Course   Beginning and Intermediate Algebra

Julie Miller

Special Edition for
Norwalk Community College

http://create.mheducation.com

ISBN-10: 1307043232   ISBN-13: 9781307043235

Contents

iv

Credits

Factoring Polynomials 585

Rational Expressions and Equations 663

Pre-Algebra Review

Chapter 1   Whole Numbers

Section 1.1   Introduction to Whole Numbers

Concepts

- Place Value
- Standard Notation and Expanded Notation
- Writing Numbers in Words
- The Number Line and Order

1. Place Value

Numbers provide the foundation that is used in mathematics. We begin this chapter by discussing how numbers are represented and named. All numbers in our numbering system are composed from the **digits** 0, 1, 2, 3, 4, 5, 6, 7, 8, and 9. In mathematics, the numbers 0, 1, 2, 3, 4, 5, 6, 7, 8, 9, 10, 11, 12, . . . are called the *whole numbers*. (The three dots are called *ellipses* and indicate that the list goes on indefinitely.)

For large numbers, commas are used to separate digits into groups of three called **periods**. For example, the number of live births in the United States in a recent year was 4,058,614. (*Source: The World Almanac*) Numbers written in this way are said to be in **standard form**. The position of each digit determines the place value of the digit. To interpret the number of births in the United States, refer to the place value chart (Figure 1-1).

Concept Connections

1. Explain the difference between the two 3's in the number 303.

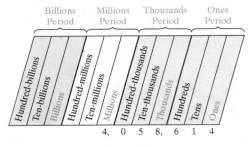

Figure 1-1

The digit 5 in 4,058,614 represents 5 ten-thousands because it is in the ten-thousands place. The digit 4 on the left represents 4 millions, whereas the digit 4 on the right represents 4 ones.

Skill Practice

Determine the place value of the digit 4.
2. 547,098,632
3. 1,659,984,036
4. 6,420

Example 1   Determining Place Value

Determine the place value of the digit 2.

   a. 417,216,900   **b.** 724   **c.** 502,000,700

Solution:

   a. 417,216,900   hundred-thousands

   b. 724   tens

   c. 502,000,700   millions

Answers

1. First 3 (on the left) represents 3 hundreds, while the second 3 (on the right) represents 3 ones.
2. Ten-millions
3. Thousands
4. Hundreds

Example 2 Determining Place Value

Mount Everest, the highest mountain on Earth, is 29,035 feet (ft) tall. Give the place value for each digit.

Solution:

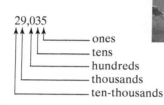

29,035
— ones
— tens
— hundreds
— thousands
— ten-thousands

2. Standard Notation and Expanded Notation

A number can also be written in an expanded form by writing each digit with its place value unit. For example, 287 can be written as

$$287 = 2 \text{ hundreds} + 8 \text{ tens} + 7 \text{ ones}$$
$$= 2 \times 100 + 8 \times 10 + 7 \times 1$$
$$= 200 + 80 + 7$$

This is called **expanded form**.

Example 3 Converting Standard Form to Expanded Form

Convert to expanded form.

a. 4,672   **b.** 257,016

Solution:

a. 4,672   4 thousands + 6 hundreds + 7 tens + 2 ones

$$= 4 \times 1,000 + 6 \times 100 + 7 \times 10 + 2 \times 1$$
$$= 4,000 + 600 + 70 + 2$$

b. 257,016   2 hundred-thousands + 5 ten-thousands +

7 thousands + 1 ten + 6 ones

$$= 2 \times 100,000 + 5 \times 10,000 + 7 \times 1,000 + 1 \times 10 + 6 \times 1$$
$$= 200,000 + 50,000 + 7,000 + 10 + 6$$

Example 4   Converting Expanded Form to Standard Form

Convert to standard form.

a. 2 hundreds + 5 tens + 9 ones

b. 1 thousand + 2 tens + 5 ones

Solution:

a. 2 hundreds + 5 tens + 9 ones = 259

b. Each place position from the thousands place to the ones place must contain a digit. In this problem, there is no reference to the hundreds place digit. Therefore, we assume 0 hundreds. Thus,

$$1 \text{ thousand} + 0 \text{ hundreds} + 2 \text{ tens} + 5 \text{ ones} = 1{,}025$$

3. Writing Numbers in Words

The word names of some two-digit numbers appear with a hyphen, while others do not. For example:

Number	Number Name
12	twelve
68	sixty-eight
40	forty
42	forty-two

To write a three-digit or larger number, begin at the leftmost group of digits. The number named in that group is followed by the period name, followed by a comma. Then the next period is named, and so on.

Example 5   Writing a Number in Words

Write 621,417,325 in words.

Solution:

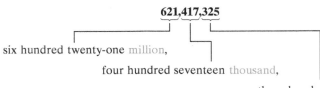

six hundred twenty-one million,

four hundred seventeen thousand,

three hundred twenty-five

Notice from Example 5 that when naming numbers, the name of the ones period is not attached to the last group of digits. Also note that for whole numbers, the word *and* should not appear in word names. For example, 405 should be written as four hundred five.

Example 6 Writing a Number in Standard Form

Write the number in standard form.

Six million, forty-six thousand, nine hundred three

Solution:

six million   nine hundred three

6,046,903

forty-six thousand

Skill Practice

11. Write the number in standard form: fourteen thousand, six hundred nine.

We have seen several examples of writing a number in standard form, in expanded form, and in words. Standard form is the most concise representation. Also note that when we write a four-digit number in standard form, the comma is often omitted. For example, 4,389 is often written as 4389.

4. The Number Line and Order

Whole numbers can be visualized as equally spaced points on a line called a *number line* (Figure 1-2).

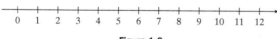

Figure 1-2

The whole numbers begin at 0 and are ordered from left to right by increasing value.

    A number is graphed on a number line by placing a dot at the corresponding point. For any two numbers graphed on a number line, the number to the left is less than the number to the right. Similarly, a number to the right is greater than the number to the left. In mathematics, the symbol $<$ is used to denote "is less than," and the symbol $>$ means "is greater than." Therefore,

$3 < 5$ means   3 is less than 5
$5 > 3$ means   5 is greater than 3

Example 7 Determining Order Between Two Numbers

Fill in the blank with the symbol $<$ or $>$.

a. 7 ☐ 0   **b.** 30 ☐ 82

Solution:

a. 7 $>$ 0

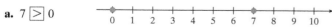

b. 30 $<$ 82

Skill Practice

Fill in the blank with the symbol $<$ or $>$.

12. 9 ☐ 5

13. 8 ☐ 18

To visualize the numbers 82 and 30 on the number line, it may be necessary to use a different scale. Rather than setting equally spaced marks in units of 1, we can use units of 10. The number 82 must be somewhere between 80 and 90 on the number line.

Answers

11. 14,609   **12.** $>$ **13.** $<$

Chapter 1 Whole Numbers

Section 1.1   Practice Exercises

Study Skills Exercise

In this text, we provide skills for you to enhance your learning experience. Each set of practice exercises begins with an activity that focuses on one of eight areas: learning about your course, using your text, taking notes, doing homework, taking an exam (test and math anxiety), managing your time, recognizing your learning style, and studying for the final exam.

Each activity requires only a few minutes and will help you to pass this class and become a better math student. Many of these skills can be carried over to other disciplines and help you become a model college student.

To begin, write down the following information.

a. Instructor's name

b. Instructor's office number

c. Instructor's telephone number

d. Instructor's email address

e. Instructor's office hours

f. Days of the week that the class meets

g. The room number in which the class meets

h. Is there a lab requirement for this course? If so, where is the lab located and how often must you go?

Vocabulary and Key Concepts

1. a. For large numbers, commas are used to separate digits into groups called _____.

b. The place values of the digits in the ones period are the ones, tens, and _____ places.

c. The place values of the digits in the _____ period are the thousands, ten-thousands, and hundred-thousands places.

Concept 1: Place Value

2. Name the place value for each digit in 36,791.

3. Name the place values for each of the digits in 8,213,457.

4. Name the place values for each of the digits in 103,596.

For Exercises 5–24, determine the place value for each underlined digit. **(See Example 1.)**

5. 3<u>2</u>1

6. 6<u>8</u>9

7. 2<u>1</u>4

8. 73<u>8</u>

9. 8,<u>7</u>10

10. 2,<u>2</u>93

11. <u>1</u>,430

12. <u>3</u>,101

13. 4<u>5</u>2,723

14. <u>6</u>55,878

15. 1,023,676,<u>2</u>07

16. 3,<u>1</u>11,901,211

17. 2<u>2</u>,422

18. <u>5</u>8,106

19. 5<u>1</u>,033,201

20. 93,971,<u>2</u>24

21. The number of U.S. travelers abroad in a recent year was 10,677,88<u>1</u>. **(See Example 2.)**

22. The area of Lake Superior is 3<u>1</u>,820 mi^2.

23. For a recent year, the total number of U.S. $1 bills in circulation was <u>7</u>,653,468,440.

24. For a certain flight, the cruising altitude of a commercial jet is <u>3</u>1,000 ft.

Concept 2: Standard Notation and Expanded Notation

For Exercises 25–32, convert the numbers to expanded form. **(See Example 3.)**

25. 58   **26.** 71   **27.** 539   **28.** 382

29. 503   **30.** 809   **31.** 10,241   **32.** 20,873

For Exercises 33–40, convert the numbers to standard form. **(See Example 4.)**

33. 5 hundreds + 2 tens + 4 ones   **34.** 3 hundreds + 1 ten + 8 ones

35. 1 hundred + 5 tens   **36.** 6 hundreds + 2 tens

37. 1 thousand + 9 hundreds + 6 ones   **38.** 4 thousands + 2 hundreds + 1 one

39. 8 ten-thousands + 5 thousands + 7 ones   **40.** 2 ten-thousands + 6 thousands + 2 ones

41. Name the first four periods of a number (from right to left).   **42.** Name the first four place values of a number (from right to left).

Concept 3: Writing Numbers in Words

For Exercises 43–50, write the number in words. **(See Example 5.)**

43. 241   **44.** 327   **45.** 603   **46.** 108

47. 31,530   **48.** 52,160   **49.** 100,234   **50.** 400,199

51. The Shuowen jiezi dictionary, an ancient Chinese dictionary that dates back to the year 100, contained 9,535 characters. Write 9,535 in words.

52. Researchers calculate that about 590,712 stone blocks were used to construct the Great Pyramid. Write 590,712 in words.

53. Mt. McKinley in Alaska is 20,320 ft high. Write 20,320 in words.

54. There are 1,800 seats in the Regal Champlain Theater in Plattsburgh, New York. Write 1,800 in words.

55. Interstate I-75 is 1,377 miles (mi) long. Write the number 1,377 in words.

56. In the United States, there are approximately 60,000,000 cats living in households. Write the number 60,000,000 in words.

Chapter 1   Whole Numbers

For Exercises 57–62, convert the number to standard form. (**See Example 6.**)

57. Six thousand, five

58. Four thousand, four

59. Six hundred seventy-two thousand

60. Two hundred forty-eight thousand

61. One million, four hundred eighty-four thousand, two hundred fifty

62. Two million, six hundred forty-seven thousand, five hundred twenty

Concept 4: The Number Line and Order

For Exercises 63–64, graph the numbers on the number line.

63. **a.** 6   **b.** 13   **c.** 8   **d.** 1

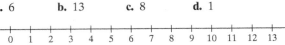

64. **a.** 5   **b.** 3   **c.** 11   **d.** 9

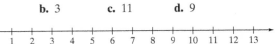

65. On a number line, what number is 4 units to the right of 6?

66. On a number line, what number is 8 units to the left of 11?

67. On a number line, what number is 3 units to the left of 7?

68. On a number line, what number is 5 units to the right of 0?

For Exercises 69–72, translate the inequality to words.

69. $8 > 2$ **70.** $6 < 11$ **71.** $3 < 7$ **72.** $14 > 12$

For Exercises 73–84, fill in the blank with the inequality symbol $<$ or $>$. (**See Example 7.**)

73. $6 \square 11$ **74.** $14 \square 13$ **75.** $21 \square 18$ **76.** $5 \square 7$

77. $3 \square 7$ **78.** $14 \square 24$ **79.** $95 \square 89$ **80.** $28 \square 30$

81. $0 \square 3$ **82.** $8 \square 0$ **83.** $90 \square 91$ **84.** $48 \square 47$

Expanding Your Skills

85. Answer true or false. 12 is a digit.

86. Answer true or false. 26 is a digit.

87. What is the greatest two-digit number?

88. What is the greatest three-digit number?

89. What is the greatest whole number?

90. What is the least whole number?

91. How many zeros are there in the number ten million?

92. How many zeros are there in the number one hundred billion?

93. What is the greatest three-digit number that can be formed from the digits 6, 9, and 4? Use each digit only once.

94. What is the greatest three-digit number that can be formed from the digits 0, 4, and 8? Use each digit only once.

Addition of Whole Numbers and Perimeter

1. Addition of Whole Numbers Using the Number Line

We use addition of whole numbers to represent an increase in quantity. For example, suppose Jonas typed 5 pages of a report before lunch. Later in the afternoon he typed 3 more pages. The total number of pages that he typed is found by adding 5 and 3.

$$5 \text{ pages} + 3 \text{ pages} = 8 \text{ pages}$$

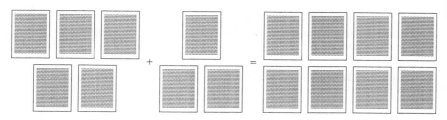

The result of an addition problem is called the **sum**, and the numbers being added are called **addends**. Thus,

$$5 + 3 = 8$$
addends   sum

The number line is a useful tool to visualize the operation of addition. To add 5 and 3 on a number line, begin at 0 and move 5 units to the right. Then move an additional 3 units to the right. The final location indicates the sum.

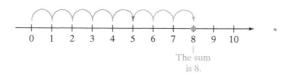

The sum
is 8.

You can use a number line to find the sum of any pair of digits. The sums for all possible pairs of one-digit numbers should be memorized (see Exercise 9). Memorizing these basic addition facts will make it easier for you to add larger numbers.

2. Addition of Whole Numbers

To add whole numbers, line up the numbers vertically by place value. Then add the digits in the corresponding place positions.

Example 1 Adding Whole Numbers

Add. $24 + 61$

Solution:

$$\begin{aligned}
24 &= 2 \text{ tens} + 4 \text{ ones} \\
+\, 61 &= 6 \text{ tens} + 1 \text{ one} \\
\hline
85 &= 8 \text{ tens} + 5 \text{ ones}
\end{aligned}$$

Concepts

1. Addition of Whole Numbers Using the Number Line
2. Addition of Whole Numbers
3. Properties of Addition
4. Translations and Applications Involving Addition
5. Perimeter

Concept Connections

1. Identify the addends and the sum.
   $3 + 7 + 12 = 22$

Skill Practice

2. Add. $\begin{aligned} 47 \\ +\,32 \end{aligned}$

Answers

1. Addends: 3, 7, and 12; sum: 22
2. 79

0   **Chapter 1**   Whole Numbers

Example 2 **Adding Whole Numbers**

Add.   261 + 28

Solution:

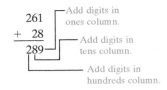

$$\begin{array}{r} 261 \\ + \ 28 \\ \hline 289 \end{array}$$

Add digits in ones column.

Add digits in tens column.

Add digits in hundreds column.

Sometimes when adding numbers, the sum of the digits in a given place position is greater than 9. If this occurs, we must do what is called *carrying* or *regrouping*. Example 3 illustrates this process.

Example 3 **Adding Whole Numbers with Carrying**

Add.   35 + 48

Solution:

$$\begin{array}{rcl} 35 &=& 3 \text{ tens} + \ 5 \text{ ones} \\ + \ 48 &=& 4 \text{ tens} + \ 8 \text{ ones} \\ \hline & & 7 \text{ tens} + 13 \text{ ones} \end{array}$$

The sum of the digits in the ones place exceeds 9. But 13 ones is the same as 1 ten and 3 ones. We can *carry* 1 ten to the tens column while leaving the 3 ones in the ones column. Notice that we placed the carried digit above the tens column.

$$\begin{array}{rcl} \overset{1 \text{ ten}}{35} &=& 3 \text{ tens} + 5 \text{ ones} \\ + \ 48 &=& 4 \text{ tens} + 8 \text{ ones} \\ \hline 83 &=& 8 \text{ tens} + 3 \text{ ones} \end{array}$$

The sum is 83.

Example 4 **Adding Whole Numbers with Carrying**

Add.   458 + 67

Solution:

$$\begin{array}{r} \overset{1}{458} \\ + \ 67 \\ \hline 5 \end{array}$$

Add the digits in the ones column: 8 + 7 = 15. Write 5 in the ones column, and carry the 1 to the tens column.

$$\begin{array}{r} \overset{11}{458} \\ + \ 67 \\ \hline 25 \end{array}$$

Add the digits in the tens column (including the carry): 1 + 5 + 6 = 12. Write the 2 in the tens column, and carry the 1 to the hundreds column.

$$\begin{array}{r} \overset{11}{458} \\ + \ 67 \\ \hline 525 \end{array}$$

Add the digits in the hundreds column. The sum is 525.

Addition of numbers may include more than two addends.

Example 5 Adding Whole Numbers

Add. $21{,}076 + 84{,}158 + 2419$

Solution:

$$
\begin{array}{r}
{}^{1}\;{}^{1\,2}\\
21{,}076\\
84{,}158\\
+\quad 2{,}419\\
\hline
107{,}653
\end{array}
$$

In this example, the sum of the digits in the ones column is 23. Therefore, we write the 3 and carry the 2.

Skill Practice

Add.

6. $\begin{array}{r} 57{,}296 \\ 4{,}089 \\ +\ 9{,}762 \\ \hline \end{array}$

3. Properties of Addition

We present three properties of addition that you may have already discovered.

Addition Property of 0

The sum of any number and 0 is that number.

Examples: $5 + 0 = 5$

$0 + 2 = 2$

Commutative Property of Addition

Changing the order of two addends does not affect the sum.

Example: $5 + 7$ is equivalent to $7 + 5$

In mathematics we use parentheses ( ) as grouping symbols. To add more than two numbers, we can group them and then add. For example:

$(2 + 3) + 8$ Parentheses indicate that $2 + 3$ is added first. Then 8 is added to the result.

$= 5 + 8$

$= 13$

$2 + (3 + 8)$ Parentheses indicate that $3 + 8$ is added first. Then the result is added to 2.

$= 2 + 11$

$= 13$

Associative Property of Addition

The manner in which addends are grouped does not affect the sum.

Example: $(1 + 7) + 3$ is equivalent to $1 + (7 + 3)$

Answer

6. 71,147

2   **Chapter 1** Whole Numbers

Example 6 Applying the Properties of Addition

a. Rewrite $9 + 6$, using the commutative property of addition.

b. Rewrite $(15 + 9) + 5$, using the associative property of addition.

Solution:

a. $9 + 6 = 6 + 9$ Change the order of the addends.

b. $(15 + 9) + 5 = 15 + (9 + 5)$ Change the grouping of the addends.

4. Translations and Applications Involving Addition

In the English language, there are many different words and phrases that imply addition. A partial list is given in Table 1-1.

Table 1-1

Word/Phrase	Example	In Symbols
Sum	The sum of 6 and 2	$6 + 2$
Added to	3 added to 8	$8 + 3$
Increased by	7 increased by 2	$7 + 2$
More than	10 more than 6	$6 + 10$
Plus	8 plus 3	$8 + 3$
Total of	The total of 9 and 6	$9 + 6$

Example 7 Translating an English Phrase to a Mathematical Statement

Translate each phrase to an equivalent mathematical statement and simplify.

a. 12 added to 109

b. The sum of 1386 and 376

Solution:

a. $109 + 12$

$$\begin{array}{r} \overset{1}{1}09 \\ +\ \ 12 \\ \hline 121 \end{array}$$

b. $1386 + 376$

$$\begin{array}{r} \overset{1\,1}{1}386 \\ +\ \ 376 \\ \hline 1762 \end{array}$$

Addition of whole numbers is sometimes necessary to solve application problems.

Example 8 Solving an Application Problem

Carlita works as a waitress at El Pinto restaurant in Albuquerque, New Mexico. Her tips for the last five nights were $30, $18, $66, $102, and $45. Find the total amount she made in tips.

Solution:

To find the total, we add.

$$\begin{array}{r} \overset{1\,2}{\$\ 30} \\ 18 \\ 66 \\ 102 \\ +\ 45 \\ \hline \$261 \end{array}$$

Carlita made $261 in tips.

Skill Practice

11. Talita received test scores of 92, 100, 84, and 96 on her first four math tests. She also earned 8 points of extra credit. How many total points did she earn?

Tables and graphs are often used to summarize information in an organized manner. Examples 9 and 10 demonstrate the interpretation of these tools.

Example 9 Solving an Application Problem Involving a Table

The following table gives the number of hits for five popular websites for a recent month. Find the total number of visitors.

Website	Number of Visitors
AOL Time Warner Network	97,995
MSN-Microsoft sites	89,819
Yahoo! sites	83,433
Google sites	37,460
Terra Lycos	36,173

Skill Practice

12. The table gives the number of gold, silver, and bronze medals won in the 2010 Winter Olympics for selected countries. Find the total number of medals won by Canada.

	Gold	Silver	Bronze
Germany	10	13	7
USA	9	15	13
Canada	14	7	5

Solution:

$$\begin{array}{r} \overset{3\,32\ 22}{97,995} \\ 89,819 \\ 83,433 \\ 37,460 \\ +\ 36,173 \\ \hline 344,880 \end{array}$$

There were 344,880 combined visitors to these websites.

Answers
11. 380 points   12. 26 medals

4 **Chapter 1** Whole Numbers

Skill Practice

13. Samira's monthly expenses are summarized in the pie graph. Find the sum of her expenses.

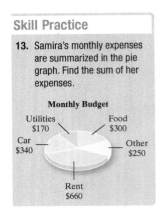

Monthly Budget

Utilities $170
Food $300
Car $340
Other $250
Rent $660

Example 10 **Solving an Application Problem Involving a Graph**

The bar graph in Figure 1-3 gives the estimated number of cases of HIV/AIDS in the United States for three selected years. The pink bars in the graph represent the values for the number of women. The blue bars in the graph represent the values for the number of men.

Find the total number of HIV/AIDS cases for women for the years 1–3.

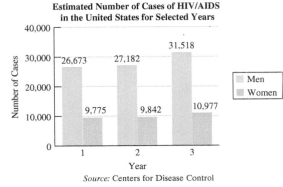

Estimated Number of Cases of HIV/AIDS in the United States for Selected Years

Source: Centers for Disease Control

Figure 1-3

Solution:

The question asks for the number of HIV/AIDS cases for women only. Therefore, add the values corresponding to the pink bars in the graph.

$$\begin{array}{r} {}^{2\ 2\ 11} \\ 9{,}775 \\ 9{,}842 \\ +\ 10{,}977 \\ \hline 30{,}594 \end{array}$$

There were 30,594 HIV/AIDS cases among women for years 1–3.

5. Perimeter

One special application of addition is to find the perimeter of a polygon. A **polygon** is a flat closed figure formed by line segments connected at their ends. Familiar figures such as triangles, rectangles, and squares are examples of polygons. See Figure 1-4.

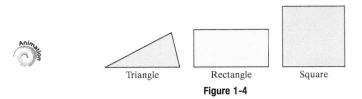

Triangle   Rectangle   Square

Figure 1-4

The **perimeter** of any polygon is the distance around the outside of the figure. To find the perimeter, add the lengths of the sides.

Section 1.2 Addition of Whole Numbers and Perimeter　　**15**

Example 11 **Finding Perimeter**

Find the perimeter of the triangle.

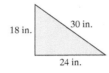

Solution:

The perimeter is the sum of the lengths of the sides.

$$
\begin{array}{r}
\overset{1}{18} \text{ in.} \\
24 \text{ in.} \\
+\ 30 \text{ in.} \\
\hline
72 \text{ in.}
\end{array}
$$

The perimeter is 72 inches.

Skill Practice

14. Find the perimeter of the rectangle.

8 ft

3 ft ☐ 3 ft

8 ft

Example 12 **Finding Perimeter**

A paving company wants to edge the perimeter of a parking lot with concrete curbing. Find the perimeter of the parking lot.

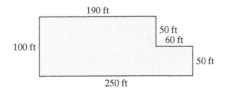

Solution:

The perimeter is the sum of the lengths of the sides.

$$
\begin{array}{r}
\overset{3}{190} \text{ ft} \\
50 \text{ ft} \\
60 \text{ ft} \\
50 \text{ ft} \\
250 \text{ ft} \\
+\ 100 \text{ ft} \\
\hline
700 \text{ ft}
\end{array}
$$

The distance around the parking lot (the perimeter) is 700 ft.

Skill Practice

15. Find the perimeter of the garden.

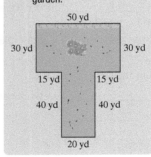

Answers

14. 22 ft
15. 240 yd

Section 1.2   Practice Exercises

Study Skills Exercise

Taking 12 credit-hours is the equivalent of a full-time job. Often students try to work too many hours while taking classes at school.

a. Write down how many hours you work per week and the number of credit-hours you are taking this term.

Number of hours worked per week _____

Number of credit-hours this term _____

b. The table gives a recommended limit on the number of hours you should work based on the number of credit-hours you are taking at school. (Keep in mind that other responsibilities in your life such as your family might also make it necessary to limit your hours at work even more.) How do your numbers from part (a) compare to those in the table? Are you working too many hours?

Number of Credit-hours	Maximum Number of Hours of Work per Week
3	40
6	30
9	20
12	10
15	0

Vocabulary and Key Concepts

1. a. The numbers being added in an addition problem are called the _____.

b. The result of an addition problem is called the _____.

c. The _____ property of addition states that the order in which two numbers are added does not affect the sum.

d. The addition property of 0 indicates that $4 + 0 =$ _____ and that $0 + 4 =$ _____.

e. The _____ property of addition states that the manner in which addends are grouped does not affect the sum.

f. A _____ is a flat closed figure formed by line segments connected at their ends.

g. The _____ of a polygon is the sum of the lengths of the sides.

Review Exercises

For Exercises 2–8, write the number in the form indicated.

2. Write 5,024 in expanded form.

3. Write 351 in expanded form.

4. Write 351 in words.

5. Write 107 in expanded form.

6. Write in standard form: two thousand, four

7. Write in standard form: four thousand, twelve

8. Write in standard form:
6 thousands + 2 hundreds + 6 ones

Concept 1: Addition of Whole Numbers Using the Number Line

9. Fill in the table. Use the number line if necessary.

+	0	1	2	3	4	5	6	7	8	9
0										
1										
2										
3										
4										
5										
6										
7										
8										
9										

For Exercises 10–15, identify the addends and the sum.

10. $5 + 9 = 14$ **11.** $2 + 8 = 10$ **12.** $12 + 5 = 17$

13. $11 + 10 = 21$ **14.** $1 + 13 + 4 = 18$ **15.** $5 + 8 + 2 = 15$

Concept 2: Addition of Whole Numbers

For Exercises 16–31, add. **(See Examples 1 and 2.)**

16. $\begin{array}{r} 42 \\ +\,33 \\ \hline \end{array}$ **17.** $\begin{array}{r} 21 \\ +\,53 \\ \hline \end{array}$ **18.** $\begin{array}{r} 39 \\ +\,20 \\ \hline \end{array}$ **19.** $\begin{array}{r} 15 \\ +\,43 \\ \hline \end{array}$

20. $\begin{array}{r} 12 \\ 15 \\ +\,32 \\ \hline \end{array}$ **21.** $\begin{array}{r} 10 \\ 8 \\ +\,30 \\ \hline \end{array}$ **22.** $\begin{array}{r} 7 \\ 21 \\ +\,10 \\ \hline \end{array}$ **23.** $\begin{array}{r} 6 \\ 11 \\ +\,2 \\ \hline \end{array}$

24. $341 + 225$ **25.** $407 + 181$ **26.** $890 + 107$ **27.** $444 + 354$

28. $4 + 13 + 102$ **29.** $11 + 221 + 5$ **30.** $31 + 7 + 430$ **31.** $24 + 14 + 160$

For Exercises 32–51, add the whole numbers with carrying. **(See Examples 3–5.)**

32. $\begin{array}{r} 76 \\ +\,45 \\ \hline \end{array}$ **33.** $\begin{array}{r} 25 \\ +\,59 \\ \hline \end{array}$ **34.** $\begin{array}{r} 87 \\ +\,24 \\ \hline \end{array}$ **35.** $\begin{array}{r} 38 \\ +\,77 \\ \hline \end{array}$

36. $\begin{array}{r} 658 \\ +\,231 \\ \hline \end{array}$ **37.** $\begin{array}{r} 642 \\ +\,295 \\ \hline \end{array}$ **38.** $\begin{array}{r} 152 \\ +\,549 \\ \hline \end{array}$ **39.** $\begin{array}{r} 462 \\ +\,388 \\ \hline \end{array}$

40. $15 + 5 + 9$ **41.** $2 + 31 + 8$ **42.** $14 + 9 + 17$ **43.** $7 + 18 + 4$

44. $79 + 112 + 12$ **45.** $62 + 907 + 34$ **46.** $331 + 422 + 76$ **47.** $87 + 119 + 630$

48. $4980 + 10{,}223$ **49.** $23{,}112 + 892$ **50.** $10{,}223 + 25{,}782 + 4980$ **51.** $92{,}377 + 5622 + 34{,}659$

8   **Chapter 1** Whole Numbers

Concept 3: Properties of Addition

For Exercises 52–55, rewrite the addition problem, using the commutative property of addition. **(See Example 6.)**

52. $12 + 6 = \square + \square$ **53.** $30 + 21 = \square + \square$ **54.** $101 + 44 = \square + \square$ **55.** $8 + 13 = \square + \square$

For Exercises 56–59, rewrite the addition problem using the associative property of addition, by inserting a pair of parentheses.

56. $(4 + 8) + 13 = 4 + 8 + 13$

57. $(23 + 9) + 10 = 23 + 9 + 10$

58. $7 + (12 + 8) = 7 + 12 + 8$

59. $41 + (3 + 22) = 41 + 3 + 22$

60. Explain the difference between the commutative and associative properties of addition.

61. Explain the addition property of 0. Then simplify the expressions.

    a. $423 + 0$ **b.** $0 + 25$ **c.** $\begin{array}{r} 67 \\ +\ 0 \\ \hline \end{array}$

Concept 4: Translations and Applications Involving Addition

For Exercises 62–70, translate the English phrase into a mathematical statement and simplify. **(See Example 7.)**

62. The sum of 13 and 7   **63.** The sum of 100 and 42   **64.** 45 added to 7

65. 81 added to 23   **66.** 5 more than 18   **67.** 2 more than 76

68. 1523 increased by 90   **69.** 1320 increased by 448   **70.** The total of 5, 39, and 81

For Exercises 71–78, write an English phrase from the mathematical statement. Answers may vary.

71. $54 + 24$ **72.** $33 + 15$ **73.** $12 + 88$ **74.** $70 + 15$

75. $4 + 23 + 77$ **76.** $11 + 41 + 53$ **77.** $10 + 8$ **78.** $25 + 14$

79. The attendance at a high school play during one weekend was as follows: 103 on Friday, 112 on Saturday, and 61 at the Sunday matinee. What was the total attendance? **(See Example 8.)**

80. To schedule enough drivers for an upcoming week, a local pizza shop manager recorded the number of deliveries each day from the previous week: 38, 54, 44, 61, 97, 103, 124. What was the total number of deliveries for the week?

81. Three top television shows entertained the following number of viewers in one week: 21,209,000 for *Dancing with the Stars,* 20,836,000 for *American Idol (Tuesday)*, and 16,448,000 for *NCIS.* Find the total number of viewers for these shows.

82. To travel from Houston to Corpus Christi, a salesperson must stop in San Antonio. If it is 195 mi from Houston to San Antonio and 228 mi from San Antonio to Corpus Christi, how far will she travel on this trip?

83. Nora earned $43,000 last year. This year her salary was increased by $2500. What is her present salary?

84. The number of participants in the Special Olympics increased by 1,205,655 since it began in 1968 with 1000 athletes. How many athletes are presently participating?

85. A portion of Jonathan's checking account register is shown. What is the total amount of the four checks written? **(See Example 9.)**

Check No.	Description	Deposit	Payment	Balance
1871	Electric bill		$60	$180
1872	Groceries		52	128
1873	Department store		75	53
	Payroll deposit	$1256		1309
1874	Restaurant		58	1251
	Deposit from savings	150		1401

86. The table gives the number of desks and chairs delivered each quarter to an office supply store. Find the total number of desks delivered for the year.

	Chairs	Desks
March	220	115
June	185	104
September	201	93
December	198	111

87. The Student Career Experience Program is a program that places students in government jobs. The bar graph displays the number of participants in the top six agencies. Find the total number of participants in the program. **(See Example 10.)**

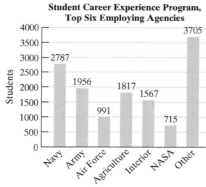

Source: U.S. Office of Personnel Management

88. The bar graph displays the number of public school teachers in the United States. Find the total number of elementary school, prekindergarten, and kindergarten teachers.

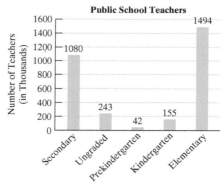

Source: National Center for Education Statistics

89. The staff for U.S. public schools is categorized in the pie graph. Determine the number of staff other than teachers.

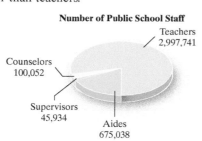

Source: National Center for Education Statistics

90. The pie graph shows the costs incurred in managing Sub-World sandwich shop for one month. From this information, determine the total cost for one month.

0   **Chapter 1** Whole Numbers

Concept 5: Perimeter

For Exercises 91–98, find the perimeter. **(See Examples 11 and 12.)**

91.

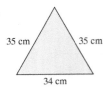

35 cm   35 cm
34 cm

92.

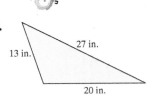

13 in.   27 in.
20 in.

93.

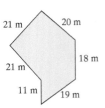

21 m   20 m
21 m   18 m
11 m   19 m

94.

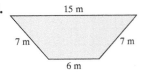

15 m
7 m   7 m
6 m

95.

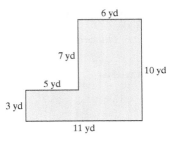

6 yd
7 yd
5 yd   10 yd
3 yd
11 yd

96.

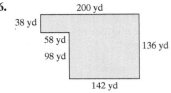

200 yd
38 yd
58 yd
98 yd   136 yd
142 yd

97. Find the perimeter of an NBA basketball court.

94 ft
50 ft   50 ft
94 ft

98. A major league baseball diamond is in the shape of a square. Find the distance a batter must run if he hits a home run. (After hitting a home run, the batter must run the perimeter of the diamond.)

90 ft   90 ft
90 ft   90 ft

Calculator Connections

Topic: Adding Whole Numbers

The following keystrokes demonstrate the procedure to add numbers on a calculator. The **ENTER** key (or, on some calculators, the **=** key or **EXE** key) tells the calculator to complete the calculation. Notice that commas used in large numbers are not entered into the calculator.

Expression	Keystrokes	Result
92,406 + 83,168	92406 **+** 83168 **ENTER**	175574

Your calculator may use the
= key or **EXE** key instead.

Calculator Exercises

For Exercises 99–106, add by using a calculator.

99. 9,084,037 + 452,903

100. 899,382 + 9406

101. 7,201,529 + 962,411

102.
```
   45,418
   81,990
    9,063
 + 56,309
```

103.
```
  9,300,050
  7,803,513
  3,480,009
 +  907,822
```

104.
```
  3,421,019
    822,761
  1,003,721
 +    9,678
```

105. The amount of money spent on television advertisements during the NCAA tournament is given in the table. This represents the four largest contributors. Determine the total amount spent on television advertisements for these four companies.

106. The number of votes tallied for the leading presidential candidates for the 2012 election is given in the table. (*Source:* Federal Election Commission) Find the total number of votes for these three candidates.

Advertisers	Amount Spent
General Motors Corporation	$64,700,000
AT&T	$36,500,000
National Collegiate Athletic Association	$24,100,000
Coca-Cola Company	$23,200,000

Candidate	Number of Votes
Obama	65,899,660
Romney	60,932,152
Johnson	1,275,804

Section 1.3   Subtraction of Whole Numbers

1. Introduction to Subtraction

Jeremy bought a case of 12 sodas, and on a hot afternoon he drank 3 of the sodas. We can use the operation of subtraction to find the number of sodas remaining.

12 sodas − 3 sodas   =   9 sodas

The symbol "−" between two numbers is a subtraction sign, and the result of a subtraction is called the **difference**. The number being subtracted (in this case, 3) is called the **subtrahend**. The number 12 from which 3 is subtracted is called the **minuend**.

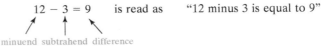

$$12 - 3 = 9 \quad \text{is read as} \quad \text{"12 minus 3 is equal to 9"}$$

minuend subtrahend difference

Subtraction is the inverse operation of addition. To find the number of sodas that remain after Jeremy takes 3 sodas away from 12 sodas, we ask the question:

"3 added to what number equals 12?"

That is,

$$12 - 3 = ? \quad \text{is equivalent to} \quad ? + 3 = 12$$

Subtraction can also be visualized on the number line. To evaluate $7 - 4$, start from the point on the number line corresponding to the minuend (7 in this case). Then move to the *left* 4 units. The resulting position on the number line is the difference.

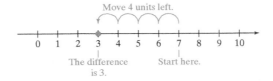

Move 4 units left.

0 1 2 3 4 5 6 7 8 9 10

The difference is 3.   Start here.

To check the result, we can use addition.

$$7 - 4 = 3 \quad \text{because} \quad 3 + 4 = 7$$

Example 1 Subtracting Whole Numbers

Subtract and check the answer, using addition.

a. $8 - 2$ **b.** $10 - 6$ **c.** $5 - 0$ **d.** $3 - 3$

Solution:

a. $8 - 2 = 6$ because $6 + 2 = 8$

b. $10 - 6 = 4$ because $4 + 6 = 10$

c. $5 - 0 = 5$ because $5 + 0 = 5$

d. $3 - 3 = 0$ because $0 + 3 = 3$

Skill Practice

Subtract. Check by using addition.

1. $11 - 5$ **2.** $8 - 0$
3. $7 - 2$ **4.** $5 - 5$

2. Subtraction of Whole Numbers

When subtracting large numbers, it is usually more convenient to write the numbers vertically. We write the minuend on top and the subtrahend below it. Starting from the ones column, we subtract digits having corresponding place values.

Example 2 Subtracting Whole Numbers

Subtract and check the answer by using addition.

a. $\begin{array}{r} 976 \\ -\ 124 \end{array}$ **b.** $\begin{array}{r} 2498 \\ -\ 197 \end{array}$

Skill Practice

Subtract. Check by using addition.

5. $\begin{array}{r} 472 \\ -\ 261 \end{array}$ **6.** $\begin{array}{r} 3947 \\ -\ 137 \end{array}$

Solution:

a. $\begin{array}{r} 976 \\ -\ 124 \\ \hline 852 \end{array}$ Check: $\begin{array}{r} 852 \\ +\ 124 \\ \hline 976 \end{array}$ ✓

Subtract the ones column digits.
Subtract the tens column digits.
Subtract the hundreds column digits.

b. $\begin{array}{r} 2498 \\ -\ 197 \\ \hline 2301 \end{array}$ Check: $\begin{array}{r} 2301 \\ +\ 197 \\ \hline 2498 \end{array}$ ✓

When a digit in the subtrahend (bottom number) is larger than the corresponding digit in the minuend (top number), we must "regroup" or borrow a value from the column to the left.

$92 = 9 \text{ tens} + 2 \text{ ones}$
$-74 = 7 \text{ tens} + 4 \text{ ones}$

In the ones column, we cannot take 4 away from 2. We will regroup by borrowing 1 ten from the minuend. Furthermore, 1 ten = 10 ones.

$\overset{8+10}{9}\ 2 = \overset{8}{9} \text{ tens} + \overset{+10\text{ ones}}{2 \text{ ones}} \Big\}$
$-\ 7\ 4 = 7 \text{ tens} + 4 \text{ ones}$

We now have 12 ones in the minuend.

$\overset{8}{9}\overset{12}{2} = \overset{8}{9} \text{ tens} + 12 \text{ ones}$
$-\ 7\ 4 = 7 \text{ tens} + \ 4 \text{ ones}$
$\ \ 1\ 8 = 1 \text{ ten} + \ 8 \text{ ones}$

TIP: The process of *borrowing* in subtraction is the reverse of *carrying* in addition.

Answers

1. 6   **2.** 8   **3.** 5   **4.** 0
5. 211   **6.** 3810

4 **Chapter 1** Whole Numbers

Skill Practice

Subtract. Check by addition.
7.   23,126
   − 6,048

Example 3 Subtracting Whole Numbers with Borrowing

Subtract and check the result with addition.

$$134{,}616$$
$$-\ 53{,}438$$

Solution:

$$\begin{array}{r}\overset{0\ 16}{134{,}6\cancel{1}\cancel{6}} \\ -\ 53{,}438 \\ \hline 8\end{array}$$ In the ones place, 8 is greater than 6. We borrow 1 ten from the tens place.

$$\begin{array}{r}\overset{5\ \overset{10}{\cancel{6}}\ 16}{134{,}\cancel{6}\cancel{1}\cancel{6}} \\ -\ 53{,}438 \\ \hline 78\end{array}$$ In the tens place, 3 is greater than 0. We borrow 1 hundred from the hundreds place.

$$\begin{array}{r}\overset{0\ 13\quad 5\ \overset{10}{\cancel{6}}\ 16}{\cancel{1}\,\cancel{3}\,4{,}\cancel{6}\cancel{1}\cancel{6}} \\ -\ 53{,}438 \\ \hline 81{,}178\end{array}$$ In the ten-thousands place, 5 is greater than 3. We borrow 1 hundred-thousand from the hundred-thousands place.

Check: $$\begin{array}{r}\overset{1\quad 11}{81{,}178} \\ +\ 53{,}438 \\ \hline 134{,}616\ ✓\end{array}$$

Example 4 Subtracting Whole Numbers with Borrowing

Skill Practice

Subtract. Check by addition.
8. 700 − 531

Subtract and check the result with addition. $500 - 247$

Solution:

$$\begin{array}{r}500 \\ -\ 247\end{array}$$ In the ones place, 7 is greater than 0. We try to borrow 1 ten from the tens place. However, the tens place digit is 0. Therefore we must first borrow from the hundreds place.

$$\begin{array}{r}\overset{4\ 10}{\cancel{5}\,\cancel{0}\,0} \\ -\ 2\,4\,7\end{array}$$

$$\begin{array}{r}\overset{4\ \overset{9}{\cancel{10}}\ 10}{\cancel{5}\,\cancel{0}\,\cancel{0}} \\ -\ 2\,4\,7 \\ \hline 2\,5\,3\end{array}$$ ←Now we can borrow 1 ten to add to the ones place.

Subtract.

Check: $$\begin{array}{r}\overset{1\ 1}{253} \\ +\ 247 \\ \hline 500\ ✓\end{array}$$

3. Translations and Applications Involving Subtraction

In applications of mathematics, several words and phrases imply subtraction. A partial list is provided in Table 1-2.

Table 1-2

Word/Phrase	Example	In Symbols
Minus	15 minus 10	$15 - 10$
Difference	The difference of 10 and 2	$10 - 2$
Decreased by	9 decreased by 1	$9 - 1$
Less than	5 less than 12	$12 - 5$
Subtract . . . from	Subtract 3 from 8	$8 - 3$

In Table 1-2, make a note of the last two entries. The phrases *less than* and *subtract . . . from* imply a specific order in which the subtraction is performed. In both cases, begin with the second number listed and subtract the first number listed.

Example 5 Translating an English Phrase to a Mathematical Statement

Translate the English phrase to a mathematical statement and simplify.

  a. The difference of 150 and 38

  b. 30 subtracted from 82

Solution:

  a. From Table 1-2, the *difference* of 150 and 38 implies $150 - 38$.

$$\begin{array}{r} {\scriptstyle 4\ 10} \\ 1\,\cancel{5}\,0 \\ -\ \ 3\,8 \\ \hline 1\,1\,2 \end{array}$$

  b. The phrase "30 subtracted from 82" implies that 30 is taken away from 82. We have $82 - 30$.

$$\begin{array}{r} 8\,2 \\ -\ 3\,0 \\ \hline 5\,2 \end{array}$$

Skill Practice

Translate the English phrase into a mathematical statement and simplify.

  9. Twelve decreased by eight
  10. Subtract three from nine.

In Section 1.2 we saw that the operation of addition is commutative. That is, the order in which two numbers are added does not affect the sum. This is *not* true for subtraction. For example, $82 - 30$ is not equal to $30 - 82$. The symbol $\neq$ means "is not equal to." Thus, $82 - 30 \neq 30 - 82$.

Most applications of subtraction generally fall into two categories.

  1. The first type is phrased as a subtraction problem in which the minuend and subtrahend are given.

Answers
  9. $12 - 8$; 4
  10. $9 - 3$; 6

Example: Shawn has $52 and then spends $40. How much money does he have left? (In this problem, we subtract $40 from $52.)

$$\$52 - \$40 = \$12$$

2. The second type is phrased as an addition problem with a missing addend.

Example: Maria received 72 points on her last math test, but needed 90 points to receive an A. How many more points would she have needed to earn an A? (In this problem, the addition problem can be translated to subtraction.)

$$72 + ? = 90 \quad \text{is equivalent to} \quad 90 - 72 = ?$$

Because $90 - 72 = 18$, Maria would have needed 18 more points.

Skill Practice

11. The temperature at 1:00 P.M. in Denver was 47°F. Three hours later, the temperature was 34°F. By how much did the temperature drop?

Example 6   **Solving an Application Problem**

A biology class started with 35 students. By midsemester, 7 students had dropped. How many students are still in the class?

Solution:

$$35 - 7 = 28 \qquad \text{There are 28 students still in the class.}$$

Skill Practice

12. Teresa earned test scores of 98, 84, and 90 on her first three exams. How many points must she score on the fourth exam to earn a total of 360 points?

Example 7   **Solving an Application Problem**

A surveyor knows that the perimeter of the lot shown is 620 ft. Find the missing length. See Figure 1-5.

Solution:

Recall that the perimeter of a polygon is the sum of the lengths of its sides. The sum of the three known side lengths in Figure 1-5 is 480 ft:

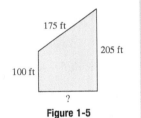

Figure 1-5

$$\begin{array}{r} \overset{1}{1}00 \\ 175 \\ +\,205 \\ \hline 480 \end{array}$$

We can subtract 480 ft from the perimeter to find the missing length:

$$620\ \text{ft} - 480\ \text{ft} = ?$$

$$\begin{array}{r} {}^{5\ 12} \\ \cancel{6}20 \\ -\,480 \\ \hline 140 \end{array}$$

The missing length is 140 ft.

A third application of subtraction is to compute a change (increase or decrease) in an amount.

Example 8   Solving an Application Problem

A criminal justice student did a study of the number of robberies that occurred in the United State over a period of several years. The bar graph shows the results for five selected years.

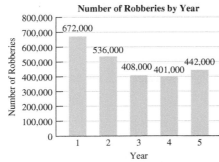

Number of Robberies by Year

Source: Federal Bureau of Investigation

Skill Practice

Refer to the graph for Example 8.

13. a. Has the number of robberies increased or decreased between year 2 and year 3?
b. Determine the amount of increase or decrease.

---

a. Find the increase in the number of reported robberies from year 4 to year 5.

b. Find the decrease in the number of reported robberies from year 1 to year 2.

Solution:

For the purpose of finding an amount of increase or decrease, we will subtract the smaller number from the larger number.

a. Because the number of robberies went *up* from year 4 to year 5, there was an *increase*. To find the amount of the increase, we subtract the smaller number from the larger number.

$$
\begin{array}{r}
442,000 \\
-\,401,000 \\
\hline
41,000
\end{array}
$$

From year 4 to year 5, there was an increase of 41,000 reported robberies in the United States.

b. Because the number of robberies went *down* from year 1 to year 2, there was a *decrease*. To find the amount of the decrease, we subtract the smaller number from the larger number.

$$
\begin{array}{r}
6\ 12 \\
6\,7\,2,000 \\
-\,536,000 \\
\hline
136,000
\end{array}
$$

From year 1 to year 2 there was a decrease of 136,000 reported robberies in the United States.

Answers
13. a. decreased   **b.** 128,000 robberies

Section 1.3   Practice Exercises

Study Skills Exercise

It is very important to attend class every day. Math is cumulative in nature, and you must master the material learned in the previous class to understand today's lesson. Because this is so important, many instructors tie attendance into the final grade. Write down the attendance policy for your class.

Vocabulary and Key Concepts

1. Given the subtraction statement $15 - 4 = 11$, the number 15 is called the _____, the number 4 is called the _____, and the number 11 is called the _____.

Review Exercises

For Exercises 2–5, add.

2. $89 + 45$

3. $330 + 821$

4.   782
           21
         + 1046

5.   46
           804
         + 49

6. Circle the true statement:

$14 > 21, 14 < 21$

7. Circle the true statement:

$0 < 10, 0 > 10$

8. Write the inequality in words:

$22 < 25$

Concept 1: Introduction to Subtraction

For Exercises 9–14, identify the minuend, subtrahend, and the difference.

9. $12 - 8 = 4$

10. $6 - 1 = 5$

11. $21 - 12 = 9$

12. $32 - 2 = 30$

13.   9
          − 6
          ───
            3

14.   17
          − 3
          ───
           14

For Exercises 15–18, write the subtraction problem as a related addition problem. For example, $19 - 6 = 13$ can be written as $13 + 6 = 19$.

15. $27 - 9 = 18$

16. $20 - 8 = 12$

17. $102 - 75 = 27$

18. $211 - 45 = 166$

For Exercises 19–24, subtract, then check the answer by using addition. **(See Example 1.)**

19. $8 - 3$ Check: ☐ $+ 3 = 8$

20. $7 - 2$ Check: ☐ $+ 2 = 7$

21. $4 - 1$ Check: ☐ $+ 1 = 4$

22. $9 - 1$ Check: ☐ $+ 1 = 9$

23. $6 - 0$ Check: ☐ $+ 0 = 6$

24. $3 - 0$ Check: ☐ $+ 0 = 3$

Concept 2: Subtraction of Whole Numbers

For Exercises 25–36, subtract and check the answer by using addition. **(See Example 2.)**

25.   68
         − 23

26.   54
         − 31

27.   88
         − 27

28.   75
         − 50

29. 1347
− 221

30. 4865
− 713

31. 1525
− 1204

32. 8843
− 5612

33. 12,806 − 2802   **34.** 12,771 − 1240   **35.** 14,356 − 13,253   **36.** 34,550 − 31,450

For Exercises 37–60, subtract the whole numbers involving borrowing. **(See Examples 3 and 4.)**

37. 76
− 59

38. 64
− 48

39. 87
− 38

40. 94
− 75

41. 240
− 136

42. 360
− 225

43. 710
− 189

44. 850
− 303

45. 4350
− 4327

46. 7293
− 7255

47. 6002
− 1238

48. 3000
− 2356

49. 10,425
− 9,022

50. 23,901
− 8,064

51. 62,088
− 59,871

52. 32,112
− 28,334

53. 470 − 92   **54.** 674 − 89   **55.** 3700 − 2987   **56.** 8000 − 3788

57. 32,439 − 1498   **58.** 21,335 − 4123   **59.** 8,007,234 − 2,345,115   **60.** 3,045,567 − 1,871,495

Concept 3: Translations and Applications Involving Subtraction

For Exercises 61–72, translate the English phrase into a mathematical statement and simplify. **(See Example 5.)**

61. 78 minus 23   **62.** 45 minus 17   **63.** 78 decreased by 6

64. 50 decreased by 12   **65.** Subtract 100 from 422.   **66.** Subtract 42 from 89.

67. 72 less than 1090   **68.** 60 less than 3111   **69.** The difference of 50 and 13

70. The difference of 405 and 103   **71.** Subtract 35 from 103.   **72.** Subtract 14 from 91.

For Exercises 73–76, write an English phrase for the mathematical statement. (Answers will vary.)

73. 93 − 27   **74.** 80 − 20   **75.** 165 − 85   **76.** 171 − 42

77. Use the expression 7 − 4 to explain why subtraction is not commutative.

78. Is subtraction associative? Use the numbers 10, 6, 2 to explain.

79. A $50 bill was used to purchase $17 worth of gasoline. Find the amount of change received. **(See Example 6.)**

80. There are 55 DVDs to shelve one evening at a video rental store. If Jason puts away 39 before leaving for the day, how many are left for Patty to put away?

81. The songwriting team of John Lennon and Paul McCartney had 118 chart hits while Mick Jagger and Keith Richards had 63. How many more chart hits did Lennon and McCartney have than Jagger and Richards?

82. Due to severe drought in the state of Alabama in 2007, a local well driller said that the minimum depth to drill for water had increased from 150 ft in 2006 to 200 ft in 2007. In 2007, the driller had to dig 505 ft to find water in one rural community. How many more feet above the 2007 minimum depth did the driller have to drill?

83. In landscaping a yard, Lily would like 26 plants for a border. If she has 18 plants in her truck, how many more will she need to finish the job?

84. A collection is taken to buy flowers for a co-worker who is in the hospital. If $37 has been collected and the flower arrangement costs $50, how much more needs to be collected?

85. A recent report indicated that the play, *The Lion King*, had been performed 5149 times on Broadway. At that time, the play, *Wicked*, had been performed 2670 times on Broadway. How many more times had *The Lion King* been performed than *Wicked*?

86. At the time of Kurt Warner's retirement from football, his total passing yardage was 32,344 yd. Drew Brees had 30,646 yd as of 2009. How many more yards does Drew Brees need to reach Kurt Warner's total?

For Exercises 87 and 88, for each figure find the missing length.

87. The perimeter of the triangle is 39 m.

88. The perimeter of the figure is 547 cm.

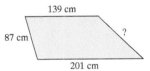

89. A homeowner knows that the perimeter of his backyard is 56 yd. Find the missing length.
(See Example 7.)

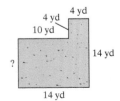

90. Barbara has 15 ft of molding to install in her bathroom, as shown in the figure. What is the missing length? *Note:* There will be no molding by the tub or door.

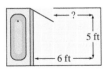

For Exercises 91–94, use the information from the bar graph. **(See Example 8.)**

91. What is the difference in the number of marriages between year 3 and year 4?

92. Find the decrease in the number of marriages in the United States between year 4 and year 5.

93. What is the difference in the number of marriages between the year having the greatest and the year having the least?

94. Between which two consecutive years did the greatest increase in the number of marriages occur? What is the increase?

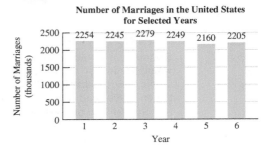

Number of Marriages in the United States for Selected Years

Source: National Center for Health Statistics

Figure for Exercises 91–94

Calculator Connections

Topic: Subtracting Whole Numbers

To subtract numbers on a calculator, use the subtraction key − . Do not confuse the subtraction key with the (−) key. The (−) is presented later to enter negative numbers.

Expression	Keystrokes	Result
345,899 − 43,018	345899 − 43018 **ENTER**	302881

Calculator Exercises

For Exercises 95–97, subtract by using a calculator.

95. 4,905,620
− 458,318

96. 953,400,415
− 56,341,902

97. 82,025,160
−79,118,705

For Exercises 98–101, refer to the table showing the land area for five states.

98. Find the difference in land area between Colorado and Wisconsin.

99. Find the difference in land area between Tennessee and West Virginia.

100. Find the difference in land area between the state with the greatest land area and the state with the least land area.

101. How much more land area does Wisconsin have than Tennessee?

State	Land Area (mi²)
Rhode Island	1,045
Tennessee	41,217
West Virginia	24,078
Wisconsin	54,310
Colorado	103,718

Section 1.4 Rounding and Estimating

1. Rounding

Rounding a whole number is a common practice when we do not require an exact value. For example, Madagascar lost 3956 mi^2 of rainforest between 1990 and 2008. We might round this number to the nearest thousand and say that there was approximately 4000 mi^2 lost. In mathematics, we use the symbol ≈ to read "is approximately equal to." Therefore, 3956 mi^2 ≈ 4000 mi^2.

A number line is a helpful tool to understand rounding. For example, 48 is closer to 50 than it is to 40. Therefore, 48 rounded to the nearest ten is 50.

Round up to 50.

Concept Connections

1. Is 82 closer to 80 or to 90? Round 82 to the nearest ten.
2. Is 65 closer to 60 or to 70? Round the number to the nearest ten.

On the other hand, 43 is closer to 40 than to 50. Therefore, 43 rounded to the nearest ten is 40.

Round down to 40.

Note 45 is halfway between 40 and 50. In such a case, our convention will be to round *up* to the next-larger ten.

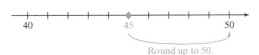

Round up to 50.

The decision to round up or down to a given place value is determined by the digit to the *right* of the given place value. The following steps outline the procedure.

Rounding Whole Numbers

Step 1 Identify the digit one position to the right of the given place value.

Step 2 If the digit in step 1 is a 5 or greater, add 1 to the digit in the given place value. Then replace each digit to the right of the given place value by 0.

Step 3 If the digit in step 1 is less than 5, replace it and each digit to its right by 0. Note that in this case, the digit in the original given place value does not change.

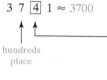 **Rounding a Whole Number**

Round 3741 to the nearest hundred.

Solution:

$3\ 7\ \boxed{4}\ 1 \approx 3700$

hundreds place

This is the digit to the right of the hundreds place. Because 4 is less than 5, the digit in the hundreds place remains the same and replace the digits to its right by zeros.

Skill Practice

3. Round 12,461 to the nearest thousand.

Example 1 could also have been solved by drawing a number line. Use the part of a number line between 3700 and 3800.

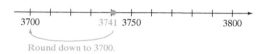

Round down to 3700.

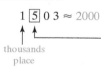 **Rounding a Whole Number**

Round 1,790,641 to the nearest hundred-thousand.

Solution:

$1,\ 7\ \boxed{9}\ 0,\ 6\ 4\ 1 \approx 1,800,000$

hundred-thousands place

This is the digit to the right of the given place value. Because 9 is greater than 5, add 1 to the hundred-thousands place, add: $7 + 1 = 8$. Replace the digits to the right of the hundred-thousands place by zeros.

Skill Practice

4. Round 147,316 to the nearest ten-thousand.

Example 3 **Rounding a Whole Number**

Round 1503 to the nearest thousand.

Solution:

$1\ \boxed{5}\ 0\ 3 \approx 2000$

thousands place

This is the digit to the right of the thousands place. Because this digit is 5, we round up. We increase the thousands place digit by 1. That is, $1 + 1 = 2$. Replace the digits to its right by zeros.

Skill Practice

5. Round 7,521,460 to the nearest million.

Answers

3. 12,000   **4.** 150,000
5. 8,000,000

Skill Practice

6. Round 39,823 to the nearest thousand.

Example 4   Rounding a Whole Number

Round the number 24,961 to the hundreds place.

Solution:

$$2\,4,\overset{+1}{9}\,\boxed{6}\,1 \approx 25,000$$

This value is greater than 5. Therefore, add 1 to the hundreds place digit. Replace the digits to the right of the hundreds place with 0.

2. Estimation

We use the process of rounding to estimate the result of numerical calculations. For example, to estimate the following sum, we can round each addend to the nearest ten.

31	rounds to	⟶	30
12	rounds to	⟶	10
+ 49	rounds to	⟶	+ 50
			90

The estimated sum is 90 (the actual sum is 92).

Skill Practice

Estimate the sum by rounding each number to the nearest hundred.

7. 3162 + 4931 + 2206

Example 5   Estimating a Sum

Estimate the sum by rounding to the nearest thousand.

$$6109 + 976 + 4842 + 11{,}619$$

Solution:

6,109	rounds to	⟶	$\overset{1}{6{,}000}$
976	rounds to	⟶	1,000
4,842	rounds to	⟶	5,000
+ 11,619	rounds to	⟶	+ 12,000
			24,000

The estimated sum is 24,000 (the actual sum is 23,546).

Skill Practice

Estimate the difference by rounding each number to the nearest million.

8. 35,264,000 − 21,906,210

Example 6   Estimating a Difference

Estimate the difference 4817 − 2106 by rounding each number to the nearest hundred.

Solution:

4817	rounds to	⟶	4800
− 2106	rounds to	⟶	− 2100
			2700

The estimated difference is 2700 (the actual difference is 2711).

3. Using Estimation in Applications

Example 7 Estimating a Sum in an Application

A driver for a delivery service must drive from Chicago, Illinois, to Dallas, Texas, and make several stops on the way. The driver follows the route given on the map. Estimate the total mileage by rounding each distance to the nearest hundred miles.

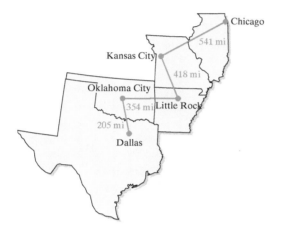

Solution:

541	rounds to ⟶	500
418	rounds to ⟶	400
354	rounds to ⟶	400
+ 205	rounds to ⟶	+ 200
		1500

The driver traveled approximately 1500 mi.

Example 8 Estimating a Difference in an Application

In a recent year, the U.S. Census Bureau reported that the number of males over the age of 18 was 100,994,367. The same year, the number of females over 18 was 108,133,727. Round each value to the nearest million. Estimate how many more females over 18 there were than males over 18.

Solution:

The number of males was approximately 101,000,000. The number of females was approximately 108,000,000.

$$
\begin{array}{r}
108{,}000{,}000 \\
- 101{,}000{,}000 \\
\hline
7{,}000{,}000
\end{array}
$$

There were approximately 7 million more women over age 18 in the United States than men.

6 **Chapter 1** Whole Numbers

Section 1.4 Practice Exercises

Study Skills Exercise

Purchase a three-ring binder for your math notes and homework. Use section dividers to separate each chapter that you cover in the text. Keep your homework and notes in the appropriate section. What other course materials might you keep organized in your notebook?

Vocabulary and Key Concepts

1. A process called _____ is common practice when the exact value of a number is not required.

Review Exercises

2. A triangle has sides of length 5 ft, 12 ft, and 13 ft. Find the perimeter.

For Exercises 3–6, add or subtract as indicated.

3. 59
   − 33

4. 130
   − 98

5. 4009
   + 998

6. 12,033
   + 23,441

7. Determine the place value of the digit 6 in the number 1,860,432.

8. Determine the place value of the digit 4 in the number 1,860,432.

Concept 1: Rounding

9. Explain how to round a whole number to the hundreds place.

10. Explain how to round a whole number to the tens place.

For Exercises 11–28, round each number to the given place value. **(See Examples 1–4.)**

11. 342; tens

12. 834; tens

13. 725; tens

14. 445; tens

15. 9384; hundreds

16. 8363; hundreds

17. 8539; hundreds

18. 9817; hundreds

19. 34,992; thousands

20. 76,831; thousands

21. 2578; thousands

22. 3511; thousands

23. 9982; hundreds

24. 7974; hundreds

25. 109,337; thousands

26. 437,208; thousands

27. 489,090; ten-thousands

28. 388,725; ten-thousands

29. In the first weekend of its release, the movie *Avatar* grossed $77,025,481. Round this number to the millions place.

30. The average per capita personal income in the United States in a recent year was $33,050. Round this number to the nearest thousand.

31. The average center-to-center distance from the Earth to the Moon is 238,863 mi. Round this to the thousands place.

32. A shopping center in Edmonton, Alberta, Canada, covers an area of 492,000 square meters (m^2). Round this number to the hundred-thousands place.

Concept 2: Estimation

For Exercises 33–36, estimate the sum by first rounding each number to the nearest ten. **(See Example 5.)**

33.   57
82
+ 21

34.   33
78
+ 41

35.   41
12
+ 129

36.   29
73
+ 113

For Exercises 37–40, estimate the difference by first rounding each number to the nearest hundred. **(See Example 6.)**

37.   898
− 422

38.   731
− 584

39.   3412
− 1252

40.   9771
− 4544

Concept 3: Using Estimation in Applications

For Exercises 41 and 42, refer to the table.

Brand	Manufacturer	Sales ($)
M&Ms	Mars	97,404,576
Hershey's Milk Chocolate	Hershey Chocolate	81,296,784
Reese's Peanut Butter Cups	Hershey Chocolate	54,391,268
Snickers	Mars	53,695,428
KitKat	Hershey Chocolate	38,168,580

41. Round the sales to the nearest million to estimate the total sales brought in by the Mars company. **(See Example 7.)**

42. Round the sales to the nearest million to estimate the total sales brought in by the Hershey Chocolate Company.

43. Neil Diamond earned $71,339,710 in U.S. tours in one year while Paul McCartney earned $59,684,076. Round each value to the nearest million dollars to estimate how much more Neil Diamond earned. **(See Example 8.)**

44. The average annual salary for a public school teacher in Iowa is $43,130. The average salary for a public school teacher in California is $63,640. Round each value to the nearest thousand to estimate how much more a school teacher in California makes compared to one from Iowa.

For Exercises 45–48, use the given table.

45. Round the revenue to the nearest hundred-thousand to estimate the total revenue for the years 1 through 3.

46. Round the revenue to the nearest hundred-thousand to estimate the total revenue for the years 4 through 6.

47. a. Determine the year with the greatest revenue. Round this revenue to the nearest hundred-thousand.

Beach Parking Revenue for Daytona Beach, Florida	
Year	Revenue
1	$3,316,897
2	3,272,028
3	3,360,289
4	3,470,295
5	3,173,050
6	1,970,380

Source: Daytona Beach News Journal
Table for Exercises 45–48

b. Determine the year with the least revenue. Round this revenue to the nearest hundred-thousand.

48. Estimate the difference between the year with the greatest revenue and the year with the least revenue.

8 **Chapter 1** Whole Numbers

For Exercises 49–52, use the bar graph provided.

49. Determine the state with the greatest number of students enrolled in grades 6–12. Round this number to the nearest thousand.

50. Determine the state with the least number of students enrolled in grades 6–12. Round this number to the nearest thousand.

51. Use the information in Exercises 49 and 50 to estimate the difference between the number of students in the state with the highest enrollment and that of the lowest enrollment.

52. Estimate the total number of students enrolled in grades 6–12 in the selected states by first rounding the number of students to the thousands place.

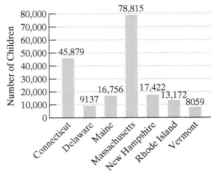

Number of Students Enrolled in Grades 6–12 for Selected States

Source: National Center for Education Statistics

Figure for Exercises 49–52

53. If you were to estimate the following sum, what place value would you round to and why?

389,220 + 2988 + 12,824 + 101,333

54. Identify the place value that you would round to when estimating the answer to the following problem. Then round the values and estimate the answer.

4208 − 932 + 1294

Expanding Your Skills

For Exercises 55–58, round the numbers to estimate the perimeter of each figure. (Answers may vary.)

55.

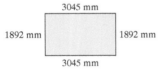

56.

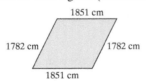

57.

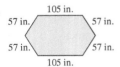

58.

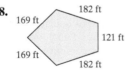

Multiplication of Whole Numbers and Area

1. Introduction to Multiplication

Suppose that Carmen buys three cartons of eggs to prepare a large family brunch. If there are 12 eggs per carton, then the total number of eggs can be found by adding three 12s.

12 eggs

12 eggs

$$\dfrac{+\ 12\ \text{eggs}}{36\ \text{eggs}}$$

When each addend in a sum is the same, we have what is called *repeated* addition. Repeated addition is also called **multiplication**. We use the multiplication sign $\times$ to express repeated addition more concisely.

$$12 + 12 + 12 \qquad \text{is equal to} \qquad 3 \times 12$$

The expression 3×12 is read "3 times 12" to signify that the number 12 is added 3 times. The numbers 3 and 12 are called **factors**, and the result, 36, is called the **product**.

The symbol $\cdot$ may also be used to denote multiplication such as in the expression $3 \cdot 12 = 36$. Two factors written adjacent to each other with no other operator between them also implies multiplication. The quantity $2y$, for example, is understood to be 2 times y. If we use this notation to multiply two numbers, parentheses are used to group one or both factors. For example:

$$3(12) = 36 \qquad (3)12 = 36 \qquad \text{and} \qquad (3)(12) = 36$$

all represent the product of 3 and 12.

> **TIP:** In the expression 3(12), the parentheses are necessary because two adjacent factors written together with no grouping symbol would look like the number 312.

The products of one-digit numbers such as $4 \times 5 = 20$ and $2 \times 7 = 14$ are basic facts. All products of one-digit numbers should be memorized (see Exercise 6).

Example 1   **Identifying Factors and Products**

Identify the factors and the product.

a. $6 \times 3 = 18$ **b.** $5 \cdot 2 \cdot 7 = 70$

Solution:

a. Factors: 6, 3; product: 18   **b.** Factors: 5, 2, 7; product: 70

2. Properties of Multiplication

Recall from Section 1.2 that the order in which two numbers are added does not affect the result. The same is true for multiplication. This is stated formally as the *commutative property of multiplication*.

Concepts

1. Introduction to Multiplication
2. Properties of Multiplication
3. Multiplying Many-Digit Whole Numbers
4. Estimating Products by Rounding
5. Translations and Applications Involving Multiplication
6. Area of a Rectangle

Concept Connections

1. How can multiplication be used to compute the sum $4 + 4 + 4 + 4 + 4 + 4 + 4$?

Skill Practice

Identify the factors and the product.
2. $3 \times 11 = 33$
3. $2 \cdot 5 \cdot 8 = 80$

Answers

1. 7×4
2. Factors: 3 and 11; product: 33
3. Factors: 2, 5, and 8; product: 80

Commutative Property of Multiplication

Changing the order of two factors does not affect the product.

Example: 2×5 is equivalent to 5×2

Rectangular arrays help us visualize the commutative property of multiplication.

$2 \times 5 = 10$ 2 rows of 5

$5 \times 2 = 10$ 5 rows of 2

Multiplication is also an associative operation.

Associative Property of Multiplication

The manner in which factors are grouped under multiplication does not affect the product.

Example: $(3 \times 5) \times 2$ is equivalent to $3 \times (5 \times 2)$

Consider these products.

$$
\begin{array}{ll}
(3 \times 5) \times 2 & 3 \times (5 \times 2) \\
= 15 \times 2 & = 3 \times 10 \\
= 30 & = 30
\end{array}
$$

Skill Practice

4. Rewrite the expression 6×5, using the commutative property of multiplication. Then find the product.

5. Rewrite the expression $3 \times (1 \times 7)$, using the associative property of multiplication. Then find the product.

Example 2 Applying Properties of Multiplication

a. Rewrite the expression 3×9, using the commutative property of multiplication. Then find the product.

b. Rewrite the expression $(4 \times 2) \times 3$, using the associative property of multiplication. Then find the product.

Solution:

a. $3 \times 9 = 9 \times 3$. The product is 27.

b. $(4 \times 2) \times 3 = 4 \times (2 \times 3)$.

To find the product, we have

$$
\begin{array}{l}
4 \times (2 \times 3) \\
= 4 \times (6) \\
= 24
\end{array}
$$

The product is 24.

Two other important properties of multiplication involve factors of 0 and 1.

Multiplication Property of 0

The product of any number and 0 is 0.

Examples: $5 \times 0 = 0$

$0 \times 12 = 0$

The product $5 \times 0 = 0$ can easily be understood by writing the product as repeated addition.

$$\underbrace{0 + 0 + 0 + 0 + 0}_{\text{Add 0 five times.}} = 0$$

Multiplication Property of 1

The product of any number and 1 is that number.

Examples: $1 \times 4 = 4$

$3 \times 1 = 3$

The last property of multiplication involves both addition and multiplication. First consider the expression $2(4 + 3)$. By performing the operation within parentheses first, we have

$$2(4 + 3) = 2(7) = 14$$

We get the same result by multiplying 2 times each addend within the parentheses:

$$2(4 + 3) = (2 \times 4) + (2 \times 3) = 8 + 6 = 14$$

This result illustrates the distributive property of multiplication over addition (sometimes we simply say *distributive property* for short).

Distributive Property of Multiplication over Addition

The product of a number and a sum can be found by multiplying the number by each addend.

Example: $5(7 + 3) = (5 \times 7) + (5 \times 3)$

Example 3 **Applying the Distributive Property of Multiplication Over Addition**

Apply the distributive property and simplify.

a. $3(4 + 8)$ **b.** $7(3 + 0)$

Solution:

a. $3(4 + 8) = (3 \times 4) + (3 \times 8) = 12 + 24 = 36$

b. $7(3 + 0) = (7 \times 3) + (7 \times 0) = 21 + 0 = 21$

Skill Practice

Apply the distributive property and simplify.

6. $2(6 + 4)$

7. $5(0 + 8)$

Answers

6. $(2 \times 6) + (2 \times 4)$; 20

7. $(5 \times 0) + (5 \times 8)$; 40

3. Multiplying Many-Digit Whole Numbers

When multiplying numbers with several digits, it is sometimes necessary to carry. To see why, consider the product 3×29. By writing the factors in expanded form, we can apply the distributive property. In this way, we see that 3 is multiplied by both 20 and 9.

$$3 \times 29 = 3(20 + 9) = (3 \times 20) + (3 \times 9)$$
$$= 60 + 27$$
$$= 6 \text{ tens} + 2 \text{ tens} + 7 \text{ ones}$$
$$= 8 \text{ tens} + 7 \text{ ones}$$
$$= 87$$

Now we will multiply 29×3 in vertical form.

Multiply $3 \times 9 = 27$. Write the 7 in the ones column and carry the 2.

Multiply 3×2 tens $= 6$ tens. Add the carry: 6 tens $+$ 2 tens $=$ 8 tens. Write the 8 in the tens place.

Example 4   Multiplying a Many-Digit Number by a One-Digit Number

Multiply.   368
            × 5

Solution:

Using the distributive property, we have

$$5(300 + 60 + 8) = 1500 + 300 + 40 = 1840$$

This can be written vertically as:

$$
\begin{array}{r}
368 \\
\times\ 5 \\
\hline
40 \\
300 \\
+\ 1500 \\
\hline
1840
\end{array}
$$

Multiply 5×8.
Multiply 5×60.
Multiply 5×300.
Add.

The numbers 40, 300, and 1500 are called *partial products*. The product of 386 and 5 is found by adding the partial products. The product is 1840.

The solution to Example 4 can also be found by using a shorter form of multiplication. We outline the procedure:

$$
\begin{array}{r}
{}^{4}\ \\
368 \\
\times\ 5 \\
\hline
0
\end{array}
$$

Multiply $5 \times 8 = 40$. Write the 0 in the ones place and carry the 4.

$$
\begin{array}{r}
^{3\,4}\\
368\\
\times\ \ \ 5\\
\hline
40
\end{array}
$$

Multiply 5×6 tens $= 300$. Add the carry. $300 + 4$ tens $= 340$.
Write the 4 in the tens place and carry the 3.

$$
\begin{array}{r}
^{3\,4}\\
368\\
\times\ \ \ 5\\
\hline
1840
\end{array}
$$

Multiply 5×3 hundreds $= 1500$. Add the carry. $1500 + 3$
hundreds $= 1800$. Write the 8 in the hundreds place and the
1 in the thousands place.

Example 5 demonstrates the process to multiply two factors with many digits.

Example 5 Multiplying a Many-Digit Number by a Many-Digit Number

Multiply.
$$
\begin{array}{r}
72\\
\times\ 83
\end{array}
$$

Solution:

Writing the problem vertically and computing the partial products, we have

$$
\begin{array}{r}
^{1}\\
72\\
\times\ 83\\
\hline
216\\
+\ 5760\\
\hline
5976
\end{array}
$$

Multiply 3×72.
Multiply 80×72.
Add.

The product is 5976.

Example 6 Multiplying Two Multidigit Whole Numbers

Multiply. 368×497

Solution:

$$
\begin{array}{r}
^{2\,3}\\
^{6\,7}\\
^{4\,5}\\
368\\
\times\ 497\\
\hline
2576\\
33120\\
+\ 147200\\
\hline
182{,}896
\end{array}
$$

---

4. Estimating Products by Rounding

A special pattern occurs when one or more factors in a product end in zero. Consider the following products:

$12 \times 20 = 240$	$120 \times 20 = 2400$
$12 \times 200 = 2400$	$1200 \times 20 = 24{,}000$
$12 \times 2000 = 24{,}000$	$12{,}000 \times 20 = 240{,}000$

Notice in each case the product is $12 \times 2 = 24$ followed by the total number of zeros from each factor. Consider the product 1200×20.

$$
\begin{array}{r|l}
12 & 00 \\
\times\ 2 & 0 \\
\hline
24 & 000
\end{array}
$$

Shift the numbers 1200 and 20 so that the zeros appear to the right of the multiplication process. Multiply $12 \times 2 = 24$.
Write the product 24 followed by the total number of zeros from each factor.

Skill Practice

11. Estimate the product 421×869 by rounding each factor to the nearest hundred.

Example 7 **Estimating a Product**

Estimate the product 795×4060 by rounding 795 to the nearest hundred and 4060 to the nearest thousand.

Solution:

$$
\begin{array}{rcl}
795 & \text{rounds to} \longrightarrow & 800 \\
4060 & \text{rounds to} \longrightarrow & 4000
\end{array}
\qquad
\begin{array}{r|l}
8 & 00 \\
\times\ 4 & 000 \\
\hline
32 & 00000
\end{array}
$$

The product is approximately 3,200,000.

Skill Practice

12. A small newspaper has 16,850 subscribers. Each subscription costs $149 per year. Estimate the revenue for the year by rounding the number of subscriptions to the nearest thousand and the cost to the nearest ten.

Example 8 **Estimating a Product in an Application**

For a trip from Atlanta to Los Angeles, the average cost of a plane ticket was $495. If the plane carried 218 passengers, estimate the total revenue for the airline. (*Hint*: Round each number to the hundreds place and find the product.)

Solution:

$$
\begin{array}{rcl}
\$495 & \text{rounds to} \longrightarrow & \$\ 5 \\
218 & \text{rounds to} \longrightarrow & \times 2
\end{array}
\qquad
\begin{array}{r|l}
\$\ 5 & 00 \\
\times\ 2 & 00 \\
\hline
\$10 & 0000
\end{array}
$$

The airline received approximately $100,000 in revenue.

5. Translations and Applications Involving Multiplication

In English there are many different words that imply multiplication. A partial list is given in Table 1-3.

Table 1-3

Word/Phrase	Example	In Symbols
Product	The product of 4 and 7	4×7
Times	8 times 4	8×4
Multiply . . . by . . .	Multiply 6 by 3	6×3

Multiplication may also be warranted in applications involving unit rates. In Example 8, we multiplied the cost per customer ($495) by the number of customers (218). The value $495 is a unit rate because it gives the cost per one customer (per one unit).

Example 9 Solving an Application Involving Multiplication

The average weekly income for production workers is $489. How much does a production worker make in 1 year (assume 52 weeks in 1 year)?

Solution:

The value $489 per week is a unit rate. The total earnings for 1 year is given by $489 × 52.

$$
\begin{array}{r}
^{44} \\
^{11} \\
489 \\
\times\ 52 \\
\hline
978 \\
+\ 24450 \\
\hline
25{,}428
\end{array}
$$
  The yearly earnings are $25,428.

> **Skill Practice**
>
> **13.** Ella can type 65 words per minute. How many words can she type in 45 minutes?

TIP: This product can be estimated quickly by rounding the factors.

$$
\begin{array}{rcl}
489 & \text{rounds to} \longrightarrow & 5\,|00 \\
52 & \text{rounds to} \longrightarrow & \times\ 5\,|0 \\
\hline
& & 25\,|000
\end{array}
$$

The total yearly income is approximately $25,000. Estimating gives a quick approximation of a product. Furthermore, it also checks for the reasonableness of our exact product. In this case $25,000 is close to our exact value of $25,428.

6. Area of a Rectangle

Another application of multiplication of whole numbers lies in finding the area of a region. **Area** measures the amount of surface contained within the region. For example, a square that is 1 in. by 1 in. occupies an area of 1 square inch, denoted as 1 in.^{2}. Similarly, a square that is 1 centimeter (cm) by 1 cm occupies an area of 1 square centimeter. This is denoted by 1 cm^2.

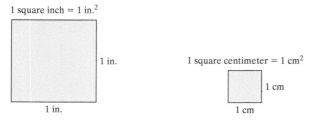

The units of square inches and square centimeters (in.^{2} and cm^2) are called *square units*. To find the area of a region, measure the number of square units occupied in that region. For example, the region in Figure 1-6 occupies 6 cm^2.

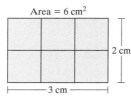

Figure 1-6

Answer

13. 2925 words

The 3-cm by 2-cm region in Figure 1-6 suggests that to find the **area of a rectangle**, multiply the length by the width. If the area is represented by A, the length is represented by l, and the width is represented by w, then we have

$$\text{Area of rectangle} = (\text{length}) \times (\text{width})$$

$$A = l \times w$$

The letters A, l, and w are called **variables** because their values *vary* as they are replaced by different numbers.

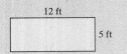
Example 10 **Finding the Area of a Rectangle**

Find the area and perimeter of the rectangle.

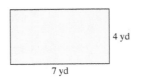
4 yd
7 yd

Solution:

Area:

$$A = l \times w$$

$$A = (7 \text{ yd}) \times (4 \text{ yd})$$

$$= 28 \text{ yd}^2$$

Recall from Section 1.2 that the perimeter of a polygon is the sum of the lengths of the sides. In a rectangle the opposite sides are equal in length.

Perimeter:

$$P = 7 \text{ yd} + 4 \text{ yd} + 7 \text{ yd} + 4 \text{ yd}$$

$$= 22 \text{ yd}$$

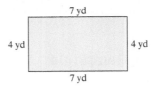
7 yd
4 yd
4 yd
7 yd

The area is 28 yd^2 and the perimeter is 22 yd.

Example 11 **Finding Area in an Application**

The state of Wyoming is approximately the shape of a rectangle (Figure 1-7). Its length is 355 mi and its width is 276 mi. Approximate the total area of Wyoming by rounding the length and width to the nearest ten.

WY   276 mi
355 mi
Figure 1-7

Solution:

$$
\begin{array}{ll}
355 & \text{rounds to} \longrightarrow \\
276 & \text{rounds to} \longrightarrow
\end{array}
\quad
\begin{array}{r}
\overset{1}{\underset{}{}}\overset{4}{} \\
36\,|\,0 \\
\times\, 28\,|\,0 \\
\hline
288 \\
720 \\
\hline
1008\,|\,00
\end{array}
$$

The area of Wyoming is approximately 100,800 mi^2.

Section 1.5   Practice Exercises

Study Skills Exercise

> Write down your instructor's policies for the following:
> **a.** Missing a test   **b.** Missing a class   **c.** Doing homework   **d.** Late homework policy

Vocabulary and Key Concepts

1. a. Two numbers being multiplied are called _____ and the result is called the _____.

b. The _____ property of multiplication states that the order of factors does not affect the product.

c. The _____ property of multiplication indicates that the manner in which factors are grouped under multiplication does not affect the product.

d. The multiplication property of 0 indicates that $7 \cdot 0 =$ _____ and $0 \cdot 7 =$ _____.

e. The multiplication property of 1 indicates that $7 \cdot 1 =$ _____ and $1 \cdot 7 =$ _____.

f. The statement $3(4 + 6) = 3 \cdot 4 + 3 \cdot 6$ is an example of the _____ property of multiplication over addition.

g. The _____ of a region measures the amount of surface contained within the region.

h. Given a rectangle of length l and width w, the area A is given by $A =$ _____.

Review Exercises

For Exercises 2–5, estimate the answer by rounding to the indicated place value.

2. $5981 + 7206$; thousands

3. $869{,}240 + 34{,}921 + 108{,}332$; ten-thousands

4. $907{,}801 - 413{,}560$; hundred-thousands

5. $8821 - 3401$; hundreds

Concept 1: Introduction to Multiplication

6. Fill in the table of multiplication facts.

×	0	1	2	3	4	5	6	7	8	9
0										
1										
2										
3										
4										
5										
6										
7										
8										
9										

For Exercises 7–10, write the repeated addition as multiplication and simplify.

7. $5 + 5 + 5 + 5 + 5 + 5$

8. $2 + 2 + 2 + 2 + 2 + 2 + 2 + 2 + 2$

9. $9 + 9 + 9$

10. $7 + 7 + 7 + 7$

For Exercises 11–14, identify the factors and the product. (**See Example 1.**)

11. $13 \times 42 = 546$

12. $26 \times 9 = 234$

13. $3 \cdot 5 \cdot 2 = 30$

14. $4 \cdot 3 \cdot 8 = 96$

15. Write the product of 5 and 12, using three different notations. (Answers may vary.)

16. Write the product of 23 and 14, using three different notations. (Answers may vary.)

Concept 2: Properties of Multiplication

For Exercises 17–22, match the property with the statement.

17. $8 \times 1 = 8$

a. Commutative property of multiplication

18. $6 \cdot 13 = 13 \cdot 6$

b. Associative property of multiplication

19. $2(6 + 12) = 2 \cdot 6 + 2 \cdot 12$

c. Multiplication property of 0

20. $5 \cdot (3 \cdot 2) = (5 \cdot 3) \cdot 2$

d. Multiplication property of 1

21. $0 \times 4 = 0$

e. Distributive property of multiplication over addition

22. $7(14) = 14(7)$

For Exercises 23–28, rewrite the expression, using the indicated property. (**See Examples 2 and 3.**)

23. 14×8; commutative property of multiplication

24. 3×9; commutative property of multiplication

25. $6 \times (2 \times 10)$; associative property of multiplication

26. $(4 \times 15) \times 5$; associative property of multiplication

27. $5(7 + 4)$; distributive property of multiplication over addition

28. $3(2 + 6)$; distributive property of multiplication over addition

Concept 3: Multiplying Many-Digit Whole Numbers

For Exercises 29–60, multiply. (**See Examples 4–6.**)

29.
$$\begin{array}{r} 24 \\ \times\ 6 \\ \hline \end{array}$$

30.
$$\begin{array}{r} 18 \\ \times\ 5 \\ \hline \end{array}$$

31.
$$\begin{array}{r} 26 \\ \times\ 2 \\ \hline \end{array}$$

32.
$$\begin{array}{r} 71 \\ \times\ 3 \\ \hline \end{array}$$

33.
$$\begin{array}{r} 131 \\ \times\ 5 \\ \hline \end{array}$$

34.
$$\begin{array}{r} 725 \\ \times\ 3 \\ \hline \end{array}$$

35.
$$\begin{array}{r} 344 \\ \times\ 4 \\ \hline \end{array}$$

36.
$$\begin{array}{r} 105 \\ \times\ 9 \\ \hline \end{array}$$

37.
$$\begin{array}{r} 1410 \\ \times\ 8 \\ \hline \end{array}$$

38.
$$\begin{array}{r} 2016 \\ \times\ 6 \\ \hline \end{array}$$

39.
$$\begin{array}{r} 3312 \\ \times\ 7 \\ \hline \end{array}$$

40.
$$\begin{array}{r} 4801 \\ \times\ 5 \\ \hline \end{array}$$

41. 42,014
$\times\ 9$

42. 51,006
$\times\ 8$

43. 32
$\times\ 14$

44. 41
$\times\ 21$

45. 68 · 24

46. 55 · 41

47. 72 · 12

48. 13 · 46

49. (143)(17)

50. (722)(28)

51. (349)(19)

52. (512)(31)

53. 151
$\times\ 127$

54. 703
$\times\ 146$

55. 222
$\times\ 841$

56. 387
$\times\ 506$

57. 3532
$\times\ 6014$

58. 2810
$\times\ 1039$

59. 4122
$\times\ \ 982$

60. 7026
$\times\ \ 528$

Concept 4: Estimating Products by Rounding

For Exercises 61–68, multiply the numbers, using the method found on page 44. **(See Example 7.)**

61. 600
$\times\ 40$

62. 900
$\times\ 50$

63. 3000
$\times\ 700$

64. 4000
$\times\ 400$

65. 8000
$\times\ 9000$

66. 1000
$\times\ 2000$

67. 90,000
$\times\ \ 400$

68. 50,000
$\times\ 6000$

For Exercises 69–72, estimate the product by first rounding the number to the indicated place value.

69. 11,784 × 5201; thousands place

70. 45,046 × 7812; thousands place

71. 82,941 × 29,740; ten-thousands place

72. 630,229 × 71,907; ten-thousands place

73. Suppose a hotel room costs $189 per night. Round this number to the nearest hundred to estimate the cost for a five-night stay. **(See Example 8.)**

74. The science department of Comstock High School must purchase a set of calculators for a class. If the cost of one calculator is $129, estimate the cost of 28 calculators by rounding the numbers to the tens place.

75. The average price for a ticket to see Kenny Chesney is $272. If a concert stadium seats 10,256 fans, estimate the amount of money received during that performance by rounding the number of seats to the nearest ten-thousand.

76. A breakfast buffet at a local restaurant serves 48 people. Estimate the maximum revenue for one week (7 days) if the price of a breakfast is $12.

Concept 5: Translations and Applications Involving Multiplication

77. The 4-gigabyte (4-GB) iPod nano is advertised to store approximately 1000 songs. Assuming the average length of a song is 4 minutes, how many minutes of music can be stored on the iPod nano? **(See Example 9.)**

78. One CD can hold 700 megabytes (MB) of data. How many megabytes can 15 CDs hold?

79. It costs about $45 for a cat to have a medical exam. If a humane society has 37 cats, find the cost of medical exams for their cats.

80. A can of Coke contains 12 fluid ounces (fl oz). Find the number of ounces in a case of Coke containing 12 cans.

81. PaperWorld shipped 115 cases of copy paper to a business. There are 5 reams of paper in each case and 500 sheets of paper in each ream. Find the number of sheets of paper delivered to the business.

82. A dietary supplement bar has 14 grams (g) of protein. If Kathleen eats 2 bars a day for 6 days, how many grams of protein will she get from this supplement?

83. Tylee's car gets 31 miles per gallon (mpg) on the highway. How many miles can he travel if he has a full tank of gas (12 gal)?

84. Sherica manages a small business called Pizza Express. She has 23 employees who work an average of 32 hours (hr) per week. How many hours of work does Sherica have to schedule each week?

Concept 6: Area of a Rectangle

For Exercises 85–88, find the area. (See Example 10.)

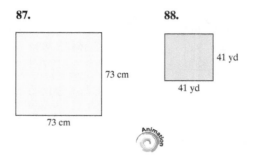

85.

12 ft
23 ft

86.

31 m
2 m

87.

73 cm
73 cm

88.

41 yd
41 yd

89. The state of Colorado is approximately the shape of a rectangle. Its length is 388 mi and its width is 269 mi. Approximate the total area of Colorado by rounding the length and width to the nearest ten. (See Example 11.)

90. A parcel of land has a width of 132 yd and a length of 149 yd. Approximate the total area by rounding each dimension to the nearest ten.

91. The front of a building has windows that are 44 in. by 58 in.

 a. Approximate the area of one window.

 b. If the building has three floors and each floor has 14 windows, how many windows are there?

 c. What is the approximate total area of all of the windows?

92. The length of a carport is 51 ft and its width is 29 ft. Approximate the area of the carport.

93. Mr. Slackman wants to paint his garage door that is 8 ft by 16 ft. To decide how much paint to buy, he must find the area of the door. What is the area of the door?

94. To carpet a rectangular room, Erika must find the area of the floor. If the dimensions of the room are 10 yd by 15 yd, how much carpeting does she need?

Division of Whole Numbers

1. Introduction to Division

Suppose 12 pieces of pizza are to be divided evenly among 4 children (Figure 1-8). The number of pieces that each child would receive is given by $12 \div 4$, read "12 divided by 4."

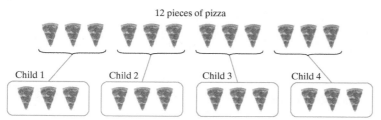

Figure 1-8

Concepts

1. Introduction to Division
2. Properties of Division
3. Long Division
4. Dividing by a Many-Digit Divisor
5. Translations and Applications Involving Division

The process of separating 12 pieces of pizza evenly among 4 children is called **division**. The statement $12 \div 4 = 3$ indicates that each child receives 3 pieces of pizza. The number 12 is called the **dividend**. It represents the number to be divided. The number 4 is called the **divisor**, and it represents the number of groups. The result of the division (in this case 3) is called the **quotient**. It represents the number of items in each group.

Division can be represented in several ways. For example, the following are all equivalent statements.

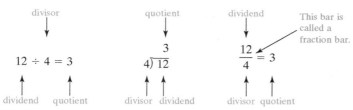

Recall that subtraction is the inverse operation of addition. In the same way, division is the inverse operation of multiplication. For example, we say $12 \div 4 = 3$ because $3 \times 4 = 12$.

Example 1 Identifying the Dividend, Divisor, and Quotient

Simplify each expression. Then identify the dividend, divisor, and quotient.

a. $48 \div 6$ **b.** $9\overline{)36}$ **c.** $\dfrac{63}{7}$

Solution:

a. $48 \div 6 = 8$ because $8 \times 6 = 48$
   The dividend is 48, the divisor is 6, and the quotient is 8.

b. $9\overline{)36}^{\,4}$ because $4 \times 9 = 36$
   The dividend is 36, the divisor is 9, and the quotient is 4.

c. $\dfrac{63}{7} = 9$ because $9 \times 7 = 63$
   The dividend is 63, the divisor is 7, and the quotient is 9.

Skill Practice

Identify the dividend, divisor, and quotient.

1. $56 \div 7$
2. $4\overline{)20}$
3. $\dfrac{18}{2}$

Answers

1. Dividend: 56; divisor: 7; quotient: 8
2. Dividend: 20; divisor: 4; quotient: 5
3. Dividend: 18; divisor: 2; quotient: 9

2   **Chapter 1**   Whole Numbers

2. Properties of Division

Example 2 illustrates the important properties of division.

Example 2   **Dividing Whole Numbers**

Divide.

a. $8 \div 8$ **b.** $\dfrac{6}{6}$ **c.** $5 \div 1$

d. $1\overline{)7}$ **e.** $0 \div 6$ **f.** $\dfrac{0}{4}$ **g.** $6 \div 0$

Solution:

a. $8 \div 8 = 1$ because $1 \times 8 = 8$

b. $\dfrac{6}{6} = 1$ because $1 \times 6 = 6$

c. $5 \div 1 = 5$ because $5 \times 1 = 5$

d. $1\overline{)7}^{\,7}$ because $7 \times 1 = 7$

e. $0 \div 6 = 0$ because $0 \times 6 = 0$

f. $\dfrac{0}{4} = 0$ because $0 \times 4 = 0$

g. $6 \div 0$ is *undefined* because there is no number that when multiplied by 0 will produce a product of 6.

Properties of Division

1. Any nonzero number divided by itself is 1.
    Example: $9 \div 9 = 1$
2. Any number divided by 1 is the number itself.
    Example: $3 \div 1 = 3$
3. Zero divided by any nonzero number is zero.
    Example: $0 \div 5 = 0$
4. Any number divided by zero is undefined.
    Example: $9 \div 0$ is undefined

To help remember the difference between $0 \div 2$ and $2 \div 0$, consider this application:

$\$8 \div 2 = \$4$ means that if we divide $\$8$ between 2 people, each will receive $\$4$.

$\$0 \div 2 = \$0$ means that if we divide $\$0$ between 2 people, each will receive $\$0$.

But $\$2 \div 0$ means that we would like to divide $\$2$ between 0 people. This cannot be done. So $2 \div 0$ is undefined.

You should also note that unlike addition and multiplication, division is neither commutative nor associative. In other words, reversing the order of the dividend and divisor may produce a different quotient. Similarly, changing the manner in which numbers are grouped with division may affect the outcome. See Exercises 31 and 32.

3. Long Division

To divide larger numbers we use a process called **long division**. This process uses a series of estimates to find the quotient. We illustrate long division in Example 3.

Example 3 **Using Long Division**

Divide. $7\overline{)161}$

Solution:

Estimate $7\overline{)161}$ by first estimating $7\overline{)16}$ and writing the result in the tens place of the quotient. Since $7 \times 2 = 14$, there are at least 2 sevens in 16.

$$
\begin{array}{r}
2 \\
7\overline{)161} \\
-140 \\
\hline
21
\end{array}
$$

The 2 in the tens place represents 20 in the quotient.
←Multiply 7×20 and write the result under the dividend.
Subtract 140. We see that our estimate leaves 21.

Repeat the process. Now divide $7\overline{)21}$ and write the result in the ones place of the quotient.

$$
\begin{array}{r}
23 \\
7\overline{)161} \\
-140 \\
\hline
21 \\
-21 \\
\hline
0
\end{array}
$$

← Multiply 7×3.
Subtract.

The quotient is 23.

Check: $\begin{array}{r} 23 \\ \times\, 7 \\ \hline 161 \end{array}$ ✔

Skill Practice

Divide.
12. $8\overline{)136}$

We can streamline the process of long division by "bringing down" digits of the dividend one at a time.

Example 4 **Using Long Division**

Divide. $6138 \div 9$

Solution:

$$
\begin{array}{r}
682 \\
9\overline{)6138} \\
-54 \\
\hline
73 \\
-72 \\
\hline
18 \\
-18 \\
\hline
0
\end{array}
$$

$9 \times 6 = 54$ and subtract.
Bring down the 3.
$9 \times 8 = 72$ and subtract.
Bring down the 8.
$9 \times 2 = 18$ and subtract.

The quotient is 682.

Check: $\begin{array}{r} {\scriptstyle 7\,1} \\ 682 \\ \times\; 9 \\ \hline 6138 \end{array}$ ✔

Skill Practice

Divide.
13. $2891 \div 7$

Answers

12. 17   **13.** 413

In many instances, quotients do not come out evenly. For example, suppose we had 13 pieces of pizza to distribute among 4 children (Figure 1-9).

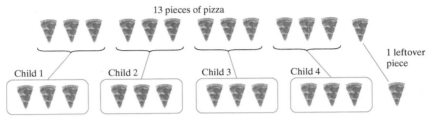

13 pieces of pizza

Child 1   Child 2   Child 3   Child 4   1 leftover piece

Figure 1-9

The mathematical term given to the "leftover" piece is called the **remainder**. The division process may be written as

$$\begin{array}{r} 3\ \text{R}1 \\ 4\overline{)13} \\ -12 \\ \hline 1 \end{array}$$

The remainder is written next to the 3.

The **whole part of the quotient** is 3, and the remainder is 1. Notice that the remainder is written next to the whole part of the quotient.

We can check a division problem that has a remainder. To do so, multiply the divisor by the whole part of the quotient and then add the remainder. The result must equal the dividend. That is,

$$(\text{Divisor})(\text{whole part of quotient}) + \text{remainder} = \text{dividend}$$

Thus,

$$(4)(3) + 1 \stackrel{?}{=} 13$$
$$12 + 1 \stackrel{?}{=} 13$$
$$13 = 13 \ ✔$$

Example 5   **Using Long Division**

Divide.   1253 ÷ 6

Solution:

$$\begin{array}{r} 208\ \text{R}5 \\ 6\overline{)1253} \\ -12 \\ \hline 05 \\ -00 \\ \hline 53 \\ -48 \\ \hline 5 \end{array}$$

6 × 2 = 12 and subtract.

Bring down the 5.

Note that 6 does not divide into 5, so we put a 0 in the quotient.

Bring down the 3.

6 × 8 = 48 and subtract.

The remainder is 5.

To check, verify that 6 × 208 + 5 = 1253. ✔

4. Dividing by a Many-Digit Divisor

When the divisor has more than one digit, we still use a series of estimations to find the quotient.

Example 6   Dividing by a Two-Digit Number

Divide. $32\overline{)1259}$

Divide.

Solution:

To estimate the leading digit of the quotient, estimate the number of times 30 will go into 125. Since $30 \cdot 4 = 120$, our estimate is 4.

$$\begin{array}{r} 4 \\ 32\overline{)1259} \\ -128 \end{array}$$

$32 \times 4 = 128$ is too big. We cannot subtract 128 from 125. Revise the estimate in the quotient to 3.

$$\begin{array}{r} 3 \\ 32\overline{)1259} \\ -96 \\ \hline 299 \end{array}$$

$32 \times 3 = 96$ and subtract.
Bring down the 9.

Now estimate the number of times 30 will go into 299. Because $30 \times 9 = 270$, our estimate is 9.

$$\begin{array}{r} 39 \;\; R11 \\ 32\overline{)1259} \\ -96 \\ \hline 299 \\ -288 \\ \hline 11 \end{array}$$

$32 \times 9 = 288$ and subtract.
The remainder is 11.

To check, verify that $32 \times 39 + 11 = 1259$. ✔

Example 7   Dividing by a Many-Digit Number

Divide. $\dfrac{82{,}705}{602}$

Solution:

$$\begin{array}{r} 137 \;\; R231 \\ 602\overline{)82{,}705} \\ -602 \\ \hline 2250 \\ -1806 \\ \hline 4445 \\ -4214 \\ \hline 231 \end{array}$$

$602 \times 1 = 602$ and subtract.
Bring down the 0.
$602 \times 3 = 1806$ and subtract.
Bring down the 5.
$602 \times 7 = 4214$ and subtract.
The remainder is 231.

To check, verify that $602 \times 137 + 231 = 82{,}705$. ✔

5. Translations and Applications Involving Division

Several words and phrases imply division. A partial list is given in Table 1-4.

Table 1-4

Word/Phrase	Example	In Symbols		
Divide	Divide 12 by 3	$12 \div 3$ or	$\dfrac{12}{3}$ or	$3\overline{)12}$
Quotient	The quotient of 20 and 2	$20 \div 2$ or	$\dfrac{20}{2}$ or	$2\overline{)20}$
Per	110 mi per 2 hr	$110 \div 2$ or	$\dfrac{110}{2}$ or	$2\overline{)110}$
Divides into	4 divides into 28	$28 \div 4$ or	$\dfrac{28}{4}$ or	$4\overline{)28}$
Divided, or shared equally among	64 shared equally among 4	$64 \div 4$ or	$\dfrac{64}{4}$ or	$4\overline{)64}$

Skill Practice

17. Four players play Hearts with a standard 52-card deck of cards. If the cards are equally distributed, how many cards does each player get?

Example 8 Solving an Application Involving Division

A painting business employs 3 painters. The business collects $1950 for painting a house. If all painters are paid equally, how much does each person make?

Solution:

This is an example where $1950 is shared equally among 3 people. Therefore, we divide.

$$
\begin{array}{r}
650 \\
3\overline{)1950} \\
\end{array}
$$

$$-18 \qquad 3 \times 6 = 18 \text{ and subtract.}$$
$$15 \qquad \text{Bring down the 5.}$$
$$-15 \qquad 3 \times 5 = 15 \text{ and subtract.}$$
$$00 \qquad \text{Bring down the 0.}$$
$$-0 \qquad 3 \times 0 = 0 \text{ and subtract.}$$
$$0 \qquad \text{The remainder is 0.}$$

Each painter makes $650.

Skill Practice

18. A college has budgeted $4800 to buy graphing calculators. Each calculator costs $119. Estimate the number of calculators that the college can buy by rounding the cost to the nearest ten.

Example 9 Solving an Application Involving Division with Estimation

Elaine and Max drove from South Bend, Indiana, to Bonita Springs, Florida. The total driving distance was 1089 mi, and the driving time was approximately 20 hr. Estimate the average speed by rounding the distance to the nearest hundred.

Answers

7. 13 cards   18. 40 calculators

Solution:

1089 mi rounds to 1100 mi. The speed is represented by 1100 mi per 20 hr, or

$$
\begin{array}{r}
55 \\
20{\overline{\smash{\big)}\,1100}} \\
\underline{-100} \\
\cdot 100 \\
\underline{-100} \\
0
\end{array}
$$

$20 \times 5 = 100$ and subtract.

Bring down the 0.

$20 \times 5 = 100$ and subtract.

Max and Elaine averaged approximately 55 miles per hour (mph).

Example 10 **Solving an Application Involving Division**

The bar graph in Figure 1-10 depicts the number of calories burned per hour for selected activities.

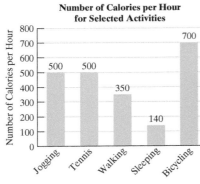

Number of Calories per Hour for Selected Activities

Figure 1-10

a. Janie wants to burn 3500 calories per week exercising. For how many hours must she jog?

b. For how many hours must Janie bicycle to burn 3500 calories?

Solution:

a. The total number of calories must be divided into 500-calorie increments. Thus, the number of hours required is given by $3500 \div 500$.

$$
\begin{array}{r}
7 \\
500{\overline{\smash{\big)}\,3500}} \\
\underline{-3500} \\
0
\end{array}
$$

Janie requires 7 hr of jogging to burn 3500 calories.

b. 3500 calories must be divided into 700-calorie increments. The number of hours required is given by $3500 \div 700$.

$$
\begin{array}{r}
5 \\
700{\overline{\smash{\big)}\,3500}} \\
\underline{-3500} \\
0
\end{array}
$$

Janie requires 5 hr of bicycling to burn 3500 calories.

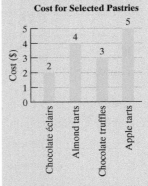
Answers

19. a. 180 chocolate éclairs
     b. 72 apple tarts

Section 1.6   Practice Exercises

Study Skills Exercise

In your next math class, take notes by drawing a vertical line about three-fourths of the way across the paper, as shown. On the left side, write down what your instructor puts on the board or overhead. On the right side, make your own comments about important words, procedures, or questions that you have.

Vocabulary and Key Concepts

1. **a.** Given the division statement $15 \div 3 = 5$, the number 15 is called the _____, the number 3 is called the _____, and the number 5 is called the _____.

   b. $5 \div 5 =$ _____

   c. $5 \div 1 =$ _____

   d. $0 \div 5 =$ _____

   e. $5 \div 0$ is _____ because no number multiplied by 0 equals 5.

   f. If 17 is divided by 5, the whole part of the quotient is 3 and the _____ is 2.

Review Exercises

2. Rewrite each statement using the indicated property.

   a. $2 + 5 =$ _____; commutative property of addition

   b. $2 \cdot 5 =$ _____; commutative property of multiplication

   c. $3 + (10 + 2) =$ _____; associative property of addition

   d. $3 \cdot (10 \cdot 2) =$ _____; associative property of multiplication

For Exercises 3–10, add, subtract, or multiply as indicated.

3. $48 \cdot 103$

4. $678 - 83$

5. $1008 + 245$

6. $14(220)$

7. 5230×127

8. $789(25)$

9. $4890 - 3988$

10. $38{,}002 + 3902$

Concept 1: Introduction to Division

For Exercises 11–16, simplify each expression. Then identify the dividend, divisor, and quotient. **(See Example 1.)**

11. $72 \div 8$

12. $32 \div 4$

13. $8\overline{)64}$

14. $5\overline{)35}$

15. $\dfrac{45}{9}$

16. $\dfrac{20}{5}$

Concept 2: Properties of Division

17. In your own words, explain the difference between dividing a number by zero and dividing zero by a number.

18. Explain what happens when a number is either divided or multiplied by 1.

For Exercises 19–30, use the properties of division to simplify the expression, if possible. **(See Example 2.)**

19. $15 \div 1$

20. $21\overline{)21}$

21. $0 \div 10$

22. $\dfrac{0}{3}$

23. $0\overline{)9}$

24. $4 \div 0$

25. $\dfrac{20}{20}$

26. $1\overline{)9}$

27. $\dfrac{16}{0}$

28. $\dfrac{5}{1}$

29. $8\overline{)0}$

30. $13 \div 13$

31. Show that $6 \div 3 = 2$ but $3 \div 6 \neq 2$ by using multiplication to check.

32. Show that division is not associative, using the numbers 36, 12, and 3.

Concept 3: Long Division

33. Explain the process for checking a division problem when there is no remainder.

34. Show how checking by multiplication can help us remember that $0 \div 5 = 0$ and that $5 \div 0$ is undefined.

For Exercises 35–46, divide and check by multiplying. **(See Examples 3 and 4.)**

35. $78 \div 6$
Check: $6 \times \square = 78$

36. $364 \div 7$
Check: $7 \times \square = 364$

37. $5\overline{)205}$
Check: $5 \times \square = 205$

38. $8\overline{)152}$
Check: $8 \times \square = 152$

39. $\dfrac{972}{2}$

40. $\dfrac{582}{6}$

41. $1227 \div 3$

42. $236 \div 4$

43. $5\overline{)1015}$

44. $5\overline{)2035}$

45. $\dfrac{4932}{6}$

46. $\dfrac{3619}{7}$

For Exercises 47–54, check each division problem. If it is incorrect, find the correct answer.

47. $4\overline{)224}^{\,56}$

48. $7\overline{)574}^{\,82}$

49. $761 \div 3 = 253$

50. $604 \div 5 = 120$

51. $\dfrac{1021}{9} = 113\text{ R}4$

52. $\dfrac{1311}{6} = 218\text{ R}3$

53. $8\overline{)203}^{\,25\text{ R}6}$

54. $7\overline{)821}^{\,117\text{ R}5}$

For Exercises 55–70, divide and check the answer. **(See Example 5.)**

55. $61 \div 8$

56. $89 \div 3$

57. $9\overline{)92}$

58. $5\overline{)74}$

59. $\dfrac{55}{2}$

60. $\dfrac{49}{3}$

61. $593 \div 3$

62. $801 \div 4$

63. $\dfrac{382}{9}$

64. $\dfrac{428}{8}$

65. $3115 \div 2$

66. $4715 \div 6$

67. $6014 \div 8$

68. $9013 \div 7$

69. $6\overline{)5012}$

70. $2\overline{)1101}$

0 **Chapter 1** Whole Numbers

Concept 4: Dividing by a Many-Digit Divisor

For Exercises 71–82, divide. **(See Examples 6 and 7.)**

71. $9110 \div 19$

72. $3505 \div 13$

73. $24\overline{)1051}$

74. $41\overline{)8104}$

75. $\dfrac{8008}{26}$

76. $\dfrac{9180}{15}$

77. $68{,}012 \div 54$

78. $92{,}013 \div 35$

79. $69{,}712 \div 304$

80. $51{,}107 \div 221$

81. $114\overline{)34{,}428}$

82. $421\overline{)87{,}989}$

Concept 5: Translations and Applications Involving Division

For Exercises 83–88, for each English sentence, write a mathematical expression and simplify.

83. Find the quotient of 497 and 71.

84. Find the quotient of 1890 and 45.

85. Divide 877 by 14.

86. Divide 722 by 53.

87. Divide 6 into 42.

88. Divide 9 into 108.

89. There are 392 students signed up for Anatomy 101. If each classroom can hold 28 students, find the number of classrooms needed. **(See Example 8.)**

90. A wedding reception is planned to take place in the fellowship hall of a church. The bride anticipates 120 guests, and each table will seat 8 people. How many tables should be set up for the reception to accommodate all the guests?

91. A case of tomato sauce contains 32 cans. If a grocer has 168 cans, how many cases can he fill completely? How many cans will be left over?

92. Austin has $425 to spend on dining room chairs. If each chair costs $52, does he have enough to purchase 8 chairs? If so, will he have any money left over?

93. Pauline drove 312 mi in 6 hr. Find Pauline's average speed (in miles per hour).

94. A house cleaning company charges $144 to clean a 3-room apartment. At this rate, how much does it cost to clean one room?

95. If it takes 2200 lb of grapes to make 100 gal of white wine, how many pounds are needed for 1 gal?

96. There are 7280 acres of ferns in Florida that are owned by 260 farmers. Find the average size of each farm.

97. Suppose Genny can type 1234 words in 22 min. Round each number to estimate her rate in words per minute. **(See Example 9.)**

98. On a trip to California from Illinois, Lavu drove 2780 mi. The gas tank in his car allows him to travel 405 mi. Round each number to the hundreds place to estimate the number of tanks of gas needed for the trip.

99. A group of 18 people go to a concert. Ticket prices are given in the bar graph. If the group has $450, can they all attend the concert? If so, which type of seats can they buy?   **(See Example 10.)**

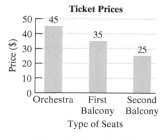

Ticket Prices

Figure for Exercise 99

100. The bar graph gives the average annual income for four professions: teacher, professor, CEO, and programmer. Find the monthly income for each of the four professions.

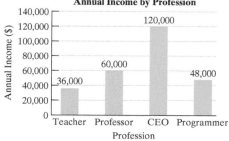

Annual Income by Profession

Figure for Exercise 100

101. The labels on most laundry detergents include the total number of wash loads that can be done. This makes comparison shopping easier since the amount of soap to be used can vary from one brand to the next. The label on Planet laundry detergent does not show the total number of loads. The instructions on the back label suggest using 4 fl oz of detergent per load of laundry.

    a. How many loads of laundry can be done with a 50-fl-oz bottle of Planet?

    b. How many ounces of detergent are left over?

102. At an elementary school, parents may pick up their children in a loading area in front of the school. Nine cars are allowed to pull up at one time, and it takes approximately 2 min to load and release the group of 9 cars. If it takes 26 minutes to get all cars through the line, how many cars are in line waiting to pick up children?

Calculator Connections

Topic: Multiplying and Dividing Whole Numbers

To multiply and divide numbers on a calculator, use the $\boxed{\times}$ and $\boxed{\div}$ keys, respectively.

Expression	Keystrokes	Result
$38{,}319 \times 1561$	38319 $\boxed{\times}$ 1561 **ENTER**	59815959
$2{,}449{,}216 \div 6248$	2449216 $\boxed{\div}$ 6248 **ENTER**	392

Calculator Exercises

For Exercises 103–106, solve the problem. Use a calculator to perform the calculations.

103. The United States consumes approximately 21,000,000 barrels (bbl) of oil per day. (*Source:* U.S. Energy Information Administration) How much does it consume in 1 year?

104. The average time to commute to work for people living in Washington State is 26 min (round trip 52 min). (*Source:* U.S. Census Bureau) How much time does a person spend commuting to and from work in 1 year if the person works 5 days a week for 50 weeks per year?

105. The budget for the U.S. federal government for 2010 was approximately $3552 billion. (*Source:* www.gpo.gov) How much could the government spend each quarter and still stay within its budget?

106. At a weigh station, a truck carrying 96 crates weighs in at 34,080 lb. If the truck weighs 9600 lb when empty, how much does each crate weigh?

Section 4.1 | Decimal Notation and Rounding

1. Decimal Notation

In Chapters 2 and 3, we studied fraction notation to denote equal parts of a whole. In this chapter, we introduce decimal notation to denote equal parts of a whole. We first introduce the concept of a decimal fraction. A **decimal fraction** is a fraction whose denominator is a power of 10. The following are examples of decimal fractions.

$$\frac{3}{10} \text{ is read as "three-tenths"}$$

$$\frac{7}{100} \text{ is read as "seven-hundredths"}$$

$$\frac{9}{1000} \text{ is read as "nine-thousandths"}$$

We now want to write these fractions in **decimal notation**. This means that we will write the numbers by using place values, as we did with whole numbers. The place value chart from Section 1.1 can be extended as shown in Figure 4-1.

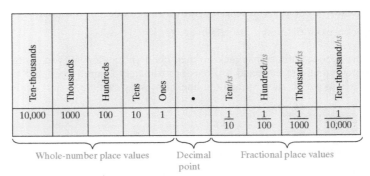

Figure 4-1

From Figure 4-1, we see that the decimal point separates the whole-number part from the fractional part. The place values for decimal fractions are located to the right of the decimal point. Their place value names are similar to those for whole numbers, but end in *ths*. Notice the correspondence between the tens place and the ten*ths* place. Similarly notice the hundreds place and the hundred*ths* place. Each place value on the left has a corresponding place value on the right, with the exception of the ones place. There is no "one*ths*" place.

Example 1　**Identify the Place Values**

Identify the place value of each underlined digit.

a. 30,804.0<u>9</u>　　　　**b.** 0.84692<u>0</u>　　　**c.** 2<u>9</u>3.604

Solution:

a. 30,804.0<u>9</u>　　　The digit 9 is in the hundredths place.

b. 0.84692<u>0</u>　　　The digit 2 is in the hundred-thousandths place.

c. 2<u>9</u>3.604　　　　The digit 9 is in the tens place.

For a whole number, the decimal point is understood to be after the ones place, and is usually not written. For example:

$$42. = 42$$

Using Figure 4-1, we can write the numbers $\frac{3}{10}$, $\frac{7}{100}$, and $\frac{9}{1000}$ in decimal notation.

Fraction	Word name	Decimal notation
$\dfrac{3}{10}$	Three-tenths	0.3 ↑ tenths place
$\dfrac{7}{100}$	Seven-hundredths	0.07 ↑ hundredths place
$\dfrac{9}{1000}$	Nine-thousandths	0.009 ↑ thousandths place

TIP: The 0 to the left of the decimal point is a place-holder so that the position of the decimal point can be easily identified. It does not contribute to the value of the number. Thus, 0.3 and .3 are equal.

Now consider the number $15\frac{7}{10}$. This value represents 1 ten + 5 ones + 7 tenths. In decimal form we have 15.7.

1 ten ————— ————— 7 tenths
5 ones

The decimal point is interpreted as the word *and*. Thus, 15.7 is read as "fifteen *and* seven tenths." The number 356.29 can be represented as

$$356 + 2 \text{ tenths} + 9 \text{ hundredths} = 356 + \frac{2}{10} + \frac{9}{100}$$

$$= 356 + \frac{20}{100} + \frac{9}{100} \qquad \text{We can use the LCD of } 100 \text{ to add the fractions.}$$

$$= 356\frac{29}{100}$$

We can read the number 356.29 as "three hundred fifty-six *and* twenty-nine hundredths."

This discussion leads to a quicker method to read decimal numbers.

Concept Connections

4. Where is the decimal point located for the number 65?

> **Reading a Decimal Number**
> **Step 1**   The part of the number to the left of the decimal point is read as a whole number. *Note:* If there is no whole-number part, skip to step 3.
> **Step 2**   The decimal point is read *and*.
> **Step 3**   The part of the number to the right of the decimal point is read as a whole number but is followed by the name of the place position of the digit farthest to the right.

Skill Practice

Write a word name for each number.
  5. 1004.6   **6.** 3.042
  7. 0.0063

Example 2   **Reading Decimal Numbers**

Write the word name for each number.

  a. 1028.4   **b.** 2.0736   **c.** 0.478

Solution:

  a. 1028.4   is written as "one thousand, twenty-eight and four-tenths."

  b. 2.0736   is written as "two and seven hundred thirty-six ten-thousandths."

  c. 0.478   is written as "four hundred seventy-eight thousandths."

Skill Practice

Write the word name as a numeral.
  8. Two hundred and two hundredths
  9. Seventy-nine and sixteen thousandths

Example 3   **Writing a Numeral from a Word Name**

Write the word name as a numeral.

  a. Four hundred eight and fifteen ten-thousandths

  b. Five thousand eight hundred and twenty-three hundredths

Solution:

  a. Four hundred eight and fifteen ten-thousandths: 408.0015

Place "15" so that the digit "5" is in the ten-thousandths place. Then place zeros as placeholders in the tenths place and hundredths place.

  b. Five thousand eight hundred and twenty-three hundredths: 5800.23

2. Writing Decimals as Mixed Numbers or Fractions

A fractional part of a whole may be written as a fraction or as a decimal. To convert a decimal to an equivalent fraction, it is helpful to think of the decimal in words. For example:

Decimal	Word Name	Fraction	
0.3	Three tenths	$\dfrac{3}{10}$	
0.67	Sixty-seven hundredths	$\dfrac{67}{100}$	
0.048	Forty-eight thousandths	$\dfrac{48}{1000} = \dfrac{6}{125}$	(simplified)
6.8	Six and eight-tenths	$6\dfrac{8}{10} = 6\dfrac{4}{5}$	(simplified)

Answers
. One thousand, four and six-tenths
. Three and forty-two thousandths
. Sixty-three ten-thousandths
. 200.02   **9.** 79.016

From the list, we notice several patterns that can be summarized as follows.

> ## Converting a Decimal to a Mixed Number or Proper Fraction
> **Step 1** The digits to the right of the decimal point are written as the numerator of the fraction.
> **Step 2** The place value of the digit farthest to the right of the decimal point determines the denominator.
> **Step 3** The whole-number part of the number is left unchanged.
> **Step 4** Once the number is converted to a fraction or mixed number, simplify the fraction to lowest terms, if possible.

Example 4 **Writing Decimals as Proper Fractions or Mixed Numbers**

Write the decimals as proper fractions or mixed numbers and simplify.

a. 0.847　　**b.** 0.0025　　**c.** 4.16

Solution:

a. $0.847 = \dfrac{847}{1000}$

thousandths place

b. $0.0025 = \dfrac{25}{10{,}000} = \dfrac{\overset{1}{25}}{\underset{400}{10{,}000}} = \dfrac{1}{400}$

ten-thousandths place

c. $4.16 = 4\dfrac{16}{100} = 4\dfrac{\overset{4}{16}}{\underset{25}{100}} = 4\dfrac{4}{25}$

hundredths place

Skill Practice

Write the decimals as proper fractions or mixed numbers.
10. 0.034　　**11.** 0.00086
12. 3.184

A decimal number greater than 1 can be written as a mixed number or as an improper fraction. The number 4.16 from Example 4(c) can be expressed as follows.

$$4.16 = 4\frac{16}{100} = 4\frac{4}{25} \quad \text{or} \quad \frac{104}{25}$$

A quick way to obtain an improper fraction for a decimal number greater than 1 is outlined here.

Concept Connections

13. Which is a correct representation of 3.17?
$3\dfrac{17}{100}$　or　$\dfrac{317}{100}$

> ## Writing a Decimal Number Greater Than 1 as an Improper Fraction
> **Step 1** The denominator is determined by the place position of the last digit to the right of the decimal point.
> **Step 2** The numerator is obtained by removing the decimal point of the original number. The resulting whole number is then written over the denominator.
> **Step 3** Simplify the improper fraction to lowest terms, if possible.

Answers

10. $\dfrac{17}{500}$　**11.** $\dfrac{43}{50{,}000}$　**12.** $3\dfrac{23}{125}$
13. They are both correct representations.

24 **Chapter 4** Decimals

For example:

Remove decimal point.

$$4.16 = \frac{416}{100} = \frac{104}{25} \quad \text{(simplified)}$$

hundredths place

Example 5 **Writing Decimals as Improper Fractions**

Write the decimals as improper fractions and simplify.

a. 40.2 **b.** 2.113

Solution:

a. $40.2 = \dfrac{402}{10} = \dfrac{\overset{201}{\cancel{402}}}{\underset{5}{\cancel{10}}} = \dfrac{201}{5}$

b. $2.113 = \dfrac{2113}{1000}$ Note that the fraction is already in lowest terms.

3. Ordering Decimal Numbers

It is often necessary to compare the values of two decimal numbers. One way of doing this is to compare the numbers in fractional form. First note that adding 0 after the last digit in a decimal number does not change its value. For example,

$$0.7 = 0.70 \quad \text{because} \quad \frac{7}{10} = \frac{70}{100}$$

Example 6 **Comparing Decimal Numbers**

Write the numbers from least to greatest.

$$2.1, \quad 2.09, \quad 2.15$$

Solution:

First write each number with the same number of digits to the right of the decimal point.

2.10,   2.09,   2.15   We can now write each number as a decimal
                            fraction with the same denominator. The value
$\dfrac{210}{100},$ $\dfrac{209}{100},$ $\dfrac{215}{100}$ 209 hundredths is less than 210 hundredths,
                            which is less than 215 hundredths.

Writing the numbers from least to greatest, we have 2.09, 2.1, and 2.15.

A quicker way to compare two decimals is outlined next.

Comparing Two Decimal Numbers
Step 1 Starting at the left (and moving toward the right), compare the digits in each corresponding place position.
Step 2 As we move from left to right, the first instance in which the digits differ determines the order of the numbers. The number having the greater digit is greater overall.

Section 4.1   Decimal Notation and Rounding   **225**

Example 7   **Ordering Decimals**

Fill in the blank with $<$ or $>$.

a. 0.68 ☐ 0.7   **b.** 3.462 ☐ 3.4619

Solution:

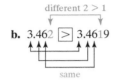

different 6 < 7   different 2 > 1

a. 0.68 $\boxed{<}$ 0.7   **b.** 3.462 $\boxed{>}$ 3.4619

same

Skill Practice

Fill in the blank with $<$ or $>$.

17. 4.163 ☐ 4.159

18. 218.38 ☐ 218.41

4. Rounding Decimals

The process to round the decimal part of a number is nearly the same as rounding whole numbers (see Section 1.4). The main difference is that the digits to the right of the rounding place position are dropped instead of being replaced by zeros.

Rounding Decimals to a Place Value to the Right of the Decimal Point

Step 1   Identify the digit one position to the right of the given place value.

Step 2   If the digit in step 1 is 5 or greater, add 1 to the given digit. If the digit in step 1 is less than 5, leave the given digit unchanged.

Step 3   Discard all digits to the right of the given digit.

Example 8   **Rounding Decimal Numbers**

a. Round 4.81542 to the thousandths place.

b. Round 52.9999 to the hundredths place.

Solution:

remaining digits discarded

a. 4.81542 ≈ 4.815

thousandths place — This digit is less than 5. Discard it and all digits to the right.

discard remaining digits

b. 5 2 . 9 9 9 9

hundredths place — This digit is greater than 5. Add 1 to the hundredths place digit.

- Since the hundredths place digit is 9, adding 1 requires us to carry 1 to the tenths place digit.
- Since the tenths place digit is 9, adding 1 requires us to carry 1 to the ones place digit.

≈ 53.00

Skill Practice

19. Round 45.372 to the hundredths place.

20. Round 134.9996 to the thousandths place.

Answers

17. $>$ **18.** $<$

19. 45.37   **20.** 135.000

26   **Chapter 4** Decimals

Example 9 Rounding Decimal Numbers

Round 14.795 to the indicated place value.

a. Tenths   **b.** Hundredths

Solution:

                                 remaining digits discarded

                  +1

a. $14.\,\overset{+1}{7}\,9\,5 \approx 14.8$

        tenths   This digit is 5 or greater. Add 1 to the tenths place.
        place

                                  remaining digit discarded

b. $14.7\,\overset{+1}{9}\,5 \approx 14.80$

  hundredths   This digit is 5 or greater. Add 1 to the hundredths place.
  place

> • Since the hundredths place digit is 9, adding 1 requires us to carry 1 to the tenths place digit.

In Example 9(b) the 0 in 14.80 indicates that the number was rounded to the hundredths place. It would be incorrect to drop the zero. Even though 14.8 has the same numerical value as 14.80, it implies a different level of accuracy. For example, when measurements are taken using some instrument such as a ruler or scale, the measured values are not exact. The place position to which a number is rounded reflects the accuracy of the measuring device. Thus, the value 14.8 lb indicates that the scale is accurate to the nearest tenth of a pound. The value 14.80 lb indicates that the scale is accurate to the nearest hundredth of a pound.

Section 4.1 Practice Exercises

Study Skills Exercise

After you get a test back, it is a good idea to correct the test so that you do not make the same errors again. One recommended approach is to use a clean sheet of paper and divide the paper down the middle vertically, as shown. For each problem that you missed on the test, rework the problem correctly on the left-hand side of the paper. Then write a written explanation on the right-hand side of the paper.

Take the time this week to make corrections from your last test.

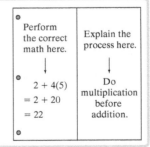

Perform the correct math here.	Explain the process here.
$2 + 4(5)$ $= 2 + 20$ $= 22$	Do multiplication before addition.

Vocabulary and Key Concepts

1. a. A _____ fraction is a fraction whose denominator is a power of 10.

   b. The first three place values to the right of the decimal point are the _____ place, the _____ place, and the _____ place.

Concept 1: Decimal Notation

2. Write the word name for the number 3005.

For Exercises 3–6, expand the powers of 10.

3. 10^2 **4.** 10^3 **5.** 10^4 **6.** 10^5

For Exercises 7–10, expand the powers of $\frac{1}{10}$.

7. $\left(\dfrac{1}{10}\right)^2$ **8.** $\left(\dfrac{1}{10}\right)^3$ **9.** $\left(\dfrac{1}{10}\right)^4$ **10.** $\left(\dfrac{1}{10}\right)^5$

For Exercises 11–22, identify the place value of each underlined digit. **(See Example 1.)**

11. 3.9̲83   **12.** 34.8̲2   **13.** 440.39̲   **14.** 24̲8.94

15. 48̲9.02   **16.** 4.0928̲4   **17.** 9.2834̲5   **18.** 0.321̲

19. 0.489̲   **20.** 58̲.211   **21.** 93̲.834   **22.** 5.000001̲

For Exercises 23–30, write the word name for each decimal fraction.

23. $\dfrac{9}{10}$ **24.** $\dfrac{7}{10}$ **25.** $\dfrac{23}{100}$ **26.** $\dfrac{19}{100}$

27. $\dfrac{33}{1000}$ **28.** $\dfrac{51}{1000}$ **29.** $\dfrac{407}{10,000}$ **30.** $\dfrac{20}{10,000}$

For Exercises 31–38, write the word name for the decimal. **(See Example 2.)**

31. 3.24   **32.** 4.26   **33.** 5.9   **34.** 3.4

35. 52.3   **36.** 21.5   **37.** 6.219   **38.** 7.338

For Exercises 39–44, write the word name as a numeral. **(See Example 3.)**

39. Eight thousand, four hundred seventy-two and fourteen thousandths

40. Sixty thousand, twenty-five and four hundred one ten-thousandths

41. Seven hundred and seven hundredths

42. Nine thousand and nine thousandths

43. Two million, four hundred sixty-nine thousand and five hundred six thousandths

44. Eighty-two million, six hundred fourteen and ninety-seven ten-thousandths

Concept 2: Writing Decimals as Mixed Numbers or Fractions

For Exercises 45–56, write the decimal as a proper fraction or as a mixed number and simplify. **(See Example 4.)**

45. 3.7   **46.** 1.9   **47.** 2.8   **48.** 4.2

49. 0.25   **50.** 0.75   **51.** 0.55   **52.** 0.45

53. 20.812   **54.** 32.905   **55.** 15.0005   **56.** 4.0015

For Exercises 57–64, write the decimal as an improper fraction and simplify. **(See Example 5.)**

57. 8.4   **58.** 2.5   **59.** 3.14   🖭 **60.** 5.65

61. 23.5   **62.** 14.6   **63.** 11.91   **64.** 21.33

Concept 3: Ordering Decimal Numbers

For Exercises 65–68, arrange the numbers from least to greatest. **(See Example 6.)**

65. 34.25, 34.2, 34.3, 34.29   **66.** 12.46, 12.4, 12.5, 12.49

67. 0.42, 0.043, $\frac{4}{10}$, 0.042, 0.43   **68.** 0.04999, 0.0499, $\frac{5}{10}$, 0.4999, 0.05001

For Exercises 69–76, fill in the blank with < or >. **(See Example 7.)**

69. 6.312 ☐ 6.321   **70.** 8.503 ☐ 8.530   🖭 **71.** 11.21 ☐ 11.2099   **72.** 10.51 ☐ 10.5098

73. 0.762 ☐ 0.76   **74.** 0.1291 ☐ 0.129   **75.** 51.72 ☐ 51.721   **76.** 49.06 ☐ 49.062

77. Which number is between 3.12 and 3.13? Circle all that apply.

   a. 3.127   **b.** 3.129   **c.** 3.134   **d.** 3.139

78. Which number is between 42.73 and 42.86? Circle all that apply.

   a. 42.81   **b.** 42.64   **c.** 42.79   **d.** 42.85

79. The batting averages for five legends are given in the table. Rank the players' batting averages from lowest to highest. (*Source:* Baseball Almanac)

Player	Average
Joe Jackson	0.3558
Ty Cobb	0.3664
Lefty O'Doul	0.3493
Ted Williams	0.3444
Rogers Hornsby	0.3585

80. The average speed, in miles per hour (mph), of the Daytona 500 for selected years is given in the table. Rank the speeds from slowest to fastest.

Year	Driver	Speed (mph)
1989	Darrell Waltrip	148.466
1991	Ernie Irvan	148.148
1997	Jeff Gordon	148.295
2007	Kevin Harvick	149.333

Source: NASCAR

Concept 4: Rounding Decimals

81. The numbers given all have equivalent value. However, suppose they represent measured values from a scale. Explain the difference in the interpretation of these numbers.

$$0.25, \quad 0.250, \quad 0.2500, \quad 0.25000$$

82. Which number properly represents 3.499999 rounded to the thousandths place?

    a. 3.500   **b.** 3.5   **c.** 3.500000   **d.** 3.499

83. Which value is rounded to the nearest tenth, 7.1 or 7.10?

84. Which value is rounded to the nearest hundredth, 34.50 or 34.5?

For Exercises 85–96, round the decimals to the indicated place values. **(See Examples 8 and 9.)**

85. 49.943; tenths   **86.** 12.7483; tenths   **87.** 33.416; hundredths

88. 4.359; hundredths   **89.** 9.0955; thousandths   **90.** 2.9592; thousandths

91. 21.0239; tenths   **92.** 16.804; hundredths   **93.** 6.9995; thousandths

94. 21.9997; thousandths   **95.** 0.0079499; ten-thousandths   **96.** 0.00084985; ten-thousandths

97. A snail moves at a rate of about 0.00362005 miles per hour. Round the decimal value to the ten-thousandths place.

For Exercises 98–101, round the number to the indicated place value.

	Number	Hundreds	Tens	Tenths	Hundredths	Thousandths
98.	349.2395					
99.	971.0948					
100.	79.0046					
101.	21.9754					

Expanding Your Skills

102. What is the least number with three places to the right of the decimal that can be created with the digits 2, 9, and 7? Assume that the digits cannot be repeated.

103. What is the greatest number with three places to the right of the decimal that can be created from the digits 2, 9, and 7? Assume that the digits cannot be repeated.

Section 4.2   Addition and Subtraction of Decimals

1. Addition and Subtraction of Decimals

In this section, we learn to add and subtract decimals. To begin, consider the sum $5.67 + 3.12$.

$$5.67 = \quad 5 + \frac{6}{10} + \frac{7}{100}$$

$$\underline{+\ 3.12} = \underline{+\ 3 + \frac{1}{10} \quad \frac{2}{100}}$$

$$8 + \frac{7}{10} + \frac{9}{100} = 8.79$$

Notice that the decimal points and place positions are lined up to add the numbers. In this way, we can add digits with the same place values because we are effectively adding decimal fractions with like denominators. The intermediate step of using fraction notation is often skipped. We can get the same result more quickly by adding digits in like place positions.

> **Adding and Subtracting Decimals**
> **Step 1** Write the numbers in a column with the decimal points and corresponding place values lined up. (You may insert additional zeros as placeholders after the last digit to the right of the decimal point.)
> **Step 2** Add or subtract the digits in columns from right to left, as you would whole numbers. The decimal point in the answer should be lined up with the decimal points from the original numbers.

Example 1   Adding Decimals

Add. $27.486 + 6.37$

Solution:

27.486	Line up the decimal points.
$+\ 6.370$	Insert an extra zero as a placeholder.

$\overset{1\ \ 1}{27.486}$	Add digits with common place values.
$+\ 6.370$	
33.856	Line up the decimal point in the answer.

With operations on decimals it is important to locate the correct position of the decimal point. A quick estimate can help you determine whether your answer is reasonable. From Example 1, we have

27.486	rounds to	27
6.370	rounds to	$\underline{+6}$
		33

The estimated value, 33, is close to the actual value of 33.856.

Example 2 **Adding Decimals**

Add. $3.7026 + 43 + 816.3$

Solution:

3.7026	Line up the decimal points.
43.0000	Insert a decimal point and four zeros after it.
+ 816.3000	Insert three zeros.

¹ ¹ 3.7026	Add the digits with common place values.
43.0000	
+ 816.3000	
863.0026	Line up the decimal point in the answer.

The sum is 863.0026.

> **TIP:** To check that the answer is reasonable, round each addend.
>
> | 3.7026 | rounds to | 4 |
> |---|---|---|
> | 43 | rounds to | ₁ 43 |
> | 816.3 | rounds to | + 816 |
> | | | 863 |
>
> which is close to the actual sum, 863.0026.

Skill Practice

Add.
3. $2.90741 + 15.13 + 3$

Example 3 **Subtracting Decimals**

Subtract.

a. $0.2868 - 0.056$ **b.** $139 - 28.63$ **c.** $192.4 - 89.387$

Solution:

a.

0.2868	Line up the decimal points.
− 0.0560	Insert an extra zero as a placeholder.
0.2308	Subtract digits with common place values.
	Decimal point in the answer is lined up.

b.

139.00	Line up the decimal points.
− 28.63	Insert extra zeros as placeholders.

⁹ 8 ₁₀ 10 13 9.0 0	Subtract digits with common place values.
− 2 8.6 3	Borrow where necessary.
1 1 0.3 7	Line up the decimal point in the answer.

c.

192.400	Line up the decimal points.
− 89.387	Insert extra zeros as placeholders.

8 12 3 ⁹ 10 10 19 2.4 0 0	Subtract digits with common place values.
− 8 9.3 8 7	Borrow where necessary.
1 0 3.0 1 3	Line up the decimal point in the answer.

Skill Practice

Subtract.
4. $3.194 - 0.512$
5. $0.397 - 0.1584$
6. $566.4 - 414.231$

Answers
3. 21.03741   **4.** 2.682
5. 0.2386   **6.** 152.169

32   **Chapter 4**   Decimals

Skill Practice

Simplify.

7. $416.04 + 67.2 - 291.76$

Example 4   Adding and Subtracting Decimals

Simplify. $27.819 - 13.78 + 9.6$

Solution:

$\underbrace{27.819 - 13.78}\; + 9.6$ We must apply the order of operations.

First subtract: $27.819 - 13.78$

$$\begin{array}{r} 27.\overset{7\;11}{8\cancel{1}9} \\ -\;13.780 \\ \hline 14.039 \end{array}$$

$= 14.039 + 9.6$ Now add 9.6 to the result.

$$\begin{array}{r} \overset{1}{14.039} \\ +\;9.600 \\ \hline 23.639 \end{array}$$

$= 23.639$

2. Applications of Addition and Subtraction of Decimals

Decimals are used often in measurements and in day-to-day applications.

Example 5   Subtracting Decimals in an Application

A graph of the U.S. population (in millions) is given for selected years (Figure 4-2).

a. What is the difference in population between the years 1970 and 1960?

b. What is the difference in population between the years 2000 and 1990?

Skill Practice

8. The following graph represents the average height (in inches) for girls for selected ages.
   a. What is the difference in height between a 9-year-old and a 3-year-old?
   b. What is the difference in height between an 11-year-old and a 9-year-old?

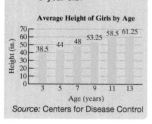

Average Height of Girls by Age

Source: Centers for Disease Control

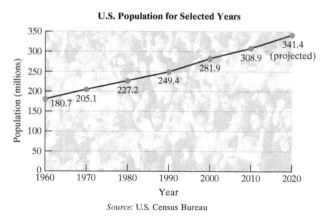

U.S. Population for Selected Years

Source: U.S. Census Bureau

Figure 4-2

Solution:

a. The difference in population between the years 1970 and 1960 is given by

$$\begin{array}{r} {\scriptstyle 1\ 10\ 4\ 11} \\ 2\,\cancel{0}\,\cancel{5}.\cancel{1} \\ -1\,8\,0.7 \\ \hline 2\,4.4 \end{array}$$ The difference in population is 24.4 million.

b. The difference in population between the years 2000 and 1990 is given by

$$\begin{array}{r} {\scriptstyle 7\ 11} \\ 2\,8\,\cancel{1}.9 \\ -\ 2\,4\,9.4 \\ \hline 3\,2.5 \end{array}$$ The difference in population is 32.5 million.

Comparing the values from parts (a) and (b), we see that the U.S. population increased during both 10-year periods. However, there was a greater increase between 1990 and 2000. This indicates that the rate of increase in population is increasing.

Example 6 **Applying Addition and Subtraction of Decimals in a Checkbook**

Fill in the balance for each line in the checkbook register, shown in Figure 4-3. What is the ending balance?

Check No.	Description	Payment	Deposit	Balance
				$684.60
2409	Doctor	$ 75.50		
2410	Mechanic	215.19		
2411	Home Depot	94.56		
	Paycheck		$981.46	
2412	Veterinarian	49.90		

Figure 4-3

Solution:

We begin with $684.60 in the checking account. For each payment, we subtract. For each deposit, we add.

Check No.	Description	Payment	Deposit	Balance	
				$ 684.60	
2409	Doctor	$ 75.50		609.10	= $684.60 − $75.50
2410	Mechanic	215.19		393.91	= $609.10 − $215.19
2411	Home Depot	94.56		299.35	= $393.91 − $94.56
	Paycheck		$981.46	1280.81	= $299.35 + $981.46
2412	Veterinarian	49.90		1230.91	= $1280.81 − $49.90

The ending balance is $1230.91.

Skill Practice

9. Fill in the balance for each line in the checkbook register.

Check	Payment	Deposit	Balance
			$437.80
1426	$82.50		
Pay		$514.02	
1427	26.04		

Answer

9.

Check	Payment	Deposit	Balance
			$ 437.80
1426	$82.50		355.30
Pay		$514.02	869.32
1427	26.04		843.28

34   **Chapter 4** Decimals

Skill Practice

Skill Practice

10. Consider the figure.

x

y

4.6 ft

2.7 ft

2.1 ft

1.8 ft

a. Find the length of side *x*.
b. Find the length of side *y*.
c. Find the perimeter.

Example 7   **Applying Decimals to Perimeter**

a. Find the length of the side labeled *x*.

b. Find the length of the side labeled *y*.

c. Find the perimeter of the figure.

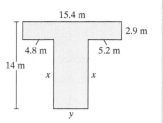

Solution:

a. If we extend the line segment labeled *x*
with the dashed line as shown below, we
see that the sum of side *x* and the dashed
line must equal 14 m. Therefore, subtract
14 − 2.9 to find the length of side *x*.

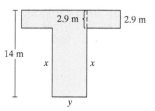

Length of side *x*: $\overset{3\ 10}{1\cancel{4}.\cancel{0}}$
                       $\underline{-\ 2.9}$
                       11.1

Side *x* is 11.1 m long.

b. The dashed line in the figure below has the same length as side *y*. We also
know that 4.8 + 5.2 + *y* must equal 15.4. Since 4.8 + 5.2 = 10.0,

$$y = 15.4 - 10.0$$
$$= 5.4$$

The length of side *y* is 5.4 m.

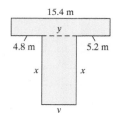

c. Now that we have the lengths of all sides, add them to get the perimeter.

$\overset{2\ 3}{15.4}$
2.9
5.2
11.1
5.4
11.1
4.8
$\underline{+\ 2.9}$
58.8

The perimeter is 58.8 m.

15.4 m

2.9 m   2.9 m

4.8 m   5.2 m

11.1 m   11.1 m

5.4 m

Section 4.2 Practice Exercises

Study Skills Exercise

Go to the online services that accompany this text. List two options that this online service offers that could help you in this course.

a. _____   **b.** _____

Review Exercises

1. Which number is equal to 2.007? Circle all that apply.

   a. 2.070   **b.** 2.0070   **c.** 2.00700   **d.** 2.7

2. Which number is equal to 5.03? Circle all that apply.

   a. 5.030   **b.** 5.30   **c.** 5.0300   **d.** 5.3

3. Which number is equal to $\frac{7}{100}$? Circle all that apply.

   a. 0.7   **b.** 0.07   **c.** 0.070   **d.** 0.007

4. Which number is equal to $\frac{9}{10}$? Circle all that apply.

   a. 0.09   **b.** 0.090   **c.** 0.90   **d.** 0.900

For Exercises 5–10, round the decimals to the indicated place values.

   5. 23.489; tenths   **6.** 42.314; hundredths   **7.** 8.6025; thousandths

   8. 0.981; tenths   **9.** 2.82998; ten-thousandths   **10.** 2.78999; thousandths

Concept 1: Addition and Subtraction of Decimals

For Exercises 11–16, add the decimal numbers. Then round the numbers and find the sum to determine if your answer is reasonable. The first estimate is done for you. **(See Examples 1 and 2.)**

Expression	Estimate		Expression	Estimate
11. 44.6 + 18.6	45 + 19 = 64		**12.** 28.2 + 23.2	
13. 5.306 + 3.645			**14.** 3.451 + 7.339	
15. 12.9 + 3.091			**16.** 4.125 + 5.9	

For Exercises 17–28, add the decimals. **(See Examples 1 and 2.)**

17. 78.9 + 0.9005	**18.** 44.2 + 0.7802	**19.** 23 + 8.0148	**20.** 7.9302 + 34
21. 34 + 23.0032 + 5.6	**22.** 23 + 8.01 + 1.0067	**23.** 68.394 + 32.02	**24.** 2.904 + 34.229
25. 103.94 + 24.5	**26.** 93.2 + 43.336	**27.** 54.2 + 23.993 + 3.87	**28.** 13.9001 + 72.4 + 34.13

36   **Chapter 4** Decimals

For Exercises 29–34, subtract the decimal numbers. Then round the numbers and find the difference to determine if your answer is reasonable. The first estimate is done for you. **(See Example 3.)**

Expression	Estimate	Expression	Estimate
29. $35.36 - 21.12$	$35 - 21 = 14$	**30.** $53.9 - 22.4$	
31. $7.24 - 3.56$		**32.** $23.3 - 20.8$	
33. $45.02 - 32.7$		**34.** $66.15 - 42.9$	

For Exercises 35–46, subtract the decimals. **(See Example 3.)**

35. $14.5 - 8.823$

36. $33.2 - 21.932$

37. $2 - 0.123$

38. $4 - 0.42$

39. $103.4 - 45.05 - 0.982$

40. $98.5 - 23.21 - 0.144$

41. $55.9 - 34.2354$

42. $49.1 - 24.481$

43. $18.003 - 3.238$

44. $21.03 - 16.446$

45. $183.01 - 23.452$

46. $164.23 - 44.3893$

Mixed Exercises

For Exercises 47–58, add and subtract as indicated. **(See Example 4.)**

47. $6.007 + 12.74 - 3.4$

48. $3.005 + 25.127 - 13.7$

49. $23.37 - 21.9 + 5.111$

50. $0.78 - 0.028 + 6.1$

51. $8.962 + 51 - 40.05$

52. $11.957 + 45 - 3.55$

53. $5.3 + 5.03 + 5.003 - 5.0003$

54. $2.6 + 2.06 + 2.006 - 2.0006$

55. $5.84 + 5.084 - 5.0084$

56. $85.3 - 47.0092 + 4.06$

57. $10 - 0.9 - 0.09 - 0.009$

58. $5 - 0.9 - 0.99 - 0.999$

Concept 2: Applications of Addition and Subtraction of Decimals

59. The amount of time that it takes Mercury, Venus, Earth, and Mars to revolve about the Sun is given in the graph. **(See Example 5.)**

  a. How much longer does it take Mars to complete a revolution around the Sun than the Earth?

  b. How much longer does it take Venus than Mercury to revolve around the Sun?

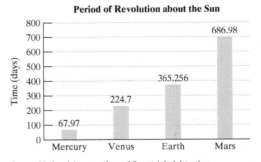

Source: National Aeronautics and Space Administration

60. The birth weights of the Dilley sextuplets are given in the graph.

  a. What is the difference between the weights of Julian and Quinn?

  b. What is the total weight of all six babies?

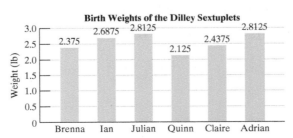

61. Water flows into a pool at a constant rate. The water level is recorded at several 1-hr intervals.

    a. From the table, how many inches is the water level rising each hour?

    b. At this rate, what will the water level be at 1:00 P.M.?

    c. At this rate, what will the water level be at 3:00 P.M.?

Time	Water Level
9:00 A.M.	4.2 in.
10:00 A.M.	5.9 in.
11:00 A.M.	7.6 in.
12:00 P.M.	9.3 in.

62. The total gross earnings in the United States for four top animated films are given in the table.

    a. What was the difference between the earnings for *Shrek 2* and *The Lion King*?

    b. What was the difference between the earnings for *Finding Nemo* and *Shrek the Third*?

    c. What was the total earnings for all four films?

Movie	Earnings ($ millions)
Shrek 2	441.2
Finding Nemo	339.7
The Lion King	328.5
Shrek the Third	322.7

63. Fill in the balance for each line in the checkbook register shown in the figure. What was the ending balance?
(See Example 6.)

Check No.	Description	Payment	Deposit	Balance
				$ 245.62
2409	Electric bill	$ 52.48		
2410	Groceries	72.44		
2411	Department store	108.34		
	Paycheck		$1084.90	
2412	Restaurant	23.87		
	Transfer from savings		200	

64. A section of a bank statement is shown in the figure. Find the mistake that was made by the bank.

Date	Action	Payment	Deposit	Balance
				$1124.35
Jan. 2	Check #4214	$749.32		375.03
Jan. 3	Check #4215	37.29		337.74
Jan. 4	Transfer from savings		$ 400.00	737.74
Jan. 5	Paycheck		1451.21	2188.95
Jan. 6	Cash withdrawal	150.00		688.95

65. A normal human red blood cell count is between 4.2 and 6.9 million cells per microliter (μL). A cancer patient undergoing chemotherapy has a red blood cell count of 2.85 million cells per microliter. How far below the lower normal limit is this?

66. A laptop computer was originally priced at $1299.99 and was discounted to $998.95. By how much was it marked down?

38   **Chapter 4**   Decimals

67. The table shows the thickness of four U.S. coins. If you stacked three quarters and a dime in one pile and two nickels and two pennies in another pile, which pile would be higher?

68. How much thicker is a nickel than a quarter?

Coin	Thickness
Quarter	1.75 mm
Dime	1.35 mm
Nickel	1.95 mm
Penny	1.55 mm

Source: U.S. Department of the Treasury

'or Exercises 69–72, find the lengths of the sides labeled *x* and *y*.
'hen find the perimeter. **(See Example 7.)**

69.

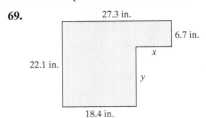

70.

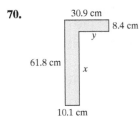

71.

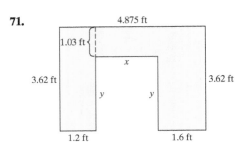

72.

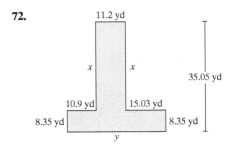

73. A city bus follows the route shown in the map. How far does it travel in one circuit?

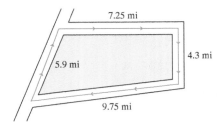

74. Santos built a new deck and needs to put a railing around the sides. He does not need railing where the deck is against the house. How much railing should he purchase?

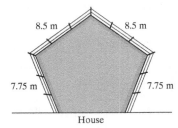

Expanding Your Skills

In a circle, the length of a line segment connecting two points on the circle and passing through the center is called a *diameter*.

Use the definition of a diameter for Exercises 75 and 76.

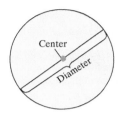

75. The wire in a cable has a diameter of 6 mm. The insulation is 0.5 mm. What is the diameter of the cable with the insulation included?

76. Find the inner diameter of the cable if the total diameter is 1.65 cm and the insulation is 0.15 cm thick.

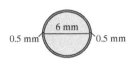

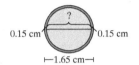

Calculator Connections

Topic: Entering Decimals on a Calculator

To enter decimals on a calculator, use the ⟨ . ⟩ key.

Expression	Keystrokes	Result
984.126 + 37.11	984 ⟨.⟩ 126 ⟨+⟩ 37 ⟨.⟩ 11 **ENTER**	1021.236

Calculator Exercises

For Exercises 77–82, refer to the table. The table gives the closing stock prices (in dollars per share) for the first day of trading for the given month.

Stock	Jan.	Feb.	March	April	May
IBM	132.45	125.53	128.57	128.25	130.46
FedEx	83.45	80.67	85.81	92.17	90.01

77. By how much did the IBM stock decrease between January and May?

78. By how much did the FedEx stock increase between January and May?

79. Between which two consecutive months did the FedEx stock increase the most? What was the amount of increase?

80. Between which two consecutive months did the IBM stock increase the most? What was the amount of increase?

81. Between which two consecutive months did the FedEx stock decrease the most? What was the amount of decrease?

82. Between which two consecutive months did the IBM stock decrease the most? What was the amount of decrease?

Section 4.3   Multiplication of Decimals

Concepts

. **Multiplication of Decimals**
. **Multiplication by a Power of 10 and by a Power of 0.1**
. **Applications Involving Multiplication of Decimals**

1. Multiplication of Decimals

Multiplication of decimals is much like multiplication of whole numbers. However, we need to know where to place the decimal point in the product. Consider the product 0.3×0.41. One way to multiply these numbers is to write them first as decimal fractions.

$$0.3 \times 0.41 = \frac{3}{10} \times \frac{41}{100} = \frac{123}{1000} \text{ or } 0.123$$

Another method multiplies the factors vertically. First we multiply the numbers as though they were whole numbers. We temporarily disregard the decimal point in the product because it will be placed later.

$$\begin{array}{r} 0.41 \\ \times\ 0.3 \\ \hline 123 \end{array}$$ ⟵ decimal point not yet placed

Concept Connections

1. How many decimal places will be in the product 2.72×1.4?
2. Explain the difference between the process to multiply 123×51 and the process to multiply 1.23×5.1.

From the first method, we know that the correct answer to this problem is 0.123. Notice that 0.123 contains the same number of decimal places as the two factors combined. That is,

$$\begin{array}{r} 0.41 \\ \times\ 0.3 \\ \hline .123 \end{array}$$

⟵ 2 decimal places
⟵ 1 decimal place
⟵ 3 decimal places

   The process to multiply decimals is summarized as follows.

> **TIP:** When multiplying decimals, it is *not* necessary to line up the decimal points as we do when we add or subtract decimals. Instead, we write the factors "right-justified."

> **Multiplying Two Decimals**
> **Step 1**   Multiply as you would whole numbers.
> **Step 2**   Place the decimal point in the product so that the number of decimal places equals the combined number of decimal places of both factors.
>
> *Note:* You may need to insert zeros to the left of the whole-number product to get the correct number of decimal places in the answer.

Skill Practice

Multiply.
3. 19.7×4.1

In Example 1, we multiply decimals by using this process.

| Example 1 | **Multiplying Decimals** |

Multiply. $\begin{array}{r} 11.914 \\ \times\ 0.8 \end{array}$

Solution:

$$\begin{array}{r} {\scriptstyle 1\,7\ \ 1\,3} \\ 11.914 \\ \times\ \ 0.8 \\ \hline 9.5312 \end{array}$$

3 decimal places
+ 1 decimal place
4 decimal places

The product is 9.5312.

Answers

. 3
. The actual process of vertical multiplication is the same for both cases. However, for the product 1.23×5.1, the decimal point must be placed so that the product has the same number of decimal places as both factors combined (in this case, 3).
. 80.77

Example 2 **Multiplying Decimals**

Multiply. Then use estimation to check the location of the decimal point.

$$29.3 \times 2.8$$

Solution:

Actual product:

$$
\begin{array}{r}
\overset{1}{}\overset{72}{} \\
29.3 \\
\times\ 2.8 \\
\hline
2344 \\
5860 \\
\hline
82.04
\end{array}
$$

1 decimal place
+ 1 decimal place

2 decimal places   The product is 82.04.

To check the answer, we can round the factors and estimate the product. The purpose of the estimate is primarily to determine whether we have placed the decimal point correctly. Therefore, it is usually sufficient to round each factor to the left-most nonzero digit. This is called **front-end rounding.** Thus,

$$
\begin{array}{ccr}
29.3 & \text{rounds to} & 30 \\
\times\ 2.8 & \text{rounds to} & \times\ 3 \\
\hline
& & 90
\end{array}
$$

The first digit for the actual product <u>8</u>2.04 and the first digit for the estimate <u>9</u>0 is the tens place. Therefore, we are reasonably sure that we have located the decimal point correctly. The estimate 90 is close to 82.04.

Example 3 **Multiplying Decimals**

Multiply. Then use estimation to check the location of the decimal point.

$$2.79 \times 0.0003$$

Solution:

Actual product: Estimate:

$$
\begin{array}{r}
\overset{2}{}\overset{2}{}79 \\
2.79 \\
\times\ 0.0003 \\
\hline
.000837
\end{array}
$$

2 decimal places
+ 4 decimal places

6 decimal places
(insert 3 zeros to the left)

$$
\begin{array}{ccr}
2.79 & \text{rounds to} & 3 \\
\times\ 0.0003 & \text{rounds to} & \times\ 0.0003 \\
\hline
& & 0.0009
\end{array}
$$

The first digit for both the actual product and the estimate is in the ten-thousandths place. We are reasonably sure the decimal point is positioned correctly.

The product is 0.000837.

42   **Chapter 4** Decimals

Skill Practice

Simplify.
  6. $(1.5)^2$

Example 4 Squaring a Decimal

Simplify. $(0.05)^2$

Solution:

$(0.05)^2 = 0.05 \times 0.05$

0.05	2 decimal places
$\times\ 0.05$	2 decimal places
0.0025	4 decimal places

When squaring a decimal, remember to count the decimal places to the right of the decimal points in both factors.

Consider: $(0.2)^2 = 0.04$
$(0.02)^2 = 0.0004$
$(0.002)^2 = 0.000004$

2. Multiplication by a Power of 10 and by a Power of 0.1

Consider the number 2.7 multiplied by the powers of 10; that is, $10, 100, 1000\ldots$

10	100	1000
$\times\ 2.7$	$\times\ 2.7$	$\times\ 2.7$
70	700	7000
200	2000	20000
27.0	270.0	2700.0

Multiplying 2.7 by 10 moves the decimal point 1 place to the right.
Multiplying 2.7 by 100 moves the decimal point 2 places to the right.
Multiplying 2.7 by 1000 moves the decimal point 3 places to the right.

This leads us to the following generalization.

> **Multiplying a Decimal by a Power of 10**
> Move the decimal point to the right the same number of decimal places as the number of zeros in the power of 10.

Skill Practice

Multiply.
  7. 81.6×1000
  8. $0.0000085 \times 10,000$
  9. $2.396 \times 10,000,000$

Example 5 Multiplying by Powers of 10

Multiply.

a. $14.78 \times 10,000$ **b.** 0.0064×100 **c.** $8.271 \times 1,000,000$

Solution:

a. $14.78 \times 10,000 = 147,800$ Move the decimal point 4 places to the right.

b. $0.0064 \times 100 = 0.64$ Move the decimal point 2 places to the right.

c. $8.271 \times 1,000,000 = 8,271,000$ Move the decimal point 6 places to the right.

Answers

  . 2.25   **7.** 81,600   **8.** 0.085
  . 23,960,000

Multiplying a decimal by 10, 100, 1000, and so on increases its value. Therefore, it makes sense to move the decimal point to the *right*. Now suppose we multiply a decimal by 0.1, 0.01, and 0.001. These numbers represent the decimal fractions $\frac{1}{10}$, $\frac{1}{100}$, and $\frac{1}{1000}$, respectively, and are easily recognized as powers of 0.1 (see Section 2.4). Taking one-tenth of a number or one-hundredth of a number makes the number smaller. To multiply by 0.1, 0.01, 0.001, and so on (powers of 0.1), move the decimal point to the *left*.

$$
\begin{array}{ccc}
3.6 & 3.6 & 3.6 \\
\times\ 0.1 & \times\ 0.01 & \times\ 0.001 \\
\hline
.36 & .036 & .0036
\end{array}
$$

Multiplying a Decimal by Powers of 0.1
Move the decimal point to the left the same number of places as there are decimal places in the power of 0.1.

Concept Connections

10. Explain the difference between multiplying a number by 100 versus 0.01.

Example 6 **Multiplying by Powers of 0.1**

Multiply.

a. 62.074×0.0001 **b.** 7965.3×0.1 **c.** 0.0057×0.00001

Solution:

a. $62.074 \times 0.0001 = 0.0062074$ Move the decimal point 4 places to the left. Insert extra zeros.

b. $7965.3 \times 0.1 = 796.53$ Move the decimal point 1 place to the left.

c. $0.0057 \times 0.00001 = 0.000000057$ Move the decimal point 5 places to the left.

Skill Practice

Multiply.

11. 471.034×0.01
12. $9,437,214.5 \times 0.00001$
13. 0.0004×0.001

Sometimes people prefer to use number names to express very large numbers. For example, we might say that the U.S. population in a recent year was approximately 280 million. To write this in decimal form, we note that 1 million = 1,000,000. In this case, we have 280 of this quantity. Thus,

$$280 \text{ million} = 280 \times 1,000,000 \text{ or } 280,000,000$$

Example 7 **Naming Large Numbers**

Write the decimal number representing each word name.

a. The distance between the Earth and Sun is approximately 92.9 million miles.

b. The number of deaths in the United States due to heart disease in 2010 was projected to be 8 hundred thousand.

c. A recent estimate claimed that collectively Americans throw away 472 billion pounds of garbage each year.

Skill Practice

Write a decimal number representing the word name.

14. The population in Bexar County, Texas, is approximately 1.6 million.
15. Light travels approximately 5.9 trillion miles in 1 year.
16. The legislative branch of the federal government employs approximately 31 thousand employees.

Answers

10. Multiplying a number by 100 increases its value. Therefore, we move the decimal point to the right two places. Multiplying a number by 0.01 decreases its value. Therefore, move the decimal point to the left two places.
11. 4.71034   **12.** 94.372145
13. 0.0000004   **14.** 1,600,000
15. 5,900,000,000,000   **16.** 31,000

44   **Chapter 4**   Decimals

Solution:

a. 92.9 million = 92.9 × 1,000,000 = 92,900,000

b. 8 hundred thousand = 8 × 100,000 = 800,000

c. 472 billion = 472 × 1,000,000,000 = 472,000,000,000

3. Applications Involving Multiplication of Decimals

Skill Practice

17. A book club ordered 12 books on www.amazon .com for $8.99 each. The shipping cost was $4.95. What was the total bill?

Example 8 **Applying Decimal Multiplication**

Jane Marie bought 8 cans of tennis balls for $1.98 each. She paid $1.03 in tax. What was the total bill?

Solution:

The cost of the tennis balls before tax is

$$8(\$1.98) = \$15.84$$

$$\begin{array}{r} {}^{7\ 6}\\ 1.98 \\ \times\ \ \ 8 \\ \hline 15.84 \end{array}$$

Adding the tax to this value, we have

$$\begin{pmatrix} \text{Total} \\ \text{cost} \end{pmatrix} = \begin{pmatrix} \text{Cost of} \\ \text{tennis balls} \end{pmatrix} + (\text{Tax})$$

$$\begin{array}{r} = \$15.84 \\ +\ 1.03 \\ \hline \$16.87 \end{array} \quad \text{The total cost is } \$16.87.$$

Skill Practice

18. The IMAX movie screen at the Museum of Science and Discovery in Ft. Lauderdale, Florida, is 18 m by 24.4 m. What is the area of the screen?

Example 9 **Finding the Area of a Rectangle**

The *Mona Lisa* is perhaps the most famous painting in the world. It was painted by Leonardo da Vinci somewhere between 1503 and 1506 and now hangs in the Louvre in Paris, France. The dimensions of the painting are 30 in. by 20.875 in. What is the total area?

Solution:

Recall that the area of a rectangle is given by

$$A = \ell \cdot w$$

$$A = (30 \text{ in.})(20.875 \text{ in.})$$

$$\begin{array}{r} {}^{2\ \ 21}\\ 20.875 \\ \times\ 30 \\ \hline 0 \\ 626250 \\ \hline 626.250 \end{array}$$

$$= 626.25 \text{ in.}^2$$

The area of the *Mona Lisa* is 626.25 in.^{2}.

Section 4.3   Practice Exercises

Study Skills Exercise

Look through this chapter and write down page numbers in which you can find the following features.

a. Avoiding Mistakes box _____   **b.** TIP box _____

c. Key term (shown in bold) _____   **d.** Skill Practice exercises _____

Vocabulary and Key Concepts

1. Rounding a number to the left-most nonzero digit is called _____ -end rounding.

Review Exercises

2. Fill in the blank with < or >. 51.4382 ☐ 51.4389

For Exercises 3–6, expand the powers of 10 and 0.1.

3. 10^3 **4.** 0.1^3 **5.** 0.1^2 **6.** 10^2

Concept 1: Multiplication of Decimals

For Exercises 7–18, multiply the decimals. **(See Examples 1–3.)**

7. $\begin{array}{r} 0.8 \\ \times\ 0.5 \\ \hline \end{array}$ **8.** $\begin{array}{r} 0.6 \\ \times\ 0.5 \\ \hline \end{array}$ **9.** $(0.9)(4)$ **10.** $(0.2)(9)$

11. $\begin{array}{r} 0.4 \\ \times\ 20 \\ \hline \end{array}$ **12.** $\begin{array}{r} 0.9 \\ \times\ 30 \\ \hline \end{array}$ **13.** $(60)(0.003)$ **14.** $(40)(0.005)$

15. $\begin{array}{r} 22.38 \\ \times\ 0.8 \\ \hline \end{array}$ **16.** $\begin{array}{r} 31.67 \\ \times\ 0.4 \\ \hline \end{array}$ **17.** $\begin{array}{r} 14 \\ \times\ 0.002 \\ \hline \end{array}$ **18.** $\begin{array}{r} 0.25 \\ \times\ 40 \\ \hline \end{array}$

For Exercises 19–26, round each number by using front-end rounding.

19. 135   **20.** 481   **21.** 28   **22.** 52

23. 0.0672   **24.** 0.0807   **25.** 0.241   **26.** 0.339

For Exercises 27–40, multiply the decimals. Then estimate the answer by rounding. The first estimate is done for you.

	Exact	Estimate		Exact	Estimate		Exact	Estimate

27. $\begin{array}{r} 8.3 \\ \times\ 4.5 \\ \hline \end{array}$ Estimate $\begin{array}{r} 8 \\ \times\ 5 \\ \hline 40 \end{array}$ **28.** $\begin{array}{r} 4.3 \\ \times\ 9.2 \\ \hline \end{array}$ **29.** $\begin{array}{r} 0.58 \\ \times\ 7.2 \\ \hline \end{array}$

30. $\begin{array}{r} 0.83 \\ \times\ 6.5 \\ \hline \end{array}$ **31.** 5.92×0.8 **32.** 9.14×0.6

33. $(0.413)(7)$ **34.** $(0.321)(6)$ **35.** 35.9×3.2 **36.** 41.7×6.1

37. 562×0.004 **38.** 984×0.009 **39.** 0.0004×3.6 **40.** 0.0008×6.5

41. Compare the quantities $(0.3)^2$ and 0.9. Are they equal?

42. Compare the quantities $(0.8)^2$ and 6.4. Are they equal?

For Exercises 43–54, simplify the expressions. **(See Example 4.)**

43. $(0.06)^2$	**44.** $(0.16)^2$	**45.** $(2.5)^2$	**46.** $(1.1)^2$
47. $(0.4)^2$	**48.** $(0.7)^2$	**49.** $(1.3)^2$	**50.** $(2.4)^2$
51. $(0.1)^3$	**52.** $(0.2)^3$	**53.** $(0.2)^4$	**54.** $(0.3)^3$

Concept 2: Multiplication by a Power of 10 and by a Power of 0.1

55. If 417.43 is multiplied by 100, will the decimal point move to the left or to the right? By how many places?

56. If 2498.613 is multiplied by 10,000, will the decimal point move to the left or to the right? By how many places?

57. Multiply the numbers.
   a. 5.1×10 **b.** 5.1×100 **c.** 5.1×1000 **d.** $5.1 \times 10,000$

58. If 256.8 is multiplied by 0.001, will the decimal point move to the left or to the right? By how many places?

59. If 0.45 is multiplied by 0.1, will the decimal point move to the left or to the right? By how many places?

60. Multiply the numbers.
   a. 5.1×0.1 **b.** 5.1×0.01 **c.** 5.1×0.001 **d.** 5.1×0.0001

For Exercises 61–72, multiply the numbers by the powers of 10 and 0.1. **(See Examples 5 and 6.)**

61. 34.9×100	**62.** 2.163×100	**63.** 96.59×1000	**64.** 18.22×1000
65. 93.3×0.01	**66.** 80.2×0.01	**67.** 54.03×0.001	**68.** 23.11×0.001
69. 2.001×10	**70.** 5.932×10	**71.** 0.5×0.0001	**72.** 0.8×0.0001

For Exercises 73–76, write the amount in terms of cents.

73. $3.24	**74.** $21.56	**75.** $0.37	**76.** $0.75

For Exercises 77–80, write the amount in terms of dollars.

77. 347¢	**78.** 512¢	**79.** 2041¢	**80.** 5712¢

81. **a.** Round $1.499 to the nearest dollar.
   b. Round $1.499 to the nearest cent.

82. **a.** Round $20.599 to the nearest dollar.
   b. Round $20.599 to the nearest cent.

For Exercises 83–88, write the decimal number representing each word name. **(See Example 7.)**

83. The number of beehives in the United States is 2.6 million. (*Source:* U.S. Department of Agriculture)

84. The people of France collectively consume 34.7 million gallons of champagne per year. (*Source:* Food and Agriculture Organization of the United Nations)

85. The most stolen make of car worldwide is Toyota. For a recent year, there were four hundred-thousand Toyota's stolen. (*Source:* Interpol)

86. The musical *Miss Saigon* ran for about 4 thousand performances in a 10-year period.

87. The people in the United States have spent over $20.549 billion on DVDs.

88. Coca-Cola Classic was the greatest selling brand of soft-drinks. For a recent year, over 4.8 billion gallons were sold in the United States. (*Source:* Beverage Marketing Corporation)

Concept 3: Applications Involving Multiplication of Decimals

89. One gallon of gasoline weighs about 6.3 lb. However, when burned, it produces 20 lb of carbon dioxide (CO_2). This is because most of the weight of the CO_2 comes from the oxygen in the air.

   a. How many pounds of gasoline does a Hummer H2 carry when its tank is full (the tank holds 32 gal).

   b. How many pounds of CO_2 does a Hummer H2 produce after burning an entire tankful of gasoline?

90. Corrugated boxes for shipping cost $2.27 each. How much will 10 boxes cost including tax of $1.59?

91. The Athletic Department at Broward College bought 20 pizzas for $12.95 each, 10 Greek salads for $5.95 each, and 60 soft drinks for $1.29 each. What was the total bill including a sales tax of $27.71? **(See Example 8.)**

92. A hotel gift shop ordered 40 T-shirts at $8.69 each, 10 hats at $3.95 each, and 20 beach towels at $4.99 each. What was the total cost of the merchandise, including the $29.21 sales tax?

93. At General Tires, one tire costs $70.20. A set of four Firestone tires costs $231.99. How much can a person save by buying the set of four Firestone tires compared to four General tires?

94. Certain DVD titles are on sale for 2 for $36. If they regularly sell for $24.99, how much can a person save by buying 4 DVDs?

For Exercises 95 and 96, find the area. **(See Example 9.)**

95.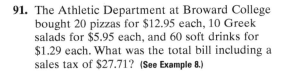

0.05 km

0.023 km

96.

4.5 yd

6.7 yd

97. Blake plans to build a rectangular patio that is 15 yd by 22.2 yd. What is the total area of the patio?

98. The front page of a newspaper is 56 cm by 31.5 cm. Find the area of the page.

Expanding Your Skills

99. Evaluate.

   a. $(0.3)^2$ **b.** $\sqrt{0.09}$

100. Evaluate.

   a. $(0.5)^2$ **b.** $\sqrt{0.25}$

For Exercises 101–104, evaluate the square roots.

101. $\sqrt{0.01}$ **102.** $\sqrt{0.04}$ **103.** $\sqrt{0.36}$ **104.** $\sqrt{0.49}$

Section 4.4 Division of Decimals

Concepts

- Division of Decimals
- Rounding a Quotient
- Applications of Decimal Division

1. Division of Decimals

Dividing decimals is much the same as dividing whole numbers. However, we must determine where to place the decimal point in the quotient.

First consider the quotient $3.5 \div 7$. We can write the numbers in fractional form and then divide.

$$3.5 \div 7 = \frac{35}{10} \div \frac{7}{1} = \frac{35}{10} \cdot \frac{1}{7} = \frac{35}{70} = \frac{5}{10} = 0.5$$

Now consider the same problem by using the efficient method of long division: $7)\overline{3.5}$.

When the divisor is a whole number, we place the decimal point directly above the decimal point in the dividend. Then we divide as we would whole numbers.

Decimal point placed above
the decimal point in the dividend.

$$\begin{array}{r} .5 \\ 7)\overline{3.5} \end{array}$$

Dividing a Decimal by a Whole Number

To divide by a whole number:

Step 1 Place the decimal point in the quotient directly above the decimal point in the dividend.

Step 2 Divide as you would whole numbers.

Skill Practice

Divide. Check by using multiplication.

1. $502.96 \div 8$

Example 1   Dividing by a Whole Number

Divide and check the answer by multiplying.

$$30.55 \div 13$$

Solution:

Locate the decimal point in the quotient.

$$13)\overline{30.55}$$

$$\begin{array}{r} 2.35 \\ 13)\overline{30.55} \\ -26 \\ \hline 45 \\ -39 \\ \hline 65 \\ -65 \\ \hline 0 \end{array}$$

Divide as you would whole numbers.

Check by multiplying:

$$\begin{array}{r} {\scriptstyle 1\ 1} \\ 2.35 \\ \times\ 13 \\ \hline 705 \\ 2350 \\ \hline 30.55\ \checkmark \end{array}$$

When dividing decimals, we do not use a remainder. Instead we insert zeros to the right of the dividend and continue dividing. This is demonstrated in Example 2.

| Example 2 | **Dividing by a Whole Number** |

Divide and check the answer by multiplying.

$$3.5 \div 4$$

Solution:

Locate the decimal point in the quotient.

$$4\overline{)3.5}$$

$$\begin{array}{r} .8 \\ 4\overline{)3.5} \\ -32 \\ \hline 3 \end{array}$$ ← Rather than using a remainder, we insert zeros in the dividend and continue dividing.

$$\begin{array}{r} .875 \\ 4\overline{)3.500} \\ -32 \\ \hline 30 \\ -28 \\ \hline 20 \\ -20 \\ \hline 0 \end{array}$$

Check by multiplying:

$$\begin{array}{r} {}^{3\ 2} \\ 0.875 \\ \times\ \ 4 \\ \hline 3.500\ \checkmark \end{array}$$

The quotient is 0.875.

Skill Practice

Divide.
2. $6.8 \div 5$

| Example 3 | **Dividing by a Whole Number** |

Divide and check the answer by multiplying. $40\overline{)5}$

Solution:

$$40\overline{)5.}$$ The dividend is a whole number, and the decimal point is understood to be to its right. Insert the decimal point above it in the quotient.

$$\begin{array}{r} .125 \\ 40\overline{)5.000} \\ -40 \\ \hline 100 \\ -80 \\ \hline 200 \\ -200 \\ \hline 0 \end{array}$$

Since 40 is greater than 5, we need to insert zeros to the right of the dividend.

Check by multiplying.

$$\begin{array}{r} {}^{1\ 2} \\ 0.125 \\ \times\ 40 \\ \hline 000 \\ 5000 \\ \hline 5.000\ \checkmark \end{array}$$

The quotient is 0.125.

Skill Practice

Divide.
3. $20\overline{)3}$

Answers

2. 1.36   **3.** 0.15

Sometimes when dividing decimals, the quotient follows a repeated pattern. The result is called a **repeating decimal**.

Skill Practice

Divide.
4. $2.4 \div 9$

Example 4   Dividing Where the Quotient Is a Repeating Decimal

Divide. $1.7 \div 30$

Solution:

$$
\begin{array}{r}
.05666\ldots \\
30\overline{)1.70000} \\
-150 \\
\hline
200 \\
-180 \\
\hline
200 \\
-180 \\
\hline
200
\end{array}
$$

Notice that as we continue to divide, we get the same values for each successive step. This causes a pattern of repeated digits in the quotient. Therefore, the quotient is a *repeating decimal*.

The quotient is $0.05666\ldots$. To denote the repeated pattern, we often use a bar over the first occurrence of the repeat cycle to the right of the decimal point. That is,

$0.05666\ldots = 0.05\overline{6}$ ←———— repeat bar

Avoiding Mistakes

In Example 4, notice that the repeat bar goes over only the 6. The 5 is not being repeated.

Skill Practice

Divide.
5. $11\overline{)57}$

Example 5   Dividing Where the Quotient Is a Repeating Decimal

Divide. $11\overline{)68}$

Solution:

$$
\begin{array}{r}
6.1818\ldots \\
11\overline{)68.0000} \\
-66 \\
\hline
20 \\
-11 \\
\hline
90 \\
-88 \\
\hline
20 \\
-11 \\
\hline
90 \\
-88 \\
\hline
20
\end{array}
$$

Could have stopped here

Once again, we see a repeated pattern. The quotient is a repeating decimal. Notice that we could have stopped dividing when we obtained the second value of 20.

Avoiding Mistakes

Be sure to put the repeating bar over the entire block of numbers that is being repeated. In Example 5, the bar extends over both the 1 and the 8. We have $6.\overline{18}$.

The quotient is $6.\overline{18}$.

The numbers $0.05\overline{6}$ and $6.\overline{18}$ are examples of repeating decimals. A decimal that "stops" is called a **terminating decimal**. For example, 6.18 is a terminating decimal, whereas $6.\overline{18}$ is a repeating decimal.

In Examples 1–5, we performed division where the divisor was a whole number. Suppose now that we have a divisor that is *not* a whole number, for example, $0.56 \div 0.7$. Because division can also be expressed in fraction notation, we have

$$0.56 \div 0.7 = \frac{0.56}{0.7}$$

If we multiply the numerator and denominator by 10, the denominator (divisor) becomes the whole number 7.

$$\frac{0.56}{0.7} = \frac{0.56 \times 10}{0.7 \times 10} = \frac{5.6}{7} \longrightarrow 7\overline{)5.6}$$

Recall that multiplying decimal numbers by 10 (or any power of 10, such as 100, 1000, etc.) moves the decimal point to the right. We use this idea to divide decimal numbers when the divisor is not a whole number.

Dividing When the Divisor Is Not a Whole Number

Step 1   Move the decimal point in the divisor to the right to make it a whole number.

Step 2   Move the decimal point in the dividend to the right the same number of places as in step 1.

Step 3   Place the decimal point in the quotient directly above the decimal point in the dividend.

Step 4   Divide as you would whole numbers.

Example 6   **Dividing Decimals**

Divide.

a. $0.56 \div 0.7$ **b.** $0.005\overline{)3.1}$

Solution:

a. $.7\overline{)}.56$ Move the decimal point in the divisor and dividend one place to the right.

$7\overline{)5.6}$ ⟵ ——— Line up the decimal point in the quotient.

$$\begin{array}{r} .8 \\ 7\overline{)5.6} \\ \underline{-5\,6} \\ 0 \end{array}$$

The quotient is 0.8.

b. $.005\overline{)3.100}$ Move the decimal point in the divisor and dividend three places to the right. Insert additional zeros in the dividend if necessary. Line up the decimal point in the quotient.

$$\begin{array}{r} 620. \\ 5\overline{)3100.} \\ \underline{-30} \\ 10 \\ \underline{-10} \\ 00 \end{array}$$

The quotient is 620.

Skill Practice

Divide.

6. $0.64 \div 0.4$ **7.** $5.4 \div 0.03$

Answers

6. 1.6   **7.** 180

Skill Practice

Divide.
8. $70 \div 0.6$

Example 7 Dividing Decimals

Divide. $50 \div 1.1$

Solution:

$$1.1\overline{)50.0}$$

Move the decimal point in the divisor and dividend one place to the right. Insert an additional zero in the dividend. Line up the decimal point in the quotient.

$$
\begin{array}{r}
45.45\ldots \\
11\overline{)500.000} \\
-44 \\
\hline
60 \\
-55 \\
\hline
50 \\
-44 \\
\hline
60 \\
-55 \\
\hline
50
\end{array}
$$

The quotient is the repeating decimal, $45.\overline{45}$.

The quotient is $45.\overline{45}$.

Calculator Connections

Repeating decimals displayed on a calculator are rounded. This is because the display cannot show an infinite number of digits.

For example, on a scientific calculator, the repeating decimal $2.\overline{66}$ may appear as

| 2.66666667 |

Avoiding Mistakes

The quotient in Example 7 is a repeating decimal. The repeat cycle actually begins to the left of the decimal point. However, the repeat bar is placed on the first repeated block of digits to the *right* of the decimal point. Therefore, we write the quotient as $45.\overline{45}$.

When we multiply a number by 10, 100, 1000, and so on, we move the decimal point to the right. However, dividing a number by 10, 100, or 1000 decreases its value. Therefore, we move the decimal point to the *left*.

For example, suppose 3.6 is divided by 10, 100, and 1000.

$$
\begin{array}{r}
.36 \\
10\overline{)3.60} \\
-30 \\
\hline
60 \\
-60 \\
\hline
0
\end{array}
\qquad
\begin{array}{r}
.036 \\
100\overline{)3.600} \\
-300 \\
\hline
600 \\
-600 \\
\hline
0
\end{array}
\qquad
\begin{array}{r}
.0036 \\
1000\overline{)3.6000} \\
-3000 \\
\hline
6000 \\
-6000 \\
\hline
0
\end{array}
$$

Dividing by a Power of 10

To divide a number by a power of 10, move the decimal point to the *left* the same number of places as there are zeros in the power of 10.

Skill Practice

Divide.
9. $162.8 \div 1000$
10. $0.0039 \div 10$

Example 8 Dividing by a Power of 10

Divide.

a. $214.3 \div 10,000$ **b.** $0.03 \div 100$

Solution:

a. $214.3 \div 10,000 = 0.02143$ Move the decimal point four places to the left. Insert an additional zero.

b. $0.03 \div 100 = 0.0003$ Move the decimal point two places to the left. Insert two additional zeros.

Answers
8. $116.\overline{6}$ 9. 0.1628 10. 0.00039

2. Rounding a Quotient

In Example 7, we found that $50 \div 1.1 = 45.\overline{45}$. To check this result, we could multiply $45.\overline{45} \times 1.1$ and show that the product equals 50. However, at this point we do not have the tools to multiply repeating decimals. What we can do is round the quotient and then multiply to see if the product is *close* to 50.

Example 9 **Rounding a Repeating Decimal**

Round $45.\overline{45}$ to the hundredths place. Then use the rounded value to estimate whether the product $45.\overline{45} \times 1.1$ is close to 50. (This will serve as a check to the division problem in Example 7.)

Solution:

To round the number $45.\overline{45}$, we must write out enough of the repeated pattern so that we can view the digit to the right of the rounding place. In this case, we must write out the number to the thousandths place.

$$45.\overline{45} = 45.454 \cdots \approx 45.45$$

hundredths place

This digit is less than 5. Discard it and all others to its right.

Now multiply the rounded value by 1.1.

$$
\begin{array}{r}
45.45 \\
\times\ 1.1 \\
\hline
4545 \\
45450 \\
\hline
49.995
\end{array}
$$

This value is close to 50. We are reasonably sure that we divided correctly in Example 7.

> **Skill Practice**
>
> Round to the indicated place value.
>
> **11.** $2.3\overline{15}$; thousandths

Sometimes we may want to round a quotient to a given place value. To do so, divide until you get a digit in the quotient one place value to the right of the rounding place. At this point, you can stop dividing and round the quotient.

Example 10 **Rounding a Quotient**

Round the quotient to the tenths place.

$$47.3 \div 5.4$$

Solution:

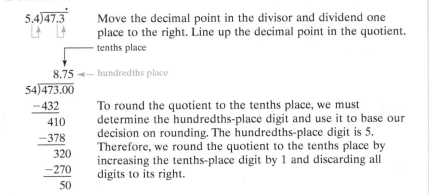

Move the decimal point in the divisor and dividend one place to the right. Line up the decimal point in the quotient.

tenths place

$$
\begin{array}{r}
8.75 \\
54)\overline{473.00} \\
-432 \\
\hline
410 \\
-378 \\
\hline
320 \\
-270 \\
\hline
50
\end{array}
$$
hundredths place

To round the quotient to the tenths place, we must determine the hundredths-place digit and use it to base our decision on rounding. The hundredths-place digit is 5. Therefore, we round the quotient to the tenths place by increasing the tenths-place digit by 1 and discarding all digits to its right.

The quotient is approximately 8.8.

> **Skill Practice**
>
> Round the quotient to the indicated place value.
>
> **12.** $42.68 \div 5.1$; hundredths

Answers
11. 2.315   **12.** 8.37

54 **Chapter 4** Decimals

3. Applications of Decimal Division

Examples 11 and 12 show how decimal division can be used in applications. Remember that division is used when we need to distribute a quantity into equal parts.

Example 11 **Applying Division of Decimals**

A lunch costs $45.80, and the bill is to be split equally among 5 people. How much must each person pay?

Solution:

We want to distribute $45.80 equally among 5 people, so we must divide $45.80 ÷ 5.

$$
\begin{array}{r}
9.16 \\
5\overline{)45.80} \\
-45 \\
\hline
08 \\
-5 \\
\hline
30 \\
-30 \\
\hline
0
\end{array}
$$

Each person must pay $9.16.

TIP: To check if your answer is reasonable, divide $45 among 5 people.

$$
\begin{array}{r}
9 \\
5\overline{)45}
\end{array}
$$

The estimated value of $9 suggests that the answer to Example 11 is correct.

Division is also used in practical applications to express rates. In Example 12, we find the rate of speed in meters per second (m/sec) for the world record time in the men's 400-m run.

Example 12 **Using Division to Find a Rate of Speed**

In a recent year, the world-record time in the men's 400-m run was 43.2 sec. What is the speed in meters per second? Round to one decimal place. (*Source:* International Association of Athletics Federations)

Solution:

To find the rate of speed in meters per second, we must divide the distance in meters by the time in seconds.

$$43.2\overline{)400.0}$$

tenths place

9.25 ← hundredths place

$$432\overline{)4000.00}$$
$$\underline{-3888}$$
$$1120$$
$$\underline{-864}$$
$$2560$$
$$\underline{-2160}$$
$$400$$

> **TIP:** In Example 12, we had to find speed in meters per second. The units of measurement required in the answer give a hint as to the order of the division. The word *per* implies division. So to obtain meters *per* second implies 400 m ÷ 43.2 sec.

To round the quotient to the tenths place, determine the hundredths-place digit and use it to make the decision on rounding. The hundredths-place digit is 5, which is 5 or greater. Therefore, add 1 to the tenths-place digit and discard all digits to its right.

The speed is approximately 9.3 m/sec.

Section 4.4 Practice Exercises

Study Skills Exercise

Meet some of the other students in your class. They can be good resources for asking questions and discussing the material that was covered in class. Write the names of two fellow students.

Vocabulary and Key Concepts

1. a. If a decimal number has an infinite number of digits with a repeated pattern, then the number is called a _____ decimal.

b. If a decimal number has a finite number of digits after the decimal point, then the number is called a _____ decimal.

Review Exercises

2. Round 34.99991 to the hundredths place.

For Exercises 3–8, perform the indicated operation.

3. 5.28×1000 **4.** $8.003 - 2.2$ **5.** 11.8×0.32

6. $102.4 + 1.239$ **7.** $16.82 - 14.8$ **8.** 5.28×0.001

Concept 1: Division of Decimals

For Exercises 9–16, divide. Check the answer by using multiplication. **(See Example 1.)**

9. $8.1 \div 9$ Check: _____ $\times 9 = 8.1$ **10.** $4.8 \div 6$ Check: _____ $\times 6 = 4.8$

11. $6\overline{)1.08}$ Check: _____ $\times 6 = 1.08$ **12.** $4\overline{)2.08}$ Check: _____ $\times 4 = 2.08$

13. $4.24 \div 8$ **14.** $5.75 \div 25$ **15.** $5\overline{)105.5}$ **16.** $7\overline{)221.2}$

56   **Chapter 4** Decimals

For Exercises 17–48, divide. **(See Examples 2–7.)**

17. $5\overline{)9.8}$ **18.** $3\overline{)2.07}$ **19.** $0.28 \div 8$ **20.** $0.54 \div 8$

21. $5\overline{)84.2}$ **22.** $2\overline{)89.1}$ **23.** $50\overline{)6}$ **24.** $80\overline{)6}$

25. $4 \div 25$ **26.** $12 \div 60$ **27.** $16 \div 3$ **28.** $52 \div 9$

29. $19 \div 6$ **30.** $9.1 \div 3$ **31.** $33\overline{)71}$ **32.** $11\overline{)42}$

33. $5.03 \div 0.01$ **34.** $3.2 \div 0.001$ **35.** $0.992 \div 0.1$ **36.** $123.4 \div 0.01$

37. $57.12 \div 1.02$ **38.** $95.89 \div 2.23$ **39.** $2.38 \div 0.8$ **40.** $5.51 \div 0.2$

41. $0.3\overline{)62.5}$ **42.** $1.05\overline{)22.4}$ **43.** $6.305 \div 0.13$ **44.** $42.9 \div 0.25$

45. $1.1 \div 0.001$ **46.** $4.44 \div 0.01$ **47.** $420.6 \div 0.01$ **48.** $0.31 \div 0.1$

49. If 45.62 is divided by 100, will the decimal point move to the right or to the left? By how many places?

50. If 5689.233 is divided by 100,000, will the decimal point move to the right or to the left? By how many places?

For Exercises 51–58, divide by the powers of 10. **(See Example 8.)**

51. $3.923 \div 100$ **52.** $5.32 \div 100$ **53.** $98.02 \div 10$ **54.** $11.033 \div 10$

55. $0.027 \div 100$ **56.** $0.665 \div 100$ **57.** $1.02 \div 1000$ **58.** $8.1 \div 1000$

Concept 2: Rounding a Quotient

59. Round $2.\overline{4}$ to the
  a. Tenths place
  b. Hundredths place
  c. Thousandths place
  (See Example 9.)

60. Round $5.\overline{2}$ to the
  a. Tenths place
  b. Hundredths place
  c. Thousandths place

61. Round $1.\overline{8}$ to the
  a. Tenths place
  b. Hundredths place
  c. Thousandths place

62. Round $4.\overline{7}$ to the
  a. Tenths place
  b. Hundredths place
  c. Thousandths place

63. Round $3.\overline{62}$ to the
  a. Tenths place
  b. Hundredths place
  c. Thousandths place

64. Round $9.\overline{38}$ to the
  a. Tenths place
  b. Hundredths place
  c. Thousandths place

For Exercises 65–73, divide. Round the answer to the indicated place value. Use the rounded quotient to check. **(See Example 10.)**

65. $7\overline{)1.8}$ hundredths   **66.** $2.1\overline{)75.3}$ hundredths   **67.** $54.9 \div 3.7$ tenths

68. $94.3 \div 21$ tenths   **69.** $0.24\overline{)4.96}$ thousandths   **70.** $2.46\overline{)27.88}$ thousandths

71. $0.9\overline{)32.1}$ hundredths   **72.** $0.6\overline{)81.4}$ hundredths   **73.** $2.13\overline{)237.1}$ tenths

Concept 3: Applications of Decimal Division

When multiplying or dividing decimals, it is important to place the decimal point correctly. For Exercises 74–77, determine whether you think the number is reasonable or unreasonable. If the number is unreasonable, move the decimal point to a position that makes more sense.

74. Steve computed the gas mileage for his Honda Civic to be 3.2 miles per gallon.

75. The sale price of a new kitchen refrigerator is $96.0.

76. Mickey makes $8.50 per hour. He estimates his weekly paycheck to be $3400.

77. Jason works in a legal office. He computes the average annual income for the attorneys in his office to be $1400 per year.

For Exercises 78–86, solve the application. Check to see if your answers are reasonable.

78. The amount that Brooke owes on her mortgage including interest is $40,540.08. If her monthly payment is $965.24, how many months does she still need to pay? How many years is this?

79. A membership at a health club costs $560 per year. The club has a payment plan in which a member can pay $50 down and the rest in 12 equal payments. How much is each payment? **(See Example 11.)**

80. It is reported that on average 42,000 tennis balls are used and 650 matches are played at the Wimbledon tennis tournament each year. On average, how many tennis balls are used per match? Round to the nearest whole unit.

81. A standard 75-watt lightbulb costs $0.75 and lasts about 800 hr. An energy efficient fluorescent bulb that gives off the same amount of light costs $5.00 and lasts about 10,000 hr.

   a. How many standard lightbulbs would be needed to provide 10,000 hr of light?

   b. How much would it cost using standard lightbulbs to provide 10,000 hr of light?

   c. Which is more cost effective long term?

82. Refer to Exercise 81.

   a. If a standard 75-watt lightbulb were left on 24 hr per day, after how many days would the lightbulb have to be changed? Round to the nearest day.

   b. If an energy efficient fluorescent bulb were left on 24 hr per day, after how many days would the lightbulb have to be changed? Round to the nearest day.

83. In baseball, the batting average is found by dividing the number of hits by the number of times a batter was at bat. Babe Ruth had 2873 hits in 8399 times at bat. What was his batting average? Round to the thousandths place.

84. Baseball legend, Ty Cobb, was at bat 11,434 times and had 4189 hits, giving him the all time best batting average. Find his average. Round to the thousandths place. (Refer to Exercise 83.)

85. Manny hikes 12 mi in 5.5 hr. What is his speed in miles per hour? Round to one decimal place. **(See Example 12.)**

86. Alicia rides her bike 33.2 mi in 2.5 hr. What is her speed in miles per hour? Round to one decimal place.

Expanding Your Skills

87. What number is halfway between 47.26 and 47.27?

88. What number is halfway between 22.4 and 22.5?

89. Which numbers when divided by 8.6 will produce a quotient less than 12.4? Circle all that apply.

   a. 111.8   **b.** 103.2   **c.** 107.5   **d.** 105.78

90. Which numbers when divided by 5.3 will produce a quotient greater than 15.8? Circle all that apply.

   a. 84.8   **b.** 84.27   **c.** 83.21   **d.** 79.5

Calculator Connections

Topic: Multiplying and Dividing Decimals on a Calculator

In some applications, the arithmetic on decimal numbers can be very tedious, and it is practical to use a calculator. To multiply or divide on a calculator, use the ⊠ and ÷ keys, respectively. However, be aware that for repeating decimals, the calculator cannot give an exact value. For example, the quotient of $17 \div 3$ is the repeating decimal $5.\overline{6}$. The calculator returns the rounded value 5.666666667. This is *not* the exact value. Also, when performing division, be careful to enter the dividend and divisor into the calculator in the correct order. For example:

Expression	Keystrokes	Result
$17 \div 3$	17 ÷ 3 =	5.666666667
$0.024\overline{)56.87}$	56.87 ÷ 0.024 =	2369.583333
$\dfrac{82.9}{3.1}$	82.9 ÷ 3.1 =	26.74193548

Calculator Exercises

For Exercises 91–96, multiply or divide as indicated.

91. $(2749.13)(418.2)$

92. $(139.241)(24.5)$

93. $(43.75)^2$

94. $(9.3)^5$

95. $21.5\overline{)2056.75}$

96. $14.2\overline{)4167.8}$

97. A Hummer H3 SUV uses 1260 gal of gas to travel 12,000 mi per year. A Honda Accord uses 375 gal of gas to go the same distance. Use the current cost of gasoline in your area, to determine the amount saved per year by driving a Honda Accord rather than a Hummer.

98. A Chevy Blazer gets 16.5 mpg and a Toyota Corolla averages 32 mpg. Suppose a driver drives 15,000 mi per year. Use the current cost of gasoline in your area to determine the amount saved per year by driving the Toyota rather than the Chevy.

99. Recently, the U.S. capacity to generate wind power was 25,369 megawatts (MW). Texas generates approximately 9410 MW of this power. (*Source:* American Wind Energy Association)

   a. What fraction of the U.S. wind power is generated in Texas? Express this fraction as a decimal number rounded to the nearest hundredth of a megawatt.

   b. Suppose there is a claim in a news article that Texas generates more than one-third of all wind power in the United States. Is this claim accurate? Explain using your answer from part (a).

100. Population density is defined to be the number of people per square mile of land area. If California has 42,475,000 people with a land area of 155,959 square miles, what is the population density? Round to the nearest whole unit. (*Source:* U.S. Census Bureau)

101. The Earth travels approximately 584,000,000 mi around the Sun each year.

   a. How many miles does the Earth travel in one day?

   b. Find the speed of the Earth in miles per hour.

102. Although we say the time for the Earth to revolve about the Sun is 365 days, the actual time is 365.256 days. Multiply the fractional amount (0.256) by 4 to explain why we have a leap year every 4 years. (A leap year is a year in which February has an extra day, February 29.)

| Section 4.5 | **Fractions as Decimals**

Concepts

. Writing Fractions as Decimals
. Writing Decimals as Fractions
. Decimals and the Number Line

1. Writing Fractions as Decimals

Sometimes it is possible to convert a fraction to its equivalent decimal form by rewriting the fraction as a decimal fraction. That is, try to multiply the numerator and denominator by a number that will make the denominator a power of 10.

For example, the fraction $\frac{3}{5}$ can easily be written as an equivalent fraction with a denominator of 10.

$$\frac{3}{5} = \frac{3 \cdot 2}{5 \cdot 2} = \frac{6}{10} = 0.6$$

The fraction $\frac{3}{25}$ can easily be converted to a fraction with a denominator of 100.

$$\frac{3}{25} = \frac{3 \cdot 4}{25 \cdot 4} = \frac{12}{100} = 0.12$$

This technique is useful in some cases. However, some fractions such as $\frac{1}{3}$ cannot be converted to a fraction with a denominator that is a power of 10. This is because 3 is not a factor of any power of 10. For this reason, we recommend dividing the numerator by the denominator.

Skill Practice

Write each fraction or mixed number as a decimal.

1. $\frac{3}{8}$

2. $\frac{43}{20}$

3. $12\frac{5}{16}$

| Example 1 | **Writing Fractions as Decimals**

Write each fraction or mixed number as a decimal.

a. $\frac{3}{5}$ **b.** $\frac{68}{25}$ **c.** $3\frac{5}{8}$

Solution:

a. $\frac{3}{5}$ means $3 \div 5$.

$$\begin{array}{r} .6 \\ 5\overline{)3.0} \\ -30 \\ \hline 0 \end{array}$$

Divide the numerator by the denominator.

$$\frac{3}{5} = 0.6$$

b. $\frac{68}{25}$ means $68 \div 25$.

$$\begin{array}{r} 2.72 \\ 25\overline{)68.00} \\ -50 \\ \hline 180 \\ -175 \\ \hline 50 \\ -50 \\ \hline 0 \end{array}$$

Divide the numerator by the denominator.

$$\frac{68}{25} = 2.72$$

c. $3\frac{5}{8} = 3 + 5 \div 8$

$$\begin{array}{r} .625 \\ 8\overline{)5.000} \\ -48 \\ \hline 20 \\ -16 \\ \hline 40 \\ -40 \\ \hline 0 \end{array}$$

Divide the numerator by the denominator.

$$3\frac{5}{8} = 3 + 0.625$$

$$= 3.625$$

Writing Fractions as Decimals

Step 1   Divide the numerator by the denominator.

Step 2   Continue the division process until the quotient is a terminating decimal or a repeating pattern is recognized.

Example 2   **Converting Fractions to Repeating Decimals**

Write each fraction as a decimal.

a. $\dfrac{4}{9}$ **b.** $\dfrac{5}{6}$ **c.** $\dfrac{4}{7}$

Solution:

a. $\dfrac{4}{9}$ means $4 \div 9$.

$$
\begin{array}{r}
.44\ldots \\
9\overline{)4.00} \\
-36 \\
\hline
40 \\
-36 \\
\hline
40
\end{array}
$$

The quotient is a repeating decimal.

$\dfrac{4}{9} = 0.\overline{4}$

b. $\dfrac{5}{6}$ means $5 \div 6$.

$$
\begin{array}{r}
.833\ldots \\
6\overline{)5.000} \\
-48 \\
\hline
20 \\
-18 \\
\hline
20
\end{array}
$$

The quotient is a repeating decimal.

$\dfrac{5}{6} = 0.8\overline{3}$

c. $\dfrac{4}{7}$ means $4 \div 7$.

$$
\begin{array}{r}
.571428\ldots \\
7\overline{)4.000000} \\
-35 \\
\hline
50 \\
-49 \\
\hline
10 \\
-7 \\
\hline
30 \\
-28 \\
\hline
20 \\
-14 \\
\hline
60 \\
-56 \\
\hline
40
\end{array}
$$

TIP: Be sure to carry out the division far enough to see the repeating digits.

The cycle will repeat.

$\dfrac{4}{7} = 0.571428571428571428571428\ldots = 0.\overline{571428}$

Skill Practice

Write each fraction as a decimal.

4. $\dfrac{8}{9}$

5. $\dfrac{1}{12}$

6. $\dfrac{3}{7}$

Answers

4. $0.\overline{8}$ **5.** $0.08\overline{3}$ **6.** $0.\overline{428571}$

62   **Chapter 4**   Decimals

Several fractions are used quite often. Their decimal forms are worth memorizing and are presented in Table 4-1.

Table 4-1

$\frac{1}{4} = 0.25$	$\frac{2}{4} = \frac{1}{2} = 0.5$	$\frac{3}{4} = 0.75$	
$\frac{1}{9} = 0.\overline{1}$	$\frac{2}{9} = 0.\overline{2}$	$\frac{3}{9} = \frac{1}{3} = 0.\overline{3}$	$\frac{4}{9} = 0.\overline{4}$
$\frac{5}{9} = 0.\overline{5}$	$\frac{6}{9} = \frac{2}{3} = 0.\overline{6}$	$\frac{7}{9} = 0.\overline{7}$	$\frac{8}{9} = 0.\overline{8}$

Example 3   **Converting Fractions to Decimals with Rounding**

Convert the fraction to a decimal rounded to the indicated place value.

a. $\frac{162}{7}$; tenths place

b. $\frac{21}{31}$; hundredths place

Solution:

a. $\frac{162}{7}$

tenths place
hundredths place

$$\begin{array}{r} 23.14 \\ 7\overline{)162.00} \\ -14 \\ \hline 22 \\ -21 \\ \hline 10 \\ -7 \\ \hline 30 \\ -28 \\ \hline 2 \end{array}$$

To round to the tenths place, we must determine the hundredths-place digit and use it to base our decision on rounding.

$23.14 \approx 23.1$

The fraction $\frac{162}{7}$ is approximately 23.1.

b. $\frac{21}{31}$

hundredths place
thousandths place

$$\begin{array}{r} .677 \\ 31\overline{)21.000} \\ -186 \\ \hline 240 \\ -217 \\ \hline 230 \\ -217 \\ \hline 13 \end{array}$$

To round to the hundredths place, we must determine the thousandths-place digit and use it to base our decision on rounding.

$0.677 \approx 0.68$

The fraction $\frac{21}{31}$ is approximately 0.68.

2. Writing Decimals as Fractions

In Section 4.1 we converted terminating decimals to fractions. We did this by writing the decimal as a decimal fraction and then reducing the fraction to lowest terms. For example:

$$0.46 = \frac{46}{100} = \frac{\overset{23}{\cancel{46}}}{\underset{50}{\cancel{100}}} = \frac{23}{50}$$

We do not yet have the tools to convert a repeating decimal to its equivalent fraction form. However, we can make use of our knowledge of the common fractions and their repeating decimal forms from Table 4-1.

Example 4   **Writing Decimals as Fractions and Fractions as Decimals**

Complete the table.

	Decimal Form	**Fractional Form**
a.	0.475	
b.		$\frac{3}{16}$
c.		$2\frac{4}{5}$
d.	$0.\overline{6}$	
e.		$\frac{19}{11}$

Solution:

a. $0.475 = \dfrac{475}{1000} = \dfrac{19 \cdot \overset{1}{\cancel{25}}}{40 \cdot \underset{1}{\cancel{25}}} = \dfrac{19}{40}$

b. $\dfrac{3}{16} = 3 \div 16$

$$
\begin{array}{r}
.1875 \\
16\overline{)3.0000} \\
\underline{-16} \\
140 \\
\underline{-128} \\
120 \\
\underline{-112} \\
80 \\
\underline{-80} \\
0
\end{array}
$$

Therefore, $\dfrac{3}{16} = 0.1875$.

c. To convert $2\frac{4}{5}$ to decimal form, we need to convert $\frac{4}{5}$ to decimal form. This can be done by dividing. Or we can easily convert $\frac{4}{5}$ to a decimal fraction with a denominator of 10.

$$\frac{4}{5} = \frac{4 \cdot 2}{5 \cdot 2} = \frac{8}{10} = 0.8$$

Therefore, $2\dfrac{4}{5} = 2.8$.

d. From Table 4-1, the decimal $0.\overline{6} = \dfrac{2}{3}$.

e. $\dfrac{19}{11}$ means $19 \div 11$.

$\dfrac{19}{11} = 1.\overline{72}$

$$
\begin{array}{r}
1.7272\ldots \\
11\overline{)19.0000} \\
\underline{-11} \\
80 \\
\underline{-77} \\
30 \\
\underline{-22} \\
80
\end{array}
$$

The cycle will repeat.

Skill Practice

Complete the table.

	Decimal Form	Fractional Form
10.	0.875	
11.		$\dfrac{7}{20}$
12.		$2\dfrac{1}{3}$
13.	$0.\overline{7}$	

Answers

10. $\frac{7}{8}$ **11.** 0.35

12. $2.\overline{3}$ **13.** $\frac{7}{9}$

We can now complete the table.

	Decimal Form	**Fractional Form**
a.	0.475	$\frac{19}{40}$
b.	0.1875	$\frac{3}{16}$
c.	2.8	$2\frac{4}{5}$
d.	$0.\overline{6}$	$\frac{2}{3}$
e.	$1.\overline{72}$	$\frac{19}{11}$

3. Decimals and the Number Line

In Example 5, we rank the numbers from least to greatest and visualize the position of the numbers on the number line.

Skill Practice

14. Rank the numbers from least to greatest. Then approximate the position of the points on the number line.
$0.161, \frac{1}{6}, 0.16$

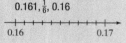

Example 5   **Ordering Decimals and Fractions**

Rank the numbers from least to greatest. Then approximate the position of the points on the number line.

$$0.\overline{45}, \quad 0.45, \quad \frac{1}{2}$$

Solution:

First note that $\frac{1}{2} = 0.5$ and that $0.\overline{45} = 0.454545\ldots$. By writing each number in decimal form, we can compare the decimals as we did in Section 4.1.

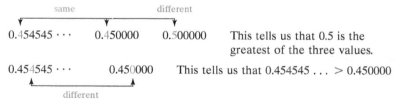

$0.454545\cdots$ 0.450000 0.500000 This tells us that 0.5 is the greatest of the three values.

$0.454545\cdots$ 0.450000 This tells us that $0.454545\ldots > 0.450000$

Ranking the numbers from least to greatest we have: $0.45, \quad 0.\overline{45}, \quad 0.5$

The position of these numbers can be seen on the number line. Note that we have expanded the segment of the number line between 0.4 and 0.5 to see more place values to the right of the decimal point.

Recall that numbers that lie to the left on the number line have lesser value than numbers that lie to the right.

Answer

4. $0.16, 0.161, \frac{1}{6}$

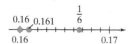

Section 4.5   Practice Exercises

Study Skills Exercise

In a study group, check which activities you might try to help you learn and understand the material.

☐ Quiz one another by asking each other questions.

☐ Practice teaching one another.

☐ Share and compare class notes.

☐ Support and encourage one another.

☐ Work together on exercises and sample problems.

Review Exercises

For Exercises 1–4, write the decimal fraction in decimal form.

1. $\dfrac{9}{10}$ **2.** $\dfrac{39}{100}$ **3.** $\dfrac{141}{1000}$ **4.** $\dfrac{71}{10,000}$

For Exercises 5–8, write the decimals as fractions.

5. 0.6   **6.** 0.0016   **7.** 0.35   **8.** 0.125

9. Round $4.\overline{25}$ to the hundredths place.

10. Round $0.\overline{37}$ to the thousandths place.

Concept 1: Writing Fractions as Decimals

For Exercises 11–14, write each fraction as a decimal fraction, that is, a fraction whose denominator is a power of 10. Then write the number in decimal form.

11. $\dfrac{2}{5}$ **12.** $\dfrac{4}{5}$ **13.** $\dfrac{49}{50}$ **14.** $\dfrac{3}{50}$

For Exercises 15–34, write each fraction or mixed number as a decimal. **(See Example 1.)**

15. $\dfrac{7}{25}$ **16.** $\dfrac{4}{25}$ **17.** $\dfrac{316}{500}$ **18.** $\dfrac{19}{500}$

19. $\dfrac{7}{8}$ **20.** $\dfrac{16}{64}$ **21.** $\dfrac{16}{5}$ **22.** $\dfrac{68}{25}$

23. $5\dfrac{3}{12}$ **24.** $4\dfrac{1}{16}$ **25.** $1\dfrac{1}{5}$ **26.** $6\dfrac{5}{8}$

27. $\dfrac{18}{24}$ **28.** $\dfrac{24}{40}$ **29.** $\dfrac{53}{16}$ **30.** $\dfrac{105}{56}$

31. $7\dfrac{9}{20}$ **32.** $3\dfrac{11}{25}$ **33.** $\dfrac{22}{25}$ **34.** $\dfrac{11}{20}$

For Exercises 35–46, write each fraction or mixed number as a repeating decimal. **(See Example 2.)**

35. $3\dfrac{8}{9}$ **36.** $4\dfrac{7}{9}$ **37.** $\dfrac{7}{15}$ **38.** $\dfrac{5}{18}$

39. $\dfrac{19}{36}$ **40.** $\dfrac{7}{12}$ **41.** $\dfrac{6}{11}$ **42.** $\dfrac{8}{33}$

43. $\dfrac{14}{111}$ **44.** $\dfrac{58}{111}$ **45.** $\dfrac{25}{22}$ **46.** $\dfrac{45}{22}$

For Exercises 47–56, convert the fraction to a decimal and round to the indicated place value. **(See Example 3.)**

47. $\dfrac{1}{7}$; thousandths   **48.** $\dfrac{2}{7}$; thousandths   **49.** $\dfrac{1}{13}$; hundredths   **50.** $\dfrac{9}{13}$; hundredths

51. $\dfrac{15}{16}$; tenths   **52.** $\dfrac{3}{11}$; tenths   **53.** $\dfrac{5}{7}$; hundredths   **54.** $\dfrac{1}{8}$; hundredths

55. $\dfrac{25}{21}$; tenths   **56.** $\dfrac{18}{13}$; tenths

57. Write the fractions as decimals. Explain how to memorize the decimal form for these fractions with a denominator of 9.

   a. $\dfrac{1}{9}$ **b.** $\dfrac{2}{9}$ **c.** $\dfrac{4}{9}$ **d.** $\dfrac{5}{9}$

58. Write the fractions as decimals. Explain how to memorize the decimal forms for these fractions with a denominator of 3.

   a. $\dfrac{1}{3}$ **b.** $\dfrac{2}{3}$

Concept 2: Writing Decimals as Fractions

For Exercises 59–62, complete the table. **(See Example 4.)**

59.

	Decimal Form	Fraction Form
a.	0.45	
b.		$\dfrac{13}{8}$ or $1\dfrac{5}{8}$
c.	$0.\overline{7}$	
d.		$\dfrac{5}{11}$

60.

	Decimal Form	Fraction Form
a.		$\dfrac{2}{3}$
b.	1.6	
c.		$\dfrac{152}{25}$
d.	$0.\overline{2}$	

61.

	Decimal Form	Fraction Form
a.	$0.\overline{3}$	
b.	2.125	
c.		$\frac{19}{22}$
d.		$\frac{42}{25}$

62.

	Decimal Form	Fraction Form
a.	0.75	
b.		$\frac{7}{11}$
c.	$1.\overline{8}$	
d.		$\frac{74}{25}$

Historically stock prices were given as fractions or mixed numbers, but are now given as decimals. For Exercises 63 and 64, complete the table that gives recent stock prices taken from the *Wall Street Journal*.

63.

Stock	Closing Price ($) (Decimal)	Closing Price ($) (Fraction)
McGraw-Hill	69.25	
Walgreens	44.95	
Home Depot		$38\frac{1}{2}$
General Electric		$37\frac{11}{25}$

64.

Stock	Closing Price ($) (Decimal)	Closing Price ($) (Fraction)
Dell	26.3	
StrideRite		$15\frac{18}{25}$
Intel	28.10	
Burger King		$24\frac{3}{20}$

Concept 3: Decimals and the Number Line

For Exercises 65–76, insert the appropriate symbol. Choose from $<$, $>$, or $=$.

65. $0.2 \ \square \ \frac{1}{5}$ **66.** $1.5 \ \square \ \frac{3}{2}$ **67.** $0.2 \ \square \ 0.\overline{2}$ **68.** $\frac{3}{5} \ \square \ 0.\overline{6}$

69. $\frac{1}{3} \ \square \ 0.3$ **70.** $\frac{2}{3} \ \square \ 0.66$ **71.** $4\frac{1}{4} \ \square \ 4.2\overline{5}$ **72.** $2.12 \ \square \ 2.\overline{12}$

73. $0.\overline{5} \ \square \ \frac{5}{9}$ **74.** $\frac{7}{4} \ \square \ 1.75$ **75.** $0.27 \ \square \ \frac{3}{11}$ **76.** $6.4\overline{3} \ \square \ 6.43$

For Exercises 77–80, rank the numbers from least to greatest. Then approximate the position of the points on the number line. **(See Example 5.)**

77. $0.\overline{1}, \frac{1}{10}, \frac{1}{5}$ **78.** $3\frac{1}{4}, 3\frac{1}{3}, 3.3$

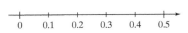

68 **Chapter 4** Decimals

79. 1.8, 1.75, 1.$\overline{7}$

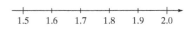

80. 5$\frac{1}{6}$, 5.$\overline{6}$, 5.0$\overline{6}$

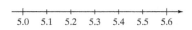

Expanding Your Skills

81. If 0.$\overline{8}$ = $\frac{8}{9}$, then what is the fraction form of 0.$\overline{9}$?

For Exercises 82–84, simplify.

82. 1.$\overline{9}$ **83.** 6.$\overline{9}$ **84.** 15.$\overline{9}$

Concepts

1. **Definition of Percent**
2. **Converting Percents to Fractions**
3. **Converting Percents to Decimals**
4. **Common Percents and Their Fraction and Decimal Forms**

1. Definition of Percent

In this chapter, we study the concept of percent. Literally, the word **percent** means *per one hundred*. To indicate percent, we use the percent symbol %. For example, 45% (read as "45 percent") of the land area in South America is rainforest (shaded in green). This means that if South America were divided into 100 squares of equal size, 45 of the 100 squares would cover rainforest. See Figures 6-1 and 6-2.

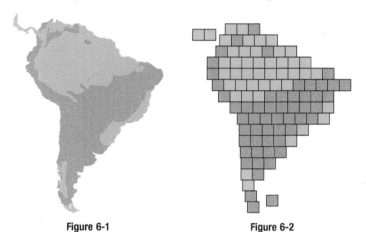

Figure 6-1   Figure 6-2

Consider another example. For a recent year, the population of Virginia could be described as follows.

21%	African American	21 out of 100 Virginians are African American
72%	Caucasian (non-Hispanic)	72 out of 100 Virginians are Caucasian (non-Hispanic)
3%	Asian American	3 out of 100 Virginians are Asian American
3%	Hispanic	3 out of 100 Virginians are Hispanic
1%	Other	1 out of 100 Virginians have other backgrounds

Figure 6-3 represents a sample of 100 residents of Virginia.

Concept Connections

1. Shade the portion of the figure represented by 18%.

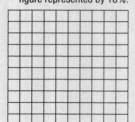

Answer

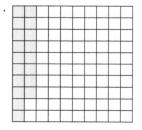

AA AA AA C C C C C C C
AA AA C C C C C C C C
AA AA C C C C C C C C
AA AA C C C C C C C H
AA AA C C C C C C C H
AA AA C C C C C C C H
AA AA C C C C C C C A
AA AA C C C C C C C A
AA AA C C C C C C C A
AA AA C C C C C C C O

AA African American
C   Caucasian (non-Hispanic)
A   Asian American
H   Hispanic
O   Other

Figure 6-3

2. Converting Percents to Fractions

By definition, a percent represents a ratio of parts per 100. Therefore, we can write percents as fractions.

Percent		Fraction	Example/Interpretation
7%	=	$\dfrac{7}{100}$	A sales tax of 7% means that 7 cents in tax is charged for every 100 cents spent.
39%	=	$\dfrac{39}{100}$	To say that 39% of households own a cat means that 39 per every 100 households own a cat.

Notice that $39\% = \dfrac{39}{100} = 39 \times \dfrac{1}{100} = 39 \div 100$.

From this discussion we have the following rule for converting percents to fractions.

Converting Percents to Fractions

Step 1   Replace the symbol % by $\times \frac{1}{100}$ (or by $\div\ 100$).
Step 2   Simplify the fraction to lowest terms, if possible.

Example 1   **Converting Percents to Fractions**

Convert each percent to a fraction.

a. 56%   **b.** 60%   **c.** 125%   **d.** 0.4%

Solution:

a. $56\% = 56 \times \dfrac{1}{100}$ Replace the % symbol by $\times \dfrac{1}{100}$.

$= \dfrac{56}{100}$ Multiply.

$= \dfrac{14}{25}$ Simplify to lowest terms.

b. $60\% = 60 \times \dfrac{1}{100}$ Replace the % symbol by $\times \dfrac{1}{100}$.

$= \dfrac{60}{100}$ Multiply.

$= \dfrac{3}{5}$ Simplify to lowest terms.

c. $125\% = 125 \times \dfrac{1}{100}$ Replace the % symbol by $\times \dfrac{1}{100}$.

$= \dfrac{125}{100}$ Multiply.

$= \dfrac{5}{4}$ or $1\dfrac{1}{4}$ Simplify to lowest terms.

Skill Practice

Convert each percent to a fraction.
2. 32%   **3.** 90%
4. 175%   **5.** 0.06%

Answers

2. $\dfrac{8}{25}$ **3.** $\dfrac{9}{10}$

4. $\dfrac{7}{4}$ **5.** $\dfrac{3}{5000}$

40   **Chapter 6** Percents

d. $0.4\% = 0.4 \times \dfrac{1}{100}$ Replace the % symbol by $\times \dfrac{1}{100}$.

$= \dfrac{4}{10} \times \dfrac{1}{100}$ Write 0.4 in fraction form.

$= \dfrac{4}{1000}$ Multiply.

$= \dfrac{1}{250}$ Simplify to lowest terms.

Note that $100\% = 100 \times \frac{1}{100} = 1$. That is, 100% represents 1 whole unit. In Example 1(c), $125\% = \frac{5}{4}$ or $1\frac{1}{4}$. This illustrates that any percent greater than 100% represents a quantity greater than 1 whole. Therefore, its fractional form may be expressed as an improper fraction or as a mixed number.

Note that $1\% = 1 \times \frac{1}{100} = \frac{1}{100}$. In Example 1(d), the value 0.4% represents a quantity less than 1%. Its fractional form is less than one-hundredth.

In Example 2 we convert some common percents to fraction form.

Concept Connections

Determine whether the percent represents a quantity greater than or less than 1 whole.

6. 1.92%
7. 19.2%
8. 192%

Skill Practice

Convert the percents to fractions.
9. 75%
10. 50%
11. $66\dfrac{2}{3}\%$

Example 2   **Converting Percents to Fractions**

Convert the percents to fractions.

a. 25%   **b.** 10%   **c.** $33\dfrac{1}{3}\%$

Solution:

a. $25\% = 25 \times \dfrac{1}{100} = \dfrac{25}{100} = \dfrac{1}{4}$ Thus, 25% represents one-quarter of a whole.

b. $10\% = 10 \times \dfrac{1}{100} = \dfrac{10}{100} = \dfrac{1}{10}$ Thus, 10% represents one-tenth of a whole.

c. $33\dfrac{1}{3}\% = 33\dfrac{1}{3} \times \dfrac{1}{100}$ Replace the % symbol by $\times \dfrac{1}{100}$.

$= \dfrac{100}{3} \times \dfrac{1}{100}$ Convert the mixed number to an improper fraction.

$= \dfrac{\overset{1}{\cancel{100}}}{3} \times \dfrac{1}{\underset{1}{\cancel{100}}}$ Simplify common factors.

$= \dfrac{1}{3}$ Thus, $33\dfrac{1}{3}\%$ represents one-third of a whole.

Example 3   **Converting Percents to Fractions**

Find the fraction form for the percent given in the sentence.

a. Forty-five percent of Americans use the Internet as a resource when planning vacations. (*Source: USA TODAY*)

b. 7.2% of adults suffer from asthma. (*Source:* National Center for Health Statistics)

Solution:

a. $45\% = 45 \times \dfrac{1}{100} = \dfrac{45}{100} = \dfrac{9}{20}$

Just under one-half of Americans planning a vacation use the Internet as a resource.

b. $7.2\% = 7.2 \times \dfrac{1}{100} = \dfrac{72}{10} \times \dfrac{1}{100}$

Write 7.2 in fraction form: $\frac{72}{10}$.

$= \dfrac{72}{1000} = \dfrac{9}{125}$

Almost one-tenth of adults have asthma.

Skill Practice

Find the fraction form for the percent given in the sentence.
12. In Pennsylvania, 15% of the residents are 65 or older.
13. One study found that teenage substance abuse rises by 40% during the summer months.

3. Converting Percents to Decimals

To express part of a whole unit, we can use a percent, a fraction, or a decimal. We would like to be able to convert from one form to another. The procedure for converting a percent to a decimal is the same as that for converting a percent to a fraction. We replace the % symbol by $\times \frac{1}{100}$. However, when converting to a decimal, it is usually more convenient to use the form $\times 0.01$.

> **Converting Percents to Decimals**
> Replace the % symbol by $\times 0.01$. (This is equivalent to $\times \frac{1}{100}$ and $\div 100$.)
> *Note:* Multiplying a decimal by 0.01 (or dividing by 100) is the same as moving the decimal point 2 places to the left.

Example 4 **Converting Percents to Decimals**

Convert each percent to its decimal form.

a. 31% **b.** 6.5% **c.** 428% **d.** $1\frac{3}{5}\%$ **e.** 0.05%

Skill Practice

Convert each percent to its decimal form.
14. 67% 15. 8.6%
16. 321% 17. $6\frac{1}{4}\%$
18. 0.7%

Solution:

a. $31\% = 31 \times 0.01$

Replace the % symbol by $\times 0.01$.

$= 0.31$

Move the decimal point 2 places to the left.

b. $6.5\% = 6.5 \times 0.01$

Replace the % symbol by $\times 0.01$.

$= 0.065$

Move the decimal point 2 places to the left.

c. $428\% = 428 \times 0.01$

Because 428% is greater than 100% we expect the decimal form to be a number greater than 1.

$= 4.28$

d. $1\frac{3}{5}\% = 1.6 \times 0.01$

Convert the mixed number to decimal form.

$= 0.016$

Because the percent is just over 1%, we expect the decimal form to be just slightly greater than one-hundredth.

e. $0.05\% = 0.05 \times 0.01$

The value 0.05% is less than 1%. We expect the decimal form to be less than one-hundredth.

$= 0.0005$

Answers

12. $\dfrac{3}{20}$ 13. $\dfrac{2}{5}$ 14. 0.67
15. 0.086 16. 3.21 17. 0.0625
18. 0.007

42 **Chapter 6** Percents

Skill Practice

Find the decimal notation for the percent given in the sentence.
19. The U.S. unemployment rate in 2010 was 9.5%.
20. Satellite Internet subscribers increased by 220% in a 4-year period.

Example 5 Converting Percents to Decimals

Find the decimal notation for the percent given in the sentence.

a. Recently, forty-eight percent of applicants to U.S. medical schools were female. (*Source:* Association of American Medical Colleges)

b. The price per gallon for regular unleaded gasoline in 2012 was 280% of what it was in 1984.

Solution:

a. $48\% = 48 \times 0.01 = 0.48$ Just under one-half of the applicants were female.

b. $280\% = 280 \times 0.01 = 2.80$ The cost of gas in 2012 was almost 3 times as great as in 1984.

Notice from Examples 1–5 that we perform the same procedure to convert a percent to either a decimal or a fraction. In each case we multiply by $\frac{1}{100}$. When converting to a decimal, it is usually easier to use the form $\times 0.01$. When converting to a fraction, it is usually easier to use the form $\times \frac{1}{100}$. In both cases, this operation is also equivalent to dividing by 100.

4. Common Percents and Their Fraction and Decimal Forms

Table 6-1 shows some common percents and their equivalent fraction and decimal forms.

Table 6-1

Percent	Fraction	Decimal	Example/Interpretation
100%	1	1.00	Of people who give birth, 100% are female.
50%	$\frac{1}{2}$	0.50	Of the population, 50% is male. That is, one-half of the population is male.
25%	$\frac{1}{4}$	0.25	Approximately 25% of the U.S. population smokes. That is, one-quarter of the population smokes.
75%	$\frac{3}{4}$	0.75	Approximately 75% of homes have computers. That is, three-quarters of homes have computers.
10%	$\frac{1}{10}$	0.10	Of the population, 10% is left-handed. That is, one-tenth of the population is left-handed.
1%	$\frac{1}{100}$	0.01	Approximately 1% of babies are born underweight. That is, about 1 in 100 babies is born underweight.
$33\frac{1}{3}\%$	$\frac{1}{3}$	$0.\overline{3}$	A basketball player made $33\frac{1}{3}\%$ of her shots. That is, she made about 1 basket for every 3 shots attempted.
$66\frac{2}{3}\%$	$\frac{2}{3}$	$0.\overline{6}$	Of the population, $66\frac{2}{3}\%$ prefers chocolate ice cream to other flavors. That is, 2 out of 3 people prefer chocolate ice cream.

Section 6.1   Practice Exercises

Study Skills Exercise

> A test is a *grading* tool for your instructor. How can you turn it into a *learning* tool for you?

Vocabulary and Key Concepts

1. The word _____ means per one hundred.

Concept 1: Definition of Percent

2. There are 100 students taking a math course. If 18% earn an A, how many students earned an A?

For Exercises 3–8, use a percent to express the shaded portion of each drawing.

3. 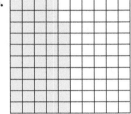   **4.** 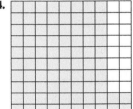   **5.**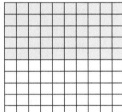

6. 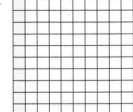   **7.** 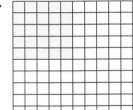   **8.**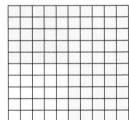

For Exercises 9–12, write a percent for each statement.

9. A bank pays $2 in interest for every $100 deposited.

10. In South Dakota, 5 out of every 100 people work in construction.

 11. Out of 100 acres, 70 acres were planted with corn.

12. On TV, 26 out of every 100 minutes are filled with commercials.

Concept 2: Converting Percents to Fractions

13. Explain the procedure to change a percent to a fraction.

14. What fraction represents 50%.

For Exercises 15–34, change the percent to a simplified fraction or mixed number. **(See Examples 1 and 2.)**

15. 3%   **16.** 7%   **17.** 84%   **18.** 32%

19. 25%   **20.** 20%   **21.** 3.4%   **22.** 5.2%

44   **Chapter 6**   Percents

23. 115%	**24.** 150%	**25.** 175%	**26.** 120%
27. 0.5%	**28.** 0.2%	**29.** 0.25%	**30.** 0.75%
31. $66\frac{2}{3}\%$	**32.** $5\frac{1}{6}\%$	**33.** $24\frac{1}{2}\%$	**34.** $6\frac{1}{4}\%$

Concept 3: Converting Percents to Decimals

35. Explain the procedure to change a percent to a decimal.

For Exercises 36–51, change the percent to a decimal. **(See Example 4.)**

36. 58%	**37.** 72%	**38.** 15%	**39.** 66%
40. 8.5%	**41.** 12.9%	**42.** 72.31%	**43.** 41.05%
44. 142%	**45.** 201%	**46.** 0.55%	**47.** 0.75%
48. $26\frac{2}{5}\%$	**49.** $16\frac{1}{4}\%$	**50.** $55\frac{1}{20}\%$	**51.** $62\frac{1}{5}\%$

Concept 4: Common Percents and Their Fraction and Decimal Forms

For Exercises 52–57, use a percent to express the shaded portion of each drawing.

52.   **53.**   **54.**

55.   **56.**    **57.**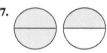

Mixed Exercises

For Exercises 58–63, match the percent with its fraction form.

58. $66\frac{2}{3}\%$	**a.** $\frac{3}{2}$
59. 10%	**b.** $\frac{3}{4}$
60. 90%	**c.** $\frac{2}{3}$
61. 75%	**d.** $\frac{1}{10}$
62. 25%	**e.** $\frac{9}{10}$
63. 150%	**f.** $\frac{1}{4}$

For Exercises 64–69, match the percent with its decimal form.

64. 30%	**a.** 0.01
65. $33\frac{1}{3}\%$	**b.** 0.50
66. 125%	**c.** 0.80
67. 50%	**d.** $0.\overline{3}$
68. 1%	**e.** 0.30
69. 80%	**f.** 1.25

70. In which direction do you move the decimal point when you convert a percent to a decimal? By how many places?

For Exercises 71–78, find the decimal and fraction equivalent of the percent given in the sentence. **(See Examples 3 and 5.)**

71. Between 2000 and 2010 the population in California grew by 7.6%.

72. Las Vegas is considered the fastest-growing city in the United States. Between 1990 and 2010 its population increased by 75%.

73. For a recent year, the unemployment rate in Kansas was 4.3%.

74. For a recent year, the unemployment rate in the United States was 5.8%.

75. From 2009 to 2010 there was a drop of 2% in electricity generated by nuclear power in the United States. (*Source:* Energy Information Administration)

76. For a recent year the average U.S. income tax rate was 18.2%.

77. Thirty-five percent of Americans say they entertain at home once or twice a year. (*Source: USA TODAY*)

78. Twenty-nine percent of Americans say they entertain at home once a month.

79. The graph represents the percent of dog owners who participate in certain activities to treat their dogs. Write the decimal and fraction forms of the percents given in the graph. (*Source:* American Animal Hospital Association)

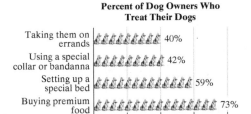

80. The graph represents the percent of people with at least a bachelor's degree for selected large cities. Write the decimal and fraction forms of the percents given in the graph. (*Source:* U.S. Census Bureau)

Section 6.2	**Fractions and Decimals and Their Percent Forms**

Concepts

- Converting Fractions and Decimals to Percents
- Approximating Percents
- Fractions, Decimals, Percents: A Summary

1. Converting Fractions and Decimals to Percents

In Section 6.1, we converted percents to their equivalent fraction and decimal forms. This is done by replacing the % symbol by $\times \frac{1}{100}$. In this section, we reverse the process. We convert fractions and decimals to percents by multiplying by 100 and applying the % symbol.

> **Converting Fractions and Decimals to Percent Form**
> Multiply the fraction or decimal by 100%.
> *Note:* Multiplying a decimal by 100 moves the decimal point 2 places to the right.

Skill Practice

Convert each decimal to its percent form.
1. 0.46
2. 3.25
3. 2
4. 0.0006
5. 2.5

TIP: Multiplying a number by 100% is equivalent to multiplying the number by 1. Thus, the value of the number is not changed.

Example 1	**Converting Decimals to Percents**

Convert each decimal to its equivalent percent form.

   a. 0.62   **b.** 1.75   **c.** 1   **d.** 0.004   **e.** 8.9

Solution:

a. $0.62 = 0.62 \times 100\%$ Multiply by 100%.

      $= 62\%$ Multiplying by 100 moves the decimal point 2 places to the right.

b. $1.75 = 1.75 \times 100\%$ Multiply by 100%.

      $= 175\%$ The decimal number 1.75 is greater than 1. Therefore, we expect a percent greater than 100%.

c. $1 = 1 \times 100\%$ Multiply by 100%.

      $= 100\%$ Recall that 1 whole is equal to 100%.

d. $0.004 = 0.004 \times 100\%$ Multiply by 100%.

      $= 00.4\%$ Move the decimal point to the right 2 places.

e. $8.9 = 8.90 \times 100\%$ Multiply by 100%.

      $= 890\%$

Example 2 **Converting a Fraction to Percent Notation**

Convert the fraction to percent notation. $\dfrac{3}{5}$

Solution:

$$\frac{3}{5} = \frac{3}{5} \times 100\% \qquad \text{Multiply by 100\%.}$$

$$= \frac{3}{5} \times \frac{100}{1}\% \qquad \text{Convert the whole number to an improper fraction.}$$

$$= \frac{3}{\overset{}{\underset{1}{5}}} \times \frac{\overset{20}{\cancel{100}}}{1}\% \qquad \text{Multiply fractions and simplify to lowest terms.}$$

$$= 60\%$$

> **TIP:** We could also have converted $\frac{3}{5}$ to decimal form first (by dividing the numerator by the denominator) and then converted the decimal to a percent.
>
> convert to decimal | convert to percent
>
> $$\frac{3}{5} = 0.60 \qquad = \qquad 0.60 \times 100\% = 60\%$$

Skill Practice

Convert the fraction to percent notation.

6. $\dfrac{7}{10}$

Example 3 **Converting a Fraction to Percent Notation**

Convert the fraction to percent notation. $\dfrac{2}{3}$

Solution:

$$\frac{2}{3} = \frac{2}{3} \times 100\% \qquad \text{Multiply by 100\%.}$$

$$= \frac{2}{3} \times \frac{100}{1}\% \qquad \text{Convert the whole number to an improper fraction.}$$

$$= \frac{200}{3}\%$$

The number $\frac{200}{3}\%$ can be written as $66\frac{2}{3}\%$ or as $66.\overline{6}\%$.

> **TIP:** First converting $\frac{2}{3}$ to a decimal before converting to percent notation is an alternative approach.
>
> convert to decimal | convert to percent
>
> $$\frac{2}{3} = 0.\overline{6} \qquad = \qquad 0.666 \ldots \times 100\% = 66.\overline{6}\%$$

Skill Practice

Convert the fraction to percent notation.

7. $\dfrac{1}{9}$

Answers

6. 70%

7. $\dfrac{100}{9}\%$ or $11\dfrac{1}{9}\%$ or $11.\overline{1}\%$

In Example 4, we convert an improper fraction and a mixed number to percent form.

Example 4   **Converting Improper Fractions and Mixed Numbers to Percents**

Convert to percent notation.

a. $2\frac{1}{4}$ **b.** $\frac{13}{10}$

Solution:

a. $2\frac{1}{4} = 2\frac{1}{4} \times 100\%$ Multiply by 100%.

$= \frac{9}{4} \times \frac{100}{1}\%$ Convert to improper fractions.

$= \frac{9}{\overset{}{4}} \times \frac{\overset{25}{\cancel{100}}}{1}\%$ Multiply and simplify to lowest terms.

$= 225\%$

b. $\frac{13}{10} = \frac{13}{10} \times 100\%$ Multiply by 100%.

$= \frac{13}{10} \times \frac{100}{1}\%$ Convert the whole number to an improper fraction.

$= \frac{13}{\underset{1}{\cancel{10}}} \times \frac{\overset{10}{\cancel{100}}}{1}\%$ Multiply and simplify to lowest terms.

$= 130\%$

Notice that both answers in Example 4 are greater than 100%. This is reasonable because any number greater than 1 whole unit represents a percent greater than 100%.

2. Approximating Percents

In Example 5 we approximate a percent from its fraction form.

Example 5   **Approximating a Percent**

Convert the fraction $\frac{5}{13}$ to percent notation rounded to the nearest tenth of a percent.

Solution:

$\frac{5}{13} = \frac{5}{13} \times 100\%$ Multiply by 100%.

$= \frac{5}{13} \times \frac{100}{1}\%$ Write the whole number as an improper fraction.

$= \frac{500}{13}\%$

Avoiding Mistakes

We converted the fraction to percent form *before* dividing and rounding. If you try to convert to decimal form first, you might round too soon.

To round to the nearest tenth of a percent, we must divide. We will obtain the hundredths-place digit in the quotient on which to base the decision on rounding.

$$38.4\overset{1}{6} \approx 38.5$$

Thus, $\dfrac{5}{13} \approx 38.5\%$.

$$
\begin{array}{r}
38.46 \\
13\overline{)500.00} \\
-39 \\
\hline
110 \\
-104 \\
\hline
60 \\
-52 \\
\hline
80 \\
-78 \\
\hline
2
\end{array}
$$

3. Fractions, Decimals, Percents: A Summary

The diagram in Figure 6-4 illustrates the methods for converting fractions, decimals, and percents.

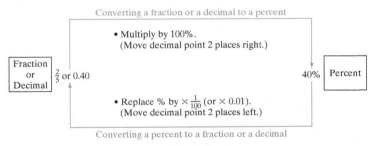

Converting a fraction or a decimal to a percent

- Multiply by 100%.
  (Move decimal point 2 places right.)

Fraction or Decimal $\frac{2}{5}$ or 0.40   40%   Percent

- Replace % by $\times \frac{1}{100}$ (or $\times 0.01$).
  (Move decimal point 2 places left.)

Converting a percent to a fraction or a decimal

Figure 6-4

Concept Connections

11. To convert a decimal to a percent, in which direction do you move the decimal point?

12. To convert a percent to a decimal, in which direction do you move the decimal point?

Example 6 **Converting Fractions, Decimals, and Percents**

Complete the table.

	Fraction	Decimal	Percent
a.		0.55	
b.	$\frac{1}{200}$		
c.			160%
d.		2.4	
e.			$66\frac{2}{3}\%$
f.	$\frac{2}{9}$		

Solution:

a. 0.55 to fraction: $0.55 = \dfrac{55}{100} = \dfrac{11}{20}$

   0.55 to percent: $0.55 \times 100\% = 55\%$

Answers

11. To the right 2 places
12. To the left 2 places

50   **Chapter 6** Percents

Skill Practice

Complete the table.

	Fraction	Decimal	Percent
13.		1.41	
14.	$\frac{1}{50}$		
15.			18%
16.		0.58	
17.			$33\frac{1}{3}\%$
18.	$\frac{7}{9}$		

b. $\frac{1}{200}$ to decimal: $1 \div 200 = 0.005$

$\frac{1}{200}$ to percent: $\frac{1}{200} \times 100\% = \frac{100}{200}\% = 0.5\%$

c. 160% to fraction: $160 \times \frac{1}{100} = \frac{160}{100} = \frac{8}{5}$ or $1\frac{3}{5}$

160% to decimal: $160 \times 0.01 = 1.6$

d. 2.4 to fraction: $\frac{24}{10} = \frac{12}{5}$ or $2\frac{2}{5}$

2.4 to percent: $2.4 \times 100\% = 240\%$

e. $66\frac{2}{3}\%$ to fraction: $66\frac{2}{3} \times \frac{1}{100} = \frac{\overset{2}{\cancel{200}}}{3} \times \frac{1}{\underset{1}{\cancel{100}}} = \frac{2}{3}$

$66\frac{2}{3}\%$ to decimal: $66\frac{2}{3} \times 0.01 = 66.\overline{6} \times 0.01 = 0.\overline{6}$

f. $\frac{2}{9}$ to decimal: $2 \div 9 = 0.\overline{2}$

$\frac{2}{9}$ to percent: $\frac{2}{9} \times 100\% = \frac{2}{9} \times \frac{100}{1}\% = \frac{200}{9}\% = 22\frac{2}{9}\%$ or $22.\overline{2}\%$

The completed table is as follows.

Answers

	Fraction	Decimal	Percent
13.	$\frac{141}{100}$ or $1\frac{41}{100}$	1.41	141%
14.	$\frac{1}{50}$	0.02	2%
15.	$\frac{9}{50}$	0.18	18%
16.	$\frac{29}{50}$	0.58	58%
17.	$\frac{1}{3}$	$0.\overline{3}$	$33\frac{1}{3}\%$
18.	$\frac{7}{9}$	$0.\overline{7}$	$77.\overline{7}\%$

	Fraction	Decimal	Percent
a.	$\frac{11}{20}$	0.55	55%
b.	$\frac{1}{200}$	0.005	0.5%
c.	$\frac{8}{5}$ or $1\frac{3}{5}$	1.6	160%
d.	$\frac{12}{5}$ or $2\frac{2}{5}$	2.4	240%
e.	$\frac{2}{3}$	$0.\overline{6}$	$66\frac{2}{3}\%$
f.	$\frac{2}{9}$	$0.\overline{2}$	$22\frac{2}{9}\%$ or $22.\overline{2}\%$

Section 6.2 Practice Exercises

Study Skills Exercise

Do you remember your instructor's name, office hours, office location, and office phone? Write them here:

Instructor's name: _____   Instructor's office hours: _____

Instructor's office location: _____   Instructor's office phone: _____

Review Exercises

1. Determine whether the given statement is true or false.

   a. $5\% = \frac{1}{2}$ **b.** $10\% = \frac{1}{10}$ **c.** $200\% = 2$

For Exercises 2–5, convert the percent to a fraction or mixed number.

2. 60% **3.** 130% **4.** $16\frac{1}{2}\%$ **5.** 0.5%

For Exercises 6–9, convert the percent to a decimal.

6. 80% **7.** $6\frac{1}{3}\%$ **8.** 143% **9.** 0.3%

Concept 1: Converting Fractions and Decimals to Percents

For Exercises 10–13, multiply.

10. $0.68 \times 100\%$ **11.** $1.62 \times 100\%$ **12.** $0.005 \times 100\%$ **13.** $0.26 \times 100\%$

14. Write the rule for multiplying a decimal by 100.

For Exercises 15–18, multiply.

15. $\dfrac{5}{4} \times 100\%$ **16.** $\dfrac{2}{5} \times 100\%$ **17.** $\dfrac{77}{100} \times 100\%$ **18.** $\dfrac{113}{100} \times 100\%$

For Exercises 19–30, convert the decimal to a percent. **(See Example 1.)**

19. 0.27 **20.** 0.51 **21.** 0.19 **22.** 0.33

23. 1.75 **24.** 2.8 **25.** 0.124 **26.** 0.277

27. 0.006 **28.** 0.0008 **29.** 1.014 **30.** 2.203

For Exercises 31–42, convert the fraction to a percent. **(See Examples 2 and 3.)**

31. $\dfrac{71}{100}$ **32.** $\dfrac{89}{100}$ **33.** $\dfrac{19}{20}$ **34.** $\dfrac{7}{20}$

35. $\dfrac{7}{8}$ **36.** $\dfrac{5}{8}$ **37.** $\dfrac{13}{16}$ **38.** $\dfrac{11}{16}$

39. $\dfrac{5}{6}$ **40.** $\dfrac{5}{12}$ **41.** $\dfrac{4}{9}$ **42.** $\dfrac{1}{9}$

For Exercises 43–48, write the fraction as a percent.

43. One-quarter of Americans say they entertain at home 2 or more times a month. (*Source: USA TODAY*)

44. According to the Centers for Disease Control (CDC), $\frac{37}{100}$ of U.S. teenage boys say they rarely or never wear their seatbelts.

45. According to the Centers for Disease Control, $\frac{1}{10}$ of teenage girls in the United States say they rarely or never wear their seatbelts.

46. In Italy, $\frac{3}{50}$ of the country's budget comes from tourism.

47. In a recent year, $\frac{2}{3}$ of the beds in U.S. hospitals were occupied.

48. Recently, $\frac{1}{8}$ of U.S. residents between the ages of 55 and 64 were not covered by health insurance. (*Source:* U.S. Bureau of the Census)

For Exercises 49–56, convert to percent notation. **(See Example 4.)**

49. $1\frac{3}{4}$ **50.** $\frac{7}{2}$ **51.** $\frac{27}{20}$ **52.** $2\frac{1}{8}$

53. $\frac{11}{9}$ **54.** $1\frac{5}{9}$ **55.** $1\frac{2}{3}$ **56.** $\frac{7}{6}$

Concept 2: Approximating Percents

For Exercises 57–64, write the fraction in percent notation to the nearest tenth of a percent. **(See Example 5.)**

57. $\frac{3}{7}$ **58.** $\frac{6}{7}$ **59.** $\frac{1}{13}$ **60.** $\frac{3}{13}$

61. $\frac{5}{11}$ **62.** $\frac{8}{11}$ **63.** $\frac{13}{15}$ **64.** $\frac{1}{15}$

Concept 3: Fractions, Decimals, Percents: A Summary

65. Explain the difference between $\frac{1}{2}$ and $\frac{1}{2}\%$.

66. Explain the difference between $\frac{3}{4}$ and $\frac{3}{4}\%$.

67. Explain the difference between 25% and 0.25%.

68. Explain the difference between 10% and 0.10%.

69. Which of the numbers represent 125%?

    a. 1.25   **b.** 0.125   **c.** $\frac{5}{4}$ **d.** $\frac{5}{4}\%$

70. Which of the numbers represent 60%?

    a. 6.0   **b.** 0.60%   **c.** 0.6   **d.** $\frac{3}{5}$

71. Which of the numbers represent 30%?

    a. $\frac{3}{10}$ **b.** $\frac{1}{3}$ **c.** 0.3   **d.** 0.03%

72. Which of the numbers represent 180%?

    a. 18   **b.** 1.8   **c.** $\frac{9}{5}$ **d.** $\frac{9}{5}\%$

Mixed Exercises

For Exercises 73–76, complete the table. **(See Example 6.)**

73.

	Fraction	Decimal	Percent
a.	$\frac{1}{4}$		
b.		0.92	
c.			15%
d.		1.6	
e.	$\frac{1}{100}$		
f.			0.5%

74.

	Fraction	Decimal	Percent
a.			0.6%
b.	$\frac{2}{5}$		
c.		2	
d.	$\frac{1}{2}$		
e.		0.12	
f.			45%

75.

	Fraction	Decimal	Percent
a.			14%
b.		0.87	
c.		1	
d.	$\frac{1}{3}$		
e.			0.2%
f.	$\frac{19}{20}$		

76.

	Fraction	Decimal	Percent
a.		1.3	
b.			22%
c.	$\frac{3}{4}$		
d.		0.73	
e.			$22.\overline{2}\%$
f.	$\frac{1}{20}$		

Expanding Your Skills

77. Is the number 1.4 less than or greater than 100%?

78. Is the number 0.0087 less than or greater than 1%?

79. Is the number 0.052 less than or greater than 50%?

80. Is the number 25 less than or greater than 25%?

Percent Proportions and Applications

1. Introduction to Percent Proportions

Recall that a percent is a ratio in parts per 100. For example, $50\% = \frac{50}{100}$. However, a percent can be represented by infinitely many equivalent fractions. Thus,

$$50\% = \frac{50}{100} = \frac{1}{2} = \frac{2}{4} = \frac{3}{6} \quad \text{and infinitely many more.}$$

Equating a percent to an equivalent ratio forms a proportion that we call a **percent proportion**. A percent proportion is a proportion in which one ratio is written with a denominator of 100. For example:

$$\frac{50}{100} = \frac{3}{6} \quad \text{is a percent proportion.}$$

Concepts

1. Introduction to Percent Proportions
2. Identifying the Parts of a Percent Proportion
3. Solving Percent Proportions
4. Applications of Percent Proportions

2. Identifying the Parts of a Percent Proportion

We will be using percent proportions to solve a variety of application problems. But first we need to identify and label the parts of a percent proportion.

A percent proportion can be written in the form:

$$\frac{\text{Amount}}{\text{Base}} = p\% \qquad \text{or} \qquad \frac{\text{Amount}}{\text{Base}} = \frac{p}{100}$$

For example:

$$\underset{\substack{| \\ \text{amount}}}{4} \text{ L out of } \underset{\substack{| \\ \text{base}}}{8} \text{ L is } \underset{\substack{| \\ p}}{50\%} \qquad \frac{4}{8} = 50\% \qquad \text{or} \qquad \frac{4}{8} = \frac{50}{100}$$

In this example, 8 L is some total (or base) quantity and 4 L is some part (or amount) of that whole. The ratio $\frac{4}{8}$ represents a fraction of the whole equal to 50%. In general, we offer the following guidelines for identifying the parts of a percent proportion.

> ### Identifying the Parts of a Percent Proportion
>
> A percent proportion can be written as
>
> $$\frac{\text{Amount}}{\text{Base}} = p\% \qquad \text{or} \qquad \frac{\text{Amount}}{\text{Base}} = \frac{p}{100}.$$
>
> - The **base** is the total or whole amount being considered. It often appears after the word *of* within a word problem.
> - The **amount** is the part being compared to the base. It sometimes appears with the word *is* within a word problem.

Example 1   Identifying Amount, Base, and *p* for a Percent Proportion

Identify the amount, base, and *p* value, and then set up a percent proportion.

a. 25% of 60 students is 15 students.   **b.** $32 is 50% of $64.

c. 5 of 1000 employees is 0.5%.

Solution:

For each problem, we recommend that you identify *p* first. It is the number in front of the symbol %. Then identify the base. In most cases it follows the word *of*. Then, by the process of elimination, find the amount.

a. $\underset{\substack{| \\ p \\ \text{(before \%} \\ \text{symbol)}}}{25\%}$ of $\underset{\substack{| \\ \text{base} \\ \text{(after the} \\ \text{word } of)}}{60}$ students is $\underset{\substack{| \\ \text{amount}}}{15}$ students.

$$\underset{\text{base} \rightarrow}{\overset{\text{amount} \rightarrow}{\frac{15}{60}}} = \underset{\leftarrow 100}{\overset{\leftarrow p}{\frac{25}{100}}}$$

b. $\underset{\substack{| \\ \text{amount}}}{\$32}$ is $\underset{\substack{| \\ p}}{50\%}$ of $\underset{\substack{| \\ \text{base}}}{\$64}$.

$$\underset{\text{base} \rightarrow}{\overset{\text{amount} \rightarrow}{\frac{32}{64}}} = \underset{\leftarrow 100}{\overset{\leftarrow p}{\frac{50}{100}}}$$

c. $\underset{\substack{| \\ \text{amount}}}{5}$ of $\underset{\substack{| \\ \text{base}}}{1000}$ employees is $\underset{\substack{| \\ p}}{0.5\%}$.

$$\underset{\text{base} \rightarrow}{\overset{\text{amount} \rightarrow}{\frac{5}{1000}}} = \underset{\leftarrow 100}{\overset{\leftarrow p}{\frac{0.5}{100}}}$$

3. Solving Percent Proportions

In Example 1, we practiced identifying the parts of a percent proportion. Now we consider percent proportions in which one of these numbers is unknown. Furthermore, we will see that the examples come in three types:

- Amount is unknown.
- Base is unknown.
- Value p is unknown.

However, the process for solving in each case is the same.

Example 2 Solving Percent Proportions—Amount Unknown

a. What is 30% of 180? **b.** 70% of 500 people is how many people?

Solution:

a. What is 30% of 180?

amount (x) p base

The base and value for p are known.

Let x represent the unknown amount.

$$\frac{x}{180} = \frac{30}{100}$$

Set up a percent proportion.

$100 \cdot x = (30)(180)$

Equate the cross products.

$100x = 5400$

$$\frac{\overset{1}{\cancel{100}}x}{\underset{1}{\cancel{100}}} = \frac{\overset{}{\cancel{5400}}}{\cancel{100}}$$

Divide both sides of the equation by 100.

$x = 54$

Simplify to lowest terms.

Therefore, 54 is 30% of 180.

> **TIP:** We can check the answer to Example 2(a) as follows. Ten percent of a number is $\frac{1}{10}$ of the number. Furthermore, $\frac{1}{10}$ of 180 is 18. Thirty percent of 180 must be 3 times this amount.
>
> $3 \times 18 = 54$ ✔

b. 70% of 500 people is how many people?

p base amount (x)

The base and value for p are known.

Let x represent the unknown amount.

$$\frac{x}{500} = \frac{70}{100}$$

Set up a percent proportion.

$100 \cdot x = (70)(500)$

Equate the cross products.

$100x = 35{,}000$

$$\frac{\overset{1}{\cancel{100}}x}{\underset{1}{\cancel{100}}} = \frac{35{,}000}{\cancel{100}}$$

Divide both sides by 100.

$x = 350$

Simplify to lowest terms.

Therefore, 70% of 500 people is 350 people.

> **Skill Practice**
>
> **4.** What is 82% of 250?
> **5.** 105% of $60 is how much?

> **TIP:** To check the solution to Example 2(b), we can compute 10% of 500, which is 50. To find 70%, multiply this by 7. We have $7(50) = 350$. ✔

56 **Chapter 6** Percents

Example 3 Solving Percent Proportions—Base Unknown

a. 40% of what number is 25?   **b.** $13.50 is 150% of how many dollars?

Solution:

a. 40% of what number is 25?   The amount and value of p are known.

p · base (x) · amount   Let x represent the unknown base.

$$\frac{25}{x} = \frac{40}{100}$$ Set up a percent proportion.

$$(25)(100) = 40 \cdot x$$ Equate the cross products.

$$2500 = 40x$$

$$\frac{2500}{40} = \frac{\overset{1}{40}x}{\underset{1}{40}}$$ Divide both sides by 40.

$$62.5 = x$$ Therefore, 40% of 62.5 is 25.

b. $13.50 is 150% of how many dollars?   The amount and value of p are known.

amount · p · base (x)   Let x represent the unknown base.

$$\frac{13.50}{x} = \frac{150}{100}$$ Set up a percent proportion.

$$150 \cdot x = (13.50)(100)$$ Equate the cross products.

$$150x = 1350$$

$$\frac{\overset{1}{150}x}{\underset{1}{150}} = \frac{1350}{150}$$ Divide both sides by 150.

$$x = 9$$ Therefore, $13.50 is 150% of $9.

Example 4 Solving Percent Proportions—p Unknown

a. What percent of 80 mi is 12.4 mi?

b. 48 is what percent of 42? Round to the nearest percent.

Solution:

a. What percent of 80 mi is 12.4 mi?   The amount and base are known.

p · base · amount   The value of p is unknown.

$$\frac{12.4}{80} = \frac{p}{100}$$ Set up a percent equation.

$$(12.4)(100) = 80 \cdot p$$ Equate the cross products.

$$1240 = 80p$$

$$\frac{1240}{80} = \frac{\overset{1}{80}p}{\underset{1}{80}}$$ Divide both sides by 80.

$$15.5 = p$$ Therefore, 15.5% of 80 mi is 12.4 mi.

b. 48 is what percent of 42? Round to the nearest percent.

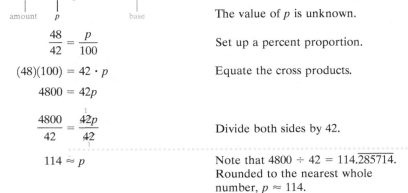

amount p base   The value of p is unknown.

$$\frac{48}{42} = \frac{p}{100}$$ Set up a percent proportion.

$(48)(100) = 42 \cdot p$ Equate the cross products.

$4800 = 42p$

$$\frac{4800}{42} = \frac{\overset{1}{\cancel{42}}p}{\underset{1}{\cancel{42}}}$$ Divide both sides by 42.

$114 \approx p$ Note that $4800 \div 42 = 114.\overline{285714}$. Rounded to the nearest whole number, $p \approx 114$.

Therefore, 48 is approximately 114% of 42.

Avoiding Mistakes

Remember that p represents the number of *parts* per 100. However, Example 4 asked us to find the value of p%. Therefore, it was necessary to attach the % symbol to our value of p.
For Example 4(b), $p \approx 114$.
Therefore, $p\% = 114\%$

4. Applications of Percent Proportions

We now use percent proportions to solve application problems involving percents.

Example 5   **Using Percents in Meteorology**

Buffalo, New York, receives an average of 94 in. of snow each year. This year it had 120% of the normal annual snowfall. How much snow did Buffalo get this year?

Solution:

This situation can be translated as:

"The amount of snow Buffalo received is 120% of 94 in."

amount (x) p base

$$\frac{x}{94} = \frac{120}{100}$$ Set up a percent proportion.

$100 \cdot x = (120)(94)$ Equate the cross products.

$100x = 11{,}280$

$$\frac{\overset{1}{\cancel{100}}x}{\underset{1}{\cancel{100}}} = \frac{11{,}280}{100}$$ Divide both sides by 100.

$x = 112.8$

This year, Buffalo had 112.8 in. of snow.

Skill Practice

10. In a recent year it was estimated that 24.7% of U.S. adults smoked tobacco products regularly. In a group of 2000 adults, how many would be expected to be smokers?

TIP: In a word problem, it is always helpful to check the reasonableness of your answer. In Example 5, we are looking for 120% of 94 in. But 120% must be *more* than the base amount of 94 in. Therefore, we suspect that our solution is reasonable.

Answer

10. 494 people

| Example 6 | **Using Percents in Statistics** |

Recently, a Harvard University's freshman class had 18% Asian American students. If this represented 380 students, how many students were admitted to the freshman class? Round to the nearest student.

Solution:

This situation can be translated as:

"380 is 18% of what number?"

$$\underset{\text{amount}}{380} \text{ is } \underset{p}{18\%} \text{ of } \underset{\text{base }(x)}{\text{what number?}}$$

$$\frac{380}{x} = \frac{18}{100}$$ Set up a percent proportion.

$$(380)(100) = (18) \cdot x$$ Equate the cross products.

$$38{,}000 = 18x$$

$$\frac{38{,}000}{18} = \frac{\overset{1}{\cancel{18}}x}{\underset{1}{\cancel{18}}}$$ Note that $38{,}000 \div 18 \approx 2111.1$. Rounded to the nearest whole unit (whole person), this is 2111.

$$2111 \approx x$$

The freshman class at Harvard had approximately 2111 students.

TIP: We can check the answer to Example 6 by substituting $x = 2111$ back into the original proportion. The cross products will not be exactly the same because we had to round the value of x. However, the cross products should be *close*.

$$\frac{380}{2111} \overset{?}{\approx} \frac{18}{100}$$ Substitute $x = 2111$ into the proportion.

$$(380)(100) \overset{?}{\approx} (18)(2111)$$

$$38{,}000 \approx 37{,}998 \quad ✔ \quad \text{The values are very close.}$$

| Example 7 | **Using Percents in Business** |

Suppose a tennis pro who is ranked 90th in the world on the men's professional tour earns $280,000 per year in tournament winnings and endorsements. He pays his coach $100,000 per year. What percent of his income goes toward his coach? Round to the nearest tenth of a percent.

Solution:

This can be translated as:

"What *percent* of $280,000 is $100,000?"

The value of p is unknown.	base (x)	amount

$$\frac{100{,}000}{280{,}000} = \frac{p}{100}$$ Set up a percent proportion.

$$\frac{100{,}\cancel{000}}{280{,}\cancel{000}} = \frac{p}{100}$$ The ratio on the left side of the equation can be simplified by a factor of 10,000. "Strike through" four zeros in the numerator and denominator.

$$\frac{10}{28} = \frac{p}{100}$$

$(10)(100) = (28) \cdot p$ Equate the cross products.

$1000 = 28p$

$$\frac{1000}{28} = \frac{\overset{1}{\cancel{28}}p}{\underset{1}{\cancel{28}}}$$ Divide both sides by 28.

$$\frac{1000}{28} = p$$

$35.7 \approx p$ Dividing $1000 \div 28$, we get approximately 35.7.

The tennis pro spends about 35.7% of his income on his coach.

$$\begin{array}{r} 35.71 \\ 28\overline{)1000.00} \\ -84 \\ \hline 160 \\ -140 \\ \hline 200 \\ -196 \\ \hline 40 \\ -28 \\ \hline 12 \end{array}$$

Section 6.3 Practice Exercises

Study Skills Exercise

Do you believe that you have math anxiety? If yes, why do you think so?

Of the list below, circle the activities that you think can help someone with math anxiety.

Deep breathing   Reading a book about math anxiety

Scheduling extra study time   Keeping a positive attitude

Vocabulary and Key Concepts

1. **a.** A _____ proportion is a proportion in which one ratio is written with a denominator of 100.

   b. The first step to solve a percent proportion is to equate the _____ products.

60   **Chapter 6** Percents

Review Exercises

For Exercises 2–4, convert the decimal to a percent.

2. 0.55

3. 1.30

4. 0.0006

For Exercises 5–7, convert the fraction to a percent.

5. $\dfrac{3}{8}$

6. $\dfrac{5}{2}$

7. $\dfrac{1}{100}$

For Exercises 8–10, convert the percent to a fraction.

8. $62\frac{1}{2}\%$

9. 2%

10. 77%

For Exercises 11–13, convert the percent to a decimal.

11. 82%

12. 0.3%

13. 100%

Concept 1: Introduction to Percent Proportions

For Example 14–19, determine if the proportion is a percent proportion.

14. $\dfrac{7}{100} = \dfrac{14}{200}$

15. $\dfrac{150}{300} = \dfrac{50}{100}$

16. $\dfrac{5}{7} = \dfrac{25}{35}$

17. $\dfrac{2}{3} = \dfrac{6}{9}$

18. $\dfrac{1\frac{1}{2}}{100} = \dfrac{3}{200}$

19. $\dfrac{\frac{3}{4}}{100} = \dfrac{3}{400}$

For Exercises 20–24, shade the figure to estimate the amount. The first exercise is given as an example.

Example: Find 60% of 80. (Answer: 48)

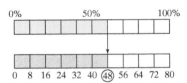

20. Find 40% of 60.

21. Find 75% of 60.

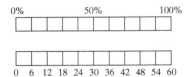

22. Find 15% of 240.

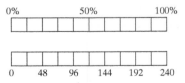

23. Find 80% of 40.

24. Find 10% of 30.

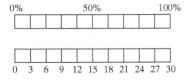

Concept 2: Identifying the Parts of a Percent Proportion

For Exercises 25–30, identify the amount, base, and p value. **(See Example 1.)**

25. 12 balloons is 60% of 20 balloons.

26. 25% of 400 cars is 100 cars.

27. $99 of $200 is 49.5%.

28. 45 of 50 children is 90%.

29. 50 hr is 125% of 40 hr.

30. 175% of 2 in. of rainfall is 3.5 in.

For Exercises 31–36, write the percent proportion.

31. 10% of 120 trees is 12 trees.

32. 15% of 20 pictures is 3 pictures.

33. 72 children is 80% of 90 children.

34. 21 dogs is 20% of 105 dogs.

35. 21,684 college students is 104% of 20,850 college students.

36. 103% of $40,000 is $41,200.

Concept 3: Solving Percent Proportions

For Exercises 37–46, solve the percent problems with an unknown amount. **(See Example 2.)**

37. Compute 54% of 200 employees.

38. Find 35% of 412.

39. What is $\frac{1}{2}$% of 40?

40. What is 1.8% of 900 grams?

41. Find 112% of 500.

42. Compute 106% of 1050.

43. Pedro pays 28% of his salary in income tax. If he makes $72,000 in taxable income, how much income tax does he pay?

44. A car dealer sets the sticker price of a car by taking 115% of the wholesale price. If a car sells wholesale at $19,000, what is the sticker price?

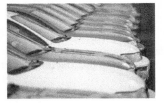

45. A recent study in Missouri showed that over a 2-year period, 72% of the teens (ages 15–19) killed in traffic accidents were not wearing seat belts. If a total of 304 teens were killed, approximately how many were not wearing seat belts? (Round to the nearest whole number.)

46. In a psychology class, 61.9% of the class consists of freshmen. If there are 42 students, how many are freshmen? Round to the nearest whole unit.

For Exercises 47–56, solve the percent problems with an unknown base. **(See Example 3.)**

47. 18 is 50% of what number?

48. 22% of what length is 44 ft?

49. 30% of what weight is 69 lb?

50. 70% of what number is 28?

51. 9 is $\frac{2}{3}$% of what number?

52. 9.5 is 200% of what number?

53. Albert saves $120 per month. If this is 7.5% of his monthly income, how much does he make per month?

54. Janie and Don left their house in South Bend, Indiana, to visit friends in Chicago. They drove 80% of the distance before stopping for lunch. If they had driven 56 mi before lunch, what would be the total distance from their house to their friends' house in Chicago?

62   **Chapter 6**   Percents

55. Amiee read 14 e-mails, which was only 40% of her total e-mails. What is her total number of e-mails?

56. A recent survey found that 5% of the population of the United States is unemployed. If Charlotte, North Carolina, has 32,000 unemployed, what is the population of Charlotte?

For Exercises 57–64, solve the percent problems with p unknown. **(See Example 4.)**

57. What percent of $120 is $42?

58. 112 is what percent of 400?

59. 84 is what percent of 70?

60. What percent of 12 letters is 4 letters?

61. What percent of 320 mi is 280 mi?

62. 54¢ is what percent of 48¢?

63. A student answered 29 problems correctly on a final exam of 40 problems. What percent of the questions did she answer correctly?

64. During his college basketball season, Jeff made 520 baskets out of 1280 attempts. What was his shooting percentage? Round to the nearest whole percent.

For Exercises 65–68, use the table given. The data represent 600 police officers broken down by gender and by the number of officers promoted.

	Promoted	Not Promoted	Total
Male	140	340	480
Female	20	100	120
Total	160	440	600

65. What percent of the officers are female?

66. What percent of the officers are male?

67. What percent of the officers were promoted? Round to the nearest tenth of a percent.

68. What percent of the officers were not promoted? Round to the nearest tenth of a percent.

Concept 4: Applications of Percent Proportions (Mixed Exercises)

69. The rainfall at Birmingham Airport in the United Kingdom averages 56 mm per month. In August the amount of rain that fell was 125% of the average monthly rainfall. How much rain fell in August? **(See Example 5.)**

70. In a recent survey 38% of people in the United States say that gas prices have affected the type of vehicle they will buy. In a sample of 500 people who are in the market for a new vehicle, how many would you expect to be influenced by gas prices?

71. Harvard University reported that 209 African American students were admitted to the freshman class in a recent year. If this represents 11% of the total freshman class, how many freshmen were admitted? **(See Example 6.)**

72. Yellowstone National Park has 3366 mi^2 of undeveloped land. If this represents 99% of the total area, find the total area of the park.

73. During the 2009–2010 basketball season, Jason Terry of the Dallas Mavericks made 136 three-point shots out of 373 attempts. To the nearest tenth of a percent, find the percent of three-point shots made. **(See Example 7.)**

74. During the 2009–2010 football season, Peyton Manning had completed 393 passes out of 571 attempts. Find his completion percentage to the nearest tenth of a percent.

75. The graph shows the percent of households that own dogs according to the number of people residing in the household. (*Source:* American Veterinary Medical Association)

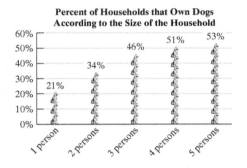

Percent of Households that Own Dogs According to the Size of the Household

   a. If 200 five-person households are surveyed, how many would you expect to own dogs?

   b. If 50 three-person households are surveyed, how many would you expect to own dogs?

76. A computer has 74.4 GB (gigabytes) of memory available. If 7.56 GB is used, what percent of the memory is used? Round to the nearest percent.

A used car dealership sells several makes of vehicles. For Exercises 77–80, refer to the graph. Round the answers to the nearest whole unit.

77. If the dealership sold 215 vehicles in one month, how many were Chevys?

78. If the dealership sold 182 vehicles in one month, how many were Fords?

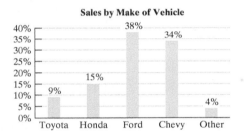

Sales by Make of Vehicle

79. If the dealership sold 27 Hondas in one month, how many total vehicles were sold?

80. If the dealership sold 10 cars in the "Other" category, how many total vehicles were sold?

Expanding Your Skills

81. Carson had $600 and spent 44% of it on clothes. Then he spent 20% of the remaining money on dinner. How much did he spend altogether?

82. Jasmine took $52 to the mall and spent 24% on makeup. Then she spent one-half of the remaining money on lunch. How much did she spend altogether?

It is customary to leave a 15–20% tip for the server in a restaurant. However, when you are at a restaurant in a social setting, you probably do not want to take out a pencil and piece of paper to figure out the tip. It is more effective to compute the tip mentally. Try this method.

Step 1:   First, if the bill is not a whole dollar amount, simplify the calculations by rounding the bill to the next-higher whole dollar.

Step 2:   Take 10% of the bill. This is the same as taking one-tenth of the bill. Move the decimal point to the left 1 place.

Step 3:   If you want to leave a 20% tip, double the value found in step 2.

Step 4:   If you want to leave a 15% tip, first note that 15% is 5% + 10%. Therefore, add one-half of the value found in step 2 to the number in step 2.

83. Estimate a 20% tip on a bill of $57.65. (*Hint:* Round up to $58 first.)

84. Estimate a 20% tip on a bill of $18.79.

85. Estimate a 15% tip on a dinner bill of $42.00.

86. Estimate a 15% tip on a luncheon bill of $12.00.

Section 6.4	**Percent Equations and Applications**

1. Solving Percent Equations—Amount Unknown

In this section, we investigate an alternative method to solve applications involving percents. We use percent equations. A **percent equation** represents a percent proportion in an alternative form. For example, recall that we can write a percent proportion as follows:

$$\frac{\text{Amount}}{\text{Base}} = p\% \qquad \text{percent proportion}$$

This is equivalent to writing $\text{Amount} = (p\%) \cdot (\text{base})$ percent equation

To set up a percent equation, it is necessary to translate an English sentence into a mathematical equation. As you read through the examples in this section, you will notice several key words. In the phrase *percent of*, the word *of* implies multiplication. The verb *to be* (am, is, are, was, were, been) often implies =.

Skill Practice

Use a percent equation to solve.
1. What is 40% of 90?

Example 1 Solving a Percent Equation—Amount Unknown

What is 30% of 60?

Solution:

We translate the words to mathematical symbols.

What is 30% of 60?

$$x \ = (30\%) \cdot (60)$$

In this context, the word *of* means to multiply.

Let x represent the unknown amount.

To find x, we must multiply 30% by 60. However, 30% means $\frac{30}{100}$ or 0.30. For the purpose of calculation, we *must* convert 30% to its equivalent decimal or fraction form. The equation becomes

$$x = (0.30)(60)$$
$$= 18$$

TIP: The solution to Example 1 can be checked by noting that 10% of 60 is 6. Therefore, 30% is equal to $(3)(6) = 18$.

The value 18 is 30% of 60.

Skill Practice

Use a percent equation to solve.
2. 235% of 60 amounts to what number?

Example 2 Equations—Amount Unknown

142% of 75 amounts to what number?

Solution:

142% of 75 amounts to what number?

$$(142\%) \cdot (75) \qquad = \qquad x$$

$$(1.42)(75) = x$$

$$106.5 = x$$

Let x represent the unknown amount.
The word *of* implies multiplication.
The phrase *amounts to* implies =.

Convert 142% to its decimal form (1.42).

Multiply.

Therefore, 142% of 75 amounts to 106.5.

Examples 1 and 2 illustrate that the percent equation gives us a quick way to find an unknown amount. For example, because $(p\%) \cdot (\text{base}) = \text{amount}$, we have

$$50\% \text{ of } 80 \; = 0.50(80) \; = 40$$
$$25\% \text{ of } 20 \; = 0.25(20) \; = 5$$
$$87\% \text{ of } 600 = 0.87(600) = 522$$
$$250\% \text{ of } 90 = 2.50(90) \; = 225$$

2. Solving Percent Equations—Base Unknown

Examples 3 and 4 illustrate the case in which the base is unknown.

Example 3   Solving a Percent Equation—Base Unknown

225 is 40% of what number?

Solution:

225 is 40% of what number?   Let x represent the base number.

$225 = (0.40) \cdot \quad x$ Notice that we immediately converted 40% to its decimal form 0.40 so that we would not forget.

$225 = 0.40x$

$\dfrac{225}{0.40} = \dfrac{0.40x}{0.40}$ Divide both sides of the equation by the number multiplied by the variable x. In this case, divide by 0.40.

$562.5 = x$ Divide: $225 \div 0.40 = 562.5$.

The value 225 is 40% of 562.5.

Skill Practice

Use a percent equation to solve.
3. 94 is 80% of what number?

Example 4   Solving a Percent Equation—Base Unknown

0.19 is 0.2% of what number?

Solution:

0.19 is 0.2% of what number?   Let x represent the base number.

$0.19 = (0.002) \cdot x$ Convert 0.2% to its decimal form 0.002.

$0.19 = 0.002x$

$\dfrac{0.19}{0.002} = \dfrac{0.002x}{0.002}$ Divide both sides by 0.002.

$95 = x$ Divide: $0.19 \div 0.002 = 95$.

Therefore, 0.19 is 0.2% of 95.

Skill Practice

Use a percent equation to solve.
4. 5.6 is 0.8% of what number?

3. Solving Percent Equations—Percent Unknown

Examples 5 and 6 demonstrate the process to find an unknown percent.

Answers
3. 117.5   **4.** 700

Example 5 Solving a Percent Equation—Percent Unknown

75 is what percent of 250?

Solution:

75 is what percent of 250?

$$75 = x \cdot (250) \quad \text{Let } x \text{ represent the unknown percent.}$$

$$75 = 250x$$

$$\frac{75}{250} = \frac{\overset{1}{250}x}{\underset{1}{250}} \qquad \text{Divide both sides by 250.}$$

$$0.3 = x \qquad \text{Divide: } 75 \div 250 = 0.3.$$

At this point, we have $x = 0.3$. To write the value of x in percent form, multiply by 100%.

$$x = 0.3$$
$$= 0.3 \times 100\%$$
$$= 30\% \dotfill$$

Thus, 75 is 30% of 250.

Avoiding Mistakes

When solving for an unknown percent using a percent equation, it is necessary to convert x to its percent form.

Example 6 Solving a Percent Equation—Percent Unknown

What percent of $60 is $92? Round to the nearest tenth of a percent.

Solution:

What percent of $60 is $92?

$$x \cdot (60) = 92 \qquad \text{Let } x \text{ represent the unknown percent.}$$

$$60x = 92$$

$$\frac{\overset{1}{60}x}{\underset{1}{60}} = \frac{92}{60} \qquad \text{Divide both sides by 60.}$$

$$x = 1.5\overline{3} \qquad \text{Divide: } 92 \div 60 = 1.5\overline{3}.$$

At this point, we have $x = 1.5\overline{3}$. To convert x to its percent form, multiply by 100%.

$$x = 1.5\overline{3}$$
$$= 1.5\overline{3} \times 100\% \qquad \text{Convert from decimal form to percent form.}$$
$$= (1.53333\ldots) \times 100\%$$
$$= 153.333\ldots\% \dotfill$$

The hundredths-place digit is less than 5. Discard it and the digits to its right.

Round to the nearest tenth of a percent.

$$\approx 153.3\%$$

Therefore, $92 is approximately 153.3% of $60. (Notice that $92 is just over $1\frac{1}{2}$ times $60, so our answer seems reasonable.)

4. Applications of Percent Equations

In Examples 7, 8, and 9, we use percent equations in application problems. An important part of this process is to extract the base, amount, and percent from the wording of the problem.

Example 7 Using a Percent Equation in Ecology

Forty-six panthers are thought to live in Florida's Big Cypress National Preserve. This represents 53% of the panthers living in Florida. How many panthers are there in Florida? Round to the nearest whole unit. (*Source:* U.S. Fish and Wildlife Services)

Solution:

This problem translates to

"46 is 53% of the number of panthers living in Florida."

$$46 = (0.53) \cdot x$$

Let x represent the total number of panthers.

$$46 = 0.53x$$

$$\frac{46}{0.53} = \frac{0.53x}{0.53}$$

Divide both sides by 0.53.

$$87 \approx x$$

Divide: $46 \div 0.53 \approx 87$ (rounded to the nearest whole number).

There are approximately 87 panthers in Florida.

Skill Practice

7. Brianna read 143 pages in a book. If this represents 22% of the book, how many pages are in the book?

Example 8 Using a Percent Equation in Sports Statistics

At one time, Steve Young of the San Francisco 49ers was ranked as the NFL's best passer (based on quarterback rating points). For one particular game he completed 23 of 30 passes. What percent of passes did he complete? Round to the nearest tenth of a percent.

Solution:

This problem translates to

"23 is what percent of 30?"

$$23 = x \cdot 30$$

Let x represent the unknown.

$$23 = 30x$$

$$\frac{23}{30} = \frac{30x}{30}$$

Divide both sides by 30.

$$0.767 \approx x$$

Divide: $23 \div 30 \approx 0.767$.

Skill Practice

8. Tyrone had $60 in his wallet to take himself and a date to dinner and a movie. If he spent $28 on dinner and $19 on the movie, what percent of his money did he spend? Round to the nearest tenth of a percent.

Answers

7. The book is 650 pages long.
8. Tyrone spent about 78.3% of his money.

68   **Chapter 6** Percents

The decimal value 0.767 has been rounded to 3 decimal places. We did this because the next step is to convert the decimal to a percent. Move the decimal point to the right 2 places and attach the % symbol. We have 76.7% which is rounded to the nearest tenth of a percent.

$$x \approx 0.767$$
$$= 0.767 \times 100\%$$
$$= 76.7\%$$

Steve Young completed approximately 76.7% of his passes.

Example 9   **Using a Percent Equation in Ecology**

On April 20, 2010, an explosion occurred on an offshore oil rig in the Gulf of Mexico. The explosion left 11 crewmembers dead and an uncontained oil leak that threatened the ecosystem in the Gulf of Mexico and surrounding beaches.

The United States consumes approximately 20 million barrels of oil per day. If the oil obtained from the Gulf of Mexico represents 8% of U.S. daily consumption, how much oil does the United States produce from the Gulf of Mexico?

Solution:

This situation translates to

"What number is 8% of 20?"

↓	↓	↓	↓	↓

$$x \quad = 0.08 \cdot 20 \qquad \text{Write 8\% in decimal form.}$$

$$= (0.08)(20) \qquad \text{Let } x \text{ represent the number of barrels produced by the United States per day in the Gulf of Mexico.}$$

$$= 1.6 \qquad \text{Multiply.}$$

The United States produces approximately 1.6 million barrels of oil per day from the Gulf of Mexico.

Section 6.4   **Practice Exercises**

Study Skills Exercise

There's a saying, "Leave no stone unturned." In math, this means "leave no homework problem undone." Did you do all the assigned homework in Section 6.3? Do you understand the concepts well enough to move on to the homework in this section?

Review Exercises

1. Explain how to solve the equation $26x = 65$.

2. Explain how to solve the equation $54 = 6x$.

Section 6.4   Percent Equations and Applications   **369**

For Exercises 3–8, solve the equation for the variable.

3. $3x = 27$

4. $12x = 48$

5. $0.15x = 45$

6. $0.32x = 60$

7. $1.02x = 841.5$

8. $1.06x = 90.1$

For Exercises 9 and 10, solve the proportion.

9. $\dfrac{165}{100} = \dfrac{693}{x}$

10. $\dfrac{16}{100} = \dfrac{x}{60}$

Concept 1: Solving Percent Equations—Amount Unknown

For Exercises 11–16, write the percent equation. Then solve for the unknown amount. **(See Examples 1 and 2.)**

11. What is 35% of 700?

12. Find 12% of 625.

13. 0.55% of 900 is what number?

14. What is 0.4% of 75?

15. Find 133% of 600.

16. 120% of 40.4 is what number?

17. What is a quick way to find 50% of a number?

18. What is a quick way to find 10% of a number?

19. Compute 200% of 14 mentally.

20. Compute 75% of 80 mentally.

21. Compute 50% of 40 mentally.

22. Compute 10% of 32 mentally.

23. Household bleach is 6% sodium hypochlorite (active ingredient). In a 64-oz bottle, how much is active ingredient?

24. One antifreeze solution is 40% alcohol. How much alcohol is in a 12.5-L mixture?

25. In football, Dan Marino completed 60% of his passes. If he attempted 8358 passes, how many did he complete? Round to the nearest whole unit.

26. To pass an exit exam, a student must pass a 60-question test with a score of 80% or better. What is the minimum number of questions she must answer correctly?

Concept 2: Solving Percent Equations—Base Unknown

For Exercises 27–32, write the percent equation. Then solve for the unknown base. **(See Examples 3 and 4.)**

27. 18 is 40% of what number?

28. 72 is 30% of what number?

29. 92% of what number is 41.4?

30. 84% of what number is 100.8?

31. 3.09 is 103% of what number?

32. 189 is 105% of what number?

33. In tests of a new anti-inflammatory drug, it was found that 47 subjects experienced nausea. If this represents 4% of the sample, how many subjects were tested?

34. Ted typed 80% of his research paper before taking a break.

   a. If he typed 8 pages, how many total pages are in the paper?

   b. How many pages does he have left to type?

35. In a recent report, approximately 61.6 million Americans had some form of heart and blood vessel disease. If this represents 22% of the population, approximate the total population of the United States.

36. A city has a population of 245,300 which is 110% of the population from the previous year. What was the population the previous year?

Concept 3: Solving Percent Equations—Percent Unknown

For Exercises 37–44, convert the decimal to a percent.

37. 0.13   **38.** 0.4   **39.** 1.08   **40.** 2.2

41. 0.005   **42.** 0.007   **43.** 0.17   **44.** 0.9

For Exercises 45–50, write the percent equation. Then solve for the unknown percent. Round to the nearest tenth of a percent if necessary. **(See Examples 5 and 6.)**

45. What percent of 480 is 120?   **46.** 180 is what percent of 2000?   **47.** 666 is what percent of 740?

48. What percent of 60 is 2.88?   **49.** What percent of 300 is 400?   **50.** 28 is what percent of 24?

51. At a softball game, the concession stand had 120 hot dogs and sold 84 of them. What percent was sold?

52. The YMCA wants to raise $2500 for its summer program for disadvantaged children. If the YMCA has already raised $900, what percent of its goal has been achieved?

For Exercises 53 and 54, refer to the table that shows the 1-year absentee record for a business.

53. a. Determine the total number of employees.

  b. What percent missed exactly 3 days of work?

  c. What percent missed between 1 and 5 days, inclusive?

54. a. What percent missed at least 4 days?

  b. What percent did not miss any days?

Number of Days Missed	Number of Employees
0	4
1	2
2	14
3	10
4	16
5	18
6	10
7	6

Concept 4: Applications of Percent Equations (Mixed Exercises)

55. In a recent year, children and adolescents comprised 6.3 million hospital stays. If this represents 18% of all hospital stays, what was the total number of hospital stays? **(See Example 7.)**

56. One fruit drink advertised that it contained "10% real fruit juice." In one bottle, this was found to be 4.8 oz of real juice.

  a. How many ounces of drink does the bottle contain?

  b. How many ounces is something other than fruit juice?

57. Of the 87 panthers living in the wild in Florida, 11 are thought to live in Everglades National Park. To the nearest tenth of a percent, what percent is this? (*Source:* U.S. Fish and Wildlife Services) **(See Example 8.)**

58. Forty-four percent of Americans use online travel sites to book hotel or airline reservations. If 400 people need to make airline or hotel reservations, how many would be expected to use online travel sites?

59. Fifty-two percent of American parents have started to put money away for their children's college educations. In a survey of 800 parents, how many would be expected to have started saving for their children's education? (*Source: USA TODAY*) **(See Example 9.)**

60. The Earth is covered by approximately 360 million km² of water. If the total surface area is 510 million km², what percent is water? (Round to the nearest tenth of a percent.)

61. Brian has been saving money to buy a 61-in. Samsung Projection HDTV. He has saved $1440 so far, but this is only 60% of the total cost of the television. What is the total cost?

62. Recently, the number of females that were homeschooled for grades K–12 was 875 thousand. This is 202% of the number of females homeschooled in 1999. How many females were homeschooled in 1999? Round to the nearest thousand. (*Source:* National Center for Educational Statistics)

63. A television station plays commercials for 26% of its air time. In 60 min, how many minutes of commercials would be expected?

64. Sixty-five percent of the human body is water. For a 150-lb person, how much is water?

For Exercises 65–68, use the graph.

65. If there were 10,000,000 people in the workforce in the 25–34 age group, how many made over $10 per hour?

66. If there were 6,600,000 people in the workforce in the 55–64 age group, how many made over $10 per hour?

67. If 4,000,000 people in the 16–24 age group made over $10 per hour, how many total workers in this age group are there?

68. If 9,000,000 people in the 45–54 age group made over $10 per hour, how many total workers in this age group are there?

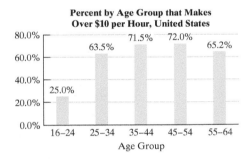

Percent by Age Group that Makes Over $10 per Hour, United States

Expanding Your Skills

The maximum recommended heart rate (in beats per minute) is given by 220 minus a person's age. For aerobic activity, it is recommended that individuals exercise at 60%–85% of their maximum recommended heart rate. This is called the aerobic range. Use this information for Exercises 69 and 70.

69. a. Find the maximum recommended heart rate for a 20-year-old.

    b. Find the aerobic range for a 20-year-old.

70. a. Find the maximum recommended heart rate for a 42-year-old.

    b. Find the aerobic range for a 42-year-old.

The Set of Real Numbers

The Set of Real Numbers

Numbers in Our World

Imagine a world where the only numbers known are the counting or natural numbers (1, 2, 3, 4, . . .). Now imagine that you want to sell only a fraction of your land to another person, or that you owe twenty dollars and fifteen cents to your bank. How could these values be written without formal numerical symbols? Living in such a world would deter the growth of a complex society like ours.

It is difficult to fathom that the use of zero, fractions, and negative numbers was formally accepted only about a thousand years ago! Before that time, communicating about parts of items, the absence of value, and owing money to a lender was likely done in creative but arduous ways. When we talk about a *third* of a parcel of land, temperatures below *zero* such as *negative* 20 degrees, and the number π, we make use of the many subsets of the **set of real numbers**.

© Zephyr_p/Shutterstock RF

Real numbers enable us to talk about parts of things, to expand our thinking to explain phenomena in precise ways, and to operate with numbers in a consistent and predicable manner. In this chapter we will explore how real numbers are used, and the way they open the door to algebra.

6   **Chapter 1**   The Set of Real Numbers

Section 1.1   Fractions

1. Basic Definitions

The study of algebra involves many of the operations and procedures used in arithmetic. Therefore, we begin this text by reviewing the basic operations of addition, subtraction, multiplication, and division on fractions and mixed numbers.

We begin with the numbers used for counting:

the **natural numbers:** 1, 2, 3, 4, . . .

and

the **whole numbers:** 0, 1, 2, 3, . . .

Whole numbers are used to count the number of whole units in a quantity. A fraction is used to express part of a whole unit. If a child gains $2\frac{1}{2}$ lb, the child has gained two whole pounds plus a portion of a pound. To express the additional half pound mathematically, we may use the fraction, $\frac{1}{2}$.

A Fraction and Its Parts

Fractions are numbers of the form $\frac{a}{b}$, where $\frac{a}{b} = a \div b$ and b does not equal zero.

In the fraction $\frac{a}{b}$, the **numerator** is a, and the **denominator** is b.

The denominator of a fraction indicates how many equal parts divide the whole. The numerator indicates how many parts are being represented. For instance, suppose Jack wants to plant carrots in $\frac{2}{5}$ of a rectangular garden. He can divide the garden into five equal parts and use two of the parts for carrots (Figure 1-1).

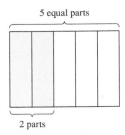

5 equal parts

2 parts

The shaded region represents $\dfrac{2}{5}$ of the garden.

Figure 1-1

Proper Fractions, Improper Fractions, and Mixed Numbers

1. If the numerator of a fraction is less than the denominator, the fraction is a **proper fraction**. A proper fraction represents a quantity that is less than a whole unit.
2. If the numerator of a fraction is greater than or equal to the denominator, then the fraction is an **improper fraction**. An improper fraction represents a quantity greater than or equal to a whole unit.
3. A **mixed number** is a whole number added to a proper fraction.

Proper Fractions: $\dfrac{3}{5}$ $\dfrac{1}{8}$

Improper Fractions: $\dfrac{7}{5}$ $\dfrac{8}{8}$

Mixed Numbers: $1\dfrac{1}{5}$ $2\dfrac{3}{8}$

2. Prime Factorization

To perform operations on fractions it is important to understand the concept of a factor. For example, when the numbers 2 and 6 are multiplied, the result (called the **product**) is 12.

$$2 \times 6 = 12$$
$$\underbrace{}_{\text{factors}} \ \underbrace{}_{\text{product}}$$

The numbers 2 and 6 are said to be **factors** of 12. (In this context, we refer only to natural number factors.) The number 12 is said to be factored when it is written as the product of two or more natural numbers. For example, 12 can be factored in several ways:

$$12 = 1 \times 12 \qquad 12 = 2 \times 6 \qquad 12 = 3 \times 4 \qquad 12 = 2 \times 2 \times 3$$

A natural number greater than 1 that has only two factors, 1 and itself, is called a **prime number**. The first several prime numbers are 2, 3, 5, 7, 11, and 13. A natural number greater than 1 that is not prime is called a **composite number**. That is, a composite number has factors other than itself and 1. The first several composite numbers are 4, 6, 8, 9, 10, 12, 14, 15, and 16.

> **Avoiding Mistakes**
> The number 1 is neither prime nor composite.

Example 1   **Writing a Natural Number as a Product of Prime Factors**

Write each number as a product of prime factors.

  a. 12   **b.** 30

Solution:

  a. $12 = 2 \times 2 \times 3$ Divide 12 by prime numbers until the result is also a prime number.

$$\begin{array}{r} 2\overline{)12} \\ 2\overline{)6} \\ \overline{3} \end{array}$$

Or use a factor tree

  b. $30 = 2 \times 3 \times 5$

$$\begin{array}{r} 2\overline{)30} \\ 3\overline{)15} \\ \overline{5} \end{array}$$

Skill Practice Write the number as a product of prime factors.

  1. 40   **2.** 72

Answers
1. $2 \times 2 \times 2 \times 5$
2. $2 \times 2 \times 2 \times 3 \times 3$

8   **Chapter 1**   The Set of Real Numbers

3. Simplifying Fractions to Lowest Terms

The process of factoring numbers can be used to reduce or simplify fractions to lowest terms. A fractional portion of a whole can be represented by infinitely many fractions. For example, Figure 1-2 shows that $\frac{1}{2}$ is equivalent to $\frac{2}{4}$, $\frac{3}{6}$, $\frac{4}{8}$, and so on.

   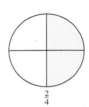  

$$\frac{1}{2} \qquad \frac{2}{4} \qquad \frac{3}{6} \qquad \frac{4}{8}$$

Figure 1-2

The fraction $\frac{1}{2}$ is said to be in **lowest terms** because the numerator and denominator share no common factor other than 1.

To simplify a fraction to lowest terms, we use the following important principle.

Fundamental Principle of Fractions

Suppose that a number, c, is a common factor in the numerator and denominator of a fraction. Then

$$\frac{a \times c}{b \times c} = \frac{a}{b} \times \frac{c}{c} = \frac{a}{b} \times 1 = \frac{a}{b}$$

To simplify a fraction, we begin by factoring the numerator and denominator into prime factors. This will help identify the common factors.

Example 2   **Simplifying a Fraction to Lowest Terms**

Simplify $\dfrac{45}{30}$ to lowest terms.

Solution:

$$\frac{45}{30} = \frac{3 \times 3 \times 5}{2 \times 3 \times 5} \qquad \text{Factor the numerator and denominator.}$$

$$= \frac{3}{2} \times \frac{3}{3} \times \frac{5}{5} \qquad \text{Apply the fundamental principle of fractions.}$$

$$= \frac{3}{2} \times 1 \times 1 \qquad \text{Any nonzero number divided by itself is 1.}$$

$$= \frac{3}{2} \qquad \text{Any number multiplied by 1 is itself.}$$

Skill Practice Simplify to lowest terms.

   3. $\dfrac{20}{50}$

Answer

3. $\dfrac{2}{5}$

In Example 2, we showed numerous steps to reduce fractions to lowest terms. However, the process is often simplified. Notice that the same result can be obtained by dividing out the greatest common factor from the numerator and denominator. (The **greatest common factor** is the largest factor that is common to both numerator and denominator.)

$$\frac{45}{30} = \frac{3 \times 15}{2 \times 15}$$ The greatest common factor of 45 and 30 is 15.

$$= \frac{3 \times \cancel{15}^{1}}{2 \times \cancel{15}_{1}}$$ The symbol / is often used to show that a common factor has been divided out.

$$= \frac{3}{2}$$ Notice that "dividing out" the common factor of 15 has the same effect as dividing the numerator and denominator by 15. This is often done mentally.

$$\frac{\overset{3}{\cancel{45}}}{\underset{2}{\cancel{30}}} = \frac{3}{2}$$ ←— 45 divided by 15 equals 3.
←— 30 divided by 15 equals 2.

| **Example 3** | **Simplifying a Fraction to Lowest Terms** |

Simplify $\frac{14}{42}$ to lowest terms.

Solution:

$$\frac{14}{42} = \frac{1 \times 14}{3 \times 14}$$ The greatest common factor of 14 and 42 is 14.

$$= \frac{1 \times \cancel{14}^{1}}{3 \times \cancel{14}_{1}}$$

$$= \frac{1}{3}$$ $\dfrac{\overset{1}{\cancel{14}}}{\underset{3}{\cancel{42}}} = \dfrac{1}{3}$ ←— 14 divided by 14 equals 1.
←— 42 divided by 14 equals 3.

Skill Practice Simplify to lowest terms.

4. $\dfrac{32}{12}$

> **Avoiding Mistakes**
>
> In Example 3, the common factor 14 in the numerator and denominator simplifies to 1. It is important to remember to write the factor of 1 in the numerator. The simplified form of the fraction is $\frac{1}{3}$.

4. Multiplying Fractions

> **Multiplying Fractions**
>
> If b is not zero and d is not zero, then
> $$\frac{a}{b} \times \frac{c}{d} = \frac{a \times c}{b \times d}$$
> To multiply fractions, multiply the numerators and multiply the denominators.

Answer

4. $\dfrac{8}{3}$

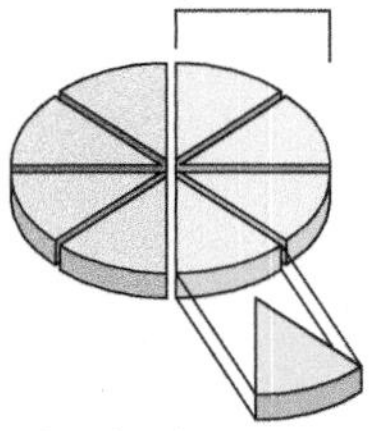

10   **Chapter 1**   The Set of Real Numbers

$\frac{1}{2}$ of a pie

$\frac{1}{4}$ of $\frac{1}{2}$ is $\frac{1}{8}$ of the pie

Figure 1-3

| Example 4 | **Multiplying Fractions** |

Multiply the fractions: $\frac{1}{4} \times \frac{1}{2}$

Solution:

$$\frac{1}{4} \times \frac{1}{2} = \frac{1 \times 1}{4 \times 2} = \frac{1}{8}$$ Multiply the numerators. Multiply the denominators.

Notice that the product $\frac{1}{4} \times \frac{1}{2}$ represents a quantity that is $\frac{1}{4}$ of $\frac{1}{2}$. Taking $\frac{1}{4}$ of a quantity is equivalent to dividing the quantity by 4. One-half of a pie divided into four pieces leaves pieces that each represent $\frac{1}{8}$ of the pie (Figure 1-3).

Skill Practice   Multiply.

5. $\frac{2}{7} \times \frac{3}{5}$

| Example 5 | **Multiplying Fractions** |

Multiply the fractions.

   a. $\frac{7}{10} \times \frac{15}{14}$ **b.** $\frac{2}{13} \times \frac{13}{2}$ **c.** $5 \times \frac{1}{5}$

Solution:

a. $\frac{7}{10} \times \frac{15}{14} = \frac{7 \times 15}{10 \times 14}$ Multiply the numerators. Multiply the denominators.

$$= \frac{\overset{1}{7} \times \overset{3}{15}}{\underset{2}{10} \times \underset{2}{14}}$$ Divide out the common factors.

$$= \frac{3}{4}$$ Multiply.

b. $\frac{2}{13} \times \frac{13}{2} = \frac{2 \times 13}{13 \times 2} = \frac{\overset{1}{2} \times \overset{1}{13}}{\underset{1}{13} \times \underset{1}{2}} = \frac{1}{1} = 1$ Multiply $1 \times 1 = 1$.

     Multiply $1 \times 1 = 1$.

c. $5 \times \frac{1}{5} = \frac{5}{1} \times \frac{1}{5}$ The whole number 5 can be written as $\frac{5}{1}$.

$$= \frac{\overset{1}{5} \times 1}{1 \times \underset{1}{5}} = \frac{1}{1} = 1$$ Divide out the common factors and multiply.

TIP: The same result can be obtained by dividing out common factors *before* multiplying.

$$\frac{\overset{1}{7}}{\underset{2}{10}} \times \frac{\overset{3}{15}}{\underset{2}{14}} = \frac{3}{4}$$

Skill Practice   Multiply.

6. $\frac{8}{9} \times \frac{3}{4}$ **7.** $\frac{4}{5} \times \frac{5}{4}$ **8.** $10 \times \frac{1}{10}$

Answers

5. $\frac{6}{35}$ **6.** $\frac{2}{3}$ **7.** 1   **8.** 1

5. Dividing Fractions

Before we divide fractions, we need to know how to find the reciprocal of a fraction. Notice from Example 5 that $\frac{2}{13} \times \frac{13}{2} = 1$ and $5 \times \frac{1}{5} = 1$. The numbers $\frac{2}{13}$ and $\frac{13}{2}$ are said to be reciprocals because their product is 1. Likewise the numbers 5 and $\frac{1}{5}$ are reciprocals.

The Reciprocal of a Number

Two nonzero numbers are **reciprocals** of each other if their product is 1. Therefore, the reciprocal of the fraction

$$\frac{a}{b} \text{ is } \frac{b}{a} \qquad \text{because} \qquad \frac{a}{b} \times \frac{b}{a} = 1$$

Number	Reciprocal	Product
$\frac{2}{15}$	$\frac{15}{2}$	$\frac{2}{15} \times \frac{15}{2} = 1$
$\frac{1}{8}$	$\frac{8}{1}$ (or equivalently 8)	$\frac{1}{8} \times 8 = 1$
6 $\left(\text{or equivalently } \frac{6}{1}\right)$	$\frac{1}{6}$	$6 \times \frac{1}{6} = 1$

To understand the concept of dividing fractions, consider a pie that is half-eaten. Suppose the remaining half must be divided among three people, that is, $\frac{1}{2} \div 3$. However, dividing by 3 is equivalent to taking $\frac{1}{3}$ of the remaining $\frac{1}{2}$ of the pie (Figure 1-4).

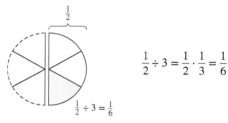

$$\frac{1}{2} \div 3 = \frac{1}{2} \cdot \frac{1}{3} = \frac{1}{6}$$

Figure 1-4

This example illustrates that dividing two numbers is equivalent to multiplying the first number by the reciprocal of the second number.

Dividing Fractions

Let a, b, c, and d be numbers such that b, c, and d are not zero. Then,

$$\frac{a}{b} \div \frac{c}{d} = \frac{a}{b} \times \frac{d}{c}$$

To divide fractions, multiply the first fraction by the reciprocal of the second fraction.

12 **Chapter 1** The Set of Real Numbers

| Example 6 | **Dividing Fractions** |

Divide the fractions.

a. $\dfrac{8}{5} \div \dfrac{3}{10}$ **b.** $\dfrac{12}{13} \div 6$

Solution:

a. $\dfrac{8}{5} \div \dfrac{3}{10} = \dfrac{8}{5} \times \dfrac{10}{3}$ Multiply by the reciprocal of $\frac{3}{10}$, which is $\frac{10}{3}$.

$= \dfrac{8 \times \overset{2}{10}}{\underset{1}{5} \times 3} = \dfrac{16}{3}$ Divide out the common factors and multiply.

b. $\dfrac{12}{13} \div 6 = \dfrac{12}{13} \div \dfrac{6}{1}$ Write the whole number 6 as $\frac{6}{1}$.

$= \dfrac{12}{13} \times \dfrac{1}{6}$ Multiply by the reciprocal of $\frac{6}{1}$, which is $\frac{1}{6}$.

$= \dfrac{\overset{2}{12} \times 1}{13 \times \underset{1}{6}} = \dfrac{2}{13}$ Divide out the common factors and multiply.

Avoiding Mistakes

Always check that the final answer is in lowest terms.

Skill Practice Divide.

9. $\dfrac{12}{25} \div \dfrac{8}{15}$ **10.** $\dfrac{1}{4} \div 2$

6. Adding and Subtracting Fractions

Adding and Subtracting Fractions

Two fractions can be added or subtracted if they have a common denominator. Let a, b, and c be numbers such that b does not equal zero. Then,

$$\frac{a}{b} + \frac{c}{b} = \frac{a+c}{b} \qquad \text{and} \qquad \frac{a}{b} - \frac{c}{b} = \frac{a-c}{b}$$

To add or subtract fractions with the same denominator, add or subtract the numerators and write the result over the common denominator.

| Example 7 | **Adding and Subtracting Fractions with the Same Denominator** |

Add or subtract as indicated.

a. $\dfrac{1}{12} + \dfrac{7}{12}$ **b.** $\dfrac{13}{5} - \dfrac{3}{5}$

Answers

9. $\dfrac{9}{10}$ **10.** $\dfrac{1}{8}$

Solution:

a. $\dfrac{1}{12} + \dfrac{7}{12} = \dfrac{1+7}{12}$ Add the numerators.

$\phantom{\dfrac{1}{12} + \dfrac{7}{12}} = \dfrac{8}{12}$

$\phantom{\dfrac{1}{12} + \dfrac{7}{12}} = \dfrac{2}{3}$ Simplify to lowest terms.

b. $\dfrac{13}{5} - \dfrac{3}{5} = \dfrac{13-3}{5}$ Subtract the numerators.

$\phantom{\dfrac{13}{5} - \dfrac{3}{5}} = \dfrac{10}{5}$ Simplify.

$\phantom{\dfrac{13}{5} - \dfrac{3}{5}} = 2$ Simplify to lowest terms.

TIP: The sum $\frac{1}{12} + \frac{7}{12}$ can be visualized as the sum of the pink and blue sections of the figure.

Skill Practice Add or subtract as indicated.

11. $\dfrac{2}{3} + \dfrac{5}{3}$ **12.** $\dfrac{5}{8} - \dfrac{1}{8}$

In Example 7, we added and subtracted fractions with the same denominators. To add or subtract fractions with different denominators, we must first become familiar with the idea of the least common multiple between two or more numbers. The **least common multiple (LCM)** of two numbers is the smallest whole number that is a multiple of each number. For example, the LCM of 6 and 9 is 18.

multiples of 6:   6, 12, 18, 24, 30, 36, . . .
multiples of 9:   9, 18, 27, 36, 45, 54, . . .

Listing the multiples of two or more given numbers can be a cumbersome way to find the LCM. Therefore, we offer the following method to find the LCM of two numbers.

> **Finding the LCM of Two Numbers**
> **Step 1**   Write each number as a product of prime factors.
> **Step 2**   The LCM is the product of unique prime factors from *both* numbers. Use repeated factors the maximum number of times they appear in *either* factorization.

Example 8   **Finding the LCM of Two Numbers**

Find the LCM of 9 and 15.

Solution:

	3's	5's
9 =	3 × 3	
15 =	3 ×	5

LCM $= 3 \times 3 \times 5 = 45$

For the factors of 3 and 5, we circle the greatest number of times each occurs. The LCM is the product.

Skill Practice Find the LCM.

13. 10 and 25

Answers

11. $\dfrac{7}{3}$ or $2\dfrac{1}{3}$ **12.** $\dfrac{1}{2}$ **13.** 50

14   **Chapter 1**   The Set of Real Numbers

To add or subtract fractions with *different* denominators, we must first write each fraction as an equivalent fraction with a common denominator. A common denominator may be *any* common multiple of the denominators. However, we will use the least common denominator. The **least common denominator (LCD)** of two or more fractions is the LCM of the denominators of the fractions. The following example uses the fundamental principle of fractions to rewrite fractions with the desired denominator. *Note:* Multiplying the numerator and denominator by the *same* nonzero quantity will not change the value of the fraction.

Example 9	**Writing Equivalent Fractions and Subtracting Fractions**

a. Write each of the fractions $\frac{1}{9}$ and $\frac{1}{15}$ as an equivalent fraction with the LCD as its denominator.

b. Subtract $\dfrac{1}{9} - \dfrac{1}{15}$.

Solution:

From Example 8, we know that the LCM for 9 and 15 is 45. Therefore, the LCD of $\frac{1}{9}$ and $\frac{1}{15}$ is 45.

a. $\quad \dfrac{1}{19} = \dfrac{}{45} \qquad\qquad \dfrac{1 \times 5}{9 \times 5} = \dfrac{5}{45} \qquad$ So, $\dfrac{1}{9}$ is equivalent to $\dfrac{5}{45}$.

What number must we multiply 9 by to get 45?   Multiply numerator and denominator by 5.

$\quad \dfrac{1}{15} = \dfrac{}{45} \qquad\qquad \dfrac{1 \times 3}{15 \times 3} = \dfrac{3}{45} \qquad$ So, $\dfrac{1}{15}$ is equivalent to $\dfrac{3}{45}$.

What number must we multiply 15 by to get 45?   Multiply numerator and denominator by 3.

b. $\dfrac{1}{9} - \dfrac{1}{15}$

$\quad = \dfrac{5}{45} - \dfrac{3}{45} \qquad$ Write $\frac{1}{9}$ and $\frac{1}{15}$ as equivalent fractions with the same denominator.

$\quad = \dfrac{2}{45} \qquad$ Subtract.

Skill Practice

14. Write each of the fractions $\frac{5}{8}$ and $\frac{5}{12}$ as an equivalent fraction with the LCD as its denominator.

15. Subtract. $\dfrac{5}{8} - \dfrac{5}{12}$

Answers

14. $\dfrac{5}{8} = \dfrac{15}{24}$ and $\dfrac{5}{12} = \dfrac{10}{24}$ **15.** $\dfrac{5}{24}$

| Example 10 | **Adding and Subtracting Fractions** |

Simplify. $\dfrac{5}{12} + \dfrac{3}{4} - \dfrac{1}{2}$

Solution:

$\dfrac{5}{12} + \dfrac{3}{4} - \dfrac{1}{2}$

To find the LCD, we have:
LCD $= 2 \times 2 \times 3 = 12$

	2's	3's
12 =	$\boxed{2 \times 2}$	$\boxed{3}$
4 =	2×2	
2 =	2	

$= \dfrac{5}{12} + \dfrac{3 \times 3}{4 \times 3} - \dfrac{1 \times 6}{2 \times 6}$

Write each fraction as an equivalent fraction with the LCD as its denominator.

$= \dfrac{5}{12} + \dfrac{9}{12} - \dfrac{6}{12}$

$= \dfrac{5 + 9 - 6}{12}$ Add and subtract the numerators.

$= \dfrac{8}{12}$ Simplify to lowest terms.

$= \dfrac{2}{3}$

Skill Practice Add.

16. $\dfrac{2}{3} + \dfrac{1}{2} + \dfrac{5}{6}$

7. Operations on Mixed Numbers

Recall that a mixed number is a whole number added to a fraction. The number $3\frac{1}{2}$ represents the sum of three wholes plus a half, that is, $3\frac{1}{2} = 3 + \frac{1}{2}$. For this reason, any mixed number can be converted to an improper fraction by using addition.

$$3\frac{1}{2} = 3 + \dfrac{1}{2} = \dfrac{6}{2} + \dfrac{1}{2} = \dfrac{7}{2}$$

TIP: A shortcut to writing a mixed number as an improper fraction is to multiply the whole number by the denominator of the fraction. Then add this value to the numerator of the fraction, and write the result over the denominator.

$3\frac{1}{2}$ ⟶   Multiply the whole number by the denominator: $3 \times 2 = 6$
Add the numerator: $6 + 1 = 7$
Write the result over the denominator: $\frac{7}{2}$

To add, subtract, multiply, or divide mixed numbers, we will first write the mixed number as an improper fraction.

Answer

16. 2

16   **Chapter 1**   The Set of Real Numbers

Example 11	**Operations on Mixed Numbers**

Subtract. $5\frac{1}{3} - 2\frac{1}{4}$

Solution:

$5\frac{1}{3} - 2\frac{1}{4}$

$= \dfrac{16}{3} - \dfrac{9}{4}$ Write the mixed numbers as improper fractions.

$= \dfrac{16 \times 4}{3 \times 4} - \dfrac{9 \times 3}{4 \times 3}$ The LCD is 12. Multiply numerators and denominators by the missing factors from the denominators.

$= \dfrac{64}{12} - \dfrac{27}{12}$

$= \dfrac{37}{12}$ or $3\frac{1}{12}$ Subtract the fractions.

Skill Practice Subtract.

17. $2\frac{3}{4} - 1\frac{1}{3}$

TIP: An improper fraction can also be written as a mixed number. Both answers are acceptable. Note that

$$\frac{37}{12} = \frac{36}{12} + \frac{1}{12} = 3 + \frac{1}{12}, \text{ or } 3\frac{1}{12}$$

This can easily be found by dividing.

$$\frac{37}{12} \longrightarrow \begin{array}{r} 3 \\ 12\overline{)37} \\ -36 \\ \hline 1 \end{array} \qquad 3\frac{1}{12}$$

quotient · remainder · divisor

Example 12	**Operations on Mixed Numbers**

Divide. $7\frac{1}{2} \div 3$

Solution:

$7\frac{1}{2} \div 3$

$= \dfrac{15}{2} \div \dfrac{3}{1}$ Write the mixed number and whole number as fractions.

$= \dfrac{\overset{5}{\cancel{15}}}{2} \times \dfrac{1}{\underset{1}{\cancel{3}}}$ Multiply by the reciprocal of $\frac{3}{1}$, which is $\frac{1}{3}$.

$= \dfrac{5}{2}$ or $2\frac{1}{2}$ The answer may be written as an improper fraction or as a mixed number.

Avoiding Mistakes

Remember that when dividing (or multiplying) fractions, a common denominator is not necessary.

Answer

17. $\frac{17}{12}$ or $1\frac{5}{12}$

Skill Practice Divide.

18. $5\frac{5}{6} \div 3\frac{2}{3}$

Answer

18. $\frac{35}{22}$ or $1\frac{13}{22}$

Section 1.1   Practice Exercises

Study Skills Exercise

To enhance your learning experience, we provide study skills that focus on eight areas: learning about your course, using your text, taking notes, doing homework, taking an exam (test and math anxiety), managing your time, recognizing your learning style, and studying for the final exam.

   Each activity requires only a few minutes and will help you pass this course and become a better math student. Many of these skills can be carried over to other disciplines and help you become a model college student. To begin, write down the following information:

a. Instructor's name

b. Instructor's office number

c. Instructor's telephone number

d. Instructor's e-mail address

e. Instructor's office hours

f. Days of the week that the class meets

g. The room number in which the class meets

h. Is there a lab requirement for this course? How often must you attend lab and where is it located?

Vocabulary and Key Concepts

1. a. A _____ is the result of multiplying two or more numbers.

  b. The numbers being multiplied in a product are called _____.

  c. Given a fraction $\frac{a}{b}$ with $b \neq 0$, the value a is the _____ and _____ is the denominator.

  d. A fraction is said to be in _____ terms if the numerator and denominator share no common factor other than 1.

  e. The fraction $\frac{4}{4}$ can also be written as the whole number _____, and the fraction $\frac{4}{1}$ can be written as the whole number _____.

  f. Two nonzero numbers $\frac{a}{b}$ and $\frac{b}{a}$ are _____ because their product is 1.

  g. The least common multiple (LCM) of two numbers is the smallest whole number that is a _____ of both numbers.

  h. The _____ common denominator of two or more fractions is the LCM of their denominators.

Concept 1: Basic Definitions

For Exercises 2–10, identify the numerator and denominator of each fraction. Then determine if the fraction is a proper fraction or an improper fraction.

2. $\frac{7}{8}$

3. $\frac{2}{3}$

4. $\frac{9}{5}$

5. $\frac{5}{2}$

6. $\frac{6}{6}$

7. $\frac{4}{4}$

8. $\frac{12}{1}$

9. $\frac{5}{1}$

10. $\frac{6}{7}$

18   **Chapter 1**   The Set of Real Numbers

For Exercises 11–18, write a proper or improper fraction associated with the shaded region of each figure.

11.    **12.**

13.    **14.**

15.    **16.** 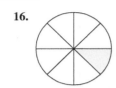   **17.** 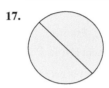   **18.**

For Exercises 19–22, write both an improper fraction and a mixed number associated with the shaded region of each figure.

19. 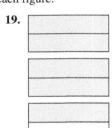   **20.**    **21.** 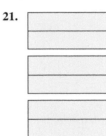   **22.**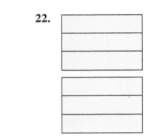

23. Explain the difference between the set of whole numbers and the set of natural numbers.

24. Explain the difference between a proper fraction and an improper fraction.

25. Write a fraction that simplifies to $\frac{1}{2}$. (Answers may vary.)

26. Write a fraction that simplifies to $\frac{1}{3}$. (Answers may vary.)

Concept 2: Prime Factorization

For Exercises 27–34, identify each number as either a prime number or a composite number.

27. 5   **28.** 9   **29.** 4   **30.** 2

31. 39   **32.** 23   **33.** 53   **34.** 51

For Exercises 35–42, write each number as a product of prime factors. **(See Example 1.)**

35. 36   **36.** 70   **37.** 42   **38.** 35

39. 110   **40.** 136   **41.** 135   **42.** 105

Concept 3: Simplifying Fractions to Lowest Terms

For Exercises 43–54, simplify each fraction to lowest terms. **(See Examples 2–3.)**

43. $\dfrac{3}{15}$ **44.** $\dfrac{8}{12}$ **45.** $\dfrac{16}{6}$ **46.** $\dfrac{20}{12}$

47. $\dfrac{42}{48}$ **48.** $\dfrac{35}{80}$ **49.** $\dfrac{48}{64}$ **50.** $\dfrac{32}{48}$

51. $\dfrac{110}{176}$ **52.** $\dfrac{70}{120}$ **53.** $\dfrac{200}{150}$ **54.** $\dfrac{210}{119}$

Concepts 4–5: Multiplying and Dividing Fractions

For Exercises 55–56, determine if the statement is true or false. If it is false, rewrite as a true statement.

55. When multiplying or dividing fractions, it is necessary to have a common denominator.

56. When dividing two fractions, it is necessary to multiply the first fraction by the reciprocal of the second fraction.

For Exercises 57–68, multiply or divide as indicated. **(See Examples 4–6.)**

57. $\dfrac{10}{13} \times \dfrac{26}{15}$ **58.** $\dfrac{15}{28} \times \dfrac{7}{9}$ **59.** $\dfrac{3}{7} \div \dfrac{9}{14}$ **60.** $\dfrac{7}{25} \div \dfrac{1}{5}$

61. $\dfrac{9}{10} \times 5$ **62.** $\dfrac{3}{7} \times 14$ **63.** $\dfrac{12}{5} \div 4$ **64.** $\dfrac{20}{6} \div 5$

65. $\dfrac{5}{2} \times \dfrac{10}{21} \times \dfrac{7}{5}$ **66.** $\dfrac{55}{9} \times \dfrac{18}{32} \times \dfrac{24}{11}$ **67.** $\dfrac{9}{100} \div \dfrac{13}{1000}$ **68.** $\dfrac{1000}{17} \div \dfrac{10}{3}$

69. Gus decides to save $\frac{1}{3}$ of his pay each month. If his monthly pay is $2112, how much will he save each month?

70. Stephen's take-home pay is $4200 a month. If he budgeted $\frac{1}{4}$ of his pay for rent, how much is his rent?

71. In Professor Foley's Beginning Algebra class, $\frac{5}{6}$ of the students passed the first test. If there are 42 students in the class, how many passed the test?

72. Shontell had only enough paper to print out $\frac{3}{5}$ of her book report before school. If the report is 10 pages long, how many pages did she print out?

73. Marty will reinforce a concrete walkway by cutting a steel rod (called rebar) that is 4 yd long. How many pieces can he cut if each piece must be $\frac{1}{2}$ yd in length?

74. There are 4 cups of oatmeal in a box. If each serving is $\frac{1}{3}$ of a cup, how many servings are contained in the box?

75. Anita buys 6 lb of mixed nuts to be divided into decorative jars that will each hold $\frac{3}{4}$ lb of nuts. How many jars will she be able to fill?

76. Beth has a $\frac{7}{8}$-in. nail that she must hammer into a board. Each strike of the hammer moves the nail $\frac{1}{16}$ in. into the board. How many strikes of the hammer must she make to drive the nail completely into the board?

Concept 6: Adding and Subtracting Fractions

For Exercises 77–80, add or subtract as indicated. **(See Example 7.)**

77. $\dfrac{5}{14} + \dfrac{1}{14}$ **78.** $\dfrac{9}{5} + \dfrac{1}{5}$ **79.** $\dfrac{17}{24} - \dfrac{5}{24}$ **80.** $\dfrac{11}{18} - \dfrac{5}{18}$

20   **Chapter 1**   The Set of Real Numbers

For Exercises 81–84, find the least common multiple for each list of numbers. **(See Example 8.)**

81. 6, 15

82. 12, 30

83. 20, 8, 4

84. 24, 40, 30

For Exercises 85–100, add or subtract as indicated. **(See Examples 9–10.)**

85. $\dfrac{1}{8} + \dfrac{3}{4}$

86. $\dfrac{3}{16} + \dfrac{1}{2}$

87. $\dfrac{11}{8} - \dfrac{3}{10}$

88. $\dfrac{12}{35} - \dfrac{1}{10}$

89. $\dfrac{7}{26} - \dfrac{2}{13}$

90. $\dfrac{25}{24} - \dfrac{5}{16}$

91. $\dfrac{7}{18} + \dfrac{5}{12}$

92. $\dfrac{3}{16} + \dfrac{9}{20}$

93. $\dfrac{5}{4} - \dfrac{1}{20}$

94. $\dfrac{7}{6} - \dfrac{1}{24}$

95. $\dfrac{5}{12} + \dfrac{5}{16}$

96. $\dfrac{3}{25} + \dfrac{8}{35}$

97. $\dfrac{1}{6} + \dfrac{3}{4} - \dfrac{5}{8}$

98. $\dfrac{1}{2} + \dfrac{2}{3} - \dfrac{5}{12}$

99. $\dfrac{4}{7} + \dfrac{1}{2} + \dfrac{3}{4}$

100. $\dfrac{9}{10} + \dfrac{4}{5} + \dfrac{3}{4}$

101. For his famous brownie recipe, Chef Alfonso combines $\frac{2}{3}$ cup granulated sugar with $\frac{1}{4}$ cup brown sugar. What is the total amount of sugar in his recipe?

102. Chef Alfonso eats too many of his brownies and his waistline increased by $\frac{3}{4}$ in. during one month and $\frac{3}{8}$ in. the next month. What was his total increase for the 2-month period?

103. Currently the most popular smartphone has a thickness of $\frac{9}{25}$ in. The second most popular is $\frac{1}{2}$ in. thick. How much thicker is the second most popular smartphone?

104. The diameter of a penny is $\frac{3}{4}$ in. while the dime is $\frac{7}{10}$ in. How much larger is the penny than the dime?

Concept 7: Operations on Mixed Numbers

For Exercises 105–118, perform the indicated operations. **(See Examples 11–12.)**

105. $3\dfrac{1}{5} \times 2\dfrac{7}{8}$

106. $2\dfrac{1}{2} \times 1\dfrac{4}{5}$

107. $1\dfrac{2}{9} \div 7\dfrac{1}{3}$

108. $2\dfrac{2}{5} \div 1\dfrac{2}{7}$

109. $1\dfrac{2}{9} \div 6$

110. $2\dfrac{2}{5} \div 2$

111. $2\dfrac{1}{8} + 1\dfrac{3}{8}$

112. $1\dfrac{3}{14} + 1\dfrac{1}{14}$

113. $3\dfrac{1}{2} - 1\dfrac{7}{8}$

114. $5\dfrac{1}{3} - 2\dfrac{3}{4}$

115. $1\dfrac{1}{6} + 3\dfrac{3}{4}$

116. $4\dfrac{1}{2} + 2\dfrac{2}{3}$

117. $1 - \dfrac{7}{8}$

118. $2 - \dfrac{3}{7}$

119. A board $26\frac{3}{8}$ in. long must be cut into three pieces of equal length. Find the length of each piece.

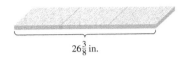

$26\frac{3}{8}$ in.

120. A futon, when set up as a sofa, measures $3\frac{5}{6}$ ft wide. When it is opened to be used as a bed, the width is increased by $1\frac{3}{4}$ ft. What is the total width of this bed?

$3\frac{5}{6}$ ft

121. A plane trip from Orlando to Detroit takes $2\frac{3}{4}$ hr. If the plane traveled for $1\frac{1}{6}$ hr, how much time remains for the flight?

122. Silvia manages a sub shop and needs to prepare smoked turkey sandwiches. She has $3\frac{3}{4}$ lb of turkey in the cooler, and each sandwich requires $\frac{3}{8}$ lb of turkey. How many sandwiches can she make?

123. José's catering company plans to prepare two different shrimp dishes for an upcoming event. One dish requires $1\frac{1}{2}$ lb of shrimp and the other requires $\frac{3}{4}$ lb of shrimp. How much shrimp should José order for the two dishes?

124. Ayako took a trip to the store $5\frac{1}{2}$ mi away. If she rode the bus for $4\frac{5}{6}$ mi and walked the rest of the way, how far did she have to walk?

125. If Tampa, Florida, averages $6\frac{1}{4}$ in. of rain during each summer month, how much total rain would be expected in June, July, August, and September?

126. Pete started working out and found that he lost approximately $\frac{3}{4}$ in. off his waistline every month. How much would he lose around his waist in 6 months?

Introduction to Algebra and the Set of Real Numbers   Section 1.2

1. Variables and Expressions

Doctors promote daily exercise as part of a healthy lifestyle. Aerobic exercise is exercise for the heart. During aerobic exercise, the goal is to maintain a heart rate level between 65% and 85% of an individual's maximum recommended heart rate. The maximum recommended heart rate, in beats per minute, for an adult of age a is given by:

$$\text{Maximum recommended heart rate} = 220 - a$$

In this example, value a is called a **variable**. This is a symbol or letter, such as x, y, z, a, and the like, that is used to represent an unknown number that is subject to change. The number 220 is called a **constant**, because it does not vary. The quantity $220 - a$ is called an algebraic expression. An algebraic **expression** is a collection of variables and constants under algebraic operations. For example, $\frac{3}{x}$, $y + 7$, and $t - 1.4$ are algebraic expressions.

The symbols used in algebraic expressions to show the four basic operations are shown here:

Addition $a + b$

Subtraction $a - b$

Multiplication $a \times b$, $a \cdot b$, $(a)b$, $a(b)$, $(a)(b)$, ab
        (*Note:* We rarely use the notation $a \times b$ because the symbol $\times$ may be confused with the variable x.)

Division $a \div b$, $\dfrac{a}{b}$, a/b, $b\overline{)a}$

Concepts

1. Variables and Expressions
2. The Set of Real Numbers
3. Inequalities
4. Opposite of a Real Number
5. Absolute Value of a Real Number

The value of an algebraic expression depends on the values of the variables within the expression.

Example 1 **Evaluating an Algebraic Expression**

The expression $220 - a$ represents the maximum recommended heart rate for an adult of age a. Determine the maximum heart rate for:

a. A 20-year-old   **b.** A 45-year-old

Solution:

a. In the expression $220 - a$, the variable, a, represents the age of the individual. To calculate the maximum recommended heart rate for a 20-year-old, we substitute 20 for a in the expression.

$220 - a$

$220 - (\ \ )$ When substituting a number for a variable, use parentheses.

$= 220 - (20)$ Substitute $a = 20.$

$= 200$ Subtract.

The maximum recommended heart rate for a 20-year-old is 200 beats per minute.

b. $220 - a$

$220 - (\ \ )$ When substituting a number for a variable, use parentheses.

$= 220 - (45)$ Substitute $a = 45.$

$= 175$ Subtract.

The maximum recommended heart rate for a 45-year-old is 175 beats per minute.

Skill Practice

1. After dining out at a restaurant, the recommended minimum amount for tipping the server is 15% of the cost of the meal. This can be represented by the expression $0.15c$, where c is the cost of the meal. Compute the tip for a meal that costs:

    a. $18   **b.** $46

Example 2 **Evaluating Algebraic Expressions**

Evaluate the algebraic expression when $p = 4$ and $q = \frac{3}{4}$.

    a. $100 - p$ **b.** pq

Solution:

a. $100 - p$

$100 - (\ \ )$ When substituting a number for a variable, use parentheses.

$= 100 - (4)$ Substitute $p = 4$ in the parentheses.

$= 96$ Subtract.

Answers

1. a. $2.70   **b.** $6.90

b. pq

$= (\ )(\ )$ When substituting a number for a variable, use parentheses.

$= (4)\left(\dfrac{3}{4}\right)$ Substitute $p = 4$ and $q = \frac{3}{4}$.

$= \dfrac{\overset{1}{\cancel{4}}}{1} \cdot \dfrac{3}{\underset{1}{\cancel{4}}}$ Write the whole number as a fraction.

$= \dfrac{3}{1}$ Multiply fractions.

$= 3$ Simplify.

Skill Practice Evaluate the algebraic expressions when $x = 5$ and $y = 2$.

2. $20 - y$ **3.** xy

2. The Set of Real Numbers

Typically, the numbers represented by variables in an algebraic expression are all part of the set of **real numbers**. These are the numbers that we work with on a day-to-day basis. The real numbers encompass zero, all positive, and all negative numbers, including those represented by fractions and decimal numbers. The set of real numbers can be represented graphically on a horizontal number line with a point labeled as 0. Positive real numbers are graphed to the right of 0, and negative real numbers are graphed to the left of 0. Zero is neither positive nor negative. Each point on the number line corresponds to exactly one real number. For this reason, this number line is called the *real number line* (Figure 1-5).

Figure 1-5

| Example 3 | **Plotting Points on the Real Number Line** |

Plot the numbers on the real number line.

a. -3 **b.** $\dfrac{3}{2}$ **c.** -4.7 **d.** $\dfrac{16}{5}$

Solution:

a. Because -3 is negative, it lies three units to the left of 0.

b. The fraction $\frac{3}{2}$ can be expressed as the mixed number $1\frac{1}{2}$ which lies halfway between 1 and 2 on the number line.

c. The negative number -4.7 lies $\frac{7}{10}$ unit to the left of -4 on the number line.

d. The fraction $\frac{16}{5}$ can be expressed as the mixed number $3\frac{1}{5}$, which lies $\frac{1}{5}$ unit to the right of 3 on the number line.

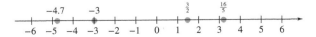

Answers

2. 18   **3.** 10

Skill Practice Plot the numbers on the real number line.

4. $\{-1, \frac{3}{4}, -2.5, \frac{10}{3}\}$

In mathematics, a well-defined collection of elements is called a **set**. "Well-defined" means the set is described in such a way that it is clear whether an element is in the set. The symbols { } are used to enclose the elements of the set. For example, the set {A, B, C, D, E} represents the set of the first five letters of the alphabet.

Several sets of numbers are used extensively in algebra and are *subsets* (or part) of the set of real numbers.

> ## Natural Numbers, Whole Numbers, and Integers
> The set of **natural numbers** is {1, 2, 3, . . .}
> The set of **whole numbers** is {0, 1, 2, 3, . . .}
> The set of **integers** is {. . . −3, −2, −1, 0, 1, 2, 3, . . .}

Notice that the set of whole numbers includes the natural numbers. Therefore, every natural number is also a whole number. The set of integers includes the set of whole numbers. Therefore, every whole number is also an integer.

Fractions are also among the numbers we use frequently. A number that can be written as a fraction whose numerator is an integer and whose denominator is a nonzero integer is called a *rational number*.

> ## Rational Numbers
> The set of **rational numbers** is the set of numbers that can be expressed in the form $\frac{p}{q}$, where both p and q are integers and q does not equal 0.

We also say that a rational number $\frac{p}{q}$ is a *ratio* of two integers, p and q, where q is not equal to zero.

Example 4   **Identifying Rational Numbers**

Show that the following numbers are rational numbers by finding an equivalent ratio of two integers.

  a. $\dfrac{-2}{3}$ b. -12 c. 0.5 d. $0.\overline{6}$

Solution:

  a. The fraction $\frac{-2}{3}$ is a rational number because it can be expressed as the ratio of -2 and 3.

  b. The number -12 is a rational number because it can be expressed as the ratio of -12 and 1, that is, $-12 = \frac{-12}{1}$. In this example, we see that an integer is also a rational number.

Answer

4.

c. The terminating decimal 0.5 is a rational number because it can be expressed as the ratio of 5 and 10, that is, $0.5 = \frac{5}{10}$. In this example, we see that a terminating decimal is also a rational number.

d. The numeral $0.\overline{6}$ represents the nonterminating, repeating decimal $0.6666666\ldots$. The number $0.\overline{6}$ is a rational number because it can be expressed as the ratio of 2 and 3, that is, $0.\overline{6} = \frac{2}{3}$. In this example, we see that a repeating decimal is also a rational number.

Skill Practice Show that each number is rational by finding an equivalent ratio of two integers.

5. $\frac{3}{7}$ **6.** -5 **7.** 0.3 **8.** $0.\overline{3}$

> **TIP:** A rational number can be represented by a terminating decimal or by a repeating decimal.

Some real numbers, such as the number π, cannot be represented by the ratio of two integers. These numbers are called irrational numbers and in decimal form are nonterminating, nonrepeating decimals. The value of π, for example, can be approximated as $\pi \approx 3.1415926535897932$. However, the decimal digits continue forever with no repeated pattern. Another example of an irrational number is $\sqrt{3}$ (read as "the positive square root of 3"). The expression $\sqrt{3}$ is a number that when multiplied by itself is 3. There is no rational number that satisfies this condition. Thus, $\sqrt{3}$ is an irrational number.

Irrational Numbers

The set of **irrational numbers** is a subset of the real numbers whose elements cannot be written as a ratio of two integers.

Note: An irrational number cannot be written as a terminating decimal or as a repeating decimal.

The set of real numbers consists of both the rational and the irrational numbers. The relationship among these important sets of numbers is illustrated in Figure 1-6 along with numerical examples.

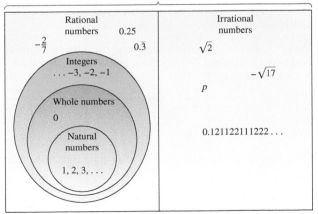

Figure 1-6

Answers
5. Ratio of 3 and 7
6. Ratio of -5 and 1
7. Ratio of 3 and 10
8. Ratio of 1 and 3

Example 5   **Classifying Numbers by Set**

Check the set(s) to which each number belongs. The numbers may belong to more than one set.

	Natural Numbers	Whole Numbers	Integers	Rational Numbers	Irrational Numbers	Real Numbers
5						
$\frac{-47}{3}$						
1.48						
$\sqrt{7}$						
0						

Solution:

	Natural Numbers	Whole Numbers	Integers	Rational Numbers	Irrational Numbers	Real Numbers
5	✓	✓	✓	✓ (ratio of 5 and 1)		✓
$\frac{-47}{3}$				✓ (ratio of −47 and 3)		✓
1.48				✓ (ratio of 148 and 100)		✓
$\sqrt{7}$					✓	✓
0		✓	✓	✓ (ratio of 0 and 1)		✓

Skill Practice Identify the sets to which each number belongs. Choose from: natural numbers, whole numbers, integers, rational numbers, irrational numbers, real numbers.

9. −4   **10.** $0.\overline{7}$ **11.** $\sqrt{13}$ **12.** 12   **13.** 1

3. Inequalities

The relative size of two real numbers can be compared using the real number line. Suppose a and b represent two real numbers. We say that a is less than b, denoted $a < b$, if a lies to the left of b on the number line.

$a < b$

We say that a is greater than b, denoted $a > b$, if a lies to the right of b on the number line.

$a > b$

Answers

9. Integers, rational numbers, real numbers
10. Rational numbers, real numbers
11. Irrational numbers, real numbers
12. Natural numbers, whole numbers, integers, rational numbers, real numbers
13. Natural numbers, whole numbers, integers, rational numbers, real numbers

Table 1-1 summarizes the relational operators that compare two real numbers a and b.

Table 1-1

Mathematical Expression	Translation	Example
$a < b$	a is less than b.	$2 < 3$
$a > b$	a is greater than b.	$5 > 1$
$a \leq b$	a is less than or equal to b.	$4 \leq 4$
$a \geq b$	a is greater than or equal to b.	$10 \geq 9$
$a = b$	a is equal to b.	$6 = 6$
$a \neq b$	a is not equal to b.	$7 \neq 0$
$a \approx b$	a is approximately equal to b.	$2.3 \approx 2$

The symbols $<$, $>$, $\leq$, $\geq$, and $\neq$ are called *inequality signs*, and the statements $a < b$, $a > b$, $a \leq b$, $a \geq b$, and $a \neq b$ are called **inequalities**.

Example 6   **Ordering Real Numbers**

The average temperatures (in degrees Celsius) for selected cities in the United States and Canada in January are shown in Table 1-2.

Table 1-2

City	Temp (°C)
Prince George, British Columbia	-12.5
Corpus Christi, Texas	13.4
Parkersburg, West Virginia	-0.9
San Jose, California	9.7
Juneau, Alaska	-5.7
New Bedford, Massachusetts	-0.2
Durham, North Carolina	4.2

Plot a point on the real number line representing the temperature of each city. Compare the temperatures between the following cities, and fill in the blank with the appropriate inequality sign: $<$ or $>$.

Solution:

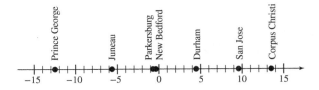

a. Temperature of San Jose $\boxed{<}$ temperature of Corpus Christi

b. Temperature of Juneau $\boxed{>}$ temperature of Prince George

c. Temperature of Parkersburg $\boxed{<}$ temperature of New Bedford

d. Temperature of Parkersburg $\boxed{>}$ temperature of Prince George

Skill Practice Fill in the blanks with the appropriate inequality sign:
< or >.

14. −11 _____ 20   **15.** −3 _____ −6

16. 0 _____ −9   **17.** −6.2 _____ −1.8

4. Opposite of a Real Number

To gain mastery of any algebraic skill, it is necessary to know the meaning of key definitions and key symbols. Two important definitions are the *opposite* of a real number and the *absolute value* of a real number.

> **The Opposite of a Real Number**
>
> Two numbers that are the same distance from 0 but on opposite sides of 0 on the number line are called **opposites** of each other. Symbolically, we denote the opposite of a real number a as $-a$.

Example 7 **Finding the Opposite of a Real Number**

a. Find the opposite of 5.   **b.** Find the opposite of $-\dfrac{4}{7}$.

Solution:

a. The opposite of 5 is −5.   **b.** The opposite of $-\dfrac{4}{7}$ is $\dfrac{4}{7}$.

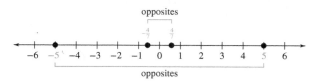

Skill Practice Find the opposite.

18. 224   **19.** −3.4

Example 8 **Finding the Opposite of a Real Number**

Evaluate each expression.

a. −(0.46)   **b.** $-\left(-\dfrac{11}{3}\right)$

Solution:

a. $-(0.46) = -0.46$ The expression $-(0.46)$ represents the opposite of 0.46.

b. $-\left(-\dfrac{11}{3}\right) = \dfrac{11}{3}$ The expression $-\left(-\dfrac{11}{3}\right)$ represents the opposite of $-\dfrac{11}{3}$.

Skill Practice Evaluate.

20. −(2.8)   **21.** $-\left(-\dfrac{1}{5}\right)$

Answers

14. <   **15.** >   **16.** >
17. <   **18.** −224   **19.** 3.4
20. −2.8   **21.** $\dfrac{1}{5}$

5. Absolute Value of a Real Number

To define the addition of real numbers, we use the concept of absolute value.

> **Informal Definition of the Absolute Value of a Real Number**
>
> The **absolute value** of a real number a, denoted $|a|$, is the distance between a and 0 on the number line.
>
> *Note:* The absolute value of any real number is positive or zero.

For example, $|3| = 3$ and $|-3| = 3$.

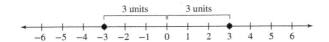

Example 9	**Finding the Absolute Value of a Real Number**

Evaluate the absolute value expressions.

a. $|-4|$ **b.** $\left|\dfrac{1}{2}\right|$ **c.** $|-6.2|$ **d.** $|0|$

Solution:

a. $|-4| = 4$ -4 is 4 units from 0 on the number line.

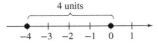

b. $\left|\dfrac{1}{2}\right| = \dfrac{1}{2}$ $\dfrac{1}{2}$ is $\dfrac{1}{2}$ unit from 0 on the number line.

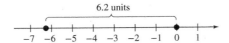

c. $|-6.2| = 6.2$ -6.2 is 6.2 units from 0 on the number line.

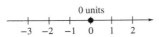

d. $|0| = 0$ 0 is 0 units from 0 on the number line.

Skill Practice Evaluate.

22. $|-99|$ **23.** $\left|\dfrac{7}{8}\right|$ **24.** $|-1.4|$ **25.** $|1|$

30   **Chapter 1**   The Set of Real Numbers

The absolute value of a number a is its distance from 0 on the number line. The definition of $|a|$ may also be given symbolically depending on whether a is negative or nonnegative.

Absolute Value of a Real Number

Let a be a real number. Then

1. If a is nonnegative (that is, $a \geq 0$), then $|a| = a$.
2. If a is negative (that is, $a < 0$), then $|a| = -a$.

This definition states that if a is a nonnegative number, then $|a|$ equals a itself. If a is a negative number, then $|a|$ equals the opposite of a. For example:

$|9| = 9$ Because 9 is positive, then $|9|$ equals the number 9 itself.

$|-7| = 7$ Because -7 is negative, then $|-7|$ equals the opposite of -7, which is 7.

Example 10   **Comparing Absolute Value Expressions**

Determine if the statements are true or false.

   a. $|3| \leq 3$ **b.** $-|5| = |-5|$

Solution:

   a. $|3| \leq 3$ $|3| \overset{?}{\leq} 3$ Simplify the absolute value.

                         $3 \overset{?}{\leq} 3$ True

   b. $-|5| = |-5|$ $-|5| \overset{?}{=} |-5|$ Simplify the absolute values.

                         $-5 \overset{?}{=} 5$ False

Skill Practice   Answer true or false.

26. $-|4| > |-4|$ **27.** $|-17| = 17$

Answers

26. False   **27.** True

Calculator Connections

Topic: Approximating Irrational Numbers on a Calculator

Scientific and graphing calculators approximate irrational numbers by using rational numbers in the form of terminating decimals. For example, consider approximating π and $\sqrt{3}$.

Scientific Calculator:

Enter: $\boxed{\pi}$ or $\boxed{2\text{nd}}$ $\boxed{\pi}$ Result: $\boxed{3.141592654}$

Enter: 3 $\boxed{\sqrt{}}$ Result: $\boxed{1.732050808}$

Graphing Calculator:

Enter: $\boxed{2\text{nd}}$ $\boxed{\pi}$ $\boxed{\text{ENTER}}$

Enter: $\boxed{2\text{nd}}$ $\boxed{\sqrt{}}$ 3 $\boxed{\text{ENTER}}$

```
π
                3.141592654
√(3)
                1.732050808
```

The symbol $\approx$ is read "is approximately equal to" and is used when writing approximations.

$$\pi \approx 3.141592654 \quad \text{and} \quad \sqrt{3} \approx 1.732050808$$

Calculator Exercises

Use a calculator to approximate the irrational numbers. Remember to use the appropriate symbol, $\approx$, when expressing answers.

1. $\sqrt{12}$ **2.** $\sqrt{99}$ **3.** 4π **4.** $\sqrt{\pi}$

Section 1.2   Practice Exercises

Study Skills Exercise

Look over the notes that you took today. Do you understand what you wrote? If there were any rules, definitions, or formulas, highlight them so that they can be easily found when studying for the test.

Vocabulary and Key Concepts

1. **a.** A _____ is a symbol or letter used to represent an unknown number.

     b. Values that do not vary are called _____.

     c. In mathematics, a well-defined collection of elements is called a _____.

     d. The statements $a < b$, $a > b$, and $a \neq b$ are examples of _____.

     e. The statement $a < b$ is read as "_____."

     f. The statement $c \geq d$ is read as "_____."

     g. The statement $5 \neq 6$ is read as "_____."

     h. Two numbers that are the same distance from 0 but on opposite sides of 0 on the number line are called _____.

     i. The absolute value of a real number, a, is denoted by _____ and is the distance between a and _____ on the number line.

Review Exercises

For Exercises 2–4, simplify.

2. $4\frac{1}{2} - 1\frac{5}{6}$ **3.** $4\frac{1}{2} \times 1\frac{5}{6}$ **4.** $4\frac{1}{2} \div 1\frac{5}{6}$

Concept 1: Variables and Expressions

For Exercises 5–14, evaluate the expressions for the given substitution. **(See Examples 1–2.)**

5. $y - 3$ when $y = 18$ **6.** $3q$ when $q = 5$

7. $\dfrac{15}{t}$ when $t = 5$ **8.** $8 + w$ when $w = 12$

9. $6d$ when $d = \dfrac{2}{3}$ **10.** $\dfrac{6}{5}h$ when $h = 10$

32   **Chapter 1**   The Set of Real Numbers

11. $c - 2 - d$ when $c = 15.4$, $d = 8.1$

12. $1.1 + t + s$ when $t = 93.2$, $s = 11.5$

13. abc when $a = \dfrac{1}{10}$, $b = \dfrac{1}{4}$, $c = \dfrac{1}{2}$

14. $x - y - z$ when $x = \dfrac{7}{8}$, $y = \dfrac{1}{2}$, $z = \dfrac{1}{4}$

15. The cost of downloading songs from the Internet can be represented by the expression $1.29s$, where s is the number of songs downloaded. Calculate the cost of downloading:

    a. 3 songs   **b.** 8 songs   **c.** 10 songs

16. The number of calories burned by a 150-lb person by walking 2 mph can be represented by the expression $240h$, where h represents the number of hours spent walking. Calculate the number of calories burned by walking:

    a. 4 hr   **b.** $2\frac{1}{2}$ hr   **c.** $1\frac{1}{4}$ hr

17. Aly is trying to limit her total calorie intake for breakfast and lunch to 850 calories. The number of calories that she can consume for lunch is given by the expression $850 - b$, where b is the number of calories consumed for breakfast. Determine the number of calories allowed for lunch assuming that she had the following number of calories at breakfast:

    a. 475 calories   **b.** 220 calories   **c.** 580 calories

18. Lorenzo knows that the gas mileage on his car is about 25 miles per gallon. The number of gallons needed to travel a certain distance is given by the expression $\frac{d}{25}$, where d is the distance traveled. Find the number of gallons of fuel needed if Lorenzo drives:

    a. 200 mi   **b.** 450 mi   **c.** 180 mi

Concept 2: The Set of Real Numbers

19. Plot the numbers on the real number line: $\left\{1, -2, -\pi, 0, -\frac{5}{2}, 5.1\right\}$ **(See Example 3.)**

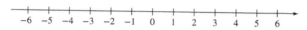

20. Plot the numbers on the real number line: $\left\{3, -4, \frac{1}{8}, -1.7, -\frac{4}{3}, 1.75\right\}$

For Exercises 21–36, describe each number as (a) a terminating decimal, (b) a repeating decimal, or (c) a nonterminating, nonrepeating decimal. Then classify the number as a rational number or as an irrational number. **(See Example 4.)**

21. 0.29 **22.** 3.8 **23.** $\dfrac{1}{9}$ **24.** $\dfrac{1}{3}$

25. $\dfrac{1}{8}$ **26.** $\dfrac{1}{5}$ **27.** 2π **28.** 3π

29. -0.125 **30.** -3.24 **31.** -3 **32.** -6

33. $0.\overline{2}$ **34.** $0.\overline{6}$ **35.** $\sqrt{6}$ **36.** $\sqrt{10}$

37. List three numbers that are real numbers but not rational numbers.

38. List three numbers that are real numbers but not irrational numbers.

39. List three numbers that are integers but not natural numbers.

40. List three numbers that are integers but not whole numbers.

41. List three numbers that are rational numbers but not integers.

For Exercises 42–48, let $A = \left\{-\frac{3}{2}, \sqrt{11}, -4, 0.\overline{6}, 0, \sqrt{7}, 1\right\}$ **(See Example 5.)**

42. Are all of the numbers in set A real numbers?

43. List all of the rational numbers in set A.

44. List all of the whole numbers in set A.

45. List all of the natural numbers in set A.

46. List all of the irrational numbers in set A.

47. List all of the integers in set A.

48. Plot the real numbers from set A on a number line. (*Hint:* $\sqrt{11} \approx 3.3$ and $\sqrt{7} \approx 2.6$)

```
 ←─┼──┼──┼──┼──┼──┼──┼──┼──┼──┼──┼──┼──→
  -6  -5  -4  -3  -2  -1   0   1   2   3   4   5   6
```

Concept 3: Inequalities

49. The women's golf scores for selected players at an LPGA event are given in the table. Compare the scores and fill in the blank with the appropriate inequality sign: $<$ or $>$. **(See Example 6.)**

a. Kane's score _____ Pak's score.

b. Sorenstam's score _____ Davies's score.

c. Pak's score _____ McCurdy's score.

d. Kane's score _____ Davies's score.

LPGA Golfers	Final Score with Respect to Par
Annika Sorenstam	7
Laura Davies	−4
Lorie Kane	0
Cindy McCurdy	3
Se Ri Pak	−8

50. The elevations of selected cities in the United States are shown in the figure. Compare the elevations and fill in the blank with the appropriate inequality sign: $<$ or $>$. (A negative number indicates that the city is below sea level.)

a. Elevation of Tucson _____ elevation of Cincinnati.

b. Elevation of New Orleans _____ elevation of Chicago.

c. Elevation of New Orleans _____ elevation of Houston.

d. Elevation of Chicago _____ elevation of Cincinnati.

Concept 4: Opposite of a Real Number

For Exercises 51–58, find the opposite of each number. **(See Example 7.)**

51. 18

52. 2

53. −6.1

54. −2.5

55. $-\dfrac{5}{8}$

56. $-\dfrac{1}{3}$

57. $\dfrac{7}{3}$

58. $\dfrac{1}{9}$

34 **Chapter 1** The Set of Real Numbers

The opposite of a is denoted as $-a$. For Exercises 59–66, simplify. **(See Example 8.)**

59. $-(-3)$

60. $-(-5.1)$

61. $-\left(\dfrac{7}{3}\right)$

62. $-(-7)$

63. $-(-8)$

64. $-(36)$

65. $-(72.1)$

66. $-\left(\dfrac{9}{10}\right)$

Concept 5: Absolute Value of a Real Number

For Exercises 67–78, simplify. **(See Example 9.)**

67. $|-2|$

68. $|-7|$

69. $|-1.5|$

70. $|-3.7|$

71. $-|-1.5|$

72. $-|-3.7|$

73. $\left|\dfrac{3}{2}\right|$

74. $\left|\dfrac{7}{4}\right|$

75. $-|10|$

76. $-|20|$

77. $-\left|-\dfrac{1}{2}\right|$

78. $-\left|-\dfrac{11}{3}\right|$

For Exercises 79–80, answer true or false. If a statement is false, explain why.

79. If n is positive, then $|n|$ is negative.

80. If m is negative, then $|m|$ is negative.

For Exercises 81–104, determine if the statements are true or false. Use the real number line to justify the answer. **(See Example 10.)**

81. $5 > 2$

82. $8 < 10$

83. $6 < 6$

84. $19 > 19$

85. $-7 \geq -7$

86. $-1 \leq -1$

87. $\dfrac{3}{2} \leq \dfrac{1}{6}$

88. $-\dfrac{1}{4} \geq -\dfrac{7}{8}$

89. $-5 > -2$

90. $6 < -10$

91. $8 \neq 8$

92. $10 \neq 10$

93. $|-2| \geq |-1|$

94. $|3| \leq |-1|$

95. $\left|-\dfrac{1}{9}\right| = \left|\dfrac{1}{9}\right|$

96. $\left|-\dfrac{1}{3}\right| = \left|\dfrac{1}{3}\right|$

97. $|7| \neq |-7|$

98. $|-13| \neq |13|$

99. $-1 < |-1|$

100. $-6 < |-6|$

101. $|-8| \geq |8|$

102. $|-11| \geq |11|$

103. $|-2| \leq |2|$

104. $|-21| \leq |21|$

Expanding Your Skills

105. For what numbers, a, is $-a$ positive?

106. For what numbers, a, is $|a| = a$?

Exponents, Square Roots, and the Order of Operations

1. Exponential Expressions

In algebra, repeated multiplication can be expressed using exponents. The expression $4 \cdot 4 \cdot 4$ can be written as

In the expression 4^3, 4 is the base, and 3 is the exponent, or power. The exponent indicates how many factors of the base to multiply.

Concepts

1. Exponential Expressions
2. Square Roots
3. Order of Operations
3. Translations

Definition of b^n

Let b represent any real number and n represent a positive integer. Then,

$$b^n = \underbrace{b \cdot b \cdot b \cdot b \cdot \ldots b}_{n \text{ factors of } b}$$

b^n is read as "b to the nth power."
b is called the **base**, and n is called the **exponent,** or **power**.
b^2 is read as "b squared," and b^3 is read as "b cubed."

The exponent, n, is the number of times the base, b, is used as a factor.

TIP: A number or variable with no exponent shown implies that there is an exponent of 1. That is, $b = b^1$.

Example 1   **Evaluating Exponential Expressions**

Translate the expression into words and then evaluate the expression.

a. 2^5 **b.** 5^2 **c.** $\left(\dfrac{3}{4}\right)^3$ **d.** 1^6

Solution:

a. The expression 2^5 is read as "two to the fifth power."
$2^5 = (2)(2)(2)(2)(2) = 32$

b. The expression 5^2 is read as "five to the second power" or "five, squared."
$5^2 = (5)(5) = 25$

c. The expression $\left(\frac{3}{4}\right)^3$ is read as "three-fourths to the third power" or "three-fourths, cubed."

$$\left(\frac{3}{4}\right)^3 = \left(\frac{3}{4}\right)\left(\frac{3}{4}\right)\left(\frac{3}{4}\right) = \frac{27}{64}$$

d. The expression 1^6 is read as "one to the sixth power."
$1^6 = (1)(1)(1)(1)(1)(1) = 1$

Skill Practice Evaluate.

1. 4^3 **2.** 2^4 **3.** $\left(\dfrac{2}{3}\right)^2$ **4.** $(1)^7$

Answers
1. 64   **2.** 16   **3.** $\dfrac{4}{9}$ **4.** 1

2. Square Roots

If we reverse the process of squaring a number, we can find the square roots of the number. For example, finding a square root of 9 is equivalent to asking "what number(s) when squared equals 9?" The symbol, $\sqrt{}$ (called a **radical sign**), is used to find the *principal* square root of a number. By definition, the principal square root of a number is nonnegative. Therefore, $\sqrt{9}$ is the nonnegative number that when squared equals 9. Hence, $\sqrt{9} = 3$ because 3 is nonnegative and $(3)^2 = 9$.

Example 2   **Evaluating Square Roots**

Evaluate the square roots.

a. $\sqrt{64}$ **b.** $\sqrt{121}$ **c.** $\sqrt{0}$ **d.** $\sqrt{\dfrac{4}{9}}$

Solution:

a. $\sqrt{64} = 8$ Because $(8)^2 = 64$

b. $\sqrt{121} = 11$ Because $(11)^2 = 121$

c. $\sqrt{0} = 0$ Because $(0)^2 = 0$

d. $\sqrt{\dfrac{4}{9}} = \dfrac{2}{3}$ Because $\dfrac{2}{3} \cdot \dfrac{2}{3} = \dfrac{4}{9}$

Skill Practice Evaluate.

5. $\sqrt{81}$ **6.** $\sqrt{100}$ **7.** $\sqrt{1}$ **8.** $\sqrt{\dfrac{9}{25}}$

A perfect square is a number whose square root is a rational number. If a positive number is not a perfect square, its square root is an irrational number that can be approximated on a calculator.

TIP: To simplify square roots, it is advisable to become familiar with the following perfect squares and square roots.

$$0^2 = 0 \longrightarrow \sqrt{0} = 0 \qquad\qquad 7^2 = 49 \longrightarrow \sqrt{49} = 7$$
$$1^2 = 1 \longrightarrow \sqrt{1} = 1 \qquad\qquad 8^2 = 64 \longrightarrow \sqrt{64} = 8$$
$$2^2 = 4 \longrightarrow \sqrt{4} = 2 \qquad\qquad 9^2 = 81 \longrightarrow \sqrt{81} = 9$$
$$3^2 = 9 \longrightarrow \sqrt{9} = 3 \qquad\qquad 10^2 = 100 \longrightarrow \sqrt{100} = 10$$
$$4^2 = 16 \longrightarrow \sqrt{16} = 4 \qquad\qquad 11^2 = 121 \longrightarrow \sqrt{121} = 11$$
$$5^2 = 25 \longrightarrow \sqrt{25} = 5 \qquad\qquad 12^2 = 144 \longrightarrow \sqrt{144} = 12$$
$$6^2 = 36 \longrightarrow \sqrt{36} = 6 \qquad\qquad 13^2 = 169 \longrightarrow \sqrt{169} = 13$$

3. Order of Operations

When algebraic expressions contain numerous operations, it is important to evaluate the operations in the proper order. Parentheses ( ), brackets [ ], and braces { } are used for grouping numbers and algebraic expressions. It is important to recognize that operations

Answers

5. 9   **6.** 10   **7.** 1   **8.** $\dfrac{3}{5}$

must be done within parentheses and other grouping symbols first. Other grouping symbols include absolute value bars, radical signs, and fraction bars.

Applying the Order of Operations

Step 1 Simplify expressions within parentheses and other grouping symbols first. These include absolute value bars, fraction bars, and radicals. If imbedded parentheses are present, start with the innermost parentheses.

Step 2 Evaluate expressions involving exponents, radicals, and absolute values.

Step 3 Perform multiplication or division in the order that they occur from left to right.

Step 4 Perform addition or subtraction in the order that they occur from left to right.

TIP: Radical signs act as grouping symbols.
$$\sqrt{16 + 9} = \sqrt{(16 + 9)}$$
$$= \sqrt{25}$$
$$= 5$$
Perform operations inside the radical first, then apply the square root.

Example 3   **Applying the Order of Operations**

Simplify the expressions.

a. $17 - 3 \cdot 2 + 2^2$ **b.** $\dfrac{1}{2}\left(\dfrac{5}{6} - \dfrac{3}{4}\right)$

Solution:

a. $17 - 3 \cdot 2 + 2^2$

$= 17 - 3 \cdot 2 + 4$ Simplify exponents.

$= 17 - 6 + 4$ Multiply before adding or subtracting.

$= 11 + 4$ Add or subtract from left to right.

$= 15$

b. $\dfrac{1}{2}\left(\dfrac{5}{6} - \dfrac{3}{4}\right)$ Subtract fractions within the parentheses.

$= \dfrac{1}{2}\left(\dfrac{10}{12} - \dfrac{9}{12}\right)$ The least common denominator is 12.

$= \dfrac{1}{2}\left(\dfrac{1}{12}\right)$

$= \dfrac{1}{24}$ Multiply fractions.

Skill Practice Simplify the expressions.

9. $14 - 3 \cdot 2 + 3^2$

10. $\dfrac{13}{4} - \dfrac{1}{4}(10 - 2)$

Answers
9. 17   **10.** $\dfrac{5}{4}$

Example 4	**Applying the Order of Operations**

Simplify the expressions.

  a. $25 - 12 \div 3 \cdot 4$

  b. $6.2 - |-2.1| + \sqrt{16 + 9}$

  c. $28 - 2[(6 - 3)^2 + 4]$

Solution:

a. $25 - 12 \div 3 \cdot 4$ Multiply or divide in order from left to right.

$= 25 - 4 \cdot 4$ Notice that the operation $12 \div 3$ is performed first (not $4 \cdot 4$).

$= 25 - 16$ Multiply $4 \cdot 4$ before subtracting.

$= 9$ Subtract.

b. $6.2 - |-2.1| + \sqrt{16 + 9}$

$= 6.2 - |-2.1| + \sqrt{25}$ Simplify within the square root.

$= 6.2 - (2.1) + 5$ Simplify the absolute value and square root.

$= 4.1 + 5$ Add or subtract from left to right.

$= 9.1$ Add.

c. $28 - 2[(6 - 3)^2 + 4]$

$= 28 - 2[(3)^2 + 4]$ Simplify within the inner parentheses first.

$= 28 - 2[(9) + 4]$ Simplify exponents.

$= 28 - 2[13]$ Add within the square brackets.

$= 28 - 26$ Multiply before subtracting.

$= 2$ Subtract.

Skill Practice   Simplify the expressions.

  11. $1 + 2 \cdot 3^2 \div 6$ **12.** $|-20| - \sqrt{20 - 4}$ **13.** $60 - 5[(7 - 4) + 2^2]$

Example 5	**Applying the Order of Operations**

Simplify the expression. $\dfrac{32 + 8 \div 2}{2 \cdot 3^2}$

Solution:

$\dfrac{32 + 8 \div 2}{2 \cdot 3^2}$ In this expression, the fraction bar acts as a grouping symbol.

$= \dfrac{32 + 4}{2 \cdot 9}$ First, simplify the expressions above and below the fraction bar using the order of operations.

$= \dfrac{36}{18}$ The last step is to simplify the fraction.

$= 2$

Answers
11. 4   **12.** 16   **13.** 25

Skill Practice Simplify the expression.

14. $\dfrac{60 - 3^2 \cdot 2}{3 + 8 \div 2}$

4. Translations

Algebra is a powerful tool used in science, business, economics, and many day-to-day applications. To apply algebra to a real-world application, we need the important skill of translating an English phrase to a mathematical expression. Table 1-3 summarizes commonly used phrases and expressions.

Table 1-3

Operation	Symbols	Translation
Addition	$a + b$	**sum** of a and b a plus b b added to a b more than a a increased by b the total of a and b
Subtraction	$a - b$	**difference** of a and b a minus b b subtracted from a a decreased by b b less than a a less b
Multiplication	$a \times b,\ a \cdot b,\ a(b),\ (a)b,\ (a)(b),\ ab$ (*Note:* From this point forward we will seldom use the notation $a \times b$ because the symbol, $\times$, might be confused with the variable, x.)	**product** of a and b a times b a multiplied by b
Division	$a \div b,\ \dfrac{a}{b},\ a/b,\ b\overline{)a}$	**quotient** of a and b a divided by b b divided into a ratio of a and b a over b a per b

Example 6 **Writing an English Phrase as an Algebraic Expression**

Translate each English phrase to an algebraic expression.

a. The quotient of x and 5

b. The difference of p and the square root of q

c. Seven less than n

d. Seven less n

e. Eight more than the absolute value of w

f. x subtracted from 18

Answer

14. 6

Solution:

a. $\dfrac{x}{5}$ or $x \div 5$ The quotient of x and 5

b. $p - \sqrt{q}$ The difference of p and the square root of q

c. $n - 7$ Seven less than n

d. $7 - n$ Seven less n

e. $|w| + 8$ Eight more than the
       absolute value of w

f. $18 - x$ x subtracted from 18

> **Avoiding Mistakes**
>
> Recall that "a less than b" is translated as $b - a$. Therefore, the statement "seven less than n" must be translated as $n - 7$, not $7 - n$.

Skill Practice Translate each English phrase to an algebraic expression.

15. The product of 6 and y
16. The difference of the square root of t and 7
17. Twelve less than x
18. Twelve less x
19. One more than two times x
20. Five subtracted from the absolute value of w

Example 7   **Writing English Phrases as Algebraic Expressions**

Translate each English phrase into an algebraic expression. Then evaluate the expression for $a = 6$, $b = 4$, and $c = 20$.

a. The product of a and the square root of b

b. Twice the sum of b and c

c. The difference of twice a and b

Solution:

a. The product of a and the square root of b
   $a\sqrt{b}$

   $= (\ \ )\sqrt{(\ \ )}$ Use parentheses to substitute a number for a variable.
   $= (6)\sqrt{(4)}$ Substitute $a = 6$ and $b = 4$.
   $= 6 \cdot 2$ Simplify the radical first.
   $= 12$ Multiply.

b. Twice the sum of b and c

   $2(b + c)$ To compute "twice the sum of b and c," it is necessary to take the sum first and then multiply by 2. To ensure the proper order, the sum of b and c must be enclosed in parentheses. The proper translation is $2(b + c)$.

   $= 2((\ \ ) + (\ \ ))$ Use parentheses to substitute a number for a variable.
   $= 2((4) + (20))$ Substitute $b = 4$ and $c = 20$.
   $= 2(24)$ Simplify within the parentheses first.
   $= 48$ Multiply.

Answers
15. $6y$ **16.** $\sqrt{t} - 7$
17. $x - 12$ **18.** $12 - x$
19. $2x + 1$ **20.** $|w| - 5$

c. The difference of twice a and b

$2a - b$

$= 2(\ \ ) - (\ \ )$ Use parentheses to substitute a number for a variable.

$= 2(6) - (4)$ Substitute $a = 6$ and $b = 4$.

$= 12 - 4$ Multiply first.

$= 8$ Subtract.

Skill Practice Translate each English phrase to an algebraic expression. Then evaluate the expression for $x = 3$, $y = 9$, $z = 10$.

21. The quotient of the square root of y and x

22. One-half the sum of x and y

23. The difference of z and twice x

Answers

21. $\dfrac{\sqrt{y}}{x}$; 1   **22.** $\dfrac{1}{2}(x + y)$; 6

23. $z - 2x$; 4

Calculator Connections

Topic: Evaluating Exponential Expressions on a Calculator

On a calculator, we enter exponents greater than the second power by using the key labeled $\boxed{y^x}$ or $\boxed{\wedge}$. For example, evaluate 2^4 and 10^6:

Scientific Calculator:

Enter: 2 $\boxed{y^x}$ 4 $\boxed{=}$ **Result:** | 16 |

Enter: 10 $\boxed{y^x}$ 6 $\boxed{=}$ **Result:** | 1000000 |

Graphing Calculator:

```
2^4
             16
10^6
        1000000
```

Topic: Applying the Order of Operations on a Calculator

Most calculators also have the capability to enter several operations at once. However, it is important to note that fraction bars and radicals require user-defined parentheses to ensure that the proper order of operations is followed. For example, evaluate the following expressions on a calculator:

a. $130 - 2(5 - 1)^3$ **b.** $\dfrac{18 - 2}{11 - 9}$ **c.** $\sqrt{25 - 9}$

Scientific Calculator:

Enter: 130 $\boxed{-}$ 2 $\boxed{\times}$ $\boxed{(}$ 5 $\boxed{-}$ 1 $\boxed{)}$ $\boxed{y^x}$ 3 $\boxed{=}$ **Result:** | 2 |

Enter: $\boxed{(}$ 18 $\boxed{-}$ 2 $\boxed{)}$ $\boxed{\div}$ $\boxed{(}$ 11 $\boxed{-}$ 9 $\boxed{)}$ $\boxed{=}$ **Result:** | 8 |

Enter: $\boxed{(}$ 25 $\boxed{-}$ 9 $\boxed{)}$ $\boxed{\sqrt{\ }}$ **Result:** | 4 |

Graphing Calculator:

```
130-2*(5-1)^3
                 2
(18-2)/(11-9)
                 8
√(25-9)
                 4
```

Calculator Exercises

Simplify each expression without the use of a calculator. Then enter the expression into the calculator to verify your answer.

1. $\dfrac{4+6}{8-3}$

2. $110 - 5(2+1) - 4$

3. $100 - 2(5-3)^3$

4. $3 + (4-1)^2$

5. $(12-6+1)^2$

6. $3 \cdot 8 - \sqrt{32 + 2^2}$

7. $\sqrt{18-2}$

8. $(4 \cdot 3 - 3 \cdot 3)^3$

9. $\dfrac{20 - 3^2}{26 - 2^2}$

Section 1.3   Practice Exercises

Study Skills Exercise

Sometimes you may run into a problem with homework or you find that you are having trouble keeping up with the pace of the class. A tutor can be a good resource.

a. Does your college offer tutoring?   **b.** Is it free?   **c.** Where would you go to sign up for a tutor?

Vocabulary and Key Concepts

1. a. Fill in the blanks with the words *sum, difference, product,* or *quotient.*

The _____ of 10 and 2 is 5. The _____ of 10 and 2 is 20.

The _____ of 10 and 2 is 12. The _____ of 10 and 2 is 8.

b. In the expression b^n, the value b is called the _____ and n is called the _____ or _____.

c. The expression _____ is read as "8-squared."

d. The expression _____ is read as "p to the 4th power."

e. The symbol $\sqrt{}$ is called a _____ sign and is used to find the principal _____ root of a nonnegative real number.

f. The set of rules that tell us the order in which to perform operations to simplify an algebraic expression is called the _____ .

Review Exercises

2. Which of the following are rational numbers? $-4, \ 5.\overline{6}, \ \sqrt{29}, \ 0, \ \pi, \ 4.02, \ \dfrac{7}{9}$

3. Evaluate. $|-56|$

4. Evaluate. $-|-14|$

5. Find the opposite of 19.

6. Find the opposite of -34.2.

Section 1.3   Exponents, Square Roots, and the Order of Operations   **43**

Concept 1: Exponential Expressions

For Exercises 7–12, write each product using exponents.

7. $\dfrac{1}{6} \cdot \dfrac{1}{6} \cdot \dfrac{1}{6} \cdot \dfrac{1}{6}$

8. $10 \cdot 10 \cdot 10 \cdot 10 \cdot 10 \cdot 10$

9. $a \cdot a \cdot a \cdot b \cdot b$

10. $7 \cdot x \cdot x \cdot y \cdot y$

11. $5c \cdot 5c \cdot 5c \cdot 5c \cdot 5c$

12. $3 \cdot w \cdot z \cdot z \cdot z \cdot z$

13. **a.** For the expression $5x^3$, what is the base for the exponent 3?

 b. Does 5 have an exponent? If so, what is it?

14. **a.** For the expression $2y^4$, what is the base for the exponent 4?

 b. Does 2 have an exponent? If so, what is it?

For Exercises 15–22, write each expression in expanded form using the definition of an exponent.

15. x^3

16. y^4

17. $(2b)^3$

18. $(8c)^2$

19. $10y^5$

20. $x^2 y^3$

21. $2wz^2$

22. $3a^3 b$

For Exercises 23–30, simplify each expression. **(See Example 1.)**

23. 6^2

24. 5^3

25. $\left(\dfrac{1}{7}\right)^2$

26. $\left(\dfrac{1}{2}\right)^5$

27. $(0.2)^3$

28. $(0.8)^2$

29. 2^6

30. 13^2

Concept 2: Square Roots

For Exercises 31–42, simplify the square roots. **(See Example 2.)**

31. $\sqrt{81}$

32. $\sqrt{64}$

33. $\sqrt{4}$

34. $\sqrt{9}$

35. $\sqrt{144}$

36. $\sqrt{49}$

37. $\sqrt{16}$

38. $\sqrt{36}$

39. $\sqrt{\dfrac{1}{9}}$

40. $\sqrt{\dfrac{1}{64}}$

41. $\sqrt{\dfrac{25}{81}}$

42. $\sqrt{\dfrac{49}{100}}$

Concept 3: Order of Operations

For Exercises 43–74, use the order of operations to simplify each expression. **(See Examples 3–5.)**

43. $8 + 2 \cdot 6$

44. $7 + 3 \cdot 4$

45. $(8 + 2) \cdot 6$

46. $(7 + 3) \cdot 4$

47. $4 + 2 \div 2 \cdot 3 + 1$

48. $5 + 12 \div 2 \cdot 6 - 1$

49. $81 - 4 \cdot 3 + 3^2$

50. $100 - 25 \cdot 2 - 5^2$

51. $\dfrac{1}{4} \cdot \dfrac{2}{3} - \dfrac{1}{6}$

52. $\dfrac{3}{4} \cdot \dfrac{2}{3} + \dfrac{2}{3}$

53. $\left(\dfrac{11}{6} - \dfrac{3}{8}\right) \cdot \dfrac{4}{5}$

54. $\left(\dfrac{9}{8} - \dfrac{1}{3}\right) \cdot \dfrac{3}{4}$

55. $3[5 + 2(8 - 3)]$

56. $2[4 + 3(6 - 4)]$

57. $10 + |-6|$

58. $18 + |-3|$

59. $21 - |8 - 2|$

60. $12 - |6 - 1|$

61. $2^2 + \sqrt{9} \cdot 5$

62. $3^2 + \sqrt{16} \cdot 2$

63. $3 \cdot 5^2$

64. $10 \cdot 2^3$

65. $\sqrt{9 + 16} - 2$

66. $\sqrt{36 + 13} - 5$

44   **Chapter 1**   The Set of Real Numbers

67. $[4^2 \cdot (6-4) \div 8] + [7 \cdot (8-3)]$

68. $(18 \div \sqrt{4}) \cdot \{[(9^2 - 1) \div 2] - 15\}$

69. $48 - 13 \cdot 3 + [(50 - 7 \cdot 5) + 2]$

70. $80 \div 16 \cdot 2 + (6^2 - |-2|)$

71. $\dfrac{7 + 3(8-2)}{(7+3)(8-2)}$

72. $\dfrac{16 - 8 \div 4}{4 + 8 \div 4 - 2}$

73. $\dfrac{15 - 5(3 \cdot 2 - 4)}{10 - 2(4 \cdot 5 - 16)}$

74. $\dfrac{5(7-3) + 8(6-4)}{4[7 + 3(2 \cdot 9 - 8)]}$

75. A person's debt-to-income ratio is the sum of all monthly installment payments (credit cards, loans, etc.) divided by monthly take-home pay. This number is often considered when one is applying for a loan. Each month, Monica makes credit card payments of $52 and $20, a student loan payment of $65, and a payment for furniture of $43. Her monthly take-home pay is $1500.

   a. Determine Monica's debt-to-income ratio.

   b. To obtain a car loan, Monica's debt-to-income ratio must be less than 0.20. Does she meet this criteria?

76. Each month, Jared makes credit card payments of $115, $63, and $95. He also makes a student loan payment of $77 and another loan payment of $100. His monthly take-home pay is $2000.

   a. Use the definition given in Exercise 75 to determine Jared's debt-to-income ratio.

   b. To obtain a loan for a new home theater system his debt-to-income ratio must be less than 0.15. Does he meet this criteria?

77. The area of a rectangle is given by $A = lw$, where l is the length of the rectangle and w is the width. Find the area for the rectangle shown.

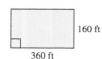
160 ft
360 ft

78. The perimeter of a rectangle is given by $P = 2l + 2w$. Find the perimeter for the rectangle shown.

79. The area of a trapezoid is given by $A = \frac{1}{2}(b_1 + b_2)h$, where b_1 and b_2 are the lengths of the two parallel sides and h is the height. A window is in the shape of a trapezoid. Find the area of the trapezoid with dimensions shown in the figure.

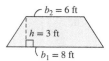
$b_2 = 6$ ft
$h = 3$ ft
$b_1 = 8$ ft

80. The volume of a rectangular solid is given by $V = lwh$, where l is the length of the box, w is the width, and h is the height. Find the volume of the box shown in the figure.

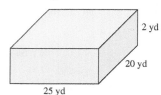
2 yd
20 yd
25 yd

Concept 4: Translations

For Exercises 81–92, write each English phrase as an algebraic expression. **(See Example 6.)**

81. The product of 3 and x

82. The sum of b and 6

83. The quotient of x and 7

84. Four divided by k

85. The difference of 2 and a

86. Three subtracted from t

87. x more than twice y

88. Nine decreased by the product of 3 and p

89. Four times the sum of x and 12

90. Twice the difference of x and 3

91. Q less than 3

92. Fourteen less than t

For Exercises 93–100, write the English phrase as an algebraic expression. Then evaluate each expression for $x = 4$, $y = 2$, and $z = 10$. **(See Example 7.)**

93. Two times y cubed

94. Three times z squared

95. The absolute value of the difference of z and 8

96. The absolute value of the difference of x and 3

97. The product of 5 and the square root of x

98. The square root of the difference of z and 1

99. The value x subtracted from the product of y and z

100. The difference of z and the product of x and y

Expanding Your Skills

For Exercises 101–104, use the order of operations to simplify each expression.

101. $\dfrac{\sqrt{\frac{1}{9}} + \frac{2}{3}}{\sqrt{\frac{4}{25}} + \frac{3}{5}}$

102. $\dfrac{5 - \sqrt{9}}{\sqrt{\frac{4}{9}} + \frac{1}{3}}$

103. $\dfrac{|-2|}{|-10| - |2|}$

104. $\dfrac{|-4|^2}{2^2 + \sqrt{144}}$

105. Some students use the following common memorization device (mnemonic) to help them remember the order of operations: the acronym PEMDAS or **P**lease **E**xcuse **M**y **D**ear **A**unt **S**ally to remember **P**arentheses, **E**xponents, **M**ultiplication, **D**ivision, **A**ddition, and **S**ubtraction. The problem with this mnemonic is that it suggests that multiplication is done before division and similarly, it suggests that addition is performed before subtraction. Explain why following this acronym may give incorrect answers for the expressions:

    a. $36 \div 4 \cdot 3$

    b. $36 - 4 + 3$

106. If you use the acronym **P**lease **E**xcuse **M**y **D**ear **A**unt **S**ally to remember the order of operations, what must you keep in mind about the last four operations?

107. Explain why the acronym **P**lease **E**xcuse **D**r. **M**ichael **S**mith's **A**unt could also be used as a memory device for the order of operations.

Addition of Real Numbers

1. Addition of Real Numbers and the Number Line

Adding real numbers can be visualized on the number line. To do so, locate the first addend on the number line. Then to add a positive number, move to the right on the number line. To add a negative number, move to the left on the number line. The following example may help to illustrate the process.

On a winter day in Detroit, suppose the temperature starts out at 5 degrees Fahrenheit (5°F) at noon, and then drops 12° two hours later when a cold front passes through. The resulting temperature can be represented by the expression $5° + (-12°)$. On the number line, start at 5 and count 12 units to the left (Figure 1-7). The resulting temperature at 2:00 P.M. is $-7°F$.

Concepts

1. Addition of Real Numbers and the Number Line
2. Addition of Real Numbers
3. Translations
4. Applications Involving Addition of Real Numbers

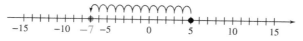

Figure 1-7

46   **Chapter 1**   The Set of Real Numbers

| Example 1 | **Using the Number Line to Add Real Numbers** |

Use the number line to add the numbers.

a. $-5 + 2$ **b.** $-1 + (-4)$ **c.** $7 + (-4)$

Solution:

a. $-5 + 2 = -3$

Start at -5, and count
2 units to the right.

> **TIP:** Note that we move to the left on the number line when we add a negative number. We move to the right when we add a positive number.

b. $-1 + (-4) = -5$

Start at -1, and count
4 units to the left.

c. $7 + (-4) = 3$

Start at 7, and count
4 units to the left.

Skill Practice   Use the number line to add the numbers.

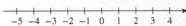

1. $-2 + 4$ **2.** $-2 + (-3)$ **3.** $5 + (-6)$

2. Addition of Real Numbers

When adding large numbers or numbers that involve fractions or decimals, counting units on the number line can be cumbersome. Study the following example to determine a pattern for adding two numbers with the *same* sign.

$1 + 4 = 5$

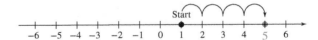

$-1 + (-4) = -5$

> **Adding Numbers with the *Same* Sign**
>
> To add two numbers with the *same* sign, add their absolute values and apply the common sign.

| Example 2 | **Adding Real Numbers with the Same Sign** |

Add.

a. $-12 + (-14)$ **b.** $-8.8 + (-3.7)$ **c.** $-\dfrac{4}{3} + \left(-\dfrac{6}{7}\right)$

Answers

1. 2   **2.** -5 **3.** -1

Solution:

a. $-12 + (-14)$

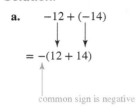

First find the absolute value of the addends. $|-12| = 12$ and $|-14| = 14$.

$= -(12 + 14)$

common sign is negative

Add their absolute values and apply the common sign (in this case, the common sign is negative).

$= -26$

The sum is -26.

b. $-8.8 + (-3.7)$

First find the absolute value of the addends. $|-8.8| = 8.8$ and $|-3.7| = 3.7$.

$= -(8.8 + 3.7)$

common sign is negative

Add their absolute values and apply the common sign (in this case, the common sign is negative).

$= -12.5$

The sum is -12.5.

c. $-\dfrac{4}{3} + \left(-\dfrac{6}{7}\right)$

The least common denominator (LCD) is 21.

$= -\dfrac{4 \cdot 7}{3 \cdot 7} + \left(-\dfrac{6 \cdot 3}{7 \cdot 3}\right)$

Write each fraction with the LCD.

$= -\dfrac{28}{21} + \left(-\dfrac{18}{21}\right)$

Find the absolute value of the addends.

$\left|-\dfrac{28}{21}\right| = \dfrac{28}{21}$ and $\left|-\dfrac{18}{21}\right| = \dfrac{18}{21}$.

$= -\left(\dfrac{28}{21} + \dfrac{18}{21}\right)$

common sign is negative

Add their absolute values and apply the common sign (in this case, the common sign is negative).

$= -\dfrac{46}{21}$

The sum is $-\dfrac{46}{21}$.

Skill Practice Add.

4. $-5 + (-25)$ **5.** $-14.8 + (-9.7)$ **6.** $-\dfrac{1}{2} + \left(-\dfrac{5}{8}\right)$

Study the following example to determine a pattern for adding two numbers with *different* signs.

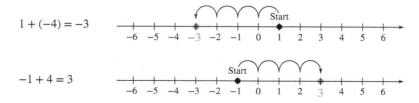

$1 + (-4) = -3$

$-1 + 4 = 3$

Answers
4. -30 **5.** -24.5 **6.** $-\dfrac{9}{8}$

48   Chapter 1   The Set of Real Numbers

Adding Numbers with *Different* Signs

To add two numbers with *different* signs, subtract the smaller absolute value from the larger absolute value. Then apply the sign of the number having the larger absolute value.

Example 3   **Adding Real Numbers with Different Signs**

Add.

   a. $12 + (-17)$ **b.** $-8 + 8$

Solution:

  a. $12 + (-17)$ First find the absolute value of the addends.
                       $|12| = 12$ and $|-17| = 17$.

                       The absolute value of -17 is greater than the absolute value of 12. Therefore, the sum is negative.

     $= -(17 - 12)$ Next, subtract the smaller absolute value from the larger absolute value.

     Apply the sign of the number with the larger absolute value.

     $= -5$

  b. $-8 + 8$ First find the absolute value of the addends.
                     $|-8| = 8$ and $|8| = 8$.

     $= 8 - 8$ The absolute values are equal. Therefore, their difference is 0. The number zero is neither positive
     $= 0$ nor negative.

Skill Practice   Add.

  7. $-15 + 16$ **8.** $6 + (-6)$

Example 4   **Adding Real Numbers with Different Signs**

Add.

   a. $-10.6 + 20.4$ **b.** $\dfrac{2}{15} + \left(-\dfrac{4}{5}\right)$

Solution:

  a. $-10.6 + 20.4$ First find the absolute value of the addends.
                       $|-10.6| = 10.6$ and $|20.4| = 20.4$.

                       The absolute value of 20.4 is greater than the absolute value of -10.6. Therefore, the sum is positive.

     $= +(20.4 - 10.6)$ Next, subtract the smaller absolute value from the larger absolute value.

     Apply the sign of the number with the larger absolute value.

     $= 9.8$

Answers

7. 1   **8.** 0

b. $\dfrac{2}{15} + \left(-\dfrac{4}{5}\right)$ The least common denominator is 15.

$= \dfrac{2}{15} + \left(-\dfrac{4 \cdot 3}{5 \cdot 3}\right)$ Write each fraction with the LCD.

$= \dfrac{2}{15} + \left(-\dfrac{12}{15}\right)$ Find the absolute value of the addends.

$\left|\dfrac{2}{15}\right| = \dfrac{2}{15}$ and $\left|-\dfrac{12}{15}\right| = \dfrac{12}{15}$.

The absolute value of $-\dfrac{12}{15}$ is greater than the absolute value of $\dfrac{2}{15}$. Therefore, the sum is negative.

$= -\left(\dfrac{12}{15} - \dfrac{2}{15}\right)$ Next, subtract the smaller absolute value from the larger absolute value.

Apply the sign of the number with the larger absolute value.

$= -\dfrac{10}{15}$ Subtract.

$= -\dfrac{2}{3}$ Simplify to lowest terms.

Skill Practice Add.

9. $27.3 + (-18.1)$ **10.** $-\dfrac{9}{10} + \dfrac{2}{5}$

3. Translations

Example 5   **Translating Expressions Involving the Addition of Real Numbers**

Write each English phrase as an algebraic expression. Then simplify the result.

a. The sum of $-12, -8, 9,$ and -1 **b.** Negative three-tenths added to $-\dfrac{7}{8}$

c. The sum of -12 and its opposite

Solution:

a. The sum of $-12, -8, 9,$ and -1

$\underbrace{-12 + (-8)} + 9 + (-1)$

$= \underbrace{-20 + 9} + (-1)$

$= \underbrace{-11 + (-1)}$ Apply the order of operations by adding from left to right.

$= -12$

b. Negative three-tenths added to $-\dfrac{7}{8}$

$-\dfrac{7}{8} + \left(-\dfrac{3}{10}\right)$

$= -\dfrac{35}{40} + \left(-\dfrac{12}{40}\right)$ The common denominator is 40.

$= -\dfrac{47}{40}$ The numbers have the same signs. Add their absolute values and keep the common sign. $-\left(\dfrac{35}{40} + \dfrac{12}{40}\right)$

Answers

9. 9.2   **10.** $-\dfrac{1}{2}$

50   **Chapter 1**   The Set of Real Numbers

> **TIP:** The sum of any number and its opposite is 0.

c. The sum of -12 and its opposite

$-12 + (12)$

$= 0$ Add.

Skill Practice Write as an algebraic expression, and simplify the result.

11. The sum of -10, 4, and -6

12. Negative 2 added to $-\frac{1}{2}$

13. -60 added to its opposite

4. Applications Involving Addition of Real Numbers

> **Example 6**   **Adding Real Numbers in Applications**

a. It is common for newborn infants to fluctuate in weight. Elise and Benjamin's baby lost 7 oz the first week after birth and gained 10 oz the second week. Write a mathematical expression to describe this situation and then simplify the result.

b. A student has $120 in her checking account. After depositing her paycheck of $215, she writes a check for $255 to cover her portion of the rent and another check for $294 to cover her car payment. Write a mathematical expression to describe this situation and then simplify the result.

© Ryan McVay/Getty Images RF

Solution:

a. $-7 + 10$ A loss of 7 oz can be interpreted as -7 oz.

     $= 3$ The infant had a net gain of 3 oz.

b. $\underbrace{120 + 215} + (-255) + (-294)$ Writing a check is equivalent to adding a negative amount to the bank account.

    $= \underbrace{335 + (-255)} + (-294)$ Use the order of operations. Add from left to right.

    $= \quad 80 + (-294)$

    $= \quad\quad -214$ The student has overdrawn her account by $214.

Skill Practice

14. A stock was priced at $32.00 per share at the beginning of the month. After the first week, the price went up $2.15 per share. At the end of the second week it went down $3.28 per share. Write a mathematical expression to describe the price of the stock and find the price of the stock at the end of the 2-week period.

Answers

11. $-10 + 4 + (-6)$; -12

12. $-\frac{1}{2} + (-2)$; $-\frac{5}{2}$

13. $60 + (-60)$; 0

14. $32.00 + 2.15 + (-3.28)$;
     $30.87 per share

Section 1.4   Practice Exercises

Study Skills Exercise

It is very important to attend class every day. Math is cumulative in nature, and you must master the material learned in the previous class to understand today's lesson. Because this is so important, many instructors have an attendance policy that may affect your final grade. Write down the attendance policy for your class.

Vocabulary and Key Concepts

1. a. If a and b are both negative, then $a + b$ will be (choose one: positive or negative).

   b. If a and b have different signs, and if $|b| > |a|$, then the sum will have the same sign as (choose one: a or b).

Review Exercises

Plot the points in set A on a number line. Then for Exercises 2–7 place the appropriate inequality ($<$, $>$) between the numbers.

$$A = \left\{ -2, \frac{3}{4}, -\frac{5}{2}, 3, \frac{9}{2}, 1.6, 0 \right\}$$

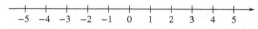

2. $-2 \;\square\; 0$

3. $\dfrac{9}{2} \;\square\; \dfrac{3}{4}$

4. $-2 \;\square\; -\dfrac{5}{2}$

5. $0 \;\square\; -\dfrac{5}{2}$

6. $\dfrac{3}{4} \;\square\; 1.6$

7. $\dfrac{3}{4} \;\square\; -\dfrac{5}{2}$

8. Evaluate the expressions.

   a. $-(-8)$ **b.** $-|-8|$

Concept 1: Addition of Real Numbers and the Number Line

For Exercises 9–16, add the numbers using the number line. **(See Example 1.)**

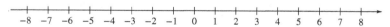

9. $-2 + (-4)$

10. $-3 + (-5)$

11. $-7 + 10$

12. $-2 + 9$

13. $6 + (-3)$

14. $8 + (-2)$

15. $2 + (-5)$

16. $7 + (-3)$

Concept 2: Addition of Real Numbers   Animation

For Exercises 17–70, add. **(See Examples 2–4.)**

17. $-19 + 2$

18. $-25 + 18$

19. $-4 + 11$

20. $-3 + 9$

21. $-16 + (-3)$

22. $-12 + (-23)$

23. $-2 + (-21)$

24. $-13 + (-1)$

52   **Chapter 1**   The Set of Real Numbers

25. $0 + (-5)$ **26.** $0 + (-4)$ **27.** $-3 + 0$ **28.** $-8 + 0$

29. $-16 + 16$ **30.** $11 + (-11)$ **31.** $41 + (-41)$ **32.** $-15 + 15$

33. $4 + (-9)$ **34.** $6 + (-9)$ **35.** $7 + (-2) + (-8)$ **36.** $2 + (-3) + (-6)$

37. $-17 + (-3) + 20$ **38.** $-9 + (-6) + 15$

39. $-3 + (-8) + (-12)$ **40.** $-8 + (-2) + (-13)$

41. $-42 + (-3) + 45 + (-6)$ **42.** $36 + (-3) + (-8) + (-25)$

43. $-5 + (-3) + (-7) + 4 + 8$ **44.** $-13 + (-1) + 5 + 2 + (-20)$

45. $23.81 + (-2.51)$ **46.** $-9.23 + 10.53$ **47.** $-\frac{2}{7} + \frac{1}{14}$ **48.** $-\frac{1}{8} + \frac{5}{16}$

49. $\frac{2}{3} + \left(-\frac{5}{6}\right)$ **50.** $\frac{1}{2} + \left(-\frac{3}{4}\right)$ **51.** $-\frac{7}{8} + \left(-\frac{1}{16}\right)$ **52.** $-\frac{1}{9} + \left(-\frac{4}{3}\right)$

53. $-\frac{1}{4} + \frac{3}{10}$ **54.** $-\frac{7}{6} + \frac{7}{8}$ **55.** $-2.1 + \left(-\frac{3}{10}\right)$ **56.** $-8.3 + \left(-\frac{9}{10}\right)$

57. $\frac{3}{4} + (-0.5)$ **58.** $-\frac{3}{2} + 0.45$ **59.** $8.23 + (-8.23)$ **60.** $-7.5 + 7.5$

61. $-\frac{7}{8} + 0$ **62.** $0 + \left(-\frac{21}{22}\right)$ **63.** $-\frac{3}{2} + \left(-\frac{1}{3}\right) + \frac{5}{6}$ **64.** $-\frac{7}{8} + \frac{7}{6} + \frac{7}{12}$

65. $-\frac{2}{3} + \left(-\frac{1}{9}\right) + 2$ **66.** $-\frac{1}{4} + \left(-\frac{3}{2}\right) + 2$ **67.** $-47.36 + 24.28$ **68.** $-0.015 + (0.0026)$

69. $-0.000617 + (-0.0015)$ **70.** $-5315.26 + (-314.89)$

71. State the rule for adding two numbers with different signs.

72. State the rule for adding two numbers with the same sign.

For Exercises 73–80, evaluate each expression for $x = -3, y = -2$, and $z = 16$.

73. $x + y + \sqrt{z}$ **74.** $2z + x + y$ **75.** $y + 3\sqrt{z}$ **76.** $-\sqrt{z} + y$

77. $|x| + |y|$ **78.** $z + x + |y|$ **79.** $-x + y$ **80.** $x + (-y) + z$

Concept 3: Translations

For Exercises 81–90, write each English phrase as an algebraic expression. Then simplify the result. **(See Example 5.)**

81. The sum of -6 and -10 **82.** The sum of -3 and 5

83. Negative three increased by 8   **84.** Twenty-one increased by 4

85. Seventeen more than -21

86. Twenty-four more than -7

87. Three times the sum of -14 and 20

88. Two times the sum of 6 and -10

89. Five more than the sum of -7 and -2

90. Negative six more than the sum of 4 and -1

Concept 4: Applications Involving Addition of Real Numbers

91. The temperature in Minneapolis, Minnesota, began at $-5°F$ (5° below zero) at 6:00 A.M. By noon, the temperature had risen 13°, and by the end of the day, the temperature had dropped 11° from its noontime high. Write an expression using addition that describes the change in temperatures during the day. Then evaluate the expression to give the temperature at the end of the day.

92. The temperature in Toronto, Ontario, Canada, began at 4°F. A cold front went through at noon, and the temperature dropped 9°. By 4:00 P.M., the temperature had risen 2° from its noontime low. Write an expression using addition that describes the changes in temperature during the day. Then evaluate the expression to give the temperature at the end of the day.

© Burke/Triolo/Brand X Pictures/Jupiterimages RF

93. For 4 months, Amara monitored her weight loss or gain. Her records showed that she lost 8 lb, gained 1 lb, gained 2 lb, and lost 5 lb. Write an expression using addition that describes Amara's total loss or gain and evaluate the expression. Interpret the result. **(See Example 6.)**

94. Alan just started an online business. His profit/loss records for the past 5 months show that he had a profit of $200, a profit of $750, a loss of $340, a loss of $290, and a profit of $900. Write an expression using addition that describes Alan's total profit or loss and evaluate the expression. Interpret the result.

95. Yoshima has $52.23 in her checking account. She writes a check for groceries for $52.95. **(See Example 6.)**

   a. Write an addition statement that expresses Yoshima's transaction.

   b. Is Yoshima's account overdrawn?

96. Mohammad has $40.02 in his checking account. He writes a check for a pair of shoes for $40.96.

   a. Write an addition statement that expresses Mohammad's transaction.

   b. Is Mohammad's account overdrawn?

97. The table gives the golf scores for a top golfer for five rounds of the LPGA Final Qualifying Tournament. Find her total score.

Score per Round	
Round 1	-5
Round 2	0
Round 3	-1
Round 4	-1
Round 5	$+1$

98. A company that has been in business for 5 years has the following profit and loss record.

   a. Write an expression using addition to describe the company's profit/loss activity.

   b. Evaluate the expression from part (a) to determine the company's net profit or loss.

Year	Profit/Loss ($)
1	$-50,000$
2	$-32,000$
3	$-5,000$
4	13,000
5	26,000

54   **Chapter 1**   The Set of Real Numbers

| **Section 1.5** | Subtraction of Real Numbers |

Concepts

1. Subtraction of Real Numbers
2. Translations
3. Applications Involving Subtraction
4. Applying the Order of Operations

1. Subtraction of Real Numbers

We have learned the rules for adding real numbers. Subtraction of real numbers is defined in terms of the addition process. For example, consider the following subtraction problem and the corresponding addition problem:

$$6 - 4 = 2 \quad \Leftrightarrow \quad 6 + (-4) = 2$$

In each case, we start at 6 on the number line and move to the left 4 units. That is, adding the opposite of 4 produces the same result as subtracting 4. This is true in general. To subtract two real numbers, add the opposite of the second number to the first number.

> **Subtracting Real Numbers**
>
> If a and b are real numbers, then $a - b = a + (-b)$.

$$\left.\begin{array}{l} 10 - 4 = 10 + (-4) = 6 \\ -10 - 4 = -10 + (-4) = -14 \end{array}\right\}$$ Subtracting 4 is the same as adding -4.

$$\left.\begin{array}{l} 10 - (-4) = 10 + (4) = 14 \\ -10 - (-4) = -10 + (4) = -6 \end{array}\right\}$$ Subtracting -4 is the same as adding 4.

| **Example 1** | **Subtracting Integers** |

Subtract the numbers.

a. $4 - (-9)$ **b.** $-6 - 9$ **c.** $-11 - (-5)$ **d.** $7 - 10$

Solution:

a. $4 - (-9)$

$= 4 + (9) = 13$

↑ Change subtraction to addition.
↑ Take the opposite of -9.

b. $-6 - 9$

$= -6 + (-9) = -15$

↑ Change subtraction to addition.
↑ Take the opposite of 9.

c. $-11 - (-5)$

$= -11 + (5) = -6$

↑ Change subtraction to addition.
↑ Take the opposite of -5.

d. $7 - 10$

$= 7 + (-10) = -3$

↑ Change subtraction to addition.
↑ Take the opposite of 10.

Skill Practice Subtract.

1. $1 - (-3)$ **2.** $-2 - 2$ **3.** $-6 - (-11)$ **4.** $8 - 15$

Answers

1. 4   **2.** -4 **3.** 5   **4.** -7

> **Example 2** **Subtracting Real Numbers**
>
> **a.** $\dfrac{3}{20} - \left(-\dfrac{4}{15}\right)$ **b.** $-2.3 - 6.04$
>
> **Solution:**
>
> **a.** $\dfrac{3}{20} - \left(-\dfrac{4}{15}\right)$ The least common denominator is 60.
>
> $\quad = \dfrac{9}{60} - \left(-\dfrac{16}{60}\right)$ Write equivalent fractions with the LCD.
>
> $\quad = \dfrac{9}{60} + \left(\dfrac{16}{60}\right)$ Rewrite subtraction in terms of addition.
>
> $\quad = \dfrac{25}{60}$ Add.
>
> $\quad = \dfrac{5}{12}$ Simplify by dividing the numerator and
>   denominator by the GCF of 5.
>
> **b.** $-2.3 - 6.04$
> $\quad -2.3 + (-6.04)$ Rewrite subtraction in terms of addition.
> $\quad -8.34$ Add.

Skill Practice Subtract.

5. $\dfrac{1}{6} - \left(-\dfrac{7}{12}\right)$ **6.** $-7.5 - 1.5$

2. Translations

> **Example 3** **Translating Expressions Involving Subtraction**
>
> Write an algebraic expression for each English phrase and then simplify
> the result.
>
> **a.** The difference of -7 and -5
>
> **b.** 12.4 subtracted from -4.7
>
> **c.** -24 decreased by the sum of -10 and 13
>
> **d.** Seven-fourths less than one-third

Solution:

a. The difference of -7 and -5
$\quad -7 - (-5)$
$\quad\quad = -7 + (5)$ Rewrite subtraction in terms of addition.
$\quad\quad = -2$ Simplify.

Answers

5. $\dfrac{3}{4}$ **6.** -9

TIP: Recall that "*b* subtracted from *a*" is translated as *a* − *b*. In Example 3(b), −4.7 is written first and then 12.4.

TIP: In Example 3(c), parentheses must be used around the sum of −10 and 13 so that −24 is decreased by the entire quantity (−10 + 13).

b. 12.4 subtracted from −4.7

$-4.7 - 12.4$

$= -4.7 + (-12.4)$ Rewrite subtraction in terms of addition.

$= -17.1$ Simplify.

c. −24 decreased by the sum of −10 and 13

$-24 - (-10 + 13)$

$= -24 - (3)$ Simplify inside parentheses.

$= -24 + (-3)$ Rewrite subtraction in terms of addition.

$= -27$ Simplify.

d. Seven-fourths less than one-third

$\dfrac{1}{3} - \dfrac{7}{4}$

$= \dfrac{1}{3} + \left(-\dfrac{7}{4}\right)$ Rewrite subtraction in terms of addition.

$= \dfrac{4}{12} + \left(-\dfrac{21}{12}\right)$ The common denominator is 12.

$= -\dfrac{17}{12}$

Skill Practice Write an algebraic expression for each phrase and then simplify.

7. 8 less than −10

8. −7.2 subtracted from −8.2

9. 10 more than the difference of −2 and 3

10. Two-fifths decreased by four-thirds

3. Applications Involving Subtraction

Example 4   **Using Subtraction of Real Numbers in an Application**

During one of his turns on *Jeopardy,* Harold selected the category "Show Tunes." He got the $200, $600, and $1000 questions correct, but he got the $400 and $800 questions incorrect. Write an expression that determines Harold's score. Then simplify the expression to find his total winnings for that category.

Solution:

$200 + 600 + 1000 - 400 - 800$

$= 200 + 600 + 1000 + (-400) + (-800)$ Add the positive numbers.

$= 1800 + (-1200)$ Add the negative numbers.

$= 600$ Harold won $600.

Skill Practice

11. During Harold's first round on *Jeopardy,* he got the $100, $200, and $400 questions correct but he got the $300 and $500 questions incorrect. Determine Harold's score for this round.

Answers

7. −10 − 8; −18

8. −8.2 − (−7.2); −1

9. (−2 − 3) + 10; 5

10. $\dfrac{2}{5} - \dfrac{4}{3}$; $-\dfrac{14}{15}$

11. −100, Harold lost $100.

| **Example 5** | **Using Subtraction of Real Numbers in an Application** |

The highest recorded temperature in North America was 134°F, recorded on July 10, 1913, in Death Valley, California. The lowest temperature of −81°F was recorded on February 3, 1947, in Snag, Yukon, Canada.

Find the difference between the highest and lowest recorded temperatures in North America.

Solution:

$134 - (-81)$

$= 134 + (81)$ Rewrite subtraction in terms of addition.

$= 215$ Add.

The difference between the highest and lowest temperatures is 215°F.

Skill Practice

12. The record high temperature for the state of Montana occurred in 1937 and was 117°F. The record low occurred in 1954 and was −70°F. Find the difference between the highest and lowest temperatures.

4. Applying the Order of Operations

| **Example 6** | **Applying the Order of Operations** |

Simplify the expressions.

a. $-6 + \{10 - [7 - (-4)]\}$ **b.** $5 - \sqrt{35 - (-14)} - 2$

Solution:

a. $-6 + \{10 - [7 - (-4)]\}$ Simplify inside the inner brackets first.

$= -6 + \{10 - [7 + (4)]\}$ Rewrite subtraction in terms of addition.

$= -6 + \{10 - (11)\}$ Simplify the expression inside brackets.

$= -6 + \{10 + (-11)\}$ Rewrite subtraction in terms of addition.

$= -6 + (-1)$ Add within the braces.

$= -7$ Add.

b. $5 - \sqrt{35 - (-14)} - 2$ Simplify inside the radical first.

$= 5 - \sqrt{35 + (14)} - 2$ Rewrite subtraction in terms of addition.

$= 5 - \sqrt{49} - 2$ Add within the radical sign.

$= 5 - 7 - 2$ Simplify the radical.

$= 5 + (-7) + (-2)$ Rewrite subtraction in terms of addition.

$= -2 + (-2)$ Add from left to right.

$= -4$

Skill Practice Simplify the expressions.

13. $-11 - \{8 - [2 - (-3)]\}$ **14.** $(12 - 5)^2 + \sqrt{4 - (-21)}$

Answers

12. 187°F   **13.** −14   **14.** 54

58 **Chapter 1** The Set of Real Numbers

Example 7 **Applying the Order of Operations**

Simplify the expressions.

a. $\left(-\dfrac{5}{8}-\dfrac{2}{3}\right)-\left(\dfrac{1}{8}+2\right)$ **b.** $-6-|7-11|+(-3+7)^2$

Solution:

a. $\left(-\dfrac{5}{8}-\dfrac{2}{3}\right)-\left(\dfrac{1}{8}+2\right)$ Simplify inside the parentheses first.

$=\left[-\dfrac{5}{8}+\left(-\dfrac{2}{3}\right)\right]-\left(\dfrac{1}{8}+2\right)$ Rewrite subtraction in terms of addition.

$=\left[-\dfrac{15}{24}+\left(-\dfrac{16}{24}\right)\right]-\left(\dfrac{1}{8}+\dfrac{16}{8}\right)$ Get a common denominator in each parentheses.

$=\left(-\dfrac{31}{24}\right)-\left(\dfrac{17}{8}\right)$ Add fractions in each parentheses.

$=\left(-\dfrac{31}{24}\right)+\left(-\dfrac{17}{8}\right)$ Rewrite subtraction in terms of addition.

$=-\dfrac{31}{24}+\left(-\dfrac{51}{24}\right)$ Get a common denominator.

$=-\dfrac{82}{24}$ Add.

$=-\dfrac{41}{12}$ Simplify to lowest terms.

b. $-6-|7-11|+(-3+7)^2$ Simplify within absolute value bars and parentheses first.

$=-6-|7+(-11)|+(-3+7)^2$ Rewrite subtraction in terms of addition.

$=-6-|-4|+(4)^2$

$=-6-(4)+16$ Simplify the absolute value and exponent.

$=-6+(-4)+16$ Rewrite subtraction in terms of addition.

$=-10+16$ Add from left to right.

$=6$

Skill Practice Simplify the expressions.

15. $\left(-1+\dfrac{1}{4}\right)-\left(\dfrac{3}{4}-\dfrac{1}{2}\right)$

16. $4-2|6+(-8)|+(4)^2$

Answers

15. -1 **16.** 16

Calculator Connections

Topic: Operations with Signed Numbers on a Calculator

Most calculators can add, subtract, multiply, and divide signed numbers. It is important to note, however, that the key used for the negative sign is different from the key used for subtraction. On a scientific calculator, the $\boxed{+/-}$ key or $\boxed{+\circ-}$ key is used to enter a negative number or to change the sign of an existing number. On a graphing calculator, the $\boxed{(-)}$ key is used. These keys should not be confused with the $\boxed{-}$ key which is used for subtraction. For example, try simplifying the following expressions.

a. $-7 + (-4) - 6$ **b.** $-3.1 - (-0.5) + 1.1$

Scientific Calculator:

Enter: 7 $\boxed{+\circ-}$ $\boxed{+}$ $\boxed{(}$ 4 $\boxed{+\circ-}$ $\boxed{)}$ $\boxed{-}$ 6 $\boxed{=}$ **Result:** $\boxed{-17}$

Enter: 3.1 $\boxed{+\circ-}$ $\boxed{-}$ $\boxed{(}$ 0.5 $\boxed{+\circ-}$ $\boxed{)}$ + 1.1 $\boxed{=}$ **Result:** $\boxed{-1.5}$

Graphing Calculator:

```
-7+( -4)-6
              -17
-3.1-( -0.5)+1.1
               -1.5
```

Calculator Exercises

Simplify the expression without the use of a calculator. Then use the calculator to verify your answer.

1. $-8 + (-5)$ **2.** $4 + (-5) + (-1)$ **3.** $627 - (-84)$ **4.** $-0.06 - 0.12$

5. $-3.2 + (-14.5)$ **6.** $-472 + (-518)$ **7.** $-12 - 9 + 4$ **8.** $209 - 108 + (-63)$

Section 1.5   Practice Exercises

Study Skills Exercise

Some instructors allow the use of calculators. What is your instructor's policy regarding calculators in class, on the homework, and on tests?

Helpful Hint: If you are not permitted to use a calculator on tests, it is a good idea to do your homework in the same way, without a calculator.

Vocabulary and Key Concepts

1. a. The expression $a - b$ is equal to $a +$ _____.

   b. If a is positive and b is negative, then the difference $a - b$ will be (choose one: positive or negative).

Review Exercises

For Exercises 2–5, write each English phrase as an algebraic expression.

2. The square root of 6

3. The square of x

4. Negative seven increased by 10

5. Two more than $-b$

60   **Chapter 1** The Set of Real Numbers

For Exercises 6–8, simplify the expression.

6. $4^2 - 6 \div 2$

7. $1 + 36 \div 9 \cdot 2$

8. $14 - |10 - 6|$

Concept 1: Subtraction of Real Numbers

For Exercises 9–14, fill in the blank to make each statement correct.

9. $5 - 3 = 5 + $ _____

10. $8 - 7 = 8 + $ _____

11. $-2 - 12 = -2 + $ _____

12. $-4 - 9 = -4 + $ _____

13. $7 - (-4) = 7 + $ _____

14. $13 - (-4) = 13 + $ _____

For Exercises 15–60, simplify. **(See Examples 1–2.)**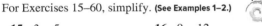

15. $3 - 5$

16. $9 - 12$

17. $3 - (-5)$

18. $9 - (-12)$

19. $-3 - 5$

20. $-9 - 12$

21. $-3 - (-5)$

22. $-9 - (-5)$

23. $23 - 17$

24. $14 - 2$

25. $23 - (-17)$

26. $14 - (-2)$

27. $-23 - 17$

28. $-14 - 2$

29. $-23 - (-23)$

30. $-14 - (-14)$

31. $-6 - 14$

32. $-9 - 12$

33. $-7 - 17$

34. $-8 - 21$

35. $13 - (-12)$

36. $20 - (-5)$

37. $-14 - (-9)$

38. $-21 - (-17)$

39. $-\dfrac{6}{5} - \dfrac{3}{10}$

40. $-\dfrac{2}{9} - \dfrac{5}{3}$

41. $\dfrac{3}{8} - \left(-\dfrac{4}{3}\right)$

42. $\dfrac{7}{10} - \left(-\dfrac{5}{6}\right)$

43. $\dfrac{1}{2} - \dfrac{1}{10}$

44. $\dfrac{2}{7} - \dfrac{3}{14}$

45. $-\dfrac{11}{12} - \left(-\dfrac{1}{4}\right)$

46. $-\dfrac{7}{8} - \left(-\dfrac{1}{6}\right)$

47. $6.8 - (-2.4)$

48. $7.2 - (-1.9)$

49. $3.1 - 8.82$

50. $1.8 - 9.59$

51. $-4 - 3 - 2 - 1$

52. $-10 - 9 - 8 - 7$

53. $6 - 8 - 2 - 10$

54. $20 - 50 - 10 - 5$

55. $10 + (-14) + 6 - 22$

56. $-3 - (-8) + (-11) - 6$

57. $-112.846 + (-13.03) - 47.312$

58. $-96.473 + (-36.02) - 16.617$

59. $0.085 - (-3.14) + 0.018$

60. $0.00061 - (-0.00057) + 0.0014$

Concept 2: Translations

For Exercises 61–70, write each English phrase as an algebraic expression. Then evaluate the expression.
(See Example 3.)

61. Six minus -7

62. Eighteen minus -1

63. Eighteen subtracted from 3

64. Twenty-one subtracted from 8

65. The difference of -5 and -11

66. The difference of -2 and -18

67. Negative thirteen subtracted from -1

68. Negative thirty-one subtracted from -19

69. Twenty less than -32

70. Seven less than -3

Concept 3: Applications Involving Subtraction

71. On the game, *Jeopardy,* Jasper selected the category "The Last." He got the first four questions correct (worth $200, $400, $600, and $800) but then missed the last question (worth $1000). Write an expression that determines Jasper's score. Then simplify the expression to find his total winnings for that category. **(See Example 4.)**

72. On Courtney's turn in *Jeopardy,* she chose the category "Birds of a Feather." She already had $1200 when she selected a Double Jeopardy question. She wagered $500 but guessed incorrectly (therefore she lost $500). On her next turn, she got the $800 question correct. Write an expression that determines Courtney's score. Then simplify the expression.

73. In Ohio, the highest temperature ever recorded was 113°F and the lowest was −39°F. Find the difference between the highest and lowest temperatures. (*Source: Information Please Almanac*) **(See Example 5.)**

74. On a recent winter day at the South Pole, the temperature was −52°F. On the same day in Springfield, Missouri, it was a pleasant summer temperature of 75°F. What was the difference in temperatures?

75. The highest mountain in the world is Mt. Everest, located in South Asia. Its height is 8848 meters (m). The lowest recorded depth in the ocean is located in the Marianas Trench in the Pacific Ocean. Its "height" relative to sea level is −11,033 m. Determine the difference in elevation, in meters, between the highest mountain in the world and the deepest ocean trench. (*Source: Information Please Almanac*)

76. The lowest point in North America is located in Death Valley, California, at an elevation of −282 ft. The highest point in North America is Denali, Alaska, at an elevation of 20,320 ft. Find the difference in elevation, in feet, between the highest and lowest points in North America. (*Source: Information Please Almanac*)

© Daniel Prudek/iStockphoto/Getty Images RF

© Comstock Images/Alamy RF

Concept 4: Applying the Order of Operations

For Exercises 77–96, perform the indicated operations. **(See Examples 6–7.)**

77. $6 + 8 - (-2) - 4 + 1$

78. $-3 - (-4) + 1 - 2 - 5$

79. $-1 - 7 + (-3) - 8 + 10$

80. $13 - 7 + 4 - 3 - (-1)$

81. $2 - (-8) + 7 + 3 - 15$

82. $8 - (-13) + 1 - 9$

83. $-6 + (-1) + (-8) + (-10)$

84. $-8 + (-3) + (-5) + (-2)$

85. $-4 - \{11 - [4 - (-9)]\}$

86. $15 - \{25 + 2[3 - (-1)]\}$

87. $-\dfrac{13}{10} + \dfrac{8}{15} - \left(-\dfrac{2}{5}\right)$

88. $\dfrac{11}{14} - \left(-\dfrac{9}{7}\right) - \dfrac{3}{2}$

62   **Chapter 1**   The Set of Real Numbers

89. $\left(\dfrac{2}{3} - \dfrac{5}{9}\right) - \left(\dfrac{4}{3} - (-2)\right)$ **90.** $\left(-\dfrac{9}{8} - \dfrac{1}{4}\right) - \left(-\dfrac{5}{6} + \dfrac{1}{8}\right)$ **91.** $\sqrt{29 + (-4)} - 7$

92. $8 - \sqrt{98 + (-3) + 5}$ **93.** $|10 + (-3)| - |-12 + (-6)|$ **94.** $|6 - 8| + |12 - 5|$

95. $\dfrac{3 - 4 + 5}{4 + (-2)}$ **96.** $\dfrac{12 - 14 + 6}{6 + (-2)}$

For Exercises 97–104, evaluate each expression for $a = -2$, $b = -6$, and $c = -1$.

97. $(a + b) - c$ **98.** $(a - b) + c$ **99.** $a - (b + c)$ **100.** $a + (b - c)$

101. $(a - b) - c$ **102.** $(a + b) + c$ **103.** $a - (b - c)$ **104.** $a + (b + c)$

Problem Recognition Exercises

Addition and Subtraction of Real Numbers

1. State the rule for adding two negative numbers.

2. State the rule for adding a negative number to a positive number.

For Exercises 3–10, perform the indicated operations.

3. a. $14 + (-8)$ **b.** $-14 + 8$ **c.** $-14 + (-8)$ **d.** $14 - (-8)$ **e.** $-14 - 8$

4. a. $-5 - (-3)$ **b.** $-5 + (-3)$ **c.** $-5 - 3$ **d.** $-5 + 3$ **e.** $5 - (-3)$

5. a. $-25 + 25$ **b.** $25 - 25$ **c.** $25 - (-25)$ **d.** $-25 - (-25)$ **e.** $-25 + (-25)$

6. a. $\dfrac{1}{2} + \left(-\dfrac{2}{3}\right)$ **b.** $-\dfrac{1}{2} + \left(\dfrac{2}{3}\right)$ **c.** $-\dfrac{1}{2} + \left(-\dfrac{2}{3}\right)$ **d.** $\dfrac{1}{2} - \left(-\dfrac{2}{3}\right)$ **e.** $-\dfrac{1}{2} - \dfrac{2}{3}$

7. a. $3.5 - 7.1$ **b.** $3.5 - (-7.1)$ **c.** $-3.5 + 7.1$ **d.** $-3.5 - (-7.1)$ **e.** $-3.5 + (-7.1)$

8. a. $6 - 1 + 4 - 5$ **b.** $6 - (1 + 4) - 5$ **c.** $6 - (1 + 4 - 5)$ **d.** $(6 - 1) - (4 - 5)$

9. a. $-100 - 90 - 80$ **b.** $-100 - (90 - 80)$ **c.** $-100 + (90 - 80)$ **d.** $-100 - (90 + 80)$

10. a. $-8 - (-10) + 20^2$ **b.** $-8 - (-10 + 20)^2$ **c.** $[-8 - (-10) + 20]^2$ **d.** $[-8 - (-10)]^2 + 20$

Multiplication and Division of Real Numbers

1. Multiplication of Real Numbers

Multiplication of real numbers can be interpreted as repeated addition. For example:

$$3(4) = 4 + 4 + 4 = 12 \qquad \text{Add 3 groups of 4.}$$
$$3(-4) = -4 + (-4) + (-4) = -12 \qquad \text{Add 3 groups of } -4.$$

Concepts

1. **Multiplication of Real Numbers**
2. **Exponential Expressions**
3. **Division of Real Numbers**
4. **Order of Operations**

These results suggest that the product of a positive number and a negative number is *negative*. Consider the following pattern of products.

$$
\begin{aligned}
4 \cdot \quad 3 &= 12 \\
4 \cdot \quad 2 &= 8 \\
4 \cdot \quad 1 &= 4 \\
4 \cdot \quad 0 &= 0 \\
4 \cdot (-1) &= -4 \\
4 \cdot (-2) &= -8 \\
4 \cdot (-3) &= -12
\end{aligned}
$$

The pattern decreases by 4 with each row.

Thus, the product of a positive number and a negative number must be *negative* for the pattern to continue.

Now suppose we have a product of two negative numbers. To determine the sign, consider the following pattern of products.

$$
\begin{aligned}
-4 \cdot \quad 3 &= -12 \\
-4 \cdot \quad 2 &= -8 \\
-4 \cdot \quad 1 &= -4 \\
-4 \cdot \quad 0 &= 0 \\
-4 \cdot (-1) &= 4 \\
-4 \cdot (-2) &= 8 \\
-4 \cdot (-3) &= 12
\end{aligned}
$$

The pattern increases by 4 with each row.

Thus, the product of two negative numbers must be *positive* for the pattern to continue.

From the first four rows, we see that the product increases by 4 for each row. For the pattern to continue, it follows that the product of two negative numbers must be *positive*.

We now summarize the rules for multiplying real numbers.

Multiplying Real Numbers

- The product of two real numbers with the *same* sign is positive.

  Examples: $(5)(6) = 30$

  $(-4)(-10) = 40$

- The product of two real numbers with *different* signs is negative.

  Examples: $(-2)(5) = -10$

  $(4)(-9) = -36$

- The product of any real number and zero is zero.

  Examples: $(8)(0) = 0$

  $(0)(-6) = 0$

| Example 1 | **Multiplying Real Numbers** |

Multiply the real numbers.

   a. $-8(-4)$ **b.** $-2.5(-1.7)$ **c.** $-7(10)$

   d. $\dfrac{1}{2}(-8)$ **e.** $0(-8.3)$ **f.** $-\dfrac{2}{7}\left(-\dfrac{7}{2}\right)$

Solution:

   a. $-8(-4) = 32$ *Same* signs. Product is positive.

   b. $-2.5(-1.7) = 4.25$ *Same* signs. Product is positive.

   c. $-7(10) = -70$ *Different* signs. Product is negative.

   d. $\dfrac{1}{2}(-8) = -4$ *Different* signs. Product is negative.

   e. $0(-8.3) = 0$ The product of any real number and zero is zero.

   f. $-\dfrac{2}{7}\left(-\dfrac{7}{2}\right) = \dfrac{14}{14}$ *Same* signs. Product is positive.

               $= 1$ Simplify.

Skill Practice Multiply.

   1. $-9(-3)$ **2.** $-1.5(-1.5)$ **3.** $-6(4)$

   4. $\dfrac{1}{3}(-15)$ **5.** $0(-4.1)$ **6.** $-\dfrac{5}{9}\left(-\dfrac{9}{5}\right)$

Observe the pattern for repeated multiplications.

$(-1)(-1)$ $\underline{(-1)(-1)}(-1)$ $\underline{(-1)(-1)}(-1)(-1)$ $\underline{(-1)(-1)}(-1)(-1)(-1)$

$= 1$ $= (1)(-1)$ $= \underline{(1)(-1)}(-1)$ $= \underline{(1)(-1)}(-1)(-1)$

            $= -1$ $= \underline{(-1)(-1)}$ $= \underline{(-1)(-1)}(-1)$

                             $= 1$ $= (1)(-1)$

                                                $= -1$

The pattern demonstrated in these examples indicates that
- The product of an even number of negative factors is positive.
- The product of an odd number of negative factors is negative.

2. Exponential Expressions

Recall that for any real number b and any positive integer, n:

$$b^n = \underbrace{b \cdot b \cdot b \cdot b \cdot \ldots \cdot b}_{n \text{ factors of } b}$$

Be particularly careful when evaluating exponential expressions involving negative numbers. An exponential expression with a negative base is written with parentheses around the base, such as $(-2)^4$.

Answers

1. 27   **2.** 2.25   **3.** −24
4. −5   **5.** 0   **6.** 1

To evaluate $(-2)^4$, the base -2 is used as a factor four times:

$$(-2)^4 = (-2)(-2)(-2)(-2) = 16$$

If parentheses are *not* used, the expression -2^4 has a different meaning:

- The expression -2^4 has a base of 2 (not -2) and can be interpreted as $-1 \cdot 2^4$.

$$-2^4 = -1(2)(2)(2)(2) = -16$$

- The expression -2^4 can also be interpreted as the opposite of 2^4.

$$-2^4 = -(2 \cdot 2 \cdot 2 \cdot 2) = -16$$

> **TIP:** The following expressions are translated as:
> $-(-3)$: opposite of negative 3
> -3^2: opposite of 3 squared
> $(-3)^2$: negative 3, squared

Example 2   **Evaluating Exponential Expressions**

Simplify.

   a. $(-5)^2$ **b.** -5^2 **c.** $(-0.4)^3$ **d.** -0.4^3 **e.** $\left(-\dfrac{1}{2}\right)^3$

Solution:

a. $(-5)^2 = (-5)(-5) = 25$ Multiply two factors of -5.

b. $-5^2 = -1(5)(5) = -25$ Multiply -1 by two factors of 5.

c. $(-0.4)^3 = (-0.4)(-0.4)(-0.4) = -0.064$ Multiply three factors of -0.4.

d. $-0.4^3 = -1(0.4)(0.4)(0.4) = -0.064$ Multiply -1 by three factors of 0.4.

e. $\left(-\dfrac{1}{2}\right)^3 = \left(-\dfrac{1}{2}\right)\left(-\dfrac{1}{2}\right)\left(-\dfrac{1}{2}\right) = -\dfrac{1}{8}$ Multiply three factors of $-\dfrac{1}{2}$.

> **Avoiding Mistakes**
> The negative sign is not part of the base unless it is in parentheses with the base. Thus, in the expression -5^2, the exponent applies only to 5 and not to the negative sign.

Skill Practice Simplify.

   7. $(-7)^2$ **8.** -7^2 **9.** $\left(-\dfrac{2}{3}\right)^3$ **10.** -0.2^3

---

3. Division of Real Numbers

Two numbers are *reciprocals* if their product is 1. For example, $-\frac{2}{7}$ and $-\frac{7}{2}$ are reciprocals because $-\frac{2}{7}\left(-\frac{7}{2}\right) = 1$. Symbolically, if a is a nonzero real number, then the reciprocal of a is $\frac{1}{a}$ because $a \cdot \frac{1}{a} = 1$. This definition also implies that a number and its reciprocal have the same sign.

> **The Reciprocal of a Real Number**
> Let a be a nonzero real number. Then, the **reciprocal** of a is $\frac{1}{a}$.

Recall that to subtract two real numbers, we add the opposite of the second number to the first number. In a similar way, division of real numbers is defined in terms of multiplication. To divide two real numbers, we multiply the first number by the reciprocal of the second number.

Answers
7. 49   **8.** -49
9. $-\dfrac{8}{27}$ **10.** -0.008

Division of Real Numbers

Let a and b be real numbers such that $b \neq 0$. Then, $a \div b = a \cdot \dfrac{1}{b}$.

Consider the quotient $10 \div 5$. The reciprocal of 5 is $\frac{1}{5}$, so we have

$$10 \div 5 = 2 \qquad \text{or equivalently,} \qquad 10 \cdot \frac{1}{5} = 2$$

Because division of real numbers can be expressed in terms of multiplication, then the sign rules that apply to multiplication also apply to division.

Dividing Real Numbers

- The quotient of two real numbers with the *same* sign is positive.

    Examples: $24 \div 4 = 6$

    $-36 \div (-9) = 4$

- The quotient of two real numbers with *different* signs is negative.

    Examples: $100 \div (-5) = -20$

    $-12 \div 4 = -3$

Example 3   **Dividing Real Numbers**

Divide the real numbers.

a. $200 \div (-10)$ b. $\dfrac{-48}{16}$ c. $\dfrac{-6.25}{-1.25}$ d. $\dfrac{-9}{-5}$

Solution:

a. $200 \div (-10) = -20$ *Different* signs. Quotient is negative.

b. $\dfrac{-48}{16} = -3$ *Different* signs. Quotient is negative.

c. $\dfrac{-6.25}{-1.25} = 5$ *Same* signs. Quotient is positive.

d. $\dfrac{-9}{-5} = \dfrac{9}{5}$ *Same* signs. Quotient is positive.

Because 5 does not divide into 9 evenly the answer can be left as a fraction.

TIP: If the numerator and denominator of a fraction are both negative, then the quotient is positive. Therefore, $\frac{-9}{-5}$ can be simplified to $\frac{9}{5}$.

Skill Practice   Divide.

11. $-14 \div 7$ 12. $\dfrac{-18}{3}$ 13. $\dfrac{-7.6}{-1.9}$ 14. $\dfrac{-7}{-3}$

Answers

11. -2 12. -6 13. 4 14. $\dfrac{7}{3}$

Example 4	**Dividing Real Numbers**

Divide the real numbers.

a. $15 \div (-25)$ **b.** $-\dfrac{3}{14} \div \dfrac{9}{7}$

Solution:

a. $15 \div (-25)$ *Different* signs. Quotient is negative.

$= \dfrac{15}{-25}$

$= -\dfrac{3}{5}$

b. $-\dfrac{3}{14} \div \dfrac{9}{7}$ *Different* signs. Quotient is negative.

$= -\dfrac{3}{14} \cdot \dfrac{7}{9}$ Multiply by the reciprocal of $\frac{9}{7}$ which is $\frac{7}{9}$.

$= -\dfrac{\overset{1}{\cancel{3}}}{14} \cdot \dfrac{\overset{1}{\cancel{7}}}{\underset{3}{\cancel{9}}}$ Divide out common factors.

$= -\dfrac{1}{6}$ Multiply the fractions.

TIP: If the numerator and denominator of a fraction have opposite signs, then the quotient will be negative. Therefore, a fraction has the same value whether the negative sign is written in the numerator, in the denominator, or in front of the fraction.

$$\frac{-3}{5} = \frac{3}{-5} = -\frac{3}{5}$$

Skill Practice Divide.

15. $12 \div (-18)$ **16.** $\dfrac{3}{4} \div \left(-\dfrac{9}{16}\right)$

Multiplication can be used to check any division problem. If $\frac{a}{b} = c$, then $bc = a$ (provided that $b \neq 0$). For example:

$$\frac{8}{-4} = -2 \;\longrightarrow\; \underline{\text{Check}}\text{: } (-4)(-2) = 8 \checkmark$$

This relationship between multiplication and division can be used to investigate division problems involving the number zero.

1. The quotient of 0 and any nonzero number is 0. For example:

$$\frac{0}{6} = 0 \qquad \text{because } 6 \cdot 0 = 0 \checkmark$$

2. The quotient of any nonzero number and 0 is undefined. For example:

$$\frac{6}{0} = ?$$

Finding the quotient $\frac{6}{0}$ is equivalent to asking, "What number times zero will equal 6?" That is, $(0)(?) = 6$. No real number satisfies this condition. Therefore, we say that division by zero is undefined.

3. The quotient of 0 and 0 cannot be determined. Evaluating an expression of the form $\frac{0}{0} = ?$ is equivalent to asking, "What number times zero will equal 0?" That is, $(0)(?) = 0$. Any real number will satisfy this requirement; however, expressions involving $\frac{0}{0}$ are usually discussed in advanced mathematics courses.

Answers

15. $-\dfrac{2}{3}$ **16.** $-\dfrac{4}{3}$

> **Division Involving Zero**
>
> Let a represent a nonzero real number. Then,
>
> **1.** $\dfrac{0}{a} = 0$ **2.** $\dfrac{a}{0}$ is undefined

4. Order of Operations

Example 5   **Applying the Order of Operations**

Simplify. $-8 + 8 \div (-2) \div (-6)$

Solution:

$-8 + 8 \div (-2) \div (-6)$

$= -8 + (-4) \div (-6)$ Perform division before addition.

$= -8 + \dfrac{4}{6}$ The quotient of -4 and -6 is positive $\frac{4}{6}$ or $\frac{2}{3}$.

$= -\dfrac{8}{1} + \dfrac{2}{3}$ Write -8 as a fraction.

$= -\dfrac{24}{3} + \dfrac{2}{3}$ Get a common denominator.

$= -\dfrac{22}{3}$ Add.

Skill Practice Simplify.

17. $-36 + 36 \div (-4) \div (-3)$

Example 6   **Applying the Order of Operations**

Simplify. $\dfrac{24 - 2[-3 + (5 - 8)]^2}{2|-12 + 3|}$

Solution:

$\dfrac{24 - 2[-3 + (5 - 8)]^2}{2|-12 + 3|}$ Simplify numerator and denominator separately.

$= \dfrac{24 - 2[-3 + (-3)]^2}{2|-9|}$ Simplify within the inner parentheses and absolute value.

$= \dfrac{24 - 2[-6]^2}{2(9)}$ Simplify within brackets, [   ]. Simplify the absolute value.

$= \dfrac{24 - 2(36)}{2(9)}$ Simplify exponents.

$= \dfrac{24 - 72}{18}$ Perform multiplication before subtraction.

$= \dfrac{-48}{18}$ or $-\dfrac{8}{3}$ Simplify to lowest terms.

Answer

17. -33

Skill Practice Simplify.

18. $\dfrac{100 - 3[-1 + (2 - 6)^2]}{|20 - 25|}$

| Example 7 | **Evaluating Algebraic Expressions** |

Given $y = -6$, evaluate the expressions.

  a. y^2 **b.** $-y^2$

Solution:

  a. y^2

    $= (\quad)^2$ When substituting a number for a variable, use parentheses.

    $= (-6)^2$ Substitute $y = -6$.

    $= 36$ Square -6, that is, $(-6)(-6) = 36$.

  b. $-y^2$

    $= -(\quad)^2$ When substituting a number for a variable, use parentheses.

    $= -(-6)^2$ Substitute $y = -6$.

    $= -(36)$ Square -6 within parentheses to get 36.

    $= -36$ Multiply by -1.

Skill Practice Given $a = -7$, evaluate the expressions.

19. a^2 **20.** $-a^2$

Answers

18. 11 **19.** 49 **20.** −49

Calculator Connections

Topic: Evaluating Exponential Expressions with Positive and Negative Bases

Be particularly careful when raising a negative number to an even power on a calculator. For example, the expressions $(-4)^2$ and -4^2 have different values. That is, $(-4)^2 = 16$ and $-4^2 = -16$. Verify these expressions on a calculator.

Scientific Calculator:

To evaluate $(-4)^2$

Enter: (4 +⊘-) x^2 **Result:** | 16 |

To evaluate -4^2 on a scientific calculator, it is important to square 4 first and then take its opposite.

Enter: 4 x^2 +⊘-   **Result:** | −16 |

Graphing Calculator:

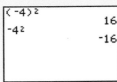

The graphing calculator allows for several methods of denoting the multiplication of two real numbers. For example, consider the product of −8 and 4.

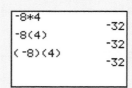

Calculator Exercises

Simplify the expression without the use of a calculator. Then use the calculator to verify your answer.

1. $-6(5)$ **2.** $\dfrac{-5.2}{2.6}$ **3.** $(-5)(-5)(-5)(-5)$ **4.** $(-5)^4$ **5.** -5^4

6. -2.4^2 **7.** $(-2.4)^2$ **8.** $(-1)(-1)(-1)$ **9.** $\dfrac{-8.4}{-2.1}$ **10.** $90 \div (-5)(2)$

Section 1.6   Practice Exercises

Study Skills Exercise

To familiarize yourself with some of the helpful features of the text, look through this section and write down a page number that contains:

a. An Avoiding Mistakes box _____

b. A Tip box _____

c. A key term (shown in bold) _____

Vocabulary and Key Concepts

1. a. If a is a nonzero real number, then the reciprocal of a is _____.

    b. If either a or b is zero then the product $ab =$ _____.

    c. If $a = 0$, and $b \neq 0$, then $\frac{a}{b} =$ _____.

    d. If $a \neq 0$ and $b = 0$, then $\frac{a}{b}$ is _____.

    e. If a and b have the same sign, then the product ab is (choose one: positive or negative).

    f. If a and b have different signs, then the quotient $\frac{a}{b}$ is (choose one: positive or negative).

    g. The product of a number and its reciprocal is _____. For example $-\frac{2}{3} \cdot (\ ) = 1$

    h. Which of the following expressions represents the product of 2 and x?

        a. $2x$ **b.** $2 \cdot x$ **c.** $2(x)$ **d.** $(2)x$ **e.** $(2)(x)$

Review Exercises

For Exercises 2–6, determine if the expression is true or false.

2. $6 + (-2) > -5 + 6$

3. $|-6| + |-14| \le |-3| + |-17|$

4. $\sqrt{36} - |-6| > 0$

5. $\sqrt{9} + |-3| \le 0$

6. $14 - |-3| \ge 12 + \sqrt{25}$

Concept 1: Multiplication of Real Numbers

For Exercises 7–14, multiply the real numbers. **(See Example 1.)**

7. $8(-7)$

8. $(-3) \cdot 4$

9. $(-11)(-13)$

10. $(-5)(-26)$

11. $(-2.2)(5.8)$

12. $(9.1)(-4.5)$

13. $\left(-\dfrac{2}{3}\right)\left(-\dfrac{9}{8}\right)$

14. $\left(-\dfrac{5}{4}\right)\left(-\dfrac{12}{25}\right)$

Concept 2: Exponential Expressions

For Exercises 15–22, simplify the exponential expressions. **(See Example 2.)**

15. $(-6)^2$

16. $(-10)^2$

17. -6^2

18. -10^2

19. $\left(-\dfrac{3}{5}\right)^3$

20. $\left(-\dfrac{5}{2}\right)^3$

21. $(-0.2)^4$

22. $(-0.1)^4$

Concept 3: Division of Real Numbers

For Exercises 23–30, divide the real numbers. **(See Examples 3–4.)**

23. $\dfrac{54}{-9}$

24. $\dfrac{-27}{3}$

25. $\dfrac{-15}{-17}$

26. $\dfrac{-21}{-16}$

27. $\dfrac{-14}{-14}$

28. $\dfrac{-21}{-21}$

29. $\dfrac{13}{-65}$

30. $\dfrac{7}{-77}$

For Exercises 31–38, show how multiplication can be used to check the division problems.

31. $\dfrac{14}{-2} = -7$

32. $\dfrac{-18}{-6} = 3$

33. $\dfrac{0}{-5} = 0$

34. $\dfrac{0}{-4} = 0$

35. $\dfrac{6}{0}$ is undefined

36. $\dfrac{-4}{0}$ is undefined

37. $-24 \div (-6) = 4$

38. $-18 \div 2 = -9$

Mixed Exercises

For Exercises 39–78, multiply or divide as indicated.

39. $2 \cdot 3$

40. $8 \cdot 6$

41. $2(-3)$

42. $8(-6)$

43. $(-24) \div 3$

44. $(-52) \div 2$

45. $(-24) \div (-3)$

46. $(-52) \div (-2)$

47. $-6 \cdot 0$

48. $-8 \cdot 0$

49. $-18 \div 0$

50. $-42 \div 0$

51. $0\left(-\dfrac{2}{5}\right)$

52. $0\left(-\dfrac{1}{8}\right)$

53. $0 \div \left(-\dfrac{1}{10}\right)$

54. $0 \div \left(\dfrac{4}{9}\right)$

72   **Chapter 1** The Set of Real Numbers

55. $\dfrac{-9}{6}$

56. $\dfrac{-15}{10}$

57. $\dfrac{-30}{-100}$

58. $\dfrac{-250}{-1000}$

59. $\dfrac{26}{-13}$

60. $\dfrac{52}{-4}$

61. $1.72(-4.6)$

62. $361.3(-14.9)$

63. $-0.02(-4.6)$

64. $-0.06(-2.15)$

65. $\dfrac{14.4}{-2.4}$

66. $\dfrac{50.4}{-6.3}$

67. $\dfrac{-5.25}{-2.5}$

68. $\dfrac{-8.5}{-27.2}$

69. $(-3)^2$

70. $(-7)^2$

71. -3^2

72. -7^2

73. $\left(-\dfrac{4}{3}\right)^3$

74. $\left(-\dfrac{1}{5}\right)^3$

75. $(-6.8) \div (-0.02)$

76. $(-12.3) \div (-0.03)$

77. $\left(-\dfrac{7}{8}\right) \div \left(-\dfrac{9}{16}\right)$

78. $\left(-\dfrac{22}{23}\right) \div \left(-\dfrac{11}{3}\right)$

Concept 4: Order of Operations

For Exercises 79–110, perform the indicated operations. **(See Examples 5–6.)**

79. $(-2)(-5)(-3)$

80. $(-6)(-1)(-10)$

81. $(-8)(-4)(-1)(-3)$

82. $(-6)(-3)(-1)(-5)$

83. $100 \div (-10) \div (-5)$

84. $150 \div (-15) \div (-2)$

85. $-12 \div (-6) \div (-2)$

86. $-36 \div (-2) \div 6$

87. $\dfrac{2}{5} \cdot \dfrac{1}{3} \cdot \left(-\dfrac{10}{11}\right)$

88. $\left(-\dfrac{9}{8}\right) \cdot \left(-\dfrac{2}{3}\right) \cdot \left(1\dfrac{5}{12}\right)$

89. $\left(1\dfrac{1}{3}\right) \div 3 \div \left(-\dfrac{7}{9}\right)$

90. $-\dfrac{7}{8} \div \left(3\dfrac{1}{4}\right) \div (-2)$

91. $12 \div (-2)(4)$

92. $(-6) \cdot 7 \div (-2)$

93. $\left(-\dfrac{12}{5}\right) \div (-6) \cdot \left(-\dfrac{1}{8}\right)$

94. $10 \cdot \dfrac{1}{3} \div \dfrac{25}{6}$

95. $8 - 2^3 \cdot 5 + 3 - (-6)$

96. $-14 \div (-7) - 8 \cdot 2 + 3^3$

97. $-(2-8)^2 \div (-6) \cdot 2$

98. $-(3-5)^2 \cdot 6 \div (-4)$

99. $\dfrac{6(-4) - 2(5-8)}{-6-3-5}$

100. $\dfrac{3(-4) - 5(9-11)}{-9-2-3}$

101. $\dfrac{-4+5}{(-2) \cdot 5 + 10}$

102. $\dfrac{-3+10}{2(-4)+8}$

103. $-4 - 3[2 - (-5+3)] - 8 \cdot 2^2$

104. $-6 - 5[-4 - (6-12)] + (-5)^2$

105. $-|-1| - |5|$

106. $-|-10| - |6|$

107. $\dfrac{|2-9| - |5-7|}{10-15}$

108. $\dfrac{|-2+6| - |3-5|}{13-11}$

109. $\dfrac{6 - 3[2 - (6-8)]^2}{-2|2-5|}$

110. $\dfrac{12 - 4[-6 - (5-8)]^2}{4|6-10|}$

For Exercises 111–116, evaluate the expression for $x = -2$, $y = -4$, and $z = 6$. **(See Example 7.)**

111. $-x^2$

112. x^2

113. $4(2x - z)$

114. $6(3x + y)$

115. $\dfrac{3x + 2y}{y}$

116. $\dfrac{2z - y}{x}$

117. Is the expression $\dfrac{10}{5x}$ equal to 10/5x? Explain.

118. Is the expression 10/(5x) equal to $\dfrac{10}{5x}$? Explain.

For Exercises 119–126, write each English phrase as an algebraic expression. Then evaluate the expression.

119. The product of -3.75 and 0.3

120. The product of -0.4 and -1.258

121. The quotient of $\frac{16}{5}$ and $\left(-\frac{8}{9}\right)$

122. The quotient of $\left(-\frac{3}{14}\right)$ and $\frac{1}{7}$

123. The number -0.4 plus the quantity 6 times -0.42

124. The number 0.5 plus the quantity -2 times 0.125

125. The number $-\frac{1}{4}$ minus the quantity 6 times $-\frac{1}{3}$

126. Negative five minus the quantity $\left(-\frac{5}{6}\right)$ times $\frac{3}{8}$

127. For 3 weeks, Jim pays $2 a week for lottery tickets. Jim has one winning ticket for $3. Write an expression that describes his net gain or loss. How much money has Jim won or lost?

128. Stephanie pays $2 a week for 6 weeks for lottery tickets. Stephanie has one winning ticket for $5. Write an expression that describes her net gain or loss. How much money has Stephanie won or lost?

© Buena Vista Images/Getty Images RF

129. Lorne sells ads for the local newspaper and has a quota for the number of ads he must sell each week. For the first two days of the week, Lorne was 5 above his daily quota. For the last three days of the week, Lorne was 3 below his daily quota. Write an expression that describes the net amount he was above or below his quota. Interpret the result.

130. Valerie trades stocks each day and analyzes her results at the end of the week. The first day of the week she had a profit of $650. The next two days she had a loss of $400 each day and the last two days she had a loss of $150 each day. Write an expression that describes Valerie's profit or loss for the week. Interpret the result.

131. A pediatrician analyzed the effect of a special baby food on five toddlers. He recorded the amount of weight lost or gained (in ounces) by each child for one month as shown in the table.

Baby	A	B	C	D	E
Gain/Loss (oz)	12	−15	4	−9	3

Write an expression to calculate the average gain or loss in weight of the children and then simplify. Interpret your answer. (*Hint*: To find the *average* (mean) of a set of values, add the values and divide by the number of values.)

132. At the end of a 2-month class, a personal trainer analyzed the effect of her new exercise routine by recording the gain or loss (in inches) in waist measurements of her clients. The results are shown in the table.

Client	A	B	C	D	E	F
Gain/Loss (in.)	−1.5	−2	1.5	2.5	−3	−0.5

Write an expression to calculate the average gain or loss in waist measurement and then simplify. Interpret your answer.

133. Evaluate the expressions in parts (a) and (b).

   a. $-4 - 3 - 2 - 1$

   b. $-4(-3)(-2)(-1)$

   c. Explain the difference between the operations in parts (a) and (b).

134. Evaluate the expressions in parts (a) and (b).

   a. $-10 - 9 - 8 - 7$

   b. $-10(-9)(-8)(-7)$

   c. Explain the difference between the operations in parts (a) and (b).

74   **Chapter 1**   The Set of Real Numbers

Problem Recognition Exercises

Adding, Subtracting, Multiplying, and Dividing Real Numbers

Perform the indicated operations.

1. a. $-8 - (-4)$ **b.** $-8(-4)$ **c.** $-8 + (-4)$ **d.** $-8 \div (-4)$

2. a. $12 + (-2)$ **b.** $12 - (-2)$ **c.** $12(-2)$ **d.** $12 \div (-2)$

3. a. $-36 + 9$ **b.** $-36(9)$ **c.** $-36 \div 9$ **d.** $-36 - 9$

4. a. $27 - (-3)$ **b.** $27 + (-3)$ **c.** $27(-3)$ **d.** $27 \div (-3)$

5. a. $-5(-10)$ **b.** $-5 + (-10)$ **c.** $-5 \div (-10)$ **d.** $-5 - (-10)$

6. a. $-20 \div 4$ **b.** $-20 - 4$ **c.** $-20 + 4$ **d.** $-20(4)$

7. a. $-4(-16)$ **b.** $-4 - (-16)$ **c.** $-4 \div (-16)$ **d.** $-4 + (-16)$

8. a. $-21 \div 3$ **b.** $-21 - 3$ **c.** $-21(3)$ **d.** $-21 + 3$

9. a. $80(-5)$ **b.** $80 - (-5)$ **c.** $80 \div (-5)$ **d.** $80 + (-5)$

10. a. $-14 - (-21)$ **b.** $-14(-21)$ **c.** $-14 \div (-21)$ **d.** $-14 + (-21)$

11. a. $|-6| + |2|$ **b.** $|-6 + 2|$ **c.** $|-6| - |-2|$ **d.** $|-6 - 2|$

12. a. $-|9| - |-7|$ **b.** $|-9| - |-7|$ **c.** $-|9 - 7|$ **d.** $|-9 - 7|$

Properties of Real Numbers and Simplifying Expressions

1. Commutative Properties of Real Numbers

When getting dressed, it makes no difference whether you put on your left shoe first and then your right shoe, or vice versa. This example illustrates a process in which the order does not affect the outcome. Such a process or operation is said to be *commutative*.

In algebra, the operations of addition and multiplication are commutative because the order in which we add or multiply two real numbers does not affect the result. For example:

$$10 + 5 = 5 + 10 \quad \text{and} \quad 10 \cdot 5 = 5 \cdot 10$$

© C. Borland/PhotoLink/
Getty Images RF

Concepts

1. Commutative Properties of Real Numbers
2. Associative Properties of Real Numbers
3. Identity and Inverse Properties of Real Numbers
4. Distributive Property of Multiplication over Addition
5. Algebraic Expressions

Commutative Properties of Real Numbers

If a and b are real numbers, then

1. $a + b = b + a$ **commutative property of addition**
2. $ab = ba$ **commutative property of multiplication**

It is important to note that although the operations of addition and multiplication are commutative, subtraction and division are *not* commutative. For example:

$$\underline{10 - 5} \neq \underline{5 - 10} \quad \text{and} \quad \underline{10 \div 5} \neq \underline{5 \div 10}$$
$$5 \quad \neq \quad -5 \qquad\qquad 2 \quad \neq \quad \frac{1}{2}$$

Example 1   **Applying the Commutative Property of Addition**

Use the commutative property of addition to rewrite each expression.

a. $-3 + (-7)$ **b.** $3x^3 + 5x^4$

Solution:

a. $-3 + (-7) = -7 + (-3)$

b. $3x^3 + 5x^4 = 5x^4 + 3x^3$

Skill Practice Use the commutative property of addition to rewrite each expression.

1. $-5 + 9$ **2.** $7y + x$

Recall that subtraction is not a commutative operation. However, if we rewrite $a - b$, as $a + (-b)$, we can apply the commutative property of addition. This is demonstrated in Example 2.

Answers

1. $9 + (-5)$ **2.** $x + 7y$

Example 2	**Applying the Commutative Property of Addition**

Rewrite the expression in terms of addition. Then apply the commutative property of addition.

a. $5a - 3b$ **b.** $z^2 - \dfrac{1}{4}$

Solution:

a. $5a - 3b$

$\quad = 5a + (-3b)$ Rewrite subtraction as addition of $-3b$.

$\quad = -3b + 5a$ Apply the commutative property of addition.

b. $z^2 - \dfrac{1}{4}$

$\quad = z^2 + \left(-\dfrac{1}{4}\right)$ Rewrite subtraction as addition of $-\frac{1}{4}$.

$\quad = -\dfrac{1}{4} + z^2$ Apply the commutative property of addition.

Skill Practice Rewrite each expression in terms of addition. Then apply the commutative property of addition.

3. $8m - 2n$ **4.** $\dfrac{1}{3}x - \dfrac{3}{4}$

Example 3	**Applying the Commutative Property of Multiplication**

Use the commutative property of multiplication to rewrite each expression.

a. $12(-6)$ **b.** $x \cdot 4$

Solution:

a. $12(-6) = -6(12)$

b. $x \cdot 4 = 4 \cdot x$ (or simply $4x$)

Skill Practice Use the commutative property of multiplication to rewrite each expression.

5. $-2(5)$ **6.** $y \cdot 6$

2. Associative Properties of Real Numbers

The associative property of real numbers states that the manner in which three or more real numbers are grouped under addition or multiplication will not affect the outcome. For example:

$$(5 + 10) + 2 = 5 + (10 + 2) \qquad \text{and} \qquad (5 \cdot 10)2 = 5(10 \cdot 2)$$
$$15 + 2 = 5 + 12 \qquad\qquad\qquad (50)2 = 5(20)$$
$$17 = 17 \qquad\qquad\qquad\qquad\quad 100 = 100$$

Answers

3. $8m + (-2n);\ -2n + 8m$

4. $\dfrac{1}{3}x + \left(-\dfrac{3}{4}\right);\ -\dfrac{3}{4} + \dfrac{1}{3}x$

5. $5(-2)$ **6.** $6y$

Associative Properties of Real Numbers

If a, b, and c represent real numbers, then

1. $(a + b) + c = a + (b + c)$ **associative property of addition**

2. $(ab)c = a(bc)$ **associative property of multiplication**

Example 4   **Applying the Associative Property**

Use the associative property of addition or multiplication to rewrite each expression. Then simplify the expression if possible.

a. $(y + 5) + 6$ **b.** $4(5z)$ **c.** $-\dfrac{3}{2}\left(-\dfrac{2}{3}w\right)$

Solution:

a. $(y + 5) + 6$

$\quad = y + (5 + 6)$ Apply the associative property of addition.

$\quad = y + 11$ Simplify.

b. $4(5z)$

$\quad = (4 \cdot 5)z$ Apply the associative property of multiplication.

$\quad = 20z$ Simplify.

c. $-\dfrac{3}{2}\left(-\dfrac{2}{3}w\right)$

$\quad = \left[-\dfrac{3}{2}\left(-\dfrac{2}{3}\right)\right]w$ Apply the associative property of multiplication.

$\quad = 1w$ Simplify.

$\quad = w$

Note: In most cases, a detailed application of the associative property will not be shown. Instead, the process will be written in one step, such as

$$(y + 5) + 6 = y + 11, \quad 4(5z) = 20z, \quad \text{and} \quad -\dfrac{3}{2}\left(-\dfrac{2}{3}w\right) = w$$

Skill Practice   Use the associative property of addition or multiplication to rewrite each expression. Simplify if possible.

7. $(x + 4) + 3$ **8.** $-2(4x)$ **9.** $\dfrac{5}{4}\left(\dfrac{4}{5}t\right)$

3. Identity and Inverse Properties of Real Numbers

The number 0 has a special role under the operation of addition. Zero added to any real number does not change the number. Therefore, the number 0 is said to be the *additive identity* (also called the *identity element of addition*). For example:

$$-4 + 0 = -4 \quad 0 + 5.7 = 5.7 \quad 0 + \dfrac{3}{4} = \dfrac{3}{4}$$

Answers

7. $x + (4 + 3); x + 7$

8. $(-2 \cdot 4)x; -8x$

9. $\left(\dfrac{5}{4} \cdot \dfrac{4}{5}\right)t; t$

The number 1 has a special role under the operation of multiplication. Any real number multiplied by 1 does not change the number. Therefore, the number 1 is said to be the *multiplicative identity* (also called the *identity element of multiplication*). For example:

$$(-8)1 = -8 \quad 1(-2.85) = -2.85 \quad 1\left(\frac{1}{5}\right) = \frac{1}{5}$$

Identity Properties of Real Numbers

If a is a real number, then

1. $a + 0 = 0 + a = a$ **identity property of addition**
2. $a \cdot 1 = 1 \cdot a = a$ **identity property of multiplication**

The sum of a number and its opposite equals 0. For example, $-12 + 12 = 0$. For any real number, a, the opposite of a (also called the *additive inverse* of a) is $-a$ and $a + (-a) = -a + a = 0$. The inverse property of addition states that the sum of any number and its additive inverse is the identity element of addition, 0. For example:

Number	Additive Inverse (Opposite)	Sum
9	-9	$9 + (-9) = 0$
-21.6	21.6	$-21.6 + 21.6 = 0$
$\dfrac{2}{7}$	$-\dfrac{2}{7}$	$\dfrac{2}{7} + \left(-\dfrac{2}{7}\right) = 0$

If b is a nonzero real number, then the reciprocal of b (also called the *multiplicative inverse* of b) is $\frac{1}{b}$. The inverse property of multiplication states that the product of b and its multiplicative inverse is the identity element of multiplication, 1. Symbolically, we have $b \cdot \frac{1}{b} = \frac{1}{b} \cdot b = 1$. For example:

Number	Multiplicative Inverse (Reciprocal)	Product
7	$\dfrac{1}{7}$	$7 \cdot \dfrac{1}{7} = 1$
3.14	$\dfrac{1}{3.14}$	$3.14\left(\dfrac{1}{3.14}\right) = 1$
$-\dfrac{3}{5}$	$-\dfrac{5}{3}$	$-\dfrac{3}{5}\left(-\dfrac{5}{3}\right) = 1$

Inverse Properties of Real Numbers

If a is a real number and b is a nonzero real number, then

1. $a + (-a) = -a + a = 0$ **inverse property of addition**
2. $b \cdot \dfrac{1}{b} = \dfrac{1}{b} \cdot b = 1$ **inverse property of multiplication**

---

4. Distributive Property of Multiplication over Addition

The operations of addition and multiplication are related by an important property called the **distributive property of multiplication over addition**. Consider the expression $6(2 + 3)$. The order of operations indicates that the sum $2 + 3$ is evaluated first, and then the result is multiplied by 6:

$$6(2 + 3)$$
$$= 6(5)$$
$$= 30$$

Notice that the same result is obtained if the factor of 6 is multiplied by each of the numbers 2 and 3, and then their products are added:

$6(2 + 3)$ The factor of 6 is *distributed* to the numbers 2 and 3.

$$= 6(2) + 6(3)$$
$$= \quad 12 + 18$$
$$= \quad\quad 30$$

The distributive property of multiplication over addition states that this is true in general.

> **Distributive Property of Multiplication over Addition**
>
> If a, b, and c are real numbers, then
>
> $$a(b + c) = ab + ac \quad \text{and} \quad (b + c)a = ab + ac$$

TIP: The mathematical definition of the distributive property is consistent with the everyday meaning of the word *distribute*. To distribute means to "spread out from one to many." In the mathematical context, the factor a is distributed to both b and c in the parentheses.

Example 5   **Applying the Distributive Property**

Apply the distributive property. $2(a + 6b + 7)$

Solution:

$2(a + 6b + 7)$

$= 2(a + 6b + 7)$

$= 2(a) + 2(6b) + 2(7)$ Apply the distributive property.

$= 2a + 12b + 14$ Simplify.

Skill Practice Apply the distributive property.

10. $7(x + 4y + z)$

Because the difference of two expressions $a - b$ can be written in terms of addition as $a + (-b)$, the distributive property can be applied when the operation of subtraction is present within the parentheses. For example:

$5(y - 7)$

$= 5[y + (-7)]$ Rewrite subtraction as addition of -7.

$= 5[y + (-7)]$ Apply the distributive property.

$= 5(y) + 5(-7)$

$= 5y + (-35)$, or $5y - 35$ Simplify.

Example 6   **Applying the Distributive Property**

Use the distributive property to rewrite each expression.

a. $-(-3a + 2b + 5c)$ **b.** $-6(2 - 4x)$

Solution:

a. $-(-3a + 2b + 5c)$

$= -1(-3a + 2b + 5c)$ The negative sign preceding the parentheses can be interpreted as taking the opposite of the quantity that follows or as $-1(-3a + 2b + 5c)$

$= -1(-3a + 2b + 5c)$

$= -1(-3a) + (-1)(2b) + (-1)(5c)$ Apply the distributive property.

$= 3a + (-2b) + (-5c)$ Simplify.

$= 3a - 2b - 5c$

b. $-6(2 - 4x)$

$= -6[2 + (-4x)]$ Change subtraction to addition of $-4x$.

$= -6[2 + (-4x)]$ Apply the distributive property. Notice that multiplying by -6 changes the signs of all terms to which it is applied.

$= -6(2) + (-6)(-4x)$

$= -12 + 24x$ Simplify.

TIP: Notice that a negative factor preceding the parentheses changes the signs of all the terms to which it is multiplied.

$-1(-3a + 2b + 5c)$

$= +3a - 2b - 5c$

Skill Practice   Use the distributive property to rewrite each expression.

11. $-(12x + 8y - 3z)$ **12.** $-6(-3a + 7b)$

Note: In most cases, the distributive property will be applied without as much detail as shown in Examples 5 and 6. Instead, the distributive property will be applied in one step.

$2(a + 6b + 7)$
1 step $= 2a + 12b + 14$

$-(3a + 2b + 5c)$
1 step $= -3a - 2b - 5c$

$-6(2 - 4x)$
1 step $= -12 + 24x$

Answers

11. $-12x - 8y + 3z$

12. $18a - 42b$

5. Algebraic Expressions

A **term** is a constant or the product or quotient of constants and variables. An algebraic expression is the sum of one or more terms. For example, the expression

$$-7x^2 + xy - 100 \quad \text{or} \quad -7x^2 + xy + (-100)$$

consists of the terms $-7x^2$, xy, and -100.

The terms $-7x^2$ and xy are **variable terms** and the term -100 is called a **constant term**. It is important to distinguish between a term and the factors within a term. For example, the quantity xy is one term, and the values x and y are factors within the term. The constant factor in a term is called the *numerical coefficient* (or simply **coefficient**) of the term. In the terms $-7x^2$, xy, and -100, the coefficients are -7, 1, and -100, respectively.

Terms are *like* **terms** if they each have the same variables, and the corresponding variables are raised to the same powers. For example:

Like Terms		**Unlike** Terms		
$-3b$ and $5b$		$-5c$ and $7d$		(different variables)
$9p^2q^3$ and p^2q^3		$4p^2q^3$ and $8p^3q^2$		(different powers)
$5w$ and $2w$		$5w$ and 2		(different variables)

Example 7   Identifying Terms, Factors, Coefficients, and *Like* Terms

a. List the terms of the expression $5x^2 - 3x + 2$.

b. Identify the coefficient of the term $6yz^3$.

c. Which of the pairs are *like* terms: $8b, 3b^2$ or $4c^2d, -6c^2d$?

Solution:

a. The terms of the expression $5x^2 - 3x + 2$ are $5x^2$, $-3x$, and 2.

b. The coefficient of $6yz^3$ is 6.

c. $4c^2d$ and $-6c^2d$ are *like* terms.

Skill Practice

13. List the terms in the expression. $4xy - 9x^2 + 15$
14. Identify the coefficients of each term in the expression. $2a - b + c - 80$
15. Which of the pairs are *like* terms? $5x^3, 5x$ or $-7x^2, 11x^2$

Two terms can be added or subtracted only if they are *like* terms. To add or subtract *like* terms, we use the distributive property as shown in Example 8.

Answers
13. $4xy$, $-9x^2$, 15
14. 2, -1, 1, -80
15. $-7x^2$ and $11x^2$ are *like* terms.

Example 8	**Using the Distributive Property to Add and Subtract *Like* Terms**

Add or subtract as indicated.

a. $7x + 2x$ **b.** $-2p + 3p - p$

Solution:

a. $7x + 2x$

$\quad = (7 + 2)x$ Apply the distributive property.

$\quad = 9x$ Simplify.

b. $-2p + 3p - p$

$\quad = -2p + 3p - 1p$ Note that $-p$ equals $-1p$.

$\quad = (-2 + 3 - 1)p$ Apply the distributive property.

$\quad = (0)p$ Simplify.

$\quad = 0$

Skill Practice Simplify by adding *like* terms.

16. $8x + 3x$ **17.** $-6a + 4a + a$

Although the distributive property is used to add and subtract *like* terms, it is tedious to write each step. Observe that adding or subtracting *like* terms is a matter of adding or subtracting the coefficients and leaving the variable factors unchanged. This can be shown in one step, a shortcut that we will use throughout the text. For example:

$$7x + 2x = 9x \qquad -2p + 3p - 1p = 0p = 0 \qquad -3a - 6a = -9a$$

Example 9	**Combining *Like* Terms**

Simplify by combining *like* terms.

a. $3yz + 5 - 2yz + 9$ **b.** $1.2w^3 + 5.7w^3$

Solution:

a. $3yz + 5 - 2yz + 9$

$\quad = 3yz - 2yz + 5 + 9$ Arrange *like* terms together. Notice that constants such as 5 and 9 are *like* terms.

$\quad = 1yz + 14$ Combine *like* terms.

$\quad = yz + 14$

b. $1.2w^3 + 5.7w^3$

$\quad = 6.9w^3$ Combine *like* terms.

Skill Practice Simplify by combining *like* terms.

18. $4pq - 7 + 5pq - 8$ **19.** $8.3x^2 + 5.1x^2$

Answers

16. $11x$ **17.** $-a$

18. $9pq - 15$ **19.** $13.4x^2$

When we apply the distributive property, the parentheses are removed. Sometimes this is referred to as *clearing parentheses*. In Examples 10 and 11, we clear parentheses and combine *like* terms.

Example 10 Clearing Parentheses and Combining *Like* Terms

Simplify by *clearing parentheses* and combining *like* terms. $5 - 2(3x + 7)$

Solution:

$5 - 2(3x + 7)$ The order of operations indicates that we must perform multiplication before subtraction.

It is important to understand that a factor of -2 (not 2) will be multiplied to all terms within the parentheses. To see why this is so, we rewrite the subtraction in terms of addition.

$= 5 + (-2)(3x + 7)$	Change subtraction to addition.
$= 5 + (-2)(3x + 7)$	A factor of -2 is to be distributed to terms in the parentheses.
$= 5 + (-2)(3x) + (-2)(7)$	Apply the distributive property.
$= 5 + (-6x) + (-14)$	Simplify.
$= 5 + (-14) + (-6x)$	Arrange *like* terms together.
$= -9 + (-6x)$	Combine *like* terms.
$= -9 - 6x$	Simplify by changing addition of the opposite to subtraction.

Skill Practice Clear the parentheses and combine *like* terms.

20. $9 - 5(2x - 7)$

Example 11 Clearing Parentheses and Combining *Like* Terms

Simplify by clearing parentheses and combining *like* terms.

a. $\dfrac{1}{4}(4k + 2) - \dfrac{1}{2}(6k + 1)$ **b.** $-(4s - 6t) - (3t + 5s) - 2s$

Solution:

a. $\dfrac{1}{4}(4k + 2) - \dfrac{1}{2}(6k + 1)$

$= \dfrac{4}{4}k + \dfrac{2}{4} - \dfrac{6}{2}k - \dfrac{1}{2}$	Apply the distributive property. Notice that a factor of $-\frac{1}{2}$ is distributed through the second parentheses and changes the signs.
$= k + \dfrac{1}{2} - 3k - \dfrac{1}{2}$	Simplify fractions.
$= k - 3k + \dfrac{1}{2} - \dfrac{1}{2}$	Arrange *like* terms together.
$= -2k + 0$	Combine *like* terms.
$= -2k$	

Answer
20. $-10x + 44$

b. $-(4s - 6t) - (3t + 5s) - 2s$

$= -1(4s - 6t) - 1(3t + 5s) - 2s$ Notice that a factor of -1 is distributed through each parentheses.

$= -4s + 6t - 3t - 5s - 2s$ Apply the distributive property.

$= -4s - 5s - 2s + 6t - 3t$ Arrange *like* terms together.

$= -11s + 3t$ Combine *like* terms.

Skill Practice Clear the parentheses and combine *like* terms.

21. $\dfrac{1}{2}(8x + 4) + \dfrac{1}{3}(3x - 9)$ **22.** $-4(x + 2y) - (2x - y) - 5x$

| **Example 12** | **Clearing Parentheses and Combining *Like* Terms** |

Simplify by clearing parentheses and combining *like* terms.

$$-7a - 4[3a - 2(a + 6)] - 4$$

Solution:

$-7a - 4[3a - 2(a + 6)] - 4$

$= -7a - 4[3a - 2a - 12] - 4$ Apply the distributive property to clear the innermost parentheses.

$= -7a - 4[a - 12] - 4$ Simplify within brackets by combining *like* terms.

$= -7a - 4a + 48 - 4$ Apply the distributive property to clear the brackets.

$= -11a + 44$ Combine *like* terms.

Avoiding Mistakes

First clear the innermost parentheses and combine *like* terms within the brackets. Then use the distributive property to clear the brackets.

Skill Practice Clear the parentheses and combine *like* terms.

23. $6 - 5[-2y - 4(2y - 5)]$

Answers

21. $5x - 1$ **22.** $-11x - 7y$
23. $50y - 94$

| **Section 1.7** | **Practice Exercises** |

Study Skills Exercise

Write down the page number(s) for the Chapter Summary for this chapter. Describe one way in which you can use the Summary found at the end of each chapter.

Vocabulary and Key Concepts

1. a. Given the expression $12y + ab - 2x + 18$, the terms $12y$, ab, and $-2x$ are variable terms, whereas 18 is a _____ term.

  b. The constant factor in a term is called the _____ of the term.

  c. Given the expression x, the value of the coefficient is _____, and the exponent is _____.

  d. Terms that have the same variables, with corresponding variables raised to the same powers, are called _____terms.

Review Exercises

For Exercises 2–14, perform the indicated operations.

2. $(-6) + 14$

3. $(-2) + 9$

4. $-13 - (-5)$

5. $-1 - (-19)$

6. $18 \div (-4)$

7. $-27 \div 5$

8. $-3 \cdot 0$

9. $0(-15)$

10. $\dfrac{1}{2} + \dfrac{3}{8}$

11. $\dfrac{25}{21} - \dfrac{6}{7}$

12. $\left(-\dfrac{3}{5}\right)\left(\dfrac{4}{27}\right)$

13. $\left(-\dfrac{11}{12}\right) \div \left(-\dfrac{5}{4}\right)$

14. $25 \cdot \left(-\dfrac{4}{5}\right)$

Concept 1: Commutative Properties of Real Numbers

For Exercises 15–22, rewrite each expression using the commutative property of addition or the commutative property of multiplication. **(See Examples 1 and 3.)**

15. $5 + (-8)$

16. $7 + (-2)$

17. $8 + x$

18. $p + 11$

19. $5(4)$

20. $10(8)$

21. $x(-12)$

22. $y(-23)$

For Exercises 23–26, rewrite each expression using addition. Then apply the commutative property of addition.
(See Example 2.)

23. $x - 3$

24. $y - 7$

25. $4p - 9$

26. $3m - 12$

Concept 2: Associative Properties of Real Numbers

For Exercises 27–38, use the associative property of addition or multiplication to rewrite each expression. Then simplify the expression if possible. **(See Example 4.)**

27. $(x + 4) + 9$

28. $-3 + (5 + z)$

29. $-5(3x)$

30. $-12(4z)$

31. $\dfrac{6}{11}\left(\dfrac{11}{6}x\right)$

32. $\dfrac{3}{5}\left(\dfrac{5}{3}x\right)$

33. $-4\left(-\dfrac{1}{4}t\right)$

34. $-5\left(-\dfrac{1}{5}w\right)$

35. $-8 + (2 + y)$

36. $[x + (-5)] + 7$

37. $-5(2x)$

38. $-10(6t)$

Concept 3: Identity and Inverse Properties of Real Numbers

39. What is another name for multiplicative inverse?

40. What is another name for additive inverse?

41. What is the additive identity?

42. What is the multiplicative identity?

Concept 4: Distributive Property of Multiplication over Addition

For Exercises 43–62, use the distributive property to clear parentheses. **(See Examples 5–6.)**

43. $6(5x + 1)$

44. $2(x + 7)$

45. $-2(a + 8)$

46. $-3(2z + 9)$

47. $3(5c - d)$

48. $4(w - 13z)$

49. $-7(y - 2)$

50. $-2(4x - 1)$

51. $-\dfrac{2}{3}(x - 6)$

52. $-\dfrac{1}{4}(2b - 8)$

53. $\dfrac{1}{3}(m - 3)$

54. $\dfrac{2}{5}(n - 5)$

55. $-(2p + 10)$

56. $-(7q + 1)$

57. $-2(-3w - 5z + 8)$

58. $-4(-7a - b - 3)$

59. $4(x + 2y - z)$

60. $-6(2a - b + c)$

61. $-(-6w + x - 3y)$

62. $-(-p - 5q - 10r)$

86   **Chapter 1**   The Set of Real Numbers

Mixed Exercises

For Exercises 63–70, use the associative property or distributive property to clear parentheses.

63. $2(3 + x)$ **64.** $5(4 + y)$ **65.** $4(6z)$ **66.** $8(2p)$

67. $-2(7x)$ **68.** $3(-11t)$ **69.** $-4(1 + x)$ **70.** $-9(2 + y)$

For Exercises 71–79, match each statement with the property that describes it.

71. $6 \cdot \dfrac{1}{6} = 1$ **a.** Commutative property of addition

72. $7(4 \cdot 9) = (7 \cdot 4)\, 9$ **b.** Inverse property of multiplication

73. $2(3 + k) = 6 + 2k$ **c.** Commutative property of multiplication

74. $3 \cdot 7 = 7 \cdot 3$ **d.** Associative property of addition

75. $5 + (-5) = 0$ **e.** Identity property of multiplication

76. $18 \cdot 1 = 18$ **f.** Associative property of multiplication

77. $(3 + 7) + 19 = 3 + (7 + 19)$ **g.** Inverse property of addition

78. $23 + 6 = 6 + 23$ **h.** Identity property of addition

79. $3 + 0 = 3$ **i.** Distributive property of multiplication over addition

Concept 5: Algebraic Expressions

For Exercises 80–83, for each expression list the terms and their coefficients. **(See Example 7.)**

80. $3xy - 6x^2 + y - 17$

Term	Coefficient

81. $2x - y + 18xy + 5$

Term	Coefficient

82. $x^4 - 10xy + 12 - y$

Term	Coefficient

83. $-x + 8y - 9x^2y - 3$

Term	Coefficient

84. Explain why $12x$ and $12x^2$ are not *like* terms.

85. Explain why $3x$ and $3xy$ are not *like* terms.

86. Explain why $7z$ and $\sqrt{13}z$ are *like* terms.

87. Explain why πx and $8x$ are *like* terms.

88. Write three different *like* terms.

89. Write three terms that are not *like*.

For Exercises 90–98, simplify by combining *like* terms. **(See Examples 8–9.)**

90. $5k - 10k$

91. $-4p - 2p$

92. $-7x^2 + 14x^2$

93. $2y^2 - 5y^2 - 3y^2$

94. $2ab + 5 + 3ab - 2$

95. $8x^3y + 3 - 7 - x^3y$

96. $\frac{1}{4}a + b - \frac{3}{4}a - 5b$

97. $\frac{2}{5} + 2t - \frac{3}{5} + t - \frac{6}{5}$

98. $2.8z - 8.1z + 6 - 15.2$

For Exercises 99–126, simplify by clearing parentheses and combining *like* terms. **(See Examples 10–12.)**

99. $-3(2x - 4) + 10$

100. $-2(4a + 3) - 14$

101. $4(w + 3) - 12$

102. $5(2r + 6) - 30$

103. $5 - 3(x - 4)$

104. $4 - 2(3x + 8)$

105. $-3(2t + 4w) + 8(2t - 4w)$

106. $-5(5y + 9z) + 3(3y + 6z)$

107. $2(q - 5u) - (2q + 8u)$

108. $6(x + 3y) - (6x - 5y)$

109. $-\frac{1}{3}(6t + 9) + 10$

110. $-\frac{3}{4}(8 + 4q) + 7$

111. $10(5.1a - 3.1) + 4$

112. $100(-3.14p - 1.05) + 212$

113. $-4m + 2(m - 3) + 2m$

114. $-3b + 4(b + 2) - 8b$

115. $\frac{1}{2}(10q - 2) + \frac{1}{3}(2 - 3q)$

116. $\frac{1}{5}(15 - 4p) - \frac{1}{10}(10p + 5)$

117. $7n - 2(n - 3) - 6 + n$

118. $8k - 4(k - 1) + 7 - k$

119. $6(x + 3) - 12 - 4(x - 3)$

120. $5(y - 4) + 3 - 6(y - 7)$

121. $0.2(6c - 1.6) + c$

122. $-1.1(5 + 8x) - 3.1$

123. $6 + 2[-8 - 3(2x + 4)] + 10x$

124. $-3 + 5[-3 - 4(y + 2)] - 8y$

125. $1 - 3[2(z + 1) - 5(z - 2)]$

126. $1 - 6[3(2t + 2) - 8(t + 2)]$

Expanding Your Skills

For Exercises 127–134, determine if the expressions are equivalent. If two expressions are not equivalent, state why.

127. $3a + b, \; b + 3a$

128. $4y + 1, \; 1 + 4y$

129. $2c + 7, \; 9c$

130. $5z + 4, \; 9z$

131. $5x - 3, \; 3 - 5x$

132. $6d - 7, \; 7 - 6d$

133. $5x - 3, \; -3 + 5x$

134. $8 - 2x, \; -2x + 8$

135. As a small child in school, the great mathematician Karl Friedrich Gauss (1777–1855) was said to have found the sum of the integers from 1 to 100 mentally:

$$1 + 2 + 3 + 4 + \cdots + 99 + 100$$

Rather than adding the numbers sequentially, he added the numbers in pairs:

$$(1 + 99) + (2 + 98) + (3 + 97) + \cdots + 100$$

a. Use this technique to add the integers from 1 to 10.

$$1 + 2 + 3 + 4 + 5 + 6 + 7 + 8 + 9 + 10$$

b. Use this technique to add the integers from 1 to 20.

88   **Chapter 1**   The Set of Real Numbers

Evaluating Formulas Using a Calculator

Materials: A calculator

Estimated Time: 20 minutes

Group Size: 2

In this chapter, we learned one of the most important concepts in mathematics—the order of operations. The proper order of operations is required whenever we evaluate any mathematical expression. The following formulas are taken from applications from science, mathematics, statistics, and business. These are just some samples of what you may encounter as you work your way through college.

For Exercises 1–8, substitute the given values into the formula. Then use a calculator and the proper order of operations to simplify the result. Round to three decimal places if necessary.

1. $F = \dfrac{9}{5}C + 32$ (biology) $C = 35$

2. $V = \dfrac{nRT}{P}$ (chemistry) $n = 1.00, R = 0.0821, T = 273.15, P = 1.0$

3. $R = k\left(\dfrac{L}{r^2}\right)$ (electronics) $k = 0.05, L = 200, r = 0.5$

4. $m = \dfrac{y_2 - y_1}{x_2 - x_1}$ (mathematics) $x_1 = -8.3, x_2 = 3.3, y_1 = 4.6, y_2 = -9.2$

5. $z = \dfrac{\bar{x} - \mu}{\frac{\sigma}{\sqrt{n}}}$ (statistics) $\bar{x} = 69, \mu = 55, \sigma = 20, n = 25$

6. $S = R\left[\dfrac{(1 + i)^n - 1}{i}\right]$ (finance) $R = 200, i = 0.08, n = 30$

7. $x = \dfrac{-b + \sqrt{b^2 - 4ac}}{2a}$ (mathematics) $a = 2, b = -7, c = -15$

8. $h = \dfrac{1}{2}gt^2 + v_0 t + h_0$ (physics) $g = -32, t = 2.4, v_0 = 192, h_0 = 288$

Chapter 1   Summary

Section 1.1   Fractions

Key Concepts	Examples

Key Concepts

Simplifying Fractions

Divide the numerator and denominator by their greatest common factor.

Multiplication of Fractions

$$\frac{a}{b} \times \frac{c}{d} = \frac{a \times c}{b \times d}$$

Division of Fractions

$$\frac{a}{b} \div \frac{c}{d} = \frac{a}{b} \times \frac{d}{c}$$

Addition and Subtraction of Fractions

$$\frac{a}{b} + \frac{c}{b} = \frac{a+c}{b} \quad \text{and} \quad \frac{a}{b} - \frac{c}{b} = \frac{a-c}{b}$$

To perform operations on mixed numbers, convert to improper fractions.

Examples

Example 1

$$\frac{60}{84} = \frac{5 \times \overset{1}{\cancel{12}}}{7 \times \underset{1}{\cancel{12}}} = \frac{5}{7}$$

Example 2

$$\frac{25}{108} \times \frac{27}{40} = \frac{\overset{5}{\cancel{25}}}{\underset{4}{\cancel{108}}} \times \frac{\overset{1}{\cancel{27}}}{\underset{8}{\cancel{40}}}$$

$$= \frac{5 \times 1}{4 \times 8} = \frac{5}{32}$$

Example 3

$$\frac{95}{49} \div \frac{65}{42} = \frac{\overset{19}{\cancel{95}}}{\underset{7}{\cancel{49}}} \times \frac{\overset{6}{\cancel{42}}}{\underset{13}{\cancel{65}}}$$

$$= \frac{19 \times 6}{7 \times 13} = \frac{114}{91}$$

Example 4

$$\frac{8}{9} + \frac{2}{15} = \frac{8 \times 5}{9 \times 5} + \frac{2 \times 3}{15 \times 3}$$

$$= \frac{40}{45} + \frac{6}{45} = \frac{46}{45}$$

The least common denominator (LCD) of 9 and 15 is 45.

Example 5

$$2\frac{5}{6} - 1\frac{1}{3} = \frac{17}{6} - \frac{4}{3}$$

The LCD is 6.

$$= \frac{17}{6} - \frac{4 \times 2}{3 \times 2} = \frac{17}{6} - \frac{8}{6}$$

$$= \frac{9}{6}$$

$$= \frac{3}{2} \text{ or } 1\frac{1}{2}$$

| **Section 1.2** | **Introduction to Algebra and the Set of Real Numbers** |

Key Concepts

A **variable** is a symbol or letter used to represent an unknown number.

A **constant** is a value that is not variable.

An algebraic **expression** is a collection of variables and constants under algebraic operations.

Natural numbers: $\{1, 2, 3, \ldots\}$

Whole numbers: $\{0, 1, 2, 3, \ldots\}$

Integers: $\{\ldots -3, -2, -1, 0, 1, 2, 3, \ldots\}$

Rational numbers: The set of numbers that can be expressed in the form $\frac{p}{q}$, where p and q are integers and q does not equal 0. In decimal form, rational numbers are terminating or repeating decimals.

Irrational numbers: A subset of the real numbers whose elements cannot be written as a ratio of two integers. In decimal form, irrational numbers are nonterminating, nonrepeating decimals.

Real numbers: The set of both the rational numbers and the irrational numbers.

Examples

Example 1

Variables: x, y, z, a, b

Constants: $2, -3, \pi$

Expressions: $2x + 5, 3a + b^2$

Example 2

$-5, 0,$ and 4 are integers.

$-\dfrac{5}{2}, -0.5,$ and $0.\overline{3}$ are rational numbers.

$\sqrt{7}, -\sqrt{2},$ and π are irrational numbers.

Example 3

All real numbers can be located on the real number line.

$a < b$ "a is less than b."

$a > b$ "a is greater than b."

$a \leq b$ "a is less than or equal to b."

$a \geq b$ "a is greater than or equal to b."

    Two numbers that are the same distance from zero but on opposite sides of zero on the number line are called **opposites**. The opposite of a is denoted $-a$.

    The **absolute value** of a real number, a, denoted $|a|$, is the distance between a and 0 on the number line.

If $a \geq 0, |a| = a$

If $a < 0, |a| = -a$

Example 4

$5 < 7$ "5 is less than 7."

$-2 > -10$ "−2 is greater than −10."

$y \leq 3.4$ "y is less than or equal to 3.4."

$x \geq \frac{1}{2}$ "x is greater than or equal to $\frac{1}{2}$."

Example 5

5 and −5 are opposites.

Example 6

$|7| = 7$

$|-7| = 7$

Section 1.3   Exponents, Square Roots, and the Order of Operations

Key Concepts

$b^n = \underbrace{b \cdot b \cdot b \cdot b \cdot \ldots b}_{n \text{ factors of } b}$ b is the **base**,
   n is the **exponent**

$\sqrt{x}$ is the positive **square root** of x.

The Order of Operations

1. Simplify expressions within parentheses and other grouping symbols first.
2. Evaluate expressions involving exponents, radicals, and absolute values.
3. Perform multiplication or division in the order that they occur from left to right.
4. Perform addition or subtraction in the order that they occur from left to right.

Examples

Example 1

$5^3 = 5 \cdot 5 \cdot 5 = 125$

Example 2

$\sqrt{49} = 7$

Example 3

$10 + 5(3-1)^2 - \sqrt{5-1}$

$= 10 + 5(2)^2 - \sqrt{4}$ Work within grouping symbols.

$= 10 + 5(4) - 2$ Simplify exponents and radicals.

$= 10 + 20 - 2$ Perform multiplication.

$= 30 - 2$ Add and subtract, left to right.

$= 28$

Section 1.4   Addition of Real Numbers

Key Concepts

Addition of Two Real Numbers

Same Signs.   Add the absolute values of the numbers and apply the common sign to the sum.

Different Signs.   Subtract the smaller absolute value from the larger absolute value. Then apply the sign of the number having the larger absolute value.

Examples

Example 1

$-3 + (-4) = -7$

$-1.3 + (-9.1) = -10.4$

Example 2

$-5 + 7 = 2$

$\frac{2}{3} + \left(-\frac{7}{3}\right) = -\frac{5}{3}$

Section 1.5	Subtraction of Real Numbers

Key Concepts

Subtraction of Two Real Numbers

Add the opposite of the second number to the first number. That is,

$$a - b = a + (-b)$$

Examples

Example 1

$$7 - (-5) = 7 + (5) = 12$$

$$-3 - 5 = -3 + (-5) = -8$$

$$-11 - (-2) = -11 + (2) = -9$$

Section 1.6	Multiplication and Division of Real Numbers

Key Concepts

Multiplication and Division of Two Real Numbers

Same Signs

Product is positive.

Quotient is positive.

Different Signs

Product is negative.

Quotient is negative.

The **reciprocal** of a nonzero number a is $\dfrac{1}{a}$.

Multiplication and Division Involving Zero

The product of any real number and 0 is 0.

The quotient of 0 and any nonzero real number is 0.

The quotient of any nonzero real number and 0 is undefined.

Examples

Example 1

$$(-5)(-2) = 10 \qquad \frac{-20}{-4} = 5$$

Example 2

$$(-3)(7) = -21 \qquad \frac{-4}{8} = -\frac{1}{2}$$

Example 3

$$-3^4 = -1(3 \cdot 3 \cdot 3 \cdot 3) = -81$$

$$(-3)^4 = (-3)(-3)(-3)(-3) = 81$$

Example 4

The reciprocal of -6 is $-\frac{1}{6}$.

Example 5

$$4 \cdot 0 = 0$$

$$0 \div 4 = 0$$

$4 \div 0$ is undefined.

Section 1.7   ## Properties of Real Numbers and Simplifying Expressions

Key Concepts

Properties of Real Numbers

Commutative Properties

$a + b = b + a$

$ab = ba$

Associative Properties

$(a + b) + c = a + (b + c)$

$(ab)c = a(bc)$

Identity Properties

$0 + a = a$

$1 \cdot a = a$

Inverse Properties

$a + (-a) = 0$

$b \cdot \dfrac{1}{b} = 1$ for $b \neq 0$

Distributive Property of Multiplication over Addition

$a(b + c) = ab + ac$

A **term** is a constant or the product or quotient of constants and variables. The **coefficient** of a term is the numerical factor of the term.

Like **terms** have the same variables, and the corresponding variables have the same powers.

Terms can be added or subtracted if they are *like* terms. Sometimes it is necessary to clear parentheses before adding or subtracting *like* terms.

Examples

Example 1

$(-5) + (-7) = (-7) + (-5)$

$3 \cdot 8 = 8 \cdot 3$

Example 2

$(2 + 3) + 10 = 2 + (3 + 10)$

$(2 \cdot 4) \cdot 5 = 2 \cdot (4 \cdot 5)$

Example 3

$0 + (-5) = -5$

$1(-8) = -8$

Example 4

$1.5 + (-1.5) = 0$

$6 \cdot \dfrac{1}{6} = 1$

Example 5

$-2(x - 3y) = (-2)x + (-2)(-3y)$

$\qquad\qquad = -2x + 6y$

Example 6

$-2x$ is a term with coefficient -2.

yz^2 is a term with coefficient 1.

$3x$ and $-5x$ are *like* terms.

$4a^2b$ and $4ab$ are not *like* terms.

Example 7

$-2w - 4(w - 2) + 3$

$= -2w - 4w + 8 + 3$ Clear parentheses.

$= -6w + 11$ Combine *like* terms.

94   **Chapter 1**   The Set of Real Numbers

Chapter 1   Review Exercises

Section 1.1

For Exercises 1–4, identify as a proper or improper fraction.

1. $\dfrac{14}{5}$ 2. $\dfrac{1}{6}$ 3. $\dfrac{3}{3}$ 4. $\dfrac{7}{1}$

5. Write 112 as a product of primes.

6. Simplify. $\dfrac{84}{70}$

For Exercises 7–12, perform the indicated operations.

7. $\dfrac{2}{9} + \dfrac{3}{4}$ 8. $\dfrac{7}{8} - \dfrac{1}{16}$ 9. $\dfrac{21}{24} \times \dfrac{16}{49}$

10. $\dfrac{68}{34} \div \dfrac{20}{12}$ 11. $5\dfrac{1}{3} \div 1\dfrac{7}{9}$ 12. $3\dfrac{4}{5} - 2\dfrac{1}{10}$

13. The surface area of the Earth is approximately 510 million km². If water covers about $\frac{7}{10}$ of the surface, how many square kilometers of the Earth is covered by water?

Section 1.2

14. Given the set $\left\{7, \frac{1}{3}, -4, 0, -\sqrt{3}, -0.\overline{2}, \pi, 1\right\}$,

   a. List the natural numbers.

   b. List the integers.

   c. List the whole numbers.

   d. List the rational numbers.

   e. List the irrational numbers.

   f. List the real numbers.

For Exercises 15–18, determine the absolute value.

15. $\left|\dfrac{1}{2}\right|$ 16. $|-6|$ 17. $|-\sqrt{7}|$ 18. $|0|$

For Exercises 19–27, identify whether the inequality is true or false.

19. $-6 > -1$ 20. $0 < -5$ 21. $-10 \le 0$

22. $5 \ne -5$ 23. $7 \ge 7$ 24. $7 \ge -7$

25. $0 \le -3$ 26. $-\dfrac{2}{3} \le -\dfrac{2}{3}$ 27. $|-3| > -|3|$

For Exercises 28–31, evaluate each expression for $x = 8, y = 4$, and $z = 1$.

28. $x - 2y$ 29. $x^2 - y$

30. $\sqrt{x + z}$ 31. $\sqrt{x + 2y}$

Section 1.3

For Exercises 32–37, write each English phrase as an algebraic expression.

32. The product of x and $\dfrac{2}{3}$

33. The quotient of 7 and y

34. The sum of 2 and $3b$

35. The difference of a and 5

36. Two more than $5k$

37. Seven less than $13z$

For Exercises 38–43, simplify the expressions.

38. 6^3 39. 15^2 40. $\sqrt{36}$

41. $\dfrac{1}{\sqrt{100}}$ 42. $\left(\dfrac{1}{4}\right)^2$ 43. $\left(\dfrac{3}{2}\right)^3$

For Exercises 44–47, perform the indicated operations.

44. $15 - 7 \cdot 2 + 12$ 45. $|-11| + |5| - (7 - 2)$

46. $4^2 - (5 - 2)^2$ 47. $22 - 3(8 \div 4)^2$

Section 1.4

For Exercises 48–60, add.

48. $-6 + 8$ 49. $14 + (-10)$

50. $21 + (-6)$ 51. $-12 + (-5)$

52. $\dfrac{2}{7} + \left(-\dfrac{1}{9}\right)$ 53. $\left(-\dfrac{8}{11}\right) + \left(\dfrac{1}{2}\right)$

54. $\left(-\dfrac{1}{10}\right) + \left(-\dfrac{5}{6}\right)$ 55. $\left(-\dfrac{5}{2}\right) + \left(-\dfrac{1}{5}\right)$

56. $-8.17 + 6.02$ 57. $2.9 + (-7.18)$

58. $13 + (-2) + (-8)$

59. $-5 + (-7) + 20$

60. $2 + 5 + (-8) + (-7) + 0 + 13 + (-1)$

61. Under what conditions will the expression $a + b$ be negative?

62. Richard's checkbook was overdrawn by $45 (that is, his balance was -45). He deposited $117 but then wrote a check for $80. Was the deposit enough to cover the check? Explain.

Section 1.5

For Exercises 63–75, subtract.

63. $13 - 25$

64. $31 - (-2)$

65. $-8 - (-7)$

66. $-2 - 15$

67. $\left(-\dfrac{7}{9}\right) - \dfrac{5}{6}$

68. $\dfrac{1}{3} - \dfrac{9}{8}$

69. $7 - 8.2$

70. $-1.05 - 3.2$

71. $-16.1 - (-5.9)$

72. $7.09 - (-5)$

73. $\dfrac{11}{2} - \left(-\dfrac{1}{6}\right) - \dfrac{7}{3}$

74. $-\dfrac{4}{5} - \dfrac{7}{10} - \left(-\dfrac{13}{20}\right)$

75. $6 - 14 - (-1) - 10 - (-21) - 5$

76. Under what conditions will the expression $a - b$ be negative?

For Exercises 77–81, write an algebraic expression and simplify.

77. -18 subtracted from -7

78. The difference of -6 and 41

79. Seven decreased by 13

80. Five subtracted from the difference of 20 and -7

81. The sum of 6 and -12, decreased by 21

82. In Nevada, the highest temperature ever recorded was $125°F$ and the lowest was $-50°F$. Find the difference between the highest and lowest temperatures. (*Source: Information Please Almanac*)

Section 1.6

For Exercises 83–100, multiply or divide as indicated.

83. $10(-17)$

84. $(-7)13$

85. $(-52) \div 26$

86. $(-48) \div (-16)$

87. $\dfrac{7}{4} \div \left(-\dfrac{21}{2}\right)$

88. $\dfrac{2}{3}\left(-\dfrac{12}{11}\right)$

89. $-\dfrac{21}{5} \cdot 0$

90. $\dfrac{3}{4} \div 0$

91. $0 \div (-14)$

92. $(-0.45)(-5)$

93. $\dfrac{-21}{14}$

94. $\dfrac{-13}{-52}$

95. $(5)(-2)(3)$

96. $(-6)(-5)(15)$

97. $\left(-\dfrac{1}{2}\right)\left(\dfrac{7}{8}\right)\left(-\dfrac{4}{7}\right)$

98. $\left(\dfrac{12}{13}\right)\left(-\dfrac{1}{6}\right)\left(\dfrac{13}{14}\right)$

99. $40 \div 4 \div (-5)$

100. $\dfrac{10}{11} \div \dfrac{7}{11} \div \dfrac{5}{9}$

For Exercises 101–106, perform the indicated operations.

101. $9 - 4[-2(4 - 8) - 5(3 - 1)]$

102. $\dfrac{8(-3) - 6}{-7 - (-2)}$

103. $\dfrac{2}{3} - \left(\dfrac{3}{8} + \dfrac{5}{6}\right) \div \dfrac{5}{3}$

104. $5.4 - (0.3)^2 \div 0.09$

105. $\dfrac{5 - [3 - (-4)^2]}{36 \div (-2)(3)}$

106. $|-8 + 5| - \sqrt{5^2 - 3^2}$

For Exercises 107–110, evaluate each expression given the values $x = 4$ and $y = -9$.

107. $3(x + 2) \div y$

108. $\sqrt{x} - y$

109. $-xy$

110. $3x + 2y$

111. In statistics the formula $x = \mu + z\sigma$ is used to find cutoff values for data that follow a bellshaped curve Find x if $\mu = 100$, $z = -1.96$, and $\sigma = 15$.

96   **Chapter 1**   The Set of Real Numbers

For Exercises 112–118, answer true or false. If a statement is false, explain why.

112. If n is positive, then $-n$ is negative

113. If m is negative, then m^4 is negative.

114. If m is negative, then m^3 is negative.

115. If $m > 0$ and $n > 0$, then $mn > 0$.

116. If $p < 0$ and $q < 0$, then $pq < 0$.

117. A number and its reciprocal have the same signs.

118. A nonzero number and its opposite have different signs.

Section 1.7

For Exercises 119–126, answers may vary.

119. Give an example of the commutative property of addition.

120. Give an example of the associative property of addition.

121. Give an example of the inverse property of addition.

122. Give an example of the identity property of addition.

123. Give an example of the commutative property of multiplication.

124. Give an example of the associative property of multiplication.

125. Give an example of the inverse property of multiplication.

126. Give an example of the identity property of multiplication.

127. Explain why $5x - 2y$ is the same as $-2y + 5x$.

128. Explain why $3a - 9y$ is the same as $-9y + 3a$.

129. List the terms of the expression:
$3y + 10x - 12 + xy$

130. Identify the coefficients for the terms listed in Exercise 129.

For Exercises 131–132, simplify by combining *like* terms.

131. $3a + 3b - 4b + 5a - 10$

132. $-6p + 2q + 9 - 13q - p + 7$

For Exercises 133–134, use the distributive property to clear the parentheses.

133. $-2(4z + 9)$ **134.** $5(4w - 8y + 1)$

For Exercises 135–140, simplify each expression.

135. $2p - (p + 5w) + 3w$

136. $6(h + 3m) - 7h - 4m$

137. $\frac{1}{2}(-6q) + q - 4\left(3q + \frac{1}{4}\right)$

138. $0.3b + 12(0.2 - 0.5b)$

139. $-4[2(x + 1) - (3x + 8)]$

140. $5[(7y - 3) + 3(y + 8)]$

Chapter 1   Test

1. Simplify. $\dfrac{135}{36}$

2. Add and subtract. $\dfrac{5}{4} - \dfrac{5}{12} + \dfrac{2}{3}$

3. Divide. $4\dfrac{1}{12} \div 1\dfrac{1}{3}$

4. Subtract. $4\dfrac{1}{4} - 1\dfrac{7}{8}$

5. Is $0.\overline{315}$ a rational number or an irrational number? Explain your reasoning.

6. Use the definition of exponents to expand the expressions:

    a. $(4x)^3$ **b.** $4x^3$

7. Plot the points on a number line: $|3|,\ 0,\ -2,\ 0.5,\ \left|-\frac{3}{2}\right|,\ \sqrt{16}.$

8. Use the number line in Exercise 7 to identify whether the statements are true or false.

    a. $|3| < -2$ **b.** $0 \le \left|-\frac{3}{2}\right|$

    c. $-2 < 0.5$ **d.** $|3| \ge \left|-\frac{3}{2}\right|$

9. Identify the property that justifies each statement.

    a. $6(-8) = (-8)6$ **b.** $5 + 0 = 5$

    c. $(2 + 3) + 4 = 2 + (3 + 4)$

    d. $\frac{1}{7} \cdot 7 = 1$ **e.** $8[7(-3)] = (8 \cdot 7)(-3)$

10. Write each expression as an English phrase.

    a. $2(a - b)$.

    b. $2a - b$. (Answers may vary.)

11. Write the phrase as an algebraic expression: "The quotient of the square root of c and the square of d."

For Exercises 12–14, write each English statement as an algebraic expression. Then simplify the expression.

12. Subtract -4 from 12

13. Find the difference of 6 and 8

14. The quotient of 10 and -12

For Exercises 15–29, perform the indicated operations.

15. $-\frac{1}{8} + \left(-\frac{3}{4}\right)$ **16.** $-84 \div 7$

17. $21 - (-7)$ **18.** $-15 - (-3)$

19. $-14 + (-2) - 16$

20. $(-16)(-2)(-1)(-3)$

21. $-22 \cdot 0$

22. $38 \div 0$

23. $18 + (-12)$

24. $-10.06 - (-14.72)$

25. $7(-4)$

26. $\frac{2}{5} \div \left(-\frac{7}{10}\right) \cdot \left(-\frac{7}{6}\right)$

27. $\dfrac{\sqrt{5^2 - 4^2}}{|-12 + 3|}$

28. $8 - [(2 - 4) - (8 - 9)]$

29. $(8 - 10) \cdot \frac{3}{2} + (-5)$

30. The average high temperature in January for Nova Scotia, Canada, is $-1.2°C$. The average low is $-10.7°C$. Find the difference between the average high and the average low.

31. In the third quarter of a football game, a quarterback made a 5-yd gain, a 2-yd gain, a 10-yd loss, and then a 4-yd gain.

    a. Write an expression using addition to describe the quarterback's movement.

    b. Evaluate the expression from part (a) to determine the quarterback's net gain or loss in yards.

For Exercises 32–36, simplify each expression.

32. $3k - 20 + (-9k) + 12$

33. $-5x - 4y + 3 - 7x + 6y - 7$

34. $4(p - 5) - (8p + 3)$

35. $-3(4m + 8p - 7)$

36. $\frac{1}{2}(12p - 4) + \frac{1}{3}(2 - 6p)$

For Exercises 37–40, evaluate each expression given the values $x = 4$ and $y = -3$ and $z = -7$.

37. $y^2 - x$ **38.** $3x - 2y$

39. $y(x - 2)$ **40.** $-y^2 - 4x + z$

Linear Equations and Inequalities

Linear Equations and Inequalities

2

CHAPTER OUTLINE

Mathematics as a Language

Languages make use of symbols to represent sounds and other conventions used in speech and writing. The letters of the alphabet and punctuation marks are all examples of these symbols. Mathematicians cleverly adopted the use of symbols as a way to give a temporary nickname to *unknowns* in order to simplify the problem-solving process.

Suppose that the maximum recommended heart rate for an adult is given by 220 minus the age (in years) of the adult. If we let a be the age of an adult in years, then the expression $220 - a$ represents the adult's maximum recommended heart rate.

© Blend Images/Ariel Skelley/Getty Images RF

If Alan is 60 years old, his maximum heart rate is found by substituting 60 for a. Thus, Alan's maximum recommended heart rate is $220 - 60$, which is 160 beats per minute.

If we know that Ben's recommended heart rate is 178, then we can solve an equation to determine his age, a.

$$220 - a = 178$$
$$-a = 178 - 220$$
$$-a = -42$$
$$a = 42 \quad \text{Ben is 42 years old.}$$

100   **Chapter 2**   Linear Equations and Inequalities

Section 2.1   Addition, Subtraction, Multiplication, and Division Properties of Equality

Concepts

1. Definition of a Linear Equation in One Variable
2. Addition and Subtraction Properties of Equality
3. Multiplication and Division Properties of Equality
4. Translations

1. Definition of a Linear Equation in One Variable

An **equation** is a statement that indicates that two expressions are equal. The following are equations.

$$x = 5 \qquad y + 2 = 12 \qquad -4z = 28$$

All equations have an equal sign. Furthermore, notice that the equal sign separates the equation into two parts, the left-hand side and the right-hand side. A **solution to an equation** is a value of the variable that makes the equation a true statement. Substituting a solution into an equation for the variable makes the right-hand side equal to the left-hand side.

Equation	Solution	Check	
$x = 5$	5	$x = 5$ $\downarrow$ $5 = 5$ ✓	Substitute 5 for x. Right-hand side equals left-hand side.
$y + 2 = 12$	10	$y + 2 = 12$ $\downarrow$ $10 + 2 = 12$ ✓	Substitute 10 for y. Right-hand side equals left-hand side.
$-4z = 28$	-7	$-4z = 28$ $\downarrow$ $-4(-7) = 28$ ✓	Substitute -7 for z. Right-hand side equals left-hand side.

Avoiding Mistakes

Be sure to notice the difference between solving an equation versus simplifying an expression. For example, $2x + 1 = 7$ is an equation, whose solution is 3, while $2x + 1 + 7$ is an expression that simplifies to $2x + 8$.

Example 1   **Determining Whether a Number Is a Solution to an Equation**

Determine whether the given number is a solution to the equation.

a. $4x + 7 = 5$; $-\frac{1}{2}$ **b.** $-4 = 6w - 14$;   3

Solution:

a.
$$4x + 7 = 5$$
$$4\left(-\tfrac{1}{2}\right) + 7 \stackrel{?}{=} 5 \qquad \text{Substitute } -\tfrac{1}{2} \text{ for } x.$$
$$-2 + 7 \stackrel{?}{=} 5 \qquad \text{Simplify.}$$
$$5 \stackrel{?}{=} 5 ✓ \qquad \text{Right-hand side equals the left-hand side.}$$
$$\text{Thus, } -\tfrac{1}{2} \text{ is a solution to the equation } 4x + 7 = 5.$$

b. $-4 = 6w - 14$
$$-4 \stackrel{?}{=} 6(3) - 14 \qquad \text{Substitute 3 for } w.$$
$$-4 \stackrel{?}{=} 18 - 14 \qquad \text{Simplify.}$$
$$-4 \neq 4 \qquad \text{Right-hand side does not equal left-hand side.}$$
$$\text{Thus, 3 is not a solution to the equation } -4 = 6w - 14.$$

Skill Practice   Determine whether the given number is a solution to the equation.

1. $4x - 1 = 7$;   3   **2.** $9 = -2y + 5$; -2

Answers

1. No   **2.** Yes

The set of all solutions to an equation is called the **solution set** and is written with set braces. For example, the solution set for Example 1(a) is $\{-\frac{1}{2}\}$.

In the study of algebra, you will encounter a variety of equations. In this chapter, we will focus on a specific type of equation called a linear equation in one variable.

Definition of a Linear Equation in One Variable

Let a, b, and c be real numbers such that $a \neq 0$. A **linear equation in one variable** is an equation that can be written in the form

$$ax + b = c$$

Note: A linear equation in one variable is often called a first-degree equation because the variable x has an implied exponent of 1.

Examples	Notes
$2x + 4 = 20$	$a = 2, b = 4, c = 20$
$-3x - 5 = 16$ can be written as $-3x + (-5) = 16$	$a = -3, b = -5, c = 16$
$5x + 9 - 4x = 1$ can be written as $x + 9 = 1$	$a = 1, b = 9, c = 1$

---

2. Addition and Subtraction Properties of Equality

If two equations have the same solution set, then the equations are equivalent. For example, the following equations are equivalent because the solution set for each equation is $\{6\}$.

Equivalent Equations		Check the Solution 6
$2x - 5 = 7$	$\longrightarrow$	$2(6) - 5 \overset{?}{=} 7 \Rightarrow 12 - 5 \overset{?}{=} 7 \checkmark$
$2x = 12$	$\longrightarrow$	$2(6) \overset{?}{=} 12 \Rightarrow 12 \overset{?}{=} 12 \checkmark$
$x = 6$	$\longrightarrow$	$6 \overset{?}{=} 6 \Rightarrow 6 \overset{?}{=} 6 \checkmark$

To solve a linear equation, $ax + b = c$, the goal is to find *all* values of x that make the equation true. One general strategy for solving an equation is to rewrite it as an equivalent but simpler equation. This process is repeated until the equation can be written in the form $x = $ number. We call this "isolating the variable." The addition and subtraction properties of equality help us isolate the variable.

Addition and Subtraction Properties of Equality

Let a, b, and c represent algebraic expressions.

1. **Addition property of equality:**   If $a = b$,
   then $a + c = b + c$

2. ***Subtraction property of equality:***   If $a = b$,
   then $a - c = b - c$

*The subtraction property of equality follows directly from the addition property, because subtraction is defined in terms of addition.

If $a + (-c) = b + (-c)$
then, $a - c = b - c$

The addition and subtraction properties of equality indicate that adding or subtracting the same quantity on each side of an equation results in an equivalent equation. This means that if two equal quantities are increased or decreased by the same amount, then the resulting quantities will also be equal (Figure 2-1).

$$50 = 50$$
$$50 + 20 = 50 + 20$$
$$70 = 70$$

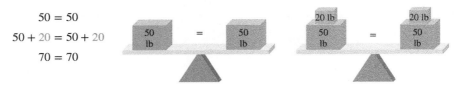

Figure 2-1

| Example 2 | **Applying the Addition and Subtraction Properties of Equality** |

Solve the equations.

a. $p - 4 = 11$ **b.** $w + 5 = -2$

Solution:

In each equation, the goal is to isolate the variable on one side of the equation. To accomplish this, we use the fact that the sum of a number and its opposite is zero and the difference of a number and itself is zero.

a.
$$p - 4 = 11$$
$$p - 4 + 4 = 11 + 4 \qquad \text{To isolate } p, \text{ add } 4 \text{ to both sides } (-4 + 4 = 0).$$
$$p + 0 = 15 \qquad \text{Simplify.}$$
$$p = 15 \qquad \text{Check by substituting } p = 15 \text{ into the original equation.}$$

$$\underline{\text{Check}}: \quad p - 4 = 11$$
$$15 - 4 \stackrel{?}{=} 11$$
$$11 \stackrel{?}{=} 11 \checkmark \quad \text{True}$$

The solution set is $\{15\}$.

b.
$$w + 5 = -2$$
$$w + 5 - 5 = -2 - 5 \qquad \text{To isolate } w, \text{ subtract } 5 \text{ from both sides.}$$
$$(5 - 5 = 0).$$
$$w + 0 = -7 \qquad \text{Simplify.}$$
$$w = -7 \qquad \text{Check by substituting } w = -7 \text{ into the original equation.}$$

$$\underline{\text{Check}}: \quad w + 5 = -2$$
$$-7 + 5 \stackrel{?}{=} -2$$
$$-2 \stackrel{?}{=} -2 \checkmark \quad \text{True}$$

The solution set is $\{-7\}$.

Skill Practice   Solve the equations.

3. $v - 7 = 2$ **4.** $x + 4 = 4$

Answers

3. $\{9\}$ **4.** $\{0\}$

Example 3	**Applying the Addition and Subtraction Properties of Equality**

Solve the equations.

a. $\dfrac{9}{4} = q - \dfrac{3}{4}$ **b.** $-1.2 + z = 4.6$

Solution:

a.
$$\dfrac{9}{4} = q - \dfrac{3}{4}$$

$$\dfrac{9}{4} + \dfrac{3}{4} = q - \dfrac{3}{4} + \dfrac{3}{4} \qquad \text{To isolate } q, \text{ add } \tfrac{3}{4} \text{ to both sides } \left(-\tfrac{3}{4} + \tfrac{3}{4} = 0\right).$$

$$\dfrac{12}{4} = q + 0 \qquad \text{Simplify.}$$

$$3 = q \quad \text{or equivalently,} \quad q = 3$$

> **TIP:** The variable may be isolated on either side of the equation.

Check: $\dfrac{9}{4} = q - \dfrac{3}{4}$

$\dfrac{9}{4} \overset{?}{=} 3 - \dfrac{3}{4}$ Substitute $q = 3$.

$\dfrac{9}{4} \overset{?}{=} \dfrac{12}{4} - \dfrac{3}{4}$ Common denominator

The solution set is $\{3\}$.

$\dfrac{9}{4} \overset{?}{=} \dfrac{9}{4}$ ✓   True

b.
$$-1.2 + z = 4.6$$

$$-1.2 + 1.2 + z = 4.6 + 1.2 \qquad \text{To isolate } z, \text{ add } 1.2 \text{ to both sides.}$$

$$0 + z = 5.8$$

$$z = 5.8$$

Check: $-1.2 + z = 4.6$

$-1.2 + 5.8 \overset{?}{=} 4.6$ Substitute $z = 5.8$.

The solution set is $\{5.8\}$.

$4.6 \overset{?}{=} 4.6$ ✓   True

Skill Practice   Solve the equations.

5. $\dfrac{1}{4} = a - \dfrac{2}{3}$ **6.** $-8.1 + w = 11.5$

3. Multiplication and Division Properties of Equality

Adding or subtracting the same quantity to both sides of an equation results in an equivalent equation. In a similar way, multiplying or dividing both sides of an equation by the same nonzero quantity also results in an equivalent equation. This is stated formally as the multiplication and division properties of equality.

Answers

5. $\left\{\dfrac{11}{12}\right\}$ **6.** $\{19.6\}$

> **Multiplication and Division Properties of Equality**
>
> Let a, b, and c represent algebraic expressions, $c \neq 0$.
>
> 1. **Multiplication property of equality:** If $a = b$,
>
>   then $ac = bc$
>
> 2. ***Division property of equality:*** If $a = b$
>
>   then $\dfrac{a}{c} = \dfrac{b}{c}$
>
> *The division property of equality follows directly from the multiplication property because division is defined as multiplication by the reciprocal.
>
> If $a \cdot \dfrac{1}{c} = b \cdot \dfrac{1}{c}$
>
> then, $\dfrac{a}{c} = \dfrac{b}{c}$

To understand the multiplication property of equality, suppose we start with a true equation such as $10 = 10$. If both sides of the equation are multiplied by a constant such as 3, the result is also a true statement (Figure 2-2).

$10 = 10$

$3 \cdot 10 = 3 \cdot 10$

$30 = 30$

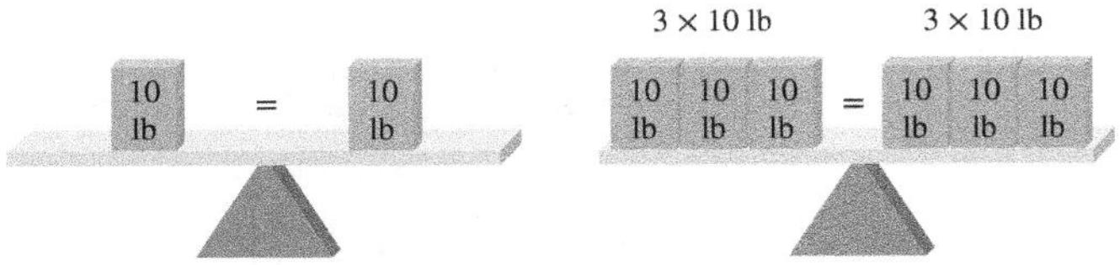

Figure 2-2

Similarly, if both sides of the equation are divided by a nonzero real number such as 2, the result is also a true statement (Figure 2-3).

$10 = 10$

$\dfrac{10}{2} = \dfrac{10}{2}$

$5 = 5$

Figure 2-3

> **TIP:** The product of a number and its reciprocal is always 1. For example:
>
> $\dfrac{1}{5}(5) = 1$
>
> $-\dfrac{7}{2}\left(-\dfrac{2}{7}\right) = 1$

To solve an equation in the variable x, the goal is to write the equation in the form $x =$ number. In particular, notice that we desire the coefficient of x to be 1. That is, we want to write the equation as $1x =$ number. Therefore, to solve an equation such as $5x = 15$, we can multiply both sides of the equation by the reciprocal of the x-term coefficient. In this case, multiply both sides by the reciprocal of 5, which is $\frac{1}{5}$.

$5x = 15$

$\dfrac{1}{5}(5x) = \dfrac{1}{5}(15)$ Multiply by $\dfrac{1}{5}$.

$1x = 3$ The coefficient of the x-term is now 1.

$x = 3$

The division property of equality can also be used to solve the equation $5x = 15$ by dividing both sides by the coefficient of the x-term. In this case, divide both sides by 5 to make the coefficient of x equal to 1.

$$5x = 15$$

$$\frac{5x}{5} = \frac{15}{5} \qquad \text{Divide by } 5.$$

$$1x = 3 \qquad \text{The coefficient of the } x\text{-term is now 1.}$$

$$x = 3$$

> **TIP:** The quotient of a nonzero real number and itself is always 1. For example:
>
> $$\frac{5}{5} = 1$$
>
> $$\frac{-3.5}{-3.5} = 1$$

| **Example 4** | **Applying the Division Property of Equality** |

Solve the equations using the division property of equality.

a. $12x = 60$ **b.** $48 = -8w$ **c.** $-x = 8$

Solution:

a. $12x = 60$

$$\frac{12x}{12} = \frac{60}{12} \qquad \text{To obtain a coefficient of 1 for the } x\text{-term,}$$
$$\text{divide both sides by } 12.$$

$$1x = 5 \qquad \text{Simplify.}$$

$$x = 5 \qquad \underline{\text{Check:}} \quad 12x = 60$$

$$12(5) \overset{?}{=} 60$$

The solution set is $\{5\}$. $60 \overset{?}{=} 60 \checkmark$ True

b. $48 = -8w$

$$\frac{48}{-8} = \frac{-8w}{-8} \qquad \text{To obtain a coefficient of 1 for the } w\text{-term, divide}$$
$$\text{both sides by } -8.$$

$$-6 = 1w \qquad \text{Simplify.}$$

$$-6 = w \qquad \underline{\text{Check:}}\ 48 = -8w$$

$$48 \overset{?}{=} -8(-6)$$

The solution set is $\{-6\}$. $48 \overset{?}{=} 48 \checkmark$ True

c. $-x = 8$ Note that $-x$ is equivalent to $-1 \cdot x$.

$$-1x = 8$$

$$\frac{-1x}{-1} = \frac{8}{-1} \qquad \text{To obtain a coefficient of 1 for the } x\text{-term, divide}$$
$$\text{by } -1.$$

$$x = -8 \qquad \underline{\text{Check:}}\ -x = 8$$

$$-(-8) \overset{?}{=} 8$$

The solution set is $\{-8\}$. $8 \overset{?}{=} 8 \checkmark$ True

> **TIP:** In Example 4(c), we could also have *multiplied* both sides by −1 to create a coefficient of 1 on the x-term.
>
> $$-x = 8$$
> $$(-1)(-x) = (-1)8$$
> $$x = -8$$

Skill Practice   Solve the equations.

7. $4x = -20$ **8.** $100 = -4p$ **9.** $-y = -11$

Answers

7. $\{-5\}$ **8.** $\{-25\}$ **9.** $\{11\}$

106   **Chapter 2**   Linear Equations and Inequalities

Example 5   **Applying the Multiplication Property of Equality**

Solve the equation by using the multiplication property of equality.

$$-\frac{2}{9}q = \frac{1}{3}$$

Solution:

$$-\frac{2}{9}q = \frac{1}{3}$$

$$\left(-\frac{9}{2}\right)\left(-\frac{2}{9}q\right) = \frac{1}{3}\left(-\frac{9}{2}\right)$$ To obtain a coefficient of 1 for the q-term, multiply by the reciprocal of $-\frac{2}{9}$, which is $-\frac{9}{2}$.

$$1q = -\frac{3}{2}$$ Simplify. The product of a number and its reciprocal is 1.

$$q = -\frac{3}{2}$$ Check: $-\frac{2}{9}q = \frac{1}{3}$

$$-\frac{2}{9}\left(-\frac{3}{2}\right) \overset{?}{=} \frac{1}{3}$$

The solution set is $\left\{-\frac{3}{2}\right\}$. $\frac{1}{3} \overset{?}{=} \frac{1}{3}$ ✓   True

Skill Practice   Solve the equation.

10. $-\frac{2}{3}a = \frac{1}{4}$

TIP: When applying the multiplication or division property of equality to obtain a coefficient of 1 for the variable term, we will generally use the following convention:

- If the coefficient of the variable term is expressed as a fraction, we will usually multiply both sides by its reciprocal, as in Example 5.
- If the coefficient of the variable term is an integer or decimal, we will divide both sides by the coefficient itself, as in Example 6.

Example 6   **Applying the Division Property of Equality**

Solve the equation by using the division property of equality.

$$-3.43 = -0.7z$$

Solution:

$$-3.43 = -0.7z$$

$$\frac{-3.43}{-0.7} = \frac{-0.7z}{-0.7}$$ To obtain a coefficient of 1 for the z-term, divide by -0.7.

$$4.9 = 1z$$ Simplify.

$$4.9 = z$$

$$z = 4.9$$ Check: $-3.43 = -0.7z$

$$-3.43 \overset{?}{=} -0.7(4.9)$$

Answer

The solution set is $\{4.9\}$. $-3.43 \overset{?}{=} -3.43$ ✓   True

10. $\left\{-\frac{3}{8}\right\}$

Skill Practice   Solve the equation.

11. $6.82 = 2.2w$

Example 7   **Applying the Multiplication Property of Equality**

Solve the equation by using the multiplication property of equality.

$$\frac{d}{6} = -4$$

Solution:

$$\frac{d}{6} = -4$$

$$\frac{1}{6}d = -4 \qquad\qquad \frac{d}{6} \text{ is equivalent to } \frac{1}{6}d.$$

$$\frac{6}{1} \cdot \frac{1}{6}d = -4 \cdot \frac{6}{1} \qquad \text{To obtain a coefficient of 1 for the } d\text{-term,}$$
$$\text{multiply by the reciprocal of } \frac{1}{6}, \text{ which is } \frac{6}{1}.$$

$$1d = -24 \qquad\qquad \text{Simplify.}$$

$$d = -24 \qquad\qquad \underline{\text{Check:}} \; \frac{d}{6} = -4$$

$$\frac{-24}{6} \stackrel{?}{=} -4$$

The solution set is $\{-24\}$. $-4 \stackrel{?}{=} -4 \checkmark$ True

---

Skill Practice   Solve the equation.

12. $\dfrac{x}{5} = -8$

It is important to distinguish between cases where the addition or subtraction properties of equality should be used to isolate a variable versus those in which the multiplication or division property of equality should be used. Remember the goal is to isolate the variable term and obtain a coefficient of 1. Compare the equations:

$$5 + x = 20 \qquad \text{and} \qquad 5x = 20$$

In the first equation, the relationship between 5 and x is addition. Therefore, we want to reverse the process by subtracting 5 from both sides. In the second equation, the relationship between 5 and x is multiplication. To isolate x, we reverse the process by dividing by 5 or equivalently, multiplying by the reciprocal, $\frac{1}{5}$.

$$5 + x = 20 \qquad \text{and} \qquad 5x = 20$$

$$5 - 5 + x = 20 - 5 \qquad\qquad \frac{5x}{5} = \frac{20}{5}$$

$$x = 15 \qquad\qquad\qquad x = 4$$

Answers

11. $\{3.1\}$ **12.** $\{-40\}$

4. Translations

We have already practiced writing an English sentence as a mathematical equation. Recall that several key words translate to the algebraic operations of addition, subtraction, multiplication, and division.

Example 8	**Translating to a Linear Equation**

Write an algebraic equation to represent each English sentence. Then solve the equation.

   a. The quotient of a number and 4 is 6.

   b. The product of a number and 4 is 6.

   c. Negative twelve is equal to the sum of -5 and a number.

   d. The value 1.4 subtracted from a number is 5.7.

Solution:

For each case we will let x represent the unknown number.

   a. The quotient of a number and 4 is 6.

$$\frac{x}{4} = 6$$

$$4 \cdot \frac{x}{4} = 4 \cdot 6 \qquad \text{Multiply both sides by } 4.$$

$$\frac{4}{1} \cdot \frac{x}{4} = 4 \cdot 6$$

$$x = 24 \qquad \underline{\text{Check:}} \ \frac{24}{4} \overset{?}{=} 6 \checkmark \quad \text{True}$$

The number is 24.

   b. The product of a number and 4 is 6.

$$4x = 6$$

$$\frac{4x}{4} = \frac{6}{4} \qquad \text{Divide both sides by } 4.$$

$$x = \frac{3}{2} \qquad \underline{\text{Check:}} \ 4\left(\frac{3}{2}\right) \overset{?}{=} 6 \checkmark \quad \text{True}$$

The number is $\frac{3}{2}$.

   c. Negative twelve is equal to the sum of -5 and a number.

$$-12 = -5 + x$$

$$-12 + 5 = -5 + 5 + x \qquad \text{Add } 5 \text{ to both sides.}$$

$$-7 = x \qquad \underline{\text{Check:}} \ -12 \overset{?}{=} -5 + (-7) \checkmark \quad \text{True}$$

The number is -7.

d. The value 1.4 subtracted from a number is 5.7.

$$x - 1.4 = 5.7$$

$$x - 1.4 + 1.4 = 5.7 + 1.4 \qquad \text{Add } 1.4 \text{ to both sides.}$$

$$x = 7.1 \qquad \underline{\text{Check}}: \quad 7.1 - 1.4 \overset{?}{=} 5.7 \checkmark \quad \text{True}$$

The number is 7.1.

Skill Practice   Write an algebraic equation to represent each English sentence. Then solve the equation.

13. The quotient of a number and −2 is 8.

14. The product of a number and −3 is −24.

15. The sum of a number and 6 is −20.

16. 13 is equal to 5 subtracted from a number.

Answers

13. $\frac{x}{-2} = 8$; The number is −16.

14. $-3x = -24$; The number is 8.

15. $y + 6 = -20$; The number is −26.

16. $13 = x - 5$; The number is 18.

Section 2.1   Practice Exercises

Study Skills Exercise

After getting a test back, it is a good idea to correct the test so that you do not make the same errors again. One recommended approach is to use a clean sheet of paper, and divide the paper down the middle vertically as shown. For each problem that you missed on the test, rework the problem correctly on the left-hand side of the paper. Then give a written explanation on the right-hand side of the paper. To reinforce the correct procedure, do four more problems of that type.

Take the time this week to make corrections from your last test.

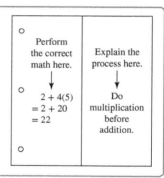

Vocabulary and Key Concepts

1. **a.** An _____ is a statement that indicates that two expressions are equal.

   b. A _____ to an equation is a value of the variable that makes the equation a true statement.

   c. An equation that can be written in the form $ax + b = c$ $(a \neq 0)$ is called a _____ equation in one variable.

   d. The set of all solutions to an equation is called the _____.

Concept 1: Definition of a Linear Equation in One Variable

For Exercises 2–6, identify the following as either an expression or an equation.

2. $2 - 8x + 10$ **3.** $x - 4 + 5x$ **4.** $8x + 2 = 7$ **5.** $9 = 2x - 4$ **6.** $3x^2 + x = -3$

7. Explain how to determine if a number is a solution to an equation.

8. Explain why the equations $6x = 12$ and $x = 2$ are *equivalent equations*.

110   **Chapter 2**   Linear Equations and Inequalities

For Exercises 9–14, determine whether the given number is a solution to the equation. **(See Example 1.)**

9. $x - 1 = 5;$ 4

10. $x - 2 = 1;$ -1

11. $5x = -10;$ -2

12. $3x = 21;$ 7

13. $3x + 9 = 3;$ -2

14. $2x - 1 = -3;$ -1

Concept 2: Addition and Subtraction Properties of Equality

For Exercises 15–34, solve each equation using the addition or subtraction property of equality. Be sure to check your answers. **(See Examples 2–3.)**

15. $x + 6 = 5$

16. $x - 2 = 10$

17. $q - 14 = 6$

18. $w + 3 = -5$

19. $2 + m = -15$

20. $-6 + n = 10$

21. $-23 = y - 7$

22. $-9 = -21 + b$

23. $4 + c = 4$

24. $-13 + b = -13$

25. $4.1 = 2.8 + a$

26. $5.1 = -2.5 + y$

27. $5 = z - \dfrac{1}{2}$

28. $-7 = p + \dfrac{2}{3}$

29. $x + \dfrac{5}{2} = \dfrac{1}{2}$

30. $\dfrac{7}{3} = x - \dfrac{2}{3}$

31. $-6.02 + c = -8.15$

32. $p + 0.035 = -1.12$

33. $3.245 + t = -0.0225$

34. $-1.004 + k = 3.0589$

Concept 3: Multiplication and Division Properties of Equality

For Exercises 35–54, solve each equation using the multiplication or division property of equality. Be sure to check your answers. **(See Examples 4–7.)**

35. $6x = 54$

36. $2w = 8$

37. $12 = -3p$

38. $6 = -2q$

39. $-5y = 0$

40. $-3k = 0$

41. $-\dfrac{y}{5} = 3$

42. $-\dfrac{z}{7} = 1$

43. $\dfrac{4}{5} = -t$

44. $-\dfrac{3}{7} = -h$

45. $\dfrac{2}{5}a = -4$

46. $\dfrac{3}{8}b = -9$

47. $-\dfrac{1}{5}b = -\dfrac{4}{5}$

48. $-\dfrac{3}{10}w = \dfrac{2}{5}$

49. $-41 = -x$

50. $32 = -y$

51. $3.81 = -0.03p$

52. $2.75 = -0.5q$

53. $5.82y = -15.132$

54. $-32.3x = -0.4522$

Concept 4: Translations

For Exercises 55–66, write an algebraic equation to represent each English sentence. (Let x represent the unknown number.) Then solve the equation. **(See Example 8.)**

55. The sum of negative eight and a number is forty-two.

56. The sum of thirty-one and a number is thirteen.

57. The difference of a number and negative six is eighteen.

58. The sum of negative twelve and a number is negative fifteen.

59. The product of a number and seven is the same as negative sixty-three.

60. The product of negative three and a number is the same as twenty-four.

61. The value 3.2 subtracted from a number is 2.1.

62. The value -3 subtracted from a number is 4.

63. The quotient of a number and twelve is one-third.

64. Eighteen is equal to the quotient of a number and two.

65. The sum of a number and $\frac{5}{8}$ is $\frac{13}{8}$.

66. The difference of a number and $\frac{2}{3}$ is $\frac{1}{3}$.

Mixed Exercises

For Exercises 67–90, solve each equation using the appropriate property of equality.

67. a. $x - 9 = 1$

    b. $-9x = 1$

68. a. $k - 2 = -4$

    b. $-2k = -4$

69. a. $-\dfrac{2}{3}h = 8$

    b. $\dfrac{2}{3} + h = 8$

70. a. $\dfrac{3}{4}p = 15$

    b. $\dfrac{3}{4} + p = 15$

71. $\dfrac{r}{3} = -12$

72. $\dfrac{d}{-4} = 5$

73. $k + 16 = 32$

74. $-18 = -9 + t$

75. $16k = 32$

76. $-18 = -9t$

77. $7 = -4q$

78. $-3s = 10$

79. $-4 + q = 7$

80. $s - 3 = 10$

81. $-\dfrac{1}{3}d = 12$

82. $-\dfrac{2}{5}m = 10$

83. $4 = \dfrac{1}{2} + z$

84. $3 = \dfrac{1}{4} + p$

85. $1.2y = 4.8$

86. $4.3w = 8.6$

87. $4.8 = 1.2 + y$

88. $8.6 = w - 4.3$

89. $0.0034 = y - 0.405$

90. $-0.98 = m + 1.0034$

For Exercises 91–98, determine if the equation is a linear equation in one variable. Answer yes or no.

91. $4p + 5 = 0$

92. $3x - 5y = 0$

93. $4 + 2a^2 = 5$

94. $-8t = 7$

95. $x - 4 = 9$

96. $2x^3 + y = 0$

97. $19b = -3$

98. $13 + x = 19$

Expanding Your Skills

For Exercises 99–104, construct an equation with the given solution set. Answers will vary.

99. $\{6\}$

100. $\{2\}$

101. $\{-4\}$

102. $\{-10\}$

103. $\{0\}$

104. $\{1\}$

For Exercises 105–108, simplify by collecting the *like* terms. Then solve the equation.

105. $5x - 4x + 7 = 8 - 2$

106. $2 + 3 = 2y + 1 - y$

107. $6p - 3p = 15 + 6$

108. $12 - 20 = 2t + 2t$

Section 2.2	Solving Linear Equations

Concepts

1. Linear Equations Involving Multiple Steps
2. Procedure for Solving a Linear Equation in One Variable
3. Conditional Equations, Identities, and Contradictions

1. Linear Equations Involving Multiple Steps

Previously we studied a one-step process to solve linear equations by using the addition, subtraction, multiplication, and division properties of equality. In Example 1, we solve the equation $-2w - 7 = 11$. Solving this equation will require multiple steps. To understand the proper steps, always remember that the ultimate goal is to isolate the variable. Therefore, we will first isolate the *term* containing the variable before dividing both sides by -2.

Example 1	Solving a Linear Equation

Solve the equation. $-2w - 7 = 11$

Solution:

$$-2w - 7 = 11$$

$$-2w - 7 + 7 = 11 + 7 \qquad \text{Add } 7 \text{ to both sides of the equation. This isolates the } w\text{-term.}$$

$$-2w = 18$$

$$\frac{-2w}{-2} = \frac{18}{-2} \qquad \text{Next, apply the division property of equality to obtain a coefficient of 1 for } w. \text{ Divide by } -2 \text{ on both sides.}$$

$$w = -9$$

<u>Check:</u>

$$-2w - 7 = 11$$

$$-2(-9) - 7 \overset{?}{=} 11 \qquad \text{Substitute } w = -9 \text{ in the original equation.}$$

$$18 - 7 \overset{?}{=} 11$$

$$11 \overset{?}{=} 11 \checkmark \qquad \text{True}$$

The solution set is $\{-9\}$.

Skill Practice Solve the equation.

1. $-5y - 5 = 10$

Example 2	Solving a Linear Equation

Solve the equation. $2 = \frac{1}{5}x + 3$

Solution:

$$2 = \frac{1}{5}x + 3$$

$$2 - 3 = \frac{1}{5}x + 3 - 3 \qquad \text{Subtract 3 from both sides. This isolates the } x\text{-term.}$$

$$-1 = \frac{1}{5}x \qquad \text{Simplify.}$$

Answer

1. $\{-3\}$

$$5(-1) = 5 \cdot \left(\frac{1}{5}x\right)$$ Next, apply the multiplication property of equality to obtain a coefficient of 1 for x.

$$-5 = 1x$$

$$-5 = x$$ Simplify. The answer checks in the original equation.

The solution set is $\{-5\}$.

Skill Practice Solve the equation.

2. $2 = \frac{1}{2}a - 7$

In Example 3, the variable x appears on both sides of the equation. In this case, apply the addition or subtraction property of equality to collect the variable terms on one side of the equation and the constant terms on the other side. Then use the multiplication or division property of equality to get a coefficient equal to 1 on the variable term.

Example 3   **Solving a Linear Equation**

Solve the equation. $6x - 4 = 2x - 8$

Solution:

$$6x - 4 = 2x - 8$$

$$6x - 2x - 4 = 2x - 2x - 8$$ Subtract $2x$ from both sides leaving $0x$ on the right-hand side.

$$4x - 4 = 0x - 8$$ Simplify.

$$4x - 4 = -8$$ The x-terms have now been combined on one side of the equation.

$$4x - 4 + 4 = -8 + 4$$ Add 4 to both sides of the equation. This combines the constant terms on the *other* side of the equation.

$$4x = -4$$

$$\frac{4x}{4} = \frac{-4}{4}$$ To obtain a coefficient of 1 for x, divide both sides of the equation by 4.

$$x = -1$$ The answer checks in the original equation.

The solution set is $\{-1\}$.

Skill Practice Solve the equation.

3. $10x - 3 = 4x - 2$

Answers

2. $\{18\}$ **3.** $\left\{\frac{1}{6}\right\}$

> **TIP:** It is important to note that the variable may be isolated on either side of the equation. We will solve the equation from Example 3 again, this time isolating the variable on the right-hand side.

$$6x - 4 = 2x - 8$$

$$6x - 6x - 4 = 2x - 6x - 8 \qquad \text{Subtract } 6x \text{ on both sides.}$$

$$0x - 4 = -4x - 8$$

$$-4 = -4x - 8$$

$$-4 + 8 = -4x - 8 + 8 \qquad \text{Add } 8 \text{ to both sides.}$$

$$4 = -4x$$

$$\frac{4}{-4} = \frac{-4x}{-4} \qquad \text{Divide both sides by } -4.$$

$$-1 = x \quad \text{or equivalently } x = -1$$

2. Procedure for Solving a Linear Equation in One Variable

In some cases, it is necessary to simplify both sides of a linear equation before applying the properties of equality. Therefore, we offer the following steps to solve a linear equation in one variable.

Solving a Linear Equation in One Variable

Step 1 Simplify both sides of the equation.
  - Clear parentheses
  - Combine *like* terms

Step 2 Use the addition or subtraction property of equality to collect the variable terms on one side of the equation.

Step 3 Use the addition or subtraction property of equality to collect the constant terms on the other side of the equation.

Step 4 Use the multiplication or division property of equality to make the coefficient of the variable term equal to 1.

Step 5 Check your answer.

Example 4	**Solving a Linear Equation**

Solve the equation. $7 + 3 = 2(p - 3)$

Solution:

$$7 + 3 = 2(p - 3)$$

$$10 = 2p - 6 \qquad \textbf{Step 1:} \quad \text{Simplify both sides of the equation by clearing parentheses and combining } like \text{ terms.}$$

$$ \qquad \textbf{Step 2:} \quad \text{The variable terms are already on one side.}$$

$$10 + 6 = 2p - 6 + 6 \qquad \textbf{Step 3:} \quad \text{Add } 6 \text{ to both sides to collect the constant terms on the other side.}$$

$$16 = 2p$$

$$\frac{16}{2} = \frac{2p}{2}$$

Step 4: Divide both sides by 2 to obtain a coefficient of 1 for p.

$8 = p$

Step 5: Check:

$$7 + 3 = 2(p - 3)$$

$$10 \overset{?}{=} 2(8 - 3)$$

$$10 \overset{?}{=} 2(5)$$

The solution set is $\{8\}$.

$$10 \overset{?}{=} 10 \checkmark \quad \text{True}$$

Skill Practice Solve the equation.

4. $12 + 2 = 7(3 - y)$

Example 5   **Solving a Linear Equation**

Solve the equation. $2.2y - 8.3 = 6.2y + 12.1$

Solution:

$$2.2y - 8.3 = 6.2y + 12.1$$

Step 1: The right- and left-hand sides are already simplified.

$$2.2y - 2.2y - 8.3 = 6.2y - 2.2y + 12.1$$
$$-8.3 = 4y + 12.1$$

Step 2: Subtract $2.2y$ from both sides to collect the variable terms on one side of the equation.

$$-8.3 - 12.1 = 4y + 12.1 - 12.1$$
$$-20.4 = 4y$$

Step 3: Subtract 12.1 from both sides to collect the constant terms on the other side.

$$\frac{-20.4}{4} = \frac{4y}{4}$$

$$-5.1 = y$$

$$y = -5.1$$

Step 4: To obtain a coefficient of 1 for the y-term, divide both sides of the equation by 4.

Step 5: Check:

$$2.2y - 8.3 = 6.2y + 12.1$$

$$2.2(-5.1) - 8.3 \overset{?}{=} 6.2(-5.1) + 12.1$$

$$-11.22 - 8.3 \overset{?}{=} -31.62 + 12.1$$

The solution set is $\{-5.1\}$.

$$-19.52 \overset{?}{=} -19.52 \checkmark \text{ True}$$

TIP: In Examples 5 and 6 we collected the variable terms on the right side to avoid negative coefficients on the variable term.

Skill Practice Solve the equation.

5. $1.5t + 2.3 = 3.5t - 1.9$

Answers

4. $\{1\}$ **5.** $\{2.1\}$

116   **Chapter 2**   Linear Equations and Inequalities

Example 6   Solving a Linear Equation

Solve the equation. $2 + 7x - 5 = 6(x + 3) + 2x$

Solution:

$$2 + 7x - 5 = 6(x + 3) + 2x$$
$$-3 + 7x = 6x + 18 + 2x$$ **Step 1:** Add *like* terms on the left. Clear parentheses on the right.

$$-3 + 7x = 8x + 18$$ Combine *like* terms.
$$-3 + 7x - 7x = 8x - 7x + 18$$ **Step 2:** Subtract $7x$ from both sides.
$$-3 = x + 18$$ Simplify.
$$-3 - 18 = x + 18 - 8$$ **Step 3:** Subtract 18 from both sides.
$$-21 = x$$ **Step 4:** Because the coefficient of the x term is already 1, there is no need to apply the multiplication or division property of equality.
$$x = -21$$

The solution set is $\{-21\}$.   **Step 5:** The check is left to the reader.

Skill Practice Solve the equation.

6. $4(2y - 1) + y = 6y + 3 - y$

Example 7   Solving a Linear Equation

Solve the equation. $9 - (z - 3) + 4z = 4z - 5(z + 2) - 6$

Solution:

$$9 - (z - 3) + 4z = 4z - 5(z + 2) - 6$$
$$9 - z + 3 + 4z = 4z - 5z - 10 - 6$$ **Step 1:** Clear parentheses.
$$12 + 3z = -z - 16$$ Combine *like* terms.
$$12 + 3z + z = -z + z - 16$$ **Step 2:** Add z to both sides.
$$12 + 4z = -16$$
$$12 - 12 + 4z = -16 - 12$$ **Step 3:** Subtract 12 from both sides.
$$4z = -28$$
$$\frac{4z}{4} = \frac{-28}{4}$$ **Step 4:** Divide both sides by 4.
$$z = -7$$ **Step 5:** The check is left for the reader.

The solution set is $\{-7\}$.

Avoiding Mistakes

When distributing a negative number through a set of parentheses, be sure to change the signs of every term within the parentheses.

Skill Practice Solve the equation.

7. $10 - (x + 5) + 3x = 6x - 5(x - 1) - 3$

Answers

6. $\left\{\frac{7}{4}\right\}$ **7.** $\{-3\}$

3. Conditional Equations, Identities, and Contradictions

The solutions to an equation are the values of x that make the equation a true statement. A linear equation in one variable has one unique solution. Some types of equations, however, have no solution while others have infinitely many solutions.

I. Conditional Equations

An equation that is true for some values of the variable but false for other values is called a **conditional equation**. The equation $x + 4 = 6$, for example, is true on the condition that $x = 2$. For other values of x, the statement $x + 4 = 6$ is false.

$$x + 4 = 6$$
$$x + 4 - 4 = 6 - 4$$
$$x = 2 \quad \text{(Conditional equation)} \quad \text{Solution set: } \{2\}$$

II. Contradictions

Some equations have no solution, such as $x + 1 = x + 2$. There is no value of x, that when increased by 1 will equal the same value increased by 2. If we try to solve the equation by subtracting x from both sides, we get the contradiction $1 = 2$. This indicates that the equation has no solution. An equation that has no solution is called a **contradiction**. The solution set is the empty set. The **empty set** is the set with no elements and is denoted by { }.

$$x + 1 = x + 2$$
$$x - x + 1 = x - x + 2$$
$$1 = 2 \quad \text{(Contradiction)} \quad \text{Solution set: } \{\ \}$$

TIP: The empty set is also called the null set and can be expressed by the symbol $\emptyset$.

III. Identities

An equation that has all real numbers as its solution set is called an **identity**. For example, consider the equation, $x + 4 = x + 4$. Because the left- and right-hand sides are *identical*, any real number substituted for x will result in equal quantities on both sides. If we subtract x from both sides of the equation, we get the identity $4 = 4$. In such a case, the solution is the set of all real numbers.

$$x + 4 = x + 4$$
$$x - x + 4 = x - x + 4$$
$$4 = 4 \quad \text{(Identity)} \quad \text{Solution set: } \text{The set of real numbers.}$$

Avoiding Mistakes

There are two ways to express the empty set: { } or $\emptyset$. Be sure that you do not use them together. It would be incorrect to write $\{\emptyset\}$.

Example 8   **Identifying Conditional Equations, Contradictions, and Identities**

Solve the equation. Identify each equation as a conditional equation, a contradiction, or an identity.

a. $4k - 5 = 2(2k - 3) + 1$ **b.** $2(b - 4) = 2b - 7$ **c.** $3x + 7 = 2x - 5$

Solution:

a.
$$4k - 5 = 2(2k - 3) + 1$$
$$4k - 5 = 4k - 6 + 1 \qquad \text{Clear parentheses.}$$
$$4k - 5 = 4k - 5 \qquad \text{Combine } like \text{ terms.}$$
$$4k - 4k - 5 = 4k - 4k - 5 \qquad \text{Subtract } 4k \text{ from both sides.}$$
$$-5 = -5 \quad \text{(Identity)}$$

This is an identity. Solution set: The set of real numbers.

b. $2(b-4) = 2b - 7$

$2b - 8 = 2b - 7$ Clear parentheses.

$2b - 2b - 8 = 2b - 2b - 7$ Subtract $2b$ from both sides.

$-8 = -7$ (Contradiction)

This is a contradiction. Solution set: { }

c. $3x + 7 = 2x - 5$

$3x - 2x + 7 = 2x - 2x - 5$ Subtract $2x$ from both sides.

$x + 7 = -5$ Simplify.

$x + 7 - 7 = -5 - 7$ Subtract 7 from both sides.

$x = -12$ (Conditional equation)

This is a conditional equation. The solution set is $\{-12\}$. (The equation is true only on the condition that $x = -12$.)

Skill Practice Solve the equation. Identify the equation as a conditional equation, a contradiction, or an identity.

8. $4(2t + 1) - 1 = 8t + 3$ **9.** $3x - 5 = 4x + 1 - x$ **10.** $6(v - 2) = 2v - 4$

Answers

8. The set of real numbers; identity
9. { }; contradiction
10. {2}; conditional equation

Section 2.2   Practice Exercises

Study Skills Exercise

Several strategies are given here about taking notes. Check the activities that you routinely do and discuss how the other suggestions may improve your learning.

_____ Read your notes after class and fill in details.

_____ Highlight important terms and definitions.

_____ Review your notes from the previous class.

_____ Bring pencils (more than one) and paper to class.

_____ Sit in class where you can clearly read the board and hear your instructor.

_____ Turn off your cell phone and keep it off your desk to avoid distraction.

Vocabulary and Key Concepts

1. a. A _____ equation is true for some values of the variable, but false for other values.

b. An equation that has no solution is called a _____.

c. The set containing no elements is called the _____ set.

d. An equation that has all real numbers as its solution set is called an _____.

Review Exercises

For Exercises 2–5, simplify each expression by clearing parentheses and combining *like* terms.

2. $5z + 2 - 7z - 3z$ **3.** $10 - 4w + 7w - 2 + w$

4. $-(-7p + 9) + (3p - 1)$ **5.** $8y - (2y + 3) - 19$

6. Explain the difference between simplifying an expression and solving an equation.

For Exercises 7–12, solve each equation using the addition, subtraction, multiplication, or division property of equality.

7. $7 = p - 12$

8. $5w = -30$

9. $-7y = 21$

10. $x + 8 = -15$

11. $z - 23 = -28$

12. $-\dfrac{9}{8} = -\dfrac{3}{4}k$

Concept 1: Linear Equations Involving Multiple Steps

For Exercises 13–36, solve each equation using the steps outlined in the text. **(See Examples 1–3.)**

13. $6z + 1 = 13$

14. $5x + 2 = -13$

15. $3y - 4 = 14$

16. $-7w - 5 = -19$

17. $-2p + 8 = 3$

18. $2b - \dfrac{1}{4} = 5$

19. $0.2x + 3.1 = -5.3$

20. $-1.8 + 2.4a = -6.6$

21. $\dfrac{5}{8} = \dfrac{1}{4} - \dfrac{1}{2}p$

22. $\dfrac{6}{7} = \dfrac{1}{7} + \dfrac{5}{3}r$

23. $7w - 6w + 1 = 10 - 4$

24. $5v - 3 - 4v = 13$

25. $11h - 8 - 9h = -16$

26. $6u - 5 - 8u = -7$

27. $3a + 7 = 2a - 19$

28. $6b - 20 = 14 + 5b$

29. $-4r - 28 = -58 - r$

30. $-6x - 7 = -3 - 8x$

31. $-2z - 8 = -z$

32. $-7t + 4 = -6t$

33. $\dfrac{5}{6}x + \dfrac{2}{3} = -\dfrac{1}{6}x - \dfrac{5}{3}$

34. $\dfrac{3}{7}x - \dfrac{1}{4} = -\dfrac{4}{7}x - \dfrac{5}{4}$

35. $3y - 2 = 5y - 2$

36. $4 + 10t = -8t + 4$

Concept 2: Procedure for Solving a Linear Equation in One Variable

For Exercises 37–58, solve each equation using the steps outlined in the text. **(See Examples 4–7.)**

37. $4q + 14 = 2$

38. $6 = 7m - 1$

39. $-9 = 4n - 1$

40. $-\dfrac{1}{2} - 4x = 8$

41. $3(2p - 4) = 15$

42. $4(t + 15) = 20$

43. $6(3x + 2) - 10 = -4$

44. $4(2k + 1) - 1 = 5$

45. $3.4x - 2.5 = 2.8x + 3.5$

46. $5.8w + 1.1 = 6.3w + 5.6$

47. $17(s + 3) = 4(s - 10) + 13$

48. $5(4 + p) = 3(3p - 1) - 9$

49. $6(3t - 4) + 10 = 5(t - 2) - (3t + 4)$

50. $-5y + 2(2y + 1) = 2(5y - 1) - 7$

51. $5 - 3(x + 2) = 5$

52. $1 - 6(2 - h) = 7$

53. $3(2z - 6) - 4(3z + 1) = 5 - 2(z + 1)$

54. $-2(4a + 3) - 5(2 - a) = 3(2a + 3) - 7$

120   **Chapter 2**   Linear Equations and Inequalities

55. $-2[(4p + 1) - (3p - 1)] = 5(3 - p) - 9$

56. $5 - (6k + 1) = 2[(5k - 3) - (k - 2)]$

57. $3(-0.9n + 0.5) = -3.5n + 1.3$

58. $7(0.4m - 0.1) = 5.2m + 0.86$

Concept 3: Conditional Equations, Identities, and Contradictions

For Exercises 59–64, solve each equation. Identify as a conditional equation, an identity, or a contradiction. **(See Example 8.)**

59. $2(k - 7) = 2k - 13$

60. $5h + 4 = 5(h + 1) - 1$

61. $7x + 3 = 6(x - 2)$

62. $3y - 1 = 1 + 3y$

63. $3 - 5.2p = -5.2p + 3$

64. $2(q + 3) = 4q + q - 9$

65. A conditional linear equation has (choose one): one solution, no solution, or infinitely many solutions.

66. An equation that is a contradiction has (choose one): one solution, no solution, or infinitely many solutions.

67. An equation that is an identity has (choose one): one solution, no solution, or infinitely many solutions.

68. If the only solution to a linear equation is 5, then is the equation a conditional equation, an identity, or a contradiction?

Mixed Exercises

For Exercises 69–92, solve each equation.

69. $4p - 6 = 8 + 2p$

70. $\frac{1}{2}t - 2 = 3$

71. $2k - 9 = -8$

72. $3(y - 2) + 5 = 5$

73. $7(w - 2) = -14 - 3w$

74. $0.24 = 0.4m$

75. $2(x + 2) - 3 = 2x + 1$

76. $n + \frac{1}{4} = -\frac{1}{2}$

77. $0.5b = -23$

78. $3(2r + 1) = 6(r + 2) - 6$

79. $8 - 2q = 4$

80. $\frac{x}{7} - 3 = 1$

81. $2 - 4(y - 5) = -4$

82. $4 - 3(4p - 1) = -8$

83. $0.4(a + 20) = 6$

84. $2.2r - 12 = 3.4$

85. $10(2n + 1) - 6 = 20(n - 1) + 12$

86. $\frac{2}{5}y + 5 = -3$

87. $c + 0.123 = 2.328$

88. $4(2z + 3) = 8(z - 3) + 36$

89. $\frac{4}{5}t - 1 = \frac{1}{5}t + 5$

90. $6g - 8 = 4 - 3g$

91. $8 - (3q + 4) = 6 - q$

92. $6w - (8 + 2w) = 2(w - 4)$

Expanding Your Skills

93. Suppose the solution set for x in the equation $x + a = 10$ is $\{-5\}$. Find the value of a.

94. Suppose the solution set for x in the equation $x + a = -12$ is $\{6\}$. Find the value of a.

95. Suppose the solution set for x in the equation $ax = 12$ is $\{3\}$. Find the value of a.

96. Suppose the solution set for x in the equation $ax = 49.5$ is $\{11\}$. Find the value of a.

97. Write an equation that is an identity. Answers may vary.

98. Write an equation that is a contradiction. Answers may vary.

Linear Equations: Clearing Fractions and Decimals

1. Linear Equations Containing Fractions

Linear equations that contain fractions can be solved in different ways. The first procedure, illustrated here, uses the method previously outlined.

$$\frac{5}{6}x - \frac{3}{4} = \frac{1}{3}$$

$$\frac{5}{6}x - \frac{3}{4} + \frac{3}{4} = \frac{1}{3} + \frac{3}{4} \qquad \text{To isolate the variable term, add } \frac{3}{4} \text{ to both sides.}$$

$$\frac{5}{6}x = \frac{4}{12} + \frac{9}{12} \qquad \text{Find the common denominator on the right-hand side.}$$

$$\frac{5}{6}x = \frac{13}{12} \qquad \text{Simplify.}$$

$$\frac{6}{5}\left(\frac{5}{6}x\right) = \frac{\cancel{6}}{5}\left(\frac{13}{\cancel{12}_2}\right) \qquad \text{Multiply by the reciprocal of } \frac{5}{6}, \text{ which is } \frac{6}{5}.$$

$$x = \frac{13}{10} \qquad \text{The solution set is } \left\{\frac{13}{10}\right\}.$$

Sometimes it is simpler to solve an equation with fractions by eliminating the fractions first by using a process called **clearing fractions**. To clear fractions in the equation $\frac{5}{6}x - \frac{3}{4} = \frac{1}{3}$, we can apply the multiplication property of equality to multiply both sides of the equation by the least common denominator (LCD). In this case, the LCD of $\frac{5}{6}x$, $-\frac{3}{4}$, and $\frac{1}{3}$ is 12. Because each denominator in the equation is a factor of 12, we can simplify common factors to leave integer coefficients for each term.

Example 1   **Solving a Linear Equation by Clearing Fractions**

Solve the equation by clearing fractions first. $\dfrac{5}{6}x - \dfrac{3}{4} = \dfrac{1}{3}$

Solution:

$$\frac{5}{6}x - \frac{3}{4} = \frac{1}{3} \qquad \text{The LCD of } \frac{5}{6}x, -\frac{3}{4}, \text{ and } \frac{1}{3} \text{ is 12.}$$

$$12\left(\frac{5}{6}x - \frac{3}{4}\right) = 12\left(\frac{1}{3}\right) \qquad \text{Multiply both sides of the equation by the LCD, 12.}$$

$$\frac{\cancel{12}^2}{1}\left(\frac{5}{6}x\right) - \frac{\cancel{12}^3}{1}\left(\frac{3}{4}\right) = \frac{\cancel{12}^4}{1}\left(\frac{1}{3}\right) \qquad \text{Apply the distributive property (recall that } 12 = \frac{12}{1}\text{).}$$

$$2(5x) - 3(3) = 4(1) \qquad \text{Simplify common factors to clear the fractions.}$$

$$10x - 9 = 4$$

$$10x - 9 + 9 = 4 + 9 \qquad \text{Add 9 to both sides.}$$

$$10x = 13$$

$$\frac{10x}{10} = \frac{13}{10} \qquad \text{Divide both sides by 10.}$$

$$x = \frac{13}{10} \qquad \text{The solution set is } \left\{\frac{13}{10}\right\}.$$

TIP: Recall that the multiplication property of equality indicates that multiplying both sides of an equation by a nonzero constant results in an equivalent equation.

122   **Chapter 2**   Linear Equations and Inequalities

> **TIP:** The fractions in this equation can be eliminated by multiplying both sides of the equation by *any* common multiple of the denominators. These include 12, 24, 36, 48, and so on. We chose 12 because it is the *least* common multiple.

Skill Practice   Solve the equation by clearing fractions.

1. $\dfrac{2}{5}y + \dfrac{1}{2} = -\dfrac{7}{10}$

In this section, we combine the process for clearing fractions and decimals with the general strategies for solving linear equations. To solve a linear equation, it is important to follow these steps.

> ### Solving a Linear Equation in One Variable
> **Step 1** Simplify both sides of the equation.
> - Clear parentheses
> - Consider clearing fractions and decimals (if any are present) by multiplying both sides of the equation by a common denominator of all terms
> - Combine *like* terms
>
> **Step 2** Use the addition or subtraction property of equality to collect the variable terms on one side of the equation.
>
> **Step 3** Use the addition or subtraction property of equality to collect the constant terms on the other side of the equation.
>
> **Step 4** Use the multiplication or division property of equality to make the coefficient of the variable term equal to 1.
>
> **Step 5** Check your answer.

Example 2   **Solving a Linear Equation Containing Fractions**

Solve the equation. $\dfrac{1}{6}x - \dfrac{2}{3} = \dfrac{1}{5}x - 1$

Solution:

$$\frac{1}{6}x - \frac{2}{3} = \frac{1}{5}x - 1$$ The LCD of $\frac{1}{6}x$, $-\frac{2}{3}$, $\frac{1}{5}x$, and $\frac{-1}{1}$ is 30.

$$30\left(\frac{1}{6}x - \frac{2}{3}\right) = 30\left(\frac{1}{5}x - 1\right)$$ Multiply by the LCD, 30.

$$\frac{\overset{5}{\cancel{30}}}{1} \cdot \frac{1}{6}x - \frac{\overset{10}{\cancel{30}}}{1} \cdot \frac{2}{3} = \frac{\overset{6}{\cancel{30}}}{1} \cdot \frac{1}{5}x - 30(1)$$ Apply the distributive property (recall $30 = \frac{30}{1}$).

$$5x - 20 = 6x - 30$$ Clear fractions.

$$5x - 6x - 20 = 6x - 6x - 30$$ Subtract $6x$ from both sides.

$$-x - 20 = -30$$

Answers

1. $\{-3\}$

$$-x - 20 + 20 = -30 + 20 \qquad \text{Add } 20 \text{ to both sides.}$$

$$-x = -10$$

$$\frac{-x}{-1} = \frac{-10}{-1} \qquad \text{Divide both sides by } -1.$$

$$x = 10 \qquad \text{The check is left to the reader.}$$

The solution set is $\{10\}$.

Skill Practice   Solve the equation.

2. $\dfrac{2}{5}x - \dfrac{1}{2} = \dfrac{7}{4} + \dfrac{3}{10}x$

Example 3   **Solving a Linear Equation Containing Fractions**

Solve the equation. $\dfrac{1}{3}(x + 7) - \dfrac{1}{2}(x + 1) = 4$

Solution:

$$\frac{1}{3}(x + 7) - \frac{1}{2}(x + 1) = 4$$

$$\frac{1}{3}x + \frac{7}{3} - \frac{1}{2}x - \frac{1}{2} = 4 \qquad \text{Clear parentheses.}$$

$$6\left(\frac{1}{3}x + \frac{7}{3} - \frac{1}{2}x - \frac{1}{2}\right) = 6(4) \qquad \begin{array}{l}\text{The LCD of} \\ \tfrac{1}{3}x, \tfrac{7}{3}, -\tfrac{1}{2}x, -\tfrac{1}{2}, \text{ and } \tfrac{4}{1} \text{ is } 6.\end{array}$$

$$\frac{\overset{2}{\cancel{6}}}{1} \cdot \frac{1}{\cancel{3}}x + \frac{\overset{2}{\cancel{6}}}{1} \cdot \frac{7}{\cancel{3}} + \frac{\overset{3}{\cancel{6}}}{1}\left(-\frac{1}{\cancel{2}}x\right) + \frac{\overset{3}{\cancel{6}}}{1}\left(-\frac{1}{\cancel{2}}\right) = 6(4) \qquad \begin{array}{l}\text{Apply the distributive} \\ \text{property.}\end{array}$$

$$2x + 14 - 3x - 3 = 24$$

$$-x + 11 = 24 \qquad \text{Combine } like \text{ terms.}$$

$$-x + 11 - 11 = 24 - 11 \qquad \text{Subtract } 11.$$

$$-x = 13$$

$$\frac{-x}{-1} = \frac{13}{-1} \qquad \text{Divide by } -1.$$

$$x = -13 \qquad \begin{array}{l}\text{The check is left to the} \\ \text{reader.}\end{array}$$

The solution set is $\{-13\}$.

Skill Practice   Solve the equation.

3. $\dfrac{1}{5}(z + 1) + \dfrac{1}{4}(z + 3) = 2$

TIP: In Example 3 both parentheses and fractions are present within the equation. In such a case, we recommend that you clear parentheses first. Then clear the fractions.

Avoiding Mistakes

When multiplying an equation by the LCD, be sure to multiply all terms on both sides of the equation, including terms that are not fractions.

Answers

2. $\left\{\dfrac{45}{2}\right\}$ **3.** $\left\{\dfrac{7}{3}\right\}$

| **Example 4** | **Solving a Linear Equation Containing Fractions** |

Solve the equation. $\dfrac{x-2}{5} - \dfrac{x-4}{2} = 2$

Solution:

$$\frac{x-2}{5} - \frac{x-4}{2} = \frac{2}{1} \qquad \text{The LCD of } \tfrac{x-2}{5}, \tfrac{x-4}{2}, \text{ and } \tfrac{2}{1} \text{ is } 10.$$

$$10\left(\frac{x-2}{5} - \frac{x-4}{2}\right) = 10\left(\frac{2}{1}\right) \qquad \text{Multiply both sides by } 10.$$

$$\frac{\overset{2}{10}}{1}\cdot\left(\frac{x-2}{\overset{}{5}}\right) - \frac{\overset{5}{10}}{1}\cdot\left(\frac{x-4}{\overset{}{2}}\right) = \frac{10}{1}\cdot\left(\frac{2}{1}\right) \qquad \text{Apply the distributive property.}$$

$$2(x-2) - 5(x-4) = 20 \qquad \text{Clear fractions.}$$

$$2x - 4 - 5x + 20 = 20 \qquad \text{Apply the distributive property.}$$

$$-3x + 16 = 20 \qquad \text{Simplify both sides of the equation.}$$

$$-3x + 16 - 16 = 20 - 16 \qquad \text{Subtract } 16 \text{ from both sides.}$$

$$-3x = 4$$

$$\frac{-3x}{-3} = \frac{4}{-3} \qquad \text{Divide both sides by } -3.$$

$$x = -\frac{4}{3} \qquad \text{The check is left to the reader.}$$

The solution set is $\left\{-\dfrac{4}{3}\right\}$.

> **Avoiding Mistakes**
>
> In Example 4, several of the fractions in the equation have two terms in the numerator. It is important to enclose these fractions in parentheses when clearing fractions. In this way, we will remember to use the distributive property to multiply the factors shown in blue with both terms from the numerator of the fractions.

Skill Practice   Solve the equation.

4. $\dfrac{x+1}{4} + \dfrac{x+2}{6} = 1$

2. Linear Equations Containing Decimals

The same procedure used to clear fractions in an equation can be used to **clear decimals**. For example, consider the equation

$$2.5x + 3 = 1.7x - 6.6$$

Recall that any terminating decimal can be written as a fraction. Therefore, the equation can be interpreted as

$$\frac{25}{10}x + 3 = \frac{17}{10}x - \frac{66}{10}$$

A convenient common denominator of all terms is 10. Therefore, we can multiply the original equation by 10 to clear decimals.

$$10(2.5x + 3) = 10(1.7x - 6.6)$$
$$25x + 30 = 17x - 66$$

Multiplying by the appropriate power of 10 moves the decimal points so that all coefficients become integers.

Answer

4. $\{1\}$

| **Example 5** | **Solving a Linear Equation Containing Decimals** |

Solve the equation by clearing decimals. $2.5x + 3 = 1.7x - 6.6$

Solution:

$$2.5x + 3 = 1.7x - 6.6$$

$$10(2.5x + 3) = 10(1.7x - 6.6) \quad \text{Multiply both sides of the equation by 10.}$$

$$25x + 30 = 17x - 66 \quad \text{Apply the distributive property.}$$

$$25x - 17x + 30 = 17x - 17x - 66 \quad \text{Subtract } 17x \text{ from both sides.}$$

$$8x + 30 = -66$$

$$8x + 30 - 30 = -66 - 30 \quad \text{Subtract } 30 \text{ from both sides.}$$

$$8x = -96$$

$$\frac{8x}{8} = \frac{-96}{8} \quad \text{Divide both sides by 8.}$$

$$x = -12 \quad \text{The check is left to the reader.}$$

The solution set is $\{-12\}$.

> **TIP:** Notice that multiplying a decimal number by 10 has the effect of moving the decimal point one place to the right. Similarly, multiplying by 100 moves the decimal point two places to the right, and so on.

Skill Practice   Solve the equation.

5. $1.2w + 3.5 = 2.1 + w$

| **Example 6** | **Solving a Linear Equation Containing Decimals** |

Solve the equation by clearing decimals. $0.2(x + 4) - 0.45(x + 9) = 12$

Solution:

$$0.2(x + 4) - 0.45(x + 9) = 12$$

$$0.2x + 0.8 - 0.45x - 4.05 = 12 \quad \text{Clear parentheses first.}$$

$$100(0.2x + 0.8 - 0.45x - 4.05) = 100(12) \quad \text{Multiply both sides by 100.}$$

$$20x + 80 - 45x - 405 = 1200 \quad \text{Apply the distributive property.}$$

$$-25x - 325 = 1200 \quad \text{Simplify both sides.}$$

$$-25x - 325 + 325 = 1200 + 325 \quad \text{Add 325 to both sides.}$$

$$-25x = 1525$$

$$\frac{-25x}{-25} = \frac{1525}{-25} \quad \text{Divide both sides by } -25.$$

$$x = -61 \quad \text{The check is left to the reader.}$$

The solution set is $\{-61\}$.

> **TIP:** The terms with the most digits following the decimal point are $-0.45x$ and -4.05. Each of these is written to the hundredths place. Therefore, we multiply both sides by 100.

Skill Practice   Solve the equation.

6. $0.25(x + 2) - 0.15(x + 3) = 4$

Answers
5. $\{-7\}$ **6.** $\{39.5\}$

126   **Chapter 2**   Linear Equations and Inequalities

Section 2.3   Practice Exercises

Study Skills Exercise

Instructors vary in what they emphasize on tests. For example, test material may come from the textbook, notes, handouts, or homework. What does your instructor emphasize?

Vocabulary and Key Concepts

1. **a.** The process of eliminating fractions in an equation by multiplying both sides of the equation by the LCD is called _____ _____.

   b. The process of eliminating decimals in an equation by multiplying both sides of the equation by a power of 10 is called _____ _____.

Review Exercises

For Exercises 2–8, solve each equation.

2. $-5t - 17 = -2t + 49$

3. $5(x + 2) - 3 = 4x + 5$

4. $-2(2x - 4x) = 6 + 18$

5. $3(2y + 3) - 4(-y + 1) = 7y - 10$

6. $-(3w + 4) + 5(w - 2) - 3(6w - 8) = 10$

7. $7x + 2 = 7(x - 12)$

8. $2(3x - 6) = 3(2x - 4)$

Concept 1: Linear Equations Containing Fractions

For Exercises 9–14, determine which of the values could be used to clear fractions or decimals in the given equation.

9. $\frac{2}{3}x - \frac{1}{6} = \frac{x}{9}$

   Values: 6, 9, 12, 18, 24, 36

10. $\frac{1}{4}x - \frac{2}{7} = \frac{1}{2}x + 2$

    Values: 4, 7, 14, 21, 28, 42

11. $0.02x + 0.5 = 0.35x + 1.2$

    Values: 10; 100; 1000; 10,000

12. $0.003 - 0.002x = 0.1x$

    Values: 10; 100; 1000; 10,000

13. $\frac{1}{6}x + \frac{7}{10} = x$

    Values: 3, 6, 10, 30, 60

14. $2x - \frac{5}{2} = \frac{x}{3} - \frac{1}{4}$

    Values: 2, 3, 4, 6, 12, 24

For Exercises 15–36, solve each equation. **(See Examples 1–4.)**

15. $\frac{1}{2}x + 3 = 5$

16. $\frac{1}{3}y - 4 = 9$

17. $\frac{2}{15}z + 3 = \frac{7}{5}$

18. $\frac{1}{6}y + 2 = \frac{5}{12}$

19. $\frac{1}{3}q + \frac{3}{5} = \frac{1}{15}q - \frac{2}{5}$

20. $\frac{3}{7}x - 5 = \frac{24}{7}x + 7$

21. $\frac{12}{5}w + 7 = 31 - \frac{3}{5}w$

22. $-\frac{1}{9}p - \frac{5}{18} = -\frac{1}{6}p + \frac{1}{3}$

23. $\frac{1}{4}(3m - 4) - \frac{1}{5} = \frac{1}{4}m + \frac{3}{10}$

24. $\frac{1}{25}(20 - t) = \frac{4}{25}t - \frac{3}{5}$

25. $\frac{1}{6}(5s + 3) = \frac{1}{2}(s + 11)$

26. $\frac{1}{12}(4n - 3) = \frac{1}{4}(2n + 1)$

27. $\frac{2}{3}x + 4 = \frac{2}{3}x - 6$

28. $-\dfrac{1}{9}a + \dfrac{2}{9} = \dfrac{1}{3} - \dfrac{1}{9}a$

29. $\dfrac{1}{6}(2c - 1) = \dfrac{1}{3}c - \dfrac{1}{6}$

30. $\dfrac{3}{2}b - 1 = \dfrac{1}{8}(12b - 8)$

31. $\dfrac{2x + 1}{3} + \dfrac{x - 1}{3} = 5$

32. $\dfrac{4y - 2}{5} - \dfrac{y + 4}{5} = -3$

33. $\dfrac{3w - 2}{6} = 1 - \dfrac{w - 1}{3}$

34. $\dfrac{z - 7}{4} = \dfrac{6z - 1}{8} - 2$

35. $\dfrac{x + 3}{3} - \dfrac{x - 1}{2} = 4$

36. $\dfrac{5y - 1}{2} - \dfrac{y + 4}{5} = 1$

Concept 2: Linear Equations Containing Decimals

For Exercises 37–54, solve each equation. **(See Examples 5–6.)**

37. $9.2y - 4.3 = 50.9$

38. $-6.3x + 1.5 = -4.8$

39. $0.05z + 0.2 = 0.15z - 10.5$

40. $21.1w + 4.6 = 10.9w + 35.2$

41. $0.2p - 1.4 = 0.2(p - 7)$

42. $0.5(3q + 87) = 1.5q + 43.5$

43. $0.20x + 53.60 = x$

44. $z + 0.06z = 3816$

45. $0.15(90) + 0.05p = 0.1(90 + p)$

46. $0.25(60) + 0.10x = 0.15(60 + x)$

47. $0.40(y + 10) - 0.60(y + 2) = 2$

48. $0.75(x - 2) + 0.25(x + 4) = 0.5$

49. $0.12x + 3 - 0.8x = 0.22x - 0.6$

50. $0.4x + 0.2 = -3.6 - 0.6x$

51. $0.06(x - 0.5) = 0.06x + 0.01$

52. $0.125x = 0.025(5x + 1)$

53. $-3.5x + 1.3 = -0.3(9x - 5)$

54. $x + 4 = 2(0.4x + 1.3)$

Mixed Exercises

For Exercises 55–64, solve each equation.

55. $0.2x - 1.8 = -3$

56. $9.8h + 2 = 3.8h + 20$

57. $\dfrac{1}{4}(x + 4) = \dfrac{1}{5}(2x + 3)$

58. $\dfrac{2}{3}(y - 1) = \dfrac{3}{4}(3y - 2)$

59. $0.05(2t - 1) - 0.03(4t - 1) = 0.2$

60. $0.3(x + 6) - 0.7(x + 2) = 4$

61. $\dfrac{2k + 5}{4} = 2 - \dfrac{k + 2}{3}$

62. $\dfrac{3d - 4}{6} + 1 = \dfrac{d + 1}{8}$

63. $\dfrac{1}{8}v + \dfrac{2}{3} = \dfrac{1}{6}v + \dfrac{3}{4}$

64. $\dfrac{2}{5}z - \dfrac{1}{4} = \dfrac{3}{10}z + \dfrac{1}{2}$

Expanding Your Skills

For Exercises 65–68, solve each equation.

65. $\dfrac{1}{2}a + 0.4 = -0.7 - \dfrac{3}{5}a$

66. $\dfrac{3}{4}c - 0.11 = 0.23(c - 5)$

67. $0.8 + \dfrac{7}{10}b = \dfrac{3}{2}b - 0.8$

68. $0.78 - \dfrac{1}{25}h = \dfrac{3}{5}h - 0.5$

Problem Recognition Exercises

Equations vs. Expressions

For Exercises 1–32, identify each exercise as an expression or an equation. Then simplify the expression or solve the equation.

1. $2b + 23 - 6b - 5$

2. $10p - 9 + 2p - 3 + 8p - 18$

3. $\dfrac{y}{4} = -2$

4. $-\dfrac{x}{2} = 7$

5. $3(4h - 2) - (5h - 8) = 8 - (2h + 3)$

6. $7y - 3(2y + 5) = 7 - (10 - 10y)$

7. $3(8z - 1) + 10 - 6(5 + 3z)$

8. $-5(1 - x) - 3(2x + 3) + 5$

9. $6c + 3(c + 1) = 10$

10. $-9 + 5(2y + 3) = -7$

11. $0.5(2a - 3) - 0.1 = 0.4(6 + 2a)$

12. $0.07(2v - 4) = 0.1(v - 4)$

13. $-\dfrac{5}{9}w + \dfrac{11}{12} = \dfrac{23}{36}$

14. $\dfrac{3}{8}t - \dfrac{5}{8} = \dfrac{1}{2}t + \dfrac{1}{8}$

15. $\dfrac{3}{4}x + \dfrac{1}{2} - \dfrac{1}{8}x + \dfrac{5}{4}$

16. $\dfrac{7}{3}(6 - 12t) + \dfrac{1}{2}(4t + 8)$

17. $2z - 7 = 2(z - 13)$

18. $-6x + 2(x + 1) = -2(2x + 3)$

19. $\dfrac{2x - 1}{4} + \dfrac{3x + 2}{6} = 2$

20. $\dfrac{w - 4}{6} - \dfrac{3w - 1}{2} = -1$

21. $4b - 8 - b = -3b + 2(3b - 4)$

22. $-k - 41 - 2 - k = -2(20 + k) - 3$

23. $\dfrac{4}{3}(6y - 3) = 0$

24. $\dfrac{1}{2}(2c - 4) + 3 = \dfrac{1}{3}(6c + 3)$

25. $3(x + 6) - 7(x + 2) - 4(1 - x)$

26. $-10(2k + 1) - 4(4 - 5k) + 25$

27. $3 - 2[4a - 5(a + 1)]$

28. $-9 - 4[3 - 2(q + 3)]$

29. $4 + 2[8 - (6 + x)] = -2(x - 1) - 4 + x$

30. $-1 - 5[2 + 3(w - 2)] = 5(w + 4)$

31. $\dfrac{1}{6}y + y - \dfrac{1}{3}(4y - 1)$

32. $\dfrac{1}{2} - \dfrac{1}{5}\left(x + \dfrac{1}{2}\right) + \dfrac{9}{10}x$

Section 2.4	Applications of Linear Equations: Introduction to Problem Solving

Concepts

1. Problem-Solving Strategies

Linear equations can be used to solve many real-world applications. However, with "word problems," students often do not know where to start. To help organize the problem-solving process, we offer the following guidelines:

Problem-Solving Flowchart for Word Problems

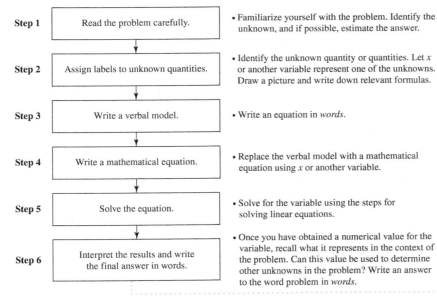

Step 1 — Read the problem carefully.
• Familiarize yourself with the problem. Identify the unknown, and if possible, estimate the answer.

Step 2 — Assign labels to unknown quantities.
• Identify the unknown quantity or quantities. Let x or another variable represent one of the unknowns. Draw a picture and write down relevant formulas.

Step 3 — Write a verbal model.
• Write an equation in *words*.

Step 4 — Write a mathematical equation.
• Replace the verbal model with a mathematical equation using x or another variable.

Step 5 — Solve the equation.
• Solve for the variable using the steps for solving linear equations.

Step 6 — Interpret the results and write the final answer in words.
• Once you have obtained a numerical value for the variable, recall what it represents in the context of the problem. Can this value be used to determine other unknowns in the problem? Write an answer to the word problem in *words*.

> **Avoiding Mistakes**
>
> Once you have reached a solution to a word problem, verify that it is reasonable in the context of the problem.

2. Translations Involving Linear Equations

We have already practiced translating an English sentence to a mathematical equation. Recall that several key words translate to the algebraic operations of addition, subtraction, multiplication, and division.

Example 1   **Translating to a Linear Equation**

The sum of a number and negative eleven is negative fifteen. Find the number.

Solution:

Let x represent the unknown number.

the sum of   is

$$(\text{a number}) + (-11) = (-15)$$

$$x + (-11) = -15$$

$$x + (-11) + 11 = -15 + 11$$

$$x = -4$$

The number is -4.

Step 1: Read the problem.

Step 2: Label the unknown.

Step 3: Write a verbal model.

Step 4: Write an equation.

Step 5: Solve the equation.

Step 6: Write the final answer in words.

Skill Practice

1. The sum of a number and negative seven is 12. Find the number.

Answer

1. The number is 19.

Example 2 **Translating to a Linear Equation**

Forty less than five times a number is fifty-two less than the number. Find the number.

Solution:

	Step 1: Read the problem.
Let x represent the unknown number.	**Step 2:** Label the unknown.

$$\left(\begin{array}{c}5 \text{ times} \\ \text{a number}\end{array}\right) \overset{\text{less}}{-} (40) \overset{\text{is}}{=} \left(\begin{array}{c}\text{the} \\ \text{number}\end{array}\right) \overset{\text{less}}{-} (52)$$

Step 3: Write a verbal model.

$$5x \quad - \quad 40 \quad = \quad x \quad - \quad 52$$

Step 4: Write an equation.

$$5x - 40 = x - 52$$

Step 5: Solve the equation.

$$5x - x - 40 = x - x - 52$$

$$4x - 40 = -52$$

$$4x - 40 + 40 = -52 + 40$$

$$4x = -12$$

$$\frac{4x}{4} = \frac{-12}{4}$$

$$x = -3$$

The number is -3.

Step 6: Write the final answer in words.

Avoiding Mistakes

It is important to remember that subtraction is not a commutative operation. Therefore, the order in which two real numbers are subtracted affects the outcome. The expression "forty less than five times a number" must be translated as: $5x - 40$ (not $40 - 5x$). Similarly, "fifty-two less than the number" must be translated as: $x - 52$ (not $52 - x$).

Skill Practice

2. Thirteen more than twice a number is 5 more than the number. Find the number.

Example 3 **Translating to a Linear Equation**

Twice the sum of a number and six is two more than three times the number. Find the number.

Solution:

	Step 1: Read the problem.
Let x represent the unknown number.	**Step 2:** Label the unknown.

$$\overset{\text{twice}}{2} \cdot \overset{\text{the sum}}{(x + 6)} \overset{\text{is}}{=} \overset{\text{2 more than}}{3x + 2}$$

three times
a number

Step 3: Write a verbal model.

Step 4: Write an equation.

Answer

2. The number is -8.

$$2(x + 6) = 3x + 2$$

Step 5:   Solve the equation.

$$2x + 12 = 3x + 2$$

$$2x - 2x + 12 = 3x - 2x + 2$$

$$12 = x + 2$$

$$12 - 2 = x + 2 - 2$$

$$10 = x$$

The number is 10.

Step 6:   Write the final answer in words.

> **Avoiding Mistakes**
>
> It is important to enclose "the sum of a number and six" within parentheses so that the entire quantity is multiplied by 2. Forgetting the parentheses would imply that only the x-term is multiplied by 2.
>
> Correct: $2(x + 6)$
>
> Incorrect: $2x + 6$

Skill Practice

3. Three times the sum of a number and eight is 4 more than the number. Find the number.

3. Consecutive Integer Problems

The word *consecutive* means "following one after the other in order without gaps." The numbers 6, 7, and 8 are examples of three **consecutive integers**. The numbers $-4, -2, 0$, and 2 are examples of **consecutive even integers**. The numbers 23, 25, and 27 are examples of **consecutive odd integers**.

Notice that any two consecutive integers differ by 1. Therefore, if x represents an integer, then $(x + 1)$ represents the next larger consecutive integer (Figure 2-4).

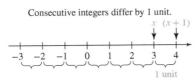

Consecutive integers differ by 1 unit.

Figure 2-4

Any two consecutive even integers differ by 2. Therefore, if x represents an even integer, then $(x + 2)$ represents the next consecutive larger even integer (Figure 2-5).

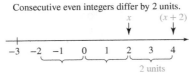

Consecutive even integers differ by 2 units.

Figure 2-5

Likewise, any two consecutive odd integers differ by 2. If x represents an odd integer, then $(x + 2)$ is the next larger odd integer (Figure 2-6).

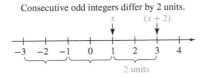

Consecutive odd integers differ by 2 units.

Figure 2-6

Answer

3. The number is -10.

| **Example 4** | **Solving an Application Involving Consecutive Integers** |

The sum of two consecutive odd integers is -188. Find the integers.

Solution:

In this example we have two unknown integers. We can let x represent either of the unknowns.

| | **Step 1:** | Read the problem. |

Suppose x represents the first odd integer.   **Step 2:**   Label the unknowns.

Then $(x + 2)$ represents the second odd integer.

$$\binom{\text{First}}{\text{integer}} + \binom{\text{second}}{\text{integer}} = (\text{total})$$ **Step 3:**   Write a verbal model.

$$\quad x \quad + \quad (x + 2) \quad = -188$$ **Step 4:**   Write a mathematical equation.

$$x + (x + 2) = -188$$

$$2x + 2 = -188$$ **Step 5:**   Solve for x.

$$2x + 2 - 2 = -188 - 2$$

$$2x = -190$$

$$\frac{2x}{2} = \frac{-190}{2}$$

$$x = -95$$

The first integer is $x = -95$.   **Step 6:**   Interpret the results and write the answer in words.

The second integer is $x + 2 = -95 + 2 = -93$.

The two integers are -95 and -93.

> **TIP:** With word problems, it is advisable to check that the answer is reasonable.
>   The numbers -95 and -93 are consecutive odd integers. Furthermore, their sum is -188 as desired.

Skill Practice

4. The sum of two consecutive even integers is 66. Find the integers.

| **Example 5** | **Solving an Application Involving Consecutive Integers** |

Ten times the smallest of three consecutive integers is twenty-two more than three times the sum of the integers. Find the integers.

Solution:

| | **Step 1:** | Read the problem. |

Let x represent the first integer.   **Step 2:**   Label the unknowns.

$x + 1$ represents the second consecutive integer.

$x + 2$ represents the third consecutive integer.

Answer

4. The integers are 32 and 34.

$$\begin{pmatrix} 10 \text{ times} \\ \text{the first} \\ \text{integer} \end{pmatrix} = \begin{pmatrix} 3 \text{ times} \\ \text{the sum of} \\ \text{the integers} \end{pmatrix} + 22$$

Step 3: Write a verbal model.

$$10x = \underbrace{3[(x) + (x + 1) + (x + 2)]}_{\text{the sum of the integers}} + 22$$

10 times the first integer — is — 3 times — 22 more than

Step 4: Write a mathematical equation.

$$10x = 3(x + x + 1 + x + 2) + 22$$

Step 5: Solve the equation.

$$10x = 3(3x + 3) + 22$$

Clear parentheses.

$$10x = 9x + 9 + 22$$

Combine *like* terms.

$$10x = 9x + 31$$

$$10x - 9x = 9x - 9x + 31$$

Isolate the x-terms on one side.

$$x = 31$$

The first integer is $x = 31$.

The second integer is $x + 1 = 31 + 1 = 32$.

The third integer is $x + 2 = 31 + 2 = 33$.

The three integers are 31, 32, and 33.

Step 6: Interpret the results and write the answer in words.

Skill Practice

5. Five times the smallest of three consecutive integers is 17 less than twice the sum of the integers. Find the integers.

---

4. Applications of Linear Equations

Example 6   Using a Linear Equation in an Application

A carpenter cuts a 6-ft board in two pieces. One piece must be three times as long as the other. Find the length of each piece.

Solution:

In this problem, one piece must be three times as long as the other. Thus, if x represents the length of one piece, then $3x$ can represent the length of the other.

Step 1: Read the problem completely.

x represents the length of the smaller piece.
$3x$ represents the length of the longer piece.

Step 2: Label the unknowns. Draw a figure.

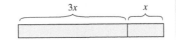

Answer

5. The integers are 11, 12, and 13.

$$\begin{pmatrix} \text{Length of} \\ \text{one piece} \end{pmatrix} + \begin{pmatrix} \text{length of} \\ \text{other piece} \end{pmatrix} = \begin{pmatrix} \text{total length} \\ \text{of the board} \end{pmatrix}$$ **Step 3:**   Write a verbal model.

$$x \quad + \quad 3x \quad = \quad 6$$ **Step 4:**   Write an equation.

$$4x = 6$$ **Step 5:**   Solve the equation.

$$\frac{4x}{4} = \frac{6}{4}$$

> **TIP:** The variable can represent either unknown. In Example 6, if we let x represent the length of the longer piece of board, then $\frac{1}{3}x$ would represent the length of the smaller piece. The equation would become $x + \frac{1}{3}x = 6$. Try solving this equation and interpreting the result.

$$x = 1.5$$

The smaller piece is $x = 1.5$ ft.   **Step 6:**   Interpret the results.

The longer piece is $3x$ or $3(1.5 \text{ ft}) = 4.5$ ft.

Skill Practice

6. A plumber cuts a 96-in. piece of pipe into two pieces. One piece is five times longer than the other piece. How long is each piece?

Example 7   **Using a Linear Equation in an Application**

In a recent Olympics, the United States won the greatest number of overall medals, followed by China. The United States won 16 more medals than China, and together they brought home a total of 192 medals. How many medals did each country win?

Source: U.S. Department of Defense

Solution:

In this example, we have two unknowns. The variable x can represent either quantity. However, the number of medals won by the United States is given in terms of the number won by China.   **Step 1:**   Read the problem.

Let x represent the number of medals won by China.   **Step 2:**   Label the variables.

Then let $x + 16$ represent the number of medals won by the United States.

$$\begin{pmatrix} \text{Number of} \\ \text{medals won} \\ \text{by China} \end{pmatrix} + \begin{pmatrix} \text{Number of medals} \\ \text{won by the} \\ \text{United States} \end{pmatrix} = \begin{pmatrix} \text{Total} \\ \text{number} \\ \text{of medals} \end{pmatrix}$$ **Step 3:**   Write a verbal model.

$$x \quad + \quad (x + 16) \quad = \quad 192$$ **Step 4:**   Write an equation.

$$2x + 16 = 192$$ **Step 5:**   Solve the equation.

$$2x = 176$$

$$x = 88$$

- Medals won by China, $x = 88$
- Medals won by the United States, $x + 16 = (88) + 16 = 104$

China won 88 medals and the United States won 104 medals.

Answer

6. One piece is 80 in. and the other is 16 in.

Skill Practice

7. There are 40 students in an algebra class. There are 4 more women than men. How many women and how many men are in the class?

Answer

7. There are 22 women and 18 men.

Section 2.4   Practice Exercises

Study Skills Exercise

After doing a section of homework, check the answers to the odd-numbered exercises in the back of the text. Choose a method to identify the exercises that gave you trouble (i.e., circle the number or put a star by the number). List some reasons why it is important to label these problems.

Vocabulary and Key Concepts

1. a. Integers that follow one after the other without "gaps" are called _____ integers.

   b. The integers -2, 0, 2, and 4 are examples of consecutive _____ integers.

   c. The integers -3, -1, 1, and 3 are examples of consecutive _____ integers.

   d. Two consecutive integers differ by _____.

   e. Two consecutive odd integers differ by _____.

   f. Two consecutive even integers differ by _____.

Concept 2: Translations Involving Linear Equations

For Exercises 2–8, write an expression representing the unknown quantity.

2. In a math class, the number of students who received an "A" in the class was 5 more than the number of students who received a "B." If x represents the number of "B" students, write an expression for the number of "A" students.

3. There are 5,682,080 fewer men than women on a particular social media site. If x represents the number of women using that site, write an expression for the number of men using that site.

4. At a recent motorcycle rally, the number of men exceeded the number of women by 216. If x represents the number of women, write an expression for the number of men.

5. There are 10 times as many users of a social media site than there are of a social news site. If x represents the number of users of the news site, write an expression for the number of users of the social media site.

6. Rebecca downloaded twice as many songs as Nigel. If x represents the number of songs downloaded by Nigel, write an expression for the number downloaded by Rebecca.

7. Sidney made $20 less than three times Casey's weekly salary. If x represents Casey's weekly salary, write an expression for Sidney's weekly salary.

8. David scored 26 points less than twice the number of points Rich scored in a video game. If x represents the number of points scored by Rich, write an expression representing the number of points scored by David.

© McGraw-Hill Education/
Mark Dierker

For Exercises 9–18, use the Problem-Solving Flowchart for Word Problems. **(See Examples 1–3.)**

9. Six less than a number is −10. Find the number.

10. Fifteen less than a number is 41. Find the number.

11. Twice the sum of a number and seven is eight. Find the number.

12. Twice the sum of a number and negative two is sixteen. Find the number.

13. A number added to five is the same as twice the number. Find the number.

14. Three times a number is the same as the difference of twice the number and seven. Find the number.

15. The sum of six times a number and ten is equal to the difference of the number and fifteen. Find the number.

16. The difference of fourteen and three times a number is the same as the sum of the number and negative ten. Find the number.

17. If the difference of a number and four is tripled, the result is six less than the number. Find the number.

18. Twice the sum of a number and eleven is twenty-two less than three times the number. Find the number.

Concept 3: Consecutive Integer Problems

19. a. If x represents the smallest of three consecutive integers, write an expression to represent each of the next two consecutive integers.

b. If x represents the largest of three consecutive integers, write an expression to represent each of the previous two consecutive integers.

20. a. If x represents the smallest of three consecutive odd integers, write an expression to represent each of the next two consecutive odd integers.

b. If x represents the largest of three consecutive odd integers, write an expression to represent each of the previous two consecutive odd integers.

For Exercises 21–30, use the Problem-Solving Flowchart for Word Problems. **(See Examples 4–5.)**

21. The sum of two consecutive integers is −67. Find the integers.

22. The sum of two consecutive odd integers is 52. Find the integers.

23. The sum of two consecutive odd integers is 28. Find the integers.

24. The sum of three consecutive even integers is 66. Find the integers.

25. The perimeter of a pentagon (a five-sided polygon) is 80 in. The five sides are represented by consecutive integers. Find the lengths of the sides.

26. The perimeter of a triangle is 96 in. The lengths of the sides are represented by consecutive integers. Find the lengths of the sides.

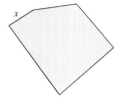

27. The sum of three consecutive even integers is 48 less than twice the smallest of the three integers. Find the integers.

28. The sum of three consecutive odd integers is 89 less than twice the largest integer. Find the integers.

29. Eight times the sum of three consecutive odd integers is 210 more than ten times the middle integer. Find the integers.

30. Five times the sum of three consecutive even integers is 140 more than ten times the smallest of the integers. Find the integers.

Concept 4: Applications of Linear Equations

For Exercises 31–42, use the Problem-Solving Flowchart for Word Problems to solve the problems.

31. A board is 86 cm in length and must be cut so that one piece is 20 cm longer than the other piece. Find the length of each piece. **(See Example 6.)**

x $x + 20$

32. A rope is 54 in. in length and must be cut into two pieces. If one piece must be twice as long as the other, find the length of each piece.

x $2x$

33. Karen's music library contains 12 fewer playlists than Clarann's music library. The total number of playlists for both music libraries is 58. Find the number of playlists in each person's music library.

34. Maria has 15 fewer apps on her phone than Orlando. If the total number of apps on both phones is 29, how many apps are on each phone?

35. For a recent year, 31 more Democrats than Republicans were in the U.S. House of Representatives. If the total number of representatives in the House from these two parties was 433, find the number of representatives from each party.

36. For a recent year, the number of men in the U.S. Senate totaled 4 more than five times the number of women. Find the number of men and the number of women in the Senate given that the Senate has 100 members.

37. A car dealership sells SUVs and passenger cars. For a recent year, 40 more SUVs were sold than passenger cars. If a total of 420 vehicles were sold, determine the number of each type of vehicle sold. **(See Example 7.)**

38. Two of the largest Internet retailers are eBay and Amazon. Recently, the estimated U.S. sales of eBay were $0.1 billion less than twice the sales of Amazon. Given the total sales of $5.6 billion, determine the sales of eBay and Amazon.

39. The longest river in Africa is the Nile. It is 2455 km longer than the Congo River, also in Africa. The sum of the lengths of these rivers is 11,195 km. What is the length of each river?

40. The average depth of the Gulf of Mexico is three times the depth of the Red Sea. The difference between the average depths is 1078 m. What is the average depth of the Gulf of Mexico and the average depth of the Red Sea?

41. Asia and Africa are the two largest continents in the world. The land area of Asia is approximately 14,514,000 km^2 larger than the land area of Africa. Together their total area is 74,644,000 km^2. Find the land area of Asia and the land area of Africa.

42. Mt. Everest, the highest mountain in the world, is 2654 m higher than Mt. McKinley, the highest mountain in the United States. If the sum of their heights is 15,042 m, find the height of each mountain.

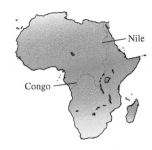

© J. Luke/PhotoLink/Getty Images RF

Mixed Exercises

43. A group of hikers walked from Hawk Mt. Shelter to Blood Mt. Shelter along the Appalachian Trail, a total distance of 20.5 mi. It took 2 days for the walk. The second day the hikers walked 4.1 mi less than they did on the first day. How far did they walk each day?

© Corbis/age fotostock RF

44. $120 is to be divided among three restaurant servers. Angie made $10 more than Marie. Gwen, who went home sick, made $25 less than Marie. How much money should each server get?

45. A 4-ft piece of PVC pipe is cut into three pieces. The longest piece is 5 in. shorter than three times the shortest piece. The middle piece is 8 in. longer than the shortest piece. How long is each piece?

46. A 6-ft piece of copper wire must be cut into three pieces. The shortest piece is 16 in. less than the middle piece. The longest piece is twice as long as the middle piece. How long is each piece?

© Comstock Images/
Masterfile RF

47. Three consecutive integers are such that three times the largest exceeds the sum of the two smaller integers by 47. Find the integers.

48. Four times the smallest of three consecutive odd integers is 236 more than the sum of the other two integers. Find the integers.

49. The winner and runner-up of a TV music contest had lucrative earnings immediately after the show's finale. The runner-up earned $2 million less than half of the winner's earnings. If their combined earnings totaled $19 million, how much did each person make?

50. One TV series ran 97 fewer episodes than twice the number of a second TV series. If the total number of episodes is 998, determine the number of each show produced.

51. Five times the difference of a number and three is four less than four times the number. Find the number.

52. Three times the difference of a number and seven is one less than twice the number. Find the number.

53. The sum of the page numbers on two facing pages in a book is 941. What are the page numbers?

54. Three raffle tickets are represented by three consecutive integers. If the sum of the three integers is 2,666,031, find the numbers.

55. If three is added to five times a number, the result is forty-three more than the number. Find the number.

56. If seven is added to three times a number, the result is thirty-one more than the number. Find the number.

57. The deepest point in the Pacific Ocean is 676 m more than twice the deepest point in the Arctic Ocean. If the deepest point in the Pacific is 10,920 m, how many meters is the deepest point in the Arctic Ocean?

58. The area of Greenland is 201,900 km² less than three times the area of New Guinea. What is the area of New Guinea if the area of Greenland is 2,175,600 km²?

59. The sum of twice a number and $\frac{3}{4}$ is the same as the difference of four times the number and $\frac{1}{8}$. Find the number.

60. The difference of a number and $-\frac{11}{12}$ is the same as the difference of three times the number and $\frac{1}{6}$. Find the number.

61. The product of a number and 3.86 is equal to 7.15 more than the number. Find the number.

62. The product of a number and 4.6 is 33.12 less than the number. Find the number.

Applications Involving Percents

1. Basic Percent Equations

Recall that the word *percent* as meaning "per hundred."

Percent	Interpretation
63% of homes have a computer	63 out of 100 homes have a computer.
5% sales tax	5¢ in tax is charged for every 100¢ in merchandise.
15% commission	$15 is earned in commission for every $100 sold.

Percents come up in a variety of applications in day-to-day life. Many such applications follow the basic percent equation:

$$\text{Amount} = (\text{percent})(\text{base}) \qquad \text{Basic percent equation}$$

In Example 1, we apply the basic percent equation to compute sales tax.

Concepts

1. Basic Percent Equations
2. Applications Involving Simple Interest
3. Applications Involving Discount and Markup

Example 1   **Computing Sales Tax**

A new digital camera costs $429.95.

a. Compute the sales tax if the tax rate is 4%.

b. Determine the total cost, including tax.

Solution:

a. Let x represent the amount of tax.

$$\text{Amount} = (\text{percent}) \cdot (\text{base})$$
$$\downarrow \qquad\qquad \downarrow \qquad\qquad \downarrow$$
$$\text{Sales tax} = (\text{tax rate})(\text{price of merchandise})$$

$$x = (0.04)(\$429.95)$$

$$x = \$17.198$$
$$x = \$17.20$$

The tax on the merchandise is $17.20.

Step 1: Read the problem.

Step 2: Label the variable.

Step 3: Write a verbal model. Apply the percent equation to compute sales tax.

Step 4: Write a mathematical equation.

Step 5: Solve the equation.
Round to the nearest cent.

Step 6: Interpret the results.

© BrandX/Punchstock RF

Avoiding Mistakes

Be sure to use the decimal form of a percent within an equation.

$$4\% = 0.04$$

b. The total cost is found by:

total cost = cost of merchandise + amount of tax

Therefore, the total cost is $429.95 + $17.20 = $447.15.

Skill Practice

1. Find the amount of tax on a portable CD player that sells for $89. Assume the tax rate is 6%.

2. Find the total cost including tax.

In Example 2, we solve a problem in which the percent is unknown.

> **Example 2**   Finding an Unknown Percent

A group of 240 college men were asked what intramural sport they most enjoyed playing. The results are in the graph. What percent of the men surveyed preferred tennis?

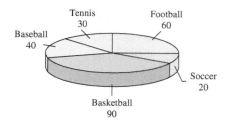

Tennis
30

Football
60

Baseball
40

Soccer
20

Basketball
90

Solution:

	Step 1: Read the problem.
Let x represent the unknown percent (in decimal form).	**Step 2:** Label the variable.
The problem can be rephrased as:	
30 is what percent of 240?	**Step 3:** Write a verbal model.
$30 = x \cdot 240$	**Step 4:** Write a mathematical equation.
$30 = 240x$	**Step 5:** Solve the equation.
$\dfrac{30}{240} = \dfrac{240x}{240}$	Divide both sides by 240.
$0.125 = x$	
$0.125 \times 100\% = 12.5\%$	**Step 6:** Interpret the results. Change the value of x to a percent form by multiplying by 100%.
In this survey, 12.5% of men prefer tennis.	

Skill Practice   Refer to the graph in Example 2.

3. What percent of the men surveyed prefer basketball as their favorite intramural sport?

Answers

1. The amount of tax is $5.34.
2. The total cost is $94.34.
3. 37.5% of the men surveyed prefer basketball.

Example 3	**Solving a Percent Equation with an Unknown Base**

Andrea spends 20% of her monthly paycheck on rent each month. If her rent payment is $950, what is her monthly paycheck?

Solution:

© Stockbyte/Getty Images RF

	Step 1: Read the problem.
Let x represent the amount of Andrea's monthly paycheck.	**Step 2:** Label the variables.
The problem can be rephrased as:	
$950 is 20% of what number?	**Step 3:** Write a verbal model.
$\downarrow \quad \downarrow \quad \downarrow \quad \downarrow \quad \downarrow$	
$950 = 0.20 \cdot x$	**Step 4:** Write a mathematical equation.
$950 = 0.20x$	**Step 5:** Solve the equation.
$\dfrac{950}{0.20} = \dfrac{0.20x}{0.20}$	Divide both sides by 0.20.
$4750 = x$	
Andrea's monthly paycheck is $4750.	**Step 6:** Interpret the results.

Skill Practice

4. In order to pass an exam, a student must answer 70% of the questions correctly. If answering 42 questions correctly results in a 70% score, how many questions are on the test?

2. Applications Involving Simple Interest

One important application of percents is in computing simple interest on a loan or on an investment.

Simple interest is interest that is earned or owed on principal (the original amount of money invested or borrowed). The following formula is used to compute simple interest.

$$\begin{pmatrix} \text{Simple} \\ \text{interest} \end{pmatrix} = (\text{principal}) \begin{pmatrix} \text{annual} \\ \text{interest rate} \end{pmatrix} \begin{pmatrix} \text{time} \\ \text{in years} \end{pmatrix}$$

This formula is often written symbolically as $I = Prt$. In this formula, I represents the simple interest, P represents the principal, r represents the annual interest rate, and t is the time of the investment in years.

For example, to find the simple interest earned on $2000 invested at 7.5% interest for 3 years, we have $P = \$2000$, $r = 0.075$, and $t = 3$. Thus,

$$I = Prt$$
$$\text{Interest} = (\$2000)(0.075)(3)$$
$$= \$450$$

Answer

4. There are 60 questions on the test.

Example 4   Applying Simple Interest

Jorge wants to save money to buy a car in 5 years. If Jorge needs to have $20,250 at the end of 5 years, how much money would he need to invest in a certificate of deposit (CD) at a 2.5% interest rate?

Solution:

© Ingram Publishing RF

Avoiding Mistakes

The interest is computed on the original principal, P, not on the total amount $20,250. That is, the interest is $P(0.025)(5)$, not ($20,250)(0.025)(5).

	Step 1: Read the problem.
Let P represent the original amount invested.	**Step 2:** Label the variables.
$\left(\begin{array}{c}\text{Original}\\\text{principal}\end{array}\right) + (\text{interest}) = (\text{total})$	**Step 3:** Write a verbal model.
$\qquad\downarrow\qquad\qquad\downarrow\qquad\quad\downarrow$	
$\quad P\quad + \quad Prt\quad = \text{total}$	**Step 4:** Write a mathematical equation.
$\quad P\quad + \ P(0.025)(5) = 20{,}250$	
$P + 0.125P = 20{,}250$	**Step 5:** Solve the equation.
$1.125P = 20{,}250$	
$\dfrac{1.125P}{1.125} = \dfrac{20{,}250}{1.125}$	
$P = 18{,}000$	

The original investment should be $18,000.

Step 6: Interpret the results and write the answer in words.

Skill Practice

5. Cassandra invested some money in her bank account, and after 10 years at 4% simple interest, it has grown to $7700. What was the initial amount invested?

3. Applications Involving Discount and Markup

Applications involving percent increase and percent decrease are abundant in many real-world settings. Sales tax, for example, is essentially a markup by a state or local government. It is important to understand that percent increase or decrease is always computed on the original amount given.

In Example 5, we illustrate an example of percent decrease in an application where merchandise is discounted.

Example 5   Applying Percents to a Discount Problem

After a 38% discount, a used treadmill costs $868 on eBay. What was the original cost of the treadmill?

Solution:

	Step 1: Read the problem.
Let x be the original cost of the treadmill.	**Step 2:** Label the variables.

Answer

5. The initial investment was $5500.

$\left(\begin{array}{c}\text{Original}\\\text{cost}\end{array}\right) - (\text{discount}) = \left(\begin{array}{c}\text{sale}\\\text{price}\end{array}\right)$ **Step 3:** Write a verbal model.

$x \quad - \quad 0.38(x) \quad = \quad 868$ **Step 4:** Write a mathematical equation. The discount is a percent of the *original* amount.

$x - 0.38x = 868$ **Step 5:** Solve the equation.

$0.62x = 868$ Combine *like* terms.

$\dfrac{0.62x}{0.62} = \dfrac{868}{0.62}$ Divide by 0.62.

$x = 1400$

© Comstock Images/Alamy RF

The original cost of the treadmill was $1400.   **Step 6:** Interpret the result.

Skill Practice

6. A camera is on sale for $151.20. This is after a 20% discount. What was the original cost?

Answer

6. The camera originally cost $189.

Section 2.5   Practice Exercises

Study Skills Exercise

It is always helpful to read the material in a section and make notes before it is presented in class. Writing notes ahead of time will free you to listen more in class and to pay special attention to the concepts that need clarification. Refer to your class syllabus and identify the next two sections that will be covered in class. Then determine a time when you can read these sections before class.

Vocabulary and Key Concepts

1. **a.** Interest that is earned on principal is called _____ interest.

    b. 82% means 82 out of _____.

Review Exercises

For Exercises 2–4, use the steps for problem solving to find the unknown quantities.

2. The difference of four times a number and 17 is 5 less than the number. Find the number.

3. Find two consecutive integers such that three times the larger is the same as 45 more than the smaller.

4. The height of the Great Pyramid of Giza is 17 m more than twice the height of the pyramid found in Saqqara. If the difference in their heights is 77 m, find the height of each pyramid.

Concept 1: Basic Percent Equations

For Exercises 5–16, find the missing values.

5. 45 is what percent of 360?

6. 338 is what percent of 520?

7. 544 is what percent of 640?

8. 576 is what percent of 800?

9. What is 0.5% of 150?

10. What is 9.5% of 616?

11. What is 142% of 740?

12. What is 156% of 280?

13. 177 is 20% of what number?

14. 126 is 15% of what number?

15. 275 is 12.5% of what number?

16. 594 is 45% of what number?

17. A drill is on sale for $99.99. If the sales tax rate is 7%, how much will Molly have to pay for the drill? **(See Example 1.)**

18. Patrick purchased four new tires that were regularly priced at $94.99 each, but are on sale for $20 off per tire. If the sales tax rate is 6%, how much will be charged to Patrick's VISA card?

For Exercises 19–22, use the graph showing the distribution for leading forms of cancer in men. (*Source:* Centers for Disease Control)

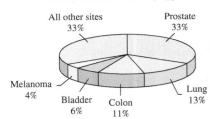

Percent of Cancer Cases by Type (Men)

19. If there are 700,000 cases of cancer in men in the United States, approximately how many are prostate cancer?

20. Approximately how many cases of lung cancer would be expected in 700,000 cancer cases among men in the United States?

21. There were 14,000 cases of cancer of the pancreas diagnosed out of 700,000 cancer cases. What percent is this? **(See Example 2.)**

22. There were 21,000 cases of leukemia diagnosed out of 700,000 cancer cases. What percent is this?

23. Javon is in a 28% tax bracket for his federal income tax. If the amount of money that he paid for federal income tax was $23,520, what was his taxable income? **(See Example 3.)**

24. In a recent survey of college-educated adults, 155 indicated that they regularly work more than 50 hr a week. If this represents 31% of those surveyed, how many people were in the survey?

Concept 2: Applications Involving Simple Interest

25. Aidan is trying to save money and has $1800 to set aside in some type of savings account. He checked his bank one day, and found that the rate for a 12-month CD had an annual percentage yield (APY) of 1.25%. The interest rate on his savings account was 0.75% APY. How much more simple interest would Aidan earn if he invested in a CD for 12 months rather than leaving the $1800 in a regular savings account?

26. How much interest will Roxanne have to pay if she borrows $2000 for 2 years at a simple interest rate of 4%?

27. Bob borrowed money for 1 year at 5% simple interest. If he had to pay back a total of $1260, how much did he originally borrow? **(See Example 4.)**

28. Andrea borrowed some money for 2 years at 6% simple interest. If she had to pay back a total of $3640, how much did she originally borrow?

29. If $1500 grows to $1950 after 5 years, find the simple interest rate.

30. If $9000 grows to $10,440 in 2 years, find the simple interest rate.

31. Perry is planning a vacation to Europe in 2 years. How much should he invest in an account that pays 3% simple interest to get the $3500 that he needs for the trip? Round to the nearest dollar.

32. Sherica invested in a mutual fund and at the end of 20 years she has $14,300 in her account. If the mutual fund returned an average yield of 8%, how much did she originally invest?

Concept 3: Applications Involving Discount and Markup

33. A hands-free kit for a car costs $62. An electronics store has it on sale for 12% off with free installation.

   a. What is the discount on the hands-free kit?

   b. What is the sale price?

34. A tablet originally selling for $550 is on sale for 10% off.

   a. What is the discount on the tablet?

   b. What is the sale price?

35. A digital camera is on sale for $400. This price is 15% off the original price. What was the original price? Round to the nearest cent. **(See Example 5.)**

36. A Blu-ray disc is on sale for $18. If this represents an 18% discount rate, what was the original price?

37. The original price of an Audio Jukebox was $250. It is on sale for $220. What percent discount does this represent?

38. During its first year, a gaming console sold for $425 in stores. This product was in such demand that it sold for $800 online. What percent markup does this represent? (Round to the nearest whole percent.)

39. A doctor ordered a dosage of medicine for a patient. After 2 days, she increased the dosage by 20% and the new dosage came to 18 cc. What was the original dosage?

40. In one area, the cable company marked up the monthly cost by 6%. The new cost is $63.60 per month. What was the cost before the increase?

Mixed Exercises

41. Sun Lei bought a laptop computer for $1800. The total cost, including tax, came to $1890. What is the tax rate?

42. Jamie purchased a beach umbrella and paid $32.04, including tax. If the price before tax is $29.80, what is the sales tax rate (round to the nearest tenth of a percent)?

© Creatas/PictureQuest RF

© Tero Hakala/123RF

43. To discourage tobacco use and to increase state revenue, several states tax tobacco products. One year, the state of New York increased taxes on tobacco, resulting in a 11% increase in the retail price of a pack of cigarettes. If the new price of a pack of cigarettes is $12.85, what was the cost before the increase in tax?

44. A hotel room rented for 5 nights costs $706.25 including 13% in taxes. Find the original price of the room (before tax) for the 5 nights. Then find the price per night.

45. Deon purchased a house and sold it for a 24% profit. If he sold the house for $260,400, what was the original purchase price?

© Comstock/PunchStock RF

46. To meet the rising cost of energy, the yearly membership at a YMCA had to be increased by 12.5% from the past year. The yearly membership fee is currently $450. What was the cost of membership last year?

© Image100/Corbis RF

47. Alina earns $1600 per month plus a 12% commission on pharmaceutical sales. If she sold $25,000 in pharmaceuticals one month, what was her salary that month?

48. Dan sold a beachfront home for $650,000. If his commission rate is 4%, what did he earn in commission?

49. Diane sells women's sportswear at a department store. She earns a regular salary and, as a bonus, she receives a commission of 4% on all sales over $200. If Diane earned an extra $25.80 last week in commission, how much merchandise did she sell over $200?

50. For selling software, Tom received a bonus commission based on sales over $500. If he received $180 in commission for selling a total of $2300 worth of software, what is his commission rate?

Section 2.6 Formulas and Applications of Geometry

Concepts

1. Literal Equations and Formulas
2. Geometry Applications

1. Literal Equations and Formulas

A *literal equation* is an equation that has more than one variable. A formula is a literal equation with a specific application. For example, the perimeter of a triangle (distance around the triangle) can be found by the formula $P = a + b + c$, where a, b, and c are the lengths of the sides (Figure 2-7).

$b = 7$ ft
$a = 5$ ft
$c = 8$ ft

$P = a + b + c$
$ = 5 \text{ ft} + 7 \text{ ft} + 8 \text{ ft}$
$ = 20 \text{ ft}$

Figure 2-7

In this section, we will learn how to rewrite formulas to solve for a different variable within the formula. Suppose, for example, that the perimeter of a triangle is known and two of the sides are known (say, sides a and b). Then the third side, c, can be found by subtracting the lengths of the known sides from the perimeter (Figure 2-8).

If the perimeter is 20 ft, then
$c = P - a - b$
$= 20 \text{ ft} - 5 \text{ ft} - 7 \text{ ft}$
$= 8 \text{ ft}$

Figure 2-8

To solve a formula for a different variable, we use the same properties of equality outlined in the earlier sections of this chapter. For example, consider the two equations $2x + 3 = 11$ and $wx + y = z$. Suppose we want to solve for x in each case:

$2x + 3 = 11$
$2x + 3 - 3 = 11 - 3$ Subtract 3.
$2x = 8$
$\dfrac{2x}{2} = \dfrac{8}{2}$ Divide by 2.
$x = 4$

$wx + y = z$
$wx + y - y = z - y$ Subtract y.
$wx = z - y$
$\dfrac{wx}{w} = \dfrac{z - y}{w}$ Divide by w.
$x = \dfrac{z - y}{w}$

The equation on the left has only one variable and we are able to simplify the equation to find a numerical value for x. The equation on the right has multiple variables. Because we do not know the values of w, y, and z, we are not able to simplify further. The value of x is left as a formula in terms of w, y, and z.

Example 1   **Solving for an Indicated Variable**

Solve for the indicated variable.

a. $d = rt$ for t **b.** $5x + 2y = 12$ for y

Solution:

a. $d = rt$ for t The goal is to isolate the variable t.

$\dfrac{d}{r} = \dfrac{rt}{r}$ Because the relationship between r and t is multiplication, we reverse the process by dividing both sides by r.

$\dfrac{d}{r} = t$, or equivalently $t = \dfrac{d}{r}$

b. $5x + 2y = 12$ for y The goal is to solve for y.

$5x - 5x + 2y = 12 - 5x$ Subtract $5x$ from both sides to isolate the y term.

$2y = -5x + 12$ $-5x + 12$ is the same as $12 - 5x$.

$\dfrac{2y}{2} = \dfrac{-5x + 12}{2}$ Divide both sides by 2 to isolate y.

$y = \dfrac{-5x + 12}{2}$

148   **Chapter 2**   Linear Equations and Inequalities

Avoiding Mistakes

In the expression $\dfrac{-5x + 12}{2}$ do not try to divide the 2 into the 12. The divisor of 2 is dividing the entire quantity, $-5x + 12$ (not just the 12).

We may, however, apply the divisor to each term individually in the numerator. That is, $y = \dfrac{-5x + 12}{2}$ can be written in several different forms. Each is correct.

$$y = \frac{-5x + 12}{2} \quad \text{or} \quad y = \frac{-5x}{2} + \frac{12}{2} \;\Rightarrow\; y = -\frac{5}{2}x + 6$$

Skill Practice Solve for the indicated variable.

1. $A = lw$ for l **2.** $-2a + 4b = 7$ for a

Example 2   **Solving for an Indicated Variable**

The formula $C = \frac{5}{9}(F - 32)$ is used to find the temperature, C, in degrees Celsius for a given temperature expressed in degrees Fahrenheit, F. Solve the formula $C = \frac{5}{9}(F - 32)$ for F.

Solution:

$$C = \frac{5}{9}(F - 32)$$

$$C = \frac{5}{9}F - \frac{5}{9} \cdot 32 \qquad \text{Clear parentheses.}$$

$$C = \frac{5}{9}F - \frac{160}{9} \qquad \text{Multiply: } \frac{5}{9} \cdot \frac{32}{1} = \frac{160}{9}$$

$$9(C) = 9\left(\frac{5}{9}F - \frac{160}{9}\right) \qquad \text{Multiply by the LCD to clear fractions.}$$

$$9C = \frac{9}{1} \cdot \frac{5}{9}F - \frac{9}{1} \cdot \frac{160}{9} \qquad \text{Apply the distributive property.}$$

$$9C = 5F - 160 \qquad \text{Simplify.}$$

$$9C + 160 = 5F - 160 + 160 \qquad \text{Add 160 to both sides.}$$

$$9C + 160 = 5F$$

$$\frac{9C + 160}{5} = \frac{5F}{5} \qquad \text{Divide both sides by 5.}$$

$$\frac{9C + 160}{5} = F$$

The answer may be written in several forms:

$$F = \frac{9C + 160}{5} \quad \text{or} \quad F = \frac{9C}{5} + \frac{160}{5} \;\Rightarrow\; F = \frac{9}{5}C + 32$$

Answers

1. $l = \dfrac{A}{w}$

2. $a = \dfrac{7 - 4b}{-2}$ or $a = \dfrac{4b - 7}{2}$ or $a = 2b - \dfrac{7}{2}$

3. $x = 3y + 7$

Skill Practice Solve for the indicated variable.

3. $y = \frac{1}{3}(x - 7)$ for x.

2. Geometry Applications

In Examples 3 through 6 and the related exercises, we use facts and formulas from geometry.

Example 3	**Solving a Geometry Application Involving Perimeter**

The length of a rectangular lot is 1 m less than twice the width. If the perimeter is 190 m, find the length and width.

Solution:

Step 1:   Read the problem.

Let x represent the width of the rectangle.

Step 2:   Label the variables.

Then $2x - 1$ represents the length.

$$P = 2l + 2w$$ **Step 3:**   Write the formula for perimeter.

$$190 = 2(2x - 1) + 2(x)$$ **Step 4:**   Write an equation in terms of x.

$$190 = 4x - 2 + 2x$$ **Step 5:**   Solve for x.

$$190 = 6x - 2$$

$$192 = 6x$$

$$\frac{192}{6} = \frac{6x}{6}$$

$$32 = x$$

The width is $x = 32$.

Step 6:   Interpret the results and write the answer in words.

The length is $2x - 1 = 2(32) - 1 = 63$.

The width of the rectangular lot is 32 m and the length is 63 m.

Skill Practice

4. The length of a rectangle is 10 ft less than twice the width. If the perimeter is 178 ft, find the length and width.

Recall some facts about angles.

- Two angles are complementary if the sum of their measures is 90°.
- Two angles are supplementary if the sum of their measures is 180°.
- The sum of the measures of the angles within a triangle is 180°.
- The measures of vertical angles are equal.

Answer

4. The length is 56 ft, and the width is 33 ft.

150   **Chapter 2**   Linear Equations and Inequalities

$(7x + 4)°$

$x°$

| **Example 4** | ### Solving a Geometry Application Involving Complementary Angles |

Two complementary angles are drawn such that one angle is 4° more than seven times the other angle. Find the measure of each angle.

Solution:

| | **Step 1:** | Read the problem. |
| Let x represent the measure of one angle. | **Step 2:** | Label the variables. |

Then $7x + 4$ represents the measure of the other angle.

The angles are complementary, so their sum must be 90°.

$$\left(\begin{matrix}\text{Measure of}\\\text{first angle}\end{matrix}\right) + \left(\begin{matrix}\text{measure of}\\\text{second angle}\end{matrix}\right) = 90°$$ **Step 3:** Write a verbal model.

$$\qquad\quad x \qquad + \qquad 7x + 4 \qquad = \quad 90$$ **Step 4:** Write a mathematical equation.

$$8x + 4 = 90$$ **Step 5:** Solve for x.

$$8x = 86$$

$$\frac{8x}{8} = \frac{86}{8}$$

$$x = 10.75$$

One angle is $x = 10.75$.   **Step 6:** Interpret the results and write the answer in words.

The other angle is $7x + 4 = 7(10.75) + 4 = 79.25$.

The angles are $10.75°$ and $79.25°$.

Skill Practice

5. Two complementary angles are constructed so that one measures 1° less than six times the other. Find the measures of the angles.

| **Example 5** | ### Solving a Geometry Application Involving Angles in a Triangle |

One angle in a triangle is twice as large as the smallest angle. The third angle is 10° more than seven times the smallest angle. Find the measure of each angle.

Animation

Solution:

| | **Step 1:** | Read the problem. |

| | **Step 2:** | Label the variables. |
| Let x represent the measure of the smallest angle. | | |

Then $2x$ and $7x + 10$ represent the measures of the other two angles.

The sum of the angles must be 180°.

$x°$ $(7x + 10)°$ $(2x)°$

Answer

5. The angles are 13° and 77°.

$$\binom{\text{Measure of}}{\text{first angle}} + \binom{\text{measure of}}{\text{second angle}} + \binom{\text{measure of}}{\text{third angle}} = 180° \quad \textbf{Step 3:} \quad \text{Write a verbal model.}$$

$$x \quad + \quad 2x \quad + \quad (7x + 10) \quad = 180 \quad \textbf{Step 4:} \quad \text{Write a mathematical equation.}$$

$$x + 2x + 7x + 10 = 180 \qquad \textbf{Step 5:} \quad \text{Solve for } x.$$
$$10x + 10 = 180$$
$$10x = 170$$
$$x = 17 \qquad \textbf{Step 6:} \quad \text{Interpret the results and write the answer in words.}$$

The smallest angle is $x = 17$.

The other angles are $2x = 2(17) = 34$

$$7x + 10 = 7(17) + 10 = 129$$

The angles are $17°$, $34°$, and $129°$.

Skill Practice

6. In a triangle, the measure of the first angle is $80°$ greater than the measure of the second angle. The measure of the third angle is twice that of the second. Find the measures of the angles.

| Example 6 | **Solving a Geometry Application Involving Circumference** |

The distance around a circular garden is 188.4 ft. Find the radius to the nearest tenth of a foot. Use 3.14 for π.

Solution:

$$C = 2\pi r \qquad \text{Use the formula for the circumference of a circle.}$$

$$188.4 = 2\pi r \qquad \text{Substitute 188.4 for } C.$$

$$\frac{188.4}{2\pi} = \frac{2\pi r}{2\pi} \qquad \text{Divide both sides by } 2\pi.$$

$$\frac{188.4}{2\pi} = r$$

$$r \approx \frac{188.4}{2(3.14)}$$

$$= 30.0$$

$C = 188.4$ ft

The radius is approximately 30.0 ft.

Skill Practice

7. The circumference of a drain pipe is 12.5 cm. Find the radius. Round to the nearest tenth of a centimeter.

Answers

6. The angles are $25°$, $50°$, and $105°$.
7. The radius is 2.0 cm.

152   **Chapter 2** Linear Equations and Inequalities

Calculator Connections

Topic: Using the π Key on a Calculator

In Example 6 we could have obtained a more accurate result if we had used the π key on a calculator.

Note that parentheses are required to divide 188.4 by the quantity 2π. This guarantees that the calculator follows the implied order of operations. Without parentheses, the calculator would divide 188.4 by 2 and then multiply the result by π.

Scientific Calculator

Enter: 188.4 ÷ (2 × π) =   **Result:** $\boxed{29.98479128}$ correct

Enter: 188.4 ÷ 2 × π =   **Result:** $\boxed{295.938028}$ incorrect

Graphing Calculator

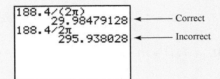

```
188.4/(2π)
          29.98479128  ← Correct
188.4/2π
          295.938028   ← Incorrect
```

Calculator Exercises

Approximate the expressions with a calculator. Round to three decimal places if necessary.

1. $\dfrac{880}{2\pi}$ 2. $\dfrac{1600}{\pi(4)^2}$ 3. $\dfrac{20}{5\pi}$ 4. $\dfrac{10}{7\pi}$

Section 2.6   Practice Exercises

Study Skills Exercise

A good technique for studying for a test is to choose four problems from each section of the chapter and write the problems along with the directions on 3 × 5 cards. On the back of each card, put the page number where you found that problem. Then shuffle the cards and test yourself on the procedure to solve each problem. If you find one that you do not know how to solve, look at the page number and do several of that type. Write four problems you would choose for this section.

Review Exercises

For Exercises 1–8, solve the equation.

1. $3(2y + 3) - 4(-y + 1) = 7y - 10$

2. $-(3w + 4) + 5(w - 2) - 3(6w - 8) = 10$

3. $\dfrac{1}{2}(x - 3) + \dfrac{3}{4} = 3x - \dfrac{3}{4}$

4. $\dfrac{5}{6}x + \dfrac{1}{2} = \dfrac{1}{4}(x - 4)$

5. $0.5(y + 2) - 0.3 = 0.4y + 0.5$

6. $0.25(500 - x) + 0.15x = 75$

7. $8b + 6(7 - 2b) = -4(b + 1)$

8. $2 - 5(t - 3) + t = 7t - (6t + 8)$

Concept 1: Literal Equations and Formulas

For Exercises 9–40, solve for the indicated variable. **(See Examples 1–2.)**

9. $P = a + b + c$ for a

10. $P = a + b + c$ for b

11. $x = y - z$ for y

12. $c + d = e$ for d

13. $p = 250 + q$ for q

14. $y = 35 + x$ for x

15. $A = bh$ for b

16. $d = rt$ for r

17. $PV = nrt$ for t

18. $P_1 V_1 = P_2 V_2$ for V_1

19. $x - y = 5$ for x

20. $x + y = -2$ for y

21. $3x + y = -19$ for y

22. $x - 6y = -10$ for x

23. $2x + 3y = 6$ for y

24. $7x + 3y = 1$ for y

25. $-2x - y = 9$ for x

26. $3x - y = -13$ for x

27. $4x - 3y = 12$ for y

28. $6x - 3y = 4$ for y

29. $ax + by = c$ for y

30. $ax + by = c$ for x

31. $A = P(1 + rt)$ for t

32. $P = 2(L + w)$ for L

33. $a = 2(b + c)$ for c

34. $3(x + y) = z$ for x

35. $Q = \dfrac{x + y}{2}$ for y

36. $Q = \dfrac{a - b}{2}$ for a

37. $M = \dfrac{a}{S}$ for a

38. $A = \dfrac{1}{3}(a + b + c)$ for c

39. $P = I^2 R$ for R

40. $F = \dfrac{GMm}{d^2}$ for m

Concept 2: Geometry Applications

For Exercises 41–62, use the Problem-Solving Flowchart for Word Problems.

41. The perimeter of a rectangular garden is 24 ft. The length is 2 ft more than the width. Find the length and the width of the garden. **(See Example 3.)**

42. In a small rectangular wallet photo, the width is 7 cm less than the length. If the perimeter of the photo is 34 cm, find the length and width.

43. The length of a rectangular parking area is four times the width. The perimeter is 300 yd. Find the length and width of the parking area.

44. The width of Jason's workbench is $\frac{1}{2}$ the length. The perimeter is 240 in. Find the length and the width of the workbench.

45. A builder buys a rectangular lot of land such that the length is 5 m less than two times the width. If the perimeter is 590 m, find the length and the width.

46. The perimeter of a rectangular pool is 140 yd. If the length is 20 yd less than twice the width, find the length and the width.

w

$2w - 5$

w

$2w - 20$

47. A triangular parking lot has two sides that are the same length, and the third side is 5 m longer. If the perimeter is 71 m, find the lengths of the sides.

48. The perimeter of a triangle is 16 ft. One side is 3 ft longer than the shortest side. The third side is 1 ft longer than the shortest side. Find the lengths of the sides.

49. Sometimes memory devices are helpful for remembering mathematical facts. Recall that the sum of two complementary angles is 90°. That is, two complementary angles when added together form a right angle or "corner." The words *Complementary* and *Corner* both start with the letter "*C*." Derive your own memory device for remembering that the sum of two supplementary angles is 180°.

$x° + y° = 90°$

Complementary angles form a "Corner"

$x° + y° = 180°$

Supplementary angles . . .

50. Two angles are complementary. One angle is 20° less than the other angle. Find the measures of the angles.

51. Two angles are complementary. One angle is 4° less than three times the other angle. Find the measures of the angles. **(See Example 4.)**

52. Two angles are supplementary. One angle is three times as large as the other angle. Find the measures of the angles.

53. Two angles are supplementary. One angle is 6° more than four times the other. Find the measures of the angles.

54. Refer to the figure. The angles, $\angle a$ and $\angle b$, are vertical angles.

  a. If the measure of $\angle a$ is 32°, what is the measure of $\angle b$?

  b. What is the measure of the supplement of $\angle a$?

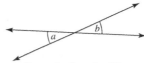

Figure for Exercise 54

55. Find the measures of the vertical angles labeled in the figure by first solving for *x*.

$(2x − 3)°$

$(x + 17)°$

56. Find the measures of the vertical angles labeled in the figure by first solving for *y*.

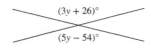

$(3y + 26)°$

$(5y − 54)°$

57. The largest angle in a triangle is three times the smallest angle. The middle angle is two times the smallest angle. Given that the sum of the angles in a triangle is 180°, find the measure of each angle. **(See Example 5.)**

$(3x)°$ $x°$

$(2x)°$

58. The smallest angle in a triangle measures 90° less than the largest angle. The middle angle measures 60° less than the largest angle. Find the measure of each angle.

59. The smallest angle in a triangle is half the largest angle. The middle angle measures 30° less than the largest angle. Find the measure of each angle.

60. The largest angle of a triangle is three times the middle angle. The smallest angle measures 10° less than the middle angle. Find the measure of each angle.

$x°$

61. Find the value of x and the measure of each angle labeled in the figure.

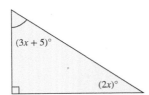

63. a. A rectangle has length l and width w. Write a formula for the area.

     b. Solve the formula for the width, w.

     c. The area of a rectangular volleyball court is 1740.5 ft^2 and the length is 59 ft. Find the width.

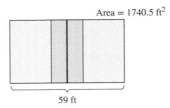

Area = 1740.5 ft^2

59 ft

65. a. A rectangle has length l and width w. Write a formula for the perimeter.

     b. Solve the formula for the length, l.

     c. The perimeter of the soccer field at Giants Stadium is 338 m. If the width is 66 m, find the length.

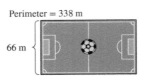

Perimeter = 338 m

66 m

67. a. A circle has a radius of r. Write a formula for the circumference. **(See Example 6.)**

     b. Solve the formula for the radius, r.

     c. The circumference of the circular Buckingham Fountain in Chicago is approximately 880 ft. Find the radius. Round to the nearest foot.

© Brand X Pictures/Getty Images RF

62. Find the value of y and the measure of each angle labeled in the figure.

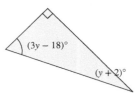

64. a. A parallelogram has height h and base b. Write a formula for the area.

     b. Solve the formula for the base, b.

     c. Find the base of the parallelogram pictured if the area is 40 m^2.

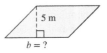

5 m

$b = ?$

66. a. A triangle has height h and base b. Write a formula for the area.

     b. Solve the formula for the height, h.

     c. Find the height of the triangle pictured if the area is 12 km^2.

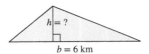

$h = ?$

$b = 6$ km

68. a. The length of each side of a square is s. Write a formula for the perimeter of the square.

     b. Solve the formula for the length of a side, s.

     c. The Pyramid of Khufu (known as the Great Pyramid) at Giza has a square base. If the distance around the bottom is 921.6 m, find the length of the sides at the bottom of the pyramid.

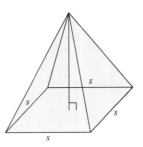

156   **Chapter 2** Linear Equations and Inequalities

Expanding Your Skills

For Exercises 69–70, find the indicated area or volume. Be sure to include the proper units and round each answer to two decimal places if necessary.

 69. a. Find the area of a circle with radius 11.5 m. Use the π key on the calculator.

     b. Find the volume of a right circular cylinder with radius 11.5 m and height 25 m.

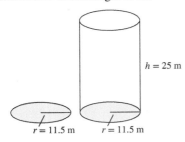

70. a. Find the area of a parallelogram with base 30 in. and height 12 in.

     b. Find the area of a triangle with base 30 in. and height 12 in.

     c. Compare the areas found in parts (a) and (b).

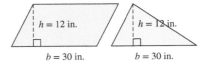

1. Applications Involving Cost

In Examples 1 and 2, we will look at different kinds of mixture problems. The first example "mixes" two types of theater tickets, adult tickets that sell for \$12 and children's tickets that sell for \$9. Furthermore, there were 300 tickets sold for a total revenue of \$3060. Before attempting the problem, we should try to gain some familiarity. Let's try a few combinations to see how many of each type of ticket might have been sold.

Suppose 100 adult tickets were sold and 200 children's tickets were sold (a total of 300 tickets).

- 100 adult tickets at \$12 each gives $100(\$12) = \$1200$
- 200 children's tickets at \$9 each gives $\underline{200(\$9) = \$1800}$

Total revenue: \$3000 (not enough)

Suppose 150 adult tickets were sold and 150 children's tickets were sold (a total of 300 tickets).

- 150 adult tickets at \$12 each gives $150(\$12) = \$1800$
- 150 children's tickets at \$9 each gives $\underline{150(\$9) = \$1350}$

Total revenue: \$3150 (too much)

As you can see, the trial-and-error process can be tedious and time consuming. Therefore, we will use algebra to determine the correct combination of each type of ticket.

Suppose we let x represent the number of adult tickets. Then the number of children's tickets is the *total minus* x. That is,

$$\begin{pmatrix} \text{Number of} \\ \text{children's tickets} \end{pmatrix} = \begin{pmatrix} \text{total number} \\ \text{of tickets} \end{pmatrix} - \begin{pmatrix} \text{number of} \\ \text{adult tickets, } x \end{pmatrix}$$

Number of children's tickets $= 300 - x$.

Notice that the number of tickets sold times the price per ticket gives the revenue:

- x adult tickets at \$12 each gives a revenue of: $x(\$12)$ or simply $12x$.
- $300 - x$ children's tickets at \$9 each gives: $(300 - x)(\$9)$ or $9(300 - x)$.

This will help us set up an equation in Example 1.

| Example 1 | Solving a Mixture Problem Involving Ticket Sales |

At a community theater, 300 tickets were sold. Adult tickets cost \$12 and tickets for children cost \$9. If the total revenue from ticket sales was \$3060, determine the number of each type of ticket sold.

© Uppercut/Getty Images RF

Solution:

Step 1: Read the problem.

Let x represent the number of adult tickets sold.
$300 - x$ is the number of children's tickets.

Step 2: Label the variables.

	\$12 Tickets	**\$9 Tickets**	**Total**
Number of tickets	x	$300 - x$	300
Revenue	$12x$	$9(300 - x)$	3060

$$\left(\begin{array}{c}\text{Revenue from}\\\text{adult tickets}\end{array}\right) + \left(\begin{array}{c}\text{revenue from}\\\text{children's tickets}\end{array}\right) = \left(\begin{array}{c}\text{total}\\\text{revenue}\end{array}\right)$$

Step 3: Write a verbal model.

$$12x \quad + \quad 9(300 - x) \quad = \quad 3060$$

Step 4: Write a mathematical equation.

$$12x + 9(300 - x) = 3060$$

Step 5: Solve the equation.

$$12x + 2700 - 9x = 3060$$

$$3x + 2700 = 3060$$

$$3x = 360$$

$$x = 120$$

Step 6: Interpret the results.

There were 120 adult tickets sold.
The number of children's tickets is $300 - x$ which is 180.

Avoiding Mistakes

Check that the answer is reasonable. 120 adult tickets and 180 children's tickets makes 300 total tickets.

Furthermore, 120 adult tickets at \$12 each amounts to \$1440, and 180 children's tickets at \$9 each amounts to \$1620. The total revenue is \$3060 as expected.

Skill Practice

1. At a Performing Arts Center, seats in the orchestra section cost \$18 and seats in the balcony cost \$12. If there were 120 seats sold for one performance, for a total revenue of \$1920, how many of each type of seat were sold?

Answer

1. There were 80 seats in the orchestra section, and there were 40 in the balcony.

2. Applications Involving Mixtures

Example 2   **Solving a Mixture Application**

How many liters (L) of a 60% antifreeze solution must be added to 8 L of a 10% antifreeze solution to produce a 20% antifreeze solution?

Solution:

The information can be organized in a table. Notice that an algebraic equation is derived from the second row of the table. This relates the number of liters of pure antifreeze in each container.

Step 1: Read the problem.

	60% Antifreeze	10% Antifreeze	Final Mixture: 20% Antifreeze
Number of liters of solution	x	8	$(8 + x)$
Number of liters of pure antifreeze	$0.60x$	$0.10(8)$	$0.20(8 + x)$

Step 2: Label the variables.

TIP: To determine the amount of pure antifreeze in a given solution, multiply the concentration rate by the amount of solution. For example, 8 L of a 10% solutions means that

$$(0.10)(8\ \text{L}) = 0.8\ \text{L}$$

of the solution is pure antifreeze. The rest is something else such as water.

The amount of pure antifreeze in the final solution equals the sum of the amounts of antifreeze in the first two solutions.

$$\begin{pmatrix}\text{Pure antifreeze}\\\text{from solution 1}\end{pmatrix} + \begin{pmatrix}\text{pure antifreeze}\\\text{from solution 2}\end{pmatrix} = \begin{pmatrix}\text{pure antifreeze}\\\text{in the final solution}\end{pmatrix}$$

Step 3: Write a verbal model.

$$0.60x \quad + \quad 0.10(8) \quad = \quad 0.20(8 + x)$$

$$0.60x + 0.10(8) = 0.20(8 + x)$$

Step 4: Write a mathematical equation.

$$0.6x + 0.8 = 1.6 + 0.2x$$

Step 5: Solve the equation.

$$0.6x - 0.2x + 0.8 = 1.6 + 0.2x - 0.2x$$

Subtract $0.2x$.

$$0.4x + 0.8 = 1.6$$

$$0.4x + 0.8 - 0.8 = 1.6 - 0.8$$

Subtract 0.8.

$$0.4x = 0.8$$

$$\frac{0.4x}{0.4} = \frac{0.8}{0.4}$$

Divide by 0.4.

$$x = 2$$

Step 6: Interpret the result.

Therefore, 2 L of 60% antifreeze solution is necessary to make a final solution that is 20% antifreeze.

Skill Practice

2. How many gallons of a 5% bleach solution must be added to 10 gallons (gal) of a 20% bleach solution to produce a solution that is 15% bleach?

Answer

2. 5 gal is needed.

3. Applications Involving Uniform Motion

The formula (distance) = (rate)(time) or simply, $d = rt$, relates the distance traveled to the rate of travel and the time of travel.

For example, if a car travels at 60 mph for 3 hours, then

$$d = (60 \text{ mph})(3 \text{ hours})$$
$$= 180 \text{ miles}$$

If a car travels at 60 mph for x hours, then

$$d = (60 \text{ mph})(x \text{ hours})$$
$$= 60x \text{ miles}$$

© Adam Gault/Getty Images RF

| Example 3 | **Solving an Application Involving Distance, Rate, and Time** |

One bicyclist rides 4 mph faster than another bicyclist. The faster rider takes 3 hr to complete a race, while the slower rider takes 4 hr. Find the speed for each rider.

Solution:

Step 1: Read the problem.

The problem is asking us to find the speed of each rider.

Let x represent the speed of the slower rider. Then $(x + 4)$ is the speed of the faster rider.

Step 2: Label the variables and organize the information given in the problem. A distance-rate-time chart may be helpful.

	Distance	Rate	Time
Faster rider	$3(x + 4)$	$x + 4$	3
Slower rider	$4(x)$	x	4

To complete the first column, we can use the relationship, $d = rt$.

Because the riders are riding in the same race, their distances are equal.

$$\begin{pmatrix} \text{Distance} \\ \text{by faster rider} \end{pmatrix} = \begin{pmatrix} \text{distance} \\ \text{by slower rider} \end{pmatrix}$$

Step 3: Write a verbal model.

$$3(x + 4) = 4(x)$$

Step 4: Write a mathematical equation.

$$3x + 12 = 4x$$

Step 5: Solve the equation.

$$12 = x$$

Subtract $3x$ from both sides.

The variable x represents the slower rider's rate. The quantity $x + 4$ is the faster rider's rate. Thus, if $x = 12$, then $x + 4 = 16$.

The slower rider travels 12 mph and the faster rider travels 16 mph.

Avoiding Mistakes

Check that the answer is reasonable. If the slower rider rides at 12 mph for 4 hr, he travels 48 mi. If the faster rider rides at 16 mph for 3 hr, he also travels 48 mi as expected.

Skill Practice

3. An express train travels 25 mph faster than a cargo train. It takes the express train 6 hr to travel a route, and it takes 9 hr for the cargo train to travel the same route. Find the speed of each train.

Answer

3. The express train travels 75 mph, and the cargo train travels 50 mph.

Example 4   ## Solving an Application Involving Distance, Rate, and Time

Two families that live 270 mi apart plan to meet for an afternoon picnic at a park that is located between their two homes. Both families leave at 9.00 A.M., but one family averages 12 mph faster than the other family. If the families meet at the designated spot $2\frac{1}{2}$ hr later, determine

© BananaStock/PictureQuest RF

a. The average rate of speed for each family.

b. The distance each family traveled to the picnic.

Solution:

For simplicity, we will call the two families, Family A and Family B. Let Family A be the family that travels at the slower rate (Figure 2-9).

Step 1: Read the problem and draw a sketch.

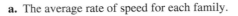

270 miles

Family A ⟶   ⟵ Family B

Figure 2-9

Let x represent the rate of Family A. Then $(x + 12)$ is the rate of Family B.

Step 2: Label the variables.

	Distance	Rate	Time
Family A	$2.5x$	x	2.5
Family B	$2.5(x + 12)$	$x + 12$	2.5

To complete the first column, we can multiply rate and time: $d = rt$.

To set up an equation, recall that the total distance between the two families is given as 270 mi.

$$\begin{pmatrix} \text{Distance} \\ \text{traveled by} \\ \text{Family A} \end{pmatrix} + \begin{pmatrix} \text{distance} \\ \text{traveled by} \\ \text{Family B} \end{pmatrix} = \begin{pmatrix} \text{total} \\ \text{distance} \end{pmatrix}$$

Step 3: Write a verbal model.

$$2.5x \quad + \quad 2.5(x + 12) \quad = \quad 270$$

Step 4: Write a mathematical equation.

$$2.5x + 2.5(x + 12) = 270$$
$$2.5x + 2.5x + 30 = 270$$
$$5.0x + 30 = 270$$
$$5x = 240$$
$$x = 48$$

Step 5: Solve for x.

a. Family A traveled 48 mph.

Family B traveled $x + 12 = 48 + 12 = 60$ mph.

Step 6: Interpret the results and write the answer in words.

b. To compute the distance each family traveled, use $d = rt$.

Family A traveled (48 mph)(2.5 hr) = 120 mi.

Family B traveled (60 mph)(2.5 hr) = 150 mi.

Skill Practice

4. A Piper airplane has an average air speed that is 10 mph faster than a Cessna 150 airplane. If the combined distance traveled by these two small planes is 690 mi after 3 hr, what is the average speed of each plane?

Answer

4. The Cessna's speed is 110 mph, and the Piper's speed is 120 mph.

Section 2.7   Practice Exercises

Study Skills Exercise

The following is a list of steps to help you solve word problems. Check those that you follow on a regular basis when solving a word problem. Place an asterisk next to the steps that you need to improve.

_____   Read through the entire problem before writing anything down.

_____   Write down exactly what you are being asked to find.

_____   Write down what is known and assign variables to what is unknown.

_____   Draw a figure or diagram if it will help you understand the problem.

_____   Highlight key words like total, sum, difference, etc.

_____   Translate the word problem to a mathematical problem.

_____   After solving, check that your answer makes sense.

Review Exercises

For Exercises 1–3, solve for the indicated variable.

1. $ax - by = c$ for x

2. $cd = r$ for c

3. $7x + xy = 18$ for y

For Exercises 4–6, solve each equation.

4. $-2d + 11 = 4 - d$

5. $3(2y + 5) - 8(y - 1) = 3y + 3$

6. $0.02x + 0.04(10 - x) = 1.26$

Concept 1: Applications Involving Cost

For Exercises 7–12, write an algebraic expression as indicated.

7. Two numbers total 200. Let t represent one of the numbers. Write an algebraic expression for the other number.

8. The total of two numbers is 43. Let s represent one of the numbers. Write an algebraic expression for the other number.

9. Olivia needs to bring 100 cookies to her friend's party. She has already baked x cookies. Write an algebraic expression for the number of cookies Olivia still needs to bake.

© Comstock Images/Jupiter Images RF

10. Rachel needs a mixture of 55 pounds (lb) of nuts consisting of peanuts and cashews. Let p represent the number of pounds of peanuts in the mixture. Write an algebraic expression for the number of pounds of cashews that she needs to add.

© McGraw-Hill Education/Jill Braaten, photographer

11. Max has a total of $3000 in two bank accounts. Let y represent the amount in one account. Write an algebraic expression for the amount in the other account.

12. Roberto has a total of $7500 in two savings accounts. Let z represent the amount in one account. Write an algebraic expression for the amount in the other account.

13. A church had an ice cream social and sold tickets for $3 and $2. When the social was over, 81 tickets had been sold totaling $215. How many of each type of ticket did the church sell? **(See Example 1.)**

	$3 Tickets	$2 Tickets	Total
Number of tickets			
Cost of tickets			

14. Anna is a teacher at an elementary school. She purchased 72 tickets to take the first-grade children and some parents on a field trip to the zoo. She purchased children's tickets for $10 each and adult tickets for $18 each. She spent a total of $856. How many of each type of ticket did she buy?

	Adults	Children	Total
Number of tickets			
Cost of tickets			

15. Josh downloaded 25 songs from an online site. Some songs cost $1.29 and some cost $1.49. He spent a total of $33.85. How many songs at each price were purchased?

16. During the past year, Kris purchased 30 books at a wholesale club store. She purchased softcover books for $4.50 each and hardcover books for $13.50 each. The total cost of the books was $216. How many of each type of book did she purchase?

17. During the past year, Amber purchased 32 books for her e-reader. She purchased some books for $6.99 and others for $9.99. If she spent a total of $256.68, how many books from each price category did she buy?

© Royalty Free/Corbis RF

18. Steven wants to buy some candy with his birthday money. He can choose from jelly beans that sell for $6.99 per pound and a variety mix that sells for $3.99. He likes to have twice the amount of jelly beans as the variety mix. If he spent a total of $53.91, how many pounds of each type of candy did he buy?

Concept 2: Applications Involving Mixtures

For Exercises 19–22, write an algebraic expression as indicated.

19. A container holds 7 ounces (oz) of liquid. Let x represent the number of ounces of liquid in another container. Write an expression for the total amount of liquid.

20. A bucket contains 2.5 L of a bleach solution. Let n represent the number of liters of bleach solution in a second bucket. Write an expression for the total amount of bleach solution.

21. If Charlene invests $2000 in a certificate of deposit and *d* dollars in a stock, write an expression for the total amount she invested.

22. James has $5000 in one savings account. Let *y* represent the amount he has in another savings account. Write an expression for the total amount of money in both accounts.

23. How much of a 5% ethanol fuel mixture should be mixed with 2000 gal of 10% ethanol fuel mixture to get a mixture that is 9% ethanol. **(See Example 2.)**

	5% Ethanol	10% Ethanol	Final Mixture: 9% Ethanol
Number of gallons of fuel mixture			
Number of gallons of pure ethanol			

24. How many ounces of a 50% antifreeze solution must be mixed with 10 oz of an 80% antifreeze solution to produce a 60% antifreeze solution?

	50% Antifreeze	80% Antifreeze	Final Mixture: 60% Antifreeze
Number of ounces of solution			
Number of ounces of pure antifreeze			

25. A pharmacist needs to mix a 1% saline (salt) solution with 24 milliliters (mL) of a 16% saline solution to obtain a 9% saline solution. How many milliliters of the 1% solution must she use?

26. A landscaper needs to mix a 75% pesticide solution with 30 gal of a 25% pesticide solution to obtain a 60% pesticide solution. How many gallons of the 75% solution must he use?

27. To clean a concrete driveway, a contractor needs a solution that is 30% acid. How many ounces of a 50% acid solution must be mixed with 15 oz of a 21% solution to obtain a 30% acid solution?

28. A veterinarian needs a mixture that contains 12% of a certain medication to treat an injured bird. How many milliliters of a 16% solution should be mixed with 6 mL of a 7% solution to obtain a solution that is 12% medication?

Concept 3: Applications Involving Uniform Motion

29. a. If a car travels 60 mph for 5 hr, find the distance traveled.

    b. If a car travels at *x* miles per hour for 5 hr, write an expression that represents the distance traveled.

    c. If a car travels at *x* + 12 mph for 5 hr, write an expression that represents the distance traveled.

30. a. If a plane travels 550 mph for 2.5 hr, find the distance traveled.

    b. If a plane travels at *x* miles per hour for 2.5 hr, write an expression that represents the distance traveled.

    c. If a plane travels at *x* − 100 mph for 2.5 hr, write an expression that represents the distance traveled.

31. A woman can walk 2 mph faster down a trail to Cochita Lake than she can on the return trip uphill. It takes her 2 hr to get to the lake and 4 hr to return. What is her speed walking down to the lake? **(See Example 3.)**

	Distance	Rate	Time
Downhill to the lake			
Uphill from the lake			

32. A car travels 20 mph slower in a bad rain storm than in sunny weather. The car travels the same distance in 2 hr in sunny weather as it does in 3 hr in rainy weather. Find the speed of the car in sunny weather.

	Distance	Rate	Time
Rain storm			
Sunny weather			

33. Bryan hiked up to the top of City Creek in 3 hr and then returned down the canyon to the trailhead in another 2 hr. His speed downhill was 1 mph faster than his speed uphill. How far up the canyon did he hike?

34. Laura hiked up Lamb's Canyon in 2 hr and then ran back down in 1 hr. Her speed running downhill was 2.5 mph faster than her speed hiking uphill. How far up the canyon did she hike?

35. Hazel and Emilie fly from Atlanta to San Diego. The flight from Atlanta to San Diego is against the wind and takes 4 hr. The return flight with the wind takes 3.5 hr. If the wind speed is 40 mph, find the speed of the plane in still air.

36. A boat on the Potomac River travels the same distance downstream with the current in $\frac{2}{3}$ hr as it does going upstream against the current in 1 hr. If the speed of the current is 3 mph, find the speed of the boat in still water.

37. Two cars are 200 mi apart and travel toward each other on the same road. They meet in 2 hr. One car travels 4 mph faster than the other. What is the speed of each car? **(See Example 4.)**

38. Two cars are 238 mi apart and travel toward each other along the same road. They meet in 2 hr. One car travels 5 mph slower than the other. What is the speed of each car?

39. After Hurricane Katrina, a rescue vehicle leaves a station at noon and heads for New Orleans. An hour later a second vehicle traveling 10 mph faster leaves the same station. By 4:00 P.M., the first vehicle reaches its destination, and the second is still 10 mi away. How fast is each vehicle?

40. A truck leaves a truck stop at 9:00 A.M. and travels toward Sturgis, Wyoming. At 10:00 A.M., a motorcycle leaves the same truck stop and travels the same route. The motorcycle travels 15 mph faster than the truck. By noon, the truck has traveled 20 mi farther than the motorcycle. How fast is each vehicle?

41. In the Disney Marathon, Jeanette's speed running is twice Sarah's speed walking. After 2 hr, Jeanette is 7 mi ahead of Sarah. Find Jeanette's speed and Sarah's speed.

42. Two canoes travel down a river, starting at 9:00 A.M. One canoe travels twice as fast as the other. After 3.5 hr, the canoes are 5.25 mi apart. Find the speed of each canoe.

Mixed Exercises

43. A certain granola mixture is 10% peanuts.

    a. If a container has 20 lb of granola, how many pounds of peanuts are there?

    b. If a container has x pounds of granola, write an expression that represents the number of pounds of peanuts in the granola.

    c. If a container has $x + 3$ lb of granola, write an expression that represents the number of pounds of peanuts.

44. A certain blend of coffee sells for $9.00 per pound.

    a. If a container has 20 lb of coffee, how much will it cost?

    b. If a container has x pounds of coffee, write an expression that represents the cost.

    c. If a container has $40 - x$ pounds of this coffee, write an expression that represents the cost.

45. The Coffee Company mixes coffee worth $12 per pound with coffee worth $8 per pound to produce 50 lb of coffee worth $8.80 per pound. How many pounds of the $12 coffee and how many pounds of the $8 coffee must be used?

46. The Nut House sells pecans worth $4 per pound and cashews worth $6 per pound. How many pounds of pecans and how many pounds of cashews must be mixed to form 16 lb of a nut mixture worth $4.50 per pound?

	$12 Coffee	$8 Coffee	Total
Number of pounds			
Value of coffee			

	$4 Pecans	$6 Cashews	Total
Number of pounds			
Value of nuts			

47. A boat in distress, 21 nautical miles from a marina, travels toward the marina at 3 knots (nautical miles per hour). A coast guard cruiser leaves the marina and travels toward the boat at 25 knots. How long will it take for the boats to reach each other?

48. An air traffic controller observes a plane heading from New York to San Francisco traveling at 450 mph. At the same time, another plane leaves San Francisco and travels 500 mph to New York. If the distance between the airports is 2850 mi, how long will it take for the planes to pass each other?

© Dennis MacDonald/Alamy RF

49. Surfer Sam purchased a total of 21 items at the surf shop. He bought wax for $3.00 per package and sunscreen for $8.00 per bottle. He spent a total of $88.00. How many of each item did he purchase?

50. Tonya Toast loves jam. She purchased 30 jars of gourmet jam for $178.50. She bought raspberry jam for $6.25 per jar and strawberry jam for $5.50 per jar. How many jars of each did she purchase?

51. How many quarts of 85% chlorine solution must be mixed with 5 quarts of 25% chlorine solution to obtain a 45% chlorine solution?

52. How many liters of a 58% sugar solution must be added to 14 L of a 40% sugar solution to obtain a 50% sugar solution?

Expanding Your Skills

53. How much pure water must be mixed with 12 L of a 40% alcohol solution to obtain a 15% alcohol solution? (*Hint:* Pure water is 0% alcohol.)

54. How much pure water must be mixed with 10 oz of a 60% alcohol solution to obtain a 25% alcohol solution?

55. Amtrak Acela Express is a high-speed train that runs in the United States between Washington, D.C. and Boston. In Japan, a bullet train along the Sanyo line operates at an average speed of 60 km/hr faster than the Amtrak Acela Express. It takes the Japanese bullet train 2.7 hr to travel the same distance as the Acela Express can travel in 3.375 hr. Find the speed of each train.

56. Amtrak Acela Express is a high-speed train along the northeast corridor between Washington, D.C. and Boston. Since its debut, it cuts the travel time from 4 hr 10 min to 3 hr 20 min. On average, if the Acela Express is 30 mph faster than the old train, find the speed of the Acela Express. (*Hint:* 4 hr 10 min $= 4\frac{1}{6}$ hr.)

Linear Inequalities

1. Graphing Linear Inequalities

Consider the following two statements.

$$2x + 7 = 11 \quad \text{and} \quad 2x + 7 < 11$$

The first statement is an equation (it has an $=$ sign). The second statement is an inequality (it has an inequality symbol, $<$). In this section, we will learn how to solve linear *inequalities*, such as $2x + 7 < 11$.

Concepts

1. Graphing Linear Inequalities
2. Set-Builder Notation and Interval Notation
3. Addition and Subtraction Properties of Inequality
4. Multiplication and Division Properties of Inequality
5. Inequalities of the Form $a < x < b$
6. Applications of Linear Inequalities

> **A Linear Inequality in One Variable**
>
> A **linear inequality in one variable**, x, is any inequality that can be written in the form:
>
> $$ax + b < c, \ ax + b \leq c, \ ax + b > c, \text{ or } ax + b \geq c, \text{ where } a \neq 0.$$

The following inequalities are linear equalities in one variable.

$$2x - 3 < 11 \qquad -4z - 3 > 0 \qquad a \leq 4 \qquad 5.2y \geq 10.4$$

The number line is a useful tool to visualize the solution set of an equation or inequality. For example, the solution set to the equation $x = 2$ is $\{2\}$ and may be graphed as a single point on the number line.

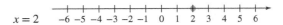

The solution set to an inequality is the set of real numbers that make the inequality a true statement. For example, the solution set to the inequality $x \geq 2$ is all real numbers 2 or greater. Because the solution set has an infinite number of values, we cannot list all of the individual solutions. However, we can graph the solution set on the number line.

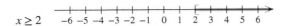

The square bracket symbol, [, is used on the graph to indicate that the point $x = 2$ is included in the solution set. By convention, square brackets, either [or], are used to *include* a point on a number line. Parentheses, (or), are used to *exclude* a point on a number line.

The solution set of the inequality $x > 2$ includes the real numbers greater than 2 but not equal to 2. Therefore, a "(" symbol is used on the graph to indicate that $x = 2$ is not included.

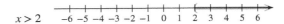

In Example 1, we demonstrate how to graph linear inequalities. To graph an inequality means that we graph its solution set. That is, we graph all of the values on the number line that make the inequality true.

Example 1   **Graphing Linear Inequalities**

Graph the solution sets.

a. $x > -1$ **b.** $c \leq \dfrac{7}{3}$ **c.** $3 > y$

Solution:

a. $x > -1$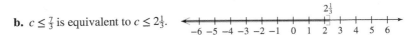

The solution set is the set of all real numbers strictly greater than -1. Therefore, we graph the region on the number line to the right of -1. Because $x = -1$ is not included in the solution set, we use the "(" symbol at $x = -1$.

b. $c \leq \frac{7}{3}$ is equivalent to $c \leq 2\frac{1}{3}$.

The solution set is the set of all real numbers less than or equal to $2\frac{1}{3}$. Therefore, graph the region on the number line to the left of and including $2\frac{1}{3}$. Use the symbol] to indicate that $c = 2\frac{1}{3}$ is included in the solution set.

c. $3 > y$ This inequality reads "3 is greater than y." This is equivalent to saying, "y is less than 3." The inequality $3 > y$ can also be written as $y < 3$.

$y < 3$ ← —|—|—|—|—|—|—|—|—|—|—)—|—|—|— →
$\qquad\qquad$ -6 -5 -4 -3 -2 -1 $\;0\;$ 1 2 3 4 5 6

The solution set is the set of real numbers less than 3. Therefore, graph the region on the number line to the left of 3. Use the symbol ")" to denote that the endpoint, 3, is not included in the solution.

Skill Practice Graph the solution sets.

1. $y < 0$ **2.** $x \geq -\dfrac{5}{4}$ **3.** $5 \geq a$

TIP: Some textbooks use a closed circle or an open circle (● or ○) rather than a bracket or parenthesis to denote inclusion or exclusion of a value on the real number line. For example, the solution sets for the inequalities $x > -1$ and $c \leq \frac{7}{3}$ are graphed here.

$x > -1$ —|—|—|—|—|—|—○—|—|—|—|—|—|— →
$\qquad\quad$ -6 -5 -4 -3 -2 -1 $\;0\;$ 1 2 3 4 5 6

$\qquad\qquad\qquad\qquad\qquad\qquad\qquad\qquad \frac{7}{3}$
$c \leq \frac{7}{3}$ ← —|—|—|—|—|—|—|—|—●—|—|—|— →
$\qquad\quad$ -6 -5 -4 -3 -2 -1 $\;0\;$ 1 2 3 4 5 6

A statement that involves more than one inequality is called a **compound inequality**. One type of compound inequality is used to indicate that one number is between two others. For example, the inequality $-2 < x < 5$ means that $-2 < x$ and $x < 5$. In words, this is easiest to understand if we read the variable first: x is greater than -2 and x is less than 5. The numbers satisfied by these two conditions are those between -2 and 5.

Example 2   **Graphing a Compound Inequality**

Graph the solution set of the inequality: $-4.1 < y \leq -1.7$

Solution:

$-4.1 < y \leq -1.7$ means that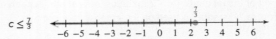

$-4.1 < y$ and $y \leq -1.7$

Shade the region of the number line greater than -4.1 and less than or equal to -1.7.

Skill Practice Graph the solution set.

4. $0 \leq y \leq 8.5$

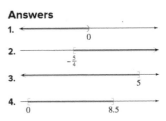

2. Set-Builder Notation and Interval Notation

Graphing the solution set to an inequality is one way to define the set. Two other methods are to use **set-builder notation** or **interval notation**.

Set-Builder Notation

The solution to the inequality $x \geq 2$ can be expressed in set-builder notation as follows:

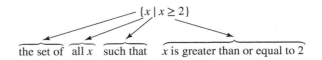

$$\{x \mid x \geq 2\}$$

the set of   all x such that x is greater than or equal to 2

Interval Notation

To understand interval notation, first think of a number line extending infinitely far to the right and infinitely far to the left. Sometimes we use the infinity symbol, ∞, or negative infinity symbol, $-\infty$, to label the far right and far left ends of the number line (Figure 2-10).

Figure 2-10

To express the solution set of an inequality in interval notation, sketch the graph first. Then use the endpoints to define the interval.

Inequality	Graph	Interval Notation
$x \geq 2$		$[2, \infty)$

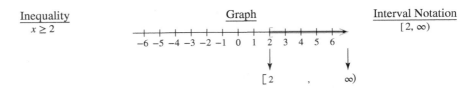

The graph of the solution set $x \geq 2$ begins at 2 and extends infinitely far to the right. The corresponding interval notation begins at 2 and extends to ∞. Notice that a square bracket [is used at 2 for both the graph and the interval notation. A parenthesis is always used at ∞ and for $-\infty$, because there is no endpoint.

Using Interval Notation

- The endpoints used in interval notation are always written from left to right. That is, the smaller number is written first, followed by a comma, followed by the larger number.
- A parenthesis, (or), indicates that an endpoint is *excluded* from the set.
- A square bracket, [or], indicates that an endpoint is *included* in the set.
- A parenthesis, (or), is always used with $-\infty$ or ∞, respectively.

In Table 2-1, we present examples of eight different scenarios for interval notation and the corresponding graph.

Table 2-1

Interval Notation	Graph	Interval Notation	Graph
(a, ∞)	a	$[a, \infty)$	a
$(-\infty, a)$	a	$(-\infty, a]$	a
(a, b)	$a \quad b$	$[a, b]$	$a \quad b$
$(a, b]$	$a \quad b$	$[a, b)$	$a \quad b$

Example 3   **Using Set-Builder Notation and Interval Notation**

Complete the chart.

Set-Builder Notation	Graph	Interval Notation
	$-6\ -5\ -4\ -3\ -2\ -1\ \ 0\ \ 1\ \ 2\ \ 3\ \ 4\ \ 5\ \ 6$	
		$[-\frac{1}{2}, \infty)$
$\{y \mid -2 \le y < 4\}$		

Solution:

Set-Builder Notation	Graph	Interval Notation
$\{x \mid x < -3\}$	$-6\ -5\ -4\ -3\ -2\ -1\ \ 0\ \ 1\ \ 2\ \ 3\ \ 4\ \ 5\ \ 6$	$(-\infty, -3)$
$\{x \mid x \ge -\frac{1}{2}\}$	$-6\ -5\ -4\ -3\ -2\ -1\ \ 0\ \ 1\ \ 2\ \ 3\ \ 4\ \ 5\ \ 6$ $\quad -\frac{1}{2}$	$[-\frac{1}{2}, \infty)$
$\{y \mid -2 \le y < 4\}$	$-6\ -5\ -4\ -3\ -2\ -1\ \ 0\ \ 1\ \ 2\ \ 3\ \ 4\ \ 5\ \ 6$	$[-2, 4)$

Skill Practice Express each of the following in set-builder notation and interval notation.

5. $\quad -2$ 6. $x < \dfrac{3}{2}$ 7. $\quad -3 \qquad 1$

3. Addition and Subtraction Properties of Inequality

The process to solve a linear inequality is very similar to the method used to solve linear equations. Recall that adding or subtracting the same quantity to both sides of an equation results in an equivalent equation. The addition and subtraction properties of inequality state that the same is true for an inequality.

Answers

5. $\{x \mid x \ge -2\}; [-2, \infty)$
6. $\left\{x \mid x < \dfrac{3}{2}\right\}; \left(-\infty, \dfrac{3}{2}\right)$
7. $\{x \mid -3 < x \le 1\}; (-3, 1]$

Addition and Subtraction Properties of Inequality

Let a, b, and c represent real numbers.

1. *Addition Property of Inequality: If $a < b$,
                                          then $a + c < b + c$

2. *Subtraction Property of Inequality: If $a < b$,
                                          then $a - c < b - c$

*These properties may also be stated for $a \leq b$, $a > b$, and $a \geq b$.

To illustrate the addition and subtraction properties of inequality, consider the inequality $5 > 3$. If we add or subtract a real number such as 4 to both sides, the left-hand side will still be greater than the right-hand side. (See Figure 2-11.)

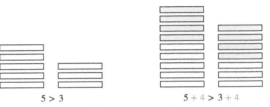

$$5 > 3 \qquad\qquad 5 + 4 > 3 + 4$$

Figure 2-11

Example 4   **Solving a Linear Inequality**

Solve the inequality and graph the solution set. Express the solution set in set-builder notation and in interval notation.

$$-2p + 5 < -3p + 6$$

Solution:

$-2p + 5 < -3p + 6$	
$-2p + 3p + 5 < -3p + 3p + 6$	Addition property of inequality (add $3p$ to both sides).
$p + 5 < 6$	Simplify.
$p + 5 - 5 < 6 - 5$	Subtraction property of inequality.
$p < 1$	

Graph:

```
  <──+──+──+──+──+──+──○──+──+──+──+──+──+──>
    -6 -5 -4 -3 -2 -1  0  1  2  3  4  5  6
```

Set-builder notation: $\{p \mid p < 1\}$

Interval notation: $(-\infty, 1)$

Skill Practice   Solve the inequality and graph the solution set. Express the solution set in set-builder notation and interval notation.

8. $2y - 5 < y - 11$

Answer

8.
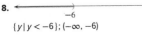

$\{y \mid y < -6\};\ (-\infty, -6)$

TIP: The solution to an inequality gives a set of values that make the original inequality true. Therefore, you can test your final answer by using *test points*. That is, pick a value in the proposed solution set and verify that it makes the original inequality true. Furthermore, any test point picked outside the solution set should make the original inequality false. For example,

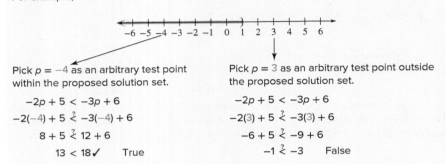

Pick $p = -4$ as an arbitrary test point within the proposed solution set.

$$-2p + 5 < -3p + 6$$
$$-2(-4) + 5 \overset{?}{<} -3(-4) + 6$$
$$8 + 5 \overset{?}{<} 12 + 6$$
$$13 < 18 \checkmark \qquad \text{True}$$

Pick $p = 3$ as an arbitrary test point outside the proposed solution set.

$$-2p + 5 < -3p + 6$$
$$-2(3) + 5 \overset{?}{<} -3(3) + 6$$
$$-6 + 5 \overset{?}{<} -9 + 6$$
$$-1 \overset{?}{<} -3 \qquad \text{False}$$

4. Multiplication and Division Properties of Inequality

Multiplying both sides of an equation by the same quantity results in an equivalent equation. However, the same is not always true for an inequality. If you multiply or divide an inequality by a negative quantity, the direction of the inequality symbol must be reversed.

For example, consider multiplying or dividing the inequality, $4 < 5$ by -1.

$$\begin{array}{ll} \text{Multiply/Divide} & 4 < 5 \\ \text{by } -1 & -4 > -5 \end{array}$$

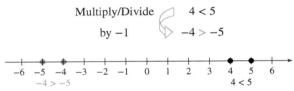

Figure 2-12

The number 4 lies to the left of 5 on the number line. However, -4 lies to the right of -5 (Figure 2-12). Changing the sign of two numbers changes their relative position on the number line. This is stated formally in the multiplication and division properties of inequality.

Multiplication and Division Properties of Inequality

Let a, b, and c represent real numbers, $c \neq 0$.

*If c is positive and $a < b$, then $ac < bc$ and $\dfrac{a}{c} < \dfrac{b}{c}$

*If c is negative and $a < b$, then $ac > bc$ and $\dfrac{a}{c} > \dfrac{b}{c}$

The second statement indicates that if both sides of an inequality are multiplied or divided by a negative quantity, the inequality sign must be reversed.

*These properties may also be stated for $a \leq b$, $a > b$, and $a \geq b$.

172   **Chapter 2** Linear Equations and Inequalities

Example 5   **Solving a Linear Inequality**

Solve the inequality and graph the solution set. Express the solution set in set-builder notation and in interval notation.

$$-5x - 3 \leq 12$$

Solution:

$$-5x - 3 \leq 12$$

$$-5x - 3 + 3 \leq 12 + 3 \qquad \text{Add } 3 \text{ to both sides.}$$

$$-5x \leq 15$$

$$\frac{-5x}{-5} \geq \frac{15}{-5} \qquad \text{Divide by } -5. \text{ Reverse the direction of the inequality sign.}$$

$$x \geq -3$$

Set-builder notation: $\{x \mid x \geq -3\}$

Interval notation: $[-3, \infty)$

TIP: The inequality $-5x - 3 \leq 12$, could have been solved by isolating x on the right-hand side of the inequality. This would create a positive coefficient on the variable term and eliminate the need to divide by a negative number.

$$-5x - 3 \leq 12$$

$$-3 \leq 5x + 12$$

$$-15 \leq 5x \qquad \text{Notice that the coefficient of } x \text{ is positive.}$$

$$\frac{-15}{5} \leq \frac{5x}{5} \qquad \text{Do not reverse the inequality sign because we are dividing by a positive number.}$$

$$-3 \leq x, \text{ or equivalently, } x \geq -3$$

Skill Practice Solve the inequality and graph the solution set. Express the solution set in set-builder notation and in interval notation.

9. $-5p + 2 > 22$

Example 6   **Solving a Linear Inequality**

Solve the inequality and graph the solution set. Express the solution set in set-builder notation and in interval notation.

$$12 - 2(y + 3) < -3(2y - 1) + 2y$$

Solution:

$$12 - 2(y + 3) < -3(2y - 1) + 2y$$

$$12 - 2y - 6 < -6y + 3 + 2y \qquad \text{Clear parentheses.}$$

$$-2y + 6 < -4y + 3 \qquad \text{Combine } like \text{ terms.}$$

$$-2y + 4y + 6 < -4y + 4y + 3 \qquad \text{Add } 4y \text{ to both sides.}$$

$$2y + 6 < 3 \qquad \text{Simplify.}$$

$$2y + 6 + (-6) < 3 + (-6) \qquad \text{Add } -6 \text{ to both sides.}$$

$$2y < -3 \qquad \text{Simplify.}$$

$$\frac{2y}{2} < \frac{-3}{2} \qquad \text{Divide by } 2. \text{ The direction of the inequality sign is } not \text{ reversed because we divided by a positive number.}$$

$$y < -\frac{3}{2}$$

Answer

9.

$\{p \mid p < -4\}; (-\infty, -4)$

Set-builder notation: $\left\{ y \mid y < -\dfrac{3}{2} \right\}$

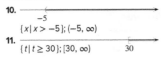

Interval notation: $\left(-\infty, -\dfrac{3}{2} \right)$

Skill Practice Solve the inequality and graph the solution set. Express the solution set in set-builder notation and in interval notation.

10. $-8 - 8(2x - 4) > -5(4x - 5) - 21$

Example 7   **Solving a Linear Inequality**

Solve the inequality and graph the solution set. Express the solution set in set-builder notation and in interval notation.

$$-\frac{1}{4}k + \frac{1}{6} \le 2 + \frac{2}{3}k$$

Solution:

$$-\frac{1}{4}k + \frac{1}{6} \le 2 + \frac{2}{3}k$$

$$12\left(-\frac{1}{4}k + \frac{1}{6}\right) \le 12\left(2 + \frac{2}{3}k\right)$$

Multiply both sides by 12 to clear fractions. (Because we multiplied by a positive number, the inequality sign is not reversed.)

$$\frac{12}{1}\left(-\frac{1}{4}k\right) + \frac{12}{1}\left(\frac{1}{6}\right) \le 12(2) + \frac{12}{1}\left(\frac{2}{3}k\right)$$

Apply the distributive property.

$$-3k + 2 \le 24 + 8k$$

Simplify.

$$-3k - 8k + 2 \le 24 + 8k - 8k$$

Subtract $8k$ from both sides.

$$-11k + 2 \le 24$$

$$-11k + 2 - 2 \le 24 - 2$$

Subtract 2 from both sides.

$$-11k \le 22$$

$$\frac{-11k}{-11} \ge \frac{22}{-11}$$

Divide both sides by -11. Reverse the inequality sign.

$$k \ge -2$$

Set-builder notation: $\{k \mid k \ge -2\}$

Interval notation: $[-2, \infty)$

Skill Practice Solve the inequality and graph the solution set. Express the solution set in set-builder notation and in interval notation.

11. $\dfrac{1}{5}t + 7 \le \dfrac{1}{2}t - 2$

Answers

10.

$\{x \mid x > -5\}; (-5, \infty)$

11.

$\{t \mid t \ge 30\}; [30, \infty)$

5. Inequalities of the Form $a < x < b$

To solve a compound inequality of the form $a < x < b$ we can work with the inequality as a three-part inequality and isolate the variable, x, as demonstrated in Example 8.

Example 8   **Solving a Compound Inequality of the Form $a < x < b$**

Solve the inequality and graph the solution set. Express the solution set in set-builder notation and in interval notation.

$$-3 \leq 2x + 1 < 7$$

Solution:

To solve the compound inequality $-3 \leq 2x + 1 < 7$ isolate the variable x in the middle. The operations performed on the middle portion of the inequality must also be performed on the left-hand side and right-hand side.

$$-3 \leq 2x + 1 < 7$$

$$-3 - 1 \leq 2x + 1 - 1 < 7 - 1 \qquad \text{Subtract } 1 \text{ from all three parts of the inequality.}$$

$$-4 \leq 2x < 6 \qquad \text{Simplify.}$$

$$\frac{-4}{2} \leq \frac{2x}{2} < \frac{6}{2} \qquad \text{Divide by } 2 \text{ in all three parts of the inequality.}$$

$$-2 \leq x < 3$$

Set-builder notation: $\{x \mid -2 \leq x < 3\}$

Interval notation: $[-2, 3)$

```
 ┼──┼──┼──┼──┼━━┼──┼──┼──┼──┼━━┼──┼──┼──┼─▶
-6 -5 -4 -3 -2 -1  0  1  2  3  4  5  6
```

Skill Practice Solve the inequality and graph the solution set. Express the solution set in set-builder notation and in interval notation.

12. $-3 \leq -5 + 2y < 11$

6. Applications of Linear Inequalities

Table 2-2 provides several commonly used translations to express inequalities.

Table 2-2

English Phrase	Mathematical Inequality
a is less than b	$a < b$
a is greater than b a exceeds b	$a > b$
a is less than or equal to b a is at most b a is no more than b	$a \leq b$
a is greater than or equal to b a is at least b a is no less than b	$a \geq b$

Answer

12.
$\{y \mid 1 \leq y < 8\}; [1, 8)$

Example 9 Translating Expressions Involving Inequalities

Write the English phrases as mathematical inequalities.

a. Claude's annual salary, s, is no more than $40,000.

b. A citizen must be at least 18 years old to vote. (Let a represent a citizen's age.)

c. An amusement park ride has a height requirement between 48 in. and 70 in. (Let h represent height in inches.)

Solution:

a. $s \leq 40{,}000$ Claude's annual salary, s, is no more than $40,000.

b. $a \geq 18$ A citizen must be at least 18 years old to vote.

c. $48 < h < 70$ An amusement park ride has a height requirement between 48 in. and 70 in.

Skill Practice Write the English phrase as a mathematical inequality.

13. Bill needs a score of at least 92 on the final exam. Let x represent Bill's score.

14. Fewer than 19 cars are in the parking lot. Let c represent the number of cars.

15. The heights, h, of women who wear petite size clothing are typically between 58 in. and 63 in., inclusive.

Linear inequalities are found in a variety of applications. Example 10 can help you determine the minimum grade you need on an exam to get an A in your math course.

Example 10 Solving an Application with Linear Inequalities

To earn an A in a math class, Alsha must average at least 90 on all of her tests. Suppose Alsha has scored 79, 86, 93, 90, and 95 on her first five math tests. Determine the minimum score she needs on her sixth test to get an A in the class.

Solution:

Let x represent the score on the sixth exam.   Label the variable.

$\left(\begin{array}{c}\text{Average of}\\ \text{all tests}\end{array}\right) \geq 90$ Create a verbal model.

$\dfrac{79 + 86 + 93 + 90 + 95 + x}{6} \geq 90$ The average score is found by taking the sum of the test scores and dividing by the number of scores.

$\dfrac{443 + x}{6} \geq 90$ Simplify.

$6\left(\dfrac{443 + x}{6}\right) \geq (90)6$ Multiply both sides by 6 to clear fractions.

$443 + x \geq 540$ Solve the inequality.

$x \geq 540 - 443$ Subtract 443 from both sides.

$x \geq 97$ Interpret the results.

Alsha must score at least 97 on her sixth exam to receive an A in the course.

Skill Practice

16. To get at least a B in math, Simon must average at least 80 on all tests. Suppose Simon has scored 60, 72, 98, and 85 on the first four tests. Determine the minimum score he needs on the fifth test to receive a B.

Answers
13. $x \geq 92$
14. $c < 19$
15. $58 \leq h \leq 63$
16. Simon needs at least 85.

176   **Chapter 2** Linear Equations and Inequalities

Section 2.8   Practice Exercises

Study Skills Exercise

Find the page numbers for the Chapter Review Exercises, the Chapter Test, and the Cumulative Review Exercises for this chapter.

Chapter Review Exercises _____   Chapter Test _____

Cumulative Review Exercises _____

Compare these features and state the advantages of each.

Vocabulary and Key Concepts

1. a. A relationship of the form $ax + b > c$ or $ax + b < c$ $(a \neq 0)$ is called a _____ in one variable.

b. A statement that involves more than one _____ is called a compound inequality.

c. The notation $\{x \mid x > -9\}$ is an example of _____ notation, whereas $(-9, \infty)$ is an example of _____ notation.

Review Problems

For Exercises 2–4, solve the equation.

2. $10y - 7(y + 8) + 13 = 13 - 6(2y + 1)$

3. $3(x + 2) - (2x - 7) = -(5x - 1) - 2(x + 6)$

4. $6 - 8(x + 3) + 5x = 5x - (2x - 5) + 13$

Concept 1: Graphing Linear Inequalities

For Exercises 5–16, graph the solution set of each inequality. **(See Examples 1–2.)**

5. $x > 5$

6. $x \geq -7.2$

7. $x \leq \dfrac{5}{2}$

8. $x < -1$

9. $13 > p$

10. $-12 \geq t$

11. $2 \leq y \leq 6.5$

12. $-3 \leq m \leq \dfrac{8}{9}$

13. $0 < x < 4$

14. $-4 < y < 1$

15. $1 < p \leq 8$

16. $-3 \leq t < 3$

Concept 2: Set-Builder Notation and Interval Notation

For Exercises 17–22, graph each inequality and write the solution set in interval notation. **(See Example 3.)**

Set-Builder Notation	Graph	Interval Notation
17. $\{x \mid x \geq 6\}$		
18. $\left\{x \mid \dfrac{1}{2} < x \leq 4\right\}$		
19. $\{x \mid x \leq 2.1\}$		
20. $\left\{x \mid x > \dfrac{7}{3}\right\}$		
21. $\{x \mid -2 < x \leq 7\}$		
22. $\{x \mid x < -5\}$		

Animation

For Exercises 23–28, write each set in set-builder notation and in interval notation. **(See Example 3.)**

Set-Builder Notation	Graph	Interval Notation
23.	$\frac{3}{4}$	
24.	-0.3	
25.	-1 8	
26.	0	
27.	-14	
28.	0 9	

For Exercises 29–34, graph each set and write the set in set-builder notation. **(See Example 3.)**

Set-Builder Notation	Graph	Interval Notation
29.		$[18, \infty)$
30.		$[-10, -2]$
31.		$(-\infty, -0.6)$
32.		$\left(-\infty, \dfrac{5}{3}\right)$
33.		$[-3.5, 7.1)$
34.		$[-10, \infty)$

Concepts 3–4: Properties of Inequality

For Exercises 35–42, solve the equation in part (a). For part (b), solve the inequality and graph the solution set. Write the answer in set-builder notation and interval notation. **(See Examples 4–7.)**

35. a. $x + 3 = 6$

   b. $x + 3 > 6$

36. a. $y - 6 = 12$

   b. $y - 6 \geq 12$

37. a. $p - 4 = 9$

   b. $p - 4 \leq 9$

38. a. $k + 8 = 10$

   b. $k + 8 < 10$

39. a. $4c = -12$

   b. $4c < -12$

40. a. $5d = -35$

   b. $5d > -35$

41. a. $-10z = 15$

   b. $-10z \leq 15$

42. a. $-2w = 14$

   b. $-2w < 14$

Concept 5: Inequalities of the Form $a < x < b$

For Exercises 43–48, graph the solution and write the set in interval notation. **(See Example 8.)**

43. $-1 < y \leq 4$

44. $2.5 \leq t < 5.7$

45. $0 < x + 3 < 8$

46. $-2 \leq x - 4 \leq 3$

47. $8 \leq 4x \leq 24$

48. $-9 < 3x < 12$

178   **Chapter 2**   Linear Equations and Inequalities

Mixed Exercises

For Exercises 49–96, solve the inequality and graph the solution set. Write the solution set in (a) set-builder notation and (b) interval notation. **(See Exercises 4–8.)**

49. $x + 5 \le 6$

50. $y - 7 < 6$

51. $3q - 7 > 2q + 3$

52. $5r + 4 \ge 4r - 1$

53. $4 < 1 + x$

54. $3 > z - 6$

55. $3c > 6$

56. $4d \le 12$

57. $-3c > 6$

58. $-4d \le 12$

59. $-h \le -14$

60. $-q > -7$

61. $12 \ge -\dfrac{x}{2}$

62. $6 < -\dfrac{m}{3}$

63. $-2 \le p + 1 < 4$

64. $0 < k + 7 < 6$

65. $-3 < 6h - 3 < 12$

66. $-6 \le 4a - 2 \le 12$

67. $-24 < -2x < -20$

68. $-12 \le -3x \le 6$

69. $-3 \le \dfrac{1}{4}x - 1 < 5$

70. $-2 < \dfrac{1}{3}x - 2 \le 2$

71. $-\dfrac{2}{3}y < 6$

72. $\dfrac{3}{4}x \le -12$

73. $-2x - 4 \le 11$

74. $-3x + 1 > 0$

75. $-12 > 7x + 9$

76. $8 < 2x - 10$

77. $-7b - 3 \le 2b$

78. $3t \ge 7t - 35$

79. $4n + 2 < 6n + 8$

80. $2w - 1 \le 5w + 8$

81. $8 - 6(x - 3) > -4x + 12$

82. $3 - 4(h - 2) > -5h + 6$

83. $3(x + 1) - 2 \le \dfrac{1}{2}(4x - 8)$

84. $8 - (2x - 5) \ge \dfrac{1}{3}(9x - 6)$

85. $4(z - 1) - 6 \ge 6(2z + 3) - 12$

86. $3(2x + 5) + 2 < 5(2x + 2) + 3$

87. $2a + 3(a + 5) > -4a - (3a - 1) + 6$

88. $13 + 7(2y - 3) \le 12 + 3(3y - 1)$

89. $\dfrac{7}{6}p + \dfrac{4}{3} \ge \dfrac{11}{6}p - \dfrac{7}{6}$

90. $\dfrac{1}{3}w - \dfrac{1}{2} \le \dfrac{5}{6}w + \dfrac{1}{2}$

91. $\dfrac{y-6}{3} > y + 4$

92. $\dfrac{5t+7}{2} < t - 4$

93. $-1.2a - 0.4 < -0.4a + 2$

94. $-0.4c + 1.2 > -2c - 0.4$

95. $-2x + 5 \geq -x + 5$

96. $4x - 6 < 5x - 6$

For Exercises 97–100, determine whether the given number is a solution to the inequality.

97. $-2x + 5 < 4;$ $x = -2$

98. $-3y - 7 > 5;$ $y = 6$

99. $4(p + 7) - 1 > 2 + p;$ $p = 1$

100. $3 - k < 2(-1 + k);$ $k = 4$

Concept 6: Applications of Linear Inequalities

For Exercises 101–110, write each English phrase as a mathematical inequality. **(See Example 9.)**

101. The length of a fish, L, was at least 10 in.

102. Tasha's average test score, t, exceeded 90.

103. The wind speed, w, exceeded 75 mph.

104. The height of a cave, h, was no more than 2 ft.

105. The temperature of the water in Blue Spring, t, is no more than 72°F.

106. The temperature on the tennis court, t, was no less than 100°F.

107. The length of the hike, L, was no less than 8 km.

108. The depth, d, of a certain pool was at most 10 ft.

109. The snowfall, h, in Monroe County is between 2 in. and 5 in.

110. The cost, c, of carpeting a room is between $300 and $400.

111. The average summer rainfall for Miami, Florida, for June, July, and August is 7.4 in. per month. If Miami receives 5.9 in. of rain in June and 6.1 in. in July, how much rain is required in August to exceed the 3-month summer average? **(See Example 10.)**

© Royalty Free/Corbis RF

112. The average winter snowfall for Burlington, Vermont, for December, January, and February is 18.7 in. per month. If Burlington receives 22 in. of snow in December and 24 in. in January, how much snow is required in February to exceed the 3-month winter average?

113. To earn a B in chemistry, Trevor's average on his five tests must be at least 80. Suppose that Trevor has scored 85, 75, 72, and 82 on his first four chemistry tests. Determine the minimum score needed on his fifth test to get a B in the class.

114. In speech class, Carolyn needs at least a B+ to keep her financial aid. To earn a B+, the average of her four speeches must be at least an 85. On the first three speeches she scored 87, 75, and 82. Determine the minimum score on her fourth speech to get a B+.

115. An artist paints wooden birdhouses. She buys the birdhouses for $9 each. However, for large orders, the price per birdhouse is discounted by a percentage off the original price. Let x represent the number of birdhouses ordered. The corresponding discount is given in the table.

a. If the artist places an order for 190 birdhouses, compute the total cost.

b. Which costs more: 190 birdhouses or 200 birdhouses? Explain your answer.

Size of Order	Discount
$x \leq 49$	0%
$50 \leq x \leq 99$	5%
$100 \leq x \leq 199$	10%
$x \geq 200$	20%

116. A wholesaler sells T-shirts to a surf shop at $8 per shirt. However, for large orders, the price per shirt is discounted by a percentage off the original price. Let x represent the number of shirts ordered. The corresponding discount is given in the table.

Number of Shirts Ordered	Discount
$x \leq 24$	0%
$25 \leq x \leq 49$	2%
$50 \leq x \leq 99$	4%
$100 \leq x \leq 149$	6%
$x \geq 150$	8%

  a. If the surf shop orders 50 shirts, compute the total cost.

  b. Which costs more: 148 shirts or 150 shirts? Explain your answer.

117. To print a flyer for a new business, Company A charges $39.99 for the design plus $0.50 per flyer. Company B charges $0.60 per flyer but has no design fee. For how many flyers would Company A be a better deal?

118. Melissa runs a landscaping business. She has equipment and fuel expenses of $313 per month. If she charges $45 for each lawn, how many lawns must she service to make a profit of at least $600 a month?

119. Madison is planning a 5-night trip to Cancun, Mexico, with her friends. The airfare is $475, her share of the hotel room is $54 per night, and her budget for food and entertainment is $350. She has $700 in savings and has a job earning $10 per hour babysitting. What is the minimum number of hours of babysitting that Madison needs so that she will have enough money to take the trip?

120. Luke and Landon are both tutors. Luke charges $50 for an initial assessment and $25 per hour for each hour he tutors. Landon charges $100 for an initial assessment and $20 per hour for tutoring. After how many hours of tutoring will Luke surpass Landon in earnings?

Group Activity

Computing Body Mass Index (BMI)

Materials: Calculator

Estimated Time: 10 minutes

Group Size: 2

Body mass index is a statistical measure of an individual's weight in relation to the person's height. It is computed by

$$BMI = \frac{703W}{h^2}$$ where W is a person's weight in *pounds*.
h is the person's height in *inches*.

The National Institutes of Health (NIH) categorizes body mass indices as shown in the table.

Body Mass Index (BMI)	Weight Status
$18.5 \leq BMI \leq 24.9$	considered ideal
$25.0 \leq BMI \leq 29.9$	considered overweight
$BMI \geq 30.0$	considered obese

1. Compute the body mass index for a person 5′4″ tall weighing 160 lb. Is this person's weight considered ideal?

2. At the time that basketball legend Michael Jordan played for the Chicago Bulls, he was 210 lb and stood 6′6″ tall. What was Michael Jordan's body mass index?

3. For a fixed height, body mass index is a function of a person's weight only. For example, for a person 72 in. tall (6 ft), solve the following inequality to determine the person's ideal weight range.

$$18.5 \leq \frac{703W}{(72)^2} \leq 24.9$$

4. At the time that professional bodybuilder, Jay Cutler, won the Mr. Olympia contest he was 260 lb and stood 5′10″ tall.

    a. What was Jay Cutler's body mass index?

    b. As a bodybuilder, Jay Cutler has an extraordinarily small percentage of body fat. Yet, according to the chart, would he be considered overweight or obese? Why do you think that the formula is not an accurate measurement of Mr. Cutler's weight status?

Chapter 2   Summary

Section 2.1   Addition, Subtraction, Multiplication, and Division Properties of Equality

Key Concepts

An equation is an algebraic statement that indicates two expressions are equal. A **solution to an equation** is a value of the variable that makes the equation a true statement. The set of all solutions to an equation is the solution set of the equation.

    A **linear equation in one variable** can be written in the form $ax + b = c$, where $a \neq 0$.

Addition Property of Equality:

If $a = b$, then $a + c = b + c$

Subtraction Property of Equality:

If $a = b$, then $a - c = b - c$

Multiplication Property of Equality:

If $a = b$, then $ac = bc$ $(c \neq 0)$

Division Property of Equality:

If $a = b$, then $\dfrac{a}{c} = \dfrac{b}{c}$ $(c \neq 0)$

Examples

Example 1

$2x + 1 = 9$ is an equation with solution set $\{4\}$.

Check: $2(4) + 1 \overset{?}{=} 9$

$$8 + 1 \overset{?}{=} 9$$

$$9 \overset{?}{=} 9 \checkmark \quad \text{True}$$

Example 2

$$x - 5 = 12$$
$$x - 5 + 5 = 12 + 5$$
$$x = 17 \qquad \text{The solution set is } \{17\}.$$

Example 3

$$z + 1.44 = 2.33$$
$$z + 1.44 - 1.44 = 2.33 - 1.44$$
$$z = 0.89 \qquad \text{The solution set is } \{0.89\}.$$

Example 4

$$\frac{3}{4}x = 12$$

$$\frac{4}{3} \cdot \frac{3}{4}x = 12 \cdot \frac{4}{3}$$

$$x = 16 \quad \text{The solution set is } \{16\}.$$

Example 5

$$16 = 8y$$
$$\frac{16}{8} = \frac{8y}{8}$$
$$2 = y \qquad \text{The solution set is } \{2\}.$$

Section 2.2 — Solving Linear Equations

Key Concepts

Steps for Solving a Linear Equation in One Variable:

1. Simplify both sides of the equation.
   - Clear parentheses
   - Combine *like* terms
2. Use the addition or subtraction property of equality to collect the variable terms on one side of the equation.
3. Use the addition or subtraction property of equality to collect the constant terms on the other side of the equation.
4. Use the multiplication or division property of equality to make the coefficient of the variable term equal to 1.
5. Check your answer.

A **conditional equation** is true for some values of the variable but is false for other values.

An equation that has all real numbers as its solution set is an **identity**.

An equation that has no solution is a **contradiction**.

Examples

Example 1

$$5y + 7 = 3(y - 1) + 2$$

$5y + 7 = 3y - 3 + 2$	Clear parentheses.
$5y + 7 = 3y - 1$	Combine *like* terms.
$2y + 7 = -1$	Collect the variable terms.
$2y = -8$	Collect the constant terms.
$y = -4$	Divide both sides by 2.

Check:

$$5(-4) + 7 \stackrel{?}{=} 3[(-4) - 1] + 2$$
$$-20 + 7 \stackrel{?}{=} 3(-5) + 2$$
$$-13 \stackrel{?}{=} -15 + 2$$

The solution set is $\{-4\}$.　　$-13 \stackrel{?}{=} -13$ ✓ True

Example 2

$x + 5 = 7$　　is a conditional equation because it is true only on the condition that $x = 2$.

Solution set: $\{2\}$

Example 3

$$x + 4 = 2(x + 2) - x$$
$$x + 4 = 2x + 4 - x$$
$$x + 4 = x + 4$$
$$4 = 4 \quad \text{is an identity.}$$

Solution set: The set of real numbers.

Example 4

$$y - 5 = 2(y + 3) - y$$
$$y - 5 = 2y + 6 - y$$
$$y - 5 = y + 6$$
$$-5 = 6 \quad \text{is a contradiction.}$$

Solution set: $\{\ \}$

Section 2.3   Linear Equations: Clearing Fractions and Decimals

Key Concepts

Steps for Solving a Linear Equation in One Variable:

1. Simplify both sides of the equation.
   - Clear parentheses
   - Consider clearing fractions or decimals (if any are present) by multiplying both sides of the equation by a common denominator of all terms
   - Combine *like* terms
2. Use the addition or subtraction property of equality to collect the variable terms on one side of the equation.
3. Use the addition or subtraction property of equality to collect the constant terms on the other side of the equation.
4. Use the multiplication or division property of equality to make the coefficient of the variable term equal to 1.
5. Check your answer.

Examples

Example 1

$$\frac{1}{2}x - 2 - \frac{3}{4}x = \frac{7}{4}$$

$$\frac{4}{1}\left(\frac{1}{2}x - 2 - \frac{3}{4}x\right) = \frac{4}{1}\left(\frac{7}{4}\right) \quad \text{Multiply by the LCD.}$$

$$\frac{4}{1}\left(\frac{1}{2}x\right) - \frac{4}{1}\left(\frac{2}{1}\right) - \frac{4}{1}\left(\frac{3}{4}x\right) = \frac{4}{1}\left(\frac{7}{4}\right)$$

$$2x - 8 - 3x = 7 \qquad \begin{array}{l}\text{Apply distributive} \\ \text{property.}\end{array}$$

$$-x - 8 = 7 \qquad \text{Combine } like \text{ terms.}$$

$$-x = 15 \qquad \text{Add 8 to both sides.}$$

$$x = -15 \qquad \text{Divide by } -1.$$

The solution set is $\{-15\}$.

Example 2

$$-1.2x - 5.1 = 16.5$$

$$10(-1.2x - 5.1) = 10(16.5) \qquad \begin{array}{l}\text{Multiply both} \\ \text{sides by 10.}\end{array}$$

$$-12x - 51 = 165$$

$$-12x = 216$$

$$\frac{-12x}{-12} = \frac{216}{-12}$$

$$x = -18$$

The solution set is $\{-18\}$.

Section 2.4   Applications of Linear Equations: Introduction to Problem Solving

Key Concepts

Problem-Solving Steps for Word Problems:

1. Read the problem carefully.
2. Assign labels to unknown quantities.
3. Write a verbal model.
4. Write a mathematical equation.
5. Solve the equation.
6. Interpret the results and write the answer in words.

Examples

Example 1

The perimeter of a triangle is 54 m. The lengths of the sides are represented by three consecutive even integers. Find the lengths of the three sides.

1. Read the problem.

2. Let x represent one side, $x + 2$ represent the second side, and $x + 4$ represent the third side.

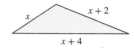

3. $\begin{pmatrix} \text{Length of} \\ \text{first side} \end{pmatrix} + \begin{pmatrix} \text{length of} \\ \text{second side} \end{pmatrix} + \begin{pmatrix} \text{length of} \\ \text{third side} \end{pmatrix}$

   $= \text{perimeter}$

4. $x + (x + 2) + (x + 4) = 54$

5. $3x + 6 = 54$
   $3x = 48$
   $x = 16$

6. $x = 16$ represents the length of the shortest side. The lengths of the other sides are given by $x + 2 = 18$ and $x + 4 = 20$.

   The lengths of the three sides are 16 m, 18 m, and 20 m.

Section 2.5   Applications Involving Percents

Key Concepts

The following formula will help you solve basic percent problems.

$$\text{Amount} = (\text{percent})(\text{base})$$

One common use of percents is in computing **sales tax**.

Another use of percents is in computing **simple interest** using the formula:

$$\begin{pmatrix}\text{Simple} \\ \text{interest}\end{pmatrix} = (\text{principal})\begin{pmatrix}\text{annual} \\ \text{interest} \\ \text{rate}\end{pmatrix}\begin{pmatrix}\text{time in} \\ \text{years}\end{pmatrix}$$

or $I = Prt$.

Examples

Example 1

A flat screen television costs $1260.00 after a 5% sales tax is included. What was the price before tax?

$$\begin{pmatrix}\text{Price} \\ \text{before tax}\end{pmatrix} + (\text{tax}) = \begin{pmatrix}\text{total} \\ \text{price}\end{pmatrix}$$

$$x \quad\quad + 0.05x = 1260$$
$$1.05x = 1260$$
$$x = 1200$$

The television costs $1200 before tax.

Example 2

John Li invests $5400 at 2.5% simple interest. How much interest does he earn after 5 years?

$$I = Prt$$
$$I = (\$5400)(0.025)(5)$$
$$I = \$675$$

Section 2.6   Formulas and Applications of Geometry

Key Concepts

A **literal equation** is an equation that has more than one variable. Often such an equation can be manipulated to solve for different variables.

Examples

Example 1

$$P = 2a + b, \text{ solve for } a.$$
$$P - b = 2a + b - b$$
$$P - b = 2a$$
$$\frac{P - b}{2} = \frac{2a}{2}$$
$$\frac{P - b}{2} = a \quad \text{or} \quad a = \frac{P - b}{2}$$

Example 2

Find the length of a side of a square whose perimeter is 28 ft.

Use the formula $P = 4s$. Substitute 28 for P and solve:

$$P = 4s$$
$$28 = 4s$$
$$7 = s$$

The length of a side of the square is 7 ft.

Section 2.7 Mixture Applications and Uniform Motion

Examples

Example 1 illustrates a mixture problem.

Example 1

How much 80% disinfectant solution should be mixed with 8 L of a 30% disinfectant solution to make a 40% solution?

	80% Solution	30% Solution	40% Solution
Amount of Solution	x	8	$x + 8$
Amount of Pure Disinfectant	$0.80x$	$0.30(8)$	$0.40(x + 8)$

$0.80x + 0.30(8) = 0.40(x + 8)$

$\begin{aligned} 0.80x + 2.4 &= 0.40x + 3.2 \\ 0.40x + 2.4 &= 3.2 \qquad \text{Subtract } 0.40x. \\ 0.40x &= 0.80 \qquad \text{Subtract } 2.4. \\ x &= 2 \qquad \text{Divide by } 0.40. \end{aligned}$

2 L of 80% solution is needed.

Examples

Example 2 illustrates a uniform motion problem.

Example 2

Jack and Diane participate in a bicycle race. Jack rides the first half of the race in 1.5 hr. Diane rides the second half at a rate 5 mph slower than Jack and completes her portion in 2 hr. How fast does each person ride?

	Distance	Rate	Time
Jack	$1.5x$	x	1.5
Diane	$2(x - 5)$	$x - 5$	2

$$\begin{pmatrix} \text{Distance} \\ \text{Jack rides} \end{pmatrix} = \begin{pmatrix} \text{distance} \\ \text{Diane rides} \end{pmatrix}$$

$\begin{aligned} 1.5x &= 2(x - 5) \\ 1.5x &= 2x - 10 \\ -0.5x &= -10 \qquad \text{Subtract } 2x. \\ x &= 20 \qquad \text{Divide by } -0.5. \end{aligned}$

Jack's speed is x. Jack rides 20 mph. Diane's speed is $x - 5$, which is 15 mph.

Section 2.8 Linear Inequalities

Key Concepts

A **linear inequality in one variable**, x, is any relationship in the form: $ax + b < c$, $ax + b > c$, $ax + b \leq c$, or $ax + b \geq c$, where $a \neq 0$.

The solution set to an inequality can be expressed as a graph or in **set-builder notation** or in **interval notation**.

When graphing an inequality or when writing interval notation, a parenthesis, (or), is used to denote that an endpoint is *not included* in a solution set. A square bracket, [or], is used to show that an endpoint *is included* in a solution set. A parenthesis (or) is always used with $-\infty$ and ∞, respectively.

The inequality $a < x < b$ is used to show that x is greater than a and less than b. That is, x is *between* a and b.

Multiplying or dividing an inequality by a negative quantity requires the direction of the inequality sign to be reversed.

Example

Example 1

$\begin{aligned} -2x + 6 &\geq 14 \\ -2x + 6 - 6 &\geq 14 - 6 \qquad \text{Subtract } 6. \\ -2x &\geq 8 \qquad \text{Simplify.} \\ \frac{-2x}{-2} &\leq \frac{8}{-2} \qquad \text{Divide by } -2. \text{ Reverse the inequality sign.} \\ x &\leq -4 \end{aligned}$

Graph:

Set-builder notation: $\{x \mid x \leq -4\}$

Interval notation: $(-\infty, -4]$

Chapter 2   Review Exercises

Section 2.1

1. Label the following as either an expression or an equation:

   a. $3x + y = 10$ **b.** $9x + 10x - 2xy$

   c. $4(x + 3) = 12$ **d.** $-5x = 7$

2. Explain how to determine whether an equation is linear in one variable.

3. Determine if the given equation is a linear equation in one variable. Answer yes or no.

   a. $4x^2 + 8 = -10$ **b.** $x + 18 = 72$

   c. $-3 + 2y^2 = 0$ **d.** $-4p - 5 = 6p$

4. For the equation, $4y + 9 = -3$, determine if the given numbers are solutions.

   a. $y = 3$ **b.** $y = -3$

For Exercises 5–12, solve each equation using the addition property, subtraction property, multiplication property, or division property of equality.

5. $a + 6 = -2$ 6. $6 = z - 9$

7. $-\dfrac{3}{4} + k = \dfrac{9}{2}$ 8. $0.1r = 7$

9. $-5x = 21$ 10. $\dfrac{t}{3} = -20$

11. $-\dfrac{2}{5}k = \dfrac{4}{7}$ 12. $-m = -27$

13. The quotient of a number and negative six is equal to negative ten. Find the number.

14. The difference of a number and $-\frac{1}{8}$ is $\frac{5}{12}$. Find the number.

15. Four subtracted from a number is negative twelve. Find the number.

16. The product of a number and $\frac{1}{4}$ is $-\frac{1}{2}$. Find the number.

Section 2.2

For Exercises 17–28, solve each equation.

17. $4d + 2 = 6$ 18. $5c - 6 = -9$

19. $-7c = -3c - 8$ 20. $-28 = 5w + 2$

21. $\dfrac{b}{3} + 1 = 0$ 22. $\dfrac{2}{3}h - 5 = 7$

23. $-3p + 7 = 5p + 1$ 24. $4t - 6 = 12t + 18$

25. $4a - 9 = 3(a - 3)$ 26. $3(2c + 5) = -2(c - 8)$

27. $7b + 3(b - 1) + 3 = 2(b + 8)$

28. $2 + (18 - x) + 2(x - 1) = 4(x + 2) - 8$

29. Explain the difference between an equation that is a contradiction and an equation that is an identity.

For Exercises 30–35, label each equation as a conditional equation, a contradiction, or an identity.

30. $x + 3 = 3 + x$ 31. $3x - 19 = 2x + 1$

32. $5x + 6 = 5x - 28$ 33. $2x - 8 = 2(x - 4)$

34. $-8x - 9 = -8(x - 9)$ 35. $4x - 4 = 3x - 2$

Section 2.3

For Exercises 36–53, solve each equation.

36. $\dfrac{x}{8} - \dfrac{1}{4} = \dfrac{1}{2}$ 37. $\dfrac{y}{15} - \dfrac{2}{3} = \dfrac{4}{5}$

38. $\dfrac{x + 5}{2} - \dfrac{2x + 10}{9} = 5$

39. $\dfrac{x - 6}{3} - \dfrac{2x + 8}{2} = 12$

40. $\dfrac{1}{10}p - 3 = \dfrac{2}{5}p$ 41. $\dfrac{1}{4}y - \dfrac{3}{4} = \dfrac{1}{2}y + 1$

42. $-\dfrac{1}{4}(2 - 3t) = \dfrac{3}{4}$ 43. $\dfrac{2}{7}(w + 4) = \dfrac{1}{2}$

44. $17.3 - 2.7q = 10.55$

45. $4.9z + 4.6 = 3.2z - 2.2$

46. $5.74a + 9.28 = 2.24a - 5.42$

47. $62.84t - 123.66 = 4(2.36 + 2.4t)$

188   **Chapter 2**   Linear Equations and Inequalities

48. $0.05x + 0.10(24 - x) = 0.75(24)$

49. $0.20(x + 4) + 0.65x = 0.20(854)$

50. $100 - (t - 6) = -(t - 1)$

51. $3 - (x + 4) + 5 = 3x + 10 - 4x$

52. $5t - (2t + 14) = 3t - 14$

53. $9 - 6(2x + 1) = -3(4z - 1)$

Section 2.4

54. Twelve added to the sum of a number and two is forty-four. Find the number.

55. Twenty added to the sum of a number and six is thirty-seven. Find the number.

56. Three times a number is the same as the difference of twice the number and seven. Find the number.

57. Eight less than five times a number is forty-eight less than the number. Find the number.

58. Three times the largest of three consecutive even integers is 76 more than the sum of the other two integers. Find the integers.

59. Ten times the smallest of three consecutive integers is 213 more than the sum of the other two integers. Find the integers.

60. The perimeter of a triangle is 78 in. The lengths of the sides are represented by three consecutive integers. Find the lengths of the sides of the triangle.

61. The perimeter of a pentagon (a five-sided polygon) is 190 cm. The lengths of the sides are represented by consecutive integers. Find the lengths of the sides.

62. Minimum salaries of major league baseball players soared after a new ruling in 1975. In 2010, the minimum salary for a major league player was $400,000. This is 25 times the minimum salary in 1975. Find the minimum salary in 1975.

63. The state of Indiana has approximately 2.1 million more people than Kentucky. Together their populations total 10.3 million. Approximately how many people are in each state?

Section 2.5

 For Exercises 64–69, solve each problem involving percents.

64. What is 35% of 68?   **65.** What is 4% of 720?

66. 53.5 is what percent of 428?

67. 68.4 is what percent of 72?

68. 24 is 15% of what number?

69. 8.75 is 0.5% of what number?

70. A couple spent a total of $50.40 for dinner. This included a 20% tip and 6% sales tax on the price of the meal. What was the price of the dinner before tax and tip?

 71. Anna Tsao invested $3000 in an account paying 8% simple interest.

    a. How much interest will she earn in $3\frac{1}{2}$ years?

    b. What will her balance be at that time?

72. Eduardo invested money in an account earning 4% simple interest. At the end of 5 years, he had a total of $14,400. How much money did he originally invest?

73. A novel is discounted 30%. The sale price is $20.65. What was the original price?

Section 2.6

For Exercises 74–81, solve for the indicated variable.

74. $C = K - 273$ for K

75. $K = C + 273$ for C

76. $P = 4s$ for s

77. $P = 3s$ for s

78. $y = mx + b$ for x

79. $a + bx = c$ for x

80. $2x + 5y = -2$ for y

81. $4(a + b) = Q$ for b

For Exercises 82–88, use an appropriate geometry formula to solve the problem.

82. Find the height of a parallelogram whose area is 42 m² and whose base is 6 m.

83. The volume of a cone is given by the formula $V = \frac{1}{3}\pi r^2 h.$

a. Solve the formula for h.

b. Find the height of a right circular cone whose volume is 47.8 in.³ and whose radius is 3 in. Round to the nearest tenth of an inch.

84. The smallest angle of a triangle is 2° more than $\frac{1}{4}$ of the largest angle. The middle angle is 2° less than the largest angle. Find the measure of each angle.

85. A carpenter uses a special saw to cut an angle on a piece of framing. If the angles are complementary and one angle is 10° more than the other, find the measure of each angle.

86. A rectangular window has width 1 ft less than its length. The perimeter is 18 ft. Find the length and the width of the window.

87. Find the measure of the vertical angles by first solving for x.

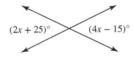

$(2x + 25)°$　　$(4x − 15)°$

88. Find the measure of angle y.

37°

y

Section 2.7

89. In stormy conditions, a delivery truck can travel a route in 14 hr. In good weather, the same trip can be made in 10.5 hr because the truck travels 15 km/hr faster. Find the speed of the truck in stormy weather and the speed in good weather.

90. Winston and Gus ride their bicycles in a relay. Each person rides the same distance. Winston rides 3 mph faster than Gus and finishes the course in 2.5 hr. Gus finishes in 3 hr. How fast does each person ride?

91. Two cars leave a rest stop on Interstate I-10 at the same time. One heads east and the other heads west. One car travels 55 mph and the other 62 mph. How long will it take for them to be 327.6 mi apart?

92. Two hikers begin at the same time at opposite ends of a 9-mi trail and walk toward each other. One hiker walks 2.5 mph and the other walks 1.5 mph. How long will it be before they meet?

93. How much ground beef with 24% fat should be mixed with 8 lb of ground sirloin that is 6% fat to make a mixture that is 9.6% fat?

94. A soldering compound with 40% lead (the rest is tin) must be combined with 80 lb of solder that is 75% lead to make a compound that is 68% lead. How much solder with 40% lead should be used?

Section 2.8

For Exercises 95–97, graph each inequality and write the set in interval notation.

95. $\{x \mid x > −2\}$

96. $\left\{x \mid x \le \dfrac{1}{2}\right\}$

97. $\{x \mid −1 < x \le 4\}$

98. A landscaper buys potted geraniums from a nursery at a price of \$5 per plant. However, for large orders, the price per plant is discounted by a percentage off the original price. Let x represent the number of potted plants ordered. The corresponding discount is given in the table.

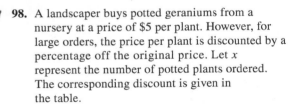

Number of Plants	Discount
$x \le 99$	0%
$100 \le x \le 199$	2%
$200 \le x \le 299$	4%
$x \ge 300$	6%

a. Find the cost to purchase 130 plants.

b. Which costs more, 300 plants or 295 plants? Explain your answer.

For Exercises 99–109, solve the inequality. Graph the solution set and write the answer in set-builder notation and interval notation.

99. $c + 6 < 23$ ⟶

100. $3w - 4 > -5$ ⟶

101. $-2x - 7 \geq 5$ ⟶

102. $5(y + 2) \leq -4$ ⟶

103. $-\dfrac{3}{7}a \leq -21$ ⟶

104. $1.3 > 0.4t - 12.5$ ⟶

105. $4k + 23 < 7k - 31$ ⟶

106. $\dfrac{6}{5}h - \dfrac{1}{5} \leq \dfrac{3}{10} + h$ ⟶

107. $-5x - 2(4x - 3) + 6 > 17 - 4(x - 1)$ ⟶

108. $-6 < 2b \leq 14$ ⟶

109. $-2 \leq z + 4 \leq 9$ ⟶

110. The summer average rainfall for Bermuda for June, July, and August is 5.3 in. per month. If Bermuda receives 6.3 in. of rain in June and 7.1 in. in July, how much rain is required in August to exceed the 3-month summer average?

111. Collette has $15.00 to spend on dinner. Of this, 25% will cover the tax and tip, resulting in $11.25 for her to spend on food. If Collette wants veggies and blue cheese, fries, and a drink, what is the maximum number of chicken wings she can get?

Wing Special

25¢ each

5:00–7:00 P.M.

*Add veggies and blue cheese for $2.50

*Add fries for $2.50

*Add a drink for $1.75

Chapter 2   Test

1. Which of the equations have $x = -3$ as a solution?

   a. $4x + 1 = 10$ **b.** $6(x - 1) = x - 21$

   c. $5x - 2 = 2x + 1$ **d.** $\dfrac{1}{3}x + 1 = 0$

2. a. Simplify: $3x - 1 + 2x + 8$

   b. Solve: $3x - 1 = 2x + 8$

For Exercises 3–13, solve each equation.

3. $-3x + 5 = -2$ **4.** $3h + 1 = 3(h + 1)$

5. $t + 3 = -13$

6. $2 + d = 2 - 3(d - 5) - 2$

7. $8 = p - 4$

8. $\dfrac{3}{7} + \dfrac{2}{5}x = -\dfrac{1}{5}x + 1$ **9.** $\dfrac{t}{8} = -\dfrac{2}{9}$

10. $2(p - 4) = p + 7$

11. $-5(x + 2) + 8x = -2 + 3x - 8$

12. $\dfrac{3x + 1}{2} - \dfrac{4x - 3}{3} = 1$

13. $0.5c - 1.9 = 2.8 + 0.6c$

14. Solve the equation for y: $3x + y = -4$

15. Solve $C = 2\pi r$ for r.

16. 13% of what is 11.7?

Cumulative Review Exercises   **191**

17. Graph the inequalities and write the sets in interval notation.

    a. $\{x \mid x < 0\}$ ⎯⎯⎯⎯⎯⎯⎯⟶

    b. $\{x \mid -2 \le x < 5\}$ ⎯⎯⎯⎯⎯⎯⎯⟶

For Exercises 18–21, solve the inequality. Graph the solution and write the solution set in set-builder notation and interval notation.

18. $5x + 14 > -2x$ ⎯⎯⎯⎯⎯⎯⟶

19. $2(3 - x) \ge 14$ ⎯⎯⎯⎯⎯⟶

20. $3(2y - 4) + 1 > 2(2y - 3) - 8$ ⎯⎯⎯⎯⟶

21. $-13 \le 3p + 2 \le 5$ ⎯⎯⎯⎯⎯⟶

22. The total bill for a pair of basketball shoes (including sales tax) is $87.74. If the tax rate is 7%, find the cost of the shoes before tax.

23. Clarita borrowed money at a 6% simple interest rate. If she paid back a total of $8000 at the end of 10 yr, how much did she originally borrow?

24. One number is four plus one-half of another. The sum of the numbers is 31. Find the numbers.

25. Two families leave their homes at the same time to meet for lunch. The families live 210 mi apart, and one family drives 5 mph slower than the other. If it takes them 2 hr to meet at a point between their homes, how fast does each family travel?

26. The average winter snowfall for Syracuse, New York, for December, January, and February is 27.5 in. per month. If Syracuse receives 24 in. of snow in December and 32 in. in January, how much snow is required in February to exceed the 3-month average?

27. The perimeter of a pentagon (a five-sided polygon) is 315 in. The lengths of the sides are represented by consecutive integers. Find the measures of the sides.

28. Matthew mixes macadamia nuts that cost $9.00 per pound with 50 lb of peanuts that cost $5.00 per pound. How many pounds of macadamia nuts should he mix to make a nut mixture that costs $6.50 per pound?

29. A couple purchased two hockey tickets and two basketball tickets for $153.92. A hockey ticket cost $4.32 more than a basketball ticket. What were the prices of the individual tickets?

30. Two angles are complementary. One angle is 26° more than the other angle. What are the measures of the angles?

31. The length of a soccer field for international matches is 40 m less than twice its width. If the perimeter is 370 m, what are the dimensions of the field?

32. Given the triangle, find the measure of each angle by first solving for y.

Chapters 1-2   Cumulative Review Exercises

For Exercises 1–5, perform the indicated operations.

1. $\left| -\dfrac{1}{5} + \dfrac{7}{10} \right|$

2. $5 - 2[3 - (4 - 7)]$

3. $-\dfrac{2}{3} + \left(\dfrac{1}{2} \right)^2$

4. $-3^2 + (-5)^2$

5. $\sqrt{5 - (-20)} - 3^2$

For Exercises 6–7, translate the mathematical expressions and simplify the results.

6. The square root of the difference of five squared and nine

7. The sum of -14 and 12

8. List the terms of the expression: $-7x^2y + 4xy - 6$

9. Simplify: $-4[2x - 3(x + 4)] + 5(x - 7)$

For Exercises 10–15, solve each equation.

10. $8t - 8 = 24$

11. $-2.5x - 5.2 = 12.8$

12. $-5(p - 3) + 2p = 3(5 - p)$

13. $\dfrac{x + 3}{5} - \dfrac{x + 2}{2} = 2$

14. $\dfrac{2}{9}x - \dfrac{1}{3} = x + \dfrac{1}{9}$

15. $-0.6w = 48$

16. The sum of two consecutive odd integers is 156. Find the integers.

17. The cost of a smartphone speaker dock (including sales tax) is \$374.50. If the tax rate is 7%, find the cost of the speaker dock before tax.

 18. The area of a triangle is 41 cm². Find the height of the triangle if the base is 12 cm.

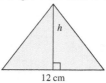

12 cm

For Exercises 19–20, solve the inequality. Graph the solution set on a number line and express the solution in set-builder notation and interval notation.

19. $-3x - 3(x + 1) < 9$ ⟶

20. $-6 \le 2x - 4 \le 14$ ⟶

Graphing Linear Equations in Two Variables

Graphing Linear Equations in Two Variables

3

Mathematics in Gaming

Imagine that you are playing a game of *Battleship*. You say "E-5" to your opponent and his face saddens as he realizes you have sunk his ship. In this game, the "E" and the "5" represent a row or column in a grid, thus defining a *location* on a map. In mathematics we use **ordered pairs**, two numbers of the form (x, y), to determine the location of a point. Furthermore, an equation involving x and y defines a line or curve in a plane that might be the path of a battleship or other object in a computer game.

© ERproductions Ltd/Getty Images RF

For example, suppose that a battleship follows the path defined by $y = 2x + 1$. The value of y depends on the value of x, where y is 1 more than double the value of x. We can determine the value of y for any given value of x by using substitution.

If $x = 1$, then $y = 2(1) + 1 = 3$. Thus, the ordered pair (1, 3) represents a point on the path of the ship.

If $x = 2$, then $y = 2(2) + 1 = 5$. Thus, the ordered pair (2, 5) represents a point on the path of the ship.

In this chapter, we will study equations in x and y and their related graphs. This is important content for a variety of applications, including computer gaming.

194   **Chapter 3**   Graphing Linear Equations in Two Variables

Rectangular Coordinate System

Concepts

1. Interpreting Graphs
2. Plotting Points in a Rectangular Coordinate System
3. Applications of Plotting and Identifying Points

1. Interpreting Graphs

Mathematics is a powerful tool used by scientists and has directly contributed to the highly technical world in which we live. Applications of mathematics have led to advances in the sciences, business, computer technology, and medicine.

One fundamental application of mathematics is the graphical representation of numerical information (or data). For example, Table 3-1 represents the number of clients admitted to a drug and alcohol rehabilitation program over a 12-month period.

Table 3-1

	Month	Number of Clients
Jan.	1	55
Feb.	2	62
March	3	64
April	4	60
May	5	70
June	6	73
July	7	77
Aug.	8	80
Sept.	9	80
Oct.	10	74
Nov.	11	85
Dec.	12	90

In table form, the information is difficult to picture and interpret. It appears that on a monthly basis, the number of clients fluctuates. However, when the data are represented in a graph, an upward trend is clear (Figure 3-1).

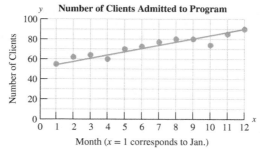

Figure 3-1

From the increase in clients shown in this graph, management for the rehabilitation center might make plans for the future. If the trend continues, management might consider expanding its facilities and increasing its staff to accommodate the expected increase in clients.

Example 1   **Interpreting a Graph**

Refer to Figure 3-1 and Table 3-1.

  a. For which month was the number of clients the greatest?

  b. How many clients were served in the first month (January)?

  c. Which month corresponds to 60 clients served?

  d. Between which two consecutive months did the number of clients decrease?

  e. Between which two consecutive months did the number of clients remain the same?

Solution:

  a. Month 12 (December) corresponds to the highest point on the graph. This represents the greatest number of clients, 90.

  b. In month 1 (January), there were 55 clients served.

  c. Month 4 (April).

  d. The number of clients decreased between months 3 and 4 and between months 9 and 10.

  e. The number of clients remained the same between months 8 and 9.

Skill Practice Refer to Figure 3-1 and Table 3-1.

  1. How many clients were served in October?
  2. Which month corresponds to 70 clients?
  3. What is the difference between the number of clients in month 12 and month 1?
  4. For which month was the number of clients the least?

2. Plotting Points in a Rectangular Coordinate System

The data in Table 3-1 represent a relationship between two variables—the month number and the number of clients. The graph in Figure 3-1 enables us to visualize this relationship. In picturing the relationship between two quantities, we often use a graph with two number lines drawn at right angles to each other (Figure 3-2). This forms a **rectangular coordinate system**. The horizontal line is called the **x-axis**, and the vertical line is called the **y-axis**. The point where the lines intersect is called the **origin**. On the x-axis, the numbers to the right of the origin are positive and the numbers to the left are negative. On the y-axis, the numbers above the origin are positive and the numbers below are negative. The x- and y-axes divide the graphing area into four regions called **quadrants**.

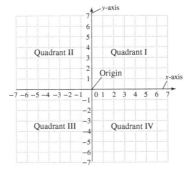

Figure 3-2

Answers

  1. 74 clients
  2. Month 5 (May)
  3. 35 clients
  4. Month 1 (January)

Points graphed in a rectangular coordinate system are defined by two numbers as an **ordered pair**, (x, y). The first number (called the **x-coordinate**, or the abscissa) is the horizontal position from the origin. The second number (called the **y-coordinate**, or the ordinate) is the vertical position from the origin. Example 2 shows how points are plotted in a rectangular coordinate system.

| **Example 2** | **Plotting Points in a Rectangular Coordinate System** |

Plot the points.

a. $(4, 5)$ **b.** $(-4, -5)$ **c.** $(-1, 3)$ **d.** $(3, -1)$

e. $\left(\frac{1}{2}, -\frac{7}{3}\right)$ **f.** $(-2, 0)$ **g.** $(0, 0)$ **h.** $(\pi, 1.1)$

Solution:

See Figure 3-3.

a. The ordered pair $(4, 5)$ indicates that $x = 4$ and $y = 5$. Beginning at the origin, move 4 units in the positive x-direction (4 units to the right), and from there move 5 units in the positive y-direction (5 units up). Then plot the point. The point is in Quadrant I.

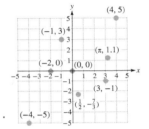

Figure 3-3

b. The ordered pair $(-4, -5)$ indicates that $x = -4$ and $y = -5$. Move 4 units in the negative x-direction (4 units to the left), and from there move 5 units in the negative y-direction (5 units down). Then plot the point. The point is in Quadrant III.

TIP: Notice that changing the order of the x- and y-coordinates changes the location of the point. For example, the point $(-1, 3)$ is in Quadrant II, whereas $(3, -1)$ is in Quadrant IV (Figure 3-3). This is why points are represented by *ordered* pairs. The order of the coordinates is important.

c. The ordered pair $(-1, 3)$ indicates that $x = -1$ and $y = 3$. Move 1 unit to the left and 3 units up. The point is in Quadrant II.

d. The ordered pair $(3, -1)$ indicates that $x = 3$ and $y = -1$. Move 3 units to the right and 1 unit down. The point is in Quadrant IV.

e. The improper fraction $-\frac{7}{3}$ can be written as the mixed number $-2\frac{1}{3}$. Therefore, to plot the point $\left(\frac{1}{2}, -\frac{7}{3}\right)$ move to the right $\frac{1}{2}$ unit, and down $2\frac{1}{3}$ units. The point is in Quadrant IV.

f. The point $(-2, 0)$ indicates $y = 0$. Therefore, the point is on the x-axis.

g. The point $(0, 0)$ is at the origin.

Avoiding Mistakes

Points that lie on either of the axes do not lie in any quadrant.

h. The irrational number, π, can be approximated as 3.14. Thus, the point $(\pi, 1.1)$ is located approximately 3.14 units to the right and 1.1 units up. The point is in Quadrant I.

Answer

5.

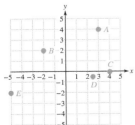

Skill Practice

5. Plot the points.

$A(3, 4)$ $B(-2, 2)$ $C(4, 0)$ $D\left(\frac{5}{2}, -\frac{1}{2}\right)$ $E(-5, -2)$

3. Applications of Plotting and Identifying Points

The effective use of graphs for mathematical models requires skill in identifying points and interpreting graphs.

Example 3   Determining Points from a Graph

A map of a national park is drawn so that the origin is placed at the ranger station (Figure 3-4). Four fire observation towers are located at points A, B, C, and D. Estimate the coordinates of the fire towers relative to the ranger station (all distances are in miles).

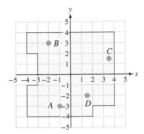

Solution:

Point A: $(-1, -3)$

Point B: $(-2, 3)$

Point C: $(3\frac{1}{2}, 1\frac{1}{2})$ or $(\frac{7}{2}, \frac{3}{2})$ or $(3.5, 1.5)$

Point D: $(1\frac{1}{2}, -2)$ or $(\frac{3}{2}, -2)$ or $(1.5, -2)$

Figure 3-4

Skill Practice

6. Towers are located at points A, B, C, and D. Estimate the coordinates of the towers.

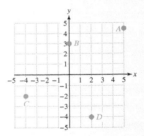

Example 4   Plotting Points in an Application

The daily low temperaures (in degrees Fahrenheit) for one week in January for Sudbury, Ontario, Canada, are given in Table 3-2.

a. Write an ordered pair for each row in the table using the day number as the x-coordinate and the temperature as the y-coordinate.

b. Plot the ordered pairs from part (a) on a rectangular coordinate system.

Table 3-2

Day Number, x	Temperature (°F), y
1	−3
2	−5
3	1
4	6
5	5
6	0
7	−4

Solution:

a. Each ordered pair represents the day number and the corresponding low temperature for that day.

$(1, -3)$ $(2, -5)$ $(3, 1)$ $(4, 6)$ $(5, 5)$ $(6, 0)$ $(7, -4)$

Answer

6. $A(5, 4\frac{1}{2})$
  $B(0, 3)$
  $C(-4, -2)$
  $D(2, -4)$

198   **Chapter 3**   Graphing Linear Equations in Two Variables

b.

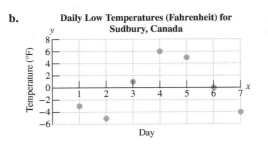

Daily Low Temperatures (Fahrenheit) for Sudbury, Canada

TIP: The graph in Example 4(b) shows only Quadrants I and IV because all x-coordinates are positive.

Answer

7.

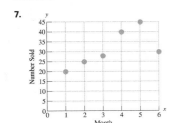

Skill Practice

7. The table shows the number of homes sold in a certain town for a 6-month period. Plot the ordered pairs.

Month, x	Number Sold, y
1	20
2	25
3	28
4	40
5	45
6	30

Section 3.1   Practice Exercisess

Study Skills Exercise

Before you begin the exercises in this section, make your test corrections for the previous test.

Vocabulary and Key Concepts

1. **a.** In a rectangular coordinate system, two number lines are drawn at right angles to each other. The horizontal line is called the _____-axis, and the vertical line is called the _____.

   b. A point in a rectangular coordinate system is defined by an _____ pair, (x, y).

   c. In a rectangular coordinate system, the point where the x- and y-axes intersect is called the _____ and is represented by the ordered pair _____.

   d. The x- and y-axes divide the coordinate plane into four regions called _____.

   e. A point with a positive x-coordinate and a _____ y-coordinate is in Quadrant IV.

   f. In Quadrant _____, both the x- and y-coordinates are negative.

Concept 1: Interpreting Graphs

For Exercises 2–6, refer to the graphs to answer the questions.
(See Example 1.)

2. The number of Botox® injection procedures (in millions) in the United States over a 6-yr period is shown in the graph.

   a. For which year was the number of procedures the greatest?

   b. Approximately how many procedures were performed in year 5?

   c. Which year corresponds to 2.3 million procedures?

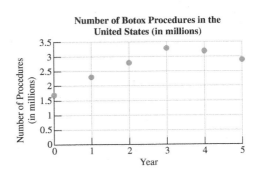

Number of Botox Procedures in the United States (in millions)

3. The number of patients served by a certain hospice care center for the first 12 months after it opened is shown in the graph.

   a. For which month was the number of patients greatest?

   b. How many patients did the center serve in the first month?

   c. Between which months did the number of patients decrease?

   d. Between which two months did the number of patients remain the same?

   e. Which month corresponds to 40 patients served?

   f. Approximately how many patients were served during the 10th month?

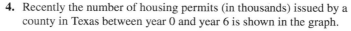

4. Recently the number of housing permits (in thousands) issued by a county in Texas between year 0 and year 6 is shown in the graph.

   a. For which year was the number of permits greatest?

   b. How many permits did the county issue in year 0?

   c. Between which years did the number of permits decrease?

   d. Between which two years did the number of permits remain the same?

   e. Which year corresponds to 7000 permits issued?

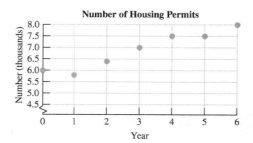

5. The price per share of a stock (in dollars) over a period of 5 days is shown in the graph.

   a. Interpret the meaning of the ordered pair (1, 89.25).

   b. What was the change in price between day 3 and day 4?

   c. What was the change in price between day 4 and day 5?

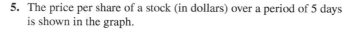

6. The price per share of a stock (in dollars) over a period of 5 days is shown in the graph.

   a. Interpret the meaning of the ordered pair (1, 10.125).

   b. What was the change between day 4 and day 5?

   c. What is the change between day 1 and day 5?

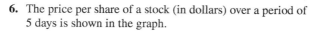
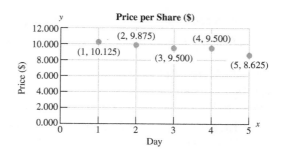

200   **Chapter 3**   Graphing Linear Equations in Two Variables

Concept 2: Plotting Points in a Rectangular Coordinate System

7. Plot the points on a rectangular coordinate system.
(See Example 2.)

   a. $(2, 6)$ **b.** $(6, 2)$ **c.** $(-7, 3)$

   d. $(-7, -3)$ **e.** $(0, -3)$ **f.** $(-3, 0)$

   g. $(6, -4)$ **h.** $(0, 5)$

8. Plot the points on a rectangular coordinate system.

   a. $(4, 5)$ **b.** $(-4, 5)$ **c.** $(-6, 0)$

   d. $(6, 0)$ **e.** $(4, -5)$ **f.** $(-4, -5)$

   g. $(0, -2)$ **h.** $(0, 0)$

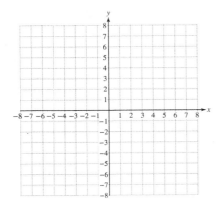

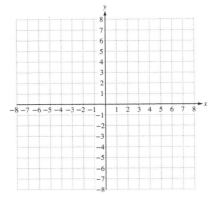

9. Plot the points on a rectangular coordinate system.

   a. $(-1, 5)$ **b.** $(0, 4)$ **c.** $\left(-2, -\dfrac{3}{2}\right)$

   d. $(2, -1.75)$ **e.** $(4, 2)$ **f.** $(-6, 0)$

10. Plot the points on a rectangular coordinate system.

   a. $(7, 0)$ **b.** $(-3, -2)$ **c.** $\left(6\tfrac{3}{5}, 1\right)$

   d. $(0, 1.5)$ **e.** $\left(\dfrac{7}{2}, -4\right)$ **f.** $\left(-\dfrac{7}{2}, 4\right)$

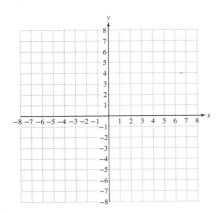

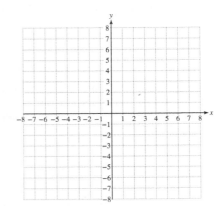

For Exercises 11–18, identify the quadrant in which the given point is located.

11. $(13, -2)$ **12.** $(25, 16)$ **13.** $(-8, 14)$ **14.** $(-82, -71)$

15. $(-5, -19)$ **16.** $(-31, 6)$ **17.** $\left(\dfrac{5}{2}, \dfrac{7}{4}\right)$ **18.** $(9, -40)$

19. Explain why the point $(0, -5)$ is *not* located in Quadrant IV.

20. Explain why the point $(-1, 0)$ is *not* located in Quadrant II.

21. Where is the point $\left(\dfrac{7}{8}, 0\right)$ located?

22. Where is the point $\left(0, \dfrac{6}{5}\right)$ located?

Concept 3: Applications of Plotting and Identifying Points

For Exercises 23–24, refer to the graph. **(See Example 3.)**

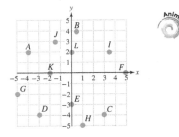

23. Estimate the coordinates of the points *A*, *B*, *C*, *D*, *E*, and *F*.

24. Estimate the coordinates of the points *G*, *H*, *I*, *J*, *K*, and *L*.

25. A map of a park is laid out with the visitor center located at the origin. Five visitors are in the park located at points *A*, *B*, *C*, *D*, and *E*. All distances are in meters.

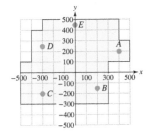

    a. Estimate the coordinates of each visitor. **(See Example 3.)**

    b. How far apart are visitors *C* and *D*?

26. A townhouse has a sprinkler system in the backyard. With the water source at the origin, the sprinkler heads are located at points *A*, *B*, *C*, *D*, and *E*. All distances are in feet.

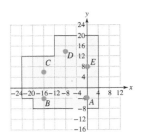

    a. Estimate the coordinates of each sprinkler head.

    b. How far is the distance from sprinkler head *B* to *C*?

27. A movie theater has kept records of popcorn sales versus movie attendance.

    a. Use the table to write the corresponding ordered pairs using the movie attendance as the *x*-variable and sales of popcorn as the *y*-variable. Interpret the meaning of the first ordered pair. **(See Example 4.)**

    b. Plot the data points on a rectangular coordinate system.

© Ryan McVay/Getty Images RF

Movie Attendance (Number of People)	Sales of Popcorn ($)
250	225
175	193
315	330
220	209
450	570
400	480
190	185

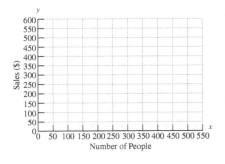

202   **Chapter 3**   Graphing Linear Equations in Two Variables

28. The age and systolic blood pressure (in millimeters of mercury, mm Hg) for eight different women are given in the table.

   a. Write the corresponding ordered pairs using the woman's age as the *x*-variable and the systolic blood pressure as the *y*-variable. Interpret the meaning of the first ordered pair.

   b. Plot the data points on a rectangular coordinate system.

Age (Years)	Systolic Blood Pressure (mm Hg)
57	149
41	120
71	158
36	115
64	151
25	110
40	118
77	165

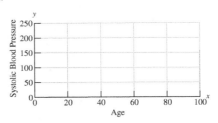

29. The following table shows the average temperature in degrees Celsius for Montreal, Quebec, Canada, by month.

   a. Write the corresponding ordered pairs, letting *x* = 1 correspond to the month of January.

   b. Plot the ordered pairs on a rectangular coordinate system.

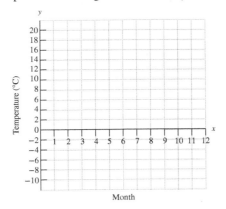

Month, *x*		Temperature (°C), *y*
Jan.	1	−10.2
Feb.	2	−9.0
March	3	−2.5
April	4	5.7
May	5	13.0
June	6	18.3
July	7	20.9
Aug.	8	19.6
Sept.	9	14.8
Oct.	10	8.7
Nov.	11	2.0
Dec.	12	−6.9

30. The table shows the average temperature in degrees Fahrenheit for Fairbanks, Alaska, by month.

   a. Write the corresponding ordered pairs, letting *x* = 1 correspond to the month of January.

   b. Plot the ordered pairs on a rectangular coordinate system.

Month, *x*		Temperature (°F), *y*
Jan.	1	−12.8
Feb.	2	−4.0
March	3	8.4
April	4	30.2
May	5	48.2
June	6	59.4
July	7	61.5
Aug.	8	56.7
Sept.	9	45.0
Oct.	10	25.0
Nov.	11	6.1
Dec.	12	−10.1

Expanding Your Skills

31. The data in the table give the percent of males and females who have completed 4 or more years of college education for selected years. Let x represent the number of years since 1960. Let y represent the percent of men and the percent of women that completed 4 or more years of college.

Year	x	Percent, y Men	Percent, y Women
1960	0	9.7	5.8
1970	10	13.5	8.1
1980	20	20.1	12.8
1990	30	24.4	18.4
2000	40	27.8	23.6
2005	45	28.9	26.5
2010	50	29.9	28.8

a. Plot the data points for men and for women on the same graph.

b. Is the percentage of men with 4 or more years of college increasing or decreasing?

c. Is the percentage of women with 4 or more years of college increasing or decreasing?

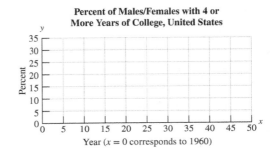

Percent of Males/Females with 4 or More Years of College, United States

32. Use the data and graph from Exercise 31 to answer the questions.

a. In which year was the difference in percentages between men and women with 4 or more years of college the greatest?

b. In which year was the difference in percentages between men and women the least?

c. If the trend continues beyond the data in the graph, does it seem possible that in the future, the percentage of women with 4 or more years of college will be greater than or equal to the percentage of men?

Linear Equations in Two Variables

1. Definition of a Linear Equation in Two Variables

Recall that an equation in the form $ax + b = c$, where $a \neq 0$, is called a linear equation in one variable. A solution to such an equation is a value of x that makes the equation a true statement. For example, $3x + 5 = -1$ has a solution of -2.

In this section, we will look at linear equations in *two* variables.

Linear Equation in Two Variables

Let A, B, and C be real numbers such that A and B are not both zero. Then, an equation that can be written in the form:

$$Ax + By = C$$

is called a **linear equation in two variables**.

Section 3.2

Concepts

1. Definition of a Linear Equation in Two Variables
2. Graphing Linear Equations in Two Variables by Plotting Points
3. x- and y-Intercepts
4. Horizontal and Vertical Lines

The equation $x + y = 4$ is a linear equation in two variables. A solution to such an equation is an ordered pair (x, y) that makes the equation a true statement. Several solutions to the equation $x + y = 4$ are listed here:

Solution:	Check:
(x, y)	$x + y = 4$
$(2, 2)$	$(2) + (2) = 4$ ✓
$(1, 3)$	$(1) + (3) = 4$ ✓
$(4, 0)$	$(4) + (0) = 4$ ✓
$(-1, 5)$	$(-1) + (5) = 4$ ✓

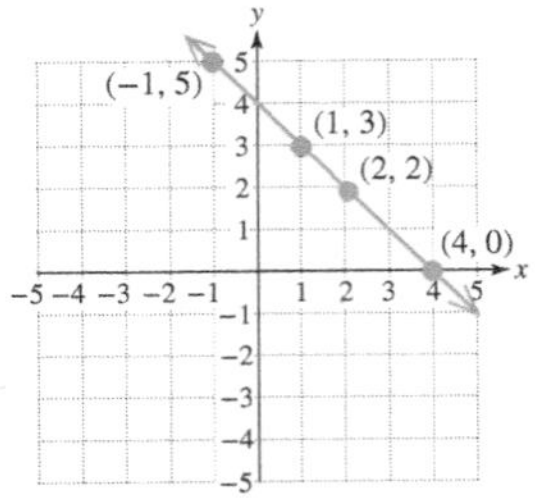

By graphing these ordered pairs, we see that the solution points line up (Figure 3-5).

Notice that there are infinitely many solutions to the equation $x + y = 4$ so they cannot all be listed. Therefore, to visualize all solutions to the equation $x + y = 4$, we draw the line through the points in the graph. Every point on the line represents an ordered pair solution to the equation $x + y = 4$, and the line represents the set of *all* solutions to the equation.

Figure 3-5

Example 1   **Determining Solutions to a Linear Equation**

For the linear equation, $6x - 5y = 12$, determine whether the given ordered pair is a solution.

a. $(2, 0)$ **b.** $(3, 1)$ **c.** $\left(1, -\dfrac{6}{5}\right)$

Solution:

a. $6x - 5y = 12$

$6(2) - 5(0) \overset{?}{=} 12$ Substitute $x = 2$ and $y = 0$.

$12 - 0 \overset{?}{=} 12$ ✓ True   The ordered pair $(2, 0)$ is a solution.

b. $6x - 5y = 12$

$6(3) - 5(1) \overset{?}{=} 12$ Substitute $x = 3$ and $y = 1$.

$18 - 5 \neq 12$ The ordered pair $(3, 1)$ is *not* a solution.

c. $6x - 5y = 12$

$6(1) - 5\left(-\dfrac{6}{5}\right) \overset{?}{=} 12$ Substitute $x = 1$ and $y = -\dfrac{6}{5}$.

$6 + 6 \overset{?}{=} 12$ ✓ True   The ordered pair $\left(1, -\dfrac{6}{5}\right)$ is a solution.

Skill Practice Given the equation $3x - 2y = -12$, determine whether the given ordered pair is a solution.

1. $(4, 0)$ **2.** $(-2, 3)$ **3.** $\left(1, \dfrac{15}{2}\right)$

2. Graphing Linear Equations in Two Variables by Plotting Points

In this section, we will graph linear equations in two variables.

Answers

1. No   **2.** Yes   **3.** Yes

The Graph of an Equation in Two Variables

The graph of an equation in two variables is the graph of all ordered pair solutions to the equation.

The word *linear* means "relating to or resembling a line." It is not surprising then that the solution set for any linear equation in two variables forms a line in a rectangular coordinate system. Because two points determine a line, to graph a linear equation it is sufficient to find two solution points and draw the line between them. We will find three solution points and use the third point as a check point. This process is demonstrated in Example 2.

Example 2   **Graphing a Linear Equation**

Graph the equation $x - 2y = 8$.

Solution:

We will find three ordered pairs that are solutions to $x - 2y = 8$. To find the ordered pairs, choose an arbitrary value of x or y. Three choices are recorded in the table. To complete the table, individually substitute each choice into the equation and solve for the missing variable. The substituted value and the solution to the equation form an ordered pair.

x	y
2		→ (2,)
	−1	→ (, −1)
0		→ (0,)

TIP: Usually we try to choose arbitrary values that will be convenient to graph.

From the first row, substitute $x = 2$:

$x - 2y = 8$
$(2) - 2y = 8$
$-2y = 6$
$y = -3$

From the second row, substitute $y = -1$:

$x - 2y = 8$
$x - 2(-1) = 8$
$x + 2 = 8$
$x = 6$

From the third row, substitute $x = 0$:

$x - 2y = 8$
$(0) - 2y = 8$
$-2y = 8$
$y = -4$

The completed table is shown with the corresponding ordered pairs.

x	y
2	−3	→ (2, −3)
6	−1	→ (6, −1)
0	−4	→ (0, −4)

To graph the equation, plot the three solutions and draw the line through the points (Figure 3-6).

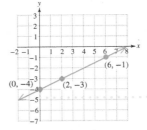

Figure 3-6

Avoiding Mistakes

Only two points are needed to graph a line. However, in Example 2, we found a third ordered pair, (0, −4). Notice that this point "lines up" with the other two points. If the three points do not line up, then we know that a mistake was made in solving for at least one of the ordered pairs.

Answer

4.

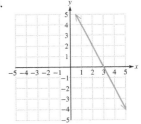

Skill Practice

4. Graph the equation $2x + y = 6$.

In Example 2, the original values for x and y given in the table were chosen arbitrarily by the authors. It is important to note, however, that once you choose an arbitrary value for x, the corresponding y-value is determined by the equation. Similarly, once you choose an arbitrary value for y, the x-value is determined by the equation.

Example 3   **Graphing a Linear Equation**

Graph the equation $4x + 3y = 15$.

Solution:

We will find three ordered pairs that are solutions to the equation $4x + 3y = 15$. In the table, we have selected arbitrary values for x and y and must complete the ordered pairs. Notice that in this case, we are choosing zero for x and zero for y to illustrate that the resulting equation is often easy to solve.

x	y
0		$\rightarrow (0,\ )$
	0	$\rightarrow (\ ,0)$
3		$\rightarrow (3,\ )$

From the first row, substitute $x = 0$:	From the second row, substitute $y = 0$:	From the third row, substitute $x = 3$:
$4x + 3y = 15$	$4x + 3y = 15$	$4x + 3y = 15$
$4(0) + 3y = 15$	$4x + 3(0) = 15$	$4(3) + 3y = 15$
$3y = 15$	$4x = 15$	$12 + 3y = 15$
$y = 5$	$x = \dfrac{15}{4}$ or $3\dfrac{3}{4}$	$3y = 3$
		$y = 1$

The completed table is shown with the corresponding ordered pairs.

x	y
0	5	$\rightarrow (0, 5)$
$3\frac{3}{4}$	0	$\rightarrow (3\frac{3}{4}, 0)$
3	1	$\rightarrow (3, 1)$

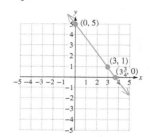

Figure 3-7

To graph the equation, plot the three solutions and draw the line through the points (Figure 3-7).

Skill Practice

5. Graph the equation $2x + 3y = 12$.

Answer

5.

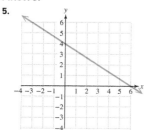

Example 4   **Graphing a Linear Equation**

Graph the equation $y = -\dfrac{1}{3}x + 1$.

Solution:

Because the y-variable is isolated in the equation, it is easy to substitute a value for x and simplify the right-hand side to find y. Since any number for x can be chosen, select numbers that are multiples of 3. These will simplify easily when multiplied by $-\frac{1}{3}$.

x	y
3	
0	
-3	

$y = -\frac{1}{3}x + 1$

Let $x = 3$:

$y = -\frac{1}{3}(3) + 1$

$y = -1 + 1$

$y = 0$

Let $x = 0$:

$y = -\frac{1}{3}(0) + 1$

$y = 0 + 1$

$y = 1$

Let $x = -3$:

$y = -\frac{1}{3}(-3) + 1$

$y = 1 + 1$

$y = 2$

x	y	
3	0	→ (3, 0)
0	1	→ (0, 1)
-3	2	→ (-3, 2)

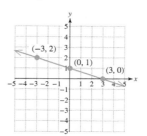

The line through the three ordered pairs (3, 0), (0, 1), and (-3, 2) is shown in Figure 3-8. The line represents the set of all solutions to the equation $y = -\frac{1}{3}x + 1$.

Figure 3-8

Skill Practice

6. Graph the equation $y = \frac{1}{2}x + 3$.

3. x- and y-Intercepts

The x- and y-intercepts are the points where the graph intersects the x- and y-axes, respectively. From Example 4, we see that the x-intercept is at the point (3, 0) and the y-intercept is at the point (0, 1). See Figure 3-8. Notice that a y-intercept is a point on the y-axis and must have an x-coordinate of 0. Likewise, an x-intercept is a point on the x-axis and must have a y-coordinate of 0.

> **Definitions of x- and y-Intercepts**
>
> An **x-intercept** of a graph is a point $(a, 0)$ where the graph intersects the x-axis.
>
> A **y-intercept** of a graph is a point $(0, b)$ where the graph intersects the y-axis.

In some applications, an x-intercept is defined as the x-coordinate of a point of intersection that a graph makes with the x-axis. For example, if an x-intercept is at the point (3, 0), it is sometimes stated simply as 3 (the y-coordinate is assumed to be 0). Similarly, a y-intercept is sometimes defined as the y-coordinate of a point of intersection that a graph makes with the y-axis. For example, if a y-intercept is at the point (0, 7), it may be stated simply as 7 (the x-coordinate is assumed to be 0).

Although any two points may be used to graph a line, in some cases it is convenient to use the x- and y-intercepts of the line. To find the x- and y-intercepts of any two-variable equation in x and y, follow these steps:

> **Finding x- and y-Intercepts**
>
> • Find the x-intercept(s) by substituting $y = 0$ into the equation and solving for x.
> • Find the y-intercept(s) by substituting $x = 0$ into the equation and solving for y.

Answer

6.

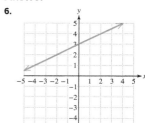

Example 5   **Finding the x- and y-Intercepts of a Line**

Given the equation $-3x + 2y = 8$,

a. Find the x-intercept.

b. Find the y-intercept.

c. Graph the equation.

Solution:

a. To find the x-intercept, substitute $y = 0$.

$$-3x + 2y = 8$$
$$-3x + 2(0) = 8$$
$$-3x = 8$$
$$\frac{-3x}{-3} = \frac{8}{-3}$$
$$x = -\frac{8}{3}$$

The x-intercept is $\left(-\frac{8}{3}, 0\right)$.

b. To find the y-intercept, substitute $x = 0$.

$$-3x + 2y = 8$$
$$-3(0) + 2y = 8$$
$$2y = 8$$
$$y = 4$$

The y-intercept is $(0, 4)$.

> **Avoiding Mistakes**
>
> Be sure to write the x- and y-intercepts as two separate ordered pairs: $\left(-\frac{8}{3}, 0\right)$ and $(0, 4)$.

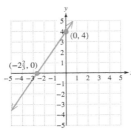

Figure 3-9

c. The line through the ordered pairs $\left(-\frac{8}{3}, 0\right)$ and $(0, 4)$ is shown in Figure 3-9. Note that the point $\left(-\frac{8}{3}, 0\right)$ can be written as $\left(-2\frac{2}{3}, 0\right)$.

The line represents the set of all solutions to the equation $-3x + 2y = 8$.

Skill Practice Given the equation $x - 3y = -4$,

7. Find the x-intercept.   **8.** Find the y-intercept.   **9.** Graph the equation.

Example 6   **Finding the x- and y-Intercepts of a Line**

Given the equation $4x + 5y = 0$,

a. Find the x-intercept.

b. Find the y-intercept.

c. Graph the equation.

Solution:

a. To find the x-intercept, substitute $y = 0$.

$$4x + 5y = 0$$
$$4x + 5(0) = 0$$
$$4x = 0$$
$$x = 0$$

The x-intercept is $(0, 0)$.

b. To find the y-intercept, substitute $x = 0$.

$$4x + 5y = 0$$
$$4(0) + 5y = 0$$
$$5y = 0$$
$$y = 0$$

The y-intercept is $(0, 0)$.

Answers

7. $(-4, 0)$ **8.** $\left(0, \frac{4}{3}\right)$

9.

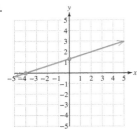

c. Because the x-intercept and the y-intercept are the same point (the origin), one or more additional points are needed to graph the line. In the table, we have arbitrarily selected additional values for x and y to find two more points on the line.

x	y
−5	
	2

Let $x = -5$:

$$4x + 5y = 0$$
$$4(-5) + 5y = 0$$
$$-20 + 5y = 0$$
$$5y = 20$$
$$y = 4$$

$(-5, 4)$ is a solution.

Let $y = 2$:

$$4x + 5y = 0$$
$$4x + 5(2) = 0$$
$$4x + 10 = 0$$
$$4x = -10$$
$$x = -\frac{10}{4}$$
$$x = -\frac{5}{2}$$

$\left(-\frac{5}{2}, 2\right)$ is a solution.

The line through the ordered pairs $(0, 0)$, $(-5, 4)$, and $\left(-\frac{5}{2}, 2\right)$ is shown in Figure 3-10. Note that the point $\left(-\frac{5}{2}, 2\right)$ can be written as $\left(-2\frac{1}{2}, 2\right)$.

The line represents the set of all solutions to the equation $4x + 5y = 0$.

x	y
−5	4
−$\frac{5}{2}$	2
0	0

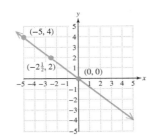

Figure 3-10

Skill Practice Given the equation $2x - 3y = 0$,

10. Find the x-intercept.   **11.** Find the y-intercept.

12. Graph the equation. (*Hint:* You may need to find an additional point.)

4. Horizontal and Vertical Lines

Recall that a linear equation can be written in the form $Ax + By = C$, where A and B are not both zero. However, if A or B is 0, then the line is either horizontal or vertical. A horizontal line either lies on the x-axis or is parallel to the x-axis. A vertical line either lies on the y-axis or is parallel to the y-axis.

Equations of Vertical and Horizontal Lines

1. A **vertical line** can be represented by an equation of the form $x = k$, where k is a constant.
2. A **horizontal line** can be represented by an equation of the form $y = k$, where k is a constant.

Answers

10. $(0, 0)$ **11.** $(0, 0)$

12.

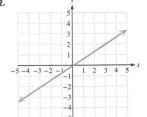

Example 7   **Graphing a Horizontal Line**

Graph the equation $y = 3$.

Solution:

Because this equation is in the form $y = k$, the line is horizontal and must cross the y-axis at $y = 3$ (Figure 3-11).

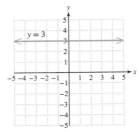

TIP: Notice that a horizontal line has a y-intercept, but does not have an x-intercept (unless the horizontal line is the x-axis itself).

Figure 3-11

Alternative Solution:

Create a table of values for the equation $y = 3$. The choice for the y-coordinate must be 3, but x can be any real number.

x	y
0	3
1	3
2	3

x can be any number. y must be 3.

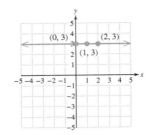

Skill Practice

13. Graph the equation. $y = -2$

Example 8   **Graphing a Vertical Line**

Graph the equation $7x = -14$.

Solution:

Because the equation does not have a y-variable, we can solve the equation for x.

$$7x = -14 \quad \text{is equivalent to} \quad x = -2$$

This equation is in the form $x = k$, indicating that the line is vertical and must cross the x-axis at $x = -2$ (Figure 3-12).

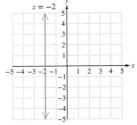

Figure 3-12

Answer

13.

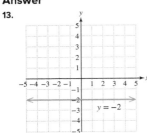

Alternative Solution:

Create a table of values for the equation $x = -2$. The choice for the x-coordinate must be -2, but y can be any real number.

x	y
-2	0
-2	3
-2	-4

x must be -2. y can be any number.

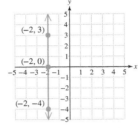

> **TIP:** Notice that a vertical line has an x-intercept but does not have a y-intercept (unless the vertical line is the y-axis itself).

Answer

14.

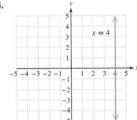

Skill Practice

14. Graph the equation. $3x = 12$

Topic: Graphing Linear Equations on an Appropriate Viewing Window

A viewing window of a graphing calculator shows a portion of a rectangular coordinate system. The standard viewing window for many calculators shows the x-axis between -10 and 10 and the y-axis between -10 and 10 (Figure 3-13). Furthermore, the scale defined by the "tick" marks on both the x- and y-axes is usually set to 1.

The "Standard Viewing Window"

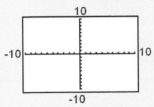

Figure 3-13

To graph an equation in x and y on a graphing calculator, the equation must be written with the y-variable isolated. For example, to graph the equation $x + 3y = 3$, we solve for y by applying the steps for solving a literal equation. The result, $y = -\frac{1}{3}x + 1$, can now be entered into a graphing calculator. To enter the equation $y = -\frac{1}{3}x + 1$, use parentheses around the fraction $\frac{1}{3}$. The *Graph* option displays the graph of the line.

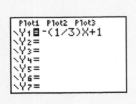

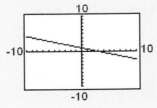

Sometimes the standard viewing window does not provide an adequate display for the graph of an equation. For example, the graph of $y = -x + 15$ is visible only in a small portion of the upper right corner of the standard viewing window.

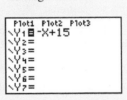

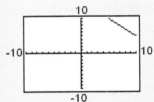

To see where this line crosses the x- and y-axes, we can change the viewing window to accommodate larger values of x and y. Most calculators have a *Range* feature or *Window* feature that allows the user to change the minimum and maximum x- and y-values.

To get a better picture of the equation $y = -x + 15$, change the minimum x-value to -10 and the maximum x-value to 20. Similarly, use a minimum y-value of -10 and a maximum y-value of 20.

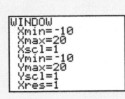

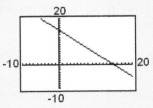

Calculator Exercises

For Exercises 1–8, graph the equations on the standard viewing window.

1. $y = -2x + 5$ **2.** $y = 3x - 1$

3. $y = \dfrac{1}{2}x - \dfrac{7}{2}$

4. $y = -\dfrac{3}{4}x + \dfrac{5}{3}$

5. $4x - 7y = 21$

6. $2x + 3y = 12$

7. $-3x - 4y = 6$

8. $-5x + 4y = 10$

For Exercises 9–12, graph the equations on the given viewing window.

9. $y = 3x + 15$ Window: $-10 \le x \le 10$
$-5 \le y \le 20$

10. $y = -2x - 25$ Window: $-30 \le x \le 30$
$-30 \le y \le 30$

Xscl = 3 (sets the x-axis tick marks to increments of 3)

Yscl = 3 (sets the y-axis tick marks to increments of 3)

11. $y = -0.2x + 0.04$
Window: $-0.1 \le x \le 0.3$
$-0.1 \le y \le 0.1$

Xscl = 0.01 (sets the x-axis tick marks to increments of 0.01)

Yscl = 0.01 (sets the y-axis tick marks to increments of 0.01)

12. $y = 0.3x - 0.5$
Window: $-1 \le x \le 3$
$-1 \le y \le 1$

Xscl = 0.1 (sets the x-axis tick marks to increments of 0.1)

Yscl = 0.1 (sets the y-axis tick marks to increments of 0.1)

Section 3.2   Practice Exercises

Study Skills Exercise

Check your progress by answering these questions.

Yes _____ No _____   Did you have sufficient time to study for the test in the previous chapter? If not, what could you have done to create more time for studying?

Yes _____ No _____   Did you work all of the assigned homework problems in the previous chapter?

Yes _____ No _____   If you encountered difficulty, did you see your instructor or tutor for help?

Yes _____ No _____   Have you taken advantage of the textbook supplements such as the *Student Solutions Manual?*

Vocabulary and Key Concepts

1. a. A linear equation in two variables is an equation that can be written in the form _____ where A and B are not both zero.

    b. A point where a graph intersects the x-axis is called a(n) _____.

    c. A point where a graph intersects the y-axis is called a(n) _____.

    d. A _____ line can be represented by an equation of the form $x = k$, where k is a constant.

    e. A _____ line can be represented by an equation of the form $y = k$, where k is a constant.

Review Exercises

For Exercises 2–8, refer to the figure to give the coordinates of the labeled points, and state the quadrant or axis where the point is located.

2. A

3. B

4. C

5. D

6. E

7. F

8. G

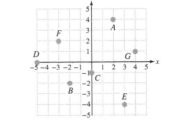

Concept 1: Definition of a Linear Equation in Two Variables

For Exercises 9–17, determine whether the given ordered pair is a solution to the equation. **(See Example 1.)**

9. $x - y = 6$; $(8, 2)$

10. $y = 3x - 2$; $(1, 1)$

11. $y = -\dfrac{1}{3}x + 3$; $(-3, 4)$

12. $y = -\dfrac{5}{2}x + 5$; $\left(\dfrac{4}{5}, -3\right)$

13. $4x + 5y = 1$; $\left(\dfrac{1}{4}, -\dfrac{2}{5}\right)$

14. $y = 7$; $(0, 7)$

15. $y = -2$; $(-2, 6)$

16. $x = 1$; $(0, 1)$

17. $x = -5$; $(-5, 6)$

Concept 2: Graphing Linear Equations in Two Variables by Plotting Points

For Exercises 18–31, complete each table, and graph the corresponding ordered pairs. Draw the line defined by the points to represent all solutions to the equation. **(See Examples 2–4.)**

18. $x + y = 3$

x	y
2	
	3
−1	
	0

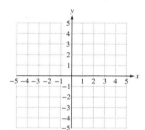

19. $x + y = -2$

x	y
1	
	0
−3	
	2

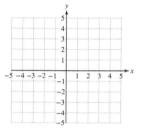

20. $y = 5x + 1$

x	y
1	
	1
−1	

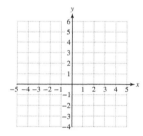

21. $y = -3x - 3$

x	y
−2	
	0
−4	

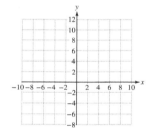

22. $2x - 3y = 6$

x	y
0	
	0
2	

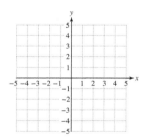

23. $4x + 2y = 8$

x	y
0	
	0
3	

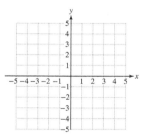

24. $y = \dfrac{2}{7}x - 5$

x	y
7	
−7	
0	

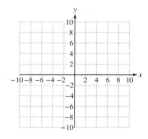

25. $y = -\dfrac{3}{5}x - 2$

x	y
0	
5	
10	

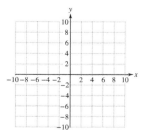

214   **Chapter 3**   Graphing Linear Equations in Two Variables

26. $y = 3$

x	y
2	
0	
−1	

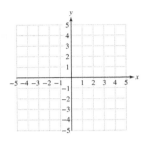

27. $y = -2$

x	y
0	
−3	
5	

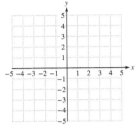

28. $x = -4$

x	y
	1
	−2
	4

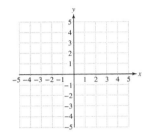

29. $x = \frac{3}{2}$

x	y
	−1
	2
	−3

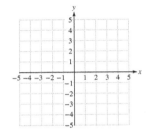

30. $y = -3.4x + 5.8$

x	y
0	
1	
2	

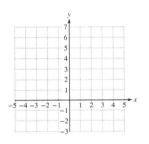

31. $y = -1.2x + 4.6$

x	y
0	
1	
2	

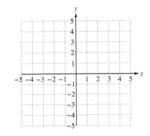

For Exercises 32–43, graph each line by making a table of at least three ordered pairs and plotting the points. **(See Example 4.)**

32. $x - y = 2$

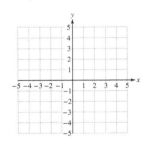

33. $x - y = 4$

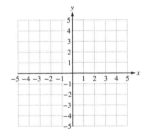

34. $-3x + y = -6$

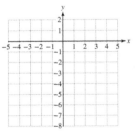

35. $2x - 5y = 10$

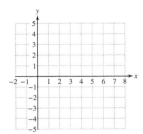

36. $y = 4x$

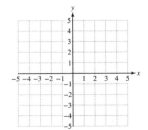

37. $y = -2x$

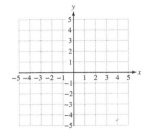

38. $y = -\frac{1}{2}x + 3$

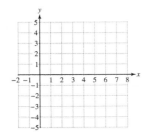

39. $y = \frac{1}{4}x - 2$

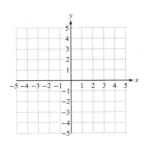

40. $x + y = 0$

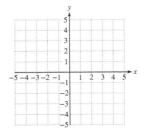

41. $-x + y = 0$

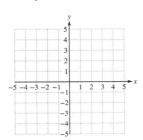

42. $50x - 40y = 200$

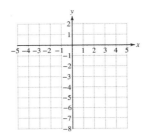

43. $-30x - 20y = 60$

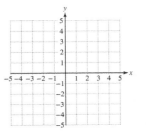

Concept 3: x- and y-Intercepts

44. The x-intercept is on which axis?

45. The y-intercept is on which axis?

For Exercises 46–49, estimate the coordinates of the x- and y-intercepts.

46.

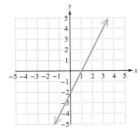

47.

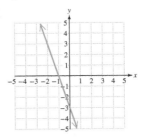

48.

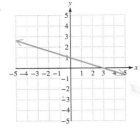

49.

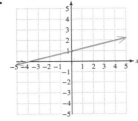

For Exercises 50–61, find the *x*- and *y*-intercepts (if they exist), and graph the line. **(See Examples 5–6.)**

50. $5x + 2y = 5$

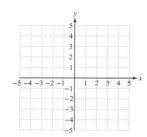

51. $4x - 3y = -9$

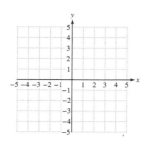

52. $y = \dfrac{2}{3}x - 1$

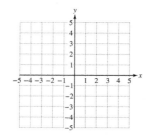

53. $y = -\dfrac{3}{4}x + 2$

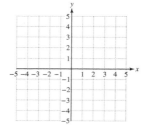

54. $x - 3 = y$

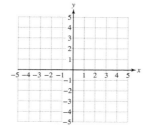

55. $2x + 8 = y$

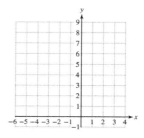

56. $-3x + y = 0$

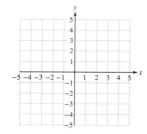

57. $2x - 2y = 0$

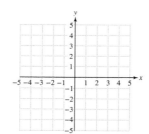

58. $25y = 10x + 100$

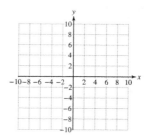

59. $20x = -40y + 200$

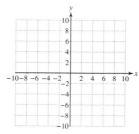

60. $x = 2y$

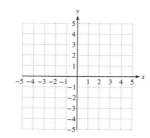

61. $x = -5y$

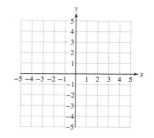

Concept 4: Horizontal and Vertical Lines

For Exercises 62–65, answer true or false. If the statement is false, rewrite it to be true.

62. The line defined by $x = 3$ is horizontal.

63. The line defined by $y = -4$ is horizontal.

64. A line parallel to the y-axis is vertical.

65. A line parallel to the x-axis is horizontal.

For Exercises 66–74,

a. Identify the equation as representing a horizontal or vertical line.

b. Graph the line.

c. Identify the x- and y-intercepts if they exist. **(See Examples 7–8.)**

66. $x = 3$

67. $y = -1$

68. $-2y = 8$

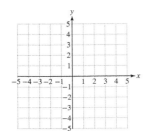
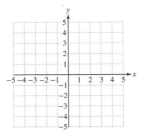
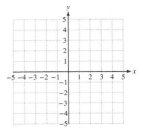

69. $5x = 20$

$$\frac{5}{5} \qquad x \cdot 4$$

70. $x - 3 = -7$

71. $y + 8 = 11$

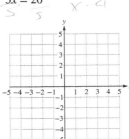
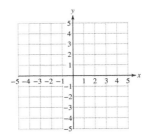
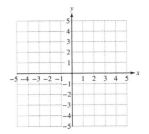

72. $3y = 0$

73. $5x = 0$

74. $2x + 7 = 10$

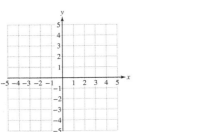
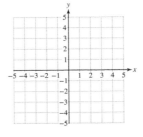
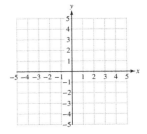

75. Explain why not every line has both an x- and a y-intercept.

76. Which of the lines has an x-intercept?

    a. $2x - 3y = 6$ **b.** $x = 5$ **c.** $2y = 8$ **d.** $-x + y = 0$

77. Which of the lines has a y-intercept?

    a. $y = 2$ **b.** $x + y = 0$ **c.** $2x - 10 = 2$ **d.** $x + 4y = 8$

Expanding Your Skills

 78. The store "CDs R US" sells all compact discs for $13.99. The following equation represents the revenue, y, (in dollars) generated by selling x CDs.

$$y = 13.99x \quad (x \geq 0)$$

a. Find y when $x = 13$.

b. Find x when $y = 279.80$.

c. Write the ordered pairs from parts (a) and (b), and interpret their meaning in the context of the problem.

d. Graph the ordered pairs and the line defined by the points.

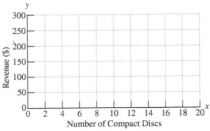

 79. The value of a car depreciates once it is driven off of the dealer's lot. For a certain sub-compact car, the value of the car is given by the equation $y = -1025x + 12{,}215$ ($x \geq 0$) where y is the value of the car in dollars x years after its purchase.

a. Find y when $x = 1$.

b. Find x when $y = 9140$.

c. Write the ordered pairs from parts (a) and (b), and interpret their meaning in the context of the problem.

218   **Chapter 3**   Graphing Linear Equations in Two Variables

Section 3.3	Slope of a Line and Rate of Change

Concepts

1. Introduction to Slope
2. Slope Formula
3. Parallel and Perpendicular Lines
4. Applications of Slope: Rate of Change

1. Introduction to Slope

The x- and y-intercepts represent the points where a line crosses the x- and y-axes. Another important feature of a line is its slope. Geometrically, the slope of a line measures the "steepness" of the line. For example, two hiking trails are depicted by the lines in Figure 3-14.

Park Trail   Mt. Dora Trail

Figure 3-14

By visual inspection, Mt. Dora Trail is "steeper" than Park Trail. To measure the slope of a line quantitatively, consider two points on the line. The **slope** of the line is the ratio of the vertical change (change in y) between the two points and the horizontal change (change in x). As a memory device, we might think of the slope of a line as "rise over run." See Figure 3-15.

$$\text{Slope} = \frac{\text{change in } y}{\text{change in } x} = \frac{\text{rise}}{\text{run}}$$

Change in x (run)

Change in y (rise)

Figure 3-15

To move from point A to point B on Park Trail, rise 2 ft and move to the right 6 ft (Figure 3-16).

To move from point A to point B on Mt. Dora Trail, rise 5 ft and move to the right 4 ft (Figure 3-17).

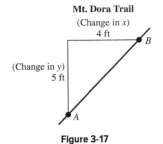

Mt. Dora Trail
(Change in x)
4 ft

(Change in y)
5 ft

B

A

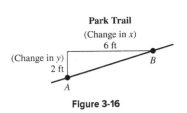

Park Trail
(Change in x)
6 ft

(Change in y)
2 ft

B

A

Figure 3-16

Figure 3-17

> **TIP:** To find the slope, you can use any two points on the line. The ratio of rise to run will be the same.

$$\text{Slope} = \frac{\text{change in } y}{\text{change in } x} = \frac{2 \text{ ft}}{6 \text{ ft}} = \frac{1}{3}$$

$$\text{Slope} = \frac{\text{change in } y}{\text{change in } x} = \frac{5 \text{ ft}}{4 \text{ ft}} = \frac{5}{4}$$

The slope of Mt. Dora Trail is greater than the slope of Park Trail, confirming the observation that Mt. Dora Trail is steeper. On Mt. Dora Trail there is a 5-ft change in elevation for every 4 ft of horizontal distance (a 5:4 ratio). On Park Trail there is only a 2-ft change in elevation for every 6 ft of horizontal distance (a 1:3 ratio).

Example 1   **Finding Slope in an Application**

Determine the slope of the ramp up the stairs.

Solution:

$$\text{Slope} = \frac{\text{change in } y}{\text{change in } x} = \frac{8 \text{ ft}}{16 \text{ ft}}$$

$$\frac{8}{16} = \frac{1}{2} \qquad \text{Write the ratio for the slope and simplify.}$$

The slope is $\frac{1}{2}$.

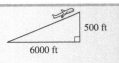

8 ft

16 ft

Skill Practice

1. Determine the slope of the aircraft's takeoff path. (Figure is not drawn to scale.)

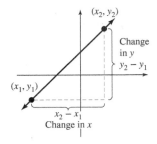

500 ft

6000 ft

---

2. Slope Formula

The slope of a line may be found using any two points on the line—call these points (x_1, y_1) and (x_2, y_2). The numbers to the right and below the variables are called *subscripts*. In this instance, the subscript 1 indicates the coordinates of the first point, and the subscript 2 indicates the coordinates of the second point. The change in y between the points can be found by taking the difference of the y values: $y_2 - y_1$. The change in x can be found by taking the difference of the x values in the same order: $x_2 - x_1$ (Figure 3-18).

The slope of a line is often symbolized by the letter m and is given by the following formula.

(x_2, y_2)

Change in y
$y_2 - y_1$

(x_1, y_1)

$x_2 - x_1$
Change in x

Figure 3-18

Answer

1. $\dfrac{500}{6000} = \dfrac{1}{12}$

> ### Slope Formula
>
> The slope of a line passing through the distinct points (x_1, y_1) and (x_2, y_2) is
>
> $$m = \frac{y_2 - y_1}{x_2 - x_1} \quad \text{provided } x_2 - x_1 \neq 0.$$
>
> *Note*: If $x_2 - x_1 = 0$, the slope is undefined.

Example 2   **Finding the Slope of a Line Given Two Points**

Find the slope of the line through the points $(-1, 3)$ and $(-4, -2)$.

Solution:

To use the slope formula, first label the coordinates of each point and then substitute the coordinates into the slope formula.

$$\underset{(x_1,\, y_1)}{(-1, 3)} \quad \text{and} \quad \underset{(x_2,\, y_2)}{(-4, -2)} \qquad \text{Label the points.}$$

$m = \dfrac{y_2 - y_1}{x_2 - x_1} = \dfrac{(-2) - (3)}{(-4) - (-1)}$	Apply the slope formula.
$\quad = \dfrac{-5}{-3}$	
$\quad = \dfrac{5}{3}$	Simplify to lowest terms.

Avoiding Mistakes

When calculating slope, always write the change in *y* in the numerator.

The slope of the line can be verified from the graph (Figure 3-19).

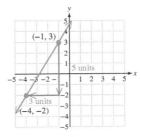

Figure 3-19

Skill Practice Find the slope of the line through the given points.

2. $(-5, 2)$ and $(1, 3)$

TIP: The slope formula is not dependent on which point is labeled (x_1, y_1) and which point is labeled (x_2, y_2). In Example 2, reversing the order in which the points are labeled results in the same slope.

$$\underset{(x_2,\, y_2)}{(-1, 3)} \quad \text{and} \quad \underset{(x_1,\, y_1)}{(-4, -2)} \qquad \text{Label the points.}$$

$$m = \frac{(3) - (-2)}{(-1) - (-4)} = \frac{5}{3} \qquad \text{Apply the slope formula.}$$

Answer

2. $\dfrac{1}{6}$

When you apply the slope formula, you will see that the slope of a line may be positive, negative, zero, or undefined.

- Lines that increase, or rise, from left to right have a positive slope.
- Lines that decrease, or fall, from left to right have a negative slope.
- Horizontal lines have a slope of zero.
- Vertical lines have an undefined slope.

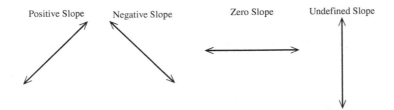

Positive Slope   Negative Slope   Zero Slope   Undefined Slope

| Example 3 | **Finding the Slope of a Line Given Two Points** |

Find the slope of the line passing through the points $\left(-5, \frac{1}{2}\right)$ and $\left(2, -\frac{3}{2}\right)$.

Solution:

$$\underset{(x_1, y_1)}{\left(-5, \frac{1}{2}\right)} \quad \text{and} \quad \underset{(x_2, y_2)}{\left(2, -\frac{3}{2}\right)} \qquad \text{Label the points.}$$

$$m = \frac{y_2 - y_1}{x_2 - x_1} = \frac{\left(-\frac{3}{2}\right) - \left(\frac{1}{2}\right)}{(2) - (-5)} \qquad \text{Apply the slope formula.}$$

$$= \frac{-\frac{4}{2}}{2 + 5} \qquad \text{Simplify.}$$

$$= \frac{-2}{7} \quad \text{or} \quad -\frac{2}{7}$$

Avoiding Mistakes

When applying the slope formula, y_2 and x_2 are taken from the same ordered pair. Likewise y_1 and x_1 are taken from the same ordered pair.

By graphing the points $\left(-5, \frac{1}{2}\right)$ and $\left(2, -\frac{3}{2}\right)$, we can verify that the slope is $-\frac{2}{7}$ (Figure 3-20). Notice that the line slopes downward from left to right.

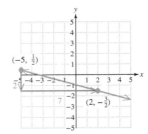

Figure 3-20

Skill Practice   Find the slope of the line through the given points.

3. $\left(\frac{2}{3}, 0\right)$ and $\left(-\frac{1}{6}, 5\right)$

Answer

3. -6

222   **Chapter 3** Graphing Linear Equations in Two Variables

Example 4   **Determining the Slope of a Vertical Line**

Find the slope of the line passing through the points $(2, -1)$ and $(2, 4)$.

Solution:

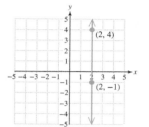

$$\underset{(x_1, y_1)}{(2, -1)} \quad \text{and} \quad \underset{(x_2, y_2)}{(2, 4)} \qquad \text{Label the points.}$$

$$m = \frac{y_2 - y_1}{x_2 - x_1} = \frac{(4) - (-1)}{(2) - (2)} \qquad \begin{array}{l}\text{Apply the slope} \\ \text{formula.}\end{array}$$

$$m = \frac{5}{0} \quad \text{Undefined}$$

Because the slope, m, is undefined, we expect the points to form a vertical line as shown in Figure 3-21.

Figure 3-21

Skill Practice Find the slope of the line through the given points.

4. $(5, 6)$ and $(5, -2)$

Example 5   **Determining the Slope of a Horizontal Line**

Find the slope of the line passing through the points $(3.4, -2)$ and $(-3.5, -2)$.

Solution:

$$\underset{(x_1, y_1)}{(3.4, -2)} \quad \text{and} \quad \underset{(x_2, y_2)}{(-3.5, -2)} \qquad \text{Label the points.}$$

$$m = \frac{y_2 - y_1}{x_2 - x_1} = \frac{(-2) - (-2)}{(-3.5) - (3.4)} \qquad \text{Apply the slope formula.}$$

$$= \frac{-2 + 2}{-3.5 - 3.4} = \frac{0}{-6.9} = 0 \qquad \text{Simplify.}$$

Because the slope is 0, we expect the points to form a horizontal line, as shown in Figure 3-22.

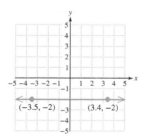

Figure 3-22

Skill Practice Find the slope of the line through the given points.

5. $(3, 8)$ and $(-5, 8)$

Answers

4. Undefined   **5.** 0

3. Parallel and Perpendicular Lines

Lines in the same plane that do not intersect are called **parallel lines**. Parallel lines have the same slope and different y-intercepts (Figure 3-23).

Lines that intersect at a right angle are **perpendicular lines**. If two lines are perpendicular then the slope of one line is the opposite of the reciprocal of the slope of the other line (provided neither line is vertical) (Figure 3-24).

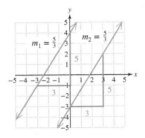

Figure 3-23

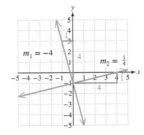

Figure 3-24

Slopes of Parallel Lines

If m_1 and m_2 represent the slopes of two parallel (nonvertical) lines, then

$$m_1 = m_2.$$

See Figure 3-23.

Slopes of Perpendicular Lines

If $m_1 \neq 0$ and $m_2 \neq 0$ represent the slopes of two perpendicular lines, then

$$m_1 = -\frac{1}{m_2} \text{ or equivalently, } m_1 m_2 = -1. \text{ See Figure 3-24.}$$

Example 6 **Determining the Slope of Parallel and Perpendicular Lines**

Suppose a given line has a slope of -6.

a. Find the slope of a line parallel to the line with the given slope.

b. Find the slope of a line perpendicular to the line with the given slope.

Solution:

a. Parallel lines must have the same slope. The slope of a line parallel to the given line is $m = -6$.

b. For perpendicular lines, the slope of one line must be the opposite of the reciprocal of the other. The slope of a line perpendicular to the given line is $m = -\left(\frac{1}{-6}\right) = \frac{1}{6}$.

Skill Practice A given line has a slope of $\frac{5}{3}$.

6. Find the slope of a line parallel to the given line.

7. Find the slope of a line perpendicular to the given line.

Answers

6. $\dfrac{5}{3}$ 7. $-\dfrac{3}{5}$

224   **Chapter 3**   Graphing Linear Equations in Two Variables

If the slopes of two lines are known, then we can compare the slopes to determine if the lines are parallel, perpendicular, or neither.

| Example 7 | Determining If Lines Are Parallel, Perpendicular, or Neither |

Lines l_1 and l_2 pass through the given points. Determine if l_1 and l_2 are parallel, perpendicular, or neither.

$$l_1: \quad (2, -7) \text{ and } (4, 1) \qquad l_2: \quad (-3, 1) \text{ and } (1, 0)$$

Solution:

Find the slope of each line.

$l_1: \quad (2, -7) \quad \text{and} \quad (4, 1)$
$\qquad (x_1, y_1) \qquad\quad (x_2, y_2)$

$l_2: \quad (-3, 1) \quad \text{and} \quad (1, 0)$
$\qquad (x_1, y_1) \qquad\quad (x_2, y_2)$

TIP: You can check that two lines are perpendicular by checking that the product of their slopes is –1.

$$4\left(-\frac{1}{4}\right) = -1$$

$$m_1 = \frac{1 - (-7)}{4 - 2} \qquad\qquad m_2 = \frac{0 - 1}{1 - (-3)}$$

$$m_1 = \frac{8}{2} \qquad\qquad\qquad m_2 = \frac{-1}{4}$$

$$m_1 = 4 \qquad\qquad\qquad m_2 = -\frac{1}{4}$$

One slope is the opposite of the reciprocal of the other slope. Therefore, the lines are perpendicular.

Skill Practice Determine if lines l_1 and l_2 are parallel, perpendicular, or neither.

8. $l_1: \quad (-2, -3) \text{ and } (4, -1)$
$\quad\; l_2: \quad (0, 2) \text{ and } (-3, 1)$

4. Applications of Slope: Rate of Change

In many applications, the interpretation of slope refers to the *rate of change* of the *y*-variable to the *x*-variable.

| Example 8 | Interpreting Slope in an Application |

The annual median income for males in the United States for selected years is shown in Figure 3-25. The trend is approximately linear. Find the slope of the line and interpret the meaning of the slope in the context of the problem.

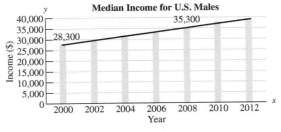

Figure 3-25

Source: U.S. Department of the Census

Answer

8. Parallel

Solution:

To determine the slope we need to know two points on the line. From the graph, the median income for males in the year 2000 was approximately $28,300. This gives us the ordered pair (2000, 28,300). In the year 2008, the income was $35,300. This gives the ordered pair (2008, 35,300).

$$\underset{(x_1,\,y_1)}{(2000,\,28{,}300)} \quad \text{and} \quad \underset{(x_2,\,y_2)}{(2008,\,35{,}300)}$$ Label the points.

$$m = \frac{y_2 - y_1}{x_2 - x_1} = \frac{35{,}300 - 28{,}300}{2008 - 2000}$$ Apply the slope formula.

$$= \frac{7000}{8}$$

$$= 875$$ Simplify.

The slope is 875. This tells us the rate of change of the y-variable (income) to the x-variable (years). This means that men's median income in the United States increased at a rate of $875 per year during this time period.

Skill Practice

9. In the year 2000, the population of Alaska was approximately 630,000. By 2010, it had grown to 700,000. Use the ordered pairs (2000, 630,000) and (2010, 700,000) to determine the slope of the line through the points. Then interpret the meaning in the context of this problem.

Answer

9. $m = 7000$; The population of Alaska increased at a rate of 7000 people per year.

Section 3.3   Practice Exercises

Study Skills Exercise

Each day after finishing your homework, choose two or three odd-numbered problems or examples from that section. Write the problem with the directions on one side of a 3×5 card. On the back write the section, page, and problem number along with the answer. Each week, shuffle your cards and pull out a few at random, to give yourself a review of $\frac{1}{2}$-hr or more.

Vocabulary and Key Concepts

1. **a.** The ratio of the vertical change and the horizontal change between two distinct points (x_1, y_1) and (x_2, y_2) on a line is called the _____ of the line. The slope can be computed from the formula $m =$ _____.

   b. Lines in the same plane that do not intersect are called _____ lines.

   c. Two lines are perpendicular if they intersect at a _____ angle.

   d. If m_1 and m_2 represent the slopes of two nonvertical perpendicular lines then $m_1 \cdot m_2 =$ _____.

   e. The slope of a vertical line is _____. The slope of a _____ line is 0.

226   **Chapter 3**   Graphing Linear Equations in Two Variables

Review Exercises

For Exercises 2–6, find the *x*- and *y*-intercepts (if they exist). Then graph the line.

2. $x - 5 = 2$

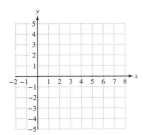

3. $x - 3y = 6$

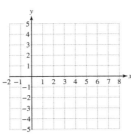

4. $y = \dfrac{2}{3}x$

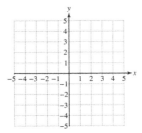

5. $2y - 3 = 0$

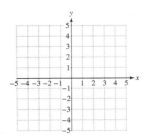

6. $2x = 4y$

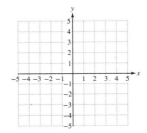

Concept 1: Introduction to Slope

7. Determine the slope of the roof.
(See Example 1.)

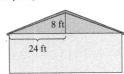

8. Determine the slope of the stairs.

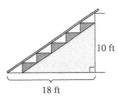

9. Calculate the slope of the handrail.

© Ryan McVay/Getty Images RF

10. Determine the slope of the treadmill

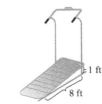

Concept 2: Slope Formula

For Exercises 11–14, fill in the blank with the appropriate term: *zero*, *negative*, *positive*, or *undefined*.

11. The slope of a line parallel to the *y*-axis is _____.

12. The slope of a horizontal line is _____.

13. The slope of a line that rises from left to right is _____.

14. The slope of a line that falls from left to right is _____.

For Exercises 15–23, determine if the slope is positive, negative, zero, or undefined.

15.

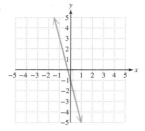

16.

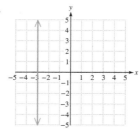

17.

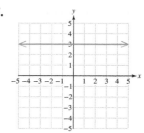

18.

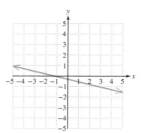

19.

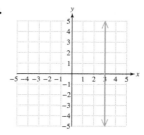

20.

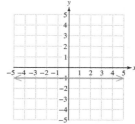

21.

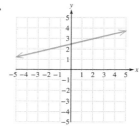

22.

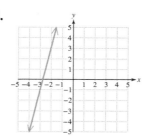

23.

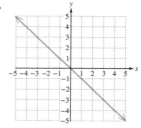

For Exercises 24–32, determine the slope by using the slope formula and any two points on the line. Check your answer by drawing a right triangle, where appropriate, and labeling the "rise" and "run."

24.

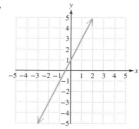

25.

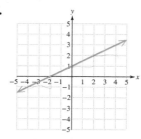

26.

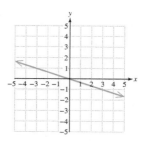

27.

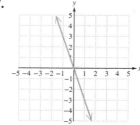

28.

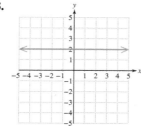

29.

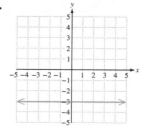

228   **Chapter 3**   Graphing Linear Equations in Two Variables

30. 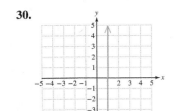   **31.** 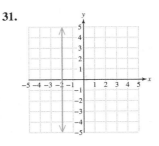   **32.**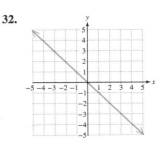

For Exercises 33–50, find the slope of the line that passes through the two points. **(See Example 2–5.)**

33. $(2, 4)$ and $(-4, 2)$

34. $(-5, 4)$ and $(-11, 12)$

35. $(-2, 3)$ and $(1, -6)$

36. $(-3, -4)$ and $(1, -5)$

37. $(1, 5)$ and $(-4, 2)$

38. $(-6, -1)$ and $(-2, -3)$

39. $(5, 3)$ and $(-2, 3)$

40. $(0, -1)$ and $(-4, -1)$

41. $(2, -7)$ and $(2, 5)$

42. $(-4, 3)$ and $(-4, -4)$

43. $\left(\dfrac{1}{2}, \dfrac{3}{5}\right)$ and $\left(\dfrac{1}{4}, -\dfrac{4}{5}\right)$

44. $\left(-\dfrac{2}{7}, \dfrac{1}{3}\right)$ and $\left(\dfrac{8}{7}, -\dfrac{5}{6}\right)$

45. $(3, -1)$ and $(-5, 6)$

46. $(-6, 5)$ and $(-10, 4)$

47. $(6.8, -3.4)$ and $(-3.2, 1.1)$

48. $(-3.15, 8.25)$ and $(6.85, -4.25)$

49. $(1994, 3.5)$ and $(2000, 2.6)$

50. $(1988, 4.65)$ and $(1998, 9.25)$

Concept 3: Parallel and Perpendicular Lines

For Exercises 51–56, the slope of a line is given. **(See Example 6.)**

a. Determine the slope of a line parallel to the line with the given slope.

b. Determine the slope of a line perpendicular to the line with the given slope.

51. $m = -2$

52. $m = \dfrac{2}{3}$

53. $m = 0$

54. The slope is undefined.

55. $m = \dfrac{4}{5}$

56. $m = -4$

For Exercises 57–62, let m_1 and m_2 represent the slopes of two lines. Determine if the lines are parallel, perpendicular, or neither. **(See Example 6.)**

57. $m_1 = -2, m_2 = \dfrac{1}{2}$

58. $m_1 = \dfrac{2}{3}, m_2 = \dfrac{3}{2}$

59. $m_1 = 1, m_2 = \dfrac{4}{4}$

60. $m_1 = \dfrac{3}{4}, m_2 = -\dfrac{8}{6}$

61. $m_1 = \dfrac{2}{7}, m_2 = -\dfrac{2}{7}$

62. $m_1 = 5, m_2 = 5$

For Exercises 63–68, find the slopes of the lines l_1 and l_2 defined by the two given points. Then determine whether l_1 and l_2 are parallel, perpendicular, or neither. **(See Example 7.)**

63. l_1: $(2, 4)$ and $(-1, -2)$
l_2: $(1, 7)$ and $(0, 5)$

64. l_1: $(0, 0)$ and $(-2, 4)$
l_2: $(1, -5)$ and $(-1, -1)$

65. l_1: $(1, 9)$ and $(0, 4)$
l_2: $(5, 2)$ and $(10, 1)$

66. l_1: $(3, -4)$ and $(-1, -8)$
l_2: $(5, -5)$ and $(-2, 2)$

67. l_1: $(4, 4)$ and $(0, 3)$
l_2: $(1, 7)$ and $(-1, -1)$

68. l_1: $(3, 5)$ and $(-2, -5)$
l_2: $(2, 0)$ and $(-4, -3)$

Concept 4: Applications of Slope: Rate of Change

69. For a recent year, the average earnings for male workers between the ages of 25 and 34 with a high school diploma was $32,000. Comparing this value in constant dollars to the average earnings 15 yr later showed that the average earnings have decreased to $29,600. Find the average rate of change in dollars per year for this time period. [*Hint:* Use the ordered pairs (0, 32,000) and (15, 29,600).]

70. In 1985, the U.S. Postal Service charged $0.22 for first class letters and cards up to 1 oz. By 2015, the price had increased to $0.49. Let x represent the year, and y represent the cost for 1 oz of first class postage. Find the average rate of change of the cost per year.

71. In 1985, there were 539 thousand male inmates in federal and state prisons. By 2010, the number increased to 1714 thousand. Let x represent the year, and let y represent the number of prisoners (in thousands). **(See Example 8.)**

    a. Using the ordered pairs (1985, 539) and (2010, 1714), find the slope of the line.

    b. Interpret the slope in the context of this problem.

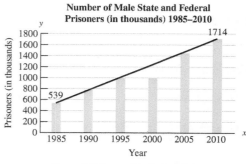

Number of Male State and Federal Prisoners (in thousands) 1985–2010

(*Source:* U.S. Bureau of Justice Statistics)

72. In the year 1985, there were 30 thousand female inmates in federal and state prisons. By 2010, the number increased to 120 thousand. Let x represent the year, and let y represent the number of prisoners (in thousands).

    a. Using the ordered pairs (1985, 30) and (2010, 120), find the slope of the line.

    b. Interpret the slope in the context of this problem.

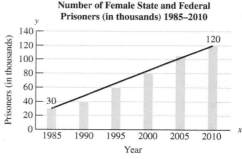

Number of Female State and Federal Prisoners (in thousands) 1985–2010

(*Source:* U.S. Bureau of Justice Statistics)

73. The distance, d (in miles), between a lightning strike and an observer is given by the equation $d = 0.2t$, where t is the time (in seconds) between seeing lightning and hearing thunder.

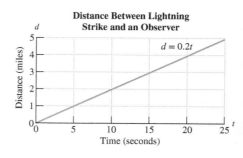

Distance Between Lightning Strike and an Observer

$$d = 0.2t$$

© Royalty Free/Corbis RF

    a. If an observer counts 5 sec between seeing lightning and hearing thunder, how far away was the lightning strike?

    b. If an observer counts 10 sec between seeing lightning and hearing thunder, how far away was the lightning strike?

    c. If an observer counts 15 sec between seeing lightning and hearing thunder, how far away was the lightning strike?

    d. What is the slope of the line? Interpret the meaning of the slope in the context of this problem.

230   **Chapter 3**   Graphing Linear Equations in Two Variables

74. Michael wants to buy an efficient Smart car that according to the latest EPA standards gets 33 mpg in the city and 40 mpg on the highway. The car that Michael picked out costs $12,600. His dad agreed to purchase the car if Michael would pay it off in equal monthly payments for the next 60 months. The equation $y = -210x + 12,600$ represents the amount, y (in dollars), that Michael owes his father after x months.

© Erica Simone Leeds

a. How much does Michael owe his dad after 5 months?

b. Determine the slope of the line and interpret its meaning in the context of this problem.

Mixed Exercises

For Exercises 75–78, determine the slope of the line passing through points A and B.

75. Point A is located 3 units up and 4 units to the right of point B.

76. Point A is located 2 units up and 5 units to the left of point B.

77. Point A is located 5 units to the right of point B.

78. Point A is located 3 units down from point B.

79. Graph the line through the point $(1, -2)$ having slope $-\frac{2}{3}$. Then give two other points on the line.

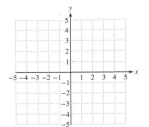

80. Graph the line through the point $(1, 2)$ having slope $-\frac{3}{4}$. Then give two other points on the line.

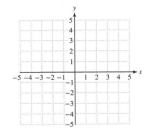

81. Graph the line through the point $(2, 2)$ having slope 3. Then give two other points on the line.

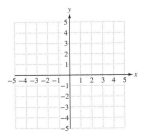

82. Graph the line through the point $(-1, 3)$ having slope 2. Then give two other points on the line.

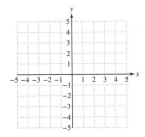

83. Graph the line through $(-3, -2)$ with an undefined slope. Then give two other points on the line.

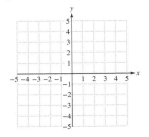

84. Graph the line through $(3, 3)$ with a slope of 0. Then give two other points on the line.

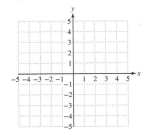

For Exercises 85–90, draw a line as indicated. Answers may vary.

85. Draw a line with a positive slope and a positive *y*-intercept.

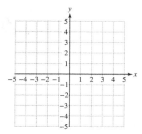

86. Draw a line with a positive slope and a negative *y*-intercept.

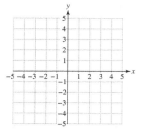

87. Draw a line with a negative slope and a negative *y*-intercept.

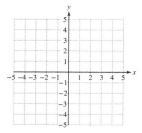

88. Draw a line with a negative slope and positive *y*-intercept.

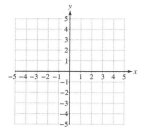

89. Draw a line with a zero slope and a positive *y*-intercept.

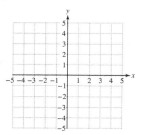

90. Draw a line with undefined slope and a negative *x*-intercept.

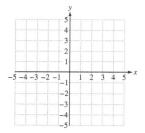

Expanding Your Skills

91. Determine the slope between the points $(a + b, 4m - n)$ and $(a - b, m + 2n)$.

92. Determine the slope between the points $(3c - d, s + t)$ and $(c - 2d, s - t)$.

93. Determine the *x*-intercept of the line $ax + by = c$.

94. Determine the *y*-intercept of the line $ax + by = c$.

95. Find another point on the line that contains the point $(2, -1)$ and has a slope of $\frac{2}{5}$.

96. Find another point on the line that contains the point $(-3, 4)$ and has a slope of $\frac{1}{4}$.

Section 3.4   Slope-Intercept Form of a Linear Equation

Concepts

1. Slope-Intercept Form of a Linear Equation
2. Graphing a Line from Its Slope and y-Intercept
3. Determining Whether Two Lines Are Parallel, Perpendicular, or Neither
4. Writing an Equation of a Line Using Slope-Intercept Form

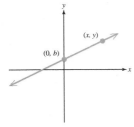

Figure 3-26

1. Slope-Intercept Form of a Linear Equation

We learned that the solutions to an equation of the form $Ax + By = C$ (where A and B are not both zero) represent a line in a rectangular coordinate system. An equation of a line written in this way is said to be in **standard form**. In this section, we will learn a new form, called **slope-intercept form**, that can be used to determine the slope and y-intercept of a line.

Let $(0, b)$ represent the y-intercept of a line. Let (x, y) represent any other point on the line. See Figure 3-26. Then the slope, m, of the line can be found as follows:

Let $(0, b)$ represent (x_1, y_1), and let (x, y) represent (x_2, y_2). Apply the slope formula.

$$m = \frac{y_2 - y_1}{x_2 - x_1} \rightarrow m = \frac{y - b}{x - 0}$$ Apply the slope formula.

$$m = \frac{y - b}{x}$$ Simplify.

$$mx = \left(\frac{y - b}{x}\right)x$$ Multiply by x to clear fractions.

$$mx = y - b$$

$$mx + b = y - b + b$$ To isolate y, add b to both sides.

$$mx + b = y \quad \text{or} \quad y = mx + b$$ The equation is in slope-intercept form.

> **Slope-Intercept Form of a Linear Equation**
>
> $y = mx + b$ is the slope-intercept form of a linear equation.
> m is the slope and the point $(0, b)$ is the y-intercept.

Example 1   **Identifying the Slope and y-Intercept From a Linear Equation**

For each equation, identify the slope and y-intercept.

a. $y = 3x - 1$ **b.** $y = -2.7x + 5$ **c.** $y = 4x$

Solution:

Each equation is written in slope-intercept form, $y = mx + b$. The slope is the coefficient of x, and the y-intercept is determined by the constant term.

a. $y = 3x - 1$ The slope is 3.   The y-intercept is $(0, -1)$.

b. $y = -2.7x + 5$ The slope is -2.7.   The y-intercept is $(0, 5)$.

c. $y = 4x$ can be written as $y = 4x + 0$.   The slope is 4.
The y-intercept is $(0, 0)$.

Skill Practice   Identify the slope and the y-intercept.

1. $y = 4x + 6$ **2.** $y = 3.5x - 4.2$ **3.** $y = -7$

Answers

1. slope: 4; y-intercept: $(0, 6)$
2. slope: 3.5; y-intercept: $(0, -4.2)$
3. slope: 0; y-intercept: $(0, -7)$

Given an equation of a line, we can write the equation in slope-intercept form by solving the equation for the y-variable. This is demonstrated in Example 2.

Example 2   **Identifying the Slope and *y*-Intercept From a Linear Equation**

Given the equation $-5x - 2y = 6$,

a. Write the equation in slope-intercept form.

b. Identify the slope and y-intercept.

Solution:

a. Write the equation in slope-intercept form, $y = mx + b$, by solving for y.

$$-5x - 2y = 6$$

$\quad\quad -2y = 5x + 6 \quad\quad$ Add $5x$ to both sides.

$\quad\quad \dfrac{-2y}{-2} = \dfrac{5x + 6}{-2} \quad\quad$ Divide both sides by -2.

$\quad\quad\quad y = \dfrac{5x}{-2} + \dfrac{6}{-2} \quad\quad$ Divide each term by -2 and simplify.

$\quad\quad\quad y = -\dfrac{5}{2}x - 3 \quad\quad$ Slope-intercept form

b. The slope is $-\frac{5}{2}$, and the y-intercept is $(0, -3)$.

Skill Practice   Given the equation $2x - 6y = -3$.

4. Write the equation in slope-intercept form.

5. Identify the slope and the y-intercept.

2. Graphing a Line from Its Slope and *y*-Intercept

Slope-intercept form is a useful tool to graph a line. The y-intercept is a known point on the line. The slope indicates the direction of the line and can be used to find a second point. Using slope-intercept form to graph a line is demonstrated in Examples 3 and 4.

Example 3   **Graphing a Line Using the Slope and *y*-Intercept**

Graph the equation $y = -\frac{5}{2}x - 3$ by using the slope and y-intercept.

Solution:

First plot the y-intercept, $(0, -3)$.

The slope $m = -\frac{5}{2}$ can be written as

$$m = \dfrac{-5}{2} \quad\begin{array}{l}\longleftarrow\text{ The change in }y\text{ is }-5.\\ \longleftarrow\text{ The change in }x\text{ is }2.\end{array}$$

To find a second point on the line, start at the y-intercept and move down 5 units and to the right 2 units. Then draw the line through the two points (Figure 3-27).

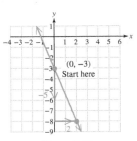

(0, −3)
Start here

Figure 3-27

Answers

4. $y = \dfrac{1}{3}x + \dfrac{1}{2}$

5. slope is $\dfrac{1}{3}$; y-intercept is $\left(0, \dfrac{1}{2}\right)$

234 **Chapter 3** Graphing Linear Equations in Two Variables

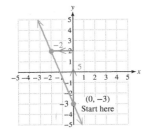

Figure 3-28

Similarly, the slope can be written as

$$m = \frac{5}{-2} \quad \underleftarrow{\hspace{1cm}} \text{The change in } y \text{ is 5.}$$
$$\underleftarrow{\hspace{1cm}} \text{The change in } x \text{ is } -2.$$

To find a second point, start at the y-intercept and move up 5 units and to the left 2 units. Then draw the line through the two points (Figure 3-28).

Skill Practice

6. Graph the equation by using the slope and y-intercept. $\quad y = 2x - 3$

 **Example 4**   **Graphing a Line Using the Slope and y-Intercept**

Graph the equation $y = 4x$ by using the slope and y-intercept.

Solution:

The equation can be written as $y = 4x + 0$. Therefore, we can plot the y-intercept at (0, 0). The slope $m = 4$ can be written as

$$m = \frac{4}{1} \quad \overset{\nwarrow \text{The change in } y \text{ is 4.}}{\underset{\swarrow \text{The change in } x \text{ is 1.}}{}}$$

 To find a second point on the line, start at the y-intercept and move up 4 units and to the right 1 unit. Then draw the line through the two points (Figure 3-29).

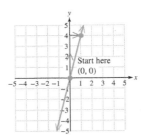

Figure 3-29

Skill Practice

7. Graph the equation by using the slope and y-intercept. $\quad y = -\frac{1}{4}x$

Answers

6–7.

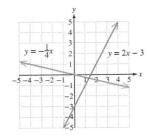

3. Determining Whether Two Lines Are Parallel, Perpendicular, or Neither

The slope-intercept form provides a means to find the slope of a line by inspection. Recall that if the slopes of two lines are known, then we can compare the slopes to determine if the lines are parallel, perpendicular, or neither parallel nor perpendicular. (Two distinct nonvertical lines are parallel if their slopes are equal. Two lines are perpendicular if the slope of one line is the opposite of the reciprocal of the slope of the other line.)

| **Example 5** | **Determining If Two Lines Are Parallel, Perpendicular, or Neither** |

For each pair of lines, determine if they are parallel, perpendicular, or neither.

a. l_1: $y = 3x - 5$ **b.** l_1: $y = \frac{3}{2}x + 2$

   l_2: $y = 3x + 1$ l_2: $y = \frac{2}{3}x + 1$

Solution:

a. l_1 : $y = 3x - 5$ The slope of l_1 is 3.

   l_2 : $y = 3x + 1$ The slope of l_2 is 3.

Because the slopes are the same, the lines are parallel.

b. l_1: $y = \frac{3}{2}x + 2$ The slope of l_1 is $\frac{3}{2}$.

   l_2: $y = \frac{2}{3}x + 1$ The slope of l_2 is $\frac{2}{3}$.

The slopes are not the same. Therefore, the lines are not parallel. The values of the slopes are reciprocals, but they are not opposite in sign. Therefore, the lines are not perpendicular. The lines are neither parallel nor perpendicular.

Skill Practice For each pair of lines determine if they are parallel, perpendicular, or neither.

8. $y = 3x - 5$ **9.** $y = \dfrac{5}{6}x - \dfrac{1}{2}$

   $y = -3x - 15$

            $y = \dfrac{5}{6}x + \dfrac{1}{2}$

| **Example 6** | **Determining If Two Lines Are Parallel, Perpendicular, or Neither** |

For each pair of lines, determine if they are parallel, perpendicular, or neither.

a. l_1: $x - 3y = -9$ **b.** l_1: $x = 2$

   l_2: $3x = -y + 4$ l_2: $2y = 8$

Solution:

a. First write the equation of each line in slope-intercept form.

l_1: $x - 3y = -9$ l_2: $3x = -y + 4$

   $-3y = -x - 9$ $3x + y = 4$

   $\dfrac{-3y}{-3} = \dfrac{-x}{-3} - \dfrac{9}{-3}$ $y = -3x + 4$

   $y = \dfrac{1}{3}x + 3$

l_1: $y = \frac{1}{3}x + 3$ The slope of l_1 is $\frac{1}{3}$.

l_2: $y = -3x + 4$ The slope of l_2 is -3.

The slope of $\frac{1}{3}$ is the opposite of the reciprocal of -3. Therefore, the lines are perpendicular.

b. The equation $x = 2$ represents a vertical line because the equation is in the form $x = k$.

The equation $2y = 8$ can be simplified to $y = 4$, which represents a horizontal line.

In this example, we do not need to analyze the slopes because vertical lines and horizontal lines are perpendicular.

Skill Practice For each pair of lines, determine if they are parallel, perpendicular, or neither.

10. $x - 5y = 10$ **11.** $y = -5$

  $5x - 1 = -y$ $x = 6$

4. Writing an Equation of a Line Using Slope-Intercept Form

The slope-intercept form of a linear equation can be used to write an equation of a line when the slope is known and the y-intercept is known.

| Example 7 | **Writing an Equation of a Line Using Slope-Intercept Form** |

Write an equation of the line whose slope is $\frac{2}{3}$ and whose y-intercept is $(0, 8)$.

Solution:

The slope is given as $m = \frac{2}{3}$, and the y-intercept $(0, b)$ is given as $(0, 8)$. Substitute the values $m = \frac{2}{3}$ and $b = 8$ into the slope-intercept form of a line.

$$y = mx + b$$
$$y = \frac{2}{3}x + 8$$

Skill Practice

12. Write an equation of the line whose slope is -4 and y-intercept is $(0, -10)$.

| Example 8 | **Writing an Equation of a Line Using Slope-Intercept Form** |

Write an equation of the line having a slope of 2 and passing through the point $(-3, 1)$.

Solution:

To find an equation of a line using slope-intercept form, it is necessary to find the value of m and b. The slope is given in the problem as $m = 2$. Therefore, the slope-intercept form becomes

$$y = mx + b$$
$$y = 2x + b$$

Answers

10. Perpendicular   **11.** Perpendicular

12. $y = -4x - 10$

Because the point $(-3, 1)$ is on the line, it is a solution to the equation. Therefore, to find b, substitute the values of x and y from the ordered pair $(-3, 1)$ and solve the resulting equation for b.

$$y = 2x + b$$
$$1 = 2(-3) + b \qquad \text{Substitute } y = 1 \text{ and } x = -3.$$
$$1 = -6 + b \qquad \text{Simplify and solve for } b.$$
$$7 = b$$

Now with m and b known, the slope-intercept form is $y = 2x + 7$.

TIP: The equation from Example 8 can be checked by graphing the line $y = 2x + 7$. The slope $m = 2$ can be written as $m = \frac{2}{1}$. Therefore, to graph the line, start at the y-intercept $(0, 7)$ and move up 2 units and to the right 1 unit.

The graph verifies that the line passes through the point $(-3, 1)$ as it should.

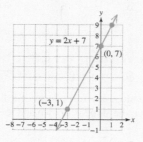

Skill Practice

13. Write an equation of the line having a slope of -3 and passing through the point $(-2, -5)$.

Answer

13. $y = -3x - 11$

Calculator Connections

Topic: Using the ZSquare Option in Zoom

In Example 6(a) we found that the equations $y = \frac{1}{3}x + 3$ and $y = -3x + 4$ represent perpendicular lines. We can verify our results by graphing the lines on a graphing calculator.

Notice that the lines do not appear perpendicular in the calculator display on the standard viewing window. That is, they do not appear to form a right angle at the point of inter-section. Because many calculators have a rectangular screen, the standard viewing window is elongated in the horizontal direction. To eliminate this distortion, try using a *ZSquare* option, which is located under the Zoom menu. This feature will set the viewing window so that equal distances on the display denote an equal number of units on the graph.

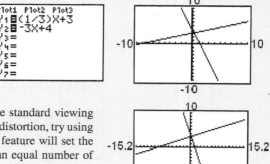

Calculator Exercises

For each pair of lines, determine if the lines are parallel, perpendicular, or neither. Then use a square viewing window to graph the lines on a graphing calculator to verify your results.

1. $x + y = 1$

$x - y = -3$

2. $3x + y = -2$

$6x + 2y = 6$

3. $2x - y = 4$

$3x + 2y = 4$

4. Graph the lines defined by $y = x + 1$ and $y = 0.99x + 3$. Are these lines parallel? Explain.

5. Graph the lines defined by $y = -2x - 1$ and $y = -2x - 0.99$. Are these lines the same? Explain.

6. Graph the line defined by $y = 0.001x + 3$. Is this line horizontal? Explain.

Section 3.4   Practice Exercises

Study Skills Exercise

When taking a test, go through the test and do all the problems that you know first. Then go back and work on the problems that were more difficult. Give yourself a time limit for how much time you spend on each problem (maybe 3 to 5 min the first time through). Circle the importance of each statement.

	not important	somewhat important	very important
a. Read through the entire test first.	1	2	3
b. If time allows, go back and check each problem.	1	2	3
c. Write out all steps instead of doing the work in your head.	1	2	3

Vocabulary and Key Terms

1. a. Consider a line with slope m and y-intercept $(0, b)$. The slope-intercept form of an equation of the line is _____.

   b. An equation of a line written in the form $Ax + By = C$ where A and B are not both zero is said to be in _____ form.

Review Exercises

2. For each equation given, determine if the line is horizontal, vertical, or slanted.

   a. $3x = 6$ b. $y + 3 = 6$ c. $x + y = 6$

For Exercises 3–10, determine the x- and y-intercepts, if they exist.

3. $x - 5y = 10$ 4. $3x + y = -12$ 5. $3y = -9$ 6. $2 + y = 5$

7. $-4x = 6y$ 8. $-x + 3 = 8$ 9. $5x = 20$ 10. $y = \frac{1}{2}x$

Concept 1: Slope-Intercept Form of a Linear Equation

For Exercises 11–30, identify the slope and y-intercept, if they exist. **(See Examples 1–2.)**

11. $y = -2x + 3$ 12. $y = \frac{2}{3}x + 5$ 13. $y = x - 2$

14. $y = -x + 6$ 15. $y = -x$ 16. $y = -5x$

17. $y = \frac{3}{4}x - 1$ 18. $y = x - \frac{5}{3}$ 19. $2x - 5y = 4$

20. $3x + 2y = 9$ 21. $3x - y = 5$ 22. $7x - 3y = -6$

23. $x + y = 6$ 24. $x - y = 1$ 25. $x + 6 = 8$

26. $-4 + x = 1$ 27. $-8y = 2$ 28. $1 - y = 9$

29. $3y - 2x = 0$ 30. $5x = 6y$

Concept 2: Graphing a Line from Its Slope and *y*-Intercept

For Exercises 31–34, graph the line using the slope and *y*-intercept. **(See Examples 3–4.)**

31. Graph the line through the point (0, 2), having a slope of −4.

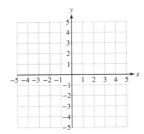

32. Graph the line through the point (0, −1), having a slope of −3.

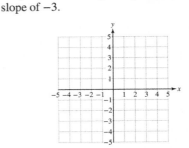

33. Graph the line through the point (0, −5), having a slope of $\frac{3}{2}$.

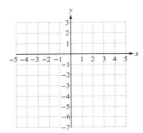

34. Graph the line through the point (0, 3), having a slope of $-\frac{1}{4}$.

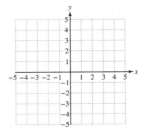

For Exercises 35–40, match the equation with the graph (a–f) by identifying if the slope is positive or negative and if the *y*-intercept is positive, negative, or zero.

35. $y = 2x + 3$

36. $y = -3x - 2$

37. $y = -\frac{1}{3}x + 3$

38. $y = \frac{1}{2}x - 2$

39. $y = x$

40. $y = -2x$

a.

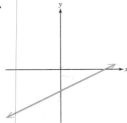

b.

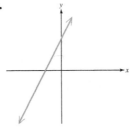

c.

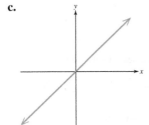

d.

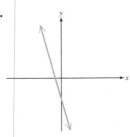

e.

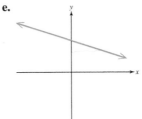

f.

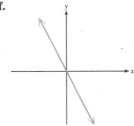

240   **Chapter 3**   Graphing Linear Equations in Two Variables

For Exercises 41–52, write each equation in slope-intercept form (if possible) and graph the line. **(See Examples 3–4.)**

41. $2x + y = 9$ **42.** $-6x + y = 8$ **43.** $x - 2y = 6$ **44.** $5x - 2y = 2$

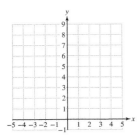   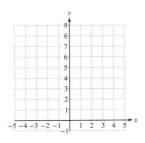   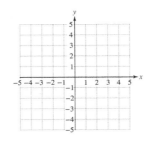   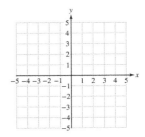

45. $2x = -4y + 6$ **46.** $6x = 2y - 14$ **47.** $x + y = 0$ **48.** $x - y = 0$

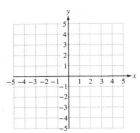   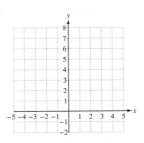   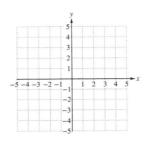   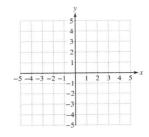

49. $5y = 4x$ **50.** $-2x = 5y$ **51.** $3y + 2 = 0$ **52.** $1 + 5y = 6$

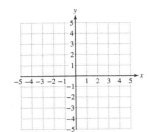   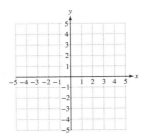   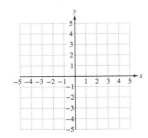   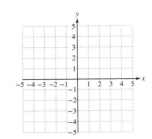

Concept 3: Determining Whether Two Lines Are Parallel, Perpendicular, or Neither

For Exercises 53–68, determine if the equations represent parallel lines, perpendicular lines, or neither. **(See Examples 5–6.)**

53. l_1: $y = -2x - 3$ **54.** l_1: $y = \frac{4}{3}x - 2$ **55.** l_1: $y = \frac{4}{5}x - \frac{1}{2}$ **56.** l_1: $y = \frac{1}{5}x + 1$

   l_2: $y = \frac{1}{2}x + 4$ l_2: $y = -\frac{3}{4}x + 6$ l_2: $y = \frac{5}{4}x - \frac{2}{3}$ l_2: $y = 5x - 3$

57. l_1: $y = -9x + 6$ **58.** l_1: $y = 4x - 1$ **59.** l_1: $x = 3$ **60.** l_1: $y = \frac{2}{3}$

   l_2: $y = -9x - 1$ l_2: $y = 4x + \frac{1}{2}$ l_2: $y = \frac{7}{4}$ l_2: $x = 6$

61. l_1: $2x = 4$ **62.** l_1: $2y = 7$ **63.** l_1: $2x + 3y = 6$ **64.** l_1: $4x + 5y = 20$

   l_2: $6 = x$ l_2: $y = 4$ l_2: $3x - 2y = 12$ l_2: $5x - 4y = 60$

65. l_1: $4x + 2y = 6$ **66.** l_1: $3x + y = 5$ **67.** l_1: $y = \frac{1}{5}x - 3$ **68.** l_1: $y = \frac{1}{3}x + 2$

   l_2: $4x + 8y = 16$ l_2: $x + 3y = 18$ l_2: $2x - 10y = 20$ l_2: $-x + 3y = 12$

Concept 4: Writing an Equation of a Line Using Slope-Intercept Form

For Exercises 69–80, write an equation of the line given the following information. Write the answer in slope-intercept form if possible. **(See Examples 7–8.)**

69. The slope is $-\frac{1}{3}$, and the y-intercept is $(0, 2)$.

70. The slope is $\frac{2}{3}$, and the y-intercept is $(0, -1)$.

71. The slope is 10, and the y-intercept is $(0, -19)$.

72. The slope is -14, and the y-intercept is $(0, 2)$.

73. The slope is 6, and the line passes through the point $(1, -2)$.

74. The slope is -4, and the line passes through the point $(4, -3)$.

75. The slope is $\frac{1}{2}$, and the line passes through the point $(-4, -5)$.

76. The slope is $-\frac{2}{3}$, and the line passes through the point $(3, -1)$.

77. The slope is 0, and the y-intercept is -11.

78. The slope is 0, and the y-intercept is $\frac{6}{7}$.

79. The slope is 5, and the line passes through the origin.

80. The slope is -3, and the line passes through the origin.

Expanding Your Skills

For Exercises 81–86, write an equation of the line that passes through two points by following these steps:

Step 1: Find the slope of the line using the slope formula, $m = \dfrac{y_2 - y_1}{x_2 - x_1}$.

Step 2: Using the slope from Step 1 and either given point, follow the procedure given in Example 8 to find an equation of the line in slope-intercept form.

81. $(2, -1)$ and $(0, 3)$

82. $(4, -8)$ and $(0, -4)$

83. $(3, 1)$ and $(-3, 3)$

84. $(2, -3)$ and $(4, -2)$

85. $(1, 3)$ and $(-2, -9)$

86. $(1, 7)$ and $(-2, 4)$

87. The number of reported cases of Lyme disease in the United States can be modeled by the equation $y = 1203x + 10{,}006$. In this equation, x represents the number of years since 1993, and y represents the number of cases of Lyme disease.

   a. What is the slope of this line and what does it mean in the context of this problem?

   b. What is the y-intercept, and what does it mean in the context of this problem?

   c. Use the model to estimate the number of cases of Lyme disease in the year 2010.

   d. During what year would the predicted number of cases be 42,487?

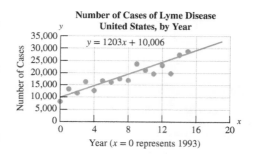

88. A phone bill is determined each month by a $16.95 flat fee plus $0.10/min of long distance. The equation, $C = 0.10x + 16.95$ represents the total monthly cost, C, for x minutes of long distance.

   a. Identify the slope. Interpret the meaning of the slope in the context of this problem.

   b. Identify the C-intercept. Interpret the meaning of the C-intercept in the context of this problem.

   c. Use the equation to determine the total cost of 234 min of long distance.

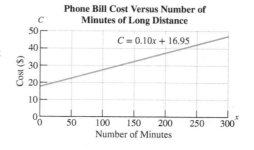

89. A linear equation is written in standard form if it can be written as $Ax + By = C$, where A and B are not both zero. Write the equation $Ax + By = C$ in slope-intercept form to show that the slope is given by the ratio, $-\frac{A}{B}$. ($B \neq 0$.)

For Exercises 90–93, use the result of Exercise 89 to find the slope of the line.

90. $2x + 5y = 8$ **91.** $6x + 7y = -9$ **92.** $4x - 3y = -5$ **93.** $11x - 8y = 4$

Problem Recognition Exercises

Linear Equations in Two Variables

For Exercises 1–20, choose the equation(s) from the column on the right whose graph satisfies the condition described. Give all possible answers.

1. Line whose slope is positive.

2. Line whose slope is negative.

3. Line that passes through the origin.

4. Line that contains the point $(3, -2)$.

5. Line whose y-intercept is $(0, 4)$.

6. Line whose y-intercept is $(0, -5)$.

7. Line whose slope is $\dfrac{1}{2}$.

8. Line whose slope is -2.

9. Line whose slope is 0.

10. Line whose slope is undefined.

11. Line that is parallel to the line with equation $y = -\dfrac{2}{3}x + 4$.

12. Line perpendicular to the line with equation $y = 2x + 9$.

13. Line that is vertical.

14. Line that is horizontal.

15. Line whose x-intercept is $(10, 0)$.

16. Line whose x-intercept is $(6, 0)$.

17. Line that is parallel to the x-axis.

18. Line that is perpendicular to the y-axis.

19. Line with a negative slope and positive y-intercept.

20. Line with a positive slope and negative y-intercept.

a. $y = 5x$

b. $2x + 3y = 12$

c. $y = \dfrac{1}{2}x - 5$

d. $3x - 6y = 10$

e. $2y = -8$

f. $y = -2x + 4$

g. $3x = 1$

h. $x + 2y = 6$

Point-Slope Formula

1. Writing an Equation of a Line Using the Point-Slope Formula

The slope-intercept form of a line can be used as a tool to construct an equation of a line. Another useful tool to determine an equation of a line is the point-slope formula. The point-slope formula can be derived from the slope formula as follows.

Suppose a line passes through a given point (x_1, y_1) and has slope m. If (x, y) is any other point on the line, then the slope is given by

$$m = \frac{y - y_1}{x - x_1} \qquad \text{Slope formula}$$

$$m(x - x_1) = \frac{y - y_1}{x - x_1}(x - x_1) \qquad \text{Clear fractions.}$$

$$m(x - x_1) = y - y_1$$
$$y - y_1 = m(x - x_1) \qquad \text{Point-slope formula}$$

Concepts

1. Writing an Equation of a Line Using the Point-Slope Formula
2. Writing an Equation of a Line Given Two Points
3. Writing an Equation of a Line Parallel or Perpendicular to Another Line
4. Different Forms of Linear Equations: A Summary

Point-Slope Formula

The **point-slope formula** is given by

$$y - y_1 = m(x - x_1)$$

where m is the slope of the line and (x_1, y_1) is any known point on the line.

Example 1 demonstrates how to use the point-slope formula to find an equation of a line when a point on the line and slope are given.

Example 1   **Writing an Equation of a Line Using the Point-Slope Formula**

Use the point-slope formula to write an equation of the line having a slope of 3 and passing through the point $(-2, -4)$. Write the answer in slope-intercept form.

Solution:

The slope of the line is given: $m = 3$

A point on the line is given: $(x_1, y_1) = (-2, -4)$

The point-slope formula:

$$y - y_1 = m(x - x_1)$$
$$y - (-4) = 3[x - (-2)] \qquad \text{Substitute } m = 3, x_1 = -2, \text{ and } y_1 = -4.$$
$$y + 4 = 3(x + 2) \qquad \text{Simplify. Because the final answer is required in slope-intercept form, simplify the equation and solve for } y.$$
$$y + 4 = 3x + 6 \qquad \text{Apply the distributive property.}$$
$$y = 3x + 2 \qquad \text{Slope-intercept form}$$

Skill Practice

1. Use the point-slope formula to write an equation of the line having a slope of -4 and passing through $(-1, 5)$. Write the answer in slope-intercept form.

The equation $y = 3x + 2$ from Example 1 is graphed in Figure 3-30. Notice that the line does indeed pass through the point $(-2, -4)$.

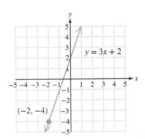

Figure 3-30

2. Writing an Equation of a Line Given Two Points

Example 2 is similar to Example 1; however, the slope must first be found from two given points.

Example 2   **Writing an Equation of a Line Given Two Points**

Use the point-slope formula to find an equation of the line passing through the points $(-2, 5)$ and $(4, -1)$. Write the final answer in slope-intercept form.

Solution:

Given two points on a line, the slope can be found with the slope formula.

$$\underset{(x_1, y_1)}{(-2, 5)} \quad \text{and} \quad \underset{(x_2, y_2)}{(4, -1)} \qquad \text{Label the points.}$$

$$m = \frac{y_2 - y_1}{x_2 - x_1} = \frac{(-1) - (5)}{(4) - (-2)} = \frac{-6}{6} = -1$$

To apply the point-slope formula, use the slope, $m = -1$ and either given point. We will choose the point $(-2, 5)$ as (x_1, y_1).

$$y - y_1 = m(x - x_1)$$
$$y - 5 = -1[x - (-2)] \qquad \text{Substitute } m = -1, x_1 = -2, \text{ and } y_1 = 5.$$
$$y - 5 = -1(x + 2) \qquad \text{Simplify.}$$
$$y - 5 = -x - 2$$
$$y = -x + 3$$

TIP: The point-slope formula can be applied using either given point for (x_1, y_1). In Example 2, using the point $(4, -1)$ for (x_1, y_1) produces the same result.

$$y - y_1 = m(x - x_1)$$
$$y - (-1) = -1(x - 4)$$
$$y + 1 = -x + 4$$
$$y = -x + 3$$

Skill Practice

2. Use the point-slope formula to write an equation of the line passing through the points $(1, -1)$ and $(-1, -5)$.

Answers

1. $y = -4x + 1$ **2.** $y = 2x - 3$

The solution to Example 2 can be checked by graphing the line $y = -x + 3$ using the slope and y-intercept. Notice that the line passes through the points $(-2, 5)$ and $(4, -1)$ as expected. See Figure 3-31.

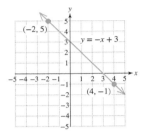

Figure 3-31

3. Writing an Equation of a Line Parallel or Perpendicular to Another Line

To write an equation of a line using the point-slope formula, the slope must be known. If the slope is not explicitly given, then other information must be used to determine the slope. In Example 2, the slope was found using the slope formula. Examples 3 and 4 show other situations in which we might find the slope.

Example 3 | **Writing an Equation of a Line Parallel to Another Line**

Use the point-slope formula to find an equation of the line passing through the point $(-1, 0)$ and parallel to the line $y = -4x + 3$. Write the final answer in slope-intercept form.

Solution:

Figure 3-32 shows the line $y = -4x + 3$ (pictured in black) and a line parallel to it (pictured in blue) that passes through the point $(-1, 0)$. The equation of the given line, $y = -4x + 3$, is written in slope-intercept form, and its slope is easily identified as -4. The line parallel to the given line must also have a slope of -4.

Apply the point-slope formula using $m = -4$ and the point $(x_1, y_1) = (-1, 0)$.

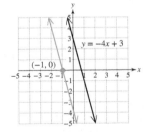

Figure 3-32

$$y - y_1 = m(x - x_1)$$
$$y - 0 = -4[x - (-1)]$$
$$y = -4(x + 1)$$
$$y = -4x - 4$$

Skill Practice

3. Use the point-slope formula to write an equation of the line passing through $(8, 2)$ and parallel to the line $y = \frac{3}{4}x - \frac{1}{2}$.

TIP: When writing an equation of a line, slope-intercept form or standard form is usually preferred. For instance, the solution to Example 3 can be written as follows.

Slope-intercept form:
$$y = -4x - 4$$

Standard form:
$$4x + y = -4$$

Answer

3. $y = \frac{3}{4}x - 4$

| Example 4 | ### Writing an Equation of a Line Perpendicular to Another Line |

Use the point-slope formula to find an equation of the line passing through the point $(-3, 1)$ and perpendicular to the line $3x + y = -2$. Write the final answer in slope-intercept form.

Solution:

The given line can be written in slope-intercept form as $y = -3x - 2$. The slope of this line is -3. Therefore, the slope of a line perpendicular to the given line is $\frac{1}{3}$.

Apply the point-slope formula with $m = \frac{1}{3}$, and $(x_1, y_1) = (-3, 1)$.

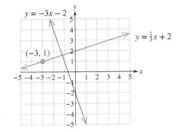

$$y - y_1 = m(x - x_1) \qquad \text{Point-slope formula}$$

$$y - (1) = \tfrac{1}{3}[x - (-3)] \qquad \text{Substitute } m = \tfrac{1}{3},\ x_1 = -3,\ \text{and } y_1 = 1.$$

$$y - 1 = \tfrac{1}{3}(x + 3) \qquad \text{To write the final answer in slope-intercept form, simplify the equation and solve for } y.$$

$$y - 1 = \tfrac{1}{3}x + 1 \qquad \text{Apply the distributive property.}$$

$$y = \tfrac{1}{3}x + 2 \qquad \text{Add 1 to both sides.}$$

A sketch of the perpendicular lines $y = \frac{1}{3}x + 2$ and $y = -3x - 2$ is shown in Figure 3-33. Notice that the line $y = \frac{1}{3}x + 2$ passes through the point $(-3, 1)$ as expected.

Figure 3-33

Skill Practice

4. Write an equation of the line passing through the point $(10, 4)$ and perpendicular to the line $x + 2y = 1$.

4. Different Forms of Linear Equations: A Summary

A linear equation can be written in several different forms, as summarized in Table 3-3.

Table 3-3

Form	Example	Comments
Standard Form $Ax + By = C$	$4x + 2y = 8$	A and B must not both be zero.
Horizontal Line $y = k$ (k is constant)	$y = 4$	The slope is zero, and the y-intercept is $(0, k)$.
Vertical Line $x = k$ (k is constant)	$x = -1$	The slope is undefined, and the x-intercept is $(k, 0)$.
Slope-Intercept Form $y = mx + b$ the slope is m y-intercept is $(0, b)$	$y = -3x + 7$ Slope $= -3$ y-intercept is $(0, 7)$	Solving a linear equation for y results in slope-intercept form. The coefficient of the x-term is the slope, and the constant defines the location of the y-intercept.
Point-Slope Formula $y - y_1 = m(x - x_1)$	$m = -3$ $(x_1, y_1) = (4, 2)$ $y - 2 = -3(x - 4)$	This formula is typically used to build an equation of a line when a point on the line is known and the slope of the line is known.

Answer

4. $y = 2x - 16$

Although standard form and slope-intercept form can be used to express an equation of a line, often the slope-intercept form is used to give a *unique* representation of the line. For example, the following linear equations are all written in standard form, yet they each define the same line.

$$2x + 5y = 10$$

$$-4x - 10y = -20$$

$$6x + 15y = 30$$

$$\frac{2}{5}x + y = 2$$

The line can be written uniquely in slope-intercept form as: $y = -\frac{2}{5}x + 2$.

Although it is important to understand and apply slope-intercept form and the point-slope formula, they are not necessarily applicable to all problems, particularly when dealing with a horizontal or vertical line.

Example 5   **Writing an Equation of a Line**

Find an equation of the line passing through the point $(2, -4)$ and parallel to the x-axis.

Solution:

Because the line is parallel to the x-axis, the line must be horizontal. Recall that all horizontal lines can be written in the form $y = k$, where k is a constant. A quick sketch can help find the value of the constant. See Figure 3-34.

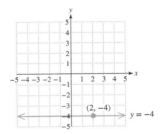

Figure 3-34

Because the line must pass through a point whose y-coordinate is -4, then the equation of the line must be $y = -4$.

Skill Practice

5. Write an equation for the vertical line that passes through the point $(-7, 2)$.

Answer

5. $x = -7$

Study Skills Exercise

Prepare a one-page summary sheet with the most important information that you need for the test. On the day of the test, look at this sheet several times to refresh your memory instead of trying to memorize new information.

Vocabulary and Key Concepts

1. **a.** The standard form of an equation of a line is _____, where A and B are not both zero and C is a constant.

   b. A line defined by an equation $y = k$, where k is a constant is a (horizontal/vertical) line.

   c. A line defined by an equation $x = k$, where k is a constant is a (horizontal/vertical) line.

   d. Given the slope-intercept form of an equation of a line, $y = mx + b$, the value of m is the _____ and b is the _____.

   e. Given a point (x_1, y_1) on a line with slope m, the point-slope formula is given by _____.

Review Exercises

For Exercises 2–6, graph each equation.

2. $-5x - 15 = 0$

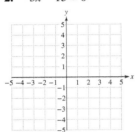

3. $2x - 3y = -3$

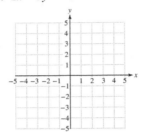

4. $y = -2x$

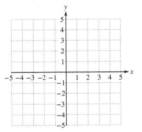

5. $3 - y = 9$

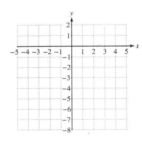

6. $y = \dfrac{4}{5}x$

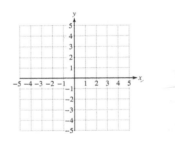

For Exercises 7–10, find the slope of the line that passes through the given points.

7. $(1, -3)$ and $(2, 6)$

8. $(2, -4)$ and $(-2, 4)$

9. $(-2, 5)$ and $(5, 5)$

10. $(6.1, 2.5)$ and $(6.1, -1.5)$

Concept 1: Writing an Equation of a Line Using the Point-Slope Formula

For Exercises 11–16, use the point-slope formula (if possible) to write an equation of the line given the following information. **(See Example 1.)**

11. The slope is 3, and the line passes through the point $(-2, 1)$.

12. The slope is -2, and the line passes through the point $(1, -5)$.

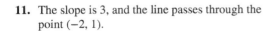**13.** The slope is -4, and the line passes through the point $(-3, -2)$.

14. The slope is 5, and the line passes through the point $(-1, -3)$.

15. The slope is $-\frac{1}{2}$, and the line passes through $(-1, 0)$.

16. The slope is $-\frac{3}{4}$, and the line passes through $(2, 0)$.

Concept 2: Writing an Equation of a Line Given Two Points

For Exercises 17–22, use the point-slope formula to write an equation of the line given the following information. **(See Example 2.)**

17. The line passes through the points $(-2, -6)$ and $(1, 0)$.

18. The line passes through the points $(-2, 5)$ and $(0, 1)$.

19. The line passes through the points $(0, -4)$ and $(-1, -3)$.

20. The line passes through the points $(1, -3)$ and $(-7, 2)$.

21. The line passes through the points $(2.2, -3.3)$ and $(12.2, -5.3)$.

22. The line passes through the points $(4.7, -2.2)$ and $(-0.3, 6.8)$.

For Exercises 23–28, find an equation of the line through the given points. Write the final answer in slope-intercept form.

23.

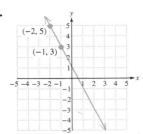

24.

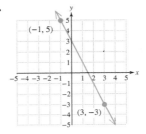

25.

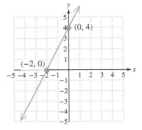

26.

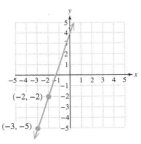

27.

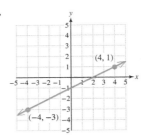

28.

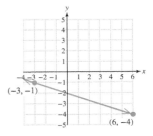

Concept 3: Writing an Equation of a Line Parallel or Perpendicular to Another Line

For Exercises 29–36, use the point-slope formula to write an equation of the line given the following information. **(See Examples 3–4.)**

29. The line passes through the point $(-3, 1)$ and is parallel to the line $y = 4x + 3$.

30. The line passes through the point $(4, -1)$ and is parallel to the line $y = 3x + 1$.

31. The line passes through the point $(4, 0)$ and is parallel to the line $3x + 2y = 8$.

32. The line passes through the point $(2, 0)$ and is parallel to the line $5x + 3y = 6$.

33. The line passes through the point $(-5, 2)$ and is perpendicular to the line $y = \frac{1}{2}x + 3$.

34. The line passes through the point $(-2, -2)$ and is perpendicular to the line $y = \frac{1}{3}x - 5$.

35. The line passes through the point $(0, -6)$ and is perpendicular to the line $-5x + y = 4$.

36. The line passes through the point $(0, -8)$ and is perpendicular to the line $2x - y = 5$.

250   **Chapter 3**   Graphing Linear Equations in Two Variables

Concept 4: Different Forms of Linear Equations: A Summary

For Exercises 37–42, match the form or formula on the left with its name on the right.

37. $x = k$

38. $y = mx + b$

39. $m = \dfrac{y_2 - y_1}{x_2 - x_1}$

40. $y - y_1 = m(x - x_1)$

41. $y = k$

42. $Ax + By = C$

i. Standard form

ii. Point-slope formula

iii. Horizontal line

iv. Vertical line

v. Slope-intercept form

vi. Slope formula

For Exercises 43–48, find an equation for the line given the following information. **(See Example 5.)**

43. The line passes through the point (3, 1) and is parallel to the line $y = -4$. See the figure.

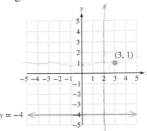

44. The line passes through the point (−1, 1) and is parallel to the line $y = 2$. See the figure.

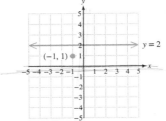

45. The line passes through the point (2, 6) and is perpendicular to the line $y = 1$. (*Hint:* Sketch the line first.)

46. The line passes through the point (0, 3) and is perpendicular to the line $y = -5$. (*Hint:* Sketch the line first.)

47. The line passes through the point (2, 2) and is perpendicular to the line $x = 0$.

48. The line passes through the point (5, −2) and is perpendicular to the line $x = 0$.

Mixed Exercises

For Exercises 49–60, write an equation of the line given the following information.

49. The slope is $\frac{1}{4}$, and the line passes through the point (−8, 6).

50. The slope is $\frac{2}{3}$, and the line passes through the point (−5, 4).

51. The line passes through the point (4, 4) and is parallel to the line $3x - y = 6$.

52. The line passes through the point (−1, −7) and is parallel to the line $5x + y = -5$.

53. The slope is 4.5, and the line passes through the point (5.2, −2.2).

54. The slope is −3.6, and the line passes through the point (10.0, 8.2).

55. The slope is undefined, and the line passes through the point (−6, −3).

56. The slope is undefined, and the line passes through the point (2, −1).

57. The slope is 0, and the line passes through the point (3, −2).

58. The slope is 0, and the line passes through the point (0, 5).

59. The line passes through the points (−4, 0) and (−4, 3).

60. The line passes through the points (1, 3) and (1, −4).

Expanding Your Skills

For Exercises 61–64, write an equation in slope-intercept form for the line shown.

61.

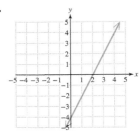

62.

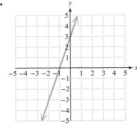

63.

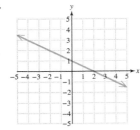

64.

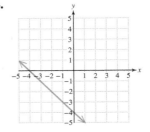

Applications of Linear Equations and Modeling

1. Interpreting a Linear Equation in Two Variables

Linear equations can often be used to describe (or model) the relationship between two variables in a real-world event.

Concepts

1. Interpreting a Linear Equation in Two Variables
2. Writing a Linear Model Using Observed Data Points
3. Writing a Linear Model Given a Fixed Value and a Rate of Change

Example 1   **Interpreting a Linear Equation**

Since the year 1900, the tiger population in India has decreased linearly. A recent study showed this decrease can be approximated by the equation $y = -350x + 42{,}000$. The variable y represents the number of tigers left in India, and x represents the number of years since 1900.

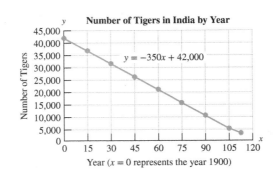

Number of Tigers in India by Year

$y = -350x + 42{,}000$

Year ($x = 0$ represents the year 1900)

a. Use the equation to estimate the number of tigers in 1960.

b. Use the equation to estimate the number of tigers in 2015.

c. Determine the slope of the line. Interpret the meaning of the slope in terms of the number of tigers and the year.

d. Determine the x-intercept. Interpret the meaning of the x-intercept in terms of the number of tigers.

Solution:

a. The year 1960 is 60 yr since 1900. Substitute $x = 60$ into the equation.

$$y = -350x + 42{,}000$$

$$y = -350(60) + 42{,}000$$

$$= 21{,}000$$ There were approximately 21,000 tigers in India in 1960.

b. The year 2015 is 115 yr since 1900. Substitute $x = 115$.

$$y = -350(115) + 42{,}000$$

$$= 1750$$ There were approximately 1750 tigers in India in 2015.

c. The slope is -350.   The slope means that the tiger population is decreasing by 350 tigers per year.

d. To find the x-intercept, substitute $y = 0$.

$$y = -350x + 42{,}000$$

$$0 = -350x + 42{,}000$$ Substitute 0 for y.

$$-42{,}000 = -350x$$

$$120 = x$$

The x-intercept is (120, 0). This means that 120 yr after the year 1900, the tiger population would be expected to reach zero. That is, in the year 2020, there will be no tigers left in India if this linear trend continues.

Skill Practice

1. The cost y (in dollars) for a local move by a small moving company is given by $y = 60x + 100$, where x is the number of hours required for the move.

a. How much would be charged for a move that requires 3 hr?

b. How much would be charged for a move that requires 8 hr?

c. What is the slope of the line and what does it mean in the context of this problem?

d. Determine the y-intercept and interpret its meaning in the context of this problem.

Answers

1. a. $280   **b.** $580

  c. 60; This means that for each additional hour of service, the cost of the move goes up by $60.

  d. (0, 100); The $100 charge is a fixed fee in addition to the hourly rate.

2. Writing a Linear Model Using Observed Data Points

Example 2	**Writing a Linear Model from Observed Data Points**

The monthly sales of hybrid cars sold in the United States are given for a recent year. The sales for the first 8 months of the year are shown in Figure 3-35. The value $x = 0$ represents January, $x = 1$ represents February, and so on.

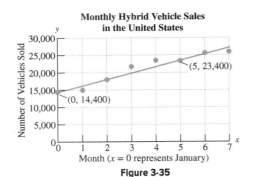

Figure 3-35

a. Use the data points from Figure 3-35 to find a linear equation that represents the monthly sales of hybrid cars in the United States. Let x represent the month number and let y represent the number of vehicles sold.

b. Use the linear equation in part (a) to estimate the number of hybrid vehicles sold in month 7 (August).

Solution:

a. The ordered pairs (0, 14,400) and (5, 23,400) are given in the graph. Use these points to find the slope.

$$\underset{(x_1, y_1)}{(0, 14{,}400)} \quad \text{and} \quad \underset{(x_2, y_2)}{(5, 23{,}400)}$$ Label the points.

$$m = \frac{y_2 - y_1}{x_2 - x_1} = \frac{23{,}400 - 14{,}400}{5 - 0}$$

$$= \frac{9000}{5}$$

$$= 1800$$ The slope is 1800. This indicates that sales increased by approximately 1800 per month during this time period.

With $m = 1800$, and the y-intercept given as (0, 14,400), we have the following linear equation in slope-intercept form.

$$y = 1800x + 14{,}400$$

b. To approximate the sales in month number 7, substitute $x = 7$ into the equation from part (a).

$$y = 1800(7) + 14{,}400$$ Substitute $x = 7$.

$$= 27{,}000$$

The monthly sales for August (month 7) would be 27,000 vehicles.

Skill Practice

2. Soft drink sales at a concession stand at a softball stadium have increased linearly over the course of the summer softball season.

   a. Use the given data points to find a linear equation that relates the sales, y, to week number, x.

   b. Use the equation to predict the number of soft drinks sold in week 10.

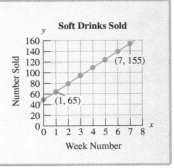

Soft Drinks Sold

---

3. Writing a Linear Model Given a Fixed Value and a Rate of Change

Another way to look at the equation $y = mx + b$ is to identify the term mx as the variable term and the term b as the constant term. The value of the term mx will change with the value of x (this is why the slope, m, is called a *rate of change*). However, the term b will remain constant regardless of the value of x. With these ideas in mind, we can write a linear equation if the rate of change and the constant are known.

Example 3   **Writing a Linear Model**

A stack of posters to advertise a production by the theater department costs $19.95 plus $1.50 per poster at the printer.

   a. Write a linear equation to compute the cost, c, of buying x posters.

   b. Use the equation to compute the cost of 125 posters.

Solution:

   a. The constant cost is $19.95. The variable cost is $1.50 per poster. If m is replaced with 1.50 and b is replaced with 19.95, the equation is

   $$c = 1.50x + 19.95 \qquad \text{where } c \text{ is the cost (in dollars) of buying } x \text{ posters.}$$

   b. Because x represents the number of posters, substitute $x = 125$.

   $$c = 1.50(125) + 19.95$$
   $$= 187.5 + 19.95$$
   $$= 207.45$$

The total cost of buying 125 posters is $207.45.

Skill Practice

3. The monthly cost for a "minimum use" cellular phone is $19.95 plus $0.10 per minute for all calls.

   a. Write a linear equation to compute the cost, c, of using t minutes.

   b. Use the equation to determine the cost of using 150 minutes.

Answers

2. a. $y = 15x + 50$ b. 200 soft drinks
3. a. $c = 0.10t + 19.95$ b. $34.95

Topic: Using the Evaluate Feature on a Graphing Calculator

In Example 3, the equation $c = 1.50x + 19.95$ was used to represent the cost, c, to buy x posters. To graph this equation on a graphing calculator, first replace the variable c by y.

$$y = 1.50x + 19.95$$

We enter the equation into the calculator and set the viewing window.

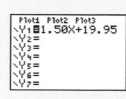 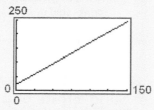

To evaluate the equation for a user-defined value of x, use the *Value* feature in the CALC menu. In this case, we entered $x = 125$, and the calculator returned $y = 207.45$.

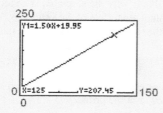

Calculator Exercises

Use a graphing calculator to graph the lines on an appropriate viewing window. Evaluate the equation at the given values of x.

1. $y = -4.6x + 27.1$ at $x = 3$

2. $y = -3.6x - 42.3$ at $x = 0$

3. $y = 40x + 105$ at $x = 6$

4. $y = 20x - 65$ at $x = 8$

Section 3.6   Practice Exercises

Study Skills Exercise

On test day, take a look at any formulas or important points that you had to memorize before you enter the classroom. Then when you sit down to take your test, write these formulas on the test or on scrap paper. This is called a memory dump. For practice write down the formulas involving slopes and equations of lines.

Review Exercises

1. Determine the slope of the line defined by $5x + 2y = -6$.

2. Determine the slope of the line defined by $2x - 8y = 15$.

For Exercises 3–8, find the x- and y-intercepts of the lines, if possible.

3. $5x + 6y = 30$

4. $3x + 4y = 1$

5. $y = -2x - 4$

6. $y = 5x$

7. $y = -9$

8. $x = 2$

256   **Chapter 3**   Graphing Linear Equations in Two Variables

Concept 1: Interpreting a Linear Equation in Two Variables

9. The minimum hourly wage, y (in dollars per hour), in the United States can be approximated by the equation $y = 0.14x + 1.60$. In this equation, x represents the number of years since 1970 ($x = 0$ represents 1970, $x = 5$ represents 1975, and so on). **(See Example 1.)**

   a. Use the equation to approximate the minimum wage in the year 1980.

   b. Use the equation to estimate the minimum wage in 2015.

   c. Determine the y-intercept. Interpret the meaning of the y-intercept in the context of this problem.

   d. Determine the slope. Interpret the meaning of the slope in the context of this problem.

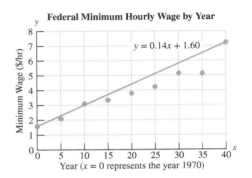

Federal Minimum Hourly Wage by Year

$y = 0.14x + 1.60$

Minimum Wage ($/hr)

Year ($x = 0$ represents the year 1970)

10. The average daily temperature in January for cities along the eastern seaboard of the United States and Canada generally decreases for cities farther north. A city's latitude in the northern hemisphere is a measure of how far north it is on the globe.

   The average temperature, y (measured in degrees Fahrenheit), can be described by the equation

   $$y = -2.333x + 124.0 \quad \text{where } x \text{ is the latitude of the city.}$$

   a. Use the equation to predict the average daily temperature in January for Philadelphia, Pennsylvania, whose latitude is 40.0°N. Round to one decimal place.

   b. Use the equation to predict the average daily temperature in January for Edmundston, New Brunswick, Canada, whose latitude is 47.4°N. Round to one decimal place.

   c. What is the slope of the line? Interpret the meaning of the slope in terms of latitude and temperature.

   d. From the equation, determine the value of the x-intercept. Round to one decimal place. Interpret the meaning of the x-intercept in terms of latitude and temperature.

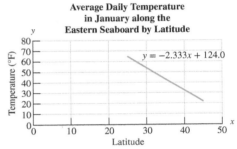

Average Daily Temperature in January along the Eastern Seaboard by Latitude

$y = -2.333x + 124.0$

Temperature (°F)

Latitude

(*Source:* U.S. National Oceanic and Atmospheric Administration)

11. Veterinarians keep records of the weights of animals that are brought in for examination. Grindel, the cat, weighed 42 oz when she was 70 days old. She weighed 46 oz when she was 84 days old. Her sister, Frisco, weighed 40 oz when she was 70 days old and 48 oz at 84 days old.

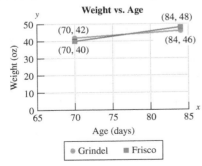

Weight vs. Age

(70, 42)   (84, 48)
(70, 40)   (84, 46)

Weight (oz)

Age (days)

● Grindel   ■ Frisco

Courtesy Rick Iossi

   a. Compute the slope of the line representing Grindel's weight.

   b. Compute the slope of the line representing Frisco's weight.

   c. Interpret the meaning of each slope in the context of this problem.

   d. Which cat gained weight more rapidly during this time period?

12. The graph depicts the rise in the number of jail inmates in the United States since 2000. Two linear equations are given: one to describe the number of female inmates and one to describe the number of male inmates by year.

Let y represent the number of inmates (in thousands). Let x represent the number of years since 2000.

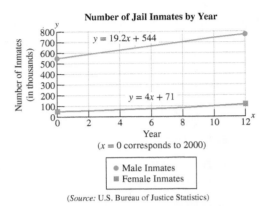

Number of Jail Inmates by Year

(*Source:* U.S. Bureau of Justice Statistics)

  a. What is the slope of the line representing the number of female inmates? Interpret the meaning of the slope in the context of this problem.

  b. What is the slope of the line representing the number of male inmates? Interpret the meaning of the slope in the context of this problem.

  c. Which group, males or females, has the larger slope? What does this imply about the rise in the number of male and female prisoners?

  d. Assuming this trend continues, use the equation to predict the number of female inmates in 2020.

13. The electric bill charge for a certain utility company is $0.095 per kilowatt-hour plus a fixed monthly tax of $11.95. The total cost, y, depends on the number of kilowatt-hours, x, according to the equation $y = 0.095x + 11.95$, $x \geq 0$.

  a. Determine the cost of using 1000 kilowatt-hours.

  b. Determine the cost of using 2000 kilowatt-hours.

  c. Determine the y-intercept. Interpret the meaning of the y-intercept in the context of this problem.

  d. Determine the slope. Interpret the meaning of the slope in the context of this problem.

14. For a recent year, children's admission to a State Fair was $8. Ride tickets were $0.75 each. The equation $y = 0.75x + 8$ represented the cost, y, in dollars to be admitted to the fair and to purchase x ride tickets.

  a. Determine the slope of the line represented by $y = 0.75x + 8$. Interpret the meaning of the slope in the context of this problem.

  b. Determine the y-intercept. Interpret its meaning in the context of this problem.

  c. Use the equation to determine how much money a child need for admission and to ride 10 rides.

Concept 2: Writing a Linear Model Using Observed Data Points

15. Meteorologists often measure the intensity of a tropical storm or hurricane by the maximum sustained wind speed and the minimum pressure. The relationship between these two quantities is approximately linear. Hurricane Katrina had a maximum sustained wind speed of 150 knots and a minimum pressure of 902 mb (millibars). Hurricane Ophelia had maximum sustained winds of 75 knots and a pressure of 976 mb. **(See Example 2.)**

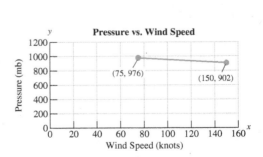

Pressure vs. Wind Speed

  a. Find the slope of the line between these two points. Round to one decimal place.

  b. Using the slope found in part (a) and the point (75, 976), find a linear model that represents the minimum pressure of a hurricane, y, versus its maximum sustained wind speed, x.

  c. Hurricane Dennis had a maximum wind speed of 130 knots. Using the equation found in part (b), predict the minimum pressure.

258   **Chapter 3**   Graphing Linear Equations in Two Variables

16. The figure depicts a relationship between a person's height, y (in inches), and the length of the person's arm, x (measured in inches from shoulder to wrist).

   a. Use the points (17, 57.75) and (24, 82.25) to find a linear equation relating height to arm length.

   b. What is the slope of the line? Interpret the slope in the context of this problem.

   c. Use the equation from part (a) to estimate the height of a person whose arm length is 21.5 in.

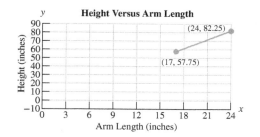

17. Wind energy is one type of renewable energy that does not produce dangerous greenhouse gases as a by-product. The graph shows the consumption of wind energy in the United States for selected years. The variable y represents the amount of wind energy in trillions of Btu, and the variable x represents the number of years since 2000.

   a. Use the points (0, 57) and (4, 143) to determine the slope of the line.

   b. Interpret the slope in the context of this problem?

   c. Use the points (0, 57) and (4, 143) to find a linear equation relating the consumption of wind energy, y, to the number of years, x, since 2000.

   d. If this linear trend continues beyond the observed data values, use the equation in part (c) to estimate the consumption of wind energy in the year 2010.

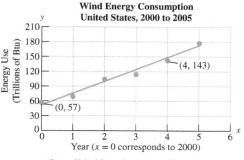

(*Source:*United States Department of Energy)

18. The graph shows the average height for boys based on age. Let x represent a boy's age, and let y represent his height (in inches).

   a. Find a linear equation that represents the height of a boy versus his age.

   b. Use the linear equation found in part (a) to predict the average height of a 5-year-old boy.

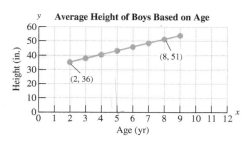

(*Source:* National Parenting Council)

Concept 3: Writing a Linear Model Given a Fixed Value and a Rate of Change

19. The owner of a restaurant franchise pays the parent company a monthly fee of $5000 plus 10% of sales. **(See Example 3.)**

   a. Write a linear model to compute the monthly payment, y, that the restaurant owner must pay the parent company for x dollars in sales.

   b. Use the equation to compute the amount that the owner has to pay if monthly sales are $11,300.

20. Anabel lives in New York and likes to keep in touch with her family in Texas. She uses 10-10-987 to call them. The cost of a long distance call is $0.83 plus $0.06 per minute.

   a. Write an equation that represents the cost, C, of a long distance call that is x minutes long.

   b. Use the equation from part (a) to compute the cost of a long distance phone call that lasted 32 minutes.

21. The cost to rent a 10 ft by 10 ft storage space is $90 per month plus a nonrefundable deposit of $105.

    a. Write a linear equation to compute the cost, y, of renting a 10 ft by 10 ft space for x months.

    b. What is the cost of renting such a storage space for 1 year (12 months)?

22. An air-conditioning and heating company has a fixed monthly cost of $5000. Furthermore, each service call costs the company $25.

    a. Write a linear equation to compute the total cost, y, for 1 month if x service calls are made.

    b. Use the equation to compute the cost for 1 month if 150 service calls are made.

23. A bakery that specializes in bread rents a booth at a flea market. The daily cost to rent the booth is $100. Each loaf of bread costs the bakery $0.80 to produce.

    a. Write a linear equation to compute the total cost, y, for 1 day if x loaves of bread are produced.

    b. Use the equation to compute the cost for 1 day if 200 loaves of bread are produced.

© Nick Gunderson/Getty Images RF

24. A beverage company rents a booth at an art show to sell lemonade. The daily cost to rent a booth is $35. Each lemonade costs $0.50 to produce.

    a. Write a linear equation to compute the total cost, y, for 1 day if x lemonades are produced.

    b. Use the equation to compute the cost for 1 day if 350 lemonades are produced.

Modeling a Linear Equation

Materials: Yardstick or other device for making linear measurements

Estimated Time: 15–20 minutes

Group Size: 3

1. The members of each group should measure the length of their arms (in inches) from elbow to wrist. Record this measurement as x and the person's height (in inches) as y. Write these values as ordered pairs for each member of the group. Then write the ordered pairs on the board.

2. Next, copy the ordered pairs collected from all groups in the class and plot the ordered pairs. (This is called a "scatter diagram.")

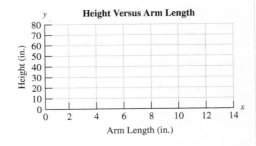

260   **Chapter 3**   Graphing Linear Equations in Two Variables

3. Select two ordered pairs that seem to follow the upward trend of the data. Using these data points, determine the slope of the line.

Slope: _____

4. Using the data points and slope from question 3, find an equation of the line through the two points. Write the equation in slope-intercept form, $y = mx + b$.

Equation: _____

5. Using the equation from question 4, estimate the height of a person whose arm length from elbow to wrist is 8.5 in.

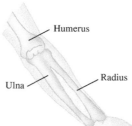

6. Suppose a crime scene investigator uncovers a partial skeleton and identifies a bone as a human ulna (the ulna is one of two bones in the forearm and extends from elbow to wrist). If the length of the bone is 12 in., estimate the height of the person before death. Would you expect this person to be male or female?

Chapter 3   Summary

Section 3.1   Rectangular Coordinate System

Key Concepts

Graphical representation of numerical data is often helpful to study problems in real-world applications.

A **rectangular coordinate system** is made up of a horizontal line called the **x-axis** and a vertical line called the **y-axis**. The point where the lines meet is the **origin**. The four regions of the plane are called **quadrants**.

The point (x, y) is an **ordered pair**. The first element in the ordered pair is the point's horizontal position from the origin. The second element in the ordered pair is the point's vertical position from the origin.

Example

Example 1

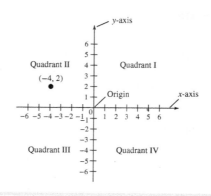

Section 3.2   Linear Equations in Two Variables

Key Concepts

An equation written in the form $Ax + By = C$ (where A and B are not both zero) is a **linear equation in two variables**.

A solution to a linear equation in x and y is an ordered pair (x, y) that makes the equation a true statement. The graph of the set of all solutions of a linear equation in two variables is a line in a rectangular coordinate system.

A linear equation can be graphed by finding at least two solutions and graphing the line through the points.

Examples

Example 1

Graph the equation $2x + y = 2$.

Select arbitrary values of x or y such as those shown in the table. Then complete the table to find the corresponding ordered pairs.

x	y	
0	2	→ (0, 2)
−1	4	→ (−1, 4)
1	0	→ (1, 0)

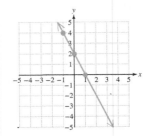

An **x-intercept** of a graph is a point $(a, 0)$ where the graph intersects the x-axis.
To find the x-intercept, let $y = 0$ and solve for x.
A **y-intercept** of a graph is a point $(0, b)$ where the graph intersects the y-axis.
To find the y-intercept, let $x = 0$ and solve for y.

Example 2

For the line $2x + y = 2$, find the x- and y-intercepts.

x-intercept	y-intercept
$2x + (0) = 2$	$2(0) + y = 2$
$2x = 2$	$0 + y = 2$
$x = 1$	$y = 2$
$(1, 0)$	$(0, 2)$

A **vertical line** can be represented by an equation of the form $x = k$.
A **horizontal line** can be represented by an equation of the form $y = k$.

Example 3

$x = 3$ represents a vertical line

$y = 3$ represents a horizontal line

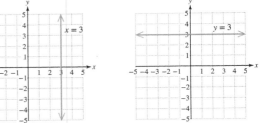

Section 3.3   Slope of a Line and Rate of Change

Key Concepts

The **slope**, m, of a line between two points (x_1, y_1) and (x_2, y_2) is given by

$$m = \frac{y_2 - y_1}{x_2 - x_1} \quad \text{or} \quad \frac{\text{change in } y}{\text{change in } x}$$

The slope of a line may be positive, negative, zero, or undefined.

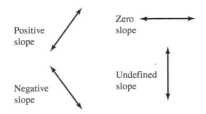

Positive slope

Zero slope

Negative slope

Undefined slope

If m_1 and m_2 represent the slopes of two **parallel lines** (nonvertical), then $m_1 = m_2$.

If $m_1 \neq 0$ and $m_2 \neq 0$ represent the slopes of two nonvertical **perpendicular lines**, then

$$m_1 = -\frac{1}{m_2} \text{ or equivalently, } m_1 m_2 = -1.$$

Examples

Example 1

Find the slope of the line between $(1, -5)$ and $(-3, 7)$.

$$m = \frac{7 - (-5)}{-3 - 1} = \frac{12}{-4} = -3$$

Example 2

The slope of the line $y = -2$ is 0 because the line is horizontal.

Example 3

The slope of the line $x = 4$ is undefined because the line is vertical.

Example 4

The slopes of two distinct lines are given. Determine whether the lines are parallel, perpendicular, or neither.

a. $m_1 = -7$ and $m_2 = -7$ Parallel

b. $m_1 = -\dfrac{1}{5}$ and $m_2 = 5$ Perpendicular

c. $m_1 = -\dfrac{3}{2}$ and $m_2 = -\dfrac{2}{3}$ Neither

Summary   **263**

Section 3.4 Slope-Intercept Form of a Linear Equation

Key Concepts

The **slope-intercept form** of a linear equation is

$$y = mx + b$$

where m is the slope of the line and $(0, b)$ is the y-intercept.

Slope-intercept form is used to identify the slope and y-intercept of a line when the equation is given.

Slope-intercept form can also be used to graph a line.

Examples

Example 1

Find the slope and y-intercept.

$$7x - 2y = 4$$
$$-2y = -7x + 4 \qquad \text{Solve for } y.$$
$$\frac{-2y}{-2} = \frac{-7x}{-2} + \frac{4}{-2}$$
$$y = \frac{7}{2}x - 2$$

The slope is $\frac{7}{2}$. The y-intercept is $(0, -2)$.

Example 2

Graph the line.

$$y = \frac{7}{2}x - 2$$

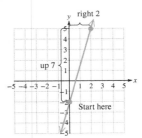

Section 3.5 Point-Slope Formula

Key Concepts

The **point-slope formula** is used primarily to construct an equation of a line given a point and the slope.

Equations of Lines—A Summary:

Standard form: $Ax + By = C$
Horizontal line: $y = k$
Vertical line: $x = k$
Slope-intercept form: $y = mx + b$
Point-slope formula: $y - y_1 = m(x - x_1)$

Example

Example 1

Find an equation of the line passing through the point $(6, -4)$ and having a slope of $-\frac{1}{2}$.

Label the given information:
$m = -\frac{1}{2}$ and $(x_1, y_1) = (6, -4)$

$$y - y_1 = m(x - x_1)$$
$$y - (-4) = -\frac{1}{2}(x - 6)$$
$$y + 4 = -\frac{1}{2}x + 3$$
$$y = -\frac{1}{2}x - 1$$

Section 3.6   Applications of Linear Equations and Modeling

Key Concepts

Linear equations can often be used to describe or model the relationship between variables in a real-world event. In such applications, the slope may be interpreted as a rate of change.

Example

Example 1

The number of drug-related arrests for a small city has been growing approximately linearly since 1985.

    Let y represent the number of drug arrests, and let x represent the number of years after 1985.

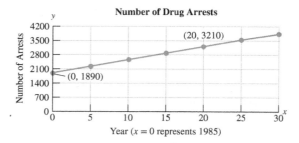

Number of Drug Arrests

Year ($x = 0$ represents 1985)

a. Use the ordered pairs $(0, 1890)$ and $(20, 3210)$ to find an equation of the line shown in the graph.

$$m = \frac{y_2 - y_1}{x_2 - x_1} = \frac{3210 - 1890}{20 - 0}$$

$$= \frac{1320}{20} = 66$$

The slope is 66, indicating that the number of drug arrests is increasing at a rate of 66 per year.
$m = 66$, and the y-intercept is $(0, 1890)$. Thus,

$$y = mx + b \quad \Rightarrow \quad y = 66x + 1890$$

b. Use the equation in part (a) to estimate the number of drug-related arrests in the year 2015. (The year 2015 is 30 years after 1985. Hence, $x = 30$.)

$$y = 66(30) + 1890$$

$$y = 3870$$

For the year 2015, the number of drug arrests was approximately 3870.

Chapter 3   Review Exercises

Section 3.1

1. Graph the points on a rectangular coordinate system.

a. $\left(\dfrac{1}{2}, 5\right)$ **b.** $(-1, 4)$ **c.** $(2, -1)$

d. $(0, 3)$ **e.** $(0, 0)$ **f.** $\left(-\dfrac{8}{5}, 0\right)$

g. $(-2, -5)$ **h.** $(3, 1)$

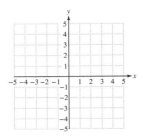

2. Estimate the coordinates of the points A, B, C, D, E, and F.

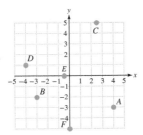

For Exercises 3–8, determine the quadrant in which the given point is located.

3. $(-2, -10)$ **4.** $(-4, 6)$

5. $(3, -5)$ **6.** $\left(\dfrac{1}{2}, \dfrac{7}{5}\right)$

7. $(\pi, -2.7)$ **8.** $(-1.2, -6.8)$

9. On which axis is the point $(2, 0)$ located?

10. On which axis is the point $(0, -3)$ located?

11. The price per share of a stock (in dollars) over a period of 5 days is shown in the graph.

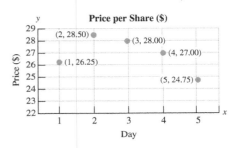

a. Interpret the meaning of the ordered pair $(1, 26.25)$.

b. On which day was the price the highest?

c. What was the increase in price between day 1 and day 2?

12. The number of space shuttle launches for selected years is given by the ordered pairs. Let x represent the number of years since 1995. Let y represent the number of launches.

$(1, 7)$ $(2, 8)$ $(3, 5)$ $(4, 3)$

$(5, 5)$ $(6, 6)$ $(7, 5)$ $(8, 1)$

a. Interpret the meaning of the ordered pair $(8, 1)$.

b. Plot the points on a rectangular coordinate system.

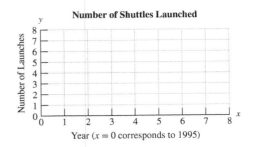

Section 3.2

For Exercises 13–16, determine if the given ordered pair is a solution to the equation.

13. $5x - 3y = 12;$ $(0, 4)$

14. $2x - 4y = -6;$ $(3, 0)$

15. $y = \dfrac{1}{3}x - 2;$ $(9, 1)$

16. $y = -\dfrac{2}{5}x + 1;$ $(-10, 5)$

For Exercises 17–20, complete the table and graph the corresponding ordered pairs. Graph the line through the points to represent all solutions to the equation.

17. $3x - y = 5$

x	y
2	
	4
1	

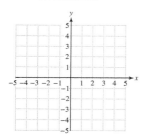

18. $\dfrac{1}{2}x + 3y = 6$

x	y
	2
-2	
	3

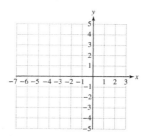

19. $y = \dfrac{2}{3}x - 1$

x	y
0	
3	
-6	

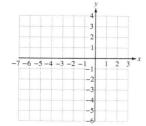

20. $y = -2x - 3$

x	y
0	
-3	
1	

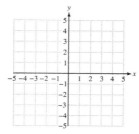

For Exercises 21–24, graph the equation.

21. $x + 2y = 4$

22. $x - y = 5$

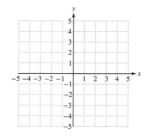
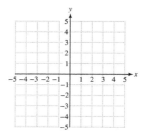

23. $y = 3x$

24. $y = \dfrac{1}{4}x$

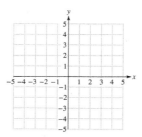
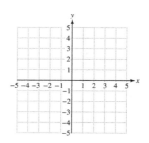

For Exercises 25–28, identify the line as horizontal or vertical. Then graph the equation.

25. $3x - 2 = 10$

26. $2x + 1 = -2$

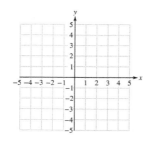
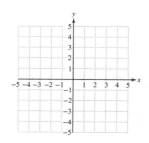

27. $6y + 1 = 13$

28. $5y - 1 = 14$

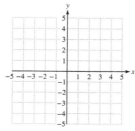
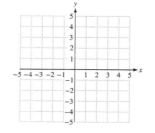

For Exercises 29–36, find the x- and y-intercepts if they exist.

29. $-4x + 8y = 12$

30. $2x + y = 6$

31. $y = 8x$

32. $5x - y = 0$

33. $6y = -24$

34. $2y - 3 = 1$

35. $2x + 5 = 0$

36. $-3x + 1 = 0$

Section 3.3

37. What is the slope of the ladder leaning up against the wall?

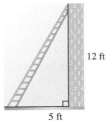

12 ft

5 ft

38. Point A is located 4 units down and 2 units to the right of point B. What is the slope of the line through points A and B?

39. Determine the slope of the line that passes through the points $(7, -9)$ and $(-5, -1)$.

40. Determine the slope of the line that has x- and y-intercepts of $(-1, 0)$ and $(0, 8)$.

41. Determine the slope of the line that passes through the points $(3, 0)$ and $(3, -7)$.

42. Determine the slope of the line given by $y = -1$.

43. A given line has a slope of -5.

   a. What is the slope of a line parallel to the given line?

   b. What is the slope of a line perpendicular to the given line?

44. A given line has a slope of 0.

   a. What is the slope of a line parallel to the given line?

   b. What is the slope of a line perpendicular to the given line?

For Exercises 45–48, find the slopes of the lines l_1 and l_2 from the two given points. Then determine whether l_1 and l_2 are parallel, perpendicular, or neither.

45. l_1: $(3, 7)$ and $(0, 5)$

   l_2: $(6, 3)$ and $(-3, -3)$

46. l_1: $(-2, 1)$ and $(-1, 9)$

   l_2: $(0, -6)$ and $(2, 10)$

47. l_1: $(0, \frac{5}{6})$ and $(2, 0)$

   l_2: $(0, \frac{6}{5})$ and $(-\frac{1}{2}, 0)$

48. l_1: $(1, 1)$ and $(1, -8)$

   l_2: $(4, -5)$ and $(7, -5)$

49. Carol's electric bill had an initial reading of 35,955 kilowatt-hours at the beginning of the month. At the end of the month the reading was 37,005 kilowatt-hours. Let x represent the day of the month and y represent the reading on the meter in kilowatt-hours.

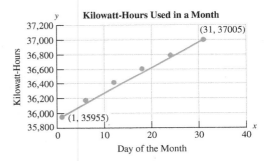

   a. Using the ordered pairs $(1, 35955)$ and $(31, 37005)$, find the slope of the line.

   b. Interpret the slope in the context of this problem.

50. New car sales were recorded over a 5-yr period in Maryland. Let x represent the year and y represent the number of new cars sold.

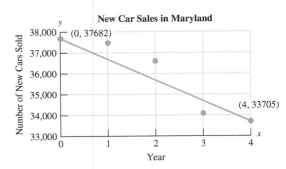

   a. Using the ordered pairs $(0, 37682)$ and $(4, 33705)$, find the slope of the line. Round to the nearest whole unit.

   b. Interpret the slope in the context of this problem.

268 **Chapter 3** Graphing Linear Equations in Two Variables

Section 3.4

For Exercises 51–56, write each equation in slope-intercept form. Identify the slope and the y-intercept.

51. $5x - 2y = 10$

52. $3x + 4y = 12$

53. $x - 3y = 0$

54. $5y - 8 = 4$

55. $2y = -5$

56. $y - x = 0$

For Exercises 57–62, determine whether the equations represent parallel lines, perpendicular lines, or neither.

57. l_1: $y = \frac{3}{5}x + 3$

l_2: $y = \frac{5}{3}x + 1$

58. l_1: $2x - 5y = 10$

l_2: $5x + 2y = 20$

59. l_1: $3x + 2y = 6$

l_2: $-6x - 4y = 4$

60. l_1: $y = \frac{1}{4}x - 3$

l_2: $-x + 4y = 8$

61. l_1: $2x = 4$

l_2: $y = 6$

62. l_1: $y = \frac{2}{9}x + 4$

l_2: $y = \frac{9}{2}x - 3$

63. Write an equation of the line whose slope is $-\frac{4}{3}$ and whose y-intercept is $(0, -1)$.

64. Write an equation of the line that passes through the origin and has a slope of 5.

65. Write an equation of the line with slope $-\frac{4}{3}$ that passes through the point $(-6, 2)$.

66. Write an equation of the line with slope 5 that passes through the point $(-1, -8)$.

Section 3.5

67. Write a linear equation in two variables in slope-intercept form. (Answers may vary.)

68. Write a linear equation in two variables in standard form. (Answers may vary.)

69. Write the slope formula to find the slope of the line between the points (x_1, y_1) and (x_2, y_2).

70. Write the point-slope formula.

71. Write an equation of a vertical line (answers may vary).

72. Write an equation of a horizontal line (answers may vary).

For Exercises 73–78, write an equation of a line given the following information.

73. The slope is -6, and the line passes through the point $(-1, 8)$.

74. The slope is $\frac{2}{3}$, and the line passes through the point $(5, 5)$.

75. The line passes through the points $(0, -4)$ and $(8, -2)$.

76. The line passes through the points $(2, -5)$ and $(8, -5)$.

77. The line passes through the point $(5, 12)$ and is perpendicular to the line $y = -\frac{5}{6}x - 3$.

78. The line passes through the point $(-6, 7)$ and is parallel to the line $4x - y = 0$.

Section 3.6

79. The graph shows the average height for girls based on age (*Source:* National Parenting Council). Let x represent a girl's age, and let y represent her height (in inches).

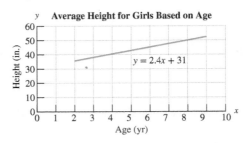

a. Use the equation to estimate the average height of a 7-year-old girl.

b. What is the slope of the line? Interpret the meaning of the slope in the context of the problem.

80. The number of drug prescriptions increased between 2000 and 2010 (see graph). Let x represent the number of years since 2000. Let y represent the number of prescriptions (in millions).

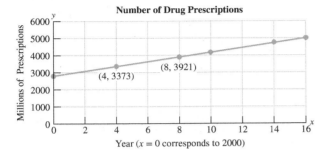

Number of Drug Prescriptions

Year ($x = 0$ corresponds to 2000)

a. Using the ordered pairs (4, 3373) and (8, 3921) find the slope of the line.

b. Interpret the meaning of the slope in the context of this problem.

c. Find a linear equation that represents the number of prescriptions, y, versus the number of years, x, since 2000.

d. Use the equation from part (c) to estimate the number of prescriptions for the year 2015.

81. A water purification company charges $20 per month and a $55 installation fee.

a. Write a linear equation to compute the total cost, y, of renting this system for x months.

b. Use the equation from part (a) to determine the total cost to rent the system for 9 months.

82. A small cleaning company has a fixed monthly cost of $700 and a variable cost of $8 per service call.

a. Write a linear equation to compute the total cost, y, of making x service calls in one month.

b. Use the equation from part (a) to determine the total cost of making 80 service calls.

Chapter 3   Test

1. In which quadrant is the given point located?

   a. $\left(-\dfrac{7}{2}, 4\right)$ **b.** $(4.6, -2)$ **c.** $(-37, -45)$

2. What is the y-coordinate for a point on the x-axis?

3. What is the x-coordinate for a point on the y-axis?

4. Bamboo is the fastest growing woody plant on earth. At a bamboo farm, the height of a black bamboo plant (phyllostachys nigra) is measured for selected days. Let x represent the day number and y represent the height of the plant.

Day, x	Height (inches), y
4	14
8	28
12	42
16	56
20	70

a. Write the data as ordered pairs and interpret the meaning of the first ordered pair.

b. Graph the ordered pairs on a rectangular coordinate system.

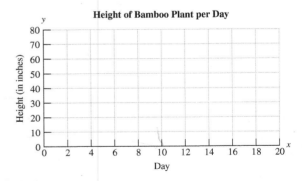

Height of Bamboo Plant per Day

Day

c. From the graph, estimate the height of the bamboo plant after 10 days.

5. Determine whether the ordered pair is a solution to the equation $2x - y = 6$.

   a. $(0, 6)$ **b.** $(4, 2)$

   c. $(3, 0)$ **d.** $\left(\dfrac{9}{2}, 3\right)$

6. Given the equation $y = \frac{1}{4}x - 2$, complete the table. Plot the ordered pairs and graph the line through the points to represent the set of all solutions to the equation.

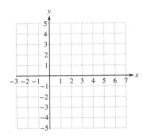

x	y
0	
4	
6	

For Exercises 7–10, graph the equations.

7. $y = 3x + 2$

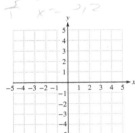

8. $2x + 5y = 0$

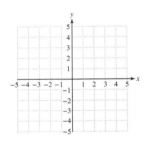

9. $3x + 2y = 8$

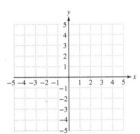

10. $y = \frac{3}{4}x - 2$

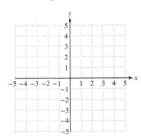

For Exercises 11–12, determine whether the equation represents a horizontal or vertical line. Then graph the line.

11. $-6y = 18$

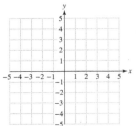

12. $5x + 1 = 8$

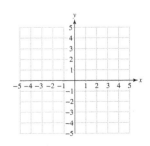

For Exercises 13–16, determine the x- and y-intercepts if they exist.

13. $-4x + 3y = 6$

14. $2y = 6x$

15. $x = 4$

16. $y - 3 = 0$

17. What is the slope of the hill?

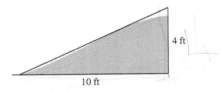

4 ft

10 ft

18. a. Find the slope of the line that passes through the points $(-2, 0)$ and $(-5, -1)$.

b. Find the slope of the line $4x - 3y = 9$.

19. a. What is the slope of a line parallel to the line $x + 4y = -16$?

b. What is the slope of a line perpendicular to the line $x + 4y = -16$?

20. a. What is the slope of the line $x = 5$?

b. What is the slope of the line $y = -3$?

21. Carlos called a local truck rental company and got quotes for renting a truck. He was told that it would cost $41.95 to rent a truck for one day to travel 20 miles. It costs $89.95 to rent the truck for one day to travel 100 miles. Let x represent the number of miles driven and y represent the cost of the rental.

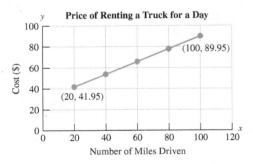

Price of Renting a Truck for a Day

a. Using the ordered pairs (20, 41.95) and (100, 89.95), find the slope of the line.

b. Interpret the slope in the context of this problem.

22. Determine whether the lines through the given points are parallel, perpendicular, or neither.

l_1: $(1, 4), (-1, -2)$ l_2: $(0, -5), (-2, -11)$

23. Determine whether the equations represent parallel lines, perpendicular lines, or neither.

l_1: $2y = 3x - 3$ l_2: $4x = -6y + 1$

24. Write an equation of the line that passes through the point $(3, 0)$ and is parallel to the line $2x + 6y = -5$.

25. Write an equation of the line that passes through the points $(2, 8)$ and $(4, 1)$.

26. Write an equation of the line that has y-intercept $(0, \frac{1}{2})$ and slope $\frac{1}{4}$.

27. Write an equation of the line that passes through the point $(-3, -1)$ and is perpendicular to the line $x + 3y = 9$.

28. Write an equation of the line that passes through the point $(2, -6)$ and is parallel to the x-axis.

29. Write an equation of the line that has slope -1 and passes through the point $(-5, 2)$.

30. To attend a state fair, the cost is $10 per person to cover exhibits and musical entertainment. There is an additional cost of $1.50 per ride.

 a. Write an equation that gives the total cost, y, of visiting the state fair and going on x rides.

 b. Use the equation from part (a) to determine the cost of going to the state fair and going on 10 rides.

31. The number of medical doctors for selected years is shown in the graph. Let x represent the number of years since 1980, and let y represent the number of medical doctors (in thousands) in the United States.

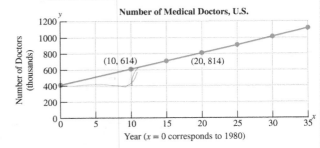

Number of Medical Doctors, U.S.

 a. Find the slope of the line shown in the graph. Interpret the meaning of the slope in the context of this problem.

 b. Find an equation of the line.

 c. Use the equation from part (b) to estimate the number of medical doctors in the United States for the year 2015.

Chapters 1–3 Cumulative Review Exercises

1. Identify the number as rational or irrational.

 a. -3 **b.** $\frac{5}{4}$ **c.** $\sqrt{10}$ **d.** 0

2. Write the opposite and the absolute value for each number.

 a. $-\frac{2}{3}$ **b.** 5.3

3. Simplify the expression using the order of operations. $32 \div 2 \cdot 4 + 5$

4. Add. $3 + (-8) + 2 + (-10)$

5. Subtract. $16 - 5 - (-7)$

For Exercises 6–7, translate the English phrase into an algebraic expression. Then evaluate the expression.

6. The quotient of $\frac{3}{4}$ and $-\frac{7}{8}$

7. The product of -2.1 and -6

8. Name the property that is illustrated by the following statement. $6 + (8 + 2) = (6 + 8) + 2$

272   **Chapter 3**   Graphing Linear Equations in Two Variables

For Exercises 9–12, solve each equation.

9. $6x - 10 = 14$ **10.** $3(m + 2) - 3 = 2m + 8$

11. $\dfrac{2}{3}y - \dfrac{1}{6} = y + \dfrac{4}{3}$ **12.** $1.7z + 2 = -2(0.3z + 1.3)$

13. The area of Texas is 267,277 mi^2. If this is 712 mi^2 less than 29 times the area of Maine, find the area of Maine.

14. For the formula $3a + b = c$, solve for a.

15. Graph the equation $-6x + 2y = 0$.

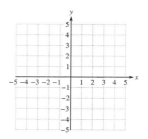

16. Find the x- and y-intercepts of $-2x + 4y = 4$.

17. Write the equation in slope-intercept form. Then identify the slope and y-intercept. $3x + 2y = -12$

18. Explain why the line $2x + 3 = 5$ has only one intercept.

19. Find an equation of a line passing through $(2, -5)$ with slope -3.

20. Find an equation of the line passing through $(0, 6)$ and $(-3, 4)$.

Systems of Linear Equations in Two Variables

Systems of Linear Equations in Two Variables

4

Mathematics in Business

Suppose that you have been invited to an end-of-semester party. You ask your friend for directions and she says, "It's on Earl Street and 10th Avenue." If we think of Earl Street and 10th Avenue as lines, then we know that the house is located where these lines intersect. In mathematics, we call these intersections **solutions** to **systems of linear equations**. Furthermore, the applications of systems of linear equations are numerous.

Imagine that the total price of buying a shirt and a tie is normally $42. If the items are on sale and priced at 60% and 90% of the original values, respectively, then the total cost is $30. To determine the original cost s of a single shirt and the original cost t of a single tie, we can set up a system of two equations.

© Lissa Harrison

Original Price: $s + t = 42$
Discounted Price: $0.60s + 0.90t = 30$

With techniques you will learn in this chapter, you can determine that the solution to this system is (26, 16). This means that the ordered pair (26, 16) satisfies both equations and that the point (26, 16) is a point of intersection of the lines defined by the equations in the system. The solution also tells us that the original cost of a shirt is $26 and the original cost of a tie is $16.

In this chapter, you will learn that some systems of linear equations have no solution, indicating that the related lines never intersect. This is similar to parallel streets that never meet. Other systems of linear equations may have infinitely many solutions. This occurs if the equations represent the same line.

274 **Chapter 4** Systems of Linear Equations in Two Variables

---

| Section 4.1 | **Solving Systems of Equations by the Graphing Method** |

Concepts

1. Solutions to a System of Linear Equations
2. Solving Systems of Linear Equations by Graphing

1. Solutions to a System of Linear Equations

Recall that a linear equation in two variables has an infinite number of solutions. The set of all solutions to a linear equation forms a line in a rectangular coordinate system. Two or more linear equations form a **system of linear equations**. For example, here are three systems of equations:

$$x - 3y = -5 \qquad\qquad y = \tfrac{1}{4}x - \tfrac{3}{4} \qquad\qquad 5a + b = 4$$
$$2x + 4y = 10 \qquad\qquad -2x + 8y = -6 \qquad\qquad -10a - 2b = 8$$

A **solution to a system of linear equations** is an ordered pair that is a solution to *both* individual linear equations.

| Example 1 | **Determining Solutions to a System of Linear Equations** |

Determine whether the ordered pairs are solutions to the system.

$$x + y = 4$$
$$-2x + y = -5$$

a. $(3, 1)$ **b.** $(0, 4)$

Solution:

a. Substitute the ordered pair $(3, 1)$ into both equations:

$$x + y = 4 \longrightarrow (3) + (1) \stackrel{?}{=} 4 \checkmark \qquad \text{True}$$
$$-2x + y = -5 \longrightarrow -2(3) + (1) \stackrel{?}{=} -5 \checkmark \qquad \text{True}$$

Avoiding Mistakes

It is important to test an ordered pair in *both* equations to determine if the ordered pair is a solution.

Because the ordered pair $(3, 1)$ is a solution to both equations, it is a solution to the *system* of equations.

b. Substitute the ordered pair $(0, 4)$ into both equations.

$$x + y = 4 \longrightarrow (0) + (4) \stackrel{?}{=} 4 \checkmark \qquad \text{True}$$
$$-2x + y = -5 \longrightarrow -2(0) + (4) \stackrel{?}{=} -5 \qquad \text{False}$$

Because the ordered pair $(0, 4)$ is not a solution to the second equation, it is *not* a solution to the system of equations.

Skill Practice Determine whether the ordered pair is a solution to the system.

$$5x - 2y = 24$$
$$2x + y = 6$$

1. $(6, 3)$ **2.** $(4, -2)$

A solution to a system of two linear equations can be interpreted graphically as a point of intersection of the two lines. Using slope-intercept form to graph the lines from Example 1, we have

Answers

1. No
2. Yes

$$l_1: \qquad x + y = 4 \longrightarrow y = -x + 4$$
$$l_2: \quad -2x + y = -5 \longrightarrow y = 2x - 5$$

All points on l_1 are solutions to the equation $y = -x + 4$.

All points on l_2 are solutions to the equation $y = 2x - 5$.

The point of intersection $(3, 1)$ is the only point that is a solution to both equations. (See Figure 4-1.)

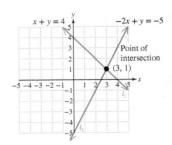

Figure 4-1

When two lines are drawn in a rectangular coordinate system, three geometric relationships are possible:

1. Two lines may intersect at *exactly one point*.

2. Two lines may intersect at *no point*. This occurs if the lines are parallel.

3. Two lines may intersect at *infinitely many points* along the line. This occurs if the equations represent the same line (the lines coincide).

If a system of linear equations has one or more solutions, the system is said to be **consistent**. If a system of linear equations has no solution, it is said to be **inconsistent**.

If two equations represent the same line, the equations are said to be **dependent equations**. In this case, all points on the line are solutions to the system. If two equations represent two different lines, the equations are said to be **independent equations**. In this case, the lines either intersect at one point or are parallel.

Solutions to Systems of Linear Equations in Two Variables

One Unique Solution	No Solution	Infinitely Many Solutions
One point of intersection	Parallel lines	Coinciding lines
• System is consistent.	• System is inconsistent.	• System is consistent.
• Equations are independent.	• Equations are independent.	• Equations are dependent.

---

2. Solving Systems of Linear Equations by Graphing

One way to find a solution to a system of equations is to graph the equations and find the point (or points) of intersection. This is called the *graphing method* to solve a system of equations.

| **Example 2** | **Solving a System of Linear Equations by Graphing** |

Solve the system by the graphing method. $y = 2x$

$y = 2$

Solution:

The equation $y = 2x$ is written in slope-intercept form as $y = 2x + 0$. The line passes through the origin, with a slope of 2.

The line $y = 2$ is a horizontal line and has a slope of 0.

Because the lines have different slopes, the lines must be different and nonparallel. From this, we know that the lines must intersect at exactly one point. Graph the lines to find the point of intersection (Figure 4-2).

The point (1, 2) appears to be the point of intersection. This can be confirmed by substituting $x = 1$ and $y = 2$ into both original equations.

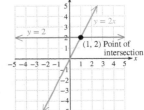

Figure 4-2

$$y = 2x \qquad (2) \overset{?}{=} 2(1)\checkmark \quad \text{True}$$

$$y = 2 \qquad (2) \overset{?}{=} 2\checkmark \qquad \text{True}$$

The solution set is $\{(1, 2)\}$.

Skill Practice Solve the system by the graphing method.

3. $y = -3x$

$x = -1$

| **Example 3** | **Solving a System of Linear Equations by Graphing** |

Solve the system by the graphing method.

$$x - 2y = -2$$

$$-3x + 2y = 6$$

Solution:

One method to graph the lines is to write each equation in slope-intercept form, $y = mx + b$.

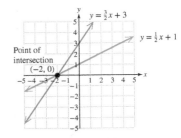

Figure 4-3

Equation 1

$x - 2y = -2$

$-2y = -x - 2$

$\dfrac{-2y}{-2} = \dfrac{-x}{-2} - \dfrac{2}{-2}$

$y = \dfrac{1}{2}x + 1$

Equation 2

$-3x + 2y = 6$

$2y = 3x + 6$

$\dfrac{2y}{2} = \dfrac{3x}{2} + \dfrac{6}{2}$

$y = \dfrac{3}{2}x + 3$

From their slope-intercept forms, we see that the lines have different slopes, indicating that the lines are different and nonparallel. Therefore, the lines must intersect at exactly one point. Graph the lines to find that point (Figure 4-3).

Answer

3. $\{(-1, 3)\}$

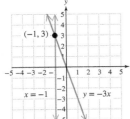

The point $(-2, 0)$ appears to be the point of intersection. This can be confirmed by substituting $x = -2$ and $y = 0$ into both equations.

$$x - 2y = -2 \longrightarrow (-2) - 2(0) \overset{?}{=} -2 \checkmark \quad \text{True}$$

$$-3x + 2y = 6 \longrightarrow -3(-2) + 2(0) \overset{?}{=} 6 \checkmark \quad \text{True}$$

The solution set is $\{(-2, 0)\}$.

Skill Practice   **Solve the system by the graphing method.**

4. $y = 2x - 3$
   $6x + 2y = 4$

> **TIP:** In Examples 2 and 3, the lines could also have been graphed by using the
> x- and y-intercepts or by using a table of points. However, the advantage of writing the
> equations in slope-intercept form is that we can compare the slopes and y-intercepts of
> the two lines.
>
>   **1.** If the slopes differ, the lines are different and nonparallel and must intersect at
>   exactly one point.
>
>   **2.** If the slopes are the same and the y-intercepts are different, the lines are parallel
>   and will not intersect.
>
>   **3.** If the slopes are the same and the y-intercepts are the same, the two equations
>   represent the same line.

Example 4   **Graphing an Inconsistent System**

Solve the system by graphing.

$$-x + 3y = -6$$
$$6y = 2x + 6$$

Solution:

To graph the lines, write each equation in slope-intercept form.

Equation 1

$-x + 3y = -6$

$3y = x - 6$

$\dfrac{3y}{3} = \dfrac{x}{3} - \dfrac{6}{3}$

$y = \dfrac{1}{3}x - 2$

Equation 2

$6y = 2x + 6$

$\dfrac{6y}{6} = \dfrac{2x}{6} + \dfrac{6}{6}$

$y = \dfrac{1}{3}x + 1$

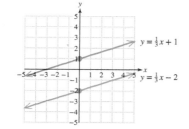

Figure 4-4

Because the lines have the same slope but different y-intercepts, they are parallel (Figure 4-4). Two parallel lines do not intersect, which implies that the system has no solution. Therefore, the solution set is the empty set, { }. The system is inconsistent.

Skill Practice Solve the system by graphing.

5. $4x + y = 8$
   $y = -4x + 3$

Answers

4. $\{(1, -1)\}$

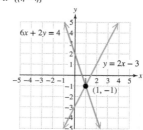

5.

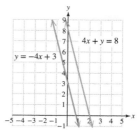

{ } The lines are parallel. The system is inconsistent.

| Example 5 | **Graphing a System of Dependent Equations** |

Solve the system by graphing. $x + 4y = 8$

$$y = -\frac{1}{4}x + 2$$

Solution:

Write the first equation in slope-intercept form. The second equation is already in slope-intercept form.

Equation 1

$x + 4y = 8$

$$4y = -x + 8$$

$$\frac{4y}{4} = \frac{-x}{4} + \frac{8}{4}$$

$$y = -\frac{1}{4}x + 2$$

Equation 2

$$y = -\frac{1}{4}x + 2$$

Figure 4-5

> **TIP:** The solution set to a system of dependent equations uses set-builder notation to describe the common line of intersection. Any form of the equation can be used. For example, in Example 5, we show the equation written in slope-intercept form and in standard form.
>
> $$\left\{ (x, y) \,\middle|\, y = -\frac{1}{4}x + 2 \right\}$$
>
> or
>
> $$\{(x, y) \mid x + 4y = 8\}$$

Notice that the slope-intercept forms of the two lines are identical. Therefore, the equations represent the same line (Figure 4-5). The equations are dependent, and the solution to the system of equations is the set of all points on the line.

Because there are infinitely many points on the line, the ordered pairs in the solution set cannot all be listed. Therefore, we can write the solution in set-builder notation: $\{(x, y) \mid y = -\frac{1}{4}x + 2\}$. This can be read as "the set of all ordered pairs (x, y) such that the ordered pairs satisfy the equation $y = -\frac{1}{4}x + 2$."

In summary:

- There are infinitely many solutions to the system of equations.
- The solution set is $\{(x, y) \mid y = -\frac{1}{4}x + 2\}$, or equivalently $\{(x, y) \mid x + 4y = 8\}$.
- The equations are dependent.

Skill Practice   Solve the system by graphing.

6. $x - 3y = 6$

$$y = \frac{1}{3}x - 2$$

Answer

6.

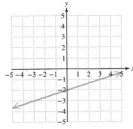

$$\left\{ (x, y) \,\middle|\, y = \frac{1}{3}x - 2 \right\}$$

The equations are dependent.

Calculator Connections

Topic: Graphing Systems of Linear Equations in Two Variables

The solution to a system of equations can be found by using either a *Trace* feature or an *Intersect* feature on a graphing calculator to find the point of intersection of two graphs.

For example, consider the system:

$$-2x + y = 6$$
$$5x + y = -1$$

First graph the equations together on the same viewing window. Recall that to enter the equations into the calculator, the equations must be written with the y variable isolated.

$$-2x + y = 6 \xrightarrow{\text{Isolate } y.} y = 2x + 6$$
$$5x + y = -1 \longrightarrow y = -5x - 1$$

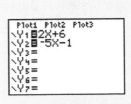 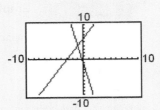

By inspection of the graph, it appears that the solution is $(-1, 4)$. The *Trace* option on the calculator may come close to $(-1, 4)$ but may not show the exact solution (Figure 4-6). However, an *Intersect* feature on a graphing calculator may provide the exact solution (Figure 4-7).

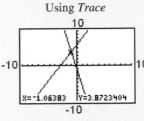

Figure 4-6   Figure 4-7

Calculator Exercises

Use a graphing calculator to graph each pair of linear equations on the same viewing window. Use a *Trace* or *Intersect* feature to find the point(s) of intersection. Then write the solution set.

1. $y = 2x - 3$
$y = -4x + 9$

2. $y = -\dfrac{1}{2}x + 2$

$y = \dfrac{1}{3}x - 3$

3. $x + y = 4$ (Example 1)
$-2x + y = -5$

4. $x - 2y = -2$ (Example 3)
$-3x + 2y = 6$

5. $-x + 3y = -6$ (Example 4)
$6y = 2x + 6$

6. $x + 4y = 8$ (Example 5)
$y = -\dfrac{1}{4}x + 2$

Section 4.1   Practice Exercises

Study Skills Exercise

It is important to keep track of your grade throughout the semester. Take a minute to compute your grade at this point. Are you earning the grade that you want? If not, maybe organizing a study group would help.

In a study group, check the activities that you might try to help you learn and understand the material.

_____ Quiz each other by asking each other questions.

_____ Practice teaching each other.

_____ Share and compare class notes.

_____ Support and encourage each other.

_____ Work together on exercises and sample problems.

280   **Chapter 4** Systems of Linear Equations in Two Variables

Vocabulary and Key Concepts

1. a. A _____ of linear equations consists of two or more linear equations.

   b. A _____ to a system of linear equations must be a solution to both individual equations in the system.

   c. Graphically, a solution to a system of linear equations in two variables is a point where the lines _____.

   d. A system of equations that has one or more solutions is said to be _____.

   e. The solution set to an inconsistent system of equations is _____.

   f. Two equations in a system of linear equations in two variables are said to be _____ if they represent the same line.

   g. Two equations in a system of linear equations in two variables are said to be _____ if they represent different lines.

Concept 1: Solutions to a System of Linear Equations

For Exercises 2–10, determine if the given point is a solution to the system. **(See Example 1.)**

2. $6x - y = -9$ $(-1, 3)$
   $x + 2y = 5$

3. $3x - y = 7$ $(2, -1)$
   $x - 2y = 4$

4. $x - y = 3$ $(4, 1)$
   $x + y = 5$

5. $4y = -3x + 12$ $(0, 4)$
   $y = \dfrac{2}{3}x - 4$

6. $y = -\dfrac{1}{3}x + 2$ $(9, -1)$
   $x = 2y + 6$

7. $3x - 6y = 9$ $\left(4, \dfrac{1}{2}\right)$
   $x - 2y = 3$

8. $x - y = 4$ $(6, 2)$
   $3x - 3y = 12$

9. $\dfrac{1}{3}x = \dfrac{2}{5}y - \dfrac{4}{5}$ $(0, 2)$
   $\dfrac{3}{4}x + \dfrac{1}{2}y = 2$

10. $\dfrac{1}{4}x + \dfrac{1}{2}y = \dfrac{3}{2}$ $(4, 1)$
   $y = \dfrac{3}{2}x - 6$

For Exercises 11–14, match the graph of the system of equations with the appropriate description of the solution.

11.

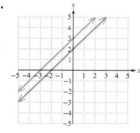

a. The solution set is $\{(1, 3)\}$.

b. $\{\ \}$

c. There are infinitely many solutions.

d. The solution set is $\{(0, 0)\}$.

12.

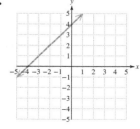

13.

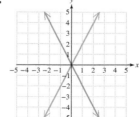

14.

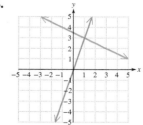

15. Graph each system of equations.

     a. $y = 2x - 3$ **b.** $y = 2x + 1$ **c.** $y = 3x - 5$

        $y = 2x + 5$ $y = 4x - 1$ $y = 3x - 5$

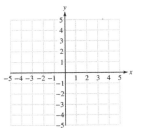 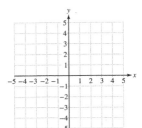 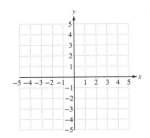

For Exercises 16–26, determine which system of equations (a, b, or c) makes the statement true. (*Hint:* Refer to the graphs from Exercise 15.)

a. $y = 2x - 3$ **b.** $y = 2x + 1$ **c.** $y = 3x - 5$

    $y = 2x + 5$ $y = 4x - 1$ $y = 3x - 5$

16. The lines are parallel.   17. The lines coincide.

18. The lines intersect at exactly one point.   19. The system is inconsistent.

20. The equations are dependent.   21. The lines have the same slope but different y-intercepts.

22. The lines have the same slope and same y-intercept.   23. The lines have different slopes.

24. The system has exactly one solution.   25. The system has infinitely many solutions.

26. The system has no solution.

Concept 2: Solving Systems of Linear Equations by Graphing

For Exercises 27–50, solve the system by graphing. For systems that do not have one unique solution, also state the number of solutions and whether the system is inconsistent or the equations are dependent. **(See Examples 2–5.)**

27. $y = -x + 4$ 28. $y = 3x + 2$ 29. $2x + y = 0$

     $y = x - 2$ $y = 2x$ $3x + y = 1$

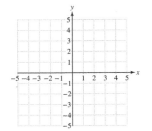 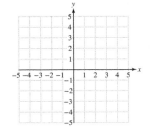 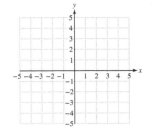

282   **Chapter 4**   Systems of Linear Equations in Two Variables

30. $x + y = -1$
$\ 2x - y = -5$

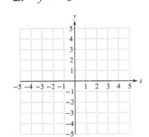

31. $2x + y = 6$
$\ x = 1$

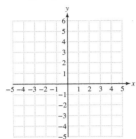

32. $4x + 3y = 9$
$\ x = 3$

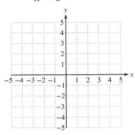

33. $-6x - 3y = 0$
$\ 4x + 2y = 4$

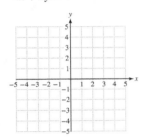

34. $2x - 6y = 12$
$\ -3x + 9y = 12$

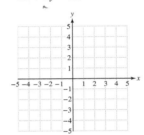

35. $-2x + y = 3$
$\ 6x - 3y = -9$

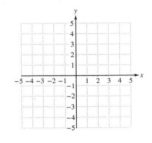

36. $x + 3y = 0$
$\ -2x - 6y = 0$

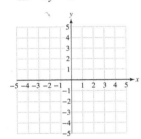

37. $y = 6$
$\ 2x + 3y = 12$

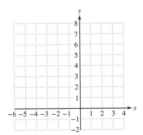

38. $y = -2$
$\ x - 2y = 10$

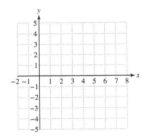

39. $x = 4 + y$
$\ 3y = -3x$

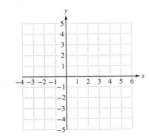

40. $3y = 4x$
$\ x - y = -1$

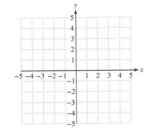

41. $-x + y = 3$
$\ 4y = 4x + 6$

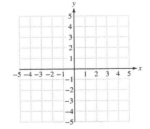

42. $x - y = 4$
$3y = 3x + 6$

43. $x = 4$
$2y = 4$

44. $-3x = 6$
$y = 2$

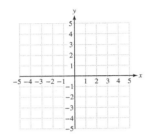

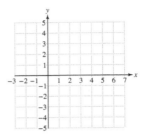

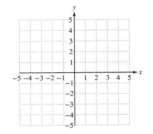

45. $2x + y = 4$
$4x - 2y = 0$

46. $3x + 3y = 3$
$2x - y = 5$

47. $y = 0.5x + 2$
$-x + 2y = 4$

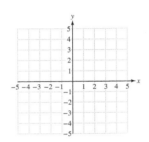

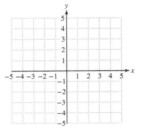

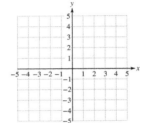

48. $3x - 4y = 6$
$-6x + 8y = -12$

49. $x - 3y = 0$
$y = -x - 4$

50. $-6x + 3y = -6$
$4x + y = -2$

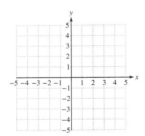

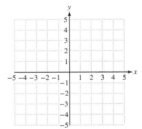

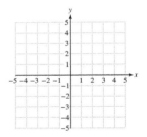

51. A wholesale club offers two types of memberships. The Executive Membership is $100 per year, including an annual 2% reward. The Business Membership is $50 per year without a reward. The total cost for membership, y, depends on the amount of money spent on merchandise, x, and can be represented by the following equations:

Executive Membership: $y = 100 - 0.02x$

Business Membership: $y = 50$

According to the graph, how much money spent on merchandise would result in the same cost for each membership?

284   **Chapter 4**   Systems of Linear Equations in Two Variables

52. The cost to rent a 10 ft by 10 ft storage space is different for two different storage companies. The Storage Bin charges $90 per month plus a nonrefundable deposit of $120. AAA Storage charges $110 per month with no deposit. The total cost, y, to rent a 10 ft by 10 ft space depends on the number of months, x, according to the equations

The Storage Bin: $y = 90x + 120$

AAA Storage: $y = 110x$

From the graph, determine the number of months required for which the cost to rent space is equal for both companies.

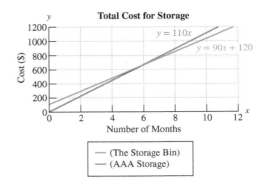

For the systems graphed in Exercises 53–54, explain why the ordered pair cannot be a solution to the system of equations.

53. $(-3, 1)$

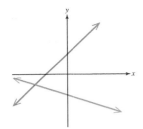

54. $(-1, -4)$

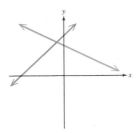

Expanding Your Skills

55. Write a system of linear equations whose solution set is $\{(2, 1)\}$.

56. Write a system of linear equations whose solution set is $\{(1, 4)\}$.

57. One equation in a system of linear equations is $x + y = 4$. Write a second equation such that the system will have no solution. (Answers may vary.)

58. One equation in a system of linear equations is $x - y = 3$. Write a second equation such that the system will have infinitely many solutions. (Answers may vary.)

| **Section 4.2** | Solving Systems of Equations by the Substitution Method |

1. Solving Systems of Linear Equations by Using the Substitution Method

We have used the graphing method to find the solution set to a system of equations. However, sometimes it is difficult to determine the solution using this method because of limitations in the accuracy of the graph. This is particularly true when the coordinates of a solution are not integer values or when the solution is a point not sufficiently close to the origin. Identifying the coordinates of the point $\left(\frac{3}{17}, -\frac{23}{9}\right)$ or $(-251, 8349)$, for example, might be difficult from a graph.

In this section, we will cover the *substitution method* to solve systems of equations. This is an algebraic method that does not require graphing the individual equations. We demonstrate the substitution method in Examples 1 through 5.

| **Example 1** | **Solving a System of Linear Equations by Using the Substitution Method** |

Solve the system by using the substitution method.

$$x = 2y - 3$$
$$-4x + 3y = 2$$

Solution:

The variable x has been isolated in the first equation. The quantity $2y - 3$ is equal to x and therefore can be substituted for x in the second equation. This leaves the second equation in terms of y only.

First equation: $\qquad x = \underline{2y - 3}$

Second equation: $\quad -4x + 3y = 2$

$\qquad -4(2y - 3) + 3y = 2$ This equation now contains only one variable.

$\qquad -8y + 12 + 3y = 2$ Solve the resulting equation.

$\qquad\qquad -5y + 12 = 2$

$\qquad\qquad\qquad -5y = -10$

$\qquad\qquad\qquad\quad y = 2$

To find x, substitute $y = 2$ back into the first equation.

$$x = 2y - 3$$
$$x = 2(2) - 3$$
$$x = 1$$

Check the ordered pair $(1, 2)$ in both original equations.

$x = 2y - 3 \longrightarrow 1 \stackrel{?}{=} 2(2) - 3$ ✓   True

$-4x + 3y = 2 \longrightarrow -4(1) + 3(2) \stackrel{?}{=} 2$ ✓   True

The solution set is $\{(1, 2)\}$.

> **Avoiding Mistakes**
>
> Remember to solve for *both* variables in the system.

Skill Practice Solve the system by using the substitution method.

1. $2x + 3y = -2$
$\quad y = x + 1$

In Example 1, we eliminated the x variable from the second equation by substituting an equivalent expression for x. The resulting equation was relatively simple to solve because it had only one variable. This is the premise of the substitution method.

The substitution method can be summarized as follows.

Solving a System of Equations by Using the Substitution Method

Step 1   Isolate one of the variables from one equation.

Step 2   Substitute the expression found in step 1 into the other equation.

Step 3   Solve the resulting equation.

Step 4   Substitute the value found in step 3 back into the equation in step 1 to find the value of the remaining variable.

Step 5   Check the ordered pair in both original equations.

Example 2   **Solving a System of Linear Equations by Using the Substitution Method**

Solve the system by using the substitution method.

$$x + y = 4$$
$$-5x + 3y = -12$$

Solution:

The x or y variable in the first equation is easy to isolate because the coefficients are both 1. While either variable can be isolated, we arbitrarily choose to solve for the x variable.

$x + y = 4 \longrightarrow x = \underline{4 - y}$ **Step 1:** Isolate x in the first equation.

$-5(4 - y) + 3y = -12$ **Step 2:** Substitute $4 - y$ for x in the other equation.

$-20 + 5y + 3y = -12$ **Step 3:** Solve for y.
$-20 + 8y = -12$
$8y = 8$
$y = 1$

$x = 4 - y$ **Step 4:** Substitute $y = 1$ into the equation $x = 4 - y$.
$x = 4 - 1$
$x = 3$

Step 5:   Check the ordered pair $(3, 1)$ in both original equations.

$$x + y = 4 \qquad (3) + (1) \overset{?}{=} 4 \checkmark \qquad \text{True}$$
$$-5x + 3y = -12 \qquad -5(3) + 3(1) \overset{?}{=} -12 \checkmark \qquad \text{True}$$

The solution set is $\{(3, 1)\}$.

Skill Practice   Solve the system by using the substitution method.

2. $x + y = 3$
$-2x + 3y = 9$

Avoiding Mistakes

Although we solved for y first, be sure to write the x-coordinate first in the ordered pair. Remember that $(1, 3)$ is not the same as $(3, 1)$.

TIP: The solution to a system of linear equations can be confirmed by graphing. The system from Example 2 is graphed here.

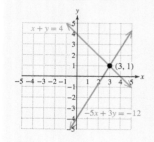

Answer

2. $\{(0, 3)\}$

Example 3	**Solving a System of Linear Equations by Using the Substitution Method**

Solve the system by using the substitution method.

$$3x + 5y = 17$$
$$2x - y = -6$$

Solution:

The y variable in the second equation is the easiest variable to isolate because its coefficient is -1.

$3x + 5y = 17$

$2x - y = -6 \longrightarrow -y = -2x - 6$

$\qquad\qquad\qquad y = \underline{2x + 6}$

Step 1: Isolate y in the second equation.

$3x + 5(2x + 6) = 17$

Step 2: Substitute the quantity $2x + 6$ for y in the other equation.

$3x + 10x + 30 = 17$

$13x + 30 = 17$

$13x = 17 - 30$

$13x = -13$

$x = -1$

Step 3: Solve for x.

$y = 2x + 6$

$y = 2(-1) + 6$

$y = -2 + 6$

$y = 4$

Step 4: Substitute $x = -1$ into the equation $y = 2x + 6$.

Step 5: The ordered pair $(-1, 4)$ can be checked in the original equations to verify the answer.

$3x + 5y = 17 \longrightarrow 3(-1) + 5(4) \overset{?}{=} 17 \longrightarrow -3 + 20 \overset{?}{=} 17$ ✓ True

$2x - y = -6 \longrightarrow 2(-1) - (4) \overset{?}{=} -6 \longrightarrow -2 - 4 \overset{?}{=} -6$ ✓ True

The solution set is $\{(-1, 4)\}$.

Avoiding Mistakes

Do not substitute $y = 2x + 6$ into the same equation from which it came. This mistake will result in an identity:

$$2x - y = -6$$
$$2x - (2x + 6) = -6$$
$$2x - 2x - 6 = -6$$
$$-6 = -6$$

Skill Practice Solve the system by using the substitution method.

3. $x + 4y = 11$
   $2x - 5y = -4$

Answer

3. $\{(3, 2)\}$

Recall that a system of linear equations may represent two parallel lines. In such a case, there is no solution to the system.

Example 4   **Solving an Inconsistent System Using Substitution**

Solve the system by using the substitution method.

$$2x + 3y = 6$$
$$y = -\tfrac{2}{3}x + 4$$

Solution:

$$2x + 3y = 6$$
$$y = \underbrace{-\tfrac{2}{3}x + 4}$$

$$2x + 3\left(-\tfrac{2}{3}x + 4\right) = 6$$

Step 1: The variable y is already isolated in the second equation.

Step 2: Substitute $y = -\tfrac{2}{3}x + 4$ from the second equation into the first equation.

$$2x - 2x + 12 = 6$$
$$12 = 6 \quad \text{(contradiction)}$$

Step 3: Solve the resulting equation.

The equation results in a contradiction. There are no values of x and y that will make 12 equal to 6. Therefore, the solution set is { }, and the system is inconsistent.

Skill Practice   Solve the system by using the substitution method.

4. $y = -\dfrac{1}{2}x + 3$

   $2x + 4y = 5$

TIP: The answer to Example 4 can be verified by writing each equation in slope-intercept form and graphing the lines.

Equation 1

$2x + 3y = 6$

$3y = -2x + 6$

$\dfrac{3y}{3} = \dfrac{-2x}{3} + \dfrac{6}{3}$

$y = -\dfrac{2}{3}x + 2$

Equation 2

$y = -\dfrac{2}{3}x + 4$

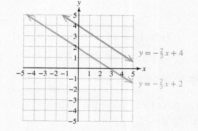

The equations indicate that the lines have the same slope but different y-intercepts. Therefore, the lines must be parallel. There is no point of intersection, indicating that the system has no solution, { }.

Answer

4. { }

Recall that a system of two linear equations may represent the same line. In such a case, the solution is the set of all points on the line.

| **Example 5** | **Solving a System of Dependent Equations Using Substitution** |

Solve the system by using the substitution method.

$$\frac{1}{2}x - \frac{1}{4}y = 1$$

$$6x - 3y = 12$$

Solution:

$\frac{1}{2}x - \frac{1}{4}y = 1$ To make the first equation easier to work with, we have the option of clearing fractions.

$6x - 3y = 12$

$\frac{1}{2}x - \frac{1}{4}y = 1 \xrightarrow{\text{Multiply by 4.}} 4\left(\frac{1}{2}x\right) - 4\left(\frac{1}{4}y\right) = 4(1) \longrightarrow 2x - y = 4$

Now the system becomes:

$2x - y = 4$ The y variable in the first equation is the easiest to isolate because its coefficient is -1.

$6x - 3y = 12$

$2x - y = 4 \xrightarrow{\text{Solve for } y.} -y = -2x + 4 \rightarrow y = \underline{2x - 4}$ **Step 1:** Isolate one of the variables.

$6x - 3y = 12$

$6x - 3(2x - 4) = 12$ **Step 2:** Substitute $y = 2x - 4$ from the first equation into the second equation.

$6x - 6x + 12 = 12$ **Step 3:** Solve the resulting equation.

$\quad\quad\quad 12 = 12 \quad (\text{identity})$

Because the equation produces an identity, all values of x make this equation true. Thus, x can be any real number. Substituting any real number, x, into the equation $y = 2x - 4$ produces an ordered pair on the line $y = 2x - 4$. Hence, the solution set to the system of equations is the set of all ordered pairs on the line $y = 2x - 4$. This can be written as $\{(x, y) \,|\, y = 2x - 4\}$. The equations are dependent.

Skill Practice Solve the system by using the substitution method.

5. $2x + \frac{1}{3}y = -\frac{1}{3}$

   $12x + 2y = -2$

Answer

5. Infinitely many solutions;
   $\{(x, y) \,|\, 12x + 2y = -2\}$; dependent equations

TIP: The solution to Example 5 can be verified by writing each equation in slope-intercept form and graphing the lines.

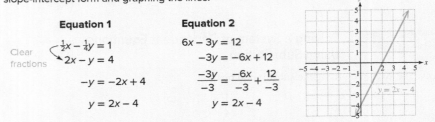

Equation 1

Clear fractions
$$\frac{1}{2}x - \frac{1}{4}y = 1$$
$$2x - y = 4$$
$$-y = -2x + 4$$
$$y = 2x - 4$$

Equation 2

$$6x - 3y = 12$$
$$-3y = -6x + 12$$
$$\frac{-3y}{-3} = \frac{-6x}{-3} + \frac{12}{-3}$$
$$y = 2x - 4$$

Notice that the slope-intercept forms for both equations are identical. The equations represent the same line, indicating that they are dependent. Each point on the line is a solution to the system of equations.

The following summary reviews the three different geometric relationships between two lines and the solutions to the corresponding systems of equations.

Interpreting Solutions to a System of Two Linear Equations

- The lines may intersect at one point (yielding one unique solution).
- The lines may be parallel and have no point of intersection (yielding no solution). This is detected algebraically when a contradiction (false statement) is obtained (for example, $0 = -3$ or $12 = 6$).
- The lines may be the same and intersect at all points on the line (yielding an infinite number of solutions). This is detected algebraically when an identity is obtained (for example, $0 = 0$ or $12 = 12$).

2. Applications of the Substitution Method

We have already encountered word problems using one linear equation and one variable. In this chapter, we investigate application problems with two unknowns. In such a case, we can use two variables to represent the unknown quantities. However, if two variables are used, we must write a system of *two* distinct equations.

Example 6   **Applying the Substitution Method**

One number is 3 more than 4 times another. Their sum is 133. Find the numbers.

Solution:

We can use two variables to represent the two unknown numbers.

Let x represent one number.
Let y represent the other number.   Label the variables.

We must now write two equations. Each of the first two sentences gives a relationship between x and y:

One number is 3 more than 4 times another. ⟶ $x = 4y + 3$ (first equation)

Their sum is 133. ⟶ $x + y = 133$ (second equation)

$$(4y + 3) + y = 133$$ Substitute $x = 4y + 3$ into the second equation, $x + y = 133$.

$$5y + 3 = 133$$ Solve the resulting equation.

$$5y = 130$$

$$y = 26$$

$$x = 4y + 3$$
$$x = 4(26) + 3$$ To solve for x, substitute $y = 26$ into the equation $x = 4y + 3$.
$$x = 104 + 3$$
$$x = 107$$

One number is 26, and the other is 107.

Skill Practice

6. One number is 16 more than another. Their sum is 92. Use a system of equations to find the numbers.

TIP: Check that the numbers 26 and 107 meet the conditions of Example 6.

- 4 times 26 is 104. Three more than 104 is 107. ✓
- The sum of the numbers should be **133**: $26 + 107 = 133$ ✓

Example 7   **Using the Substitution Method in a Geometry Application**

Two angles are supplementary. The measure of one angle is 15° more than twice the measure of the other angle. Find the measures of the two angles.

Solution:

Let x represent the measure of one angle.
Let y represent the measure of the other angle.

The sum of the measures of supplementary angles is 180°. $\longrightarrow x + y = 180$

The measure of one angle is 15° more than twice the other angle. $\longrightarrow x = 2y + 15$

$$x + y = 180$$
$$x = 2y + 15$$ The x variable in the second equation is already isolated.

$$(2y + 15) + y = 180$$ Substitute $2y + 15$ into the first equation for x.

$$2y + 15 + y = 180$$ Solve the resulting equation.

$$3y + 15 = 180$$

$$3y = 165$$

$$y = 55$$

$$x = 2y + 15$$ Substitute $y = 55$ into the equation $x = 2y + 15$.
$$x = 2(55) + 15$$
$$x = 110 + 15$$
$$x = 125$$

One angle is 55°, and the other is 125°.

TIP: Check that the angles 55° and 125° meet the conditions of Example 7.

- Because $55° + 125° = 180°$, the angles are supplementary. ✓
- The angle 125° is 15° more than twice 55°: $125° = 2(55°) + 15°$ ✓

Answer

6. One number is 38, and the other number is 54.

Skill Practice

Answer

7. The measures of the angles are
   23° and 67°.

7. The measure of one angle is 2° less than 3 times the measure of another angle. The angles are complementary. Use a system of equations to find the measures of the two angles.

Section 4.2   Practice Exercises

Review Exercises

For Exercises 1–6, write each pair of lines in slope-intercept form. Then identify whether the lines intersect in exactly one point or if the lines are parallel or coinciding.

1. $2x - y = 4$

  $-2y = -4x + 8$

2. $x - 2y = 5$

  $3x = 6y + 15$

3. $2x + 3y = 6$

  $x - y = 5$

4. $x - y = -1$

  $x + 2y = 4$

5. $2x = \dfrac{1}{2}y + 2$

  $4x - y = 13$

6. $4y = 3x$

  $3x - 4y = 15$

Concept 1: Solving Systems of Linear Equations by Using the Substitution Method

For Exercises 7–10, solve each system by using the substitution method. **(See Example 1.)**

7. $3x + 2y = -3$

  $y = 2x - 12$

8. $4x - 3y = -19$

  $y = -2x + 13$

9. $x = -4y + 16$

  $3x + 5y = 20$

10. $x = -y + 3$

  $-2x + y = 6$

11. Given the system: $4x - 2y = -6$

  $3x + y = 8$

  a. Which variable from which equation is easiest to isolate and why?

  b. Solve the system by using the substitution method.

12. Given the system: $x - 5y = 2$

  $11x + 13y = 22$

  a. Which variable from which equation is easiest to isolate and why?

  b. Solve the system by using the substitution method.

For Exercises 13–48, solve the system by using the substitution method. For systems that do not have one unique solution, also state the number of solutions and whether the system is inconsistent or the equations are dependent.
(See Examples 1–5.)

13. $x = 3y - 1$

  $2x - 4y = 2$

14. $2y = \quad x + 9$

  $y = -3x + 1$

15. $-2x + 5y = 5$

  $x = 4y - 10$

16. $y = -2x + 27$

  $3x - 7y = -2$

17. $4x - \quad y = -1$

  $2x + 4y = 13$

18. $\quad 5x - 3y = -2$

  $10x - \quad y = 1$

19. $4x - 3y = 11$

  $x = 5$

20. $y = -3x - 9$

  $y = 12$

21. $4x = 8y + 4$

  $5x - 3y = 5$

22. $3y = 6x - 6$

  $-3x + y = -4$

23. $\quad x - 3y = -11$

  $6x - \quad y = 2$

24. $-2x - \quad y = 9$

  $x + 7y = 15$

25. $3x + 2y = -1$

  $\dfrac{3}{2}x + \quad y = 4$

26. $\quad 5x - 2y = 6$

  $-\dfrac{5}{2}x + \quad y = 5$

27. $10x - 30y = -10$

  $2x - \quad 6y = -2$

28. $\quad 3x + \quad 6y = 6$

  $-6x - 12y = -12$

29. $2x + y = 3$
$\quad\quad y = -7$

30. $-3x = 2y + 23$
$\quad\quad x = -1$

31. $x + 2y = -2$
$\quad\quad 4x = -2y - 17$

32. $x + y = 1$
$\quad\quad 2x - y = -2$

33. $y = -\dfrac{1}{2}x - 4$
$\quad\quad y = \;\; 4x - 13$

34. $y = \dfrac{2}{3}x - 3$
$\quad\quad y = 6x - 19$

35. $y = 6$
$\quad\quad y - 4 = -2x - 6$

36. $x = 9$
$\quad\quad x - 3 = 6y + 12$

37. $3x + 2y = 4$
$\quad\quad 2x - 3y = -6$

38. $4x + 3y = \;\; 4$
$\quad\quad -2x + 5y = -2$

39. $y = 0.25x + 1$
$\quad\quad -x + 4y = 4$

40. $y = 0.75x - 3$
$\quad\quad -3x + 4y = -12$

41. $11x + 6y = 17$
$\quad\quad 5x - 4y = 1$

42. $3x - 8y = 7$
$\quad\quad 10x - 5y = 45$

43. $x + 2y = 4$
$\quad\quad 4y = -2x - 8$

44. $-y = x - 6$
$\quad\quad 2x + 2y = 4$

45. $2x = 3 - y$
$\quad\quad x + y = 4$

46. $2x = 4 + 2y$
$\quad\quad 3x + y = 10$

47. $\dfrac{x}{3} + \dfrac{y}{2} = -4$
$\quad\quad x - 3y = 6$

48. $x - 2y = -5$
$\quad\quad \dfrac{2x}{3} + \dfrac{y}{3} = 0$

Concept 2: Applications of the Substitution Method

For Exercises 49–58, set up a system of linear equations and solve for the indicated quantities. **(See Examples 6–7.)**

49. Two numbers have a sum of 106. One number is 10 less than the other. Find the numbers.

50. Two positive numbers have a difference of 8. The larger number is 2 less than 3 times the smaller number. Find the numbers.

51. The difference between two positive numbers is 26. The larger number is 3 times the smaller. Find the numbers.

52. The sum of two numbers is 956. One number is 94 less than 6 times the other. Find the numbers.

53. Two angles are supplementary. One angle is 15° more than 10 times the other angle. Find the measure of each angle.

54. Two angles are complementary. One angle is 1° less than 6 times the other angle. Find the measure of each angle.

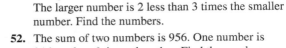

55. Two angles are complementary. One angle is 10° more than 3 times the other angle. Find the measure of each angle.

56. Two angles are supplementary. One angle is 5° less than twice the other angle. Find the measure of each angle.

57. In a right triangle, one of the acute angles is 6° less than the other acute angle. Find the measure of each acute angle.

58. In a right triangle, one of the acute angles is 9° less than twice the other acute angle. Find the measure of each acute angle.

294   **Chapter 4**   Systems of Linear Equations in Two Variables

Expanding Your Skills

59. The following system consists of dependent equations and therefore has infinitely many solutions. Find three ordered pairs that are solutions to the system of equations.

$$y = 2x + 3$$
$$-4x + 2y = 6$$

60. The following system consists of dependent equations and therefore has infinitely many solutions. Find three ordered pairs that are solutions to the system of equations.

$$y = -x + 1$$
$$2x + 2y = 2$$

294   **Chapter 4**   Systems of Linear Equations in Two Variables

Section 4.3   Solving Systems of Equations by the Addition Method

1. Solving Systems of Linear Equations by Using the Addition Method

In this section, we present another algebraic method to solve a system of linear equations. This method is called the *addition method* and its underlying principle is to add multiples of the given equations to eliminate a variable from the system. For this reason, the addition method is sometimes called the *elimination method*.

Example 1   **Solving a System of Linear Equations by Using the Addition Method**

Solve the system by using the addition method.

$$x + y = -2$$
$$x - y = -6$$

Solution:

Notice that the coefficients of the y variables are opposites:

Coefficient is 1.

$$x + 1y = -2$$
$$x - 1y = -6$$

Coefficient is -1.

Because the coefficients of the y variables are opposites, we can add the two equations to eliminate the y variable.

$$x + y = -2$$
$$\underline{x - y = -6}$$
$$2x \quad\;\; = -8 \;\; \longleftarrow \; \text{After adding the equations, we have one equation and one variable.}$$

$$2x = -8 \qquad \text{Solve the resulting equation.}$$
$$x = -4$$

To find the value of y, substitute $x = -4$ into *either* of the original equations.

$$x + y = -2 \qquad \text{First equation}$$
$$(-4) + y = -2$$
$$y = -2 + 4$$
$$y = 2 \qquad \text{The ordered pair is } (-4, 2).$$

<u>Check</u>:

$$x + y = -2 \longrightarrow (-4) + (2) \stackrel{?}{=} -2 \longrightarrow -2 \stackrel{?}{=} -2 \checkmark \quad \text{True}$$
$$x - y = -6 \longrightarrow (-4) - (2) \stackrel{?}{=} -6 \longrightarrow -6 \stackrel{?}{=} -6 \checkmark \quad \text{True}$$

The solution set is $\{(-4, 2)\}$.

Skill Practice Solve the system by using the addition method.

1. $x + y = 13$
    $2x - y = 2$

TIP: In Example 1, notice that the value $x = -4$ could have been substituted into the second equation, to obtain the same value for y.

$$x - y = -6$$
$$(-4) - y = -6$$
$$-y = -6 + 4$$
$$-y = -2$$
$$y = 2$$

It is important to note that the addition method works on the premise that the two equations have *opposite* values for the coefficients of one of the variables. Sometimes it is necessary to manipulate the original equations to create two coefficients that are opposites. This is accomplished by multiplying one or both equations by an appropriate constant. The process is outlined as follows.

Solving a System of Equations by Using the Addition Method

Step 1 Write both equations in standard form: $Ax + By = C$

Step 2 Clear fractions or decimals (optional).

Step 3 Multiply one or both equations by nonzero constants to create opposite coefficients for one of the variables.

Step 4 Add the equations from step 3 to eliminate one variable.

Step 5 Solve for the remaining variable.

Step 6 Substitute the known value from step 5 into one of the original equations to solve for the other variable.

Step 7 Check the ordered pair in both equations.

Answer

1. $\{(5, 8)\}$

> **Example 2**   ### Solving a System of Linear Equations by Using the Addition Method

Solve the system by using the addition method.

$$3x + 5y = 17$$
$$2x - y = -6$$

Solution:

$3x + 5y = 17$ **Step 1:**   Both equations are already written in standard form.

$2x - y = -6$ **Step 2:**   There are no fractions or decimals.

Notice that neither the coefficients of x nor the coefficients of y are opposites. However, multiplying the second equation by 5 creates the term $-5y$ in the second equation. This is the opposite of the term $+5y$ in the first equation.

Avoiding Mistakes		

Remember to multiply the chosen constant on *both* sides of the equation.

$$3x + 5y = 17 \qquad\qquad 3x + 5y = 17$$
$$2x - y = -6 \xrightarrow{\text{Multiply by 5.}} \underline{10x - 5y = -30}$$
$$13x \qquad = -13$$

Step 3: Multiply the second equation by 5.

Step 4: Add the equations.

$$13x = -13$$

Step 5: Solve the equation.

$$x = -1$$

TIP: In Example 2, we could have eliminated the x variable by multiplying the first equation by 2 and the second equation by -3.

$3x + 5y = 17$ First equation

$3(-1) + 5y = 17$

$-3 + 5y = 17$

$5y = 20$

$y = 4$

Step 6: Substitute $x = -1$ into one of the original equations.

Step 7: Check $(-1, 4)$ in both original equations.

<u>Check:</u>

$$3x + 5y = 17 \longrightarrow 3(-1) + 5(4) \stackrel{?}{=} 17 \longrightarrow -3 + 20 \stackrel{?}{=} 17 \checkmark \quad \text{True}$$

$$2x - y = -6 \longrightarrow 2(-1) - (4) \stackrel{?}{=} -6 \longrightarrow -2 - 4 \stackrel{?}{=} -6 \checkmark \quad \text{True}$$

The solution set is $\{(-1, 4)\}$.

Skill Practice   Solve the system by using the addition method.

2. $4x + 3y = 3$
   $x - 2y = 9$

In Example 3, the system of equations uses the variables a and b instead of x and y. In such a case, we will write the solution as an ordered pair with the variables written in alphabetical order, such as (a, b).

Answer

2. $\{(3, -3)\}$

Example 3	**Solving a System of Linear Equations by Using the Addition Method**

Solve the system by using the addition method.

$$5b = 7a + 8$$

$$-4a - 2b = -10$$

Solution:

Step 1: Write the equations in standard form.

The first equation becomes: $5b = 7a + 8 \longrightarrow -7a + 5b = 8$

The system becomes: $-7a + 5b = 8$

$$-4a - 2b = -10$$

Step 2: There are no fractions or decimals.

Step 3: We need to obtain opposite coefficients on either the a or b term.

Notice that neither the coefficients of a nor the coefficients of b are opposites. However, it is possible to change the coefficients of b to 10 and -10 (this is because the LCM of 5 and 2 is 10). This is accomplished by multiplying the first equation by 2 and the second equation by 5.

$$-7a + 5b = 8 \quad \xrightarrow{\text{Multiply by 2.}} \quad -14a + 10b = 16$$

$$-4a - 2b = -10 \quad \xrightarrow{\text{Multiply by 5.}} \quad \frac{-20a - 10b = -50}{-34a \qquad\quad = -34}$$

Step 4: Add the equations.

$$-34a = -34$$

$$\frac{-34a}{-34} = \frac{-34}{-34}$$

$$a = 1$$

Step 5: Solve the resulting equation.

$5b = 7a + 8$ First equation

Step 6: Substitute $a = 1$ into one of the original equations.

$$5b = 7(1) + 8$$

$$5b = 15$$

$$b = 3$$

Step 7: Check $(1, 3)$ in the original equations.

Check:

$$5b = 7a + 8 \longrightarrow 5(3) \overset{?}{=} 7(1) + 8 \longrightarrow 15 \overset{?}{=} 7 + 8 \checkmark \quad \text{True}$$

$$-4a - 2b = -10 \longrightarrow -4(1) - 2(3) \overset{?}{=} -10 \longrightarrow -4 - 6 \overset{?}{=} -10 \checkmark \quad \text{True}$$

The solution set is $\{(1, 3)\}$.

Skill Practice Solve the system by using the addition method.

   3. $8n = 4 - 5m$

      $7m + 6n = -10$

Answer

3. $\{(-4, 3)\}$

| Example 4 | Solving a System of Linear Equations by Using the Addition Method |

Solve the system by using the addition method.

$$34x - 22y = 4$$
$$17x - 88y = -19$$

Solution:

The equations are already in standard form. There are no fractions or decimals to clear.

$$34x - 22y = 4 \longrightarrow 34x - 22y = 4$$
$$17x - 88y = -19 \xrightarrow{\text{Multiply by } -2.} -34x + 176y = 38$$
$$\overline{154y = 42}$$

Solve for y. $154y = 42$

$$\frac{154y}{154} = \frac{42}{154}$$

Simplify. $y = \dfrac{3}{11}$

To find the value of x, we normally substitute y into one of the original equations and solve for x. In this example, we will show an alternative method for finding x. By repeating the addition method, this time eliminating y, we can solve for x. This approach enables us to avoid substitution of the fractional value for y.

$$34x - 22y = 4 \xrightarrow{\text{Multiply by } -4.} -136x + 88y = -16$$
$$17x - 88y = -19 \longrightarrow 17x - 88y = -19$$
$$\overline{-119x = -35}$$

Solve for x. $-119x = -35$

$$\frac{-119x}{-119} = \frac{-35}{-119}$$

Simplify. $x = \dfrac{5}{17}$

The ordered pair $\left(\frac{5}{17}, \frac{3}{11}\right)$ can be checked in the original equations.

$$34x - 22y = 4 \qquad\qquad\qquad 17x - 88y = -19$$

$$34\left(\frac{5}{17}\right) - 22\left(\frac{3}{11}\right) \overset{?}{=} 4 \qquad\qquad 17\left(\frac{5}{17}\right) - 88\left(\frac{3}{11}\right) \overset{?}{=} -19$$

$$10 - 6 \overset{?}{=} 4 \checkmark \quad \text{True} \qquad\qquad 5 - 24 \overset{?}{=} -19 \checkmark \quad \text{True}$$

The solution set is $\left\{\left(\dfrac{5}{17}, \dfrac{3}{11}\right)\right\}$.

Skill Practice Solve the system by using the addition method.

4. $15x - 16y = 1$
   $45x + 4y = 16$

Example 5   ## Solving an Inconsistent System by the Addition Method

Solve the system by using the addition method.

$$2x - 5y = 10$$

$$\frac{1}{2}x - \frac{5}{4}y = 1$$

Solution:

$$2x - 5y = 10$$

$$\frac{1}{2}x - \frac{5}{4}y = 1$$ **Step 1:** The equations are in standard form.

Step 2: Multiply both sides of the second equation by 4 to clear fractions.

$$\frac{1}{2}x - \frac{5}{4}y = 1 \longrightarrow 4\left(\frac{1}{2}x - \frac{5}{4}y\right) = 4(1) \longrightarrow 2x - 5y = 4$$

Now the system becomes $2x - 5y = 10$

$$2x - 5y = 4$$

To make either the x coefficients or y coefficients opposites, multiply either equation by -1.

$$2x - 5y = 10 \xrightarrow{\text{Multiply by } -1.} -2x + 5y = -10$$ **Step 3:** Create opposite coefficients.

$$2x - 5y = 4 \longrightarrow \underline{2x - 5y = 4}$$

$$0 = -6$$ **Step 4:** Add the equations.

Because the result is a contradiction, the solution set is { }, and the system of equations is inconsistent. Writing each equation in slope-intercept form verifies that the lines are parallel (Figure 4-8).

$$2x - 5y = 10 \xrightarrow{\text{slope-intercept form}} y = \frac{2}{5}x - 2$$

$$\frac{1}{2}x - \frac{5}{4}y = 1 \xrightarrow{\text{slope-intercept form}} y = \frac{2}{5}x - \frac{4}{5}$$

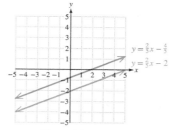

Figure 4-8

Skill Practice Solve the system by using the addition method.

5. $\dfrac{2}{3}x - \dfrac{3}{4}y = 2$

$8x - 9y = 6$

Answer

5. { }

| Example 6 | **Solving a System of Dependent Equations by the Addition Method** |

Solve the system by using the addition method.

$$3x - y = 4$$
$$2y = 6x - 8$$

Solution:

$3x - y = 4 \longrightarrow 3x - y = 4$ **Step 1:** Write the equations in standard form.

$2y = 6x - 8 \longrightarrow -6x + 2y = -8$ **Step 2:** There are no fractions or decimals.

Notice that the equations differ exactly by a factor of -2, which indicates that these two equations represent the same line. Multiply the first equation by 2 to create opposite coefficients for the variables.

$$
\begin{array}{l}
3x - y = 4 \xrightarrow{\text{Multiply by 2.}} 6x - 2y = 8 \\
-6x + 2y = -8 \qquad\qquad \underline{-6x + 2y = -8} \\
\qquad\qquad\qquad\qquad\qquad\qquad 0 = 0
\end{array}
$$

Step 3: Create opposite coefficients.

Step 4: Add the equations.

Because the resulting equation is an identity, the original equations represent the same line. This can be confirmed by writing each equation in slope-intercept form.

$$3x - y = 4 \longrightarrow -y = -3x + 4 \longrightarrow y = 3x - 4$$
$$-6x + 2y = -8 \longrightarrow 2y = 6x - 8 \longrightarrow y = 3x - 4$$

The solution is the set of all points on the line, or equivalently, $\{(x, y) \mid y = 3x - 4\}$.

Skill Practice Solve the system by using the addition method.

6. $3x = 3y + 15$
   $2x - 2y = 10$

2. Summary of Methods for Solving Systems of Linear Equations in Two Variables

If no method of solving a system of linear equations is specified, you may use the method of your choice. However, we recommend the following guidelines:

1. If one of the equations is written with a variable isolated, the substitution method is a good choice. For example:

$$2x + 5y = 2 \qquad \text{or} \qquad y = \frac{1}{3}x - 2$$
$$x = y - 6 \qquad\qquad\qquad\qquad x - 6y = 9$$

2. If both equations are written in standard form, $Ax + By = C$, where none of the variables has coefficients of 1 or -1, then the addition method is a good choice.

$$4x + 5y = 12$$
$$5x + 3y = 15$$

3. If both equations are written in standard form, $Ax + By = C$, and at least one variable has a coefficient of 1 or -1, then either the substitution method or the addition method is a good choice.

Answer

6. $\{(x, y) \mid 2x - 2y = 10\}$

Section 4.3   Practice Exercises

Study Skills Exercise

Now that you have learned three methods of solving a system of linear equations with two variables, choose a system and solve it all three ways. There are two advantages to this. One is to check your answer (you should get the same answer using all three methods). The second advantage is to show you which method is the easiest for you to use.

Solve the system by using the graphing method, the substitution method, and the addition method.

$$2x + y = -7$$
$$x - 10 = 4y$$

Review Exercises

For Exercises 1–5, check whether the given ordered pair is a solution to the system.

1. $-\dfrac{3}{4}x + 2y = -10$ $(8, -2)$

$x - \dfrac{1}{2}y = 7$

2. $x + y = 8$ $(5, 3)$

$y = x - 2$

3. $x = y + 1$ $(3, 2)$

$-x + 2y = 0$

4. $3x + 2y = 14$ $(5, -2)$

$5x - 2y = 29$

5. $x = 2y - 11$ $(-3, 4)$

$-x + 5y = 23$

Concept 1: Solving Systems of Linear Equations by Using the Addition Method

For Exercises 6–7, answer as true or false.

6. Given the system $5x - 4y = 1$

$7x - 2y = 5$

   a. To eliminate the y variable using the addition method, multiply the second equation by 2.

   b. To eliminate the x variable using the addition method, multiply the first equation by 7 and the second equation by -5.

7. Given the system $3x + 5y = -1$

$9x - 8y = -26$

   a. To eliminate the x variable using the addition method, multiply the first equation by -3.

   b. To eliminate the y variable using the addition method, multiply the first equation by 8 and the second equation by -5.

8. Given the system $3x - 4y = 2$

$17x + \ y = 35$

   a. Which variable, x or y, is easier to eliminate using the addition method?

   b. Solve the system using the addition method.

9. Given the system $-2x + 5y = -15$

$6x - 7y = 21$

   a. Which variable, x or y, is easier to eliminate using the addition method?

   b. Solve the system using the addition method.

For Exercises 10–24, solve each system using the addition method. **(See Examples 1–4.)**

10. $x + 2y = 8$

$5x - 2y = 4$

11. $2x - 3y = 11$

$-4x + 3y = -19$

12. $a + b = 3$

$3a + b = 13$

13. $-2u + 6v = 10$

$-2u + \ v = -5$

14. $-3x + \ y = 1$

$-6x - 2y = -2$

15. $5m - 2n = 4$

$3m + \ n = 9$

16. $3x - 5y = 13$

$x - 2y = 5$

17. $7a + 2b = -1$

$3a - 4b = 19$

18. $6c - 2d = -2$

$5c = -3d + 17$

19. $2s + 3t = -1$

$5s = 2t + 7$

20. $6y - 4z = -2$

$4y + 6z = 42$

21. $4k - 2r = -4$

$3k - 5r = 18$

22. $2x + 3y = 6$

$x - y = 5$

23. $6x + 6y = 8$

$9x - 18y = -3$

24. $2x - 5y = 4$

$3x - 3y = 4$

25. In solving a system of equations, suppose you get the statement $0 = 5$. How many solutions will the system have? What can you say about the graphs of these equations?

26. In solving a system of equations, suppose you get the statement $0 = 0$. How many solutions will the system have? What can you say about the graphs of these equations?

27. In solving a system of equations, suppose you get the statement $3 = 3$. How many solutions will the system have? What can you say about the graphs of these equations?

28. In solving a system of equations, suppose you get the statement $2 = -5$. How many solutions will the system have? What can you say about the graphs of these equations?

29. Suppose in solving a system of linear equations, you get the statement $x = 0$. How many solutions will the system have? What can you say about the graphs of these equations?

30. Suppose in solving a system of linear equations, you get the statement $y = 0$. How many solutions will the system have? What can you say about the graphs of these equations?

For Exercises 31–42, solve the system by using the addition method. For systems that do not have one unique solution, also state the number of solutions and whether the system is inconsistent or the equations are dependent. **(See Examples 5–6.)**

31. $-2x + y = -5$

$8x - 4y = 12$

32. $x - 3y = 2$

$-5x + 15y = 10$

33. $x + 2y = 2$

$-3x - 6y = -6$

34. $4x - 3y = 6$

$-12x + 9y = -18$

35. $3a + 2b = 11$

$7a - 3b = -5$

36. $4y + 5z = -2$

$5y - 3z = 16$

37. $3x - 5y = 7$

$5x - 2y = -1$

38. $4s + 3t = 9$

$3s + 4t = 12$

39. $2x + 2 = -3y + 9$

$3x - 10 = -4y$

40. $-3x + 6 + 7y = 5$

$5y = 2x$

41. $4x - 5y = 0$

$8(x - 1) = 10y$

42. $y = 2x + 1$

$-3(2x - y) = 0$

Concept 2: Summary of Methods for Solving Systems of Linear Equations in Two Variables

For Exercises 43–63, solve each system of equations by either the addition method or the substitution method.

43. $5x - 2y = 4$

$y = -3x + 9$

44. $-x = 8y + 5$

$4x - 3y = -20$

45. $0.1x + 0.1y = 0.6$

$0.1x - 0.1y = 0.1$

46. $0.1x + 0.1y = 0.2$

$0.1x - 0.1y = 0.3$

47. $3x = 5y - 9$

$2y = 3x + 3$

48. $10x - 5 = 3y$

$4x + 5y = 2$

49. $\dfrac{1}{10}y = -\dfrac{1}{2}x - \dfrac{1}{2}$

$\dfrac{3}{2}x - \dfrac{3}{4} = -\dfrac{3}{4}y$

50. $x + \dfrac{5}{4}y = -\dfrac{1}{2}$

$\dfrac{3}{4}x = -\dfrac{1}{2}y - \dfrac{5}{4}$

51. $x = -\dfrac{1}{2}$

$6x - 5y = -8$

52. $4x - 2y = 1$

$y = 3$

53. $0.02x + 0.04y = 0.12$

$0.03x - 0.05y = -0.15$

54. $-0.04x + 0.03y = 0.03$

$-0.06x - 0.02y = -0.02$

55. $8x - 16y = 24$

$2x - 4y = 0$

56. $y = -\dfrac{1}{2}x - 5$

$2x + 4y = -8$

57. $\dfrac{m}{2} + \dfrac{n}{5} = \dfrac{13}{10}$

$3m - 3n = m - 10$

58. $\dfrac{a}{4} - \dfrac{3b}{2} = \dfrac{15}{2}$

$a + 2b = -10$

59. $2m - 6n = m + 4$

$3m + 8 = 5m - n$

60. $m - 3n = 10$

$3m + 12n = -12$

61. $9a - 2b = 8$

$18a + 6 = 4b + 22$

62. $a = 5 + 2b$

$3a - 6b = 15$

63. $6x - 5y = 7$

$4x - 6y = 7$

For Exercises 64–69, use a system of linear equations, and solve for the indicated quantities.

64. The sum of two positive numbers is 26. Their difference is 14. Find the numbers.

65. The difference of two positive numbers is 2. The sum of the numbers is 36. Find the numbers.

66. Eight times the smaller of two numbers plus 2 times the larger number is 44. Three times the smaller number minus 2 times the larger number is zero. Find the numbers.

67. Six times the smaller of two numbers minus the larger number is −9. Ten times the smaller number plus five times the larger number is 5. Find the numbers.

68. Twice the difference of two angles is 64°. If the angles are complementary, find the measures of the angles.

69. The difference of an angle and twice another angle is 42°. If the angles are supplementary, find the measures of the angles.

For Exercises 70–72, solve the system by using each of the three methods: (a) the graphing method, (b) the substitution method, and (c) the addition method.

70. $2x + y = 1$

$-4x - 2y = -2$

71. $3x + y = 6$

$-2x + 2y = 4$

72. $2x - 2y = 6$

$5y = 5x + 5$

Expanding Your Skills

73. Explain why a system of linear equations cannot have exactly two solutions.

74. The solution to the system of linear equations is $\{(1, 2)\}$. Find A and B.

$Ax + 3y = 8$

$x + By = -7$

75. The solution to the system of linear equations is $\{(-3, 4)\}$. Find A and B.

$4x + Ay = -32$

$Bx + 6y = 18$

Problem Recognition Exercises

Systems of Equations

For Exercises 1–6 determine the number of solutions to the system without solving the system. Explain your answers.

1. $y = -4x + 2$
$\quad y = -4x + 2$

2. $y = -4x + 6$
$\quad y = -4x + 1$

3. $y = 4x - 3$
$\quad y = -4x + 5$

4. $y = 7$
$\quad 2x + 3y = 1$

5. $2x + 3y = 1$
$\quad 2x + 3y = 8$

6. $8x - 2y = 6$
$\quad 12x - 3y = 9$

For Exercises 7–10, a method of solving has been suggested for each system of equations. Explain why that method was suggested for the system and then solve the system using the method given.

7. $2x - 5y = -11$ Addition Method
$\quad 7x + 5y = -16$

8. $4x + 11y = 56$ Addition Method
$\quad -2x - 5y = -26$

9. $x = -3y + 4$ Substitution Method
$\quad 5x + 4y = -2$

10. $2x + 3y = 16$ Substitution Method
$\quad y = x - 8$

For Exercises 11–30, solve each system using the method of your choice. For systems that do not have one unique solution, also state the number of solutions and whether the system is inconsistent or the equations are dependent.

11. $x = -2y + 5$
$\quad 2x - 4y = 10$

12. $y = -3x - 4$
$\quad 2x - y = 9$

13. $3x - 2y = 22$
$\quad 5x + 2y = 10$

14. $-4x + 2y = -2$
$\quad 4x - 5y = -7$

15. $\frac{1}{3}x + \frac{1}{2}y = \frac{2}{3}$
$\quad -\frac{2}{3}x + y = -\frac{4}{3}$

16. $\frac{1}{4}x + \frac{2}{5}y = 6$
$\quad \frac{1}{2}x - \frac{1}{10}y = 3$

17. $2c + 7d = -1$
$\quad c = 2$

18. $-3w + 5z = -6$
$\quad z = -4$

19. $y = 0.4x - 0.3$
$\quad -4x + 10y = 20$

20. $x = -0.5y + 0.1$
$\quad -10x - 5y = 2$

21. $3a + 7b = -3$
$\quad -11a + 3b = 11$

22. $2v - 5w = 10$
$\quad 9v + 7w = 45$

23. $y = 2x - 14$
$\quad 4x - 2y = 28$

24. $x = 5y - 9$
$\quad -2x + 10y = 18$

25. $x + y = 3200$
$\quad 0.06x + 0.04y = 172$

26. $x + y = 4500$
$\quad 0.07x + 0.05y = 291$

27. $3x + y - 7 = x - 4$
$\quad 3x - 4y + 4 = -6y + 5$

28. $7y - 8y - 3 = -3x + 4$
$\quad 10x - 5y - 12 = 13$

29. $3x - 6y = -1$
$\quad 9x + 4y = 8$

30. $8x - 2y = 5$
$\quad 12x + 4y = -3$

Applications of Linear Equations in Two Variables

1. Applications Involving Cost

We have solved several applied problems by setting up a linear equation in one variable. When solving an application that involves two unknowns, sometimes it is convenient to use a system of linear equations in two variables.

Concepts

1. Applications Involving Cost
2. Applications Involving Principal and Interest
3. Applications Involving Mixtures
4. Applications Involving Distance, Rate, and Time

> **Example 1**   **Using a System of Linear Equations Involving Cost**

At a movie theater a couple buys one large popcorn and two small drinks for $12.50. A group of teenagers buys two large popcorns and five small drinks for $28.50. Find the cost of one large popcorn and the cost of one small drink.

Solution:

In this application we have two unknowns, which we can represent by x and y.

Let x represent the cost of one large popcorn.
Let y represent the cost of one small drink.

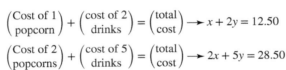

© Burke/Triolo/Brand X Pictures RF

We must now write two equations. Each of the first two sentences in the problem gives a relationship between x and y:

$$\left(\begin{array}{c}\text{Cost of 1}\\\text{popcorn}\end{array}\right) + \left(\begin{array}{c}\text{cost of 2}\\\text{drinks}\end{array}\right) = \left(\begin{array}{c}\text{total}\\\text{cost}\end{array}\right) \longrightarrow x + 2y = 12.50$$

$$\left(\begin{array}{c}\text{Cost of 2}\\\text{popcorns}\end{array}\right) + \left(\begin{array}{c}\text{cost of 5}\\\text{drinks}\end{array}\right) = \left(\begin{array}{c}\text{total}\\\text{cost}\end{array}\right) \longrightarrow 2x + 5y = 28.50$$

To solve this system, we may either use the substitution method or the addition method. We will use the substitution method by solving for x in the first equation.

$$x + 2y = 12.50 \longrightarrow x = -2y + 12.50 \qquad \text{Isolate } x \text{ in the first equation.}$$

$$2x + 5y = 28.50$$

$$2(-2y + 12.50) + 5y = 28.50 \qquad \text{Substitute } x = -2y + 12.50 \text{ into the other equation.}$$

$$-4y + 25.00 + 5y = 28.50 \qquad \text{Solve for } y.$$

$$y + 25.00 = 28.50$$

$$y = 3.50$$

$$x = -2y + 12.50$$
$$x = -2(3.50) + 12.50 \qquad \text{Substitute } y = 3.50 \text{ into the}$$
$$x = -7.00 + 12.50 \qquad \text{equation } x = -2y + 12.50.$$
$$x = 5.50$$

The cost of one large popcorn is $5.50 and the cost of one small drink is $3.50.

Check by verifying that the solution meets the specified conditions.

$$1 \text{ popcorn} + 2 \text{ drinks} = 1(\$5.50) + 2(\$3.50) = \$12.50 \checkmark \qquad \text{True}$$

$$2 \text{ popcorns} + 5 \text{ drinks} = 2(\$5.50) + 5(\$3.50) = \$28.50 \checkmark \qquad \text{True}$$

Skill Practice

1. Lynn went to a fast-food restaurant and spent $20.00. She purchased 4 hamburgers and 5 orders of fries. The next day, Ricardo went to the same restaurant and purchased 10 hamburgers and 7 orders of fries. He spent $41.20. Use a system of equations to determine the cost of a burger and the cost of an order of fries.

2. Applications Involving Principal and Interest

Simple interest is interest computed on the principal amount of money invested (or borrowed). Simple interest, I, is found by using the formula

$$I = Prt$$
where P is the principal,
r is the annual interest rate, and
t is the time in years.

In Example 2, we apply the concept of simple interest to two accounts to produce a desired amount of interest after 1 year.

Example 2 | **Using a System of Linear Equations Involving Investments**

Joanne has a total of $6000 to deposit in two accounts. One account earns 3.5% simple interest and the other earns 2.5% simple interest. If the total amount of interest at the end of 1 year is $195, find the amount she deposited in each account.

Solution:

Let x represent the principal deposited in the 2.5% account.
Let y represent the principal deposited in the 3.5% account.

	2.5% Account	3.5% Account	Total
Principal	x	y	6000
Interest ($I = Prt$)	$0.025x(1)$	$0.035y(1)$	195

Each row of the table yields an equation in x and y:

$$\begin{pmatrix} \text{Principal} \\ \text{invested} \\ \text{at } 2.5\% \end{pmatrix} + \begin{pmatrix} \text{principal} \\ \text{invested} \\ \text{at } 3.5\% \end{pmatrix} = \begin{pmatrix} \text{total} \\ \text{principal} \end{pmatrix} \longrightarrow x + y = 6000$$

$$\begin{pmatrix} \text{Interest} \\ \text{earned} \\ \text{at } 2.5\% \end{pmatrix} + \begin{pmatrix} \text{interest} \\ \text{earned} \\ \text{at } 3.5\% \end{pmatrix} = \begin{pmatrix} \text{total} \\ \text{interest} \end{pmatrix} \longrightarrow 0.025x + 0.035y = 195$$

We will choose the addition method to solve the system of equations. First multiply the second equation by 1000 to clear decimals.

Answer

1. The cost of a burger is $3.00, and the cost of an order of fries is $1.60.

$$\begin{array}{ccccc}
& & & & \text{Multiply by } -25. \\
x + y = 6000 \rightarrow & x + y = 6000 & \rightarrow & -25x - 25y = -150,000 \\
0.025x + 0.035y = 195 \rightarrow & 25x + 35y = 195,000 \rightarrow & & \underline{25x + 35y = \quad 195,000} \\
\text{Multiply by } 1000. & & & 10y = \quad 45,000
\end{array}$$

$10y = 45,000$ After eliminating the x variable, solve for y.

$\dfrac{10y}{10} = \dfrac{45,000}{10}$

$\quad y = 4500$ The amount invested in the 3.5% account is \$4500.

$x + y = 6000$ Substitute $y = 4500$ into the equation $x + y = 6000$.

$x + 4500 = 6000$

$\quad\quad x = 1500$ The amount invested in the 2.5% account is \$1500.

Joanne deposited \$1500 in the 2.5% account and \$4500 in the 3.5% account.

To check, verify that the conditions of the problem have been met.

1. The sum of \$1500 and \$4500 is \$6000 as desired. ✓   True

2. The interest earned on \$1500 at 2.5% is: 0.025(\$1500) = \$37.50
   The interest earned on \$4500 at 3.5% is: $\underline{0.035(\$4500) = \$157.50}$
   $\qquad\qquad\qquad\qquad\qquad$ Total interest: \$195.00 ✓   True

Skill Practice

2. Addie has a total of \$8000 in two accounts. One pays 5% interest, and the other pays 6.5% interest. At the end of one year, she earned \$475 interest. Use a system of equations to determine the amount invested in each account.

3. Applications Involving Mixtures

Example 3   **Using a System of Linear Equations in a Mixture Application**

According to new hospital standards, a certain disinfectant solution needs to be 20% alcohol instead of 10% alcohol. There is a 40% alcohol disinfectant available to adjust the mixture. Determine the amount of 10% solution and the amount of 40% solution to produce 30 L of a 20% solution.

Solution:

Each solution contains a percentage of alcohol plus some other mixing agent such as water. Before we set up a system of equations to model this situation, it is helpful to have background understanding of the problem. In Figure 4-9, the liquid depicted in blue is pure alcohol and the liquid shown in gray is the mixing agent (such as water). Together these liquids form a solution. (Realistically the mixture may not separate as shown, but this image may be helpful for your understanding.)

Let x represent the number of liters of 10% solution.
Let y represent the number of liters of 40% solution.

Answer

2. \$3000 is invested at 5%, and
   \$5000 is invested at 6.5%.

308   **Chapter 4**   Systems of Linear Equations in Two Variables

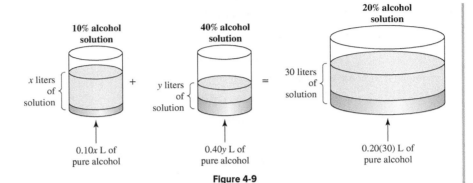

Figure 4-9

The information given in the statement of the problem can be organized in a chart.

	10% Alcohol	40% Alcohol	20% Alcohol
Number of liters of solution	x	y	30
Number of liters of pure alcohol	$0.10x$	$0.40y$	$0.20(30) = 6$

From the first row, we have

$$\left(\begin{array}{c}\text{Amount of}\\ \text{10\% solution}\end{array}\right) + \left(\begin{array}{c}\text{amount of}\\ \text{40\% solution}\end{array}\right) = \left(\begin{array}{c}\text{total amount}\\ \text{of 20\% solution}\end{array}\right) \rightarrow x + y = 30$$

From the second row, we have

$$\left(\begin{array}{c}\text{Amount of}\\ \text{alcohol in}\\ \text{10\% solution}\end{array}\right) + \left(\begin{array}{c}\text{amount of}\\ \text{alcohol in}\\ \text{40\% solution}\end{array}\right) = \left(\begin{array}{c}\text{total amount of}\\ \text{alcohol in}\\ \text{20\% solution}\end{array}\right) \rightarrow 0.10x + 0.40y = 6$$

We will solve the system with the addition method by first clearing decimals.

$$
\begin{array}{llll}
x + y = 30 & \xrightarrow{} & x + y = 30 & \xrightarrow{\text{Multiply by } -1.} & -x - y = -30 \\
0.10x + 0.40y = 6 & \xrightarrow[\text{Multiply by 10.}]{} & x + 4y = 60 & \xrightarrow{} & \underline{x + 4y = 60} \\
& & & & 3y = 30
\end{array}
$$

$3y = 30$ After eliminating the x variable, solve for y.

$y = 10$ 10 L of 40% solution is needed.

$x + y = 30$ Substitute $y = 10$ into either of the original equations.

$x + (10) = 30$

$x = 20$ 20 L of 10% solution is needed.

10 L of 40% solution must be mixed with 20 L of 10% solution.

Skill Practice

3. How many ounces of 20% and 35% acid solution should be mixed together to obtain 15 oz of 30% acid solution?

Answer

3. 10 oz of the 35% solution, and 5 oz of the 20% solution.

4. Applications Involving Distance, Rate, and Time

The following formula relates the distance traveled to the rate and time of travel.

$$d = rt \qquad \text{distance} = \text{rate} \cdot \text{time}$$

For example, if a car travels 60 mph for 3 hr, then

$$d = (60 \text{ mph})(3 \text{ hr})$$
$$= 180 \text{ mi}$$

If a car travels 60 mph for x hr, then

$$d = (60 \text{ mph})(x \text{ hr})$$
$$= 60x \text{ mi}$$

The relationship $d = rt$ is used in Example 4.

Example 4   **Using a System of Linear Equations in a Distance, Rate, and Time Application**

A plane travels with the wind from Kansas City, Missouri, to Denver, Colorado, a distance of 600 mi in 2 hr. The return trip against the same wind takes 3 hr. Find the speed of the plane in still air, and find the speed of the wind.

Solution:

Let p represent the speed of the plane in still air.
Let w represent the speed of the wind.

Notice that when the plane travels with the wind, the net speed is $p + w$. When the plane travels against the wind, the net speed is $p - w$.

The information given in the problem can be organized in a chart.

© Stockbyte/Punchstock Images RF

	Distance	Rate	Time
With the wind	600	$p + w$	2
Against the wind	600	$p - w$	3

To set up two equations in p and w, recall that $d = rt$.

From the first row, we have

$$\left(\begin{array}{c}\text{Distance}\\\text{with the wind}\end{array}\right) = \left(\begin{array}{c}\text{rate with}\\\text{the wind}\end{array}\right)\left(\begin{array}{c}\text{time traveled}\\\text{with the wind}\end{array}\right) \longrightarrow 600 = (p + w) \cdot 2$$

From the second row, we have

$$\left(\begin{array}{c}\text{Distance}\\\text{against the wind}\end{array}\right) = \left(\begin{array}{c}\text{rate against}\\\text{the wind}\end{array}\right)\left(\begin{array}{c}\text{time traveled}\\\text{against the wind}\end{array}\right) \longrightarrow 600 = (p - w) \cdot 3$$

Using the distributive property to clear parentheses produces the following system:

$$2p + 2w = 600$$
$$3p - 3w = 600$$

The coefficients of the w variable can be changed to 6 and -6 by multiplying the first equation by 3 and the second equation by 2.

$$2p + 2w = 600 \quad \xrightarrow{\text{Multiply by 3.}} \quad 6p + 6w = 1800$$
$$3p - 3w = 600 \quad \xrightarrow[\text{Multiply by 2.}]{} \quad \underline{6p - 6w = 1200}$$
$$12p \qquad\quad = 3000$$

$$12p = 3000$$

$$\frac{12p}{12} = \frac{3000}{12}$$

$$p = 250 \qquad \text{The speed of the plane in still air is 250 mph.}$$

TIP: To create opposite coefficients on the w variables, we could have divided the first equation by 2 and divided the second equation by 3:

$$2p + 2w = 600 \quad \xrightarrow{\text{Divide by 2.}} \quad p + w = 300$$
$$3p - 3w = 600 \quad \xrightarrow[\text{Divide by 3.}]{} \quad \underline{p - w = 200}$$
$$2p \qquad = 500$$
$$p = 250$$

$$2p + 2w = 600 \qquad \text{Substitute } p = 250 \text{ into the first equation.}$$

$$2(250) + 2w = 600$$

$$500 + 2w = 600$$

$$2w = 100$$

$$w = 50 \qquad \text{The speed of the wind is 50 mph.}$$

The speed of the plane in still air is 250 mph. The speed of the wind is 50 mph.

Skill Practice

Answer

4. The speed of the canoe in still water is 5 mph. The speed of the current is 3 mph.

4. Dan and Cheryl paddled their canoe 40 mi in 5 hr with the current and 16 mi in 8 hr against the current. Find the speed of the current and the speed of the canoe in still water.

Section 4.4   Practice Exercises

Review Exercises

For Exercises 1–4, solve each system of equations by three different methods:

    a. Graphing method   **b.** Substitution method   **c.** Addition method

1. $-2x + y = 6$
    $2x + y = 2$

2. $x - y = 2$
    $x + y = 6$

3. $y = -2x + 6$
    $4x - 2y = 8$

4. $2x = y + 4$
    $4x = 2y + 8$

For Exercises 5–8, set up a system of linear equations in two variables and solve for the unknown quantities.

5. One number is eight more than twice another. Their sum is 20. Find the numbers.

6. The difference of two positive numbers is 264. The larger number is three times the smaller number. Find the numbers.

7. Two angles are complementary. The measure of one angle is 10° less than nine times the measure of the other. Find the measure of each angle.

8. Two angles are supplementary. The measure of one angle is 9° more than twice the measure of the other angle. Find the measure of each angle.

Concept 1: Applications Involving Cost

9. An online store sells old video games and DVDs as a bundle. A bundle of two video games and three DVDs can be purchased for $88. A bundle of one video game and two DVDs can be purchased for $51.50. Find the cost of one video game and the cost of one DVD in the bundle. **(See Example 1.)**

10. Tanya bought three adult tickets and one children's ticket to a movie for $32.00. Li bought two adult tickets and five children's tickets for $49.50. Find the cost of one adult ticket and the cost of one children's ticket.

11. Nora bought 100 shares of a technology stock and 200 shares of a mutual fund for $3800. Her sister, Erin, bought 300 shares of the technology stock and 50 shares of the same mutual fund for $5350. Find the cost per share of the technology stock, and the cost per share of the mutual fund.

12. Eight students in Ms. Reese's class decided to purchase their textbooks from two different sources. Some students purchased the textbook from the college bookstore for $95.50. The other students purchased the textbook from an online discount store for $65 per book. If the total amount spent by the eight students is $611.50, how many students purchased the book online?

13. Mylee is a stamp collector and buys commemorative stamps. Suppose she buys a combination of 47-cent stamps and 34-cent stamps at the post office. If she spends exactly $21.55 on 50 stamps, how many of each type did she buy?

14. Zoey purchased some beef and some chicken for a family barbeque. The beef cost $6.00 per pound and the chicken cost $4.50 per pound. She bought a total of 18 lb of meat and spent $96. How much of each type of meat did she purchase?

Concept 2: Applications Involving Principal and Interest

15. Shanelle invested $10,000, and at the end of 1 year, she received $805 in interest. She invested part of the money in an account earning 10% simple interest and the remaining money in an account earning 7% simple interest. How much did she invest in each account? **(See Example 2.)**

16. $12,000 was borrowed from two sources, one that charges 12% simple interest and the other that charges 8% simple interest. If the total interest at the end of 1 year was $1240, how much money was borrowed from each source?

	10% Account	7% Account	Total
Principal invested			
Interest earned			

	12% Account	8% Account	Total
Principal borrowed			
Interest earned			

17. Troy borrowed a total of $12,000 in two different loans to help pay for his new truck. One loan charges 9% simple interest, and the other charges 6% simple interest. If he is charged $810 in interest after 1 year, find the amount borrowed at each rate.

18. Blake has a total of $4000 to invest in two accounts. One account earns 2% simple interest, and the other earns 5% simple interest. How much should be invested in each account to earn exactly $155 at the end of 1 year?

19. Suppose a rich uncle dies and leaves you an inheritance of $30,000. You decide to invest part of the money in a relatively safe bond fund that returns 8%. You invest the rest of the money in a riskier stock fund that you hope will return 12% at the end of 1 year. If you need $3120 at the end of 1 year to make a down payment on a car, how much should you invest at each rate?

20. As part of his retirement strategy, John plans to invest $200,000 in two different funds. He projects that the moderately high risk investments should return, over time, about 9% per year, while the low risk investments should return about 4% per year. If he wants a supplemental income of $12,000 a year, how should he divide his investments?

Concept 3: Applications Involving Mixtures

21. How much 50% disinfectant solution must be mixed with a 40% disinfectant solution to produce 25 gal of a 46% disinfectant solution? (See Example 3.)

	50% Mixture	40% Mixture	46% Mixture
Amount of solution			
Amount of disinfectant			

22. How many gallons of 20% antifreeze solution and a 10% antifreeze solution must be mixed to obtain 40 gal of a 16% antifreeze solution?

	20% Mixture	10% Mixture	16% Mixture
Amount of solution			
Amount of antifreeze			

23. How much 45% disinfectant solution must be mixed with a 30% disinfectant solution to produce 20 gal of a 39% disinfectant solution?

24. How many gallons of a 25% antifreeze solution and a 15% antifreeze solution must be mixed to obtain 15 gal of a 23% antifreeze solution?

25. A chemist needs 50 mL of a 16% salt solution for an experiment. She can only find a 13% salt solution and an 18% salt solution in the supply room. How many milliliters of the 13% solution should be mixed with the 18% solution to produce the desired amount of the 16% solution?

26. Meadowsilver Dairy keeps two kinds of milk on hand, skim milk that has 0.3% butterfat and whole milk that contains 3.3% butterfat. How many gallons of each type of milk does the company need to produce 300 gal of 1% milk for the P&A grocery store?

27. The cooling system in most cars requires a mixture that is 50% antifreeze. How many liters of pure antifreeze and how many liters of 40% antifreeze solution should Chad mix to obtain 6 L of 50% antifreeze solution? (*Hint:* Pure antifreeze is 100% antifreeze.)

28. Silvia wants to mix a 40% apple juice drink with pure apple juice to make 2 L of a juice drink that is 80% apple juice. How much pure apple juice should she use?

Concept 4: Applications Involving Distance, Rate, and Time

29. It takes a boat 2 hr to go 16 mi downstream with the current and 4 hr to return against the current. Find the speed of the boat in still water and the speed of the current. (See Example 4.)

	Distance	Rate	Time
Downstream			
Upstream			

30. A boat takes 1.5 hr to go 12 mi upstream against the current. It can go 24 mi downstream with the current in the same amount of time. Find the speed of the current and the speed of the boat in still water.

	Distance	Rate	Time
Upstream			
Downstream			

31. A plane can fly 960 mi with the wind in 3 hr. It takes the same amount of time to fly 840 mi against the wind. What is the speed of the plane in still air and the speed of the wind?

32. A plane flies 720 mi with the wind in 3 hr. The return trip against the wind takes 4 hr. What is the speed of the wind and the speed of the plane in still air?

33. Tony Markins flew from JFK Airport to London. It took him 6 hr to fly with the wind, and 8 hr on the return flight against the wind. If the distance is approximately 3600 mi, determine the speed of the plane in still air and the speed of the wind.

34. A riverboat cruise upstream on the Mississippi River from New Orleans, Louisiana, to Natchez, Mississippi, takes 10 hr and covers 140 mi. The return trip downstream with the current takes only 7 hr. Find the speed of the riverboat in still water and the speed of the current.

© Royalty Free/Corbis RF

© S. Solum/PhotoLink/Getty Images RF

Mixed Exercises

35. Debi has $2.80 in a collection of dimes and nickels. The number of nickels is five more than the number of dimes. Find the number of each type of coin.

36. A child collects state quarters and new $1 coins. If she has a total of 25 coins, and the number of quarters is nine more than the number of dollar coins, how many of each type of coin does she have?

37. How many quarts of water should be mixed with a 30% vinegar solution to obtain 12 qt of a 25% vinegar solution? (*Hint:* Water is 0% vinegar.)

38. How much water should be mixed with an 8% plant fertilizer solution to make a half gallon of a 6% plant fertilizer solution?

39. In the 1961–1962 NBA basketball season, Wilt Chamberlain of the Philadelphia Warriors made 2432 baskets. Some of the baskets were free throws (worth 1 point each) and some were field goals (worth 2 points each). The number of field goals was 762 more than the number of free throws.

  a. How many field goals did he make and how many free throws did he make?

  b. What was the total number of points scored?

  c. If Wilt Chamberlain played 80 games during this season, what was the average number of points per game?

40. In the 1971–1972 NBA basketball season, Kareem Abdul-Jabbar of the Milwaukee Bucks made 1663 baskets. Some of the baskets were free throws (worth 1 point each) and some were field goals (worth 2 points each). The number of field goals he scored was 151 more than twice the number of free throws.

  a. How many field goals did he make and how many free throws did he make?

  b. What was the total number of points scored?

  c. If Kareem Abdul-Jabbar played 81 games during this season, what was the average number of points per game?

41. A small plane can fly 350 mi with the wind in $1\frac{3}{4}$ hr. In the same amount of time, the same plane can travel only 210 mi against the wind. What is the speed of the plane in still air and the speed of the wind?

42. A plane takes 2 hr to travel 1000 mi with the wind. It can travel only 880 mi against the wind in the same amount of time. Find the speed of the wind and the speed of the plane in still air.

314   **Chapter 4**   Systems of Linear Equations in Two Variables

43. A total of $60,000 is invested in two accounts, one that earns 5.5% simple interest, and one that earns 6.5% simple interest. If the total interest at the end of 1 year is $3750, find the amount invested in each account.

44. Jacques borrows a total of $15,000. Part of the money is borrowed from a bank that charges 12% simple interest per year. Jacques borrows the remaining part of the money from his sister and promises to pay her 7% simple interest per year. If Jacques' total interest for the year is $1475, find the amount he borrowed from each source.

45. At the holidays, Erica likes to sell a candy/nut mixture to her neighbors. She wants to combine candy that costs $1.80 per pound with nuts that cost $1.20 per pound. If Erica needs 20 lb of mixture that will sell for $1.56 per pound, how many pounds of candy and how many pounds of nuts should she use?

46. Mary Lee's natural food store sells a combination of teas. The most popular is a mixture of a tea that sells for $3.00 per pound with one that sells for $4.00 per pound. If she needs 40 lb of tea that will sell for $3.65 per pound, how many pounds of each tea should she use?

© McGraw-Hill Education/
Jill Braaten

© Steve Mason/Getty Images RF

47. In the 1994 Super Bowl, the Dallas Cowboys scored four more points than twice the number of points scored by the Buffalo Bills. If the total number of points scored by both teams was 43, find the number of points scored by each team.

48. In the 1973 Super Bowl, the Miami Dolphins scored twice as many points as the Washington Redskins. If the total number of points scored by both teams was 21, find the number of points scored by each team.

© herreid/Getty Images RF

Expanding Your Skills

49. In a survey conducted among 500 college students, 340 said that the campus lacked adequate lighting. If $\frac{4}{5}$ of the women and $\frac{1}{2}$ of the men said that they thought the campus lacked adequate lighting, how many men and how many women were in the survey?

50. During a 1-hr television program, there were 22 commercials. Some commercials were 15 sec and some were 30 sec long. Find the number of 15-sec commercials and the number of 30-sec commercials if the total playing time for commercials was 9.5 min.

Section 4.5   Systems of Linear Equations
in Three Variables

Concepts

1. Solutions to Systems of Linear Equations in Three Variables

In this section, we will expand the discussion of solving systems of linear equations in two variables to solving systems involving three variables.

A **linear equation in three variables** can be written in the form $Ax + By + Cz = D$, where A, B, and C are not all zero. For example, the equation $2x + 3y + z = 6$ is a linear equation in three variables. Solutions to this equation are **ordered triples** of the form (x, y, z) that satisfy the equation. Some solutions to the equation $2x + 3y + z = 6$ are

Solution: Check:

$(1, 1, 1) \longrightarrow 2(1) + 3(1) + (1) = 6$ ✓ True

$(2, 0, 2) \longrightarrow 2(2) + 3(0) + (2) = 6$ ✓ True

$(0, 1, 3) \longrightarrow 2(0) + 3(1) + (3) = 6$ ✓ True

Infinitely many ordered triples serve as solutions to the equation $2x + 3y + z = 6$.

The set of all ordered triples that are solutions to a linear equation in three variables may be represented graphically by a plane in space. Figure 4-10 shows a portion of the plane $2x + 3y + z = 6$ in a 3-dimensional coordinate system.

A solution to a system of linear equations in three variables is an ordered triple that satisfies *each* equation. Geometrically, a solution is a point of intersection of the planes represented by the equations in the system.

A system of linear equations in three variables may have *one unique solution, infinitely many solutions,* or *no solution.*

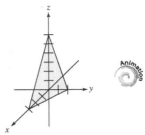

Figure 4-10

One unique solution (planes intersect at one point)

- The system is consistent.
- The equations are independent.

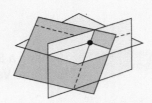

No solution (the three planes do not all intersect)

- The system is inconsistent.
- The equations are independent.

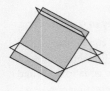 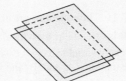 

Infinitely many solutions (planes intersect at infinitely many points)

- The system is consistent.
- The equations are dependent.

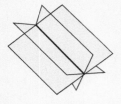 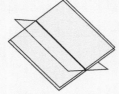 

2. Solving Systems of Linear Equations in Three Variables

To solve a system involving three variables, the goal is to eliminate one variable. This reduces the system to two equations in two variables. One strategy for eliminating a variable is to pair up the original equations two at a time.

Solving a System of Three Linear Equations in Three Variables

Step 1   Write each equation in standard form $Ax + By + Cz = D$.

Step 2   Choose a pair of equations, and eliminate one of the variables by using the addition method.

Step 3   Choose a different pair of equations and eliminate the *same* variable.

Step 4   Once steps 2 and 3 are complete, you should have two equations in two variables. Solve this system by using the substitution or the addition method.

Step 5   Substitute the values of the variables found in step 4 into any of the three original equations that contain the third variable. Solve for the third variable.

Step 6   Check the ordered triple in each of the original equations.

| **Example 1** | **Solving a System of Linear Equations in Three Variables** |

Solve the system.

$$2x + y - 3z = -7$$
$$3x - 2y + z = 11$$
$$-2x - 3y - 2z = 3$$

Solution:

$\boxed{A}$ $2x + y - 3z = -7$

$\boxed{B}$ $3x - 2y + z = 11$

$\boxed{C}$ $-2x - 3y - 2z = 3$

Step 1: The equations are already in standard form.

- It is often helpful to label the equations.
- The y variable can be easily eliminated from equations $\boxed{A}$ and $\boxed{B}$ and from equations $\boxed{A}$ and $\boxed{C}$. This is accomplished by creating opposite coefficients for the y terms and then adding the equations.

Step 2:   Eliminate the y-variable from equations $\boxed{A}$ and $\boxed{B}$.

$\boxed{A}$ $2x + y - 3z = -7$ $\xrightarrow{\text{Multiply by 2.}}$ $4x + 2y - 6z = -14$

$\boxed{B}$ $3x - 2y + z = 11$ $\xrightarrow{}$ $\underline{3x - 2y + z = 11}$

$7x - 5z = -3$ $\boxed{D}$

Step 3: Eliminate the y-variable again, this time from equations $\boxed{A}$ and $\boxed{C}$.

$\boxed{A}$ $2x + y - 3z = -7 \xrightarrow{\text{Multiply by 3.}} 6x + 3y - 9z = -21$

$\boxed{C}$ $-2x - 3y - 2z = 3 \xrightarrow{} \underline{-2x - 3y - 2z = 3}$

$ 4x - 11z = -18 \;\; \boxed{E}$

TIP: It is important to note that in steps 2 and 3, the *same* variable is eliminated.

Step 4: Now equations $\boxed{D}$ and $\boxed{E}$ can be paired up to form a linear system in two variables. Solve this system.

$\boxed{D}$ $7x - 5z = -3 \xrightarrow{\text{Multiply by } -4.} -28x + 20z = 12$

$\boxed{E}$ $4x - 11z = -18 \xrightarrow[\text{Multiply by 7.}]{} \underline{28x - 77z = -126}$

$ -57z = -114$

$ z = 2$

Once one variable has been found, substitute this value into either equation in the two-variable system, that is, either equation $\boxed{D}$ or $\boxed{E}$.

$\boxed{D}$ $7x - 5z = -3$

$ 7x - 5(2) = -3 $ Substitute $z = 2$ into equation $\boxed{D}$.

$ 7x - 10 = -3$

$ 7x = 7$

$ x = 1$

$\boxed{A}$ $2x + y - 3z = -7$

$ 2(1) + y - 3(2) = -7$

$ 2 + y - 6 = -7$

$ y - 4 = -7$

$ y = -3$

Step 5: Now that two variables are known, substitute these values for x and z into any of the original three equations to find the remaining variable y. Substitute $x = 1$ and $z = 2$ into equation $\boxed{A}$.

Step 6: Check the ordered triple, $(1, -3, 2)$, in the three original equations.

$\underline{\text{Check:}} \quad 2x + y - 3z = -7 \rightarrow 2(1) + (-3) - 3(2) = -7 \checkmark \text{ True}$

$ 3x - 2y + z = 11 \rightarrow 3(1) - 2(-3) + (2) = 11 \checkmark \text{ True}$

$ -2x - 3y - 2z = 3 \rightarrow -2(1) - 3(-3) - 2(2) = 3 \checkmark \text{ True}$

The solution set is $\{(1, -3, 2)\}$.

Skill Practice Solve the system.

1. $x + 2y + z = 1$
    $3x - y + 2z = 13$
    $2x + 3y - z = -8$

Answer
1. $\{(1, -2, 4)\}$

Example 2   Solving a System of Linear Equations in Three Variables

Solve the system.
$$3x + y - 5 = 0$$
$$z = 7 + 2y$$
$$x + 3z = 17$$

Solution:

A $\quad 3x + y \quad\quad = 5$

B $\quad\quad -2y + z = 7$

C $\quad x \quad\quad + 3z = 17$

Step 1:   Write equations in standard form, $Ax + By + Cz = D$.

Steps 2 and 3:   Note equation C is missing the y-variable. Therefore, we can eliminate the y-variable by pairing up equations A and B.

A $\quad 3x + y \quad\quad = 5$ $\xrightarrow{\text{Multiply by 2.}}$ $\quad 6x + 2y \quad\quad = 10$

B $\quad -2y + z = 7$ $\longrightarrow$ $\quad\quad\quad -2y + z = 7$

$$\overline{\quad 6x \quad\quad + z = 17 \quad \boxed{D}}$$

Step 4:   Now we pair up equations C and D to eliminate the z-variable.

C $\quad x + 3z = 17$ $\longrightarrow$ $\quad x + 3y = 17$

D $\quad 6x + z = 17$ $\longrightarrow$ $\quad \underline{-18x - 3z = -51}$

$\qquad\qquad\qquad$ Multiply by -3.

$$-17x \quad\quad = -34$$
$$x = 2$$

Step 5:   Now substitute $x = 2$ into equations A and C to find the remaining variables.

A $\quad 3x + y = 5$ $\qquad\qquad$ C $\quad x + 3z = 17$

$\quad 3(2) + y = 5$ $\qquad\qquad\qquad\quad (2) + 3z = 17$

$\quad\quad 6 + y = 5$ $\qquad\qquad\qquad\qquad\quad 3z = 15$

$\quad\quad\quad y = -1$ $\qquad\qquad\qquad\qquad\quad z = 5$

Step 6:   Check $(2, -1, 5)$ in the three original equations.

$\underline{\text{Check}}$: $3x + y - 5 = 0$ $\longrightarrow$ $3(2) + (-1) - 5 = 0$ ✔ True

$\qquad\qquad z = 7 + 2y$ $\qquad\longrightarrow$ $5 = 7 + 2(-1)$ ✔ True

$\qquad\qquad x + 3z = 17$ $\qquad\longrightarrow$ $(2) + 3(5) = 17$ ✔ True

The solution set is $\{(2, -1, 5)\}$.

Skill Practice   Solve the system.

2. $\quad 4y = x + 4$
   $\quad 2x + z = 5$
   $\quad y - 14 = 4z$

Answer

2. $\{(4, 2, -3)\}$

Example 3	**Solving a System of Dependent Equations**

Solve the system. If there is not a unique solution, state the number of solutions and whether the system is inconsistent or the equations are dependent.

$$\boxed{A}\ 3x + y - z = 8$$
$$\boxed{B}\ 2x - y + 2z = 3$$
$$\boxed{C}\ x + 2y - 3z = 5$$

Solution:

First, make a decision regarding the variable to eliminate. The y-variable is particularly easy to eliminate because the coefficients of y in equations $\boxed{A}$ and $\boxed{B}$ are already opposites. The y-variable can be eliminated from equations $\boxed{B}$ and $\boxed{C}$ by multiplying equation $\boxed{B}$ by 2.

$$\boxed{A}\quad 3x + y - z = 8$$
$$\boxed{B}\quad \underline{2x - y + 2z = 3}$$
$$\qquad 5x \quad + z = 11 \ \boxed{D}$$

Pair up equations $\boxed{A}$ and $\boxed{B}$ to eliminate y.

$$\boxed{B}\ 2x - y + 2z = 3 \xrightarrow{\text{Multiply by 2.}} 4x - 2y + 4z = 6$$
$$\boxed{C}\ x + 2y - 3z = 5 \xrightarrow{\qquad} \underline{x + 2y - 3z = 5}$$
$$\qquad\qquad\qquad\qquad\qquad 5x \quad + z = 11 \ \boxed{E}$$

Pair up equations $\boxed{B}$ and $\boxed{C}$ to eliminate y.

Because equations $\boxed{D}$ and $\boxed{E}$ are equivalent equations, this is a dependent system. By eliminating variables we obtain the identity $0 = 0$.

$$\boxed{D}\ 5x + z = 11 \xrightarrow{\text{Multiply by } -1.} -5x - z = -11$$
$$\boxed{E}\ 5x + z = 11 \xrightarrow{\qquad} \underline{5x + z = \ \ 11}$$
$$\qquad\qquad\qquad\qquad\qquad\qquad 0 = \ \ 0$$

The result $0 = 0$ indicates that there are infinitely many solutions and that the equations are dependent.

Skill Practice Solve the system. If the system does not have a unique solution, state the number of solutions and whether the system is inconsistent or the equations are dependent.

3. $\quad x + y + z = \ \ 8$
$\qquad 2x - y + z = \ \ 6$
$\quad -5x - 2y - 4z = -30$

Answer

3. Infinitely many solutions; dependent equations

Example 4 **Solving an Inconsistent System of Linear Equations**

Solve the system. If there is not a unique solution, state the number of solutions and whether the system is inconsistent or the equations are dependent.

$$2x + 3y - 7z = 4$$
$$-4x - 6y + 14z = 1$$
$$5x + y - 3z = 6$$

Solution:

We will eliminate the x-variable.

		Multiply by 2.	
A	$2x + 3y - 7z = 4$	$\longrightarrow$	$4x + 6y - 14z = 8$
B	$-4x - 6y + 14z = 1$	$\longrightarrow$	$\underline{-4x - 6y + 14z = 1}$
C	$5x + y - 3z = 6$		$0 = 9$ (contradiction)

The result $0 = 9$ is a contradiction, indicating that the system has no solution. The system is inconsistent.

Skill Practice Solve the system. If the system does not have a unique solution, state the number of solutions and whether the system is inconsistent or the equations are dependent.

4. $x - 2y + z = 5$
    $x - 3y + 2z = -7$
    $-2x + 4y - 2z = 6$

Answer

4. No solution; inconsistent system

Section 4.5 **Practice Exercises**

Vocabulary and Key Concepts

1. **a.** An equation written in the form $Ax + By + Cz = D$, where A, B, and C are not all zero, is called a _____ equation in three variables.

   b. Solutions to a linear equation in three variables are of the form (x, y, z) and are called _____ .

Review Exercises

For Exercises 2–4, solve the systems by using two methods: **(a)** the substitution method and **(b)** the addition method.

2. $3x + y = 4$
    $4x + y = 5$

3. $2x - 5y = 3$
    $-4x + 10y = 3$

4. $4x - 6y = 5$
    $x = \dfrac{3}{2}y + \dfrac{5}{4}$

5. Two cars leave Kansas City at the same time. One travels east and one travels west. After 3 hr the cars are 369 mi apart. If one car travels 7 mph slower than the other, find the speed of each car.

Concept 1: Solutions to Systems of Linear Equations in Three Variables

6. How many solutions are possible when solving a system of three equations with three variables?

7. Which of the following points are solutions to the system?

$$(2, 1, 7), (3, -10, -6), (4, 0, 2)$$

$$2x - y + z = 10$$
$$4x + 2y - 3z = 10$$
$$x - 3y + 2z = 8$$

8. Which of the following points are solutions to the system?

$$(1, 1, 3), (0, 0, 4), (4, 2, 1)$$

$$-3x - 3y - 6z = -24$$
$$-9x - 6y + 3z = -45$$
$$9x + 3y - 9z = 33$$

9. Which of the following points are solutions to the system?

$$(12, 2, -2), (4, 2, 1), (1, 1, 1)$$

$$-x - y - 4z = -6$$
$$x - 3y + z = -1$$
$$4x + y - z = 4$$

10. Which of the following points are solutions to the system?

$$(0, 4, 3), (3, 6, 10), (3, 3, 1)$$

$$x + 2y - z = 5$$
$$x - 3y + z = -5$$
$$-2x + y - z = -4$$

Concept 2: Solving Systems of Linear Equations in Three Variables

For Exercises 11–34, solve the system of equations. **(See Examples 1–2.)**

11.
$$2x + y - 3z = -12$$
$$3x - 2y - z = 3$$
$$-x + 5y + 2z = -3$$

12.
$$-3x - 2y + 4z = -15$$
$$2x + 5y - 3z = 3$$
$$4x - y + 7z = 15$$

13.
$$x - 3y - 4z = -7$$
$$5x + 2y + 2z = -1$$
$$4x - y - 5z = -6$$

14.
$$6x - 5y + z = 7$$
$$5x + 3y + 2z = 0$$
$$-2x + y - 3z = 11$$

15.
$$-3x + y - z = 8$$
$$-4x + 2y + 3z = -3$$
$$2x + 3y - 2z = -1$$

16.
$$2x + 3y + 3z = 15$$
$$3x - 6y - 6z = -23$$
$$-9x - 3y + 6z = 8$$

17.
$$4x + 2z = 12 + 3y$$
$$2x = 3x + 3z - 5$$
$$y = 2x + 7z + 8$$

18.
$$y = 2x + z + 1$$
$$-3x - 1 = -2y + 2z$$
$$5x + 3z = 16 - 3y$$

19.
$$x + y + z = 6$$
$$-x + y - z = -2$$
$$2x + 3y + z = 11$$

20.
$$x - y - z = -11$$
$$x + y - z = 15$$
$$2x - y + z = -9$$

21.
$$2x - 3y + 2z = -1$$
$$x + 2y = -4$$
$$x + z = 1$$

22.
$$x + y + z = 2$$
$$2x - z = 5$$
$$3y + z = 2$$

23.
$$4x + 9y = 8$$
$$8x + 6z = -1$$
$$6y + 6z = -1$$

24.
$$3x + 2z = 11$$
$$y - 7z = 4$$
$$x - 6y = 1$$

25.
$$2x + 3y - 2z = 8$$
$$x - 4y + z = -8$$
$$-4x + 3y + 2z = 3$$

26.
$$5x - 3y + z = 4$$
$$-x + 6y + 4z = 1$$
$$2x + 3y - z = 3$$

27.
$$5y = -7 + 4z$$
$$x + 3y + 3 = 0$$
$$2x = 14 + z$$

28.
$$4(x - z) = -1$$
$$3y + z = 1$$
$$4x = 3 + y$$

29.
$$x + z = -16 + 3y$$
$$2(y + z) = 12 - 5y$$
$$3x + 8 = y - z$$

30.
$$4(x - 2y) = 8 - 3z$$
$$4y + 13 = 3x + z$$
$$x - 3y = -2(z + 2)$$

31.
$$\tfrac{1}{3}x + \tfrac{1}{2}y + \tfrac{1}{6}z = \tfrac{1}{6}$$
$$\tfrac{1}{5}x + y - \tfrac{3}{5}z = \tfrac{4}{5}$$
$$x - \tfrac{4}{9}y + \tfrac{2}{3}z = \tfrac{1}{3}$$

32.
$$\tfrac{1}{2}x + \tfrac{5}{2}z = -1$$
$$\tfrac{1}{4}x - \tfrac{1}{6}y - \tfrac{2}{3}z = 3$$
$$-\tfrac{1}{2}x + \tfrac{5}{8}y + \tfrac{1}{8}z = -3$$

33.
$$0.1x - 0.6y + z = -6.8$$
$$0.7x - 0.3z = -14$$
$$y + 0.5z = 8$$

34.
$$0.5x + y = 10$$
$$-0.2y + 0.5z = 0.5$$
$$-0.3x - z = -6$$

Mixed Exercises

For Exercises 35–46, solve the system. If there is not a unique solution, state whether the system is inconsistent or the equations are dependent. **(See Examples 1–4.)**

35.
$$2x + y + 3z = 2$$
$$x - y + 2z = -4$$
$$-2x + 2y - 4z = 8$$

36.
$$x + y = z$$
$$2x + 4y - 2z = 6$$
$$3x + 6y - 3z = 9$$

37.
$$6x - 2y + 2z = 2$$
$$4x + 8y - 2z = 5$$
$$-2x - 4y + z = -2$$

38.
$$3x + 2y + z = 3$$
$$x - 3y + z = 4$$
$$-6x - 4y - 2z = 1$$

39.
$$\tfrac{1}{2}x + \tfrac{2}{3}y = \tfrac{5}{2}$$
$$\tfrac{1}{5}x - \tfrac{1}{2}z = -\tfrac{3}{10}$$
$$\tfrac{1}{3}y - \tfrac{1}{4}z = \tfrac{3}{4}$$

40.
$$\tfrac{1}{2}x + \tfrac{1}{4}y + z = 3$$
$$\tfrac{1}{8}x + \tfrac{1}{4}y + \tfrac{1}{4}z = \tfrac{9}{8}$$
$$x - y - \tfrac{2}{3}z = \tfrac{1}{3}$$

41.
$$3(2x + y) = 4(3z - 1)$$
$$y + 4z = 2(3 + 5x)$$
$$2(x + z) = y - 1$$

42.
$$5(y - 2z) = 9x - 11$$
$$2(3x + z) = 5 + y$$
$$3x = z + 2(y + 1)$$

43.
$$2x + y = 3(z - 1)$$
$$3x - 2(y - 2z) = 1$$
$$2(2x - 3z) = -6 - 2y$$

44.
$$2x + y = -3$$
$$2y + 16z = -10$$
$$-7x - 3y + 4z = 8$$

45.
$$-0.1y + 0.2z = 0.2$$
$$0.1x + 0.1y + 0.1z = 0.2$$
$$-0.1x + 0.3z = 0.2$$

46.
$$0.1x - 0.2y = 0$$
$$0.3y + 0.1z = -0.1$$
$$0.4x - 0.1z = 1.2$$

Expanding Your Skills

The systems in Exercises 47–50 are called homogeneous systems because each system has $(0, 0, 0)$ as a solution. However, if the equations are dependent, there will be infinitely many more solutions. For each system determine whether $(0, 0, 0)$ is the only solution or if the equations are dependent.

47.
$$2x - 4y + 8z = 0$$
$$-x - 3y + z = 0$$
$$x - 2y + 5z = 0$$

48.
$$2x - 4y + z = 0$$
$$x - 3y - z = 0$$
$$3x - y + 2z = 0$$

49.
$$4x - 2y - 3z = 0$$
$$-8x - y + z = 0$$
$$2x - y - \tfrac{3}{2}z = 0$$

50.
$$5x + y = 0$$
$$4y - z = 0$$
$$5x + 5y - z = 0$$

Applications of Systems of Linear Equations in Three Variables

1. Applications Involving Geometry

In this section we solve several applications of linear equations in three variables.

Objectives

1. Applications Involving Geometry
2. Applications Involving Mixtures

Example 1   **Applying Systems of Linear Equations in Three Variables**

In a triangle, the smallest angle measures $10°$ more than one-half of the largest angle. The middle angle measures $12°$ more than the smallest angle. Find the measure of each angle.

Solution:

Let x represent the measure of the smallest angle.

Let y represent the measure of the middle angle.

Let z represent the measure of the largest angle.

To solve for three variables, we need to establish three independent relationships among x, y, and z.

$\boxed{A}$ $\quad x = \dfrac{1}{2}z + 10$
The smallest angle measures $10°$ more than one-half the measure of the largest angle.

$\boxed{B}$ $\quad y = x + 12$
The middle angle measures $12°$ more than the measure of the smallest angle.

$\boxed{C}$ $\quad x + y + z = 180$
The sum of the interior angles of a triangle measures $180°$.

Clear fractions and write each equation in standard form.

Standard Form

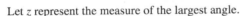

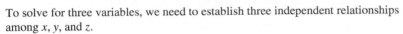

$\boxed{A}$ $\quad x \quad = \dfrac{1}{2}z + 10 \xrightarrow{\text{Multiply by 2.}} 2x = z + 20 \longrightarrow \quad 2x \quad - z = \ 20$

$\boxed{B}$ $\quad\quad y \ = \ x + 12 \xrightarrow{\hspace{4cm}} \quad -x + y \quad = \ 12$

$\boxed{C}$ $\quad x + y + z = \quad 180 \xrightarrow{\hspace{4cm}} \quad x + y + z = 180$

Notice equation $\boxed{B}$ is missing the z-variable. Therefore, we can eliminate z again by pairing up equations $\boxed{A}$ and $\boxed{C}$.

$\boxed{A}$ $\quad 2x \quad\quad - z = \ 20$
$\boxed{C}$ $\quad \underline{x + y + z = 180}$
$\quad\quad 3x + y \quad = 200$ $\boxed{D}$

$$\boxed{B}\ -x+y=12 \xrightarrow{\text{Multiply by } -1.} x-y=-12$$
$$\boxed{D}\ 3x+y=200 \longrightarrow \underline{3x+y=200}$$

Pair up equations $\boxed{B}$ and $\boxed{D}$ to form a system of two variables.

$$4x\ \ \ \ =188$$
$$x=47 \qquad \text{Solve for } x.$$

From equation $\boxed{B}$ we have $-x+y=12 \longrightarrow -47+y=12 \rightarrow y=59$

From equation $\boxed{C}$ we have $x+y+z=180 \rightarrow 47+59+z=180 \rightarrow z=74$

The smallest angle measures $47°$, the middle angle measures $59°$, and the largest angle measures $74°$.

Skill Practice

1. The perimeter of a triangle is 30 in. The shortest side is 4 in. shorter than the longest side. The longest side is 6 in. less than the sum of the other two sides. Find the length of each side.

2. Applications Involving Mixtures

Example 2 **Applying Systems of Linear Equations to Nutrition**

Doctors have become increasingly concerned about the sodium intake in the U.S. diet. Recommendations by the American Medical Association indicate that most individuals should not exceed 2400 mg of sodium per day.

Liz ate 1 slice of pizza, 1 serving of ice cream, and 1 glass of soda for a total of 1030 mg of sodium. David ate 3 slices of pizza, no ice cream, and 2 glasses of soda for a total of 2420 mg of sodium. Melinda ate 2 slices of pizza, 1 serving of ice cream, and 2 glasses of soda for a total of 1910 mg of sodium. How much sodium is in one serving of each item?

Solution:

Let x represent the sodium content of 1 slice of pizza.

Let y represent the sodium content of 1 serving of ice cream.

Let z represent the sodium content of 1 glass of soda.

From Liz's meal we have: $\boxed{A}\ x+y+\ z=1030$

From David's meal we have: $\boxed{B}\ 3x\ \ \ \ +2z=2420$

From Melinda's meal we have: $\boxed{C}\ 2x+y+2z=1910$

Equation $\boxed{B}$ is missing the y-variable. Eliminating y from equations $\boxed{A}$ and $\boxed{C}$, we have

$$\boxed{A}\ x+y+\ z=1030 \xrightarrow{\text{Multiply by } -1.} -x-y-\ z=-1030$$
$$\boxed{C}\ 2x+y+2z=1910 \longrightarrow \underline{2x+y+2z=\ \ \ 1910}$$
$$\boxed{D}\ x\ \ \ \ +z=\ \ \ \ 880$$

Solve the system formed by equations $\boxed{B}$ and $\boxed{D}$.

$$\boxed{B}\ 3x+2z=2420 \longrightarrow 3x+2z=\ \ 2420$$
$$\boxed{D}\ x+\ z=\ 880 \xrightarrow{\text{Multiply by } -2.} \underline{-2x-2z=-1760}$$
$$x\ \ \ \ =\ \ \ 660$$

Answer

1. The sides are 8 in., 10 in., and 12 in.

From equation $\boxed{D}$ we have $x + z = 800 \longrightarrow 660 + z = 880 \longrightarrow z = 220$

From equation $\boxed{A}$ we have $x + y + z = 1030 \longrightarrow 660 + y + 220 = 1030 \longrightarrow y = 150$

Therefore, 1 slice of pizza has 660 mg of sodium, 1 serving of ice cream has 150 mg of sodium, and 1 glass of soda has 220 mg of sodium.

Skill Practice

2. Annette, Barb, and Carlita work in a clothing shop. One day the three had combined sales of $1480. Annette sold $120 more than Barb. Barb and Carlita combined sold $280 more than Annette. How much did each person sell?

Answer

2. Annette sold $600, Barb sold $480, and Carlita sold $400.

Section 4.6 Practice Exercises

Review Exercises

For Exercises 1–4, solve the system. If there is not a unique solution, state whether the system is inconsistent or the equations are dependent.

1. $\begin{aligned} -5y - z &= -8 \\ x + 10y + 2z &= 9 \\ -3x + y &= 21 \end{aligned}$

2. $\begin{aligned} 8x - y + 2z &= 18 \\ x + y - 5z &= -21 \\ 4x - 0.5y + z &= 9 \end{aligned}$

3. $\begin{aligned} \frac{1}{2}x - y + \frac{5}{6}z &= 4 \\ \frac{3}{2}x - 3y + \frac{5}{2}z &= 6 \\ -\frac{1}{4}x + y - \frac{1}{3}z &= -2 \end{aligned}$

4. $\begin{aligned} 12x - y + z &= -6 \\ -6x + 2y - 3z &= 5 \\ 6x + y - z &= 3 \end{aligned}$

Concept 1: Applications Involving Geometry

5. A triangle has one angle that measures 5° more than twice the smallest angle, and the largest angle measures 11° less than 3 times the measure of the smallest angle. Find the measures of the three angles.
(See Example 1.)

6. The largest angle of a triangle measures 4° less than 5 times the measure of the smallest angle. The middle angle measures twice that of the smallest angle. Find the measures of the three angles.

7. One angle of a triangle measures 6° more than twice the measure of the smallest angle. The third angle measures 1° less than four times the smallest. Find the measures of the three angles.

8. In a triangle the smallest angle measures 12° less than the middle angle. The measure of the largest angle is equal to the sum of the other two. Find the measures of the three angles.

9. The perimeter of a triangle is 55 cm. The measure of the shortest side is 8 cm less than the middle side. The measure of the longest side is 1 cm less than the sum of the other two sides. Find the lengths of the sides.

10. The perimeter of a triangle is 5 ft. The longest side of the triangle measures 20 in. more than the shortest side. The middle side is 3 times the measure of the shortest side. Find the lengths of the three sides in *inches*.

11. The perimeter of a triangle is 4.5 ft. The shortest side measures 2 in. less than half the longest side. The longest side measures 2 in. less than the sum of the other two sides. Find the lengths of the sides in *inches*.

12. The perimeter of a triangle is 7 m. The length of the longest side is twice the length of the shortest side. The sum of the lengths of the shortest side and the middle side is 1 m more than the length of the longest side. Find the lengths of the sides.

Concept 2: Applications Involving Mixtures

13. Sean kept track of his fiber intake from three sources for 3 weeks. The first week he had 3 servings of a fiber supplement, 1 serving of oatmeal, and 4 servings of cereal, which totaled 19 g of fiber. The second week he had 2 servings of the fiber supplement, 4 servings of oatmeal, and 2 servings of cereal totaling 25 g. The third week he had 5 servings of the fiber supplement, 3 servings of oatmeal, and 2 servings of cereal for a total of 30 g. Find the amount of fiber in one serving of each of the following: the fiber supplement, the oatmeal, and the cereal. **(See Example 2.)**

14. Natalie kept track of her calcium intake from three sources for 3 days. The first day she had 1 glass of milk, 1 serving of ice cream, and 1 calcium supplement in pill form which totaled 1180 mg of calcium. The second day she had 2 glasses of milk, 1 serving of ice cream, and 1 calcium supplement totaling 1680 mg. The third day she had 1 glass of milk, 2 servings of ice cream, and 1 calcium supplement for a total of 1260 mg. Find the amount of calcium in one glass of milk, in one serving of ice cream, and in one calcium supplement.

15. Kyoki invested a total of $10,000 into bonds, mutual funds, and a Treasury note. He put the same amount of money in the money market account as he did in bonds. For 1 year, the bonds paid 5% interest, the mutual funds paid 8%, and the Treasury note paid 4%. At the end of the year, Kyoki earned $660 in interest. How much did he invest in each account?

16. Walter had $25,000 to invest. He split the money into three types of investment: small caps earning 6%, global market investments earning 10%, and a balanced fund earning 9%. He put twice as much money in the global account as he did in the balanced fund. If his earnings for the first year totaled $2160, how much did he invest in each account?

17. Winston deposited $4500 into three accounts: one pays 5% interest, another pays 5.5% interest, and the third pays 4% interest. He deposits $1000 more in the 5.5% account than he does in the 4% account. After the first year, he earned a total of $225 interest. How much did he deposit into each account?

18. Raeann deposited $8000 into three accounts at her credit union: a checking account that pays 1.2% interest, a savings account that pays 2.5% interest, and a money market account that pays 3% interest. If she put 3 times more money in the 3% account than she did in the 1.2% account, and her total interest for 1 year was $202, how much did she deposit into each account?

19. A basketball player scored 29 points in one game. In basketball, some baskets are worth 3 points, some are worth 2 points, and free throws are worth 1 point. He scored four more 2-point baskets than he did 3-point baskets. The number of free throws is one less than the number of 2-point baskets. How many free throws, 2-point shots, and 3-point shots did he make?

20. Goofie Golf has 18 holes that are par 3, par 4, or par 5. Most of the holes are par 4. In fact, there are 3 times as many par 4s as par 3s. There are 3 more par 5s than par 3s. How many of each type are there?

© Getty Images RF

21. Combining peanuts, pecans, and cashews makes a party mixture of nuts. If the amount of peanuts equals the amount of pecans and cashews combined, and if there are twice as many cashews as pecans, how many ounces of each nut is used to make 48 oz of party mixture?

22. Souvenir hats, T-shirts, and jackets are sold at a rock concert. Three hats, two T-shirts, and one jacket cost $140. Two hats, two T-shirts, and two jackets cost $170. One hat, three T-shirts, and two jackets cost $180. Find the prices of the individual items.

23. A theater charges $70 per seat for seats in section A, $65 per seat for seats in section B, and $44 per seat for seats in section C. 2400 tickets are sold for a total of $153,000 in revenue. If there are 600 more seats sold in section A than the other two sections combined, how many seats in each section were sold?

24. Annie and Maria traveled overseas for seven days and stayed in three different hotels in three different cities: Stockholm, Sweden; Oslo, Norway; and Paris, France.

The total bill for all seven nights (not including tax) was $1040. The total tax was $106. The nightly cost (excluding tax) to stay at the hotel in Paris was $80 more than the nightly cost (excluding tax) to stay in Oslo. Find the cost per night for each hotel excluding tax.

City	Number of Nights	Cost/Night ($)	Tax Rate
Paris, France	1	x	8%
Stockholm, Sweden	4	y	11%
Oslo, Norway	2	z	10%

Creating Linear Models from Data

Materials: Two pieces of rope for each group. The ropes should be of different thicknesses. The piece of thicker rope should be between 4 and 5 ft long. The thinner piece of rope should be 8 to 12 in. shorter than the thicker rope. You will also need a yardstick or other device for making linear measurements.

Estimated Time: 30–35 minutes

Group Size: 4 (2 pairs)

328   **Chapter 4** Systems of Linear Equations in Two Variables

1. Each group of 4 should divide into two pairs, and each pair will be given a piece of rope. Each pair will measure the initial length of rope. Then students will tie a series of knots in the rope and measure the new length after each knot is tied. (*Hint:* Try to tie the knots with an equal amount of force each time. Also, as the ropes are straightened for measurement, try to use the same amount of tension in the rope.) The results should be recorded in the table.

Thick Rope		Thin Rope	
Number of Knots, *x*	Length (in.), *y*	Number of Knots, *x*	Length (in.), *y*
0		0	
1		1	
2		2	
3		3	
4		4	

2. Graph each set of data points. Use a different color pen or pencil for each set of points. Does it appear that each set of data follows a linear trend? For each data set, draw a representative line.

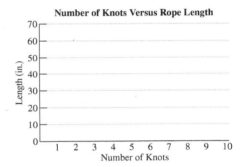

Number of Knots Versus Rope Length

3. Each time a knot is tied, the rope decreases in length. Using the results from question 1, compute the average amount of length lost per knot tied.

For the thick rope, the length decreases by _____ inches per knot tied.

For the thin rope, the length decreases by _____ inches per knot tied.

4. For each set of data points, find an equation of the line through the points. Write the equation in slope-intercept form, $y = mx + b$.

Equation for the thick rope: _____

Equation for the thin rope: _____

What does the slope of each line represent? _____

What does the *y*-intercept for each line represent? _____

5. Next, you will try to predict the number of knots that you need to tie in each rope so that the ropes will be equal in length. To do this, solve the system of equations in question 4.

Solution to the system of equations: (_____, _____)

                 number of knots, *x*   length, *y*

Interpret the meaning of the ordered pair in terms of the number of knots tied and the lengths of the ropes.

6. Check your answer from question 5 by actually tying the required number of knots in each rope. After doing this, are the ropes the same length? What is the length of each rope? Does this match the length predicted from question 5?

Chapter 4   Summary

Section 4.1   Solving Systems of Equations by the Graphing Method

Key Concepts

A **system of two linear equations** can be solved by graphing.

  A **solution to a system of linear equations** is an ordered pair that satisfies both equations in the system. Graphically, this represents a point of intersection of the lines.

  There may be one solution, infinitely many solutions, or no solution.

One solution | Infinitely many solutions | No solution
Consistent | Consistent | Inconsistent
Independent | Dependent | Independent

  A system of equations is **consistent** if there is at least one solution. A system is **inconsistent** if there is no solution.

  If two equations represent the same line, the equations are said to be **dependent equations**. In this case, all points on the line are solutions to the system. If two equations represent two different lines, the equations are said to be **independent equations**. In this case, the lines either intersect at one point or are parallel.

Examples

Example 1

Solve by using the graphing method.

$x + y = 3$

$2x - y = 0$

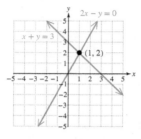

The solution set is $\{(1, 2)\}$.

Example 2

Solve by using the graphing method.

$3x - 2y = 2$

$-6x + 4y = 4$

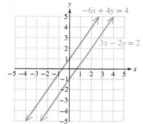

There is no solution, $\{\ \}$. The system is inconsistent.

Example 3

Solve by using the graphing method.

$x + 2y = 2$

$-3x - 6y = -6$

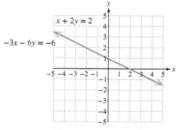

The equations are dependent, and the solution set consists of all points on the line, given by $\{(x, y) \mid x + 2y = 2\}$.

Section 4.2	Solving Systems of Equations by the Substitution Method

Key Concepts

Solving a System of Equations by Using the Substitution Method:

1. Isolate one of the variables from one equation.
2. Substitute the expression found in step 1 into the other equation.
3. Solve the resulting equation.
4. Substitute the value found in step 3 back into the equation in step 1 to find the remaining variable.
5. Check the ordered pair in both original equations.

An inconsistent system has no solution and is detected algebraically by a contradiction (such as $0 = 3$).

If two linear equations represent the same line, the equations are dependent. This is detected algebraically by an identity (such as $0 = 0$).

Examples

Example 1

Solve by using the substitution method.

$$x + 4y = -11$$
$$3x - 2y = -5$$

Isolate x in the first equation: $x = -4y - 11$
Substitute into the second equation.

$$3(-4y - 11) - 2y = -5 \qquad \text{Solve the}$$
$$-12y - 33 - 2y = -5 \qquad \text{equation.}$$
$$-14y = 28$$
$$y = -2$$

$$\qquad\qquad\qquad\qquad \text{Substitute}$$
$$x = -4y - 11 \qquad y = -2.$$
$$x = -4(-2) - 11 \qquad \text{Solve for } x.$$
$$x = -3$$

The ordered pair $(-3, -2)$ checks in the original equations. The solution set is $\{(-3, -2)\}$.

Example 2

Solve by using the substitution method.

$$3x + y = 4$$
$$-6x - 2y = 2$$

Isolate y in the first equation: $y = -3x + 4$
Substitute into the second equation.

$$-6x - 2(-3x + 4) = 2$$
$$-6x + 6x - 8 = 2$$
$$-8 = 2 \qquad \text{Contradiction}$$

The system is inconsistent and has no solution, $\{\ \}$.

Example 3

Solve by using the substitution method.

$$y = x + 2 \qquad y \text{ is already isolated.}$$
$$x - y = -2$$

$$x - (x + 2) = -2 \qquad \text{Substitute } y = x + 2 \text{ into the}$$
$$\qquad\qquad\qquad\qquad \text{second equation.}$$
$$x - x - 2 = -2$$
$$-2 = -2 \qquad \text{Identity}$$

The equations are dependent. The solution set is all points on the line $y = x + 2$ or $\{(x, y) \mid y = x + 2\}$.

| Section 4.3 | Solving Systems of Equations by the Addition Method |

Key Concepts

Solving a System of Linear Equations by Using the Addition Method:

1. Write both equations in standard form: $Ax + By = C$
2. Clear fractions or decimals (optional).
3. Multiply one or both equations by a nonzero constant to create opposite coefficients for one of the variables.
4. Add the equations to eliminate one variable.
5. Solve for the remaining variable.
6. Substitute the known value into one of the original equations to solve for the other variable.
7. Check the ordered pair in both equations.

Examples

Example 1

Solve by using the addition method.

$$5x = -4y - 7 \qquad \text{Write the first equation in}$$
$$6x - 3y = 15 \qquad \text{standard form.}$$

$$5x + 4y = -7 \xrightarrow{\text{Multiply by 3.}} 15x + 12y = -21$$
$$6x - 3y = 15 \xrightarrow[\text{Multiply by 4.}]{} \underline{24x - 12y = 60}$$
$$39x = 39$$
$$x = 1$$

$$5x = -4y - 7$$
$$5(1) = -4y - 7$$
$$5 = -4y - 7$$
$$12 = -4y$$
$$-3 = y \qquad \text{The ordered pair } (1, -3) \text{ checks in both original equations. The solution set is } \{(1, -3)\}.$$

Section 4.4   ## Applications of Linear Equations in Two Variables

Examples

Example 1

A riverboat travels 36 mi with the current in 2 hr. The return trip takes 3 hr against the current. Find the speed of the current and the speed of the boat in still water.

Let x represent the speed of the boat in still water.
Let y represent the speed of the current.

	Distance	Rate	Time
Against current	36	$x - y$	3
With current	36	$x + y$	2

Distance = (rate)(time)

$$36 = (x - y) \cdot 3 \longrightarrow 36 = 3x - 3y$$
$$36 = (x + y) \cdot 2 \longrightarrow 36 = 2x + 2y$$

$$36 = 3x - 3y \xrightarrow{\text{Multiply by 2.}} 72 = 6x - 6y$$
$$36 = 2x + 2y \xrightarrow{\text{Multiply by 3.}} \underline{108 = 6x + 6y}$$
$$180 = 12x$$
$$15 = x$$

$$36 = 2(15) + 2y$$
$$36 = 30 + 2y$$
$$6 = 2y$$
$$3 = y$$

The speed of the boat in still water is 15 mph, and the speed of the current is 3 mph.

Example 2

Diane borrows a total of $15,000. Part of the money is borrowed from a lender that charges 8% simple interest. She borrows the rest of the money from her mother and will pay back the money at 5% simple interest. If the total interest after 1 year is $900, how much did she borrow from each source?

	8%	5%	Total
Principal	x	y	15,000
Interest	$0.08x$	$0.05y$	900

$$x + \quad y = 15{,}000$$
$$0.08x + 0.05y = \quad 900$$

Substitute $x = 15{,}000 - y$ into the second equation.

$$0.08(15{,}000 - y) + 0.05y = 900$$
$$1200 - 0.08y + 0.05y = 900$$
$$1200 - 0.03y = 900$$
$$-0.03y = -300$$
$$y = 10{,}000$$

$$x = 15{,}000 - 10{,}000$$
$$= 5{,}000$$

The amount borrowed at 8% is $5,000.
The amount borrowed from her mother is $10,000.

| **Section 4.5** | **Systems of Linear Equations in Three Variables** |

Key Concepts

A **linear equation in three variables** can be written in the form $Ax + By + Cz = D$, where A, B, and C are not all zero. The graph of a linear equation in three variables is a plane in space.

A solution to a system of linear equations in three variables is an **ordered triple** that satisfies each equation. Graphically, a solution is a point of intersection among three planes.

A system of linear equations in three variables may have one unique solution, infinitely many solutions (dependent equations), or no solution (inconsistent system).

Examples

Example 1

$\boxed{A}$ $x + 2y - z = 4$

$\boxed{B}$ $3x - y + z = 5$

$\boxed{C}$ $2x + 3y + 2z = 7$

$\boxed{A}$ and $\boxed{B}$ $x + 2y - z = 4$

$\phantom{A \text{ and } B}$ $\underline{3x - y + z = 5}$

$\phantom{A \text{ and } B}$ $4x + y = 9 \;\boxed{D}$

$2 \cdot \boxed{A}$ and $\boxed{C}$ $2x + 4y - 2z = 8$

$\phantom{2 \cdot A \text{ and } C}$ $\underline{2x + 3y + 2z = 7}$

$\phantom{2 \cdot A \text{ and } C}$ $4x + 7y = 15 \;\boxed{E}$

$\boxed{D}$ $4x + y = 9$ $\xrightarrow{\text{Multiply by } -1.}$ $-4x - y = -9$

$\boxed{E}$ $4x + 7y = 15$ $\xrightarrow{}$ $\underline{4x + 7y = 15}$

$\phantom{\boxed{E} 4x + 7y = 15 \longrightarrow}$ $6y = 6$

$\phantom{\boxed{E} 4x + 7y = 15 \longrightarrow}$ $y = 1$

Substitute $y = 1$ into either equation $\boxed{D}$ or $\boxed{E}$.

$\boxed{D}$ $4x + (1) = 9$

$\phantom{\boxed{D}}$ $4x = 8$

$\phantom{\boxed{D}}$ $x = 2$

Substitute $x = 2$ and $y = 1$ into equation $\boxed{A}$, $\boxed{B}$, or $\boxed{C}$.

$\boxed{A}$ $(2) + 2(1) - z = 4$

$\phantom{\boxed{A}}$ $-z = 0$

$\phantom{\boxed{A}}$ $z = 0$

The solution set is $\{(2, 1, 0)\}$.

334   **Chapter 4**   Systems of Linear Equations in Two Variables

Section 4.6

Applications of Systems of Linear Equations in Three Variables

Key Concepts

In application problems where there are three unknowns, it is often useful to set up a system of linear equations in three variables.

With three variables, three independent relationships among x, y, and z are required.

Example

Example 1

In a triangle, the middle angle measures $55°$ more than the smallest angle. The largest angle measures $10°$ more than the sum of the other two angles. Find the measures of the angles.

Let x = measure of the smallest angle

Let y = measure of the middle angle

Let z = measure of the largest angle

First recall that the sum of the angles in a triangle is $180°$.

$$\text{standard form}$$

$$x + y + z = 180 \longrightarrow x + y + z = 180 \quad \boxed{A}$$
$$y = x + 55 \longrightarrow -x + y \quad\;\; = 55 \quad \boxed{B}$$
$$z = x + y + 10 \longrightarrow -x - y + z = 10 \quad \boxed{C}$$

$$\boxed{A} \quad x + \; y + z = 180$$
$$\boxed{B} \quad -x + \; y \qquad = 55$$
$$\overline{\qquad\qquad 2y + z = 235 \quad \boxed{D}}$$

$$\boxed{A} \quad x + y + \; z = 180$$
$$\boxed{C} \quad -x - y + \; z = 10$$
$$\overline{\qquad\qquad\quad 2z = 190 \quad \boxed{E}}$$
$$z = 95$$

From $\boxed{D}$: $2y + z = 235$

$$2y + 95 = 235$$
$$y = 70$$

From $\boxed{B}$: $-x + y = 55$

$$-x + 70 = 55$$
$$x = 15$$

Solving the system yields $x = 15$, $y = 70$, and $z = 95$.

The measures of the three angles are and $15°$, $70°$, and $95°$.

Chapter 4   Review Exercises

Section 4.1

For Exercises 1–4, determine if the ordered pair is a solution to the system.

1. $x - 4y = -4$ $(4, 2)$

   $x + 2y = 8$

2. $x - 6y = 6$ $(12, 1)$

   $-x + y = 4$

3. $3x + y = 9$ $(1, 3)$

   $y = 3$

4. $2x - y = 8$ $(2, -4)$

   $x = 2$

For Exercises 5–10, identify whether the system represents intersecting lines, parallel lines, or coinciding lines by comparing slopes and y-intercepts.

5. $y = -\dfrac{1}{2}x + 4$ **6.** $y = -3x + 4$

   $y = x - 1$ $y = 3x + 4$

7. $y = -\dfrac{4}{7}x + 3$ **8.** $y = 5x - 3$

   $y = -\dfrac{4}{7}x - 5$ $y = \dfrac{1}{5}x - 3$

9. $y = 9x - 2$ **10.** $x = -5$

   $9x - y = 2$ $y = 2$

For Exercises 11–18, solve the system by graphing. For systems that do not have one unique solution, also state the number of solutions and whether the system is inconsistent or the equations are dependent.

11. $y = -\dfrac{2}{3}x - 2$ **12.** $y = -2x - 1$

   $-x + 3y = -6$ $x + 2y = 4$

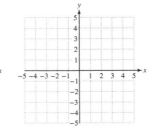

13. $4x = -2y + 10$ **14.** $10y = 2x - 10$

   $2x + y = 5$ $-x + 5y = -5$

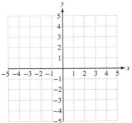   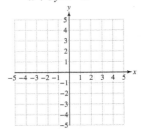

15. $6x - 3y = 9$ **16.** $5x + y = -3$

   $y = -1$ $x = -1$

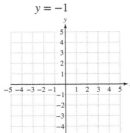   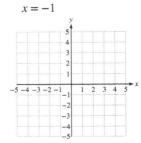

17. $x - 7y = 14$ **18.** $y = -5x + 4$

   $-2x + 14y = 14$ $10x + 2y = -4$

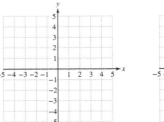   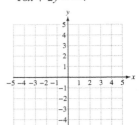

Section 4.2

19. One phone company charges $0.15 a minute for calls but adds a $3.90 charge each month. Another company does not have a monthly fee but charges $0.25 per minute. The cost per month, y_1 (in $) for the first company is given by the equation:

$y_1 = 0.15x + 3.90$ where x represents the number of minutes used.

The cost per month, y_2, (in $) for the second company is given by the equation:

$y_2 = 0.25x$ where x represents the number of minutes used.

Find the number of minutes at which the cost per month for each company is the same.

336   **Chapter 4** Systems of Linear Equations in Two Variables

For Exercises 20–23, solve each system using the substitution method.

20. $6x + y = 2$

$y = 3x - 4$

21. $2x + 3y = -5$

$x = y - 5$

22. $2x + 6y = 10$

$x = -3y + 6$

23. $4x + 2y = 4$

$y = -2x + 2$

24. Given the system: $x + 2y = 11$

$5x + 4y = 40$

a. Which variable from which equation is easiest to isolate and why?

b. Solve the system using the substitution method.

25. Given the system: $4x - 3y = 9$

$2x + y = 12$

a. Which variable from which equation is easiest to isolate and why?

b. Solve the system using the substitution method.

For Exercises 26–29, solve each system using the substitution method.

26. $3x - 2y = 23$

$x + 5y = -15$

27. $x + 5y = 20$

$3x + 2y = 8$

28. $x - 3y = 9$

$5x - 15y = 45$

29. $-3x + y = 15$

$6x - 2y = 12$

30. The difference of two positive numbers is 42. The larger number is 2 more than 6 times the smaller number. Find the numbers.

31. In a right triangle, one of the acute angles is 8° less than the other acute angle. Find the measure of each acute angle.

32. Two angles are supplementary. One angle measures 14° less than two times the other angle. Find the measure of each angle.

Section 4.3

33. Given the system. $-2x + 7y = 30$

$4x + 5y = 16$

a. Which variable, x or y, is easier to eliminate using the addition method? (Answers may vary.)

b. Solve the system using the addition method.

34. Given the system: $3x - 5y = 1$

$2x - y = -4$

a. Which variable, x or y, is easier to eliminate using the addition method? (Answers may vary.)

b. Solve the system using the addition method.

35. Given the system: $9x - 2y = 14$

$4x + 3y = 14$

a. Which variable, x or y, is easier to eliminate using the addition method? (Answers may vary.)

b. Solve the system using the addition method.

For Exercises 36–43, solve each system using the addition method.

36. $2x + 3y = 1$

$x - 2y = 4$

37. $x + 3y = 0$

$-3x - 10y = -2$

38. $8x + 8 = -6y + 6$

$10x = 9y - 8$

39. $12x = 5y + 5$

$5y = -1 - 4x$

40. $-4x - 6y = -2$

$6x + 9y = 3$

41. $-8x - 4y = 16$

$10x + 5y = 5$

42. $\frac{1}{2}x - \frac{3}{4}y = -\frac{1}{2}$

$\frac{1}{3}x + y = -\frac{10}{3}$

43. $0.5x - 0.2y = 0.5$

$0.4x + 0.7y = 0.4$

44. Given the system: $4x + 9y = -7$

$y = 2x - 13$

a. Which method would you choose to solve the system, the substitution method or the addition method? Explain your choice.

b. Solve the system

45. Given the system: $5x - 8y = -2$

$3x - 7y = 1$

a. Which method would you choose to solve the system, the substitution method or the addition method? Explain your choice.

b. Solve the system

Section 4.4

46. Zoo Miami charges $19.95 for adult admission and $15.95 for children under 13. The total bill before tax for a school group of 60 people is $989. How many adults and how many children were admitted?

47. As part of his retirement strategy Winston plans to invest $600,000 in two different funds. He projects that the high-risk investments should return, over time, about 12% per year, while the low-risk investments should return about 4% per year. If he wants a supplemental income of $30,000 a year, how should he divide his investments?

48. Suppose that whole milk with 4% fat is mixed with 1% low fat milk to make a 2% reduced fat milk. How much of the whole milk should be mixed with the low fat milk to make 60 gal of 2% reduced fat milk?

49. A boat travels 80 mi downstream with the current in 4 hr and 80 mi upstream against the current in 5 hr. Find the speed of the current and the speed of the boat in still water.

50. A plane travels 870 mi against the wind in 3 hr. Traveling with the wind, the plane travels 700 mi in 2 hr. Find the speed of the plane in still air and the speed of the wind.

51. At a sports arena, the total cost of a soft drink and a hot dog is $8.00. The price of the hot dog is $1.00 more than the cost of the soft drink. Find the cost of a soft drink and the cost of a hot dog.

52. Ray played two rounds of golf at Pebble Beach for a total score of 154. If his score in the second round is 10 more than his score in the first round, find the scores for each round.

© Royalty Free/Corbis RF

Section 4.5

For Exercises 53–58, solve the systems of equations. If a system does not have a unique solution, state whether the system is inconsistent or the equations are dependent.

53.
$$5x + 5y + 5z = 30$$
$$-x + y + z = 2$$
$$10x + 6y - 2z = 4$$

54.
$$5x + 3y - z = 5$$
$$x + 2y + z = 6$$
$$-x - 2y - z = 8$$

55.
$$x + y + z = 4$$
$$-x - 2y - 3z = -6$$
$$2x + 4y + 6z = 12$$

56.
$$3x \qquad + 4z = 5$$
$$2y + 3z = 2$$
$$2x - 5y \qquad = 8$$

57.
$$3(x - y) = -1 - 5z - y$$
$$3y + 6 = 2z + x$$
$$5x + 1 = 3(z - y) - y$$

58.
$$2a = -3c - 2$$
$$2b - 8 = 5c$$
$$7a + 3b = 5$$

Section 4.6

59. The perimeter of a right triangle is 30 ft. One leg is 2 ft longer than twice the shortest leg. The hypotenuse is 2 ft less than 3 times the shortest leg. Find the lengths of the sides of this triangle.

60. Three pumps are working to drain a construction site. Working together, the pumps can drain 950 gal/hr of water. The slowest pump drains 150 gal/hr less than the fastest pump. The fastest pump drains 150 gal/hr less than the sum of the other two pumps. How many gallons can each pump drain per hour?

61. Theresa had $12,000 to invest among three mutual funds. Fund A had a 5% yield for the year. Fund B had a 3.5% yield, and Fund C lost 2% for the year. She invested three times as much in Fund A as in Fund C. If she gained $400 in 1 year, how much was invested in each fund?

62. In a triangle, the largest angle measures 76° more than the sum of the other two angles. The middle angle measures 3 times the smallest angle. Find the measure of each angle.

Chapter 4   Test

1. Write each line in slope-intercept form. Then determine if the lines represent intersecting lines, parallel lines, or coinciding lines.

$$5x + 2y = -6$$

$$-\frac{5}{2}x - y = -3$$

For Exercises 2–3, solve each system by graphing.

2. $y = 2x - 4$

   $-2x + 3y = 0$

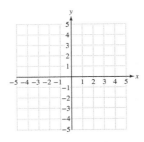

3. $2x + 4y = 12$

   $2y - 6 = -x$

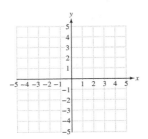

4. Solve the system using the substitution method.

$$x = 5y - 2$$

$$2x + y = -4$$

5. In an early WNBA (basketball) season, the league's leading scorer was Sheryl Swoopes from the Houston Comets. Swoopes scored 17 points more than the second leading scorer, Lauren Jackson from the Seattle Storm. Together they scored a total of 1211 points. How many points did each player score?

6. Solve the system using the addition method.

$$3x - 6y = 8$$

$$2x + 3y = 3$$

7. How many milliliters of a 50% acid solution and how many milliliters of a 20% acid solution must be mixed to produce 36 mL of a 30% acid solution?

8. a. How many solutions does a system of two linear equations have if the equations represent parallel lines?

   b. How many solutions does a system of two linear equations have if the equations represent coinciding lines?

   c. How many solutions does a system of two linear equations have if the equations represent intersecting lines?

For Exercises 9–14, solve each system using any method.

9. $\dfrac{1}{3}x + y = \dfrac{7}{3}$

   $x = \dfrac{3}{2}y - 11$

10. $2x - 12 = y$

    $2x - \dfrac{1}{2}y = x + 5$

11. $3x - 4y = 29$

    $2x + 5y = -19$

12. $2x = 6y - 14$

    $2y = 3 - x$

13. $-0.25x - 0.05y = 0.2$

    $10x + 2y = -8$

14. $3x + 3y = -2y - 7$

    $-3y = 10 - 4x$

15. Latrell buys four CDs and two DVDs for $54 from the sale rack. Kendra buys two CDs and three DVDs from the same rack for $49. What is the price per CD and the price per DVD?

16. The cost to ride a certain trolley one way is $2.25. Kelly and Hazel had to buy eight tickets for their group.

    a. What was the total amount of money required?

    b. Kelly and Hazel had only quarters and $1 bills. They also determined that they used twice as many quarters as $1 bills. How many quarters and how many $1 bills did they use?

17. Suppose a total of $5000 is borrowed from two different loans. One loan charges 10% simple interest, and the other charges 8% simple interest. How much was borrowed at each rate if $424 in interest is charged at the end of 1 year?

18. Mark needs to move to a new apartment and is trying to find the most affordable moving truck. He will only need the truck for one day. After checking the AAA Movers website, he finds that he can rent a 10-ft truck for $20.95 a day plus $1.89 per mile. He then checks the website of a local moving company and finds the charge to be $37.95 a day plus $1.19 per mile for the same size truck. Determine the number of miles for which the cost to rent from either company would be the same. Round the answer to the nearest mile.

19. A plane travels 910 mi in 2 hr against the wind and 1090 mi in 2 hr with the same wind. Find the speed of the plane in still air and the speed of the wind.

20. The number of calories in a piece of cake is 20 less than 3 times the number of calories in a scoop of ice cream. Together, the cake and ice cream have 460 calories. How many calories are in each?

© McGraw-Hill Education/Jill Braaten

21. How much 10% acid solution should be mixed with a 25% acid solution to create 100 mL of a 16% acid solution?

For Exercises 22–24, solve the system of equations.

22. $2x + 2y + 4z = -6$
$3x + y + 2z = 29$
$x - y - z = 44$

23. $2(x + z) = 6 + x - 3y$
$2x = 11 + y - z$
$x + 2(y + z) = 8$

24. $3x - 4y = 6 - 2z$
$x - 3y + 2z = 9$
$2x = y - 1$

25. The perimeter of a triangle is 43 ft. The shortest side is one-third the length of the middle side. The longest side is 3 feet more than four times the shortest side. Find the lengths of the three sides.

26. Bennet invested a total of $11,500 among three mutual funds. At the end of one year, Fund A had a 6% yield, Fund B had an 8% yield, and Fund C lost 5%. Twice as much money was invested in Fund B as in Fund C. At the end of one year, the total gain was $550. How much was invested in each fund?

27. Working together, Joanne, Kent, and Geoff can process 504 orders per day for their business. Kent can process 20 more orders per day than Joanne can process. Geoff can process 104 fewer orders per day than Kent and Joanne combined. Find the number of orders that each person can process per day.

Chapters 1–4 Cumulative Review Exercises

1. Simplify.
$$\frac{|2 - 5| + 10 \div 2 + 3}{\sqrt{10^2 - 8^2}}$$

2. Solve for x. $\frac{1}{3}x - \frac{3}{4} = \frac{1}{2}(x + 2)$

3. Solve for a. $-4(a + 3) + 2 = -5(a + 1) + a$

4. Solve for y. $3x - 2y = 6$

5. Solve for x. $z = \frac{x - m}{5}$

6. Solve for z. Graph the solution set on a number line and write the solution in interval notation.
$$-2(3z + 1) \le 5(z - 3) + 10$$

7. The largest angle in a triangle is 110°. Of the remaining two angles, one is 4° less than the other angle. Find the measure of the three angles.

340   **Chapter 4** Systems of Linear Equations in Two Variables

8. Two hikers start at opposite ends of an 18-mi trail and walk toward each other. One hiker walks predominately down hill and averages 2 mph faster than the other hiker. Find the average rate of each hiker if they meet in 3 hr.

9. Jesse Ventura became the 38th governor of Minnesota by receiving 37% of the votes. If approximately 2,060,000 votes were cast, how many did Mr. Ventura get?

10. The YMCA wants to raise $2500 for its summer program for disadvantaged children. If the YMCA has already raised $900, what percent of its goal has been achieved?

11. Two angles are complementary. One angle measures 17° more than the other angle. Find the measure of each angle.

12. Find the slope and y-intercept of the line $5x + 3y = -6$.

13. The slope of a given line is $-\frac{2}{3}$.

   a. What is the slope of a line parallel to the given line?

   b. What is the slope of a line perpendicular to the given line?

14. Find an equation of the line passing through the point $(2, -3)$ and having a slope of -3. Write the final answer in slope-intercept form.

15. Sketch the following equations on the same graph.

   a. $2x + 5y = 10$

   b. $2y = 4$

   c. Find the point of intersection and check the solution in each equation.

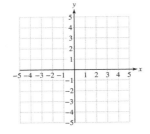

16. Solve the system of equations by using the substitution method.

$$2x + 5y = 10$$
$$2y = 4$$

17. How many gallons of a 15% antifreeze solution should be mixed with a 60% antifreeze solution to produce 60 gal of a 45% antifreeze solution?

18. Use a system of linear equations to solve for x and y.

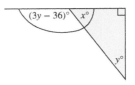

19. In 1920, the average speed for the winner of the Indianapolis 500 car race was 88.6 mph. In 1990, a track record was reached with the speed of 186.0 mph.

   a. Find the slope of the line shown in the figure. Round to one decimal place.

   b. Interpret the meaning of the slope in the context of this problem.

Average Speed for the Winning Car in the Indianapolis 500

20. Solve the system.

$$x + 3y + z = 5$$
$$2x + 4y - z = -2$$
$$6x + 2y + 5z = 26$$

Polynomials and Properties of Exponents

Polynomials and Properties of Exponents

5

Mathematics to Compute Cost

Trevor is a dance instructor and wants to host a one-day dance event. He has a fixed cost of $200 to rent the dance studio. In addition, to host the event, he has the following variable costs, which depend on the number of participants.

- $1.00 per person for coffee and breakfast snacks
- $7.00 per person for lunch
- $1.20 per person for a step-sheet booklet

If n represents the number of participants, then Trevor's cost for the event is given by

   Cost = $1.00n + 7.00n + 1.20n + 200$

This expression is called a **polynomial**. Terms of a polynomial are separated by addition, and sometimes a polynomial can be simplified by adding *like* **terms**. In this case, the terms containing the variable n are *like* terms. Thus, the polynomial representing cost can be simplified as

   Cost $= (1.00 + 7.00 + 1.20)n + 200$
   $= 9.20n + 200$

The terms $1.00n$, $7.00n$, and $1.20n$ are combined to form $9.20n$ because we're effectively consolidating the costs for breakfast, lunch, and the booklet into one overall cost per person.

   As you study polynomials in this chapter, you will encounter other applications including those involving profit and cost.

© McGraw-Hill Education/John Flournoy

Section 5.1	**Multiplying and Dividing Expressions with Common Bases**

1. Review of Exponential Notation

Recall that an **exponent** is used to show repeated multiplication of the **base**.

Definition of b^n

Let b represent any real number and n represent a positive integer. Then,

$$b^n = \underbrace{b \cdot b \cdot b \cdot b \cdot \ldots b}_{n \text{ factors of } b}$$

Example 1 **Evaluating Expressions with Exponents**

For each expression, identify the exponent and base. Then evaluate the expression.

a. 6^2 **b.** $\left(-\dfrac{1}{2}\right)^3$ **c.** 0.8^4

Solution:

Expression	**Base**	**Exponent**	**Result**
a. 6^2	6	2	$(6)(6) = 36$
b. $\left(-\dfrac{1}{2}\right)^3$	$-\dfrac{1}{2}$	3	$\left(-\dfrac{1}{2}\right)\left(-\dfrac{1}{2}\right)\left(-\dfrac{1}{2}\right) = -\dfrac{1}{8}$
c. 0.8^4	0.8	4	$(0.8)(0.8)(0.8)(0.8) = 0.4096$

Skill Practice For each expression, identify the base and exponent.

1. 8^3 **2.** $\left(-\dfrac{1}{4}\right)^2$ **3.** 0.2^4

Note that if no exponent is explicitly written for an expression, then the expression has an implied exponent of 1. For example, $x = x^1$.

Consider an expression such as $3y^6$. The factor 3 has an exponent of 1, and the factor y has an exponent of 6. That is, the expression $3y^6$ is interpreted as $3^1 y^6$.

2. Evaluating Expressions with Exponents

Particular care must be taken when evaluating exponential expressions involving negative numbers. An exponential expression with a negative base is written with parentheses around the base, such as $(-3)^2$.

To evaluate $(-3)^2$, we have: $(-3)^2 = (-3)(-3) = 9$

If no parentheses are present, the expression -3^2 is the *opposite* of 3^2, or equivalently, $-1 \cdot 3^2$.

$$-3^2 = -1(3^2) = -1(3)(3) = -9$$

| Example 2 | **Evaluating Expressions with Exponents** |

Evaluate each expression.

a. -5^4　　　**b.** $(-5)^4$　　　**c.** $(-0.2)^3$　　　**d.** -0.2^3

Solution:

a. -5^4

$= -1 \cdot 5^4$　　　　5 is the base with exponent 4.

$= -1 \cdot 5 \cdot 5 \cdot 5 \cdot 5$　　Multiply -1 by four factors of 5.

$= -625$

b. $(-5)^4$

$= (-5)(-5)(-5)(-5)$　　Parentheses indicate that -5 is the base with exponent 4.

$= 625$　　　　Multiply four factors of -5.

c. $(-0.2)^3$　　　Parentheses indicate that -0.2 is the base with exponent 3.

$= (-0.2)(-0.2)(-0.2)$　　Multiply three factors of -0.2.

$= -0.008$

d. -0.2^3

$= -1 \cdot 0.2^3$　　　0.2 is the base with exponent 3.

$= -1(0.2)(0.2)(0.2)$　　Multiply -1 by three factors of 0.2.

$= -0.008$

Skill Practice　Evaluate each expression.

4. -2^4　　　**5.** $(-2)^4$　　　**6.** $(-0.1)^3$　　　**7.** -0.1^3

| Example 3 | **Evaluating Expressions with Exponents** |

Evaluate each expression for $a = 2$ and $b = -3$.

a. $5a^2$　　　**b.** $(5a)^2$　　　**c.** $5ab^2$　　　**d.** $(b + a)^2$

Solution:

a. $5a^2$

$= 5(\ )^2$　　　Use parentheses to substitute a number for a variable.

$= 5(2)^2$　　　Substitute $a = 2$.

$= 5(4)$　　　Simplify exponents before multiplying.

$= 20$

b. $(5a)^2$

$= [5(\ )]^2$　　　Use parentheses to substitute a number for a variable. The original parentheses are replaced with brackets.

$= [5(2)]^2$　　　Substitute $a = 2$.

$= (10)^2$　　　Simplify inside the parentheses first.

$= 100$

Answers

4. -16　　　**5.** 16

6. -0.001　　　**7.** -0.001

Avoiding Mistakes

In the expression $5ab^2$, the exponent, 2, applies only to the variable b. The constant 5 and the variable a both have an implied exponent of 1.

Avoiding Mistakes

Be sure to follow the order of operations. In Example 3(d), it would be incorrect to square the terms within the parentheses before adding.

c. $5ab^2$

$= 5(2)(-3)^2$	Substitute $a = 2$, $b = -3$.
$= 5(2)(9)$	Simplify exponents before multiplying.
$= 90$	Multiply.

d. $(b + a)^2$

$= [(-3) + (2)]^2$	Substitute $b = -3$ and $a = 2$.
$= (-1)^2$	Simplify within the parentheses first.
$= 1$	

Skill Practice Evaluate each expression for $x = 2$ and $y = -5$.

8. $6x^2$ **9.** $(6x)^2$ **10.** $2xy^2$ **11.** $(y - x)^2$

3. Multiplying and Dividing Expressions with Common Bases

In this section, we investigate the effect of multiplying or dividing two quantities with the same base. For example, consider the expressions: $x^5 x^2$ and $\frac{x^5}{x^2}$. Simplifying each expression, we have:

$$x^5 x^2 = (x \cdot x \cdot x \cdot x \cdot x)(x \cdot x) = \overbrace{x \cdot x \cdot x \cdot x \cdot x \cdot x \cdot x}^{\text{7 factors of } x} = x^7$$

$$\frac{x^5}{x^2} = \frac{x \cdot x \cdot x \cdot \overset{1}{\cancel{x}} \cdot \overset{1}{\cancel{x}}}{x \cdot x} = \frac{x \cdot x \cdot x}{1} = x^3$$

These examples suggest that to multiply two quantities with the same base, we add the exponents. To divide two quantities with the same base, we subtract the exponent in the denominator from the exponent in the numerator. These rules are stated formally in the following two properties.

Multiplication of Expressions with Like Bases

Assume that b is a real number and that m and n represent positive integers. Then,

$$b^m b^n = b^{m+n}$$

Division of Expressions with Like Bases

Assume that $b \neq 0$ is a real number and that m and n represent positive integers. Then,

$$\frac{b^m}{b^n} = b^{m-n}$$

Answers

8. 24   **9.** 144   **10.** 100
11. 49

Example 4   **Simplifying Expressions with Exponents**

Simplify the expressions.   **a.** $w^3 w^4$ **b.** $2^3 \cdot 2^4$

Solution:

a. $w^3 w^4$ $(w \cdot w \cdot w)(w \cdot w \cdot w \cdot w)$

$= w^{3+4}$ To multiply expressions with like bases, add the exponents.

$= w^7$

b. $2^3 \cdot 2^4$ $(2 \cdot 2 \cdot 2)(2 \cdot 2 \cdot 2 \cdot 2)$

$= 2^{3+4}$ To multiply expressions with like bases, add the exponents (the base is unchanged).

$= 2^7$ or 128

Avoiding Mistakes
When we multiply expressions with like bases, we add the exponents. The base does not change. In Example 4(b), notice that the base 2 does not change. $2^3 \cdot 2^4 = 2^7$.

Skill Practice   Simplify the expressions.

12. $q^4 q^8$ **13.** $8^4 \cdot 8^8$

Example 5   **Simplifying Expressions with Exponents**

Simplify the expressions.   **a.** $\dfrac{t^6}{t^4}$ **b.** $\dfrac{5^6}{5^4}$

Solution:

a. $\dfrac{t^6}{t^4}$ $\dfrac{t \cdot t \cdot t \cdot t \cdot t \cdot t}{t \cdot t \cdot t \cdot t}$

$= t^{6-4}$ To divide expressions with like bases, subtract the exponents.

$= t^2$

b. $\dfrac{5^6}{5^4}$ $\dfrac{5 \cdot 5 \cdot 5 \cdot 5 \cdot 5 \cdot 5}{5 \cdot 5 \cdot 5 \cdot 5}$

$= 5^{6-4}$ To divide expressions with like bases, subtract the exponents (the base is unchanged).

$= 5^2$ or 25

Skill Practice   Simplify the expressions.

14. $\dfrac{y^{15}}{y^8}$ **15.** $\dfrac{3^{15}}{3^8}$

Answers
12. q^{12} **13.** 8^{12}
14. y^7 **15.** 3^7

| **Example 6** | **Simplifying Expressions with Exponents** |

Simplify the expressions.   **a.** $\dfrac{z^4 z^5}{z^3}$ **b.** $\dfrac{10^7}{10^2 \cdot 10}$

Solution:

a. $\dfrac{z^4 z^5}{z^3}$

$\quad = \dfrac{z^{4+5}}{z^3}$ Add the exponents in the numerator (the base is unchanged).

$\quad = \dfrac{z^9}{z^3}$

$\quad = z^{9-3}$ Subtract the exponents.

$\quad = z^6$

b. $\dfrac{10^7}{10^2 \cdot 10}$

$\quad = \dfrac{10^7}{10^2 \cdot 10^1}$ Note that 10 is equivalent to 10^1.

$\quad = \dfrac{10^7}{10^{2+1}}$ Add the exponents in the denominator (the base is unchanged).

$\quad = \dfrac{10^7}{10^3}$

$\quad = 10^{7-3}$ Subtract the exponents.

$\quad = 10^4$ or $10,000$ Simplify.

Skill Practice Simplify the expressions.

16. $\dfrac{a^3 a^8}{a^7}$ **17.** $\dfrac{5^9}{5^2 \cdot 5^5}$

4. Simplifying Expressions with Exponents

| **Example 7** | **Simplifying Expressions with Exponents** |

Use the commutative and associative properties of real numbers and the properties of exponents to simplify the expressions.

a. $(-3p^2 q^4)(2pq^5)$ **b.** $\dfrac{16w^9 z^3}{4w^8 z}$

Avoiding Mistakes

To simplify the expression in Example 7(a) we multiply the coefficients. However, to multiply expressions with like bases, we add the exponents.

Solution:

a. $(-3p^2 q^4)(2pq^5)$

$\quad = (-3 \cdot 2)(p^2 p)(q^4 q^5)$ Apply the associative and commutative properties of multiplication to group coefficients and like bases.

$\quad = (-3 \cdot 2)p^{2+1} q^{4+5}$ Add the exponents when multiplying expressions with like bases.

$\quad = -6p^3 q^9$ Simplify.

Answers

16. a^4 **17.** 5^2 or 25

b. $\dfrac{16w^9z^3}{4w^8z}$

$= \left(\dfrac{16}{4}\right)\left(\dfrac{w^9}{w^8}\right)\left(\dfrac{z^3}{z}\right)$ Group coefficients and like bases.

$= 4w^{9-8}z^{3-1}$ Subtract the exponents when dividing expressions with like bases.

$= 4wz^2$ Simplify.

> **Avoiding Mistakes**
>
> In Example 7(b) we divide the coefficients. However, to divide expressions with like bases, we subtract the exponents.

Skill Practice Simplify the expressions.

18. $(-4x^2y^3)(3x^5y^7)$ **19.** $\dfrac{81x^4y^7}{9xy^3}$

5. Applications of Exponents

Simple interest on an investment or loan is computed by the formula $I = Prt$, where P is the amount of principal, r is the annual interest rate, and t is the time in years. Simple interest is based only on the original principal. However, in most day-to-day applications, the interest computed on money invested or borrowed is compound interest. **Compound interest** is computed on the original principal and on the interest already accrued.

Suppose $1000 is invested at 8% interest for 3 years. Compare the total amount in the account if the money earns simple interest versus if the interest is compounded annually.

Simple Interest

The simple interest earned is given by $I = Prt$

$$= (\$1000)(0.08)(3)$$
$$= \$240$$

The total amount, A, at the end of 3 years is $A = P + I$

$$= \$1000 + \$240$$
$$= \$1240$$

Compound Annual Interest

The total amount, A, in an account earning compound annual interest may be computed using the following formula:

$A = P(1 + r)^t$ where P is the amount of principal, r is the annual interest rate (expressed in decimal form), and t is the number of years.

For example, for $1000 invested at 8% interest compounded annually for 3 years, we have $P = 1000$, $r = 0.08$, and $t = 3$.

$$A = P(1 + r)^t$$
$$A = 1000(1 + 0.08)^3$$
$$= 1000(1.08)^3$$
$$= 1000(1.259712)$$
$$= 1259.712$$

Rounding to the nearest cent, we have $A = \$1259.71$.

Answers

18. $-12x^7y^{10}$ **19.** $9x^3y^4$

Example 8	**Using Exponents in an Application**

Find the amount in an account after 8 years if the initial investment is $7000, invested at 2.25% interest compounded annually.

Solution:

Identify the values for each variable.

$P = 7000$

$r = 0.0225$ 　　　Note that the decimal form of a percent is used for calculations.

$t = 8$

$A = P(1 + r)^t$

$\quad = 7000(1 + 0.0225)^8$ 　　　Substitute.

$\quad = 7000(1.0225)^8$ 　　　Simplify inside the parentheses.

$\quad \approx 7000(1.194831142)$ 　　　Approximate $(1.0225)^8$.

$\quad \approx 8363.82$ 　　　Multiply (round to the nearest cent).

The amount in the account after 8 years is $8363.82.

Skill Practice

20. Find the amount in an account after 3 years if the initial investment is $4000 invested at 5% interest compounded annually.

Answer

20. $4630.50

Topic: Review of Evaluating Exponential Expressions on a Calculator

In Example 8, it was necessary to evaluate the expression $(1.0225)^8$. Recall that the $\boxed{\wedge}$ or $\boxed{y^x}$ key may be used to enter expressions with exponents.

Scientific Calculator

Enter: 　1.0225 $\boxed{y^x}$ 8 $\boxed{=}$ 　　　**Result:** 　$\boxed{1.194831142}$

Graphing Calculator

```
1.0225^8
          1.194831142
```

Calculator Exercises

Use a calculator to evaluate the expressions.

1. $(1.06)^5$ 　　　　**2.** $(1.02)^{40}$ 　　　　**3.** $5000(1.06)^5$

4. $2000(1.02)^{40}$ 　　　　**5.** $3000(1 + 0.06)^2$ 　　　　**6.** $1000(1 + 0.05)^3$

Section 5.1   Practice Exercises

For this exercise set, assume all variables represent nonzero real numbers.

Vocabulary and Key Concepts

1. a. A(n) _____ is used to show repeated multiplication of the base.

   b. Given the expression b^n, the value b is the _____ and n is the _____.

   c. Given the expression x, the value of the exponent on x is understood to be _____.

   d. The formula to compute simple interest is _____.

   e. Interest that is computed on the original principal and on the accrued interest is called _____ _____.

Concept 1: Review of Exponential Notation

For Exercises 2–13, identify the base and the exponent. **(See Example 1.)**

2. c^3 **3.** x^4 **4.** 5^2 **5.** 3^5

6. $(-4)^8$ **7.** $(-1)^4$ **8.** x **9.** 13

10. -4^2 **11.** -10^3 **12.** $-y^5$ **13.** $-t^6$

14. What base corresponds to the exponent 5 in the expression $x^3y^5z^2$?

15. What base corresponds to the exponent 2 in the expression w^3v^2?

16. What is the exponent for the factor of 2 in the expression $2x^3$?

17. What is the exponent for the factor of p in the expression pq^7?

For Exercises 18–26, write the expression using exponents.

18. $(4n)(4n)(4n)$ **19.** $(-6b)(-6b)$ **20.** $4 \cdot n \cdot n \cdot n$

21. $-6 \cdot b \cdot b$ **22.** $(x-5)(x-5)(x-5)$ **23.** $(y+2)(y+2)(y+2)(y+2)$

24. $\dfrac{4}{x \cdot x \cdot x \cdot x \cdot x}$ **25.** $\dfrac{-2}{t \cdot t \cdot t}$ **26.** $\dfrac{5 \cdot x \cdot x \cdot x}{(y-7)(y-7)}$

Concept 2: Evaluating Expressions with Exponents

For Exercises 27–34, evaluate the two expressions and compare the answers. Do the expressions have the same value? **(See Example 2.)**

27. -5^2 and $(-5)^2$ **28.** -3^4 and $(-3)^4$ **29.** -2^5 and $(-2)^5$ **30.** -5^3 and $(-5)^3$

31. $\left(\dfrac{1}{2}\right)^3$ and $\dfrac{1}{2^3}$ **32.** $\left(\dfrac{1}{5}\right)^2$ and $\dfrac{1}{5^2}$ **33.** $-(-2)^4$ and $-(2)^4$ **34.** $-(-3)^3$ and $-(3)^3$

For Exercises 35–42, evaluate each expression. **(See Example 2.)**

35. 16^1 **36.** 20^1 **37.** $(-1)^{21}$ **38.** $(-1)^{30}$

39. $\left(-\dfrac{1}{3}\right)^2$ **40.** $\left(-\dfrac{1}{4}\right)^3$ **41.** $-\left(\dfrac{2}{5}\right)^2$ **42.** $-\left(\dfrac{3}{5}\right)^2$

350   **Chapter 5** Polynomials and Properties of Exponents

For Exercises 43–50, simplify using the order of operations.

43. $3 \cdot 2^4$

44. $2 \cdot 0^5$

45. $-4(-1)^7$

46. $-3(-1)^4$

47. $6^2 - 3^3$

48. $4^3 + 2^3$

49. $2 \cdot 3^2 + 4 \cdot 2^3$

50. $6^2 - 3 \cdot 1^3$

For Exercises 51–62, evaluate each expression for $a = -4$ and $b = 5$. **(See Example 3.)**

51. $-4b^2$

52. $3a^2$

53. $(-4b)^2$

54. $(3a)^2$

55. $(a + b)^2$

56. $(a - b)^2$

57. $a^2 + 2ab + b^2$

58. $a^2 - 2ab + b^2$

59. $-10ab^2$

60. $-6a^3b$

61. $-10a^2b$

62. $-a^2b$

Concept 3: Multiplying and Dividing Expressions with Common Bases

63. Expand the following expressions first. Then simplify using exponents.

    a. $x^4 \cdot x^3$ **b.** $5^4 \cdot 5^3$

64. Expand the following expressions first. Then simplify using exponents.

    a. $y^2 \cdot y^4$ **b.** $3^2 \cdot 3^4$

For Exercises 65–76, simplify each expression. Write the answers in exponent form. **(See Example 4.)**

65. z^5z^3

66. w^4w^7

67. $a \cdot a^8$

68. p^4p

69. $4^5 \cdot 4^9$

70. $6^7 \cdot 6^5$

71. $\left(\dfrac{2}{3}\right)^3\left(\dfrac{2}{3}\right)$

72. $\left(\dfrac{1}{x}\right)\left(\dfrac{1}{x}\right)^2$

73. $c^5c^2c^7$

74. $b^7b^2b^8$

75. $x \cdot x^4 \cdot x^{10} \cdot x^3$

76. $z^7 \cdot z^{11} \cdot z^{60} \cdot z$

77. Expand the expressions. Then simplify.

    a. $\dfrac{p^8}{p^3}$ **b.** $\dfrac{8^8}{8^3}$

78. Expand the expressions. Then simplify.

    a. $\dfrac{w^5}{w^2}$ **b.** $\dfrac{4^5}{4^2}$

For Exercises 79–94, simplify each expression. Write the answers in exponent form. **(See Examples 5–6.)**

79. $\dfrac{x^8}{x^6}$

80. $\dfrac{z^5}{z^4}$

81. $\dfrac{a^{10}}{a}$

82. $\dfrac{b^{12}}{b}$

83. $\dfrac{7^{13}}{7^6}$

84. $\dfrac{2^6}{2^4}$

85. $\dfrac{5^8}{5}$

86. $\dfrac{3^5}{3}$

87. $\dfrac{y^{13}}{y^{12}}$

88. $\dfrac{w^7}{w^6}$

89. $\dfrac{h^3h^8}{h^7}$

90. $\dfrac{n^5n^4}{n^2}$

91. $\dfrac{7^2 \cdot 7^6}{7}$

92. $\dfrac{5^3 \cdot 5^8}{5}$

93. $\dfrac{10^{20}}{10^3 \cdot 10^8}$

94. $\dfrac{3^{15}}{3^2 \cdot 3^{10}}$

Concept 4: Simplifying Expressions with Exponents (Mixed Exercises)

For Exercises 95–114, use the commutative and associative properties of real numbers and the properties of exponents to simplify. **(See Example 7.)**

95. $(2x^3)(3x^4)$

96. $(10y)(2y^3)$

97. $(5a^2b)(8a^3b^4)$

98. $(10xy^3)(3x^4y)$

99. $s^3 \cdot t^5 \cdot t \cdot t^{10} \cdot s^6$

100. $c \cdot c^4 \cdot d^2 \cdot c^3 \cdot d^3$

101. $(-2v^2)(3v)(5v^5)$

102. $(10q^5)(-3q^8)(q)$

103. $\left(\frac{2}{3}m^{13}n^8\right)(24m^7n^2)$ **104.** $\left(\frac{1}{4}c^6d^6\right)(28c^2d^7)$ **105.** $\dfrac{14c^4d^5}{7c^3d}$ **106.** $\dfrac{36h^5k^2}{9h^3k}$

107. $\dfrac{z^3z^{11}}{z^4z^6}$ **108.** $\dfrac{w^{12}w^2}{w^4w^5}$ **109.** $\dfrac{25h^3jk^5}{12h^2k}$ **110.** $\dfrac{15m^5np^{12}}{4mp^9}$

111. $(-4p^6q^8r^4)(2pqr^2)$ **112.** $(-5a^4bc)(-10a^2b)$ **113.** $\dfrac{-12s^2tu^3}{4su^2}$ **114.** $\dfrac{15w^5x^{10}y^3}{-15w^4x}$

Concept 5: Applications of Exponents

Use the formula $A = P(1 + r)^t$ for Exercises 115–118. **(See Example 8.)**

115. Find the amount in an account after 2 years if the initial investment is $5000, invested at 7% interest compounded annually.

116. Find the amount in an account after 5 years if the initial investment is $2000, invested at 4% interest compounded annually.

117. Find the amount in an account after 3 years if the initial investment is $4000, invested at 6% interest compounded annually.

118. Find the amount in an account after 4 years if the initial investment is $10,000, invested at 5% interest compounded annually.

For Exercises 119–122, use appropriate geometry formulas.

119. Find the area of the pizza shown in the figure. Round to the nearest square inch.

16 in.

© Brand X Pictures/Alamy RF

120. Find the volume of the sphere shown in the figure. Round to the nearest cubic centimeter.

$r = 3$ cm

121. Find the volume of a spherical balloon that is 8 in. in diameter. Round to the nearest cubic inch.

122. Find the area of a circular pool 50 ft in diameter. Round to the nearest square foot.

Expanding Your Skills

For Exercises 123–130, simplify each expression using the addition or subtraction rules of exponents. Assume that a, b, m, and n represent positive integers.

123. $x^n x^{n+1}$ **124.** $y^a y^{2a}$ **125.** $p^{3m+5}p^{-m-2}$ **126.** $q^{4b-3}q^{-4b+4}$

127. $\dfrac{z^{b+1}}{z^b}$ **128.** $\dfrac{w^{5n+3}}{w^{2n}}$ **129.** $\dfrac{r^{3a+3}}{r^{3a}}$ **130.** $\dfrac{t^{3+2m}}{t^{2m}}$

352   **Chapter 5**   Polynomials and Properties of Exponents

Section 5.2   More Properties of Exponents

Concepts

1. Power Rule for Exponents
2. The Properties
   $(ab)^m = a^m b^m$ and
   $\left(\dfrac{a}{b}\right)^m = \dfrac{a^m}{b^m}$

1. Power Rule for Exponents

The expression $(x^2)^3$ indicates that the quantity x^2 is cubed.

$$(x^2)^3 = (x^2)(x^2)(x^2) = (x \cdot x)(x \cdot x)(x \cdot x) = x^6$$

From this example, it appears that to raise a base to successive powers, we multiply the exponents and leave the base unchanged. This is stated formally as the power rule for exponents.

> **Power Rule for Exponents**
>
> Assume that b is a real number and that m and n represent positive integers. Then,
>
> $$(b^m)^n = b^{m \cdot n}$$

Example 1   **Simplifying Expressions with Exponents**

Simplify the expressions.

   a. $(s^4)^2$ **b.** $(3^4)^2$ **c.** $(x^2 x^5)^4$

Solution:

a. $(s^4)^2$

    $= s^{4 \cdot 2}$ Multiply exponents (the base is unchanged).

    $= s^8$

b. $(3^4)^2$

    $= 3^{4 \cdot 2}$ Multiply exponents (the base is unchanged).

    $= 3^8$ or 6561

c. $(x^2 x^5)^4$

    $= (x^7)^4$ Simplify inside the parentheses by adding exponents.

    $= x^{7 \cdot 4}$ Multiply exponents (the base is unchanged).

    $= x^{28}$

Skill Practice   Simplify the expressions.

  1. $(y^3)^5$ **2.** $(2^8)^{10}$ **3.** $(q^5 q^4)^3$

2. The Properties $(ab)^m = a^m b^m$ and $\left(\frac{a}{b}\right)^m = \frac{a^m}{b^m}$

Consider the following expressions and their simplified forms:

$$(xy)^3 = (xy)(xy)(xy) = (x \cdot x \cdot x)(y \cdot y \cdot y) = x^3 y^3$$

$$\left(\frac{x}{y}\right)^3 = \left(\frac{x}{y}\right)\left(\frac{x}{y}\right)\left(\frac{x}{y}\right) = \left(\frac{x \cdot x \cdot x}{y \cdot y \cdot y}\right) = \frac{x^3}{y^3}$$

The expressions are simplified using the commutative and associative properties of multiplication. The simplified forms for each expression could have been reached in one step by applying the exponent to each factor inside the parentheses.

Answers

1. y^{15} **2.** 2^{80} **3.** q^{27}

Power of a Product and Power of a Quotient

Assume that a and b are real numbers. Let m represent a positive integer. Then,

$$(ab)^m = a^m b^m$$

$$\left(\frac{a}{b}\right)^m = \frac{a^m}{b^m}, \quad b \neq 0$$

Applying these properties of exponents, we have

$$(xy)^3 = x^3 y^3 \quad \text{and} \quad \left(\frac{x}{y}\right)^3 = \frac{x^3}{y^3}$$

Example 2   **Simplifying Expressions with Exponents**

Simplify the expressions.

a. $(-2xyz)^4$ **b.** $(5x^2 y^7)^3$ **c.** $\left(\frac{2}{5}\right)^3$ **d.** $\left(\frac{1}{3xy^4}\right)^2$

Solution:

a. $(-2xyz)^4$

$\quad = (-2)^4 x^4 y^4 z^4$ Raise each factor within parentheses to the fourth power.

$\quad = 16x^4 y^4 z^4$

b. $(5x^2 y^7)^3$

$\quad = 5^3 (x^2)^3 (y^7)^3$ Raise each factor within parentheses to the third power.

$\quad = 125 x^6 y^{21}$ Multiply exponents and simplify.

c. $\left(\frac{2}{5}\right)^3$

$\quad = \frac{(2)^3}{(5)^3}$ Raise each factor within parentheses to the third power.

$\quad = \frac{8}{125}$ Simplify.

d. $\left(\frac{1}{3xy^4}\right)^2$

$\quad = \frac{1^2}{3^2 x^2 (y^4)^2}$ Square each factor within parentheses.

$\quad = \frac{1}{9x^2 y^8}$ Multiply exponents and simplify.

Skill Practice   Simplify the expressions.

4. $(3abc)^5$ **5.** $(-2t^2 w^4)^3$ **6.** $\left(\frac{3}{4}\right)^3$ **7.** $\left(\frac{2x^3}{y^5}\right)^2$

Answers

4. $3^5 a^5 b^5 c^5$ or $243 a^5 b^5 c^5$

5. $-8t^6 w^{12}$ **6.** $\frac{27}{64}$ **7.** $\frac{4x^6}{y^{10}}$

The properties of exponents can be used along with the properties of real numbers to simplify complicated expressions.

Example 3   **Simplifying Expressions with Exponents**

Simplify the expression. $\dfrac{(x^2)^6(x^3)}{(x^7)^2}$

Solution:

$\dfrac{(x^2)^6(x^3)}{(x^7)^2}$ Clear parentheses by applying the power rule.

$= \dfrac{x^{2\cdot6}x^3}{x^{7\cdot2}}$ Multiply exponents.

$= \dfrac{x^{12}x^3}{x^{14}}$

$= \dfrac{x^{12+3}}{x^{14}}$ Add exponents in the numerator.

$= \dfrac{x^{15}}{x^{14}}$

$= x^{15-14}$ Subtract exponents.

$= x$ Simplify.

Skill Practice   Simplify the expression.

8. $\dfrac{(k^5)^2 k^8}{(k^2)^4}$

Example 4   **Simplifying Expressions with Exponents**

Simplify the expression. $(3cd^2)(2cd^3)^3$

Solution:

$(3cd^2)(2cd^3)^3$ Clear parentheses by applying the power rule.

$= 3cd^2 \cdot 2^3 c^3 d^9$ Raise each factor in the second parentheses to the third power.

$= 3 \cdot 2^3 cc^3 d^2 d^9$ Group like factors.

$= 3 \cdot 8 c^{1+3} d^{2+9}$ Add exponents on like bases.

$= 24 c^4 d^{11}$ Simplify.

Skill Practice   Simplify the expression.

9. $(4x^4y)(2x^3y^4)^4$

Answers

8. k^{10} **9.** $64x^{16}y^{17}$

| Example 5 | Simplifying Expressions with Exponents |

Simplify the expression. $\left(\dfrac{x^7yz^4}{8xz^3}\right)^2$

Solution:

$$\left(\frac{x^7yz^4}{8xz^3}\right)^2$$

$$= \left(\frac{x^{7-1}yz^{4-3}}{8}\right)^2 \qquad \text{First simplify inside the parentheses by subtracting exponents on like bases.}$$

$$= \left(\frac{x^6yz}{8}\right)^2$$

$$= \frac{(x^6)^2y^2z^2}{8^2} \qquad \text{Apply the power rule of exponents.}$$

$$= \frac{x^{12}y^2z^2}{64}$$

Skill Practice Simplify the expression.

10. $\left(\dfrac{w^2xy^4}{6xy^3}\right)^2$

Answer

10. $\dfrac{w^4y^2}{36}$

Section 5.2   Practice Exercises

For this exercise set assume all variables represent nonzero real numbers.

Review Exercises

For Exercises 1–8, simplify.

1. $4^2 \cdot 4^7$

2. $5^8 \cdot 5^3 \cdot 5$

3. $a^{13} \cdot a \cdot a^6$

4. $y^{14}y^3$

5. $\dfrac{d^{13}d}{d^5}$

6. $\dfrac{3^8 \cdot 3}{3^2}$

7. $\dfrac{7^{11}}{7^5}$

8. $\dfrac{z^4}{z^3}$

9. Explain when to add exponents versus when to multiply exponents.

10. Explain when to add exponents versus when to subtract exponents.

Concept 1: Power Rule for Exponents

For Exercises 11–22, simplify and write answers in exponent form. **(See Example 1.)**

11. $(5^3)^4$

12. $(2^8)^7$

13. $(12^3)^2$

14. $(6^4)^4$

15. $(y^7)^2$

16. $(z^6)^4$

17. $(w^5)^5$

18. $(t^3)^6$

19. $(a^2a^4)^6$

20. $(z \cdot z^3)^2$

21. $(y^3y^4)^2$

22. $(w^5w)^4$

Chapter 5   Polynomials and Properties of Exponents

two expressions and compare the
$(2^2)^3$ and $(2^3)^2$

24. Evaluate the two expressions and compare the
answers: $(4^4)^2$ and $(4^2)^4$

two expressions and compare the
hich expression is greater? Why?

4^{3^2} and $(4^3)^2$

26. Evaluate the two expressions and compare the
answers. Which expression is greater? Why?

3^{5^2} and $(3^5)^2$

Properties $(ab)^m = a^m b^m$ and $\left(\frac{a}{b}\right)^m = \frac{a^m}{b^m}$

42, use the appropriate property to clear the parentheses. **(See Example 2.)**

28. $(4y)^3$

29. $(srt)^4$

30. $(wxy)^6$

32. $\left(\frac{1}{t}\right)^8$

33. $\left(\frac{x}{y}\right)^5$

34. $\left(\frac{w}{z}\right)^7$

36. $(2x)^5$

37. $(-3abc)^3$

38. $(-5xyz)^2$

40. $\left(-\frac{1}{w}\right)^4$

41. $\left(-\frac{a}{b}\right)^2$

42. $\left(-\frac{r}{s}\right)^3$

, simplify. **(See Examples 3–5.)**

44. $(3a^5b^2)^6$

45. $5(x^2y)^4$

46. $18(u^3v^4)^2$

48. $(-k^6)^3$

49. $(-m^2)^6$

50. $(-n^3)^8$

52. $\left(\frac{2}{h^7k}\right)^3$

53. $\left(\frac{3p}{q^3}\right)^5$

54. $\left(\frac{5x^2}{y^3}\right)^4$

56. $\frac{(w^3)^2(w^4)^5}{(w^4)^2}$

57. $(x^2)^5(x^3)^7$

58. $(y^3)^4(y^2)^5$

60. $(4c^3d^5)^2(3cd^3)^2$

61. $(-2p^2q^4)^4$

62. $(-7x^4y^5)^2$

64. $(-a^3b^6)^7$

65. $\frac{(5a^3b)^4(a^2b)^4}{(5ab)^2-}$

66. $\frac{(6s^3)^2(s^4t^5)^2}{(3s^4t^2)^2}$

68. $\left(\frac{x^3y^5z}{5xy^2}\right)^2$

69. $(2c^3d^2)^5\left(\frac{c^6d^8}{4c^2d}\right)^3$

70. $\left(\frac{s^5t^6}{2s^2t}\right)^2(10s^3t^3)^2$

72. $\left(\frac{-4x^2}{y^4z}\right)^3$

73. $\frac{(-8b^6)^2(b^3)^5}{4b}$

74. $\frac{(-6a^2)^2(a^3)^4}{9a}$

lls

implify each expression. Assume that a, b, m, n, and x represent positive integers.

76. $(y^3)^n$

77. $(5a^{2n})^3$

78. $(3b^4)^m$

80. $\left(\frac{x^5}{y^3}\right)^m$

81. $\left(\frac{3a^3}{5b^4}\right)^n$

82. $\left(\frac{4m^6}{3n^2}\right)^x$

Definitions of b^0 and b^{-n}

We have learned several rules that enable us to manipulate expressions containing *positive* integer exponents. In this section, we present definitions that can be used to simplify expressions with negative exponents or with an exponent of zero.

Concepts

1. Definition of b^0
2. Definition of b^{-n}
3. Properties of Integer Exponents: A Summary

1. Definition of b^0

To begin, consider the following pattern.

$3^3 = 27$ — Divide by 3.
$3^2 = 9$ — Divide by 3.
$3^1 = 3$ — Divide by 3.
$3^0 = 1$

As the exponents decrease by 1, the resulting expressions are divided by 3.

For the pattern to continue, we define $3^0 = 1$.

This pattern suggests that we should define an expression with a zero exponent as follows.

> **Definition of b^0**
>
> Let b be a nonzero real number. Then, $b^0 = 1$.
>
> *Note*: The value of 0^0 is not defined by this definition because the base b must not equal zero.

Example 1   **Simplifying Expressions with a Zero Exponent**

Simplify. Assume that $z \neq 0$.

a. 4^0 **b.** $(-4)^0$ **c.** -4^0

d. z^0 **e.** $-4z^0$ **f.** $(4z)^0$

Solution:

a. $4^0 = 1$ By definition

b. $(-4)^0 = 1$ By definition

c. $-4^0 = -1 \cdot 4^0 = -1 \cdot 1 = -1$ The exponent 0 applies only to 4.

d. $z^0 = 1$ By definition

e. $-4z^0 = -4 \cdot z^0 = -4 \cdot 1 = -4$ The exponent 0 applies only to z.

f. $(4z)^0 = 1$ The parentheses indicate that the exponent, 0, applies to both factors 4 and z.

Skill Practice Evaluate the expressions. Assume that $x \neq 0$ and $y \neq 0$.

1. 7^0 **2.** $(-7)^0$ **3.** -5^0

4. y^0 **5.** $-2x^0$ **6.** $(2x)^0$

Answers

1. 1   **2.** 1   **3.** −1
4. 1   **5.** −2   **6.** 1

358   **Chapter 5** Polynomials and Properties of Exponents

The definition of b^0 is consistent with the other properties of exponents learned thus far. For example, we know that $1 = \frac{5^3}{5^3}$. If we subtract exponents, the result is 5^0.

Subtract exponents.

$$1 = \frac{5^3}{5^3} = 5^{3-3} = 5^0 \qquad \text{Therefore, } 5^0 \text{ must be defined as 1.}$$

2. Definition of b^{-n}

To understand the concept of a *negative* exponent, consider the following pattern.

$3^3 = 27$
Divide by 3.
$3^2 = 9$
Divide by 3.   As the exponents decrease by
$3^1 = 3$ 1, the resulting expressions are
Divide by 3.   divided by 3.
$3^0 = 1$
Divide by 3.

$3^{-1} = \dfrac{1}{3}$ ⟵———— For the pattern to continue, we define $3^{-1} = \dfrac{1}{3^1} = \dfrac{1}{3}$.

$3^{-2} = \dfrac{1}{9}$ ⟵———— For the pattern to continue, we define $3^{-2} = \dfrac{1}{3^2} = \dfrac{1}{9}$.

$3^{-3} = \dfrac{1}{27}$ ⟵———— For the pattern to continue, we define $3^{-3} = \dfrac{1}{3^3} = \dfrac{1}{27}$.

This pattern suggests that $3^{-n} = \frac{1}{3^n}$ for all integers, n. In general, we have the following definition involving negative exponents.

Definition of b^{-n}

Let n be an integer and b be a nonzero real number. Then,

$$b^{-n} = \left(\frac{1}{b}\right)^n \quad \text{or} \quad \frac{1}{b^n}$$

The definition of b^{-n} implies that to evaluate b^{-n}, take the reciprocal of the base and change the sign of the exponent.

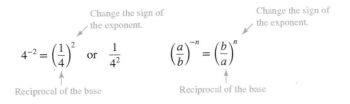

| Example 2 | **Simplifying Expressions with Negative Exponents** |

Simplify. Assume that $c \neq 0$.

  a. c^{-3} **b.** 5^{-1} **c.** $(-3)^{-4}$

Solution:

  a. $c^{-3} = \dfrac{1}{c^3}$ By definition

  b. $5^{-1} = \dfrac{1}{5^1}$ By definition

         $= \dfrac{1}{5}$ Simplify.

  c. $(-3)^{-4} = \dfrac{1}{(-3)^4}$ The base is -3 and must be enclosed in parentheses.

           $= \dfrac{1}{81}$ Simplify. Note that $(-3)^4 = (-3)(-3)(-3)(-3) = 81$.

> **Avoiding Mistakes**
>
> A negative exponent does *not* affect the sign of the base.

Skill Practice Simplify. Assume that $p \neq 0$.

  7. p^{-4} **8.** 3^{-3} **9.** $(-5)^{-2}$

| Example 3 | **Simplifying Expressions with Negative Exponents** |

Simplify. Assume that $y \neq 0$.

  a. $\left(\dfrac{1}{6}\right)^{-2}$ **b.** $\left(-\dfrac{3}{5}\right)^{-3}$ **c.** $\dfrac{1}{y^{-5}}$

Solution:

  a. $\left(\dfrac{1}{6}\right)^{-2} = 6^2$ Take the reciprocal of the base, and change the sign of the exponent.

           $= 36$ Simplify.

  b. $\left(-\dfrac{3}{5}\right)^{-3} = \left(-\dfrac{5}{3}\right)^3$ Take the reciprocal of the base, and change the sign of the exponent.

           $= -\dfrac{125}{27}$ Simplify.

  c. $\dfrac{1}{y^{-5}} = \left(\dfrac{1}{y}\right)^{-5}$ Apply the power of a quotient rule.

           $= (y)^5$ Take the reciprocal of the base, and change the sign of the exponent.

           $= y^5$

> **TIP:** Example 3(c) illustrates that $\dfrac{1}{b^{-n}} = b^n$, for $b \neq 0$.

Skill Practice Simplify. Assume that $w \neq 0$.

  10. $\left(\dfrac{1}{3}\right)^{-1}$ **11.** $\left(-\dfrac{2}{5}\right)^{-2}$ **12.** $\dfrac{1}{w^{-7}}$

Answers

7. $\dfrac{1}{p^4}$ **8.** $\dfrac{1}{3^3}$ or $\dfrac{1}{27}$

9. $\dfrac{1}{(-5)^2}$ or $\dfrac{1}{25}$ **10.** 3

11. $\dfrac{25}{4}$ **12.** w^7

360   Chapter 5   Polynomials and Properties of Exponents

| Example 4 | **Simplifying Expressions with Negative Exponents** |

Simplify. Assume that $x \neq 0$.

a. $(5x)^{-3}$ **b.** $5x^{-3}$ **c.** $-5x^{-3}$

Solution:

a. $(5x)^{-3} = \left(\dfrac{1}{5x}\right)^{3}$ Take the reciprocal of the base, and change the sign of the exponent.

$= \dfrac{(1)^3}{(5x)^3}$ Apply the exponent of 3 to each factor within parentheses.

$= \dfrac{1}{125x^3}$ Simplify.

b. $5x^{-3} = 5 \cdot x^{-3}$ Note that the exponent, -3, applies only to x.

$= 5 \cdot \dfrac{1}{x^3}$ Rewrite x^{-3} as $\dfrac{1}{x^3}$.

$= \dfrac{5}{x^3}$ Multiply.

c. $-5x^{-3} = -5 \cdot x^{-3}$ Note that the exponent, -3, applies only to x, and that -5 is a coefficient.

$= -5 \cdot \dfrac{1}{x^3}$ Rewrite x^{-3} as $\dfrac{1}{x^3}$.

$= -\dfrac{5}{x^3}$ Multiply.

Skill Practice Simplify. Assume that $w \neq 0$.

13. $(2w)^{-4}$ **14.** $2w^{-4}$ **15.** $-2w^{-4}$

It is important to note that the definition of b^{-n} is consistent with the other properties of exponents learned thus far. For example, consider the expression

$$\frac{x^4}{x^7} = \frac{\cancel{x} \cdot \cancel{x} \cdot \cancel{x} \cdot \cancel{x}}{\cancel{x} \cdot \cancel{x} \cdot \cancel{x} \cdot \cancel{x} \cdot x \cdot x \cdot x} = \frac{1}{x^3}$$

Subtract exponents.   Hence, $x^{-3} = \dfrac{1}{x^3}$.

By subtracting exponents, we have $\dfrac{x^4}{x^7} = x^{4-7} = x^{-3}$

3. Properties of Integer Exponents: A Summary

The definitions of b^0 and b^{-n} enable us to extend the properties of exponents. These are summarized in Table 5-1.

Answers

13. $\dfrac{1}{16w^4}$ **14.** $\dfrac{2}{w^4}$

15. $-\dfrac{2}{w^4}$

Table 5-1

Properties of Integer Exponents		
Assume that a and b are real numbers ($b \neq 0$) and that m and n represent integers.		
Property	Example	Details/Notes
Multiplication of Expressions with Like Bases $b^m b^n = b^{m+n}$	$b^2 b^4 = b^{2+4} = b^6$	$b^2 b^4 = (b \cdot b)(b \cdot b \cdot b \cdot b) = b^6$
Division of Expressions with Like Bases $\dfrac{b^m}{b^n} = b^{m-n}$	$\dfrac{b^5}{b^2} = b^{5-2} = b^3$	$\dfrac{b^5}{b^2} = \dfrac{\cancel{b} \cdot \cancel{b} \cdot b \cdot b \cdot b}{\cancel{b} \cdot \cancel{b}} = b^3$
The Power Rule $(b^m)^n = b^{m \cdot n}$	$(b^4)^2 = b^{4 \cdot 2} = b^8$	$(b^4)^2 = (b \cdot b \cdot b \cdot b)(b \cdot b \cdot b \cdot b) = b^8$
Power of a Product $(ab)^m = a^m b^m$	$(ab)^3 = a^3 b^3$	$(ab)^3 = (ab)(ab)(ab)$ $= (a \cdot a \cdot a)(b \cdot b \cdot b) = a^3 b^3$
Power of a Quotient $\left(\dfrac{a}{b}\right)^m = \dfrac{a^m}{b^m}$	$\left(\dfrac{a}{b}\right)^3 = \dfrac{a^3}{b^3}$	$\left(\dfrac{a}{b}\right)^3 = \left(\dfrac{a}{b}\right)\left(\dfrac{a}{b}\right)\left(\dfrac{a}{b}\right) = \dfrac{a \cdot a \cdot a}{b \cdot b \cdot b} = \dfrac{a^3}{b^3}$
Definitions		
Assume that b is a real number ($b \neq 0$) and that n represents an integer.		
Definition	Example	Details/Notes
$b^0 = 1$	$(4)^0 = 1$	Any nonzero quantity raised to the zero power equals 1.
$b^{-n} = \left(\dfrac{1}{b}\right)^n = \dfrac{1}{b^n}$	$b^{-5} = \left(\dfrac{1}{b}\right)^5 = \dfrac{1}{b^5}$	To simplify a negative exponent, take the reciprocal of the base and make the exponent positive.

Example 5   Simplifying Expressions with Exponents

Simplify the expressions. Write the answers with positive exponents only. Assume all variables are nonzero.

a. $\dfrac{a^3 b^{-2}}{c^{-5}}$ **b.** $\dfrac{x^2 x^{-7}}{x^3}$ **c.** $\dfrac{z^2}{w^{-4} w^4 z^{-8}}$

Solution:

a. $\dfrac{a^3 b^{-2}}{c^{-5}}$

$= \dfrac{a^3}{1} \cdot \dfrac{b^{-2}}{1} \cdot \dfrac{1}{c^{-5}}$

$= \dfrac{a^3}{1} \cdot \dfrac{1}{b^2} \cdot \dfrac{c^5}{1}$ Simplify negative exponents.

$= \dfrac{a^3 c^5}{b^2}$ Multiply.

b. $\dfrac{x^2 x^{-7}}{x^3}$

$\qquad = \dfrac{x^{2+(-7)}}{x^3}$ Add the exponents in the numerator.

$\qquad = \dfrac{x^{-5}}{x^3}$ Simplify.

$\qquad = x^{-5-3}$ Subtract the exponents.

$\qquad = x^{-8}$

$\qquad = \dfrac{1}{x^8}$ Simplify the negative exponent.

c. $\dfrac{z^2}{w^{-4} w^4 z^{-8}}$

$\qquad = \dfrac{z^2}{w^{-4+4} z^{-8}}$ Add the exponents in the denominator.

$\qquad = \dfrac{z^2}{w^0 z^{-8}}$

$\qquad = \dfrac{z^2}{(1) z^{-8}}$ Recall that $w^0 = 1$.

$\qquad = z^{2-(-8)}$ Subtract the exponents.

$\qquad = z^{10}$ Simplify.

Skill Practice   Simplify the expressions. Assume all variables are nonzero.

16. $\dfrac{x^{-6}}{y^4 z^{-8}}$ **17.** $\dfrac{x^3 x^{-8}}{x^4}$ **18.** $\dfrac{p^3}{w^7 w^{-7} z^{-2}}$

Example 6   **Simplifying Expressions with Exponents**

Simplify the expressions. Write the answers with positive exponents only. Assume that all variables are nonzero.

a. $\left(-4ab^{-2}\right)^{-3}$ **b.** $\left(\dfrac{2p^{-4} q^3}{5p^2 q}\right)^{-2}$

Solution:

a. $\left(-4ab^{-2}\right)^{-3}$

$\qquad = (-4)^{-3} a^{-3} (b^{-2})^{-3}$ Apply the power rule of exponents.

$\qquad = (-4)^{-3} a^{-3} b^6$

$\qquad = \dfrac{1}{(-4)^3} \cdot \dfrac{1}{a^3} \cdot b^6$ Simplify the negative exponents.

$\qquad = \dfrac{1}{-64} \cdot \dfrac{1}{a^3} \cdot b^6$ Simplify.

$\qquad = -\dfrac{b^6}{64a^3}$ Multiply fractions.

Answers

16. $\dfrac{z^8}{y^4 x^6}$ **17.** $\dfrac{1}{x^9}$ **18.** $p^3 z^2$

b. $\left(\dfrac{2p^{-4}q^3}{5p^2q}\right)^{-2}$ 　　　First simplify within the parentheses.

$= \left(\dfrac{2p^{-4-2}q^{3-1}}{5}\right)^{-2}$ 　　Divide expressions with like bases by subtracting exponents.

$= \left(\dfrac{2p^{-6}q^2}{5}\right)^{-2}$ 　　　Simplify.

$= \dfrac{(2p^{-6}q^2)^{-2}}{(5)^{-2}}$ 　　　Apply the power rule of a quotient.

$= \dfrac{2^{-2}(p^{-6})^{-2}(q^2)^{-2}}{5^{-2}}$ 　　Apply the power rule of a product.

$= \dfrac{2^{-2}p^{12}q^{-4}}{5^{-2}}$ 　　　Simplify.

$= \dfrac{5^2p^{12}}{2^2q^4}$ 　　　Simplify the negative exponents.

$= \dfrac{25p^{12}}{4q^4}$ 　　　Simplify.

> **TIP:** For Example 6(b), the power rule of exponents can be performed first. In that case, the second step would be
>
> $$\dfrac{2^{-2}p^8q^{-6}}{5^{-2}p^{-4}q^{-2}}$$

Skill Practice Simplify the expressions. Assume all variables are nonzero.

19. $(-5x^{-2}y^3)^{-2}$ 　　　**20.** $\left(\dfrac{3x^{-3}y^{-2}}{4xy^{-3}}\right)^{-2}$

Example 7 **Simplifying an Expression with Exponents**

Simplify the expression $2^{-1} + 3^{-1} + 5^0$. Write the answer with positive exponents only.

Solution:

$2^{-1} + 3^{-1} + 5^0$

$= \dfrac{1}{2} + \dfrac{1}{3} + 1$ 　　　Simplify negative exponents. Simplify $5^0 = 1$.

$= \dfrac{3}{6} + \dfrac{2}{6} + \dfrac{6}{6}$ 　　The least common denominator is 6.

$= \dfrac{11}{6}$ 　　　Simplify.

Skill Practice Simplify the expressions.

21. $2^{-1} + 4^{-2} + 3^0$

Answers

19. $\dfrac{x^4}{25y^6}$ 　　**20.** $\dfrac{16x^8}{9y^2}$ 　　**21.** $\dfrac{25}{16}$

Section 5.3   Practice Exercises

For this exercise set, assume all variables represent nonzero real numbers.

Study Skills Exercise

To help you remember the properties of exponents, write them on 3×5 cards. On each card, write a property on one side and an example using that property on the other side. Keep these cards with you, and when you have a spare moment (such as waiting at the doctor's office), pull out these cards and go over the properties.

Vocabulary and Key Concepts

1. **a.** The expression b^0 is defined to be _____ provided that $b \neq 0$.

    b. The expression b^{-n} is defined as _____ provided that $b \neq 0$.

Review Exercises

For Exercises 2–9, simplify.

2. $b^3 b^8$

3. $c^7 c^2$

4. $\dfrac{x^6}{x^2}$

5. $\dfrac{y^9}{y^8}$

6. $\dfrac{9^4 \cdot 9^8}{9}$

7. $\dfrac{3^{14}}{3^3 \cdot 3^5}$

8. $(6ab^3 c^2)^5$

9. $(7w^7 z^2)^4$

Concept 1: Definition of b^0

10. Simplify.

     a. 8^0 **b.** $\dfrac{8^4}{8^4}$

11. Simplify.

     a. d^0 **b.** $\dfrac{d^3}{d^3}$

12. Simplify.

     a. m^0 **b.** $\dfrac{m^5}{m^5}$

For Exercises 13–24, simplify. **(See Example 1.)**

13. p^0

14. k^0

15. 5^0

16. 2^0

17. -4^0

18. -1^0

19. $(-6)^0$

20. $(-2)^0$

21. $(8x)^0$

22. $(-3y^3)^0$

23. $-7x^0$

24. $6y^0$

Concept 2: Definition of b^{-n}

25. Simplify and write the answers with positive exponents.

     a. t^{-5} **b.** $\dfrac{t^3}{t^8}$

26. Simplify and write the answers with positive exponents.

     a. 4^{-3} **b.** $\dfrac{4^2}{4^5}$

For Exercises 27–46, simplify. **(See Examples 2–4.)**

27. $\left(\dfrac{2}{7}\right)^{-3}$

28. $\left(\dfrac{5}{4}\right)^{-1}$

29. $\left(-\dfrac{1}{5}\right)^{-2}$

30. $\left(-\dfrac{1}{3}\right)^{-3}$

31. a^{-3}

32. c^{-5}

33. 12^{-1}

34. 4^{-2}

35. $(4b)^{-2}$

36. $(3z)^{-1}$

37. $6x^{-2}$

38. $7y^{-1}$

39. $(-8)^{-2}$ **40.** -8^{-2} **41.** $-3y^{-4}$ **42.** $-6a^{-2}$

43. $(-t)^{-3}$ **44.** $(-r)^{-5}$ **45.** $\dfrac{1}{a^{-5}}$ **46.** $\dfrac{1}{b^{-6}}$

Concept 3: Properties of Integer Exponents: A Summary

For Exercises 47–50, correct the statement.

47. $\dfrac{x^4}{x^{-6}} = x^{4-6} = x^{-2}$ **48.** $\dfrac{y^5}{y^{-3}} = y^{5-3} = y^2$

49. $2a^{-3} = \dfrac{1}{2a^3}$ **50.** $5b^{-2} = \dfrac{1}{5b^2}$

Mixed Exercises

For Exercises 51–94, simplify each expression. Write the answer with positive exponents only. **(See Examples 5–6.)**

51. $x^{-8}x^4$ **52.** s^5s^{-6} **53.** $a^{-8}a^8$ **54.** q^3q^{-3}

55. $y^{17}y^{-13}$ **56.** $b^{20}b^{-14}$ **57.** $(m^{-6}n^9)^3$ **58.** $(c^4d^{-5})^{-2}$

59. $(-3j^{-5}k^6)^4$ **60.** $(6xy^{-11})^{-3}$ **61.** $\dfrac{p^3}{p^9}$ **62.** $\dfrac{q^2}{q^{10}}$

63. $\dfrac{r^{-5}}{r^{-2}}$ **64.** $\dfrac{u^{-2}}{u^{-6}}$ **65.** $\dfrac{a^2}{a^{-6}}$ **66.** $\dfrac{p^3}{p^{-5}}$

67. $\dfrac{y^{-2}}{y^6}$ **68.** $\dfrac{s^{-4}}{s^3}$ **69.** $\dfrac{7^3}{7^2 \cdot 7^8}$ **70.** $\dfrac{3^4 \cdot 3}{3^7}$

71. $\dfrac{a^2a}{a^3}$ **72.** $\dfrac{t^5}{t^2t^3}$ **73.** $\dfrac{a^{-1}b^2}{a^3b^8}$ **74.** $\dfrac{k^{-4}h^{-1}}{k^6h}$

75. $\dfrac{w^{-8}(w^2)^{-5}}{w^3}$ **76.** $\dfrac{p^2p^{-7}}{(p^2)^3}$ **77.** $\dfrac{3^{-2}}{3}$ **78.** $\dfrac{5^{-1}}{5}$

79. $\left(\dfrac{p^{-1}q^5}{p^{-6}}\right)^0$ **80.** $\left(\dfrac{ab^{-4}}{a^{-5}}\right)^0$ **81.** $(8x^3y^0)^{-2}$ **82.** $(3u^2v^0)^{-3}$

83. $(-8y^{-12})(2y^{16}z^{-2})$ **84.** $(5p^{-2}q^5)(-2p^{-4}q^{-1})$ **85.** $\dfrac{-18a^{10}b^6}{108a^{-2}b^6}$ **86.** $\dfrac{-35x^{-4}y^{-3}}{-21x^2y^{-3}}$

87. $\dfrac{(-4c^{12}d^7)^2}{(5c^{-3}d^{10})^{-1}}$ **88.** $\dfrac{(s^3t^{-2})^4}{(3s^{-4}t^6)^{-2}}$ **89.** $\dfrac{(2x^3y^2)^{-3}}{(3x^2y^4)^{-2}}$ **90.** $\dfrac{(5p^4q)^{-3}}{(p^3q^5)^{-4}}$

91. $\left(\dfrac{5cd^{-3}}{10d^5}\right)^{-2}$ **92.** $\left(\dfrac{4m^{10}n^4}{2m^{12}n^{-2}}\right)^{-1}$ **93.** $(2xy^3)\left(\dfrac{9xy}{4x^3y^2}\right)$ **94.** $(-3a^3)\left(\dfrac{ab}{27a^4b^2}\right)$

For Exercises 95–102, simplify. **(See Example 7.)**

95. $5^{-1} + 2^{-2}$ **96.** $4^{-2} + 8^{-1}$ **97.** $10^0 - 10^{-1}$ **98.** $3^0 - 3^{-2}$

99. $2^{-2} + 1^{-2}$ **100.** $4^{-1} + 8^{-1}$ **101.** $4 \cdot 5^0 - 2 \cdot 3^{-1}$ **102.** $2 \cdot 4^0 - 3 \cdot 4^{-1}$

366   **Chapter 5**   Polynomials and Properties of Exponents

Expanding Your Skills

For Exercises 103–106, determine the missing exponent.

103. $\dfrac{y^4 y^\square}{y^{-2}} = y^8$

104. $\dfrac{x^4 x^\square}{x^{-1}} = x^9$

105. $\dfrac{w^{-9}}{w^\square} = w^2$

106. $\dfrac{a^{-2}}{a^\square} = a^6$

Problem Recognition Exercises

Properties of Exponents

For Exercises 1–40, simplify completely. Assume that all variables represent nonzero real numbers.

1. t^3t^5

2. $2^3 2^5$

3. $\dfrac{y^7}{y^2}$

4. $\dfrac{p^9}{p^3}$

5. $(r^2 s^4)^2$

6. $(ab^3 c^2)^3$

7. $\dfrac{w^4}{w^{-2}}$

8. $\dfrac{m^{-14}}{m^2}$

9. $\dfrac{y^{-7} x^4}{z^{-3}}$

10. $\dfrac{a^3 b^{-6}}{c^{-8}}$

11. $\dfrac{x^4 x^{-3}}{x^{-5}}$

12. $\dfrac{y^{-4}}{y^7 y^{-1}}$

13. $\dfrac{t^{-2} t^4}{t^8 t^{-1}}$

14. $\dfrac{w^8 w^{-5}}{w^{-2} w^{-2}}$

15. $\dfrac{1}{p^{-6} p^{-8} p^{-1}}$

16. $p^6 p^8 p$

17. $\dfrac{v^9}{v^{11}}$

18. $(c^5 d^4)^{10}$

19. $\left(\dfrac{1}{2}\right)^{-1} + \left(\dfrac{1}{3}\right)^0$

20. $\left(\dfrac{1}{4}\right)^0 - \left(\dfrac{1}{5}\right)^{-1}$

21. $(2^5 b^{-3})^{-3}$

22. $(3^{-2} y^3)^{-2}$

23. $\left(\dfrac{3x}{2y}\right)^{-4}$

24. $\left(\dfrac{6c}{5d^3}\right)^{-2}$

25. $(3ab^2)(a^2 b)^3$

26. $(4x^2 y^3)^3 (xy^2)$

27. $\left(\dfrac{xy^2}{x^3 y}\right)^4$

28. $\left(\dfrac{a^3 b}{a^5 b^3}\right)^5$

29. $\dfrac{(t^{-2})^3}{t^{-4}}$

30. $\dfrac{(p^3)^{-4}}{p^{-5}}$

31. $\left(\dfrac{2w^2 x^3}{3y^0}\right)^3$

32. $\left(\dfrac{5a^0 b^4}{4c^3}\right)^2$

33. $\dfrac{q^3 r^{-2}}{s^{-1} t^5}$

34. $\dfrac{n^{-3} m^2}{p^{-3} q^{-1}}$

35. $\dfrac{(y^{-3})^2 (y^5)}{(y^{-3})^{-4}}$

36. $\dfrac{(w^2)^{-4}(w^{-2})}{(w^5)^{-4}}$

37. $\left(\dfrac{-2a^2 b^{-3}}{a^{-4} b^{-5}}\right)^{-3}$

38. $\left(\dfrac{-3x^{-4} y^3}{2x^5 y^{-2}}\right)^{-2}$

39. $(5h^{-2} k^0)^3 (5k^{-2})^{-4}$

40. $(6m^3 n^{-5})^{-4}(6m^0 n^{-2})^5$

Scientific Notation

1. Writing Numbers in Scientific Notation

In many applications in mathematics, it is necessary to work with very large or very small numbers. For example, the number of movie tickets sold in the United States recently is estimated to be 1,500,000,000. The weight of a flea is approximately 0.00066 lb. To avoid writing numerous zeros in very large or small numbers, scientific notation was devised as a shortcut.

The principle behind scientific notation is to use a power of 10 to express the magnitude of the number. For example, the numbers 4000 and 0.07 can be written as:

$$4000 = 4 \times 1000 = 4 \times 10^3$$
$$0.07 = 7.0 \times 0.01 = 7.0 \times 10^{-2} \qquad \text{Note that } 10^{-2} = \frac{1}{100} = 0.01$$

> **Definition of Scientific Notation**
>
> A positive number expressed in the form: $a \times 10^n$, where $1 \le a < 10$ and n is an integer, is said to be written in **scientific notation**.

To write a positive number in scientific notation, we apply the following guidelines:

1. Move the decimal point so that its new location is to the right of the first nonzero digit. The number should now be greater than or equal to 1 but less than 10. Count the number of places that the decimal point is moved.

2. If the original number is *large* (greater than or equal to 10), use the number of places the decimal point was moved as a *positive* power of 10.

$$450{,}000 = 4.5 \times 100{,}000 = 4.5 \times 10^5$$

5 places

3. If the original number is *small* (between 0 and 1), use the number of places the decimal point was moved as a *negative* power of 10.

$$0.0002 = 2.0 \times 0.0001 = 2.0 \times 10^{-4}$$

4 places

4. If the original number is greater than or equal to 1 but less than 10, use 0 as the power of 10.

$$7.592 = 7.592 \times 10^0 \qquad \textit{Note: A number between 1 and 10 is seldom written in scientific notation.}$$

5. If the original number is negative, then $-10 < a \le -1$.

$$-450{,}000 = -4.5 \times 100{,}000 = -4.5 \times 10^5$$

5 places

Example 1   Writing Numbers in Scientific Notation

Write the numbers in scientific notation.

a. 53,000   b. 0.00053

Solution:

a. $53,000. = 5.3 \times 10^4$ To write 53,000 in scientific notation, the decimal point must be moved four places to the left. Because 53,000 is larger than 10, a *positive* power of 10 is used.

b. $0.00053 = 5.3 \times 10^{-4}$ To write 0.00053 in scientific notation, the decimal point must be moved four places to the right. Because 0.00053 is between 0 and 1, a *negative* power of 10 is used.

Skill Practice Write the numbers in scientific notation.

1. 175,000,000   2. 0.000005

Example 2   Writing Numbers in Scientific Notation

Write the numbers in scientific notation.

a. The number of movie tickets sold in the United States for a recent year is estimated to be 1,500,000,000.

b. The weight of a flea is approximately 0.00066 lb.

c. The temperature on a January day in Fargo dropped to −43°F.

d. A bench is 8.2 ft long.

Solution:

a. $1,500,000,000 = 1.5 \times 10^9$ b. $0.00066 \text{ lb} = 6.6 \times 10^{-4} \text{ lb}$

c. $-43°F = -4.3 \times 10^1 \text{ °F}$ d. $8.2 \text{ ft} = 8.2 \times 10^0 \text{ ft}$

Skill Practice Write the numbers in scientific notation.

3. In the year 2011, the population of the Earth was approximately 7,000,000,000.

4. The weight of a grain of salt is approximately 0.000002 ounce.

2. Writing Numbers in Standard Form

Example 3   Writing Numbers in Standard Form

Write the numbers in standard form.

a. The mass of a proton is approximately 1.67×10^{-24} g.

b. The "nearby" star Vega is approximately 1.552×10^{14} miles from Earth.

Solution:

a. $1.67 \times 10^{-24} \text{ g} = 0.000\,000\,000\,000\,000\,000\,000\,001\,67 \text{ g}$

Because the power of 10 is negative, the value of 1.67×10^{-24} is a decimal number between 0 and 1. Move the decimal point 24 places to the *left*.

b. $1.552 \times 10^{14} \text{ miles} = 155,200,000,000,000 \text{ miles}$

Because the power of 10 is a positive integer, the value of 1.552×10^{14} is a large number greater than 10. Move the decimal point 14 places to the *right*.

Answers

1. 1.75×10^8 2. 5×10^{-6}
3. 7×10^9 4. 2×10^{-6} oz

Skill Practice Write the numbers in standard form.

5. The probability of winning the California Super Lotto Jackpot is 5.5×10^{-8}.

6. The Sun's mass is 2×10^{30} kilograms.

3. Multiplying and Dividing Numbers in Scientific Notation

To multiply or divide two numbers in scientific notation, use the commutative and associative properties of multiplication to group the powers of 10. For example:

$$400 \times 2000 = (4 \times 10^2)(2 \times 10^3) = (4 \cdot 2) \times (10^2 \cdot 10^3) = 8 \times 10^5$$

$$\frac{0.00054}{150} = \frac{5.4 \times 10^{-4}}{1.5 \times 10^2} = \left(\frac{5.4}{1.5}\right) \times \left(\frac{10^{-4}}{10^2}\right) = 3.6 \times 10^{-6}$$

Example 4 **Multiplying and Dividing Numbers in Scientific Notation**

Multiply or divide as indicated.

a. $(8.7 \times 10^4)(2.5 \times 10^{-12})$ **b.** $\dfrac{4.25 \times 10^{13}}{8.5 \times 10^{-2}}$

Solution:

a. $(8.7 \times 10^4)(2.5 \times 10^{-12})$

$= (8.7 \cdot 2.5) \times (10^4 \cdot 10^{-12})$ Regroup factors using the commutative and associative properties of multiplication.

$= 21.75 \times 10^{-8}$ The number 21.75 is not in proper scientific notation because 21.75 is not between 1 and 10.

$= (2.175 \times 10^1) \times 10^{-8}$ Rewrite 21.75 as 2.175×10^1.

$= 2.175 \times (10^1 \times 10^{-8})$ Associative property of multiplication

$= 2.175 \times 10^{-7}$ Simplify.

b. $\dfrac{4.25 \times 10^{13}}{8.5 \times 10^{-2}}$

$= \left(\dfrac{4.25}{8.5}\right) \times \left(\dfrac{10^{13}}{10^{-2}}\right)$ Regroup factors using the commutative and associative properties.

$= 0.5 \times 10^{15}$ The number 0.5×10^{15} is not in proper scientific notation because 0.5 is not between 1 and 10.

$= (5.0 \times 10^{-1}) \times 10^{15}$ Rewrite 0.5 as 5.0×10^{-1}.

$= 5.0 \times (10^{-1} \times 10^{15})$ Associative property of multiplication

$= 5.0 \times 10^{14}$ Simplify.

Skill Practice Multiply or divide as indicated.

7. $(7 \times 10^5)(5 \times 10^3)$ **8.** $\dfrac{1 \times 10^{-2}}{4 \times 10^{-7}}$

Answers

5. 0.000 000 055
6. 2,000,000,000,000,000,000,000,000,000,000
7. 3.5×10^9
8. 2.5×10^4

Calculator Connections

Topic: Using Scientific Notation

Both scientific and graphing calculators can perform calculations involving numbers written in scientific notation. Most calculators use an **EE** key or an **EXP** key to enter the power of 10.

Scientific Calculator

Enter: 2.7 **EE** 5 **=**   or   2.7 **EXP** 5 **=**   Result: 270000

Enter: 7.1 **EE** 3 **+○-** **=**   or   7.1 **EXP** 3 **+○-** **=**   Result: 0.0071

Graphing Calculator

```
2.7E5
          270000
7.1E-3
            .0071
```

We recommend that you use parentheses to enclose each number written in scientific notation when performing calculations. Try using your calculator to perform the calculations from Example 4.

a. $(8.7 \times 10^4)(2.5 \times 10^{-12})$ **b.** $\dfrac{4.25 \times 10^{13}}{8.5 \times 10^{-2}}$

Scientific Calculator

Enter: **(** 8.7 **EE** 4 **)** **×** **(** 2.5 **EE** 12 **+○-** **)** **=**   Result: 0.000000218

Enter: **(** 4.25 **EE** 13 **)** **÷** **(** 8.5 **EE** 2 **+○-** **)** **=**   Result: 5E14

Notice that the answer to part (b) is shown on the calculator in scientific notation. The calculator does not have enough room to display 14 zeros. Also notice that the calculator rounds the answer to part (a). The exact answer is 2.175×10^{-7} or 0.0000002175.

Graphing Calculator

```
(8.7E4)*(2.5E-12
)
          2.175E-7
(4.25E13)/(8.5E-
2)
             5E14
```

Avoiding Mistakes

A display of 5E14 on a calculator does not mean 5^{14}. It is scientific notation and means 5×10^{14}.

Calculator Exercises

Use a calculator to perform the indicated operations:

1. $(5.2 \times 10^6)(4.6 \times 10^{-3})$

2. $(2.19 \times 10^{-8})(7.84 \times 10^{-4})$

3. $\dfrac{4.76 \times 10^{-5}}{2.38 \times 10^9}$

4. $\dfrac{8.5 \times 10^4}{4.0 \times 10^{-1}}$

5. $\dfrac{(9.6 \times 10^7)(4.0 \times 10^{-3})}{2.0 \times 10^{-2}}$

6. $\dfrac{(5.0 \times 10^{-12})(6.4 \times 10^{-5})}{(1.6 \times 10^{-8})(4.0 \times 10^2)}$

Section 5.4 Practice Exercises

Vocabulary and Key Concepts

1. A positive number expressed in the form $a \times 10^n$, where $1 \leq a < 10$ and n is an integer is said to be written in _____ _____.

Review Exercises

For Exercises 2–13, simplify each expression. Assume all variables represent nonzero real numbers.

2. $a^3 a^{-4}$

3. $b^5 b^8$

4. $10^3 \cdot 10^{-4}$

5. $10^5 \cdot 10^8$

6. $\dfrac{x^3}{x^6}$

7. $\dfrac{y^2}{y^7}$

8. $(c^4 d^2)^3$

9. $(x^5 y^{-3})^4$

10. $\dfrac{z^9 z^4}{z^3}$

11. $\dfrac{w^{-2} w^5}{w^{-1}}$

12. $\dfrac{10^9 \cdot 10^4}{10^3}$

13. $\dfrac{10^{-2} \cdot 10^5}{10^{-1}}$

Concept 1: Writing Numbers in Scientific Notation

14. Explain how scientific notation might be valuable in studying astronomy. Answers may vary.

15. Explain how you would write the number 0.000 000 000 23 in scientific notation.

16. Explain how you would write the number 23,000,000,000,000 in scientific notation.

For Exercises 17–28, write the number in scientific notation. **(See Example 1.)**

17. 50,000

18. 900,000

19. 208,000

20. 420,000,000

21. 6,010,000

22. 75,000

23. 0.000008

24. 0.003

25. 0.000125

26. 0.00000025

27. 0.006708

28. 0.02004

For Exercises 29–34, write each number in scientific notation. **(See Example 2.)**

29. The mass of a proton is approximately 0.000 000 000 000 000 000 000 0017 g.

30. The total combined salaries of the president, vice president, senators, and representatives of the United States federal government is approximately $85,000,000.

31. A renowned foundation has over $27,000,000,000 from which it makes contributions to global charities.

32. One gram is equivalent to 0.0035 oz.

33. One of the world's largest tanker disasters spilled 68,000,000 gal of oil off Portsall, France, causing widespread environmental damage over 100 miles of Brittany coast.

34. The human heart pumps about 2100 gal of blood per day. That means that it pumps approximately 767,000 gal per year.

Concept 2: Writing Numbers in Standard Form

35. Explain how you would write the number 3.1×10^{-9} in standard form.

36. Explain how you would write the number 3.1×10^{9} in standard form.

For Exercises 37–52, write each number in standard form. **(See Example 3.)**

37. 5×10^{-5}

38. 2×10^{-7}

39. 2.8×10^{3}

40. 9.1×10^{6}

41. 6.03×10^{-4}

42. 7.01×10^{-3}

43. 2.4×10^{6}

44. 3.1×10^{4}

45. 1.9×10^{-2}

46. 2.8×10^{-6}

47. 7.032×10^{3}

48. 8.205×10^{2}

49. One picogram (pg) is equal to 1×10^{-12} g.

50. A nanometer (nm) is approximately 3.94×10^{-8} in.

51. A normal diet contains between 1.6×10^{3} Cal and 2.8×10^{3} Cal per day.

52. The total land area of Texas is approximately 2.62×10^{5} square miles.

© Ryan McVay/Getty Images RF

Concept 3: Multiplying and Dividing Numbers in Scientific Notation

For Exercises 53–72, multiply or divide as indicated. Write the answers in scientific notation. **(See Example 4.)**

53. $(2.5 \times 10^{6})(2 \times 10^{-2})$

54. $(2 \times 10^{-7})(3 \times 10^{13})$

55. $(1.2 \times 10^{4})(3 \times 10^{7})$

56. $(3.2 \times 10^{-3})(2.5 \times 10^{8})$

57. $\dfrac{7.7 \times 10^{6}}{3.5 \times 10^{2}}$

58. $\dfrac{9.5 \times 10^{11}}{1.9 \times 10^{3}}$

59. $\dfrac{9 \times 10^{-6}}{4 \times 10^{7}}$

60. $\dfrac{7 \times 10^{-2}}{5 \times 10^{9}}$

61. $80,000,000,000 \times 4000$

62. 0.0006×0.03

63. $(3.2 \times 10^{-4})(7.6 \times 10^{-7})$

64. $(5.9 \times 10^{12})(3.6 \times 10^{9})$

65. $\dfrac{210,000,000,000}{0.007}$

66. $\dfrac{160,000,000,000,000}{0.00008}$

67. $\dfrac{5.7 \times 10^{-2}}{9.5 \times 10^{-8}}$

68. $\dfrac{2.72 \times 10^{-6}}{6.8 \times 10^{-4}}$

69. $6,000,000,000 \times 0.0000000023$

70. $0.000055 \times 40,000$

71. $\dfrac{0.0000000003}{6000}$

72. $\dfrac{420,000}{0.0000021}$

Mixed Exercises

73. If a piece of paper is 3×10^{-3} in. thick, how thick is a stack of 1.25×10^{3} pieces of paper?

74. A box of staples contains 5×10^{3} staples and weighs 15 oz. How much does one staple weigh? Write your answer in scientific notation.

75. At one time, Bill Gates owned approximately 1,100,000,000 shares of Microsoft stock. If the stock price was $27 per share, how much was Bill Gates' stock worth?

77. Dinosaurs became extinct about 65 million years ago.

   a. Write the number 65 million in scientific notation.

   b. How many days is 65 million years?

   c. How many hours is 65 million years?

   d. How many seconds is 65 million years?

76. A state lottery had a jackpot of $$\$5.2 \times 10^7$$. This week the winner was a group of office employees that included 13 people. How much would each person receive?

78. The Earth is 150,000,000 km from the Sun.

   a. Write the number 150,000,000 in scientific notation.

   b. There are 1000 m in a kilometer. How many meters is the Earth from the Sun?

   c. There are 100 cm in a meter. How many centimeters is the Earth from the Sun?

Addition and Subtraction of Polynomials

1. Introduction to Polynomials

One commonly used algebraic expression is called a polynomial. A **polynomial** in one variable, x, is defined as a single term or a sum of terms of the form ax^n, where a is a real number and the exponent, n, is a nonnegative integer. For each term, a is called the **coefficient**, and n is called the **degree of the term**. For example:

Concepts

1. Introduction to Polynomials
2. Addition of Polynomials
3. Subtraction of Polynomials
4. Polynomials and Applications to Geometry

Term (Expressed in the Form ax^n)	Coefficient	Degree
$-12z^7$	-12	7
$x^3 \rightarrow$ rewrite as $1x^3$	1	3
$10w \rightarrow$ rewrite as $10w^1$	10	1
$7 \rightarrow$ rewrite as $7x^0$	7	0

If a polynomial has exactly one term, it is categorized as a **monomial**. A two-term polynomial is called a **binomial**, and a three-term polynomial is called a **trinomial**. Usually the terms of a polynomial are written in descending order according to degree. The term with highest degree is called the **leading term**, and its coefficient is called the **leading coefficient**. The **degree of a polynomial** is the greatest degree of all of its terms. A polynomial in one variable is written in **descending order** if the term with highest degree is written first, followed by the term of next highest degree and so on. Thus, for a polynomial written in descending order, the leading term determines the degree of the polynomial.

	Expression	Descending Order	Leading Coefficient	Degree of Polynomial
Monomials	$-3x^4$	$-3x^4$	-3	4
	17	17	17	0
Binomials	$4y^3 - 6y^5$	$-6y^5 + 4y^3$	-6	5
	$\dfrac{1}{2} - \dfrac{1}{4}c$	$-\dfrac{1}{4}c + \dfrac{1}{2}$	$-\dfrac{1}{4}$	1
Trinomials	$4p - 3p^3 + 8p^6$	$8p^6 - 3p^3 + 4p$	8	6
	$7a^4 - 1.2a^8 + 3a^3$	$-1.2a^8 + 7a^4 + 3a^3$	-1.2	8

> **Example 1**   **Identifying the Parts of a Polynomial**

Given the polynomial: $3a - 2a^4 + 6 - a^3$

a. List the terms of the polynomial, and state the coefficient and degree of each term.

b. Write the polynomial in descending order.

c. State the degree of the polynomial and the leading coefficient.

d. Evaluate the polynomial for $a = -2$.

Solution:

a. term: $3a$ coefficient: 3   degree: 1

  term: $-2a^4$ coefficient: -2 degree: 4

  term: 6   coefficient: 6   degree: 0

  term: $-a^3$ coefficient: -1 degree: 3

b. $-2a^4 - a^3 + 3a + 6$

c. The degree of the polynomial is 4 and the leading coefficient is -2.

d. $-2a^4 - a^3 + 3a + 6$

$= -2(-2)^4 - (-2)^3 + 3(-2) + 6$ Substitute -2 for the variable, a. Remember to use parentheses when replacing a variable.

$= -2(16) - (-8) + 3(-2) + 6$ Simplify exponents first.

$= -32 - (-8) + (-6) + 6$ Perform multiplication before addition and subtraction.

$= -24$ Simplify.

Skill Practice

1. Given the polynomial: $5x^3 - x + 8x^4 + 3x^2$

a. Write the polynomial in descending order.

b. State the degree of the polynomial.

c. State the coefficient of the leading term.

d. Evaluate the polynomial for $x = -1$.

Polynomials may have more than one variable. In such a case, the degree of a term is the sum of the exponents of the variables contained in the term. For example, the term, $32x^2y^5z$, has degree 8 because the exponents applied to x, y, and z are 2, 5, and 1, respectively. The following polynomial has a degree of 11 because the highest degree of its terms is 11.

$$32x^2y^5z \quad - \quad 2x^3y \quad + \quad 2x^2yz^8 \quad + \quad 7$$

degree 8   degree 4   degree 11   degree 0

Answers

1. a. $8x^4 + 5x^3 + 3x^2 - x$
 b. 4   **c.** 8   **d.** 7

2. Addition of Polynomials

Recall that two terms are *like* terms if they each have the same variables, and the corresponding variables are raised to the same powers.

Like Terms: $3x^2, -7x^2$ $-5yz^3, yz^3$

Unlike Terms: $9z^2, 12z^6$ $\dfrac{1}{3}w^6, \dfrac{2}{5}p^6$ $4y, 7$

Recall that the distributive property is used to add or subtract *like* terms. For example,

$3x^2 + 9x^2 - 2x^2$

$= (3 + 9 - 2)x^2$ Apply the distributive property.

$= (10)x^2$ Simplify.

$= 10x^2$

Example 2   **Adding Polynomials**

Add the polynomials. $3x^2y + 5x^2y$

Solution:

$3x^2y + 5x^2y$ The terms are *like* terms.

$= (3 + 5)x^2y$ Apply the distributive property.

$= (8)x^2y$

$= 8x^2y$ Simplify.

Skill Practice Add the polynomials.

2. $13a^2b^3 + 2a^2b^3$

It is the distributive property that enables us to add *like* terms. We shorten the process by adding the coefficients of *like* terms.

Example 3   **Adding Polynomials**

Add the polynomials. $(-3c^3 + 5c^2 - 7c) + (11c^3 + 6c^2 + 3)$

Solution:

$(-3c^3 + 5c^2 - 7c) + (11c^3 + 6c^2 + 3)$

$= -3c^3 + 11c^3 + 5c^2 + 6c^2 - 7c$ Clear parentheses, and group *like* terms.

$= 8c^3 + 11c^2 - 7c + 3$ Combine *like* terms.

Answer

2. $15a^2b^3$

> **TIP:** Polynomials can also be added by combining *like* terms in columns. The sum of the polynomials from Example 3 is shown here.
>
> $$-3c^3 + \ 5c^2 - 7c + 0$$
> $$+ \ 11c^3 + \ 6c^2 + 0c + 3$$
> $$\overline{8c^3 + 11c^2 - 7c + 3}$$
>
> Place holders such as 0 and 0c may be used to help line up *like* terms.

Skill Practice Add the polynomials.

3. $(7q^2 - 2q + 4) + (5q^2 + 6q - 9)$

Example 4   **Adding Polynomials**

Add the polynomials. $(4w^2 - 2x) + (3w^2 - 4x^2 + 6x)$

Solution:

$$(4w^2 - 2x) + (3w^2 - 4x^2 + 6x)$$
$$= 4w^2 + 3w^2 - 4x^2 - 2x + 6x \qquad \text{Clear parentheses and group } like \text{ terms.}$$
$$= 7w^2 - 4x^2 + 4x$$

Skill Practice Add the polynomials.

4. $(5x^2 - 4xy + y^2) + (-3x^2 - 5y^2)$

---

3. Subtraction of Polynomials

Subtraction of two polynomials requires us to find the opposite of the polynomial being subtracted. To find the opposite of a polynomial, take the opposite of each term. This is equivalent to multiplying the polynomial by -1.

Example 5   **Finding the Opposite of a Polynomial**

Find the opposite of the polynomials.

a. $5x$ **b.** $3a - 4b - c$ **c.** $5.5y^4 - 2.4y^3 + 1.1y$

Solution:

	Expression	**Opposite**	**Simplified Form**
a.	$5x$	$-(5x)$	$-5x$
b.	$3a - 4b - c$	$-(3a - 4b - c)$	$-3a + 4b + c$
c.	$5.5y^4 - 2.4y^3 + 1.1y$	$-(5.5y^4 - 2.4y^3 + 1.1y)$	$-5.5y^4 + 2.4y^3 - 1.1y$

> **TIP:** Notice that the sign of each term is changed when finding the opposite of a polynomial.

Skill Practice Find the opposite of the polynomials.

5. $x - 3$ **6.** $3y^2 - 2xy + 6x + 2$ **7.** $-2.1w^3 + 4.9w^2 - 1.9w$

Answers

3. $12q^2 + 4q - 5$
4. $2x^2 - 4xy - 4y^2$
5. $-x + 3$
6. $-3y^2 + 2xy - 6x - 2$
7. $2.1w^3 - 4.9w^2 + 1.9w$

Subtraction of two polynomials is similar to subtracting real numbers. Add the opposite of the second polynomial to the first polynomial.

Subtraction of Polynomials

If A and B are polynomials, then $A - B = A + (-B)$.

Example 6 **Subtracting Polynomials**

Subtract the polynomials. $(-4p^4 + 5p^2 - 3) - (11p^2 + 4p - 6)$

Solution:

$(-4p^4 + 5p^2 - 3) - (11p^2 + 4p - 6)$

$= (-4p^4 + 5p^2 - 3) + (-11p^2 - 4p + 6)$ Add the opposite of the second polynomial.

$= -4p^4 + 5p^2 - 11p^2 - 4p - 3 + 6$ Group *like* terms.

$= -4p^4 - 6p^2 - 4p + 3$ Combine *like* terms.

TIP: Two polynomials can also be subtracted in columns by adding the opposite of the second polynomial to the first polynomial. Place holders (shown in red) may be used to help line up *like* terms.

$$-4p^4 + 0p^3 + 5p^2 + 0p - 3$$
$$-(0p^4 + 0p^3 + 11p^2 + 4p - 6)$$

$\xrightarrow{\text{Add the opposite}}$

$$-4p^4 + 0p^3 + 5p^2 + 0p - 3$$
$$+ \underline{-0p^4 - 0p^3 - 11p^2 - 4p + 6}$$
$$-4p^4 \qquad - 6p^2 - 4p + 3$$

The difference of the polynomials is $-4p^4 - 6p^2 - 4p + 3$.

Skill Practice Subtract the polynomials.

8. $(x^2 + 3x - 2) - (4x^2 + 6x + 1)$

Example 7 **Subtracting Polynomials**

Subtract the polynomials. $(a^2 - 2ab + 7b^2) - (-8a^2 - 6ab + 2b^2)$

Solution:

$(a^2 - 2ab + 7b^2) - (-8a^2 - 6ab + 2b^2)$

$= (a^2 - 2ab + 7b^2) + (8a^2 + 6ab - 2b^2)$ Add the opposite of the second polynomial.

$= a^2 + 8a^2 - 2ab + 6ab + 7b^2 - 2b^2$ Group *like* terms.

$= 9a^2 + 4ab + 5b^2$ Combine *like* terms.

Skill Practice Subtract the polynomials.

9. $(-3y^2 + xy + 2x^2) - (-2y^2 - 3xy - 8x^2)$

In Example 8, we illustrate the subtraction of polynomials by first clearing parentheses and then combining *like* terms.

Answers

8. $-3x^2 - 3x - 3$

9. $-y^2 + 4xy + 10x^2$

Example 8	**Subtracting Polynomials**

Subtract $\frac{1}{3}t^4 + \frac{1}{2}t^2$ from $t^2 - 4$, and simplify the result.

Solution:

To subtract a from b, we write $b - a$. Thus, to subtract $\overset{a}{\overbrace{\frac{1}{3}t^4 + \frac{1}{2}t^2}}$ from $\overset{b}{\overbrace{t^2 - 4}}$, we have

$$\overset{b}{(t^2 - 4)} - \overset{a}{\left(\frac{1}{3}t^4 + \frac{1}{2}t^2\right)}$$

$$= t^2 - 4 - \frac{1}{3}t^4 - \frac{1}{2}t^2 \qquad \text{Apply the distributive property to clear parentheses.}$$

$$= -\frac{1}{3}t^4 + t^2 - \frac{1}{2}t^2 - 4 \qquad \text{Group } \textit{like} \text{ terms in descending order.}$$

$$= -\frac{1}{3}t^4 + \frac{2}{2}t^2 - \frac{1}{2}t^2 - 4 \qquad \begin{array}{l}\text{The } t^2\text{-terms are the only } \textit{like} \text{ terms.}\\ \text{Get a common denominator for the } t^2\text{-terms.}\end{array}$$

$$= -\frac{1}{3}t^4 + \frac{1}{2}t^2 - 4 \qquad \text{Add } \textit{like} \text{ terms.}$$

> **Avoiding Mistakes**
>
> Example 8 involves subtracting two *expressions*. This is not an equation. Therefore, we cannot clear fractions.

Skill Practice

10. Subtract $\frac{3}{4}x^2 + \frac{2}{5}$ from $x^2 + 3x$.

4. Polynomials and Applications to Geometry

Example 9	**Subtracting Polynomials in Geometry**

If the perimeter of the triangle in Figure 5-1 can be represented by the polynomial $2x^2 + 5x + 6$, find a polynomial that represents the length of the missing side.

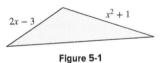

Figure 5-1

Solution:

The missing side of the triangle can be found by subtracting the sum of the two known sides from the perimeter.

$$\begin{pmatrix} \text{Length} \\ \text{of missing} \\ \text{side} \end{pmatrix} = (\text{perimeter}) - \begin{pmatrix} \text{sum of the} \\ \text{two known sides} \end{pmatrix}$$

$$\begin{pmatrix} \text{Length} \\ \text{of missing} \\ \text{side} \end{pmatrix} = (2x^2 + 5x + 6) - [(2x - 3) + (x^2 + 1)]$$

Answer

10. $\frac{1}{4}x^2 + 3x - \frac{2}{5}$

$$= 2x^2 + 5x + 6 - [2x - 3 + x^2 + 1] \qquad \text{Clear inner parentheses.}$$

$$= 2x^2 + 5x + 6 - (x^2 + 2x - 2) \qquad \begin{array}{l}\text{Combine } like \text{ terms} \\ \text{within [ ].}\end{array}$$

$$= 2x^2 + 5x + 6 - x^2 - 2x + 2 \qquad \begin{array}{l}\text{Apply the distributive} \\ \text{property.}\end{array}$$

$$= 2x^2 - x^2 + 5x - 2x + 6 + 2 \qquad \text{Group } like \text{ terms.}$$

$$= x^2 + 3x + 8 \qquad \text{Combine } like \text{ terms.}$$

The polynomial $x^2 + 3x + 8$ represents the length of the missing side.

Skill Practice

11. If the perimeter of the triangle is represented by the polynomial $6x - 9$, find the polynomial that represents the missing side.

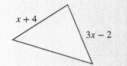

$x + 4$

$3x - 2$

Answer

11. $2x - 11$

Section 5.5   Practice Exercises

Vocabulary and Key Concepts

1. **a.** A _____ is a single term or a sum of terms.

    b. For the term ax^n, a is called the _____ and n is called the _____ of the term.

    c. Given the term x, the coefficient of the term is _____.

    d. A monomial is a polynomial with exactly _____ term(s).

    e. A _____ is a polynomial with exactly two terms.

    f. A _____ is a polynomial with exactly three terms.

    g. The term with the highest degree is called the _____ term and its coefficient is called the

    _____ _____.

    h. The degree of a polynomial is the _____ degree of all of its terms.

    i. The degree of a nonzero constant such as 5 is _____.

Review Exercises

For Exercises 2–7, simplify each expression.

2. $\dfrac{p^3 \cdot 4p}{p^2}$

3. $(3x)^2(5x^{-4})$

4. $(6y^{-3})(2y^9)$

5. $\dfrac{8t^{-6}}{4t^{-2}}$

6. $\dfrac{8^3 \cdot 8^{-4}}{8^{-2} \cdot 8^6}$

7. $\dfrac{3^4 \cdot 3^{-8}}{3^{12} \cdot 3^{-4}}$

8. Explain the difference between 3×10^7 and 3^7.

9. Explain the difference between 4×10^{-2} and 4^{-2}.

380   **Chapter 5** Polynomials and Properties of Exponents

Concept 1: Introduction to Polynomials

For Exercises 10–12,

    a. write the polynomial in descending order.

    b. identify the leading coefficient.

    c. identify the degree of the polynomial. **(See Example 1.)**

10. $10 - 8a - a^3 + 2a^2 + a^5$ **11.** $6 + 7x^2 - 7x^5 + 9x$ **12.** $\frac{1}{2}y + y^2 - 12y^4 + y^3 - 6$

For Exercises 13–22, categorize each expression as a monomial, a binomial, or a trinomial. Then evaluate the polynomial given $x = -3$, $y = 2$, and $z = -1$. **(See Example 1.)**

13. $10x^2 + 5x$ **14.** $7z + 13z^2 - 15$ **15.** $6x^2$ **16.** 9

17. $2y - y^4$ **18.** $7x + 2$ **19.** $2y^4 - 3y + 1$ **20.** 23

21. $-32xyz$ **22.** $y^4 - x^2$

Concept 2: Addition of Polynomials

23. Explain why the terms $3x$ and $3x^2$ are not *like* terms.

24. Explain why the terms $4w^3$ and $4z^3$ are not *like* terms.

For Exercises 25–42, add the polynomials. **(See Examples 2–4.)**

25. $23x^2y + 12x^2y$

26. $-5ab^3 + 17ab^3$

27. $3b^5d^2 + (5b^5d^2 - 9d)$

28. $4c^2d^3 + (3cd - 10c^2d^3)$

29. $(7y^2 + 2y - 9) + (-3y^2 - y)$

30. $(-3w^2 + 4w - 6) + (5w^2 + 2)$

31. $(5x + 3x^2 - x^3) + (2x^2 + 4x - 10)$

32. $(t^2 - 4t + t^4) + (3t^4 + 2t + 6)$

33. $(6.1y + 3.2x) + (4.8y - 3.2x)$

34. $(2.7m - 0.5h) + (-3.2m + 0.2h)$

35. $\quad 6a + 2b - 5c$
$\quad + \underline{-2a - 2b - 3c}$

36. $\quad -13x + 5y + 10z$
$\quad + \underline{-3x - 3y + \ 2z}$

37. $\left(\frac{2}{5}a + \frac{1}{4}b - \frac{5}{6}\right) + \left(\frac{3}{5}a - \frac{3}{4}b - \frac{7}{6}\right)$

38. $\left(\frac{5}{9}x + \frac{1}{10}y\right) + \left(-\frac{4}{9}x + \frac{3}{10}y\right)$

39. $\left(z - \frac{8}{3}\right) + \left(\frac{4}{3}z^2 - z + 1\right)$

40. $\left(-\frac{7}{5}r + 1\right) + \left(-\frac{3}{5}r^2 + \frac{7}{5}r + 1\right)$

41. $\quad 7.9t^3 \qquad\quad + 2.6t - 1.1$
$\quad + \underline{\qquad -3.4t^2 + 3.4t - 3.1}$

42. $\quad 0.34y^2 \qquad\quad + 1.23$
$\quad + \underline{\qquad\quad 3.42y - 7.56}$

Concept 3: Subtraction of Polynomials

For Exercises 43–48, find the opposite of each polynomial. **(See Example 5.)**

43. $4h - 5$

44. $5k - 12$

45. $-2.3m^2 + 3.1m - 1.5$

46. $-11.8n^2 - 6.7n + 9.3$

47. $3v^3 + 5v^2 + 10v + 22$

48. $7u^4 + 3v^2 + 17$

For Exercises 49–68, subtract the polynomials. **(See Examples 6–7.)**

49. $4a^3b^2 - 12a^3b^2$

50. $5yz^4 - 14yz^4$

51. $-32x^3 - 21x^3$

52. $-23c^5 - 12c^5$

53. $(7a - 7) - (12a - 4)$

54. $(4x + 3v) - (-3x + v)$

55. $4k + 3$
    $-(-12k - 6)$

56. $3h - 15$
    $-(8h + 13)$

57. $25m^4 - (23m^4 + 14m)$

58. $3x^2 - (-x^2 - 12)$

59. $(5s^2 - 3st - 2t^2) - (2s^2 + st + t^2)$

60. $(6k^2 + 2kp + p^2) - (3k^2 - 6kp + 2p^2)$

61. $10r - 6s + 2t$
    $-(12r - 3s - t)$

62. $a - 14b + 7c$
    $-(-3a - 8b + 2c)$

63. $\left(\frac{7}{8}x + \frac{2}{3}y - \frac{3}{10}\right) - \left(\frac{1}{8}x + \frac{1}{3}y\right)$

64. $\left(r - \frac{1}{12}s\right) - \left(\frac{1}{2}r - \frac{5}{12}s - \frac{4}{11}\right)$

65. $\left(\frac{2}{3}h^2 - \frac{1}{5}h - \frac{3}{4}\right) - \left(\frac{4}{3}h^2 - \frac{4}{5}h + \frac{7}{4}\right)$

66. $\left(\frac{3}{8}p^3 - \frac{5}{7}p^2 - \frac{2}{5}\right) - \left(\frac{5}{8}p^3 - \frac{2}{7}p^2 + \frac{7}{5}\right)$

67. $4.5x^4 - 3.1x^2 \qquad - 6.7$
    $-(2.1x^4 \qquad + 4.4x + 1.2)$

68. $1.3c^2 \qquad + 4.8$
    $- (4.3c^2 - 2c - 2.2)$

69. Find the difference of $(4b^3 + 6b - 7)$ and $(-12b^2 + 11b + 5)$.

70. Find the difference of $(-5y^2 + 3y - 21)$ and $(-4y^2 - 5y + 23)$.

71. Subtract $\left(\frac{3}{2}x^2 - 5x\right)$ from $(-2x^2 - 11)$.
(See Example 8.)

72. Subtract $\left(a^5 - \frac{1}{3}a^3 + 5a\right)$ from $\left(\frac{3}{4}a^5 + \frac{1}{2}a^4 + 6a\right)$.

Concept 4: Polynomials and Applications to Geometry

73. Find a polynomial that represents the perimeter of the figure.

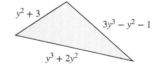

$y^2 + 3$
$3y^3 - y^2 - 1$
$y^3 + 2y^2$

74. Find a polynomial that represents the perimeter of the figure.

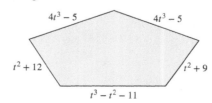

$4t^3 - 5$ $4t^3 - 5$
$t^2 + 12$ $t^2 + 9$
$t^3 - t^2 - 11$

382   Chapter 5   Polynomials and Properties of Exponents

75. If the perimeter of the figure can be represented by the polynomial $5a^2 - 2a + 1$, find a polynomial that represents the length of the missing side.
(See Example 9.)

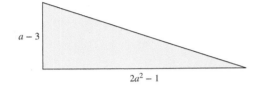

76. If the perimeter of the figure can be represented by the polynomial $6w^3 - 2w - 3$, find a polynomial that represents the length of the missing side.

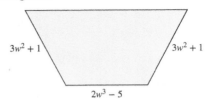

Mixed Exercises

For Exercises 77–92, perform the indicated operation.

77. $(2ab^2 + 9a^2b) + (7ab^2 - 3ab + 7a^2b)$

78. $(8x^2y - 3xy - 6xy^2) + (3x^2y - 12xy)$

79. $4z^5 \quad + z^3 - 3z + 13$
$- (\quad - z^4 - 8z^3 \quad + 15)$

80. $-15t^4 \quad - 23t^2 + 16t$
$-(\quad 21t^3 + 18t^2 + \; t)$

81. $(9x^4 + 2x^3 - x + 5) + (9x^3 - 3x^2 + 8x + 3) - (7x^4 - x + 12)$

82. $(-6y^3 - 9y^2 + 23) - (7y^2 + 2y - 11) + (3y^3 - 25)$

83. $(0.2w^2 + 3w + 1.3) - (w^3 - 0.7w + 2)$

84. $(8.1u^3 - 5.2u^2 + 4) + (2.8u^3 + 6.3u - 7)$

85. $(7p^2q - 3pq^2) - (8p^2q + pq) + (4pq - pq^2)$

86. $(12c^2d - 2cd + 8cd^2) - (-c^2d + 4cd) - (5cd - 2cd^2)$

87. $(5x - 2x^3) + (2x^3 - 5x)$

88. $(p^2 - 4p + 2) - (2 + p^2 - 4p)$

89. $2a^2b - 4ab + \; ab^2$
$-(2a^2b + \; ab - 5ab^2)$

90. $-3xy + \; 7xy^2 + 5x^2y$
$+ (-8xy - 11xy^2 + 3x^2y)$

91. $[(3y^2 - 5y) - (2y^2 + y - 1)] + (10y^2 - 4y - 5)$

92. $(12c^3 - 5c^2 - 2c) + [(7c^3 - 2c^2 + c) - (4c^3 + 4c)]$

Expanding Your Skills

93. Write a binomial of degree 3. (Answers may vary.)

94. Write a trinomial of degree 6. (Answers may vary.)

95. Write a monomial of degree 5. (Answers may vary.)

96. Write a monomial of degree 1. (Answers may vary.)

97. Write a trinomial with the leading coefficient −6. (Answers may vary.)

98. Write a binomial with the leading coefficient 13. (Answers may vary.)

Concepts

1. Multiplication of Polynomials
2. Special Case Products: Difference of Squares and Perfect Square Trinomials
3. Applications to Geometry

1. Multiplication of Polynomials

The properties of exponents can be used to simplify many algebraic expressions including the multiplication of monomials. To multiply monomials, first use the associative and commutative properties of multiplication to group coefficients and like bases. Then simplify the result by using the properties of exponents.

Example 1	**Multiplying Monomials**

Multiply the monomials.

a. $(3x^4)(4x^2)$ **b.** $(-4c^5d)(2c^2d^3e)$ **c.** $\left(\frac{1}{3}a^4b^3\right)\left(\frac{3}{4}b^7\right)$

Solution:

a. $(3x^4)(4x^2)$

$\quad = (3 \cdot 4)(x^4 x^2)$ Group coefficients and like bases.

$\quad = 12x^6$ Multiply the coefficients and add the exponents on x.

b. $(-4c^5d)(2c^2d^3e)$

$\quad = (-4 \cdot 2)(c^5c^2)(dd^3)(e)$ Group coefficients and like bases.

$\quad = -8c^7d^4e$ Simplify.

c. $\left(\frac{1}{3}a^4b^3\right)\left(\frac{3}{4}b^7\right)$

$\quad = \left(\frac{1}{3} \cdot \frac{3}{4}\right)(a^4)(b^3b^7)$ Group coefficients and like bases.

$\quad = \frac{1}{4}a^4b^{10}$ Simplify.

Skill Practice Multiply the monomials.

1. $(-5y)(6y^3)$ **2.** $(7x^2y)(-2x^3y^4)$ **3.** $\left(\frac{2}{5}w^5z^3\right)\left(\frac{15}{4}w^4\right)$

The distributive property is used to multiply polynomials: $a(b + c) = ab + ac$.

Example 2	**Multiplying a Polynomial by a Monomial**

Multiply the polynomials.

a. $2t(4t - 3)$ **b.** $-3a^2\left(-4a^2 + 2a - \frac{1}{3}\right)$

Solution:

a. $2t(4t - 3)$

$\quad = (2t)(4t) + (2t)(-3)$ Apply the distributive property by multiplying each term by $2t$.

$\quad = 8t^2 - 6t$ Simplify each term.

b. $-3a^2\left(-4a^2 + 2a - \frac{1}{3}\right)$

$\quad = (-3a^2)(-4a^2) + (-3a^2)(2a) + (-3a^2)\left(-\frac{1}{3}\right)$ Apply the distributive property by multiplying each term by $-3a^2$.

$\quad = 12a^4 - 6a^3 + a^2$ Simplify each term.

Answers

1. $-30y^4$

2. $-14x^5y^5$

3. $\frac{3}{2}w^9z^3$

Skill Practice Multiply the polynomials.

4. $-4a(5a - 3)$ **5.** $-4p\left(2p^2 - 6p + \dfrac{1}{4}\right)$

Thus far, we have illustrated polynomial multiplication involving monomials. Next, the distributive property will be used to multiply polynomials with more than one term.

$(x + 3)(x + 5) = x(x + 5) + 3(x + 5)$ Apply the distributive property.

$ = x(x + 5) + 3(x + 5)$ Apply the distributive property again.

$ = (x)(x) + (x)(5) + (3)(x) + (3)(5)$

$ = x^2 + 5x + 3x + 15$

$ = x^2 + 8x + 15$ Combine *like* terms.

Note: Using the distributive property results in multiplying each term of the first polynomial by each term of the second polynomial.

$(x + 3)(x + 5) = (x)(x) + (x)(5) + (3)(x) + (3)(5)$

$ = x^2 + 5x + 3x + 15$

$ = x^2 + 8x + 15$

Example 3   **Multiplying a Polynomial by a Polynomial**

Multiply the polynomials. $(c - 7)(c + 2)$

Solution:

$(c - 7)(c + 2)$ Multiply each term in the first polynomial by each term in the second. That is, apply the distributive property.

$= (c)(c) + (c)(2) + (-7)(c) + (-7)(2)$

$= c^2 + 2c - 7c - 14$ Simplify.

$= c^2 - 5c - 14$ Combine *like* terms.

TIP: Notice that the product of two *binomials* equals the sum of the products of the **F**irst terms, the **O**uter terms, the **I**nner terms, and the **L**ast terms. The acronym **FOIL** (First Outer Inner Last) can be used as a memory device to multiply two binomials.

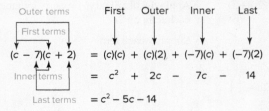

Skill Practice Multiply the polynomials.

6. $(x + 2)(x + 8)$

Example 4 **Multiplying a Polynomial by a Polynomial**

Multiply the polynomials. $(y - 2)(3y^2 + y - 5)$

Solution:

$(y - 2)(3y^2 + y - 5)$ Multiply each term in the first polynomial by each term in the second.

$= (y)(3y^2) + (y)(y) + (y)(-5) + (-2)(3y^2) + (-2)(y) + (-2)(-5)$

$= 3y^3 + y^2 - 5y - 6y^2 - 2y + 10$ Simplify each term.

$= 3y^3 - 5y^2 - 7y + 10$ Combine *like* terms.

TIP: Multiplication of polynomials can be performed vertically by a process similar to column multiplication of real numbers. For example,

$$\begin{array}{r} 235 \\ \times \;\; 21 \\ \hline 235 \\ 4700 \\ \hline 4935 \end{array}$$

$$\begin{array}{r} 3y^2 \;+\; y \;-\; 5 \\ \times \qquad\quad y \;-\; 2 \\ \hline -6y^2 \;-\; 2y \;+\; 10 \\ 3y^3 \;+\; y^2 \;-\; 5y \;+\; 0 \\ \hline 3y^3 \;-\; 5y^2 \;-\; 7y \;+\; 10 \end{array}$$

Note: When multiplying by the column method, it is important to *align like* terms vertically before adding terms.

Skill Practice Multiply the polynomials.

7. $(2y + 4)(3y^2 - 5y + 2)$

Example 5 **Multiplying Polynomials**

Multiply the polynomials. $2(10x + 3y)(2x - 4y)$

Solution:

$2(10x + 3y)(2x - 4y)$ In this case we are multiplying three polynomials—a monomial times two binomials. The associative property of multiplication enables us to choose which two polynomials to multiply first.

$= 2[(10x + 3y)(2x - 4y)]$ First we will multiply the binomials. Multiply each term in the first binomial by each term in the second binomial. That is, apply the distributive property.

$= 2[(10x)(2x) + (10x)(-4y) + (3y)(2x) + (3y)(-4y)]$

$= 2[20x^2 - 40xy + 6xy - 12y^2]$ Simplify each term.

$= 2(20x^2 - 34xy - 12y^2)$ Combine *like* terms.

$= 40x^2 - 68xy - 24y^2$ Multiply by 2 using the distributive property.

Skill Practice Multiply.

8. $3(4a - 3c)(5a - 2c)$

Answers

7. $6y^3 + 2y^2 - 16y + 8$
8. $60a^2 - 69ac + 18c^2$

2. Special Case Products: Difference of Squares and Perfect Square Trinomials

In some cases the product of two binomials takes on a special pattern.

I. The first special case occurs when multiplying the sum and difference of the same two terms. For example:

$(2x + 3)(2x - 3)$

$= 4x^2 - 6x + 6x - 9$

$= 4x^2 - 9$

Notice that the middle terms are opposites. This leaves only the difference between the square of the first term and the square of the second term. For this reason, the product is called a *difference of squares*.

Note: The binomials $2x + 3$ and $2x - 3$ are called **conjugates**. In one expression, $2x$ and 3 are added, and in the other, $2x$ and 3 are subtracted.

II. The second special case involves the square of a binomial. For example:

$(3x + 7)^2$

$= (3x + 7)(3x + 7)$

$= 9x^2 + 21x + 21x + 49$

$= 9x^2 + \quad 42x \quad + 49$

$= (3x)^2 + 2(3x)(7) + (7)^2$

When squaring a binomial, the product will be a trinomial called a *perfect square trinomial*. The first and third terms are formed by squaring each term of the binomial. The middle term equals twice the product of the terms in the binomial.

Note: The expression $(3x - 7)^2$ also expands to a perfect square trinomial, but the middle term will be negative:

$$(3x - 7)(3x - 7) = 9x^2 - 21x - 21x + 49 = 9x^2 - 42x + 49$$

Special Case Product Formulas

1. $(a + b)(a - b) = a^2 - b^2$ The product is called a **difference of squares**.

2. $(a + b)^2 = a^2 + 2ab + b^2$
$(a - b)^2 = a^2 - 2ab + b^2$ The product is called a **perfect square trinomial**.

You should become familiar with these special case products because they will be used again in the next chapter to factor polynomials.

Example 6   **Multiplying Conjugates**

Multiply the conjugates.

a. $(x - 9)(x + 9)$ **b.** $\left(\frac{1}{2}p + 6\right)\left(\frac{1}{2}p - 6\right)$

Solution:

a. $(x - 9)(x + 9)$ Apply the formula: $(a + b)(a - b) = a^2 - b^2$

$a^2 - b^2$

$= (x)^2 - (9)^2$ Substitute $a = x$ and $b = 9$.

$= x^2 - 81$

TIP: The product of two conjugates can be checked by applying the distributive property:

$(x - 9)(x + 9)$

$= x^2 + 9x - 9x - 81$

$= x^2 - 81$

b. $\left(\dfrac{1}{2}p + 6\right)\left(\dfrac{1}{2}p - 6\right)$ Apply the formula: $(a + b)(a - b) = a^2 - b^2$

$$= \left(\dfrac{1}{2}p\right)^2 - (6)^2 \qquad \text{Substitute } a = \dfrac{1}{2}p \text{ and } b = 6.$$

$$= \dfrac{1}{4}p^2 - 36 \qquad \text{Simplify each term.}$$

Skill Practice   Multiply the conjugates.

9. $(a + 7)(a - 7)$ **10.** $\left(\dfrac{4}{5}x - 10\right)\left(\dfrac{4}{5}x + 10\right)$

Example 7   **Squaring Binomials**

Square the binomials.

a. $(3w - 4)^2$ **b.** $(5x^2 + 2)^2$

Solution:

a. $(3w - 4)^2$ Apply the formula:
$(a - b)^2 = a^2 - 2ab + b^2$

$$= (3w)^2 - 2(3w)(4) + (4)^2 \qquad \text{Substitute } a = 3w, b = 4.$$

$$= 9w^2 - 24w + 16 \qquad \text{Simplify each term.}$$

TIP: The square of a binomial can be checked by explicitly writing the product of the two binomials and applying the distributive property:

$$(3w - 4)^2 = (3w - 4)(3w - 4) = 9w^2 - 12w - 12w + 16$$
$$= 9w^2 - 24w + 16$$

b. $(5x^2 + 2)^2$ Apply the formula:
$(a + b)^2 = a^2 + 2ab + b^2$

$$= (5x^2)^2 + 2(5x^2)(2) + (2)^2 \qquad \text{Substitute } a = 5x^2, b = 2.$$

$$= 25x^4 + 20x^2 + 4 \qquad \text{Simplify each term.}$$

Avoiding Mistakes

The property for squaring two factors is different than the property for squaring two terms:
$(ab)^2 = a^2b^2$ but
$(a + b)^2 = a^2 + 2ab + b^2$

Skill Practice   Square the binomials.

11. $(2x + 3)^2$ **12.** $(5c^2 - 6)^2$

Answers

9. $a^2 - 49$
10. $\frac{16}{25}x^2 - 100$
11. $4x^2 + 12x + 9$
12. $25c^4 - 60c^2 + 36$

3. Applications to Geometry

Example 8 **Using Special Case Products in an Application of Geometry**

Find a polynomial that represents the volume of the cube (Figure 5-2).

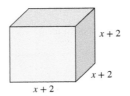

$x + 2$

$x + 2$

$x + 2$

Figure 5-2

Solution:

$$\text{Volume} = (\text{length})(\text{width})(\text{height})$$

$$V = (x + 2)(x + 2)(x + 2) \qquad \text{or} \qquad V = (x + 2)^3$$

To expand $(x + 2)(x + 2)(x + 2)$, multiply the first two factors. Then multiply the result by the last factor.

$$V = \underbrace{(x + 2)(x + 2)}(x + 2)$$

$$= (x^2 + 4x + 4)(x + 2)$$

TIP: $(x + 2)(x + 2) = (x + 2)^2$ and results in a perfect square trinomial.

$$(x + 2)^2 = (x)^2 + 2(x)(2) + (2)^2$$
$$= x^2 + 4x + 4$$

$$= (x^2)(x) + (x^2)(2) + (4x)(x) + (4x)(2) + (4)(x) + (4)(2) \qquad \text{Apply the distributive property.}$$

$$= x^3 + 2x^2 + 4x^2 + 8x + 4x + 8 \qquad \text{Group } like \text{ terms.}$$

$$= x^3 + 6x^2 + 12x + 8 \qquad \text{Combine } like \text{ terms.}$$

The volume of the cube can be represented by

$$V = (x + 2)^3 = x^3 + 6x^2 + 12x + 8$$

Skill Practice

13. Find the polynomial that represents the volume of the cube.

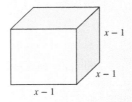

$x - 1$

$x - 1$

$x - 1$

Answer

13. The volume of the cube can be represented by $x^3 - 3x^2 + 3x - 1$.

Section 5.6   Practice Exercises

Vocabulary and Key Concepts

1. **a.** The conjugate of $5 + 2x$ is _____.

   b. When two conjugates are multiplied the resulting binomial is a difference of _____. This is given by the formula $(a + b)(a - b) =$ _____.

   c. When a binomial is squared, the resulting trinomial is a _____ square trinomial. This is given by the formula $(a + b)^2 =$ _____.

Review Exercises

For Exercises 2–9, simplify each expression (if possible).

2. $4x + 5x$
3. $2y^2 - 4y^2$
4. $(4x)(5x)$
5. $(2y^2)(-4y^2)$

6. $-5a^3b - 2a^3b$
7. $7uvw^2 + uvw^2$
8. $(-5a^3b)(-2a^3b)$
9. $(7uvw^2)(uvw^2)$

Concept 1: Multiplication of Polynomials

For Exercises 10–18, multiply the expressions. **(See Example 1.)**

10. $8(4x)$
11. $-2(6y)$
12. $-10(5z)$

13. $7(3p)$
14. $(x^{10})(4x^3)$
15. $(a^{13}b^4)(12ab^4)$

16. $(4m^3n^7)(-3m^6n)$
17. $(2c^7d)(-c^3d^{11})$
18. $(-5u^2v)(-8u^3v^2)$

For Exercises 19–54, multiply the polynomials. **(See Examples 2–5.)**

19. $8pq(2pq - 3p + 5q)$
20. $5ab(2ab + 6a - 3b)$
21. $(k^2 - 13k - 6)(-4k)$

22. $(h^2 + 5h - 12)(-2h)$
23. $-15pq(3p^2 + p^3q^2 - 2q)$
24. $-4u^2v(2u - 5uv^3 + v)$

25. $(y + 10)(y + 9)$
26. $(x + 5)(x + 6)$
27. $(m - 12)(m - 2)$

28. $(n - 7)(n - 2)$
29. $(3p - 2)(4p + 1)$
30. $(7q + 11)(q - 5)$

31. $(8 - 4w)(-3w + 2)$
32. $(-6z + 10)(4 - 2z)$
33. $(p - 3w)(p - 11w)$

34. $(y - 7x)(y - 10x)$
35. $(6x - 1)(2x + 5)$
36. $(3x + 7)(x - 8)$

37. $(4a - 9)(1.5a - 2)$
38. $(2.1y - 0.5)(y + 3)$
39. $(3t - 7)(1 + 3t^2)$

40. $(2 - 5w)(2w^2 - 5)$
41. $3(3m + 4n)(m + 2n)$
42. $2(7y + z)(3y + 5z)$

43. $(5s + 3)(s^2 + s - 2)$
44. $(t - 4)(2t^2 - t + 6)$
45. $(3w - 2)(9w^2 + 6w + 4)$

46. $(z + 5)(z^2 - 5z + 25)$
47. $(p^2 + p - 5)(p^2 + 4p - 1)$
48. $(-x^2 - 2x + 4)(x^2 + 2x - 6)$

49. $3a^2 - 4a + 9$
   $\times \underline{\quad 2a - 5}$

50. $7x^2 - 3x - 4$
   $\times \underline{\quad 5x + 1}$

51. $4x^2 - 12xy + 9y^2$
   $\times \underline{\quad 2x - 3y}$

52. $25a^2 + 10ab + b^2$
   $\times \underline{\quad 5a + b}$

53. $6x + 2y$
   $\times \underline{0.2x + 1.2y}$

54. $4.5a + 2b$
   $\times \underline{\quad 2a - 1.8b}$

Concept 2: Special Case Products: Difference of Squares and Perfect Square Trinomials

For Exercises 55–66, multiply the conjugates. **(See Example 6.)**

55. $(y - 6)(y + 6)$

56. $(x + 3)(x - 3)$

57. $(3a - 4b)(3a + 4b)$

58. $(5y + 7x)(5y - 7x)$

59. $(9k + 6)(9k - 6)$

60. $(2h - 5)(2h + 5)$

61. $\left(\dfrac{2}{3}t - 3\right)\left(\dfrac{2}{3}t + 3\right)$

62. $\left(\dfrac{1}{4}r - 1\right)\left(\dfrac{1}{4}r + 1\right)$

63. $(u^3 + 5v)(u^3 - 5v)$

64. $(8w^2 - x)(8w^2 + x)$

65. $\left(\dfrac{2}{3} - p\right)\left(\dfrac{2}{3} + p\right)$

66. $\left(\dfrac{1}{8} - q\right)\left(\dfrac{1}{8} + q\right)$

For Exercises 67–78, square the binomials. **(See Example 7.)**

67. $(a + 5)^2$

68. $(a - 3)^2$

69. $(x - y)^2$

70. $(x + y)^2$

71. $(2c + 5)^2$

72. $(5d - 9)^2$

73. $(3t^2 - 4s)^2$

74. $(u^2 + 4v)^2$

75. $(7 - t)^2$

76. $(4 + w)^2$

77. $(3 + 4q)^2$

78. $(2 - 3b)^2$

79. a. Evaluate $(2 + 4)^2$ by working within the parentheses first.

　　b. Evaluate $2^2 + 4^2$.

　　c. Compare the answers to parts (a) and (b) and make a conjecture about $(a + b)^2$ and $a^2 + b^2$.

80. a. Evaluate $(6 - 5)^2$ by working within the parentheses first.

　　b. Evaluate $6^2 - 5^2$.

　　c. Compare the answers to parts (a) and (b) and make a conjecture about $(a - b)^2$ and $a^2 - b^2$.

Concept 3: Applications to Geometry

81. Find a polynomial expression that represents the area of the rectangle shown in the figure.

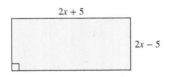

82. Find a polynomial expression that represents the area of the rectangle shown in the figure.

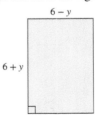

83. Find a polynomial expression that represents the area of the square shown in the figure.

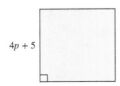

84. Find a polynomial expression that represents the area of the square shown in the figure.

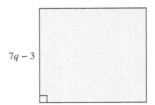

85. Find a polynomial that represents the volume of the cube shown in the figure. **(See Example 8.)**

(Recall: $V = s^3$)

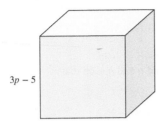

86. Find a polynomial that represents the volume of the rectangular solid shown in the figure.

(Recall: $V = lwh$)

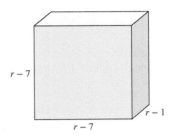

87. Find a polynomial that represents the area of the triangle shown in the figure.

(Recall: $A = \frac{1}{2}bh$)

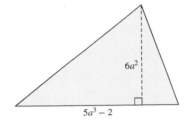

88. Find a polynomial that represents the area of the triangle shown in the figure.

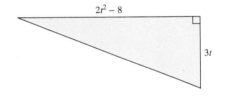

Mixed Exercises

For Exercises 89–118, multiply the expressions.

89. $(7x + y)(7x - y)$

90. $(9w - 4z)(9w + 4z)$

91. $(5s + 3t)^2$

92. $(5s - 3t)^2$

93. $(7x - 3y)(3x - 8y)$

94. $(5a - 4b)(2a - b)$

95. $\left(\frac{2}{3}t + 2\right)(3t + 4)$

96. $\left(\frac{1}{5}s + 6\right)(5s - 3)$

97. $-5(3x + 5)(2x - 1)$

98. $-4(2k - 5)(4k - 3)$

99. $(3a - 2)(5a + 1 + 2a^2)$

100. $(u + 4)(2 - 3u + u^2)$

101. $(y^2 + 2y + 4)(y - 5)$

102. $(w^2 - w + 6)(w + 2)$

103. $\left(\frac{1}{3}m - n\right)^2$

104. $\left(\frac{2}{5}p - q\right)^2$

105. $6w^2(7w - 14)$

106. $4v^3(v + 12)$

107. $(4y - 8.1)(4y + 8.1)$

108. $(2h + 2.7)(2h - 2.7)$

109. $(3c^2 + 4)(7c^2 - 8)$

110. $(5k^3 - 9)(k^3 - 2)$

111. $(3.1x + 4.5)^2$

112. $(2.5y + 1.1)^2$

113. $(k - 4)^3$

114. $(h + 3)^3$

115. $(5x + 3)^3$

116. $(2a - 4)^3$

117. $(y^2 + 2y + 1)(2y^2 - y + 3)$

118. $(2w^2 - w - 5)(3w^2 + 2w + 1)$

Expanding Your Skills

For Exercises 119–122, multiply the expressions containing more than two factors.

119. $2a(3a - 4)(a + 5)$

120. $5x(x + 2)(6x - 1)$

121. $(x - 3)(2x + 1)(x - 4)$

122. $(y - 2)(2y - 3)(y + 3)$

123. What binomial when multiplied by $(3x + 5)$ will produce a product of $6x^2 - 11x - 35$?
[*Hint:* Let the quantity $(a + b)$ represent the unknown binomial.] Then find a and b such that
$(3x + 5)(a + b) = 6x^2 - 11x - 35$.

124. What binomial when multiplied by $(2x - 4)$ will produce a product of $2x^2 + 8x - 24$?

For Exercises 125–127, determine the values of k that would create a perfect square trinomial.

125. $x^2 + kx + 25$

126. $w^2 + kw + 9$

127. $a^2 + ka + 16$

Section 5.7   Division of Polynomials

Concepts

1. Division by a Monomial
2. Long Division
3. Synthetic Division

Division of polynomials will be presented in this section as two separate cases: The first case illustrates division by a monomial divisor. The second case illustrates long division by a polynomial with two or more terms.

1. Division by a Monomial

To divide a polynomial by a monomial, divide each individual term in the polynomial by the divisor and simplify the result.

> **Dividing a Polynomial by a Monomial**
>
> If a, b, and c are polynomials such that $c \neq 0$, then
>
> $$\frac{a+b}{c} = \frac{a}{c} + \frac{b}{c} \qquad \text{Similarly,} \qquad \frac{a-b}{c} = \frac{a}{c} - \frac{b}{c}$$

Example 1   Dividing a Polynomial by a Monomial

Divide the polynomials.

a. $\dfrac{5a^3 - 10a^2 + 20}{5a}$ **b.** $(12y^2z^3 - 15yz^2 + 6y^2z) \div (-6y^2z)$

Solution:

a. $\dfrac{5a^3 - 10a^2 + 20}{5a}$

$= \dfrac{5a^3}{5a} - \dfrac{10a^2}{5a} + \dfrac{20}{5a}$ Divide each term in the numerator by $5a$.

$= a^2 - 2a + \dfrac{4}{a}$ Simplify each term using the properties of exponents.

b. $(12y^2z^3 - 15yz^2 + 6y^2z) \div (-6y^2z)$

$$= \frac{12y^2z^3 - 15yz^2 + 6y^2z}{-6y^2z}$$

$$= \frac{12y^2z^3}{-6y^2z} - \frac{15yz^2}{-6y^2z} + \frac{6y^2z}{-6y^2z} \qquad \text{Divide each term by } -6y^2z.$$

$$= -2z^2 + \frac{5z}{2y} - 1 \qquad \text{Simplify each term.}$$

Skill Practice Divide the polynomials.

1. $(36a^4 - 48a^3 + 12a^2) \div (6a^3)$ 　　**2.** $\dfrac{-15x^3y^4 + 25x^2y^3 - 5xy^2}{-5xy^2}$

2. Long Division

If the divisor has two or more terms, a *long division* process similar to the division of real numbers is used. Take a minute to review the long division process for real numbers by dividing 2273 by 5.

$$
\begin{array}{r}
454 \\
5\overline{)2273} \\
-20 \\
\hline
27 \\
-25 \\
\hline
23 \\
-20 \\
\hline
3
\end{array}
$$

454 ← Quotient

3 ← Remainder 　　Therefore, $2273 \div 5 = 454\frac{3}{5}$.

A similar procedure is used for long division of polynomials as shown in Example 2.

Example 2   **Using Long Division to Divide Polynomials**

Divide the polynomials using long division. 　　$(2x^2 - x + 3) \div (x - 3)$

Solution:

$x - 3\overline{)2x^2 - x + 3}$ 　　Divide the leading term in the dividend by the leading term in the divisor.

$$\frac{2x^2}{x} = 2x$$

This is the first term in the quotient.

$$
\begin{array}{r}
2x \\
x - 3\overline{)2x^2 - x + 3} \\
-(2x^2 - 6x)
\end{array}
$$

Multiply $2x$ by the divisor: $2x(x - 3) = 2x^2 - 6x$ and subtract the result.

> **TIP:** Recall that taking the opposite of a polynomial changes the sign of each term of the polynomial.

Answers

1. $6a - 8 + \dfrac{2}{a}$

2. $3x^2y^2 - 5xy + 1$

$$\begin{array}{r} 2x \\ x-3\overline{)2x^2-x+3} \\ \underline{-2x^2+6x} \\ 5x \end{array}$$

Subtract the quantity $2x^2 - 6x$. To do this, add the opposite.

$$\begin{array}{r} 2x+5 \\ x-3\overline{)2x^2-x+3} \\ \underline{-2x^2+6x} \downarrow \\ 5x+3 \end{array}$$

Bring down the next column, and repeat the process.

Divide the leading term by x: $(5x)/x = 5$
Place 5 in the quotient.

$$\begin{array}{r} 2x+5 \\ x-3\overline{)2x^2-x+3} \\ \underline{-2x^2+6x} \\ 5x+3 \\ -(5x-15) \end{array}$$

Multiply the divisor by 5: $5(x-3) = 5x - 15$
Subtract the result.

$$\begin{array}{r} 2x+5 \\ x-3\overline{)2x^2-x+3} \\ \underline{-2x^2+6x} \\ 5x+3 \\ \underline{-5x+15} \\ 18 \end{array}$$

Subtract the quantity $5x - 15$ by adding the opposite.

The remainder is 18.

Summary:

The quotient is	$2x + 5$
The remainder is	18
The divisor is	$x - 3$
The dividend is	$2x^2 - x + 3$

The solution to a long division problem is usually written in the form:

$$\text{quotient} + \frac{\text{remainder}}{\text{divisor}}$$

Hence,

$$(2x^2 - x + 3) \div (x - 3) = 2x + 5 + \frac{18}{x - 3}$$

Skill Practice Divide the polynomials using long division.

3. $(3x^2 + 2x - 5) \div (x + 2)$

The division of polynomials can be checked in the same fashion as the division of real numbers. To check Example 2, we use the **division algorithm**:

$$\text{Dividend} = (\text{divisor})(\text{quotient}) + \text{remainder}$$

$$2x^2 - x + 3 \overset{?}{=} (x - 3)(2x + 5) + (18)$$

$$\overset{?}{=} 2x^2 + 5x - 6x - 15 + (18)$$

$$= 2x^2 - x + 3 \checkmark$$

Answer

3. $3x - 4 + \dfrac{3}{x + 2}$

Example 3	**Using Long Division to Divide Polynomials**

Divide the polynomials using long division: $(3w^3 + 26w^2 - 3) \div (3w - 1)$

Solution:

First note that the dividend has a missing power of w and can be written as $3w^3 + 26w^2 + 0w - 3$. The term $0w$ is a place holder for the missing term. It is helpful to use the place holder to keep the powers of w lined up.

$$\begin{array}{r} w^2 \\ 3w - 1 \overline{)3w^3 + 26w^2 + 0w - 3} \\ -(3w^3 - w^2) \end{array}$$

Divide $3w^3 \div 3w = w^2$. This is the first term of the quotient.
Then multiply $w^2(3w - 1) = 3w^3 - w^2$.

$$\begin{array}{r} w^2 \\ 3w - 1 \overline{)3w^3 + 26w^2 + 0w - 3} \\ \underline{-3w^3 + w^2} \\ 27w^2 + 0w \end{array}$$

Subtract by adding the opposite.

Bring down the next column, and repeat the process.

$$\begin{array}{r} w^2 + 9w \\ 3w - 1 \overline{)3w^3 + 26w^2 + 0w - 3} \\ \underline{-3w^3 + w^2} \\ 27w^2 + 0w \\ -(27w^2 - 9w) \end{array}$$

Divide $27w^2$ by the leading term in the divisor. $27w^2 \div 3w = 9w$.
Place $9w$ in the quotient.
Multiply $9w(3w - 1) = 27w^2 - 9w$.

$$\begin{array}{r} w^2 + 9w \\ 3w - 1 \overline{)3w^3 + 26w^2 + 0w - 3} \\ \underline{-3w^3 + w^2} \\ 27w^2 + 0w \\ \underline{-27w^2 + 9w} \\ 9w - 3 \end{array}$$

Subtract by adding the opposite.

Bring down the next column, and repeat the process.

$$\begin{array}{r} w^2 + 9w + 3 \\ 3w - 1 \overline{)3w^3 + 26w^2 + 0w - 3} \\ \underline{-3w^3 + w^2} \\ 27w^2 + 0w \\ \underline{-27w^2 + 9w} \\ 9w - 3 \\ -(9w - 3) \end{array}$$

Divide $9w$ by the leading term in the divisor. $9w \div 3w = 3$.
Place 3 in the quotient.
Multiply $3(3w - 1) = 9w - 3$.

$$\begin{array}{r} w^2 + 9w + 3 \\ 3w - 1 \overline{)3w^3 + 26w^2 + 0w - 3} \\ \underline{-3w^3 + w^2} \\ 27w^2 + 0w \\ \underline{-27w^2 + 9w} \\ 9w - 3 \\ \underline{-9w + 3} \\ 0 \end{array}$$

Subtract by adding the opposite.

The remainder is 0.

The quotient is $w^2 + 9w + 3$, and the remainder is 0.

Skill Practice Divide the polynomials using long division.

4. $\dfrac{9x^3 + 11x + 10}{3x + 2}$

Answer

4. $3x^2 - 2x + 5$

396   Chapter 5   Polynomials and Properties of Exponents

In Example 3, the remainder is zero. Therefore, we say that $3w - 1$ divides evenly into $3w^3 + 26w^2 - 3$. For this reason, the divisor and quotient are factors of $3w^3 + 26w^2 - 3$. To check, we have

$$\text{Dividend} = (\text{divisor})(\text{quotient}) + \text{remainder}$$

$$3w^3 + 26w^2 - 3 \stackrel{?}{=} (3w - 1)(w^2 + 9w + 3) + 0$$

$$\stackrel{?}{=} 3w^3 + 27w^2 + 9w - w^2 - 9w - 3$$

$$= 3w^3 + 26w^2 - 3 \checkmark$$

Example 4   **Using Long Division to Divide Polynomials**

Divide the polynomials using long division.

$$\frac{2y + y^4 - 5}{1 + y^2}$$

Solution:

First note that both the dividend and divisor should be written in descending order:

$$\frac{y^4 + 2y - 5}{y^2 + 1}$$

Also note that the dividend and the divisor have missing powers of y. Leave place holders.

$$y^2 + 0y + 1\overline{)y^4 + 0y^3 + 0y^2 + 2y - 5}$$

$$\begin{array}{r} y^2 \\ y^2 + 0y + 1\overline{)y^4 + 0y^3 + 0y^2 + 2y - 5} \\ -(y^4 + 0y^3 + y^2) \end{array}$$

Divide $y^4 \div y^2 = y^2$. This is the first term of the quotient.

Multiply $y^2(y^2 + 0y + 1) = y^4 + 0y^3 + y^2$.

$$\begin{array}{r} y^2 \\ y^2 + 0y + 1\overline{)y^4 + 0y^3 + 0y^2 + 2y - 5} \\ -y^4 - 0y^3 - y^2 \\ \hline -y^2 + 2y - 5 \end{array}$$

Subtract by adding the opposite.

Bring down the next columns.

$$\begin{array}{r} y^2 -1 \\ y^2 + 0y + 1\overline{)y^4 + 0y^3 + 0y^2 + 2y - 5} \\ -y^4 - 0y^3 - y^2 \\ \hline -y^2 + 2y - 5 \\ -(-y^2 - 0y - 1) \end{array}$$

Divide $-y^2 \div y^2 = -1$.

Multiply $-1(y^2 + 0y + 1) = -y^2 - 0y - 1$.

$$\begin{array}{r} y^2 -1 \\ y^2 + 0y + 1\overline{)y^4 + 0y^3 + 0y^2 + 2y - 5} \\ -y^4 - 0y^3 - y^2 \\ \hline -y^2 + 2y - 5 \\ y^2 + 0y + 1 \\ \hline 2y - 4 \end{array}$$

Subtract by adding the opposite.

Remainder

Therefore, $\dfrac{y^4 + 2y - 5}{y^2 + 1} = y^2 - 1 + \dfrac{2y - 4}{y^2 + 1}$.

Skill Practice   Divide the polynomials using long division.

5. $(4 - x^2 + x^3) \div (2 + x^2)$

Answer

5. $x - 1 + \dfrac{-2x + 6}{x^2 + 2}$

| **Example 5** | **Determining Whether Long Division Is Necessary** |

Determine whether long division is necessary for each division of polynomials.

a. $\dfrac{2p^5 - 8p^4 + 4p - 16}{p^2 - 2p + 1}$ **b.** $\dfrac{2p^5 - 8p^4 + 4p - 16}{2p^2}$

c. $(3z^3 - 5z^2 + 10) \div (15z^3)$ **d.** $(3z^3 - 5z^2 + 10) \div (3z + 1)$

Solution:

- Long division is used when the divisor has *two or more terms*.
- If the divisor has *one term*, then divide each term in the dividend by the monomial divisor.

a. $\dfrac{2p^5 - 8p^4 + 4p - 16}{p^2 - 2p + 1}$ The divisor has three terms. Use long division.

b. $\dfrac{2p^5 - 8p^4 + 4p - 16}{2p^2}$ The divisor has one term. Long division is not necessary.

c. $(3z^3 - 5z^2 + 10) \div (15z^3)$ The divisor has one term. Long division is not necessary.

d. $(3z^3 - 5z^2 + 10) \div (3z + 1)$ The divisor has two terms. Use long division.

Skill Practice Divide the polynomials using the appropriate method of division.

6. $\dfrac{6x^3 - x^2 + 3x - 5}{2x + 3}$ **7.** $\dfrac{9w^3 - 18w^2 + 6w + 12}{3w}$

3. Synthetic Division

In this section, we introduced the process of long division to divide two polynomials. Next, we will learn another technique called **synthetic division** to divide two polynomials. Synthetic division can be used when dividing a polynomial by a first-degree divisor of the form $x - r$, where r is a constant. Synthetic division is considered a "shortcut" because it uses the coefficients of the divisor and dividend without writing the variables.

Consider dividing the polynomials $(3x^2 - 14x - 10) \div (x - 2)$.

$$
\begin{array}{r}
3x - 8 \\
x - 2 \overline{) 3x^2 - 14x - 10} \\
-(3x^2 - 6x) \\
\hline
-8x - 10 \\
-(-8x + 16) \\
\hline
-26
\end{array}
$$

Answers

6. $3x^2 - 5x + 9 + \dfrac{-32}{2x + 3}$

7. $3w^2 - 6w + 2 + \dfrac{4}{w}$

398   **Chapter 5**   Polynomials and Properties of Exponents

First note that the divisor $x - 2$ is in the form $x - r$, where $r = 2$. Therefore, synthetic division can be used to find the quotient and remainder.

Step 1: Write the value of r in a box. ⟶ $\underline{2\rfloor\ \ 3\ \ -14\ \ -10}$ ⟵ **Step 2:** Write the coefficients of the dividend to the right of the box.

$$3$$

Step 3: Skip a line and draw a horizontal line below the list of coefficients.

Step 4: Bring down the leading coefficient from the dividend and write it below the line.

$$\underline{2\rfloor\ \ 3\ \ -14\ \ -10}$$
$$6$$
$$3\quad -8$$

Step 5: Multiply the value of r by the number below the line $(2 \times 3 = 6)$. Write the result in the next column above the line.

Step 6: Add the numbers in the column above the line $(-14 + 6)$, and write the result below the line.

Repeat steps 5 and 6 until all columns have been completed.

Step 7: To get the final result, we use the numbers below the line. The number in the last column is the remainder. The other numbers are the coefficients of the quotient.

$$\underline{2\rfloor\ \ 3\ \ -14\ \ -10}$$
$$6\quad -16$$
$$3\quad -8\ \ \boxed{-26}$$

A box is usually drawn around the remainder.

Quotient: $3x - 8$,   remainder: -26

The degree of the quotient will always be 1 less than that of the dividend. Because the dividend is a second-degree polynomial, the quotient will be a first-degree polynomial. In this case, the quotient is $3x - 8$ and the remainder is -26.

| **Example 6** | **Using Synthetic Division to Divide Polynomials** |

Divide the polynomials $(5x + 4x^3 - 6 + x^4) \div (x + 3)$ by using synthetic division.

Solution:

As with long division, the terms of the dividend and divisor should be written in descending order. Furthermore, missing powers must be accounted for by using placeholders (shown here in red).

$$5x + 4x^3 - 6 + x^4$$
$$= x^4 + 4x^3 + 0x^2 + 5x - 6$$

To use synthetic division, the divisor must be in the form $(x - r)$. The divisor $x + 3$ can be written as $x - (-3)$. Hence, $r = -3$.

Avoiding Mistakes

It is important to check that the divisor is in the form $(x - r)$ before applying synthetic division. The variable x in the divisor must be of first degree, and its coefficient must be **1**.

Step 1: Write the value of r in a box.

$$-3 \,\rvert\ \ 1 \ \ \ 4 \ \ \ 0 \ \ \ 5 \ \ -6$$
$$\overline{}$$
$$1$$

Step 2: Write the coefficients of the dividend to the right of the box.

Step 3: Skip a line and draw a horizontal line below the list of coefficients.

Step 4: Bring down the leading coefficient from the dividend and write it below the line.

Step 5: Multiply the value of r by the number below the line ($-3 \times 1 = -3$). Write the result in the next column above the line.

$$-3 \,\rvert\ \ 1 \ \ \ 4 \ \ \ 0 \ \ \ 5 \ \ -6$$
$$\underline{ -3 }$$
$$1 \ \ \ 1$$

Step 6: Add the numbers in the column above the line: $4 + (-3) = 1$.

Repeat steps 5 and 6:

$$-3 \,\rvert\ \ 1 \ \ \ 4 \ \ \ \ 0 \ \ \ \ 5 \ \ \ \ -6$$
$$\underline{\ -3 \ \ -3 \ \ \ 9 \ \ -42}$$
$$1 \ \ \ 1 \ \ -3 \ \ 14 \ \ \underline{\rvert -48} \longleftarrow \text{remainder}$$
$$ \text{constant}$$
$$x\text{-term coefficient}$$
$$x^2\text{-term coefficient}$$
$$x^3\text{-term coefficient}$$

The quotient is $x^3 + x^2 - 3x + 14$.

The remainder is -48.

The answer is $x^3 + x^2 - 3x + 14 + \dfrac{-48}{x+3}$.

Skill Practice Divide the polynomials by using synthetic division.

8. $(5y^2 + 2y^3 - 5) \div (y + 2)$

TIP: It is interesting to compare the long division process to the synthetic division process. For Example 5, long division is shown on the left, and synthetic division is shown on the right. Notice that the same pattern of coefficients used in long division appears in the synthetic division process.

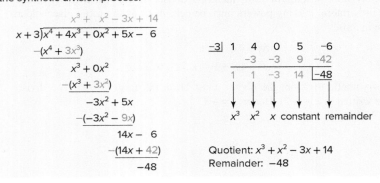

Quotient: $x^3 + x^2 - 3x + 14$
Remainder: -48

Answer
8. $2y^2 + y - 2 + \dfrac{-1}{y+2}$

Example 7	**Using Synthetic Division to Divide Polynomials**

Divide the polynomials by using synthetic division. $(p^4 - 81) \div (p - 3)$

Solution:

$(p^4 - 81) \div (p - 3)$

$(p^4 + 0p^3 + 0p^2 + 0p - 81) \div (p - 3)$ Insert placeholders (red) for missing powers of p.

$$
\begin{array}{r|rrrrr}
3 & 1 & 0 & 0 & 0 & -81 \\
  &   & 3 & 9 & 27 & 81 \\
\hline
  & 1 & 3 & 9 & 27 & \underline{0}
\end{array}
$$

Quotient: $p^3 + 3p^2 + 9p + 27$

Remainder: 0

The answer is $p^3 + 3p^2 + 9p + 27$.

Skill Practice Divide the polynomials by using synthetic division.

Answer

9. $x^2 - x + 1$

9. $(x^3 + 1) \div (x + 1)$

Section 5.7 Practice Exercises

Vocabulary and Key Concepts

1. **a.** The _____ algorithm states that: Dividend = (divisor)(_____) + (_____).

   b. _____ division or long division can be used when dividing a polynomial by a divisor of the form $x - r$, where r is a constant.

Review Exercises

2. **a.** Add. $(3x + 1) + (2x - 5)$

   b. Multiply. $(3x + 1)(2x - 5)$

3. **a.** Subtract. $(a - 10b) - (5a + b)$

   b. Multiply. $(a - 10b)(5a + b)$

4. **a.** Subtract. $(2y^2 + 1) - (y^2 - 5y + 1)$

   b. Multiply. $(2y^2 + 1)(y^2 - 5y + 1)$

5. **a.** Add. $(x^2 - x) + (6x^2 + x + 2)$

   b. Multiply. $(x^2 - x)(6x^2 + x + 2)$

For Exercises 6–8, answers may vary.

6. Write an example of a product of two binomials and simplify.

7. Write an example of the square of a binomial and simplify.

8. Write an example of the product of conjugates and simplify.

Concept 1: Division by a Monomial

For Exercises 9–24, divide the polynomials. Check your answer by multiplication. **(See Example 1.)**

9. $\dfrac{16t^4 - 4t^2 + 20t}{-4t}$

10. $\dfrac{2x^3 + 8x^2 - 2x}{-2x}$

11. $(36y + 24y^2 + 6y^3) \div (3y)$

12. $(6p^2 - 18p^4 + 30p^5) \div (6p)$

13. $(4x^3y + 12x^2y^2 - 4xy^3) \div (4xy)$

14. $(25m^5n - 10m^4n + m^3n) \div (5m^3n)$

15. $(-8y^4 - 12y^3 + 32y^2) \div (-4y^2)$

16. $(12y^5 - 8y^6 + 16y^4 - 10y^3) \div (2y^3)$

17. $(3p^4 - 6p^3 + 2p^2 - p) \div (-6p)$

18. $(-4q^3 + 8q^2 - q) \div (-12q)$

19. $(a^3 + 5a^2 + a - 5) \div (a)$

20. $(2m^5 - 3m^4 + m^3 - m^2 + 9m) \div (m^2)$

21. $\dfrac{6s^3t^5 - 8s^2t^4 + 10st^2}{-2st^4}$

22. $\dfrac{-8r^4w^2 - 4r^3w + 2w^3}{-4r^3w}$

23. $(8p^4q^7 - 9p^5q^6 - 11p^3q - 4) \div (p^2q)$

24. $(20a^5b^5 - 20a^3b^2 + 5a^2b + 6) \div (a^2b)$

Concept 2: Long Division

25. **a.** Divide $(2x^3 - 7x^2 + 5x - 1) \div (x - 2)$ and identify the divisor, quotient, and remainder.

    b. Explain how to check by using multiplication.

26. **a.** Divide $(x^3 + 4x^2 + 7x - 3) \div (x + 3)$ and identify the divisor, quotient, and remainder.

    b. Explain how to check by using multiplication.

For Exercises 27–48, divide the polynomials by using long division. Check your answer by multiplication. **(See Examples 2–4.)**

27. $(x^2 + 11x + 19) \div (x + 4)$

28. $(x^3 - 7x^2 - 13x + 3) \div (x + 2)$

29. $(3y^3 - 7y^2 - 4y + 3) \div (y - 3)$

30. $(z^3 - 2z^2 + 2z - 5) \div (z - 4)$

31. $(-12a^2 + 77a - 121) \div (3a - 11)$

32. $(28x^2 - 29x + 6) \div (4x - 3)$

33. $(9y + 18y^2 - 20) \div (3y + 4)$

34. $(-2y + 3y^2 - 1) \div (y - 1)$

35. $(18x^3 + 7x + 12) \div (3x - 2)$

36. $(8x^3 - 6x + 22) \div (2x - 1)$

37. $(8a^3 + 1) \div (2a + 1)$

38. $(81x^4 - 1) \div (3x + 1)$

39. $(x^4 - x^3 - x^2 + 4x - 2) \div (x^2 + x - 1)$

40. $(2a^5 - 7a^4 + 11a^3 - 22a^2 + 29a - 10) \div (2a^2 - 5a + 2)$

41. $(2x^3 - 10x + x^4 - 25) \div (x^2 - 5)$

42. $(-5x^3 + x^4 - 4 - 10x) \div (x^2 + 2)$

43. $(x^4 - 3x^2 + 10) \div (x^2 - 2)$

44. $(3y^4 - 25y^2 - 18) \div (y^2 - 3)$

45. $(n^4 - 16) \div (n - 2)$

46. $(m^3 + 27) \div (m + 3)$

47. $\dfrac{3y^4 + 2y + 3}{1 + y^2}$

48. $\dfrac{2x^4 + 6x + 4}{2 + x^2}$

402   **Chapter 5** Polynomials and Properties of Exponents

Concept 3: Synthetic Division

49. Explain the conditions under which you may use synthetic division to divide polynomials.

50. Can synthetic division be used directly to divide $(4x^4 + 3x^3 - 7x + 9)$ by $(2x + 5)$? Explain why or why not.

51. Can synthetic division be used to divide $(6x^5 - 3x^2 + 2x - 14)$ by $(x^2 - 3)$? Explain why or why not.

52. Can synthetic division be used to divide $(3x^4 - x + 1)$ by $(x - 5)$? Explain why or why not.

53. The following table represents the result of a synthetic division.

$$
\begin{array}{r|rrrr}
5 & 1 & -2 & -4 & 3 \\
  &   & 5 & 15 & 55 \\
\hline
  & 1 & 3 & 11 & \underline{58}
\end{array}
$$

Use x as the variable.

a. Identify the divisor.

b. Identify the quotient.

c. Identify the remainder.

54. The following table represents the result of a synthetic division.

$$
\begin{array}{r|rrrrr}
-2 & 2 & 3 & 0 & -1 & 6 \\
   &   & -4 & 2 & -4 & 10 \\
\hline
   & 2 & -1 & 2 & -5 & \underline{16}
\end{array}
$$

Use x as the variable.

a. Identify the divisor.

b. Identify the quotient.

c. Identify the remainder.

For Exercises 55–70, divide by using synthetic division. Check your answer by multiplication. **(See Examples 6–7.)**

55. $(x^2 - 2x - 48) \div (x - 8)$

56. $(x^2 - 4x - 12) \div (x - 6)$

57. $(t^2 - 3t - 4) \div (t + 1)$

58. $(h^2 + 7h + 12) \div (h + 3)$

59. $(5y^2 + 5y + 1) \div (y - 1)$

60. $(3w^2 + w - 5) \div (w + 2)$

61. $(3 + 7y^2 - 4y + 3y^3) \div (y + 3)$

62. $(2z - 2z^2 + z^3 - 5) \div (z + 3)$

63. $(x^3 - 3x^2 + 4) \div (x - 2)$

64. $(3y^4 - 25y^2 - 18) \div (y - 3)$

65. $(a^5 - 32) \div (a - 2)$

66. $(b^3 + 27) \div (b + 3)$

67. $(x^3 - 216) \div (x - 6)$

68. $(y^4 - 16) \div (y + 2)$

69. $(4w^4 - w^2 + 6w - 3) \div \left(w - \dfrac{1}{2}\right)$

70. $(-12y^4 - 5y^3 - y^2 + y + 3) \div \left(y + \dfrac{3}{4}\right)$

Mixed Exercises

For Exercises 71–82, divide the polynomials by using an appropriate method. **(See Examples 5.)**

71. $(-x^3 - 8x^2 - 3x - 2) \div (x + 4)$

72. $(8xy^2 - 9x^2y + 6x^2y^2) \div (x^2y^2)$

73. $(22x^2 - 11x + 33) \div (11x)$

74. $(2m^3 - 4m^2 + 5m - 33) \div (m - 3)$

75. $(12y^3 - 17y^2 + 30y - 10) \div (3y^2 - 2y + 5)$

76. $(90h^{12} - 63h^9 + 45h^8 - 36h^7) \div (9h^9)$

77. $(4x^4 + 6x^3 + 3x - 1) \div (2x^2 + 1)$

78. $(y^4 - 3y^3 - 5y^2 - 2y + 5) \div (y + 2)$

79. $(16k^{11} - 32k^{10} + 8k^8 - 40k^4) \div (8k^8)$

80. $(4m^3 - 18m^2 + 22m - 10) \div (2m^2 - 4m + 3)$

81. $(5x^3 + 9x^2 + 10x) \div (5x^2)$

82. $(15k^4 + 3k^3 + 4k^2 + 4) \div (3k^2 - 1)$

Problem Recognition Exercises

Operations on Polynomials

For Exercises 1–40, perform the indicated operations and simplify.

1. a. $6x^2 + 2x^2$
   b. $(6x^2)(2x^2)$

2. a. $8y^3 + y^3$
   b. $(8y^3)(y^3)$

3. a. $(4x + y)^2$
   b. $(4xy)^2$

4. a. $(2a + b)^2$
   b. $(2ab)^2$

5. a. $(2x + 3) + (4x - 2)$
   b. $(2x + 3)(4x - 2)$

6. a. $(5m^2 + 1) + (m^2 + m)$
   b. $(5m^2 + 1)(m^2 + m)$

7. a. $(3z + 2)^2$
   b. $(3z + 2)(3z - 2)$

8. a. $(6y - 7)^2$
   b. $(6y - 7)(6y + 7)$

9. a. $(2x - 4)(x^2 - 2x + 3)$
   b. $(2x - 4) + (x^2 - 2x + 3)$

10. a. $(3y^2 + 8)(-y^2 - 4)$
   b. $(3y^2 + 8) - (-y^2 - 4)$

11. a. $x + x$
   b. $x \cdot x$

12. a. $2c + 2c$
   b. $2c \cdot 2c$

13. $(7mn)^2$

14. $(8pq)^2$

15. $(-2x^4 - 6x^3 + 8x^2) \div (2x^2)$

16. $(-15m^3 + 12m^2 - 3m) \div (-3m)$

17. $(m^3 - 4m^2 - 6) - (3m^2 + 7m) + (-m^3 - 9m + 6)$

18. $(n^4 + 2n^2 - 3n) + (4n^2 + 2n - 1) - (4n^5 + 6n - 3)$

19. $(8x^3 + 2x + 6) \div (x - 2)$

20. $(-4x^3 + 2x^2 - 5) \div (x - 3)$

21. $(2x - y)(3x^2 + 4xy - y^2)$

22. $(3a + b)(2a^2 - ab + 2b^2)$

23. $(x + y^2)(x^2 - xy^2 + y^4)$

24. $(m^2 + 1)(m^4 - m^2 + 1)$

25. $(a^2 + 2b) - (a^2 - 2b)$ **26.** $(y^3 - 6z) - (y^3 + 6z)$

27. $(a^3 + 2b)(a^3 - 2b)$ **28.** $(y^3 - 6z)(y^3 + 6z)$

29. $\dfrac{8p^2 + 4p - 6}{2p - 1}$ **30.** $\dfrac{4v^2 - 8v + 8}{2v + 3}$

31. $\dfrac{12x^3y^7}{3xy^5}$ **32.** $\dfrac{-18p^2q^4}{2pq^3}$

33. $\left(\dfrac{3}{7}x - \dfrac{1}{2}\right)\left(\dfrac{3}{7}x + \dfrac{1}{2}\right)$ **34.** $\left(\dfrac{2}{5}y + \dfrac{4}{3}\right)\left(\dfrac{2}{5}y - \dfrac{4}{3}\right)$

35. $\left(\dfrac{1}{9}x^3 + \dfrac{2}{3}x^2 + \dfrac{1}{6}x - 3\right) - \left(\dfrac{4}{3}x^3 + \dfrac{1}{9}x^2 + \dfrac{2}{3}x + 1\right)$

36. $\left(\dfrac{1}{10}y^2 - \dfrac{3}{5}y - \dfrac{1}{15}\right) - \left(\dfrac{7}{5}y^2 + \dfrac{3}{10}y - \dfrac{1}{3}\right)$

37. $(0.05x^2 - 0.16x - 0.75) + (1.25x^2 - 0.14x + 0.25)$

38. $(1.6w^3 + 2.8w + 6.1) + (3.4w^3 - 4.1w^2 - 7.3)$

39. $(3x^2y)(-2xy^5)$

40. $(10ab^4)(5a^3b^2)$

404   Chapter 5   Polynomials and Properties of Exponents

The Pythagorean Theorem and a Geometric "Proof"

Estimated Time: 25–30 minutes

Group Size: 2

Right triangles occur in many applications of mathematics. By definition, a right triangle is a triangle that contains a 90° angle. The two shorter sides in a right triangle are referred to as the "legs," and the longest side is called the "hypotenuse." In the triangle shown, the legs are labeled as a and b, and the hypotenuse is labeled as c.

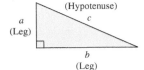

Right triangles have an important property that the sum of the squares of the two legs of a right triangle equals the square of the hypotenuse. This fact is referred to as the Pythagorean theorem. In symbols, the Pythagorean theorem is stated as:

$$a^2 + b^2 = c^2$$

1. The following triangles are right triangles. Verify that $a^2 + b^2 = c^2$. (The units may be left off when performing these calculations.)

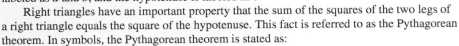

$a = 3$
$b = 4$
$c = 5$

$a =$ _____
$b =$ _____
$c =$ _____

$$a^2 + b^2 = c^2$$
$$(3)^2 + (4)^2 \stackrel{?}{=} (5)^2$$
$$9 + 16 = 25 ✓$$

$$a^2 + b^2 = c^2$$
$$(\underline{})^2 + (\underline{})^2 \stackrel{?}{=} (\underline{})^2$$
$$\underline{} + \underline{} = \underline{} \;✓$$

2. The following geometric "proof" of the Pythagorean theorem uses addition, subtraction, and multiplication of polynomials. Consider the square figure. The length of each side of the large outer square is $(a + b)$. Therefore, the area of the large outer square is $(a + b)^2$.

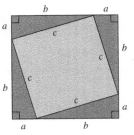

   The area of the large outer square can also be found by adding the area of the inner square (pictured in light gray) plus the area of the four right triangles (pictured in dark gray).

   Area of inner square: c^2 Area of the four right triangles: $4 \cdot \left(\frac{1}{2} a b\right)$

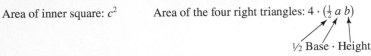

½ Base · Height

3. Now equate the two expressions representing the area of the large outer square:

$$\begin{pmatrix} \text{Area of outer} \\ \text{square} \end{pmatrix} = \begin{pmatrix} \text{area of inner} \\ \text{square} \end{pmatrix} + \begin{pmatrix} \text{4 times the area} \\ \text{of the right triangles} \end{pmatrix}$$

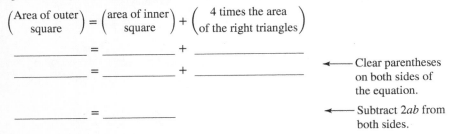

   ← Clear parentheses on both sides of the equation.

   ← Subtract $2ab$ from both sides.

Chapter 5   Summary

Section 5.1   **Multiplying and Dividing Expressions with Common Bases**

Key Concepts

Definition

$$b^n = \underbrace{b \cdot b \cdot b \cdot b \cdot \ldots b}_{n \text{ factors of } b}$$ b is the base,
n is the exponent

Multiplying Like Bases

$b^m b^n = b^{m+n}$ (m, n positive integers)

Dividing Like Bases

$\dfrac{b^m}{b^n} = b^{m-n}$ ($b \neq 0$, m, n, positive integers)

Examples

Example 1

$3^4 = 3 \cdot 3 \cdot 3 \cdot 3 = 81$ 3 is the base
4 is the exponent

Example 2

Compare: $(-5)^2$ versus -5^2

$(-5)^2 = (-5)(-5) = 25$

versus

$-5^2 = -1(5^2) = -1(5)(5) = -25$

Example 3

Simplify: $x^3 \cdot x^4 \cdot x^2 \cdot x = x^{3+4+2+1} = x^{10}$

Example 4

Simplify: $\dfrac{c^4 d^{10}}{cd^5} = c^{4-1}d^{10-5} = c^3 d^5$

Section 5.2   **More Properties of Exponents**

Key Concepts

Power Rule for Exponents

$(b^m)^n = b^{mn}$ ($b \neq 0$, m, n positive integers)

Power of a Product and Power of a Quotient

Assume m and n are positive integers and a and b are real numbers where $b \neq 0$.
Then,

$(ab)^m = a^m b^m$ and $\left(\dfrac{a}{b}\right)^m = \dfrac{a^m}{b^m}$

Examples

Example 1

Simplify: $(x^4)^5 = x^{20}$

Example 2

Simplify: $(4uv^2)^3 = 4^3 u^3 (v^2)^3 = 64 u^3 v^6$

Example 3

Simplify: $\left(\dfrac{p^5 q^3}{5pq^2}\right)^2 = \left(\dfrac{p^{5-1}q^{3-2}}{5}\right)^2 = \left(\dfrac{p^4 q}{5}\right)^2$

$= \dfrac{(p^4)^2 (q)^2}{(5)^2} = \dfrac{p^8 q^2}{25}$

406   **Chapter 5**   Polynomials and Properties of Exponents

Section 5.3   Definitions of b^0 and b^{-n}

Key Concepts

Definitions

If b is a nonzero real number and n is an integer, then:

1. $b^0 = 1$

2. $b^{-n} = \left(\dfrac{1}{b}\right)^n = \dfrac{1}{b^n}$

Examples

Example 1

Simplify: $4^0 = 1$

Example 2

Simplify: $y^{-7} = \dfrac{1}{y^7}$

Example 3

Simplify: $\dfrac{8a^0 b^{-2}}{c^{-5}d}$

$$= \frac{8(1)c^5}{b^2 d} = \frac{8c^5}{b^2 d}$$

Section 5.4   Scientific Notation

Key Concepts

A positive number written in **scientific notation** is expressed in the form:

$a \times 10^n$ where $1 \le a < 10$ and n is an integer.

$35{,}000 = 3.5 \times 10^4$

$0.000\,000\,548 = 5.48 \times 10^{-7}$

Examples

Example 1

Multiply: $(3.5 \times 10^4)(2 \times 10^{-6})$

$$= 7 \times 10^{-2}$$

Example 2

Divide: $\dfrac{2.1 \times 10^{-9}}{8.4 \times 10^3} = 0.25 \times 10^{-9-3}$

$$= 0.25 \times 10^{-12}$$
$$= (2.5 \times 10^{-1}) \times 10^{-12}$$
$$= 2.5 \times 10^{-13}$$

Section 5.5   Addition and Subtraction of Polynomials

Key Concepts

A **polynomial** in one variable is a sum of terms of the form ax^n, where a is a real number and the exponent, n, is a non-negative integer. For each term, a is called the **coefficient** of the term and n is the **degree of the term**. The term with highest degree is the **leading term**, and its coefficient is called the **leading coefficient**. The **degree of the polynomial** is the largest degree of all its terms.

To add or subtract polynomials, add or subtract *like* terms.

Examples

Example 1

Given: $4x^5 - 8x^3 + 9x - 5$

Coefficients of each term: $4, -8, 9, -5$

Degree of each term: $5, 3, 1, 0$

Leading term: $4x^5$

Leading coefficient: 4

Degree of polynomial: 5

Example 2

Perform the indicated operations:

$$(2x^4 - 5x^3 + 1) - (x^4 + 3) + (x^3 - 4x - 7)$$
$$= 2x^4 - 5x^3 + 1 - x^4 - 3 + x^3 - 4x - 7$$
$$= 2x^4 - x^4 - 5x^3 + x^3 - 4x + 1 - 3 - 7$$
$$= x^4 - 4x^3 - 4x - 9$$

Section 5.6   Multiplication of Polynomials and Special Products

Key Concepts

Multiplying Monomials

Use the commutative and associative properties of multiplication to group coefficients and like bases.

Multiplying Polynomials

Multiply each term in the first polynomial by each term in the second polynomial.

Product of Conjugates

The product of conjugates results in a **difference of squares**.
$(a + b)(a - b) = a^2 - b^2$

Square of a Binomial

The square of a binomial results in a **perfect square trinomial**.

$(a + b)^2 = a^2 + 2ab + b^2$

$(a - b)^2 = a^2 - 2ab + b^2$

Examples

Example 1

Multiply: $(5a^2b)(-2ab^3)$
$$= [5 \cdot (-2)](a^2a)(bb^3)$$
$$= -10a^3b^4$$

Example 2

Multiply: $(x - 2)(3x^2 - 4x + 11)$
$$= 3x^3 - 4x^2 + 11x - 6x^2 + 8x - 22$$
$$= 3x^3 - 10x^2 + 19x - 22$$

Example 3

Multiply: $(3w - 4v)(3w + 4v)$
$$= (3w)^2 - (4v)^2$$
$$= 9w^2 - 16v^2$$

Example 4

Multiply: $(5c - 8d)^2$
$$= (5c)^2 - 2(5c)(8d) + (8d)^2$$
$$= 25c^2 - 80cd + 64d^2$$

408   **Chapter 5**   Polynomials and Properties of Exponents

Section 5.7   Division of Polynomials

Key Concepts

Division of Polynomials

1. Division by a monomial, use the properties:

$$\frac{a+b}{c} = \frac{a}{c} + \frac{b}{c} \qquad \text{and} \qquad \frac{a-b}{c} = \frac{a}{c} - \frac{b}{c}$$

2. If the divisor has more than one term, use long division.

3. If the divisor is of the form $x - r$, then synthetic division may be used.

Examples

Example 1

Divide: $\dfrac{-3x^2 - 6x + 9}{-3x}$

$$= \frac{-3x^2}{-3x} - \frac{6x}{-3x} + \frac{9}{-3x}$$

$$= x + 2 - \frac{3}{x}$$

Example 2

Divide: $(3x^2 - 5x + 1) \div (x + 2)$

$$
\begin{array}{r}
3x - 11 \\
x + 2 \overline{)\, 3x^2 - 5x + 1} \\
\underline{-(3x^2 + 6x)} \\
-11x + 1 \\
\underline{-(-11x - 22)} \\
23
\end{array}
$$

$$3x - 11 + \frac{23}{x + 2}$$

Example 3

Divide: $(4x^3 - 2x - 5) \div (x - 1)$

$$
\begin{array}{r}
\underline{1|}\quad 4 \quad 0 \quad -2 \quad -5 \\
\quad\quad\quad 4 \quad 4 \quad 2 \\
\overline{4 \quad 4 \quad 2 \;\; |-3}
\end{array}
$$

$$4x^2 + 4x + 2 + \frac{-3}{x - 1}$$

Chapter 5   Review Exercises

Section 5.1

For Exercises 1–4, identify the base and the exponent.

1. 5^3 **2.** x^4 **3.** $(-2)^0$ **4.** y

5. Evaluate the expressions.
   a. 6^2 **b.** $(-6)^2$ **c.** -6^2

6. Evaluate the expressions.
   a. 4^3 **b.** $(-4)^3$ **c.** -4^3

For Exercises 7–18, simplify and write the answers in exponent form. Assume that all variables represent nonzero real numbers.

7. $5^3 \cdot 5^{10}$ **8.** $a^7 a^4$

9. $x \cdot x^6 \cdot x^2$ **10.** $6^3 \cdot 6 \cdot 6^5$

11. $\dfrac{10^7}{10^4}$ **12.** $\dfrac{y^{14}}{y^8}$

13. $\dfrac{b^9}{b}$ **14.** $\dfrac{7^8}{7}$

15. $\dfrac{k^2 k^3}{k^4}$ **16.** $\dfrac{8^4 \cdot 8^7}{8^{11}}$

17. $\dfrac{2^8 \cdot 2^{10}}{2^3 \cdot 2^7}$ **18.** $\dfrac{q^3 q^{12}}{q q^8}$

19. Explain why $2^2 \cdot 4^4$ does *not* equal 8^6.

20. Explain why $\frac{10^5}{5^5}$ does *not* equal 2^3.

For Exercises 21–22, use the formula

$$A = P(1 + r)^t$$

🖩 **21.** Find the amount in an account after 3 years if the initial investment is \$6000, invested at 6% interest compounded annually.

🖩 **22.** Find the amount in an account after 2 years if the initial investment is \$20,000, invested at 5% interest compounded annually.

Section 5.2

For Exercises 23–40, simplify each expression. Write the answer in exponent form. Assume all variables represent nonzero real numbers.

23. $(7^3)^4$

24. $(c^2)^6$

25. $(p^4 p^2)^3$

26. $(9^5 \cdot 9^2)^4$

27. $\left(\dfrac{a}{b}\right)^2$

28. $\left(\dfrac{1}{3}\right)^4$

29. $\left(\dfrac{5}{c^2 d^5}\right)^2$

30. $\left(-\dfrac{m^2}{4n^6}\right)^5$

31. $(2ab^2)^4$

32. $(-x^7 y)^2$

33. $\left(\dfrac{-3x^3}{5y^2 z}\right)^3$

34. $\left(\dfrac{r^3}{s^2 t^6}\right)^5$

35. $\dfrac{a^4 (a^2)^8}{(a^3)^3}$

36. $\dfrac{(8^3)^4 \cdot 8^{10}}{(8^4)^5}$

37. $\dfrac{(4h^2 k)^2 (h^3 k)^4}{(2hk^3)^2}$

38. $\dfrac{(p^3 q)^3 (2p^2 q^4)^4}{(8p)(pq^3)^2}$

39. $\left(\dfrac{2x^4 y^3}{4xy^2}\right)^2$

40. $\left(\dfrac{a^4 b^6}{ab^4}\right)^3$

Section 5.3

For Exercises 41–62, simplify each expression. Write the answers with positive exponents. Assume all variables represent nonzero real numbers.

41. 8^0

42. $(-b)^0$

43. $-x^0$

44. 1^0

45. $2y^0$

46. $(2y)^0$

47. z^{-5}

48. 10^{-4}

49. $(6a)^{-2}$

50. $6a^{-2}$

51. $4^0 + 4^{-2}$

52. $9^{-1} + 9^0$

53. $t^{-6} t^{-2}$

54. $r^8 r^{-9}$

55. $\dfrac{12x^{-2} y^3}{6x^4 y^{-4}}$

56. $\dfrac{8ab^{-3} c^0}{10a^{-5} b^{-4} c^{-1}}$

57. $(-2m^2 n^{-4})^{-4}$

58. $(3u^{-5} v^2)^{-3}$

59. $\dfrac{(k^{-6})^{-2}(k^3)}{5k^{-6} k^0}$

60. $\dfrac{(3h)^{-2}(h^{-5})^{-3}}{h^{-4} h^8}$

61. $2 \cdot 3^{-1} - 6^{-1}$

62. $2^{-1} - 2^{-2} + 2^0$

Section 5.4

63. Write the numbers in scientific notation.

    a. In a recent year there were 97,400,000 packages of M&Ms sold in the United States.

    b. The thickness of a piece of paper is 0.0042 in.

64. Write the numbers in standard form.

    a. A pH of 10 means the hydrogen ion concentration is 1×10^{-10} units.

    b. A fundraising event for neurospinal research raised $\$2.56 \times 10^5$.

For Exercises 65–68, perform the indicated operations. Write the answers in scientific notation.

65. $(41 \times 10^{-6})(2.3 \times 10^{11})$

66. $\dfrac{9.3 \times 10^3}{6 \times 10^{-7}}$

67. $\dfrac{2000}{0.000008}$

68. $(0.000078)(21,000,000)$

🖩 **69.** Use your calculator to evaluate 5^{20}. Why is scientific notation necessary on your calculator to express the answer?

🖩 **70.** Use your calculator to evaluate $(0.4)^{30}$. Why is scientific notation necessary on your calculator to express the answer?

410   Chapter 5   Polynomials and Properties of Exponents

71. The average distance between the Earth and Sun is 9.3×10^7 mi.

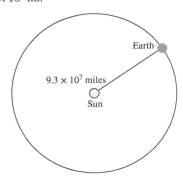

a. If the Earth's orbit is approximated by a circle, find the total distance the Earth travels around the Sun in one orbit. (*Hint:* The circumference of a circle is given by $C = 2\pi r$.) Express the answer in scientific notation.

b. If the Earth makes one complete trip around the Sun in 1 year (365 days = 8.76×10^3 hr), find the average speed that the Earth travels around the Sun in miles per hour. Express the answer in scientific notation.

72. The average distance between the planet Mercury and the Sun is 3.6×10^7 mi.

a. If Mercury's orbit is approximated by a circle, find the total distance Mercury travels around the Sun in one orbit. (*Hint:* The circumference of a circle is given by $C = 2\pi r$.) Express the answer in scientific notation.

b. If Mercury makes one complete trip around the Sun in 88 days (2.112×10^3 hr), find the average speed that Mercury travels around the Sun in miles per hour. Express the answer in scientific notation.

Section 5.5

73. For the polynomial $7x^4 - x + 6$

a. Classify as a monomial, a binomial, or a trinomial.

b. Identify the degree of the polynomial.

c. Identify the leading coefficient.

74. For the polynomial $2y^3 - 5y^7$

a. Classify as a monomial, a binomial, or a trinomial.

b. Identify the degree of the polynomial.

c. Identify the leading coefficient.

For Exercises 75–80, add or subtract as indicated.

75. $(4x + 2) + (3x - 5)$

76. $(7y^2 - 11y - 6) - (8y^2 + 3y - 4)$

77. $(9a^2 - 6) - (-5a^2 + 2a)$

78. $\left(5x^3 - \frac{1}{4}x^2 + \frac{5}{8}x + 2\right) + \left(\frac{5}{2}x^3 + \frac{1}{2}x^2 - \frac{1}{8}x\right)$

79. $8w^4 \qquad\quad - 6w + 3$
$ + 2w^4 + 2w^3 - w + 1$

80. $-0.02b^5 + b^4 \qquad\quad - 0.7b + 0.3$
$ + 0.03b^5 \qquad - 0.1b^3 + b + 0.03$

81. Subtract $(9x^2 + 4x + 6)$ from $(7x^2 - 5x)$.

82. Find the difference of $(x^2 - 5x - 3)$ and $(6x^2 + 4x + 9)$.

83. Write a trinomial of degree 2 with a leading coefficient of -5. (Answers may vary.)

84. Write a binomial of degree 5 with leading coefficient 6. (Answers may vary.)

85. Find a polynomial that represents the perimeter of the given rectangle.

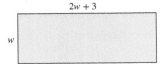

Section 5.6

For Exercises 86–103, multiply the expressions.

86. $(25x^4y^3)(-3x^2y)$ **87.** $(9a^6)(2a^2b^4)$

88. $5c(3c^3 - 7c + 5)$ **89.** $(x^2 + 5x - 3)(-2x)$

90. $(5k - 4)(k + 1)$ **91.** $(4t - 1)(5t + 2)$

92. $(q + 8)(6q - 1)$ **93.** $(2a - 6)(a + 5)$

94. $\left(7a + \frac{1}{2}\right)^2$ **95.** $(b - 4)^2$

96. $(4p^2 + 6p + 9)(2p - 3)$

97. $(2w - 1)(-w^2 - 3w - 4)$

98. $2x^2 - 3x + 4$
$\times \underline{\qquad\quad 2x - 1}$

99. $4a^2 + a - 5$
$\times \underline{\qquad\quad 3a + 2}$

100. $(b-4)(b+4)$

101. $\left(\frac{1}{3}r^4 - s^2\right)\left(\frac{1}{3}r^4 + s^2\right)$

102. $(-7z^2 + 6)^2$

103. $(2h+3)(h^4 - h^3 + h^2 - h + 1)$

104. Find a polynomial that represents the area of the given rectangle.

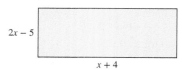

$2x - 5$

$x + 4$

Section 5.7

For Exercises 105–117, divide the polynomials.

105. $\dfrac{20y^3 - 10y^2}{5y}$

106. $(18a^3b^2 - 9a^2b - 27ab^2) \div 9ab$

107. $(12x^4 - 8x^3 + 4x^2) \div (-4x^2)$

108. $\dfrac{10z^7w^4 - 15z^3w^2 - 20zw}{-20z^2w}$

109. $\dfrac{x^2 + 7x + 10}{x + 5}$

110. $(2t^2 + t - 10) \div (t - 2)$

111. $(2p^2 + p - 16) \div (2p + 7)$

112. $\dfrac{5a^2 + 27a - 22}{5a - 3}$

113. $\dfrac{b^3 - 125}{b - 5}$

114. $(z^3 + 4z^2 + 5z + 20) \div (5 + z^2)$

115. $(y^4 - 4y^3 + 5y^2 - 3y + 2) \div (y^2 + 3)$

116. $(3t^4 - 8t^3 + t^2 - 4t - 5) \div (3t^2 + t + 1)$

117. $\dfrac{2w^4 + w^3 + 4w - 3}{2w^2 - w + 3}$

Chapter 5   Test

Assume all variables represent nonzero real numbers.

1. Expand the expression using the definition of exponents, then simplify: $\dfrac{3^4 \cdot 3^3}{3^6}$

For Exercises 2–13, simplify each expression. Write the answer with positive exponents only.

2. $9^5 \cdot 9$

3. $\dfrac{q^{10}}{q^2}$

4. $(-7)^0$

5. c^{-3}

6. $3^0 + 2^{-1} - 4^{-1}$

7. $4 \cdot 8^{-1} + 16^0$

8. $(3a^2b)^3$

9. $\left(\dfrac{2x}{y^3}\right)^4$

10. $\dfrac{14^3 \cdot 14^9}{14^{10} \cdot 14}$

11. $\dfrac{(s^2t)^3(7s^4t)^4}{(7s^2t^3)^2}$

12. $(2a^0b^{-6})^2$

13. $\left(\dfrac{6a^{-5}b}{8ab^{-2}}\right)^{-2}$

14. a. Write the number in scientific notation: 43,000,000,000

b. Write the number in standard form: 5.6×10^{-6}

15. Multiply: $(1.2 \times 10^6)(7 \times 10^{-15})$

16. Divide: $\dfrac{60,000}{0.008}$

17. The average amount of water flowing over Niagara Falls is 1.68×10^5 m^3/min.

a. How many cubic meters of water flow over the falls in one day?

b. How many cubic meters of water flow over the falls in one year?

© Alberto Fresco/Alamy RF

412   **Chapter 5** Polynomials and Properties of Exponents

18. Write the polynomial in descending order:
$4x + 5x^3 - 7x^2 + 11$

   a. Identify the degree of the polynomial.

   b. Identify the leading coefficient of the polynomial.

For Exercises 19–28, perform the indicated operations.

19. $(5t^4 - 2t^2 - 17) + (12t^3 + 2t^2 + 7t - 2)$

20. $(7w^2 - 11w - 6) + (8w^2 + 3w + 4) - (-9w^2 - 5w + 2)$

21. $-2x^3(5x^2 + x - 15)$ **22.** $(4a - 3)(2a - 1)$

23. $(4y - 5)(y^2 - 5y + 3)$ **24.** $(2 + 3b)(2 - 3b)$

25. $(5z - 6)^2$ **26.** $(5x + 3)(3x - 2)$

27. $(2x^2 + 5x) - (6x^2 - 7)$

28. $(y^2 - 5y + 2)(y - 6)$

29. Subtract $(3x^2 - 5x^3 + 2x)$ from $(10x^3 - 4x^2 + 1)$.

30. Find the perimeter and the area of the rectangle shown in the figure.

$5x + 2$

$x - 3$

For Exercises 31–35, divide the polynomials.

31. $(-12x^8 + x^6 - 8x^3) \div (4x^2)$

32. $\dfrac{16a^3b - 2a^2b^2 + 8ab}{-4ab}$

33. $\dfrac{2y^2 - 13y + 21}{y - 3}$

34. $(-5w^2 + 2w^3 - 2w + 5) \div (2w + 3)$

35. $\dfrac{3x^4 + x^3 + 4x - 33}{x^2 + 4}$

Chapters 1–5 Cumulative Review Exercises

For Exercises 1–2, simplify completely.

1. $-5 - \dfrac{1}{2}[4 - 3(-7)]$ **2.** $|-3^2 + 5|$

3. Translate the phrase into a mathematical expression and simplify:

   The difference of the square of five and the square root of four.

4. Solve for x: $\dfrac{1}{2}(x - 6) + \dfrac{2}{3} = \dfrac{1}{4}x$

5. Solve for y: $-2y - 3 = -5(y - 1) + 3y$

6. For a point in a rectangular coordinate system, in which quadrant are both the x- and y-coordinates negative?

7. For a point in a rectangular coordinate system, on which axis is the x-coordinate zero and the y-coordinate nonzero?

8. In a triangle, one angle measures $23°$ more than the smallest angle. The third angle measures $10°$ more than the sum of the other two angles. Find the measure of each angle.

9. A snow storm lasts for 9 hr and dumps snow at a rate of $1\frac{1}{2}$ in./hr. If there was already 6 in. of snow on the ground before the storm, the snow depth is given by the equation:

$y = \dfrac{3}{2}x + 6$ where y is the snow depth in inches and $x \geq 0$ is the time in hours after the storm began.

   a. Find the snow depth after 4 hr.

   b. Find the snow depth at the end of the storm.

   c. How long had it snowed when the total depth of snow was $14\frac{1}{4}$ in.?

© Brand X Photography/Veer RF

10. Solve the system of equations.

$$5x + 3y = -3$$
$$3x + 2y = -1$$

11. Solve the inequality. Graph the solution set on the real number line and express the solution in interval notation. $2 - 3(2x + 4) \leq -2x - (x - 5)$

For Exercises 12–15, perform the indicated operations.

12. $(2x^2 + 3x - 7) - (-3x^2 + 12x + 8)$

13. $(2y + 3z)(-y - 5z)$

14. $(4t - 3)^2$

15. $\left(\dfrac{2}{5}a + \dfrac{1}{3}\right)\left(\dfrac{2}{5}a - \dfrac{1}{3}\right)$

For Exercises 16–17, divide the polynomials.

16. $(12a^4b^3 - 6a^2b^2 + 3ab) \div (-3ab)$

17. $\dfrac{4m^3 - 5m + 2}{m - 2}$

For Exercises 18–19, use the properties of exponents to simplify the expressions. Write the answers with positive exponents only. Assume all variables represent nonzero real numbers.

18. $\left(\dfrac{2c^2d^4}{8cd^6}\right)^2$

19. $\dfrac{10a^{-2}b^{-3}}{5a^0b^{-6}}$

20. Perform the indicated operations, and write the final answer in scientific notation.

$$\dfrac{8.2 \times 10^{-2}}{2 \times 10^{-5}}$$

Factoring Polynomials

Factoring Polynomials

6

CHAPTER OUTLINE

Mathematics in the Workplace

Suppose that you are the manager of a laboratory that produces prototype electronics. This week you are tasked with producing 6 laptops over a 6-day period. With these constraints, you could produce 1 laptop per day for 6 days, 2 laptops per day for 3 days, 3 laptops per day for 2 days, or 6 laptops all in 1 day.

Any of these combinations will accomplish your task.

Laptops per day	Number of days	Total number of laptops
1	6	6
2	3	6
3	2	6
6	1	6

© Henrik Jonsson/Getty Images RF

The word **factor** is Latin for "maker." In this example, the numbers 1, 2, 3, and 6 are **factors** of 6 because they *make* a 6 by using multiplication. In other words, we can multiply each of the numbers 1, 2, 3, and 6 by another factor to produce 6. In essence, *factoring* is the process of breaking numbers or expressions into the elements that made them via multiplication.

Factoring (finding the factors) is used extensively in algebra to make expressions easier to use. In this chapter you will learn how to factor both numerical values and polynomials.

416   **Chapter 6**   Factoring Polynomials

Section 6.1   Greatest Common Factor and Factoring by Grouping

---

Concepts

1. Identifying the Greatest Common Factor
2. Factoring out the Greatest Common Factor
3. Factoring out a Negative Factor
4. Factoring out a Binomial Factor
5. Factoring by Grouping

1. Identifying the Greatest Common Factor

We have already learned how to multiply two or more polynomials. We now devote our study to a related operation called **factoring**. To factor an integer means to write the integer as a product of two or more integers. To factor a polynomial means to express the polynomial as a product of two or more polynomials.

In the product $2 \cdot 5 = 10$, for example, 2 and 5 are factors of 10.

In the product $(3x + 4)(2x - 1) = 6x^2 + 5x - 4$, the quantities $(3x + 4)$ and $(2x - 1)$ are factors of $6x^2 + 5x - 4$.

We begin our study of factoring by factoring integers. The number 20, for example, can be factored as $1 \cdot 20$ or $2 \cdot 10$ or $4 \cdot 5$ or $2 \cdot 2 \cdot 5$. The product $2 \cdot 2 \cdot 5$ (or equivalently $2^2 \cdot 5$) consists only of prime numbers and is called the **prime factorization**.

The **greatest common factor** (denoted **GCF**) of two or more integers is the largest factor common to each integer. To find the greatest common factor of two or more integers, it is often helpful to express the numbers as a product of prime factors as shown in the next example.

Example 1   **Identifying the Greatest Common Factor**

Find the greatest common factor.

   a. 24 and 36   **b.** 105, 40, and 60

Solution:

First find the prime factorization of each number. Then find the product of common factors.

a.
$$2\underline{|24} \qquad 2\underline{|36}$$
$$2\underline{|12} \qquad 2\underline{|18}$$
$$2\underline{|6} \qquad 3\underline{|9}$$
$$3 \qquad\quad 3$$

Factors of $24 = 2 \cdot 2 \cdot 2 \cdot 3$
Factors of $36 = 2 \cdot 2 \cdot 3 \cdot 3$ ← Common factors are circled.

The numbers 24 and 36 share two factors of 2 and one factor of 3. Therefore, the greatest common factor is $2 \cdot 2 \cdot 3 = 12$.

b.
$$5\underline{|105} \qquad 5\underline{|40} \qquad 5\underline{|60}$$
$$3\underline{|21} \qquad 2\underline{|8} \qquad 3\underline{|12}$$
$$7 \qquad\quad 2\underline{|4} \qquad 2\underline{|4}$$
$$\qquad\qquad 2 \qquad\quad 2$$

Factors of $105 = 3 \cdot 7 \cdot 5$
Factors of $40 = 2 \cdot 2 \cdot 2 \cdot 5$
Factors of $60 = 2 \cdot 2 \cdot 3 \cdot 5$

The greatest common factor is 5.

Skill Practice   Find the GCF.

   1. 12 and 20   **2.** 45, 75, and 30

Answers

1. 4   **2.** 15

In Example 2, we find the greatest common factor of two or more variable terms.

Example 2   **Identifying the Greatest Common Factor**

Find the GCF among each group of terms.

a. $7x^3$, $14x^2$, $21x^4$ **b.** $15a^4b$, $25a^3b^2$

Solution:

List the factors of each term.

a. $7x^3 = 7 \cdot x \cdot x \cdot x$
       $14x^2 = 2 \cdot 7 \cdot x \cdot x$
       $21x^4 = 3 \cdot 7 \cdot x \cdot x \cdot x \cdot x$
       The GCF is $7x^2$.

b. $15a^4b = 3 \cdot 5 \cdot a \cdot a \cdot a \cdot a \cdot b$
        $25a^3b^2 = 5 \cdot 5 \cdot a \cdot a \cdot a \cdot b \cdot b$
        The GCF is $5a^3b$.

> **TIP:** Notice in Example 2(b) the expressions $15a^4b$ and $25a^3b^2$ share factors of 5, a, and b. The GCF is the product of the common factors, where each factor is raised to the lowest power to which it occurs in all the original expressions.
>
> $15a^4b = 3^1 \cdot 5^1 a^4 b^1$ Lowest power of 5 is 1: 5^1
> $25a^3b^2 = 5^2 a^3 b^2$ Lowest power of a is 3: a^3 The GCF is $5a^3b$.
>   Lowest power of b is 1: b^1

Skill Practice   Find the GCF.

3. $10z^3$, $15z^5$, $40z$ **4.** $6w^3y^5$, $21w^4y^2$

Example 3   **Identifying the Greatest Common Factor**

Find the GCF of the terms $8c^2d^7e$ and $6c^3d^4$.

Solution:

$8c^2d^7e = 2^3c^2d^7e$
$6c^3d^4 = 2 \cdot 3c^3d^4$ The common factors are 2, c, and d.

The lowest power of 2 is 1: 2^1
The lowest power of c is 2: c^2 The GCF is $2c^2d^4$.
The lowest power of d is 4: d^4

Skill Practice   Find the GCF.

5. $9m^2np^8$, $15n^4p^5$

Sometimes polynomials share a common binomial factor, as shown in Example 4.

Answers

3. $5z$ **4.** $3w^3y^2$
5. $3np^5$

418   Chapter 6   Factoring Polynomials

> **Example 4**   **Identifying the Greatest Common Binomial Factor**
>
> Find the greatest common factor of the terms $3x(a + b)$ and $2y(a + b)$.
>
> **Solution:**
>
> $\left. \begin{array}{l} 3x(a + b) \\ 2y(a + b) \end{array} \right\}$ The only common factor is the binomial $(a + b)$.
>
> The GCF is $(a + b)$.

Skill Practice Find the GCF.

  6. $a(x + 2)$ and $b(x + 2)$

2. Factoring out the Greatest Common Factor

The process of factoring a polynomial is the reverse process of multiplying polynomials. Both operations use the distributive property: $ab + ac = a(b + c)$.

Multiply

$$5y(y^2 + 3y + 1) = 5y(y^2) + 5y(3y) + 5y(1)$$
$$= 5y^3 + 15y^2 + 5y$$

Factor

$$5y^3 + 15y^2 + 5y = 5y(y^2) + 5y(3y) + 5y(1)$$
$$= 5y(y^2 + 3y + 1)$$

> **Factoring out the Greatest Common Factor**
>
> **Step 1**   Identify the GCF of all terms of the polynomial.
> **Step 2**   Write each term as the product of the GCF and another factor.
> **Step 3**   Use the distributive property to remove the GCF.
> *Note:* To check the factorization, multiply the polynomials to remove parentheses.

> **Example 5**   **Factoring out the Greatest Common Factor**
>
> Factor out the GCF.
>
>   **a.** $4x - 20$ **b.** $6w^2 + 3w$
>
> **Solution:**
>
>   **a.** $4x - 20$ The GCF is 4.
>
> $= 4(x) - 4(5)$ Write each term as the product of the GCF and another factor.
>
> $= 4(x - 5)$ Use the distributive property to factor out the GCF.

> **TIP:** Any factoring problem can be checked by multiplying the factors:
>
> Check: $4(x - 5) = 4x - 20$ ✓

Answer

6. $(x + 2)$

b. $6w^2 + 3w$ The GCF is $3w$.

$= 3w(2w) + 3w(1)$ Write each term as the product of $3w$ and another factor.

$= 3w(2w + 1)$ Use the distributive property to factor out the GCF.

Check: $3w(2w + 1) = 6w^2 + 3w$ ✓

Avoiding Mistakes

In Example 5(b), the GCF, $3w$, is equal to one of the terms of the polynomial. In such a case, you must leave a 1 in place of that term after the GCF is factored out.

Skill Practice Factor out the GCF.

7. $6w + 18$ **8.** $21m^3 - 7m$

Example 6   **Factoring out the Greatest Common Factor**

Factor out the GCF.

a. $15y^3 + 12y^4$ **b.** $9a^4b - 18a^5b + 27a^6b$

Solution:

a. $15y^3 + 12y^4$ The GCF is $3y^3$.

$= 3y^3(5) + 3y^3(4y)$ Write each term as the product of $3y^3$ and another factor.

$= 3y^3(5 + 4y)$ Use the distributive property to factor out the GCF.

Check: $3y^3(5 + 4y) = 15y^3 + 12y^4$ ✓

TIP: When factoring out the GCF from a polynomial, the terms within parentheses are found by dividing the original terms by the GCF. For example:

$$15y^3 + 12y^4 \quad \text{The GCF is } 3y^3.$$

$$\frac{15y^3}{3y^3} = 5 \quad \text{and} \quad \frac{12y^4}{3y^3} = 4y$$

Thus, $15y^3 + 12y^4 = 3y^3(5 + 4y)$

b. $9a^4b - 18a^5b + 27a^6b$ The GCF is $9a^4b$.

$= 9a^4b(1) - 9a^4b(2a) + 9a^4b(3a^2)$ Write each term as the product of $9a^4b$ and another factor.

$= 9a^4b(1 - 2a + 3a^2)$ Use the distributive property to factor out the GCF.

Check: $9a^4b(1 - 2a + 3a^2)$

$= 9a^4b - 18a^5b + 27a^6b$ ✓

Avoiding Mistakes

The GCF is $9a^4b$, not $3a^4b$. The expression $3a^4b(3 - 6a + 9a^2)$ is not factored completely.

Skill Practice Factor out the GCF.

9. $9y^2 - 6y^5$ **10.** $50s^3t - 40st^2 + 10st$

The greatest common factor of the polynomial $2x + 5y$ is 1. If we factor out the GCF, we have $1(2x + 5y)$. A polynomial whose only factors are itself and 1 is called a **prime polynomial**.

Answers

7. $6(w + 3)$
8. $7m(3m^2 - 1)$
9. $3y^2(3 - 2y^3)$
10. $10st(5s^2 - 4t + 1)$

3. Factoring out a Negative Factor

Usually it is advantageous to factor out the *opposite* of the GCF when the leading coefficient of the polynomial is negative. This is demonstrated in Example 7. Notice that this *changes the signs* of the remaining terms inside the parentheses.

> **Example 7**   **Factoring out a Negative Factor**
>
> Factor out -3 from the polynomial $-3x^2 + 6x - 33$.
>
> **Solution:**
>
> $\quad -3x^2 + 6x - 33$ The GCF is 3. However, in this case, we will factor out the *opposite* of the GCF, -3.
>
> $\quad = -3(x^2) + (-3)(-2x) + (-3)(11)$ Write each term as the product of -3 and another factor.
>
> $\quad = -3[x^2 + (-2x) + 11]$ Factor out -3.
>
> $\quad = -3(x^2 - 2x + 11)$ Simplify. Notice that each sign within the trinomial has changed.
>
> $\quad$ Check: $-3(x^2 - 2x + 11) = -3x^2 + 6x - 33$ ✓
>
> ---
>
> **Skill Practice**   Factor out -2 from the polynomial.
>
> **11.** $-2x^2 - 10x + 16$

> **Example 8**   **Factoring out a Negative Factor**
>
> Factor out the quantity $-4pq$ from the polynomial $-12p^3q - 8p^2q^2 + 4pq^3$.
>
> **Solution:**
>
> $\quad -12p^3q - 8p^2q^2 + 4pq^3$ The GCF is $4pq$. However, in this case, we will factor out the *opposite* of the GCF, $-4pq$.
>
> $\quad = -4pq(3p^2) + (-4pq)(2pq) + (-4pq)(-q^2)$ Write each term as the product of $-4pq$ and another factor.
>
> $\quad = -4pq[3p^2 + 2pq + (-q^2)]$ Factor out $-4pq$. Notice that each sign within the trinomial has changed.
>
> $\quad = -4pq(3p^2 + 2pq - q^2)$ To verify that this is the correct factorization and that the signs are correct, multiply the factors.
>
> $\quad$ Check: $-4pq(3p^2 + 2pq - q^2) = -12p^3q - 8p^2q^2 + 4pq^3$ ✓
>
> ---
>
> **Skill Practice**   Factor out $-5xy$ from the polynomial.
>
> **12.** $-10x^2y + 5xy - 15xy^2$

4. Factoring out a Binomial Factor

The distributive property can also be used to factor out a common factor that consists of more than one term, as shown in Example 9.

Answers

11. $-2(x^2 + 5x - 8)$

12. $-5xy(2x - 1 + 3y)$

Example 9 **Factoring out a Binomial Factor**

Factor out the GCF. $2w(x + 3) - 5(x + 3)$

Solution:

$2w(x + 3) - 5(x + 3)$ The greatest common factor is the quantity $(x + 3)$.

$= (x + 3)(2w - 5)$ Use the distributive property to factor out the GCF.

Skill Practice Factor out the GCF.

13. $8y(a + b) + 9(a + b)$

5. Factoring by Grouping

When two binomials are multiplied, the product before simplifying contains four terms. For example:

$$(x + 4)(3a + 2b) = (x + 4)(3a) + (x + 4)(2b)$$

$$= (x + 4)(3a) + (x + 4)(2b)$$

$$= 3ax + 12a + 2bx + 8b$$

In Example 10, we learn how to reverse this process. That is, given a four-term polynomial, we will factor it as a product of two binomials. The process is called *factoring by grouping*.

> **Factoring by Grouping**
>
> To factor a four-term polynomial by grouping:
>
> **Step 1** Identify and factor out the GCF from all four terms.
> **Step 2** Factor out the GCF from the first pair of terms. Factor out the GCF from the second pair of terms. (Sometimes it is necessary to factor out the opposite of the GCF.)
> **Step 3** If the two terms share a common binomial factor, factor out the binomial factor.

Example 10 **Factoring by Grouping**

Factor by grouping. $3ax + 12a + 2bx + 8b$

Solution:

$3ax + 12a + 2bx + 8b$ **Step 1:** Identify and factor out the GCF from all four terms. In this case, the GCF is 1.

$= 3ax + 12a \mid + 2bx + 8b$ Group the first pair of terms and the second pair of terms.

Answer

13. $(a + b)(8y + 9)$

422   Chapter 6   Factoring Polynomials

$= 3a(x + 4) + 2b(x + 4)$ **Step 2:** Factor out the GCF from each pair of terms. *Note:* The two terms now share a common binomial factor of $(x + 4)$.

$= (x + 4)(3a + 2b)$ **Step 3:** Factor out the common binomial factor.

Check: $(x + 4)(3a + 2b) = 3ax + 2bx + 12a + 8b$ ✓

Note: Step 2 results in two terms with a common binomial factor. If the two binomials are different, step 3 cannot be performed. In such a case, the original polynomial may not be factorable by grouping, or different pairs of terms may need to be grouped and inspected.

Skill Practice Factor by grouping.

14. $5x + 10y + ax + 2ay$

TIP: One frequently asked question when factoring is whether the order can be switched between the factors. The answer is yes. Because multiplication is commutative, the order in which the factors are written does not matter.

$$(x + 4)(3a + 2b) = (3a + 2b)(x + 4)$$

Example 11   **Factoring by Grouping**

Factor by grouping. $ax + ay - x - y$

Solution:

$ax + ay - x - y$ **Step 1:** Identify and factor out the GCF from all four terms. In this case, the GCF is 1.

$= ax + ay \mid - x - y$ Group the first pair of terms and the second pair of terms.

$= a(x + y) - 1(x + y)$ **Step 2:** Factor out a from the first pair of terms.

Factor out -1 from the second pair of terms. (This causes sign changes within the second parentheses.) The terms in parentheses now match.

$= (x + y)(a - 1)$ **Step 3:** Factor out the common binomial factor.

Check: $(x + y)(a - 1) = x(a) + x(-1) + y(a) + y(-1)$
$= ax - x + ay - y$ ✓

Avoiding Mistakes

In step 2, the expression $a(x + y) - (x + y)$ is not yet factored completely because it is a *difference*, not a product. To factor the expression, you must carry it one step further.

$a(x + y) - \mathbf{1}(x + y)$
$= (x + y)(a - 1)$

The factored form must be represented as a product.

Skill Practice Factor by grouping.

15. $tu - tv - u + v$

Answers
14. $(x + 2y)(5 + a)$
15. $(u - v)(t - 1)$

| Example 12 | **Factoring by Grouping** |

Factor by grouping. $16w^4 - 40w^3 - 12w^2 + 30w$

Solution:

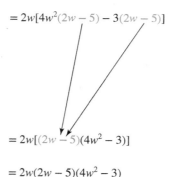

$16w^4 - 40w^3 - 12w^2 + 30w$

$= 2w[8w^3 - 20w^2 - 6w + 15]$

Step 1: Identify and factor out the GCF from all four terms. In this case, the GCF is $2w$.

$= 2w[8w^3 - 20w^2 \; | \; - 6w + 15]$

Group the first pair of terms and the second pair of terms.

$= 2w[4w^2(2w - 5) - 3(2w - 5)]$

Step 2: Factor out $4w^2$ from the first pair of terms.

Factor out -3 from the second pair of terms. (This causes sign changes within the second parentheses.) The terms in parentheses now match.

$= 2w[(2w - 5)(4w^2 - 3)]$

Step 3: Factor out the common binomial factor.

$= 2w(2w - 5)(4w^2 - 3)$

Skill Practice Factor by grouping.

16. $3ab^2 + 6b^2 - 12ab - 24b$

Answer

16. $3b(a + 2)(b - 4)$

Practice Exercises

Study Skills Exercise

> The final exam is just around the corner. Your old tests and quizzes provide good material to study for the final exam. Use your old tests to make a list of the chapters on which you need to concentrate. Ask your professor for help if there are still concepts that you do not understand.

Vocabulary and Key Concepts

1. **a.** Factoring a polynomial means to write it as a _____ of two or more polynomials.

   b. The prime factorization of a number consists of only _____ factors.

   c. The _____ _____ _____ (GCF) of two or more integers is the largest whole number that is a factor of each integer.

   d. A polynomial whose only factors are 1 and itself is called a _____ polynomial.

   e. The first step toward factoring a polynomial is to factor out the _____ _____ _____.

   f. To factor a four-term polynomial, we try the process of factoring by _____.

Concept 1: Identifying the Greatest Common Factor

2. List all the factors of 24.

424   **Chapter 6**   Factoring Polynomials

For Exercises 3–14, identify the greatest common factor. **(See Examples 1–4.)**

3. 28, 63

4. 24, 40

5. 42, 30, 60

6. 20, 52, 32

7. $3xy, 7y$

8. $10mn, 11n$

9. $12w^3z, 16w^2z$

10. $20cd, 15c^3d$

11. $8x^3y^4z^2, 12xy^5z^4, 6x^2y^8z^3$

12. $15r^2s^2t^5, 5r^3s^4t^3, 30r^4s^3t^2$

13. $7(x - y), 9(x - y)$

14. $(2a - b), 3(2a - b)$

Concept 2: Factoring out the Greatest Common Factor

15.   **a.** Use the distributive property to multiply $3(x - 2y)$.

     b. Use the distributive property to factor $3x - 6y$.

16.   **a.** Use the distributive property to multiply $a^2(5a + b)$.

     b. Use the distributive property to factor $5a^3 + a^2b$.

For Exercises 17–36, factor out the GCF. **(See Examples 5–6.)**

17. $4p + 12$

18. $3q - 15$

19. $5c^2 - 10c + 15$

20. $16d^3 + 24d^2 + 32d$

21. $x^5 + x^3$

22. $y^2 - y^3$

23. $t^4 - 4t + 8t^2$

24. $7r^3 - r^5 + r^4$

25. $2ab + 4a^3b$

26. $5u^3v^2 - 5uv$

27. $38x^2y - 19x^2y^4$

28. $100a^5b^3 + 16a^2b$

29. $6x^3y^5 - 18xy^9z$

30. $15mp^7q^4 + 12m^4q^3$

31. $5 + 7y^3$

32. $w^3 - 5u^3v^2$

33. $42p^3q^2 + 14pq^2 - 7p^4q^4$

34. $8m^2n^3 - 24m^2n^2 + 4m^3n$

35. $t^5 + 2rt^3 - 3t^4 + 4r^2t^2$

36. $u^2v + 5u^3v^2 - 2u^2 + 8uv$

Concept 3: Factoring out a Negative Factor

37. For the polynomial $-2x^3 - 4x^2 + 8x$

     a. Factor out $-2x$.   **b.** Factor out $2x$.

38. For the polynomial $-9y^5 + 3y^3 - 12y$

     a. Factor out $-3y$.   **b.** Factor out $3y$.

39. Factor out -1 from the polynomial. $-8t^2 - 9t - 2$

40. Factor out -1 from the polynomial. $-6x^3 - 2x - 5$

For Exercises 41–46, factor out the opposite of the greatest common factor. **(See Examples 7–8.)**

41. $-15p^3 - 30p^2$

42. $-24m^3 - 12m^4$

43. $-3m^4n^2 + 6m^2n - 9mn^2$

44. $-12p^3t + 2p^2t^3 + 6pt^2$

45. $-7x - 6y - 2z$

46. $-4a + 5b - c$

Concept 4: Factoring out a Binomial Factor

For Exercises 47–52, factor out the GCF. **(See Example 9.)**

47. $13(a + 6) - 4b(a + 6)$

48. $7(x^2 + 1) - y(x^2 + 1)$

49. $8v(w^2 - 2) + (w^2 - 2)$

50. $t(r + 2) + (r + 2)$

51. $21x(x + 3) + 7x^2(x + 3)$

52. $5y^3(y - 2) - 15y(y - 2)$

Concept 5: Factoring by Grouping

For Exercises 53–72, factor by grouping. **(See Examples 10–11.)**

53. $8a^2 - 4ab + 6ac - 3bc$

54. $4x^3 + 3x^2y + 4xy^2 + 3y^3$

55. $3q + 3p + qr + pr$

56. $xy - xz + 7y - 7z$

57. $6x^2 + 3x + 4x + 2$

58. $4y^2 + 8y + 7y + 14$

59. $2t^2 + 6t - t - 3$

60. $2p^2 - p - 2p + 1$

61. $6y^2 - 2y - 9y + 3$

62. $5a^2 + 30a - 2a - 12$

63. $b^4 + b^3 - 4b - 4$

64. $8w^5 + 12w^2 - 10w^3 - 15$

65. $3j^2k + 15k + j^2 + 5$

66. $2ab^2 - 6ac + b^2 - 3c$

67. $14w^6x^6 + 7w^6 - 2x^6 - 1$

68. $18p^4x - 4x - 9p^5 + 2p$

69. $ay + bx + by + ax$
(*Hint:* Rearrange the terms.)

70. $2c + 3ay + ac + 6y$

71. $vw^2 - 3 + w - 3wv$

72. $2x^2 + 6m + 12 + x^2m$

Mixed Exercises

For Exercises 73–78, factor out the GCF first. Then factor by grouping. **(See Example 12.)**

73. $15x^4 + 15x^2y^2 + 10x^3y + 10xy^3$

74. $2a^3b - 4a^2b + 32ab - 64b$

75. $4abx - 4b^2x - 4ab + 4b^2$

76. $p^2q - pq^2 - rp^2q + rpq^2$

77. $6st^2 - 18st - 6t^4 + 18t^3$

78. $15j^3 - 10j^2k - 15j^2k^2 + 10jk^3$

79. The formula $P = 2l + 2w$ represents the perimeter, P, of a rectangle given the length, l, and the width, w. Factor out the GCF and write an equivalent formula in factored form.

80. The formula $P = 2a + 2b$ represents the perimeter, P, of a parallelogram given the base, b, and an adjacent side, a. Factor out the GCF and write an equivalent formula in factored form.

81. The formula $S = 2\pi r^2 + 2\pi rh$ represents the surface area, S, of a cylinder with radius, r, and height, h. Factor out the GCF and write an equivalent formula in factored form.

82. The formula $A = P + Prt$ represents the total amount of money, A, in an account that earns simple interest at a rate, r, for t years. Factor out the GCF and write an equivalent formula in factored form.

Expanding Your Skills

83. Factor out $\frac{1}{7}$ from $\frac{1}{7}x^2 + \frac{3}{7}x - \frac{5}{7}$.

84. Factor out $\frac{1}{5}$ from $\frac{6}{5}y^2 - \frac{4}{5}y + \frac{1}{5}$.

85. Factor out $\frac{1}{4}$ from $\frac{5}{4}w^2 + \frac{3}{4}w + \frac{9}{4}$.

86. Factor out $\frac{1}{6}$ from $\frac{1}{6}p^2 - \frac{3}{6}p + \frac{5}{6}$.

87. Write a polynomial that has a GCF of $3x$. (Answers may vary.)

88. Write a polynomial that has a GCF of $7y$. (Answers may vary.)

89. Write a polynomial that has a GCF of $4p^2q$. (Answers may vary.)

90. Write a polynomial that has a GCF of $2ab^2$. (Answers may vary.)

Section 6.2   Factoring Trinomials of the Form $x^2 + bx + c$

Concept

1. Factoring Trinomials with a Leading Coefficient of 1

1. Factoring Trinomials with a Leading Coefficient of 1

We have already learned how to multiply two binomials. We also saw that such a product often results in a trinomial. For example:

$$(x + 3)(x + 7) = x^2 + \underline{7x + 3x} + 21 = x^2 + 10x + 21$$

Product of first terms

Product of last terms

Sum of products of inner terms and outer terms

In this section, we want to reverse the process. That is, given a trinomial, we want to *factor* it as a product of two binomials. In particular, we begin our study with the case in which a trinomial has a leading coefficient of 1.

Consider the quadratic trinomial $x^2 + bx + c$. To produce a leading term of x^2, we can construct binomials of the form $(x +)(x +)$. The remaining terms can be obtained from two integers, p and q, whose product is c and whose sum is b.

Factors of c

$$x^2 + bx + c = (x + p)(x + q) = x^2 + qx + px + pq$$
$$= x^2 + \underline{(q + p)}x + \underline{pq}$$

Sum $= b$ Product $= c$

This process is demonstrated in Example 1.

Example 1   Factoring a Trinomial of the Form $x^2 + bx + c$

Factor. $x^2 + 4x - 45$

Solution:

$$x^2 + 4x - 45 = (x + \square)(x + \square)$$

The product of the first terms in the binomials must equal the leading term of the trinomial $x \cdot x = x^2$.

We must fill in the blanks with two integers whose product is -45 and whose sum is 4. The factors must have opposite signs to produce a negative product. The possible factorizations of -45 are:

Product $= -45$	Sum
$-1 \cdot 45$	44
$-3 \cdot 15$	12
$-5 \cdot 9$	4
$-9 \cdot 5$	-4
$-15 \cdot 3$	-12
$-45 \cdot 1$	-44

$$x^2 + 4x - 45 = (x + \square)(x + \square)$$

$$= [x + (-5)](x + 9) \qquad \text{Fill in the blanks with } -5 \text{ and } 9.$$

$$= (x - 5)(x + 9) \qquad \text{Factored form}$$

Check:

$$(x - 5)(x + 9) = x^2 + 9x - 5x - 45$$

$$= x^2 + 4x - 45 \checkmark$$

Skill Practice Factor.

1. $x^2 - 5x - 14$

Multiplication of polynomials is a commutative operation. Therefore, in Example 1, we can express the factorization as $(x - 5)(x + 9)$ or as $(x + 9)(x - 5)$.

Example 2   **Factoring a Trinomial of the Form $x^2 + bx + c$**

Factor. $w^2 - 15w + 50$

Solution:

$$w^2 - 15w + 50 = (w + \square)(w + \square) \qquad \text{The product } w \cdot w = w^2.$$

Find two integers whose product is 50 and whose sum is -15. To form a positive product, the factors must be either both positive or both negative. The sum must be negative, so we will choose negative factors of 50.

Product = 50	**Sum**
$(-1)(-50)$	-51
$(-2)(-25)$	-27
$(-5)(-10)$	-15

$$w^2 - 15w + 50 = (w + \square)(w + \square)$$

$$= [w + (-5)][w + (-10)]$$

$$= (w - 5)(w - 10) \qquad \text{Factored form}$$

Check:

$$(w - 5)(w - 10) = w^2 - 10w - 5w + 50$$

$$= w^2 - 15w + 50 \checkmark$$

Skill Practice Factor.

2. $z^2 - 16z + 48$

TIP: Practice will help you become proficient in factoring polynomials. As you do your homework, keep these important guidelines in mind:

- To factor a trinomial, write the trinomial in descending order such as $x^2 + bx + c$.
- For all factoring problems, always factor out the GCF from all terms first.

Answers

1. $(x - 7)(x + 2)$
2. $(z - 4)(z - 12)$

Furthermore, we offer the following rules for determining the signs within the binomial factors.

Sign Rules for Factoring Trinomials

Given the trinomial $x^2 + bx + c$, the signs within the binomial factors are determined as follows:

Case 1 If c is *positive*, then the signs in the binomials must be the same (either both positive or both negative). The correct choice is determined by the middle term. If the middle term is positive, then both signs must be positive. If the middle term is negative, then both signs must be negative.

c is positive.

$$x^2 + 6x + 8$$
$$(x + 2)(x + 4)$$
Same signs

c is positive.

$$x^2 - 6x + 8$$
$$(x - 2)(x - 4)$$
Same signs

Case 2 If c is *negative*, then the signs in the binomials must be different.

c is negative.

$$x^2 + 2x - 35$$
$$(x + 7)(x - 5)$$
Different signs

c is negative.

$$x^2 - 2x - 35$$
$$(x - 7)(x + 5)$$
Different signs

Example 3   **Factoring Trinomials**

Factor.   **a.** $-8p - 48 + p^2$ **b.** $-40t - 30t^2 + 10t^3$

Solution:

a. $-8p - 48 + p^2$

$= p^2 - 8p - 48$ Write in descending order.

$= (p \ \square)(p \ \square)$ Find two integers whose product is -48 and whose sum is -8. The numbers are -12 and 4.

$= (p - 12)(p + 4)$ Factored form

b. $-40t - 30t^2 + 10t^3$

$= 10t^3 - 30t^2 - 40t$ Write in descending order.

$= 10t(t^2 - 3t - 4)$ Factor out the GCF.

$= 10t(t \ \square)(t \ \square)$ Find two integers whose product is -4 and whose sum is -3. The numbers are -4 and 1.

$= 10t(t - 4)(t + 1)$ Factored form

Skill Practice Factor.

3. $-5w + w^2 - 6$ **4.** $30y^3 + 2y^4 + 112y^2$

Answers

3. $(w - 6)(w + 1)$

4. $2y^2(y + 8)(y + 7)$

| **Example 4** | **Factoring Trinomials** |

Factor.   **a.** $-a^2 + 6a - 8$ **b.** $-2c^2 - 22cd - 60d^2$

Solution:

a. $-a^2 + 6a - 8$

$= -1(a^2 - 6a + 8)$

It is generally easier to factor a trinomial with a *positive* leading coefficient. Therefore, we will factor out -1 from all terms.

$= -1(a \ \square)(a \ \square)$

Find two integers whose product is 8 and whose sum is -6. The numbers are -4 and -2.

$= -1(a - 4)(a - 2)$

$= -(a - 4)(a - 2)$

> **Avoiding Mistakes**
>
> Recall that factoring out -1 from a polynomial changes the signs of all terms within parentheses.

b. $-2c^2 - 22cd - 60d^2$

$= -2(c^2 + 11cd + 30d^2)$ Factor out -2.

$= -2(c \ \square d)(c \ \square d)$ Notice that the second pair of terms has a factor of d. This will produce a product of d^2.

$= -2(c + 5d)(c + 6d)$ Find two integers whose product is 30 and whose sum is 11. The numbers are 5 and 6.

Skill Practice Factor.

5. $-x^2 + x + 12$ **6.** $-3a^2 + 15ab - 12b^2$

To factor a trinomial of the form $x^2 + bx + c$, we must find two integers whose product is c and whose sum is b. If no such integers exist, then the trinomial is prime.

| **Example 5** | **Factoring Trinomials** |

Factor. $x^2 - 13x + 14$

Solution:

$x^2 - 13x + 14$ The trinomial is in descending order. The GCF is 1.

$= (x \ \square)(x \ \square)$ Find two integers whose product is 14 and whose sum is -13. No such integers exist.

The trinomial $x^2 - 13x + 14$ is prime.

Skill Practice Factor.

7. $x^2 - 7x + 28$

430   **Chapter 6**   Factoring Polynomials

Section 6.2 Practice Exercises

Vocabulary and Key Concepts

1. a. Given a trinomial $x^2 + bx + c$, if c is positive, then the signs in the binomial factors are either both _____ or both negative.

b. Given a trinomial $x^2 + bx + c$, if c is negative, then the signs in the binomial factors are (choose one: both positive, both negative, different).

c. Which is the correct factored form of $x^2 - 7x - 44$? The product $(x + 4)(x - 11)$ or $(x - 11)(x + 4)$?

d. Which is the complete factorization of $3x^2 + 24x + 36$? The product $(3x + 6)(x + 6)$ or $3(x + 6)(x + 2)$?

Review Exercises

For Exercises 2–6, factor completely.

2. $9a^6b^3 - 27a^3b^6 - 3a^2b^2$

3. $3t(t - 5) - 6(t - 5)$

4. $4(3x - 2) + 8x(3x - 2)$

5. $ax + 2bx - 5a - 10b$

6. $m^2 - mx - 3pm + 3px$

Concept 1: Factoring Trinomials with a Leading Coefficient of 1

For Exercises 7–20, factor completely. **(See Examples 1, 2, and 5.)**

7. $x^2 + 10x + 16$

8. $y^2 + 18y + 80$

9. $z^2 - 11z + 18$

10. $w^2 - 7w + 12$

11. $z^2 - 3z - 18$

12. $w^2 + 4w - 12$

13. $p^2 - 3p - 40$

14. $a^2 - 10a + 9$

15. $t^2 + 6t - 40$

16. $m^2 - 12m + 11$

17. $x^2 - 3x + 20$

18. $y^2 + 6y + 18$

19. $n^2 + 8n + 16$

20. $v^2 + 10v + 25$

For Exercises 21–24, assume that b and c represent positive integers.

21. When factoring a polynomial of the form $x^2 + bx + c$, pick an appropriate combination of signs.

a. (+)(+)   **b.** (−)(−)   **c.** (+)(−)

22. When factoring a polynomial of the form $x^2 + bx - c$, pick an appropriate combination of signs.

a. (+)(+)   **b.** (−)(−)   **c.** (+)(−)

23. When factoring a polynomial of the form $x^2 - bx - c$, pick an appropriate combination of signs.

a. (+)(+)   **b.** (−)(−)   **c.** (+)(−)

24. When factoring a polynomial of the form $x^2 - bx + c$, pick an appropriate combination of signs.

a. (+)(+)   **b.** (−)(−)   **c.** (+)(−)

25. Which is the correct factorization of $y^2 - y - 12$, the product $(y - 4)(y + 3)$ or $(y + 3)(y - 4)$? Explain.

26. Which is the correct factorization of $x^2 + 14x + 13$, the product $(x + 13)(x + 1)$ or $(x + 1)(x + 13)$? Explain.

27. Which is the correct factorization of $w^2 + 2w + 1$, the product $(w + 1)(w + 1)$ or $(w + 1)^2$? Explain.

28. Which is the correct factorization of $z^2 - 4z + 4$, the product $(z - 2)(z - 2)$ or $(z - 2)^2$? Explain.

29. In what order should a trinomial be written before attempting to factor it?

30. Once a polynomial is written in descending order, what is the next step to factor the polynomial?

For Exercises 31–66, factor completely. Be sure to factor out the GCF when necessary. **(See Examples 3–4.)**

31. $-13x + x^2 - 30$

32. $12y - 160 + y^2$

33. $-18w + 65 + w^2$

34. $17t + t^2 + 72$

35. $22t + t^2 + 72$

36. $10q - 1200 + q^2$

37. $3x^2 - 30x - 72$

38. $2z^2 + 4z - 198$

39. $8p^3 - 40p^2 + 32p$

40. $5w^4 - 35w^3 + 50w^2$

41. $y^4z^2 - 12y^3z^2 + 36y^2z^2$

42. $t^4u^2 + 6t^3u^2 + 9t^2u^2$

43. $-x^2 + 10x - 24$

44. $-y^2 - 12y - 35$

45. $-5a^2 + 5ax + 30x^2$

46. $-2m^2 + 10mn + 12n^2$

47. $-4 - 2c^2 - 6c$

48. $-40d - 30 - 10d^2$

49. $x^3y^3 - 19x^2y^3 + 60xy^3$

50. $y^2z^5 + 17yz^5 + 60z^5$

51. $12p^2 - 96p + 84$

52. $5w^2 - 40w - 45$

53. $-2m^2 + 22m - 20$

54. $-3x^2 - 36x - 81$

55. $c^2 + 6cd + 5d^2$

56. $x^2 + 8xy + 12y^2$

57. $a^2 - 9ab + 14b^2$

58. $m^2 - 15mn + 44n^2$

59. $a^2 + 4a + 18$

60. $b^2 - 6a + 15$

61. $2q + q^2 - 63$

62. $-32 - 4t + t^2$

63. $x^2 + 20x + 100$

64. $z^2 - 24z + 144$

65. $t^2 + 18t - 40$

66. $d^2 + 2d - 99$

67. A student factored a trinomial as $(2x - 4)(x - 3)$. The instructor did not give full credit. Why?

68. A student factored a trinomial as $(y + 2)(5y - 15)$. The instructor did not give full credit. Why?

69. What polynomial factors as $(x - 4)(x + 13)$?

70. What polynomial factors as $(q - 7)(q + 10)$?

71. Raul purchased a parcel of land in the country. The given expressions represent the lengths of the boundary lines of his property.

    a. Write the perimeter of the land as a polynomial in simplified form.

    b. Write the polynomial from part (a) in factored form.

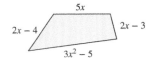

72. Jamison painted a mural in the shape of a triangle on the wall of a building. The given expressions represent the lengths of the sides of the triangle.

    a. Write the perimeter of the triangle as a polynomial in simplified form.

    b. Write the polynomial in factored form.

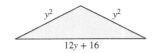

432   **Chapter 6** Factoring Polynomials

Expanding Your Skills

For Exercises 73–76, factor completely.

73. $x^4 + 10x^2 + 9$ **74.** $y^4 + 4y^2 - 21$ **75.** $w^4 + 2w^2 - 15$ **76.** $p^4 - 13p^2 + 40$

77. Find all integers, b, that make the trinomial $x^2 + bx + 6$ factorable.

78. Find all integers, b, that make the trinomial $x^2 + bx + 10$ factorable.

79. Find a value of c that makes the trinomial $x^2 + 6x + c$ factorable.

80. Find a value of c that makes the trinomial $x^2 + 8x + c$ factorable.

Section 6.3   Factoring Trinomials: Trial-and-Error Method

Concept

1. Factoring Trinomials by the Trial-and-Error Method

In this section we will learn how to factor a trinomial of the form $ax^2 + bx + c = 0$ (where $a \neq 0$). The method presented here is called the trial-and-error method.

1. Factoring Trinomials by the Trial-and-Error Method

To understand the basis of factoring trinomials of the form $ax^2 + bx + c$, first consider the multiplication of two binomials:

$$\overset{\text{Product of } 2 \cdot 1 \qquad \text{Product of } 3 \cdot 2}{(2x + 3)(1x + 2) = 2x^2 + \underline{\mathbf{4x + 3x}} + 6 = 2x^2 + 7x + 6}$$

Sum of products of inner
terms and outer terms

To factor the trinomial, $2x^2 + 7x + 6$, this operation is reversed.

$$\overset{\text{Factors of 2}}{2x^2 + 7x + 6 = (\square x \quad \square)(\square x \quad \square)}$$

Factors of 6

We need to fill in the blanks so that the product of the first terms in the binomials is $2x^2$ and the product of the last terms in the binomials is 6. Furthermore, the factors of $2x^2$ and 6 must be chosen so that the sum of the products of the inner terms and outer terms equals $7x$.

To produce the product $2x^2$, we might try the factors $2x$ and x within the binomials:

$$(2x \quad \square)(x \quad \square)$$

To produce a product of 6, the remaining terms in the binomials must either both be positive or both be negative. To produce a positive middle term, we will try positive factors of 6 in the remaining blanks until the correct product is found. The possibilities are $1 \cdot 6, 2 \cdot 3, 6 \cdot 1,$ and $3 \cdot 2$.

$(2x + 1)(x + 6) = 2x^2 + 12x + 1x + 6 = 2x^2 + 13x + 6$	Wrong middle term
$(2x + 2)(x + 3) = 2x^2 + 6x + 2x + 6 = 2x^2 + 8x + 6$	Wrong middle term
$(2x + 6)(x + 1) = 2x^2 + 2x + 6x + 6 = 2x^2 + 8x + 6$	Wrong middle term
$(2x + 3)(x + 2) = 2x^2 + 4x + 3x + 6 = 2x^2 + 7x + 6$	Correct!

The correct factorization of $2x^2 + 7x + 6$ is $(2x + 3)(x + 2)$. ✓

As this example shows, we factor a trinomial of the form $ax^2 + bx + c$ by shuffling the factors of a and c within the binomials until the correct product is obtained. However, sometimes it is not necessary to test all the possible combinations of factors. In the previous example, the GCF of the original trinomial is 1. Therefore, any binomial factor whose terms share a common factor *greater than 1* does not need to be considered. In this case, the possibilities $(2x + 2)(x + 3)$ and $(2x + 6)(x + 1)$ cannot work.

$$\underbrace{(2x + 2)}_{\substack{\text{Common} \\ \text{factor of 2}}}(x + 3) \qquad \underbrace{(2x + 6)}_{\substack{\text{Common} \\ \text{factor of 2}}}(x + 1)$$

Trial-and-Error Method to Factor $ax^2 + bx + c$

Step 1   Factor out the GCF.

Step 2   List all pairs of positive factors of a and pairs of positive factors of c. Consider the reverse order for one of the lists of factors.

Step 3   Construct two binomials of the form:

Step 4   Test each combination of factors and signs until the correct product is found.

Step 5   If no combination of factors produces the correct product, the trinomial cannot be factored further and is a *prime polynomial*.

Before we begin Example 1, keep these two important guidelines in mind:

- For any factoring problem you encounter, always factor out the GCF from all terms first.
- To factor a trinomial, write the trinomial in the form $ax^2 + bx + c$.

Example 1   Factoring a Trinomial by the Trial-and-Error Method

Factor the trinomial by the trial-and-error method. $10x^2 + 11x + 1$

Solution:

$10x^2 + 11x + 1$ **Step 1:**   Factor out the GCF from all terms. In this case, the GCF is 1.

The trinomial is written in the form $ax^2 + bx + c$.

To factor $10x^2 + 11x + 1$, two binomials must be constructed in the form:

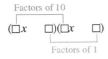

Step 2:   To produce the product $10x^2$, we might try $5x$ and $2x$, or $10x$ and $1x$. To produce a product of 1, we will try the factors $(1)(1)$ and $(-1)(-1)$.

Step 3:   Construct all possible binomial factors using different combinations of the factors of $10x^2$ and 1.

$(5x + 1)(2x + 1) = 10x^2 + 5x + 2x + 1 = 10x^2 + 7x + 1$ Wrong middle term

$(5x - 1)(2x - 1) = 10x^2 - 5x - 2x + 1 = 10x^2 - 7x + 1$ Wrong middle term

Because the numbers 1 and -1 did not produce the correct trinomial when coupled with $5x$ and $2x$, try using $10x$ and $1x$.

$(10x - 1)(1x - 1) = 10x^2 - 10x - 1x + 1 = 10x^2 - 11x + 1$ Wrong sign on the middle term

$(10x + 1)(1x + 1) = 10x^2 + 10x + 1x + 1 = 10x^2 + 11x + 1$ Correct!

Therefore, $10x^2 + 11x + 1 = (10x + 1)(x + 1)$.

Skill Practice Factor using the trial-and-error method.

1. $3b^2 + 8b + 4$

In Example 1, the factors of 1 must have the same signs to produce a positive product. Therefore, the binomial factors must both be sums or both be differences. Determining the correct signs is an important aspect of factoring trinomials. We suggest the following guidelines:

Sign Rules for the Trial-and-Error Method

Given the trinomial $ax^2 + bx + c$, $(a > 0)$, the signs can be determined as follows:

- If *c is positive*, then the signs in the binomials must be the same (either both positive or both negative). The correct choice is determined by the middle term. If the middle term is positive, then both signs must be positive. If the middle term is negative, then both signs must be negative.

c is positive	*c* is positive
↓	↓
$20x^2 + 43x + 21$	$20x^2 - 43x + 21$
$(4x + 3)(5x + 7)$	$(4x - 3)(5x - 7)$
Same signs	Same signs

- If *c is negative*, then the signs in the binomial must be different. The middle term in the trinomial determines which factor gets the positive sign and which gets the negative sign.

c is negative	*c* is negative
↓	↓
$x^2 + 3x - 28$	$x^2 - 3x - 28$
$(x + 7)(x - 4)$	$(x - 7)(x + 4)$
Different signs	Different signs

TIP: Look at the sign on the third term. If it is a sum, the signs will be the same in the two binomials. If it is a difference, the signs in the two binomials will be different: sum–same sign; difference–different signs.

Answer

1. $(3b + 2)(b + 2)$

| **Example 2** | **Factoring a Trinomial by the Trial-and-Error Method** |

Factor the trinomial. $13y - 6 + 8y^2$

Solution:

$13y - 6 + 8y^2$

$= 8y^2 + 13y - 6$ Write the polynomial in descending order.

$(\Box y \ \ \Box)(\Box y \ \ \Box)$ **Step 1:**   The GCF is 1.

Factors of 8	**Factors of 6**	

Step 2:   List the positive factors of 8 and positive factors of 6. Consider the reverse order in one list of factors.

$1 \cdot 8$ $1 \cdot 6$

$2 \cdot 4$ $2 \cdot 3$

$\left.\begin{array}{c} 3 \cdot 2 \\ 6 \cdot 1 \end{array}\right\}$ (reverse order)

Step 3:   Construct all possible binomial factors using different combinations of the factors of 8 and 6.

$\left.\begin{array}{l} (1y \ \ 1)(8y \ \ 6) \\ (1y \ \ 3)(8y \ \ 2) \\ (2y \ \ 1)(4y \ \ 6) \\ (2y \ \ 2)(4y \ \ 3) \\ (2y \ \ 3)(4y \ \ 2) \\ (2y \ \ 6)(4y \ \ 1) \end{array}\right\}$ Without regard to signs, these factorizations cannot work because the red terms in the binomials share a common factor greater than 1.

Test the remaining factorizations. Keep in mind that to produce a product of −6, the signs within the parentheses must be opposite (one positive and one negative). Also, the sum of the products of the inner terms and outer terms must be combined to form $13y$.

$(1y \ \ 6)(8y \ \ 1)$ *Incorrect.*   Wrong middle term.
Regardless of the signs, the product of inner terms, $48y$, and the product of outer terms, $1y$, cannot be combined to form the middle term $13y$.

$(1y \ \ 2)(8y \ \ 3)$ *Correct.*   The terms $16y$ and $3y$ can be combined to form the middle term $13y$, provided the signs are applied correctly. We require $+16y$ and $-3y$.

The correct factorization of $8y^2 + 13y - 6$ is $(y + 2)(8y - 3)$.

Skill Practice Factor.

2. $-25w + 6w^2 + 4$

Remember that the first step in any factoring problem is to remove the GCF. By removing the GCF, the remaining terms of the trinomial will have smaller coefficients.

Answer

2. $(6w - 1)(w - 4)$

| Example 3 | **Factoring a Trinomial by the Trial-and-Error Method** |

Factor the trinomial by the trial-and-error method. $40x^3 - 104x^2 + 10x$

Solution:

$40x^3 - 104x^2 + 10x$

$= 2x(20x^2 - 52x + 5)$ **Step 1:** The GCF is $2x$.

$= 2x(\square x \quad \square)(\square x \quad \square)$ **Step 2:** List the factors of 20 and factors of 5. Consider the reverse order in one list of factors.

TIP: Notice that when the GCF, $2x$, is removed from the original trinomial, the new trinomial has smaller coefficients. This makes the factoring process simpler. It is easier to list the factors of 20 and 5 than the factors of 40 and 10.

Factors of 20	**Factors of 5**	**Step 3:**	Construct all possible binomial factors using different combinations of the factors of 20 and factors of 5. The signs in the parentheses must both be negative.
$1 \cdot 20$	$1 \cdot 5$		
$2 \cdot 10$	$5 \cdot 1$		
$4 \cdot 5$			

$= 2x(1x - 1)(20x - 5)$
$= 2x(2x - 1)(10x - 5)$ *Incorrect.* Once the GCF has been removed from the original polynomial, the binomial factors cannot contain a GCF greater than 1.
$= 2x(4x - 1)(5x - 5)$

$= 2x(1x - 5)(20x - 1)$ *Incorrect.* Wrong middle term.

$2x(x - 5)(20x - 1)$
$= 2x(20x^2 - 1x - 100x + 5)$
$= 2x(20x^2 - 101x + 5)$

$= 2x(4x - 5)(5x - 1)$ *Incorrect.* Wrong middle term.

$2x(4x - 5)(5x - 1)$
$= 2x(20x^2 - 4x - 25x + 5)$
$= 2x(20x^2 - 29x + 5)$

$= 2x(2x - 5)(10x - 1)$ *Correct.* $2x(2x - 5)(10x - 1)$
$= 2x(20x^2 - 2x - 50x + 5)$
$= 2x(20x^2 - 52x + 5)$
$= 40x^3 - 104x^2 + 10x$

The correct factorization is $2x(2x - 5)(10x - 1)$.

Skill Practice Factor.

3. $8t^3 + 38t^2 + 24t$

Often it is easier to factor a trinomial when the leading coefficient is positive. If the leading coefficient is negative, consider factoring out the opposite of the GCF.

Answer

3. $2t(4t + 3)(t + 4)$

Example 4   **Factoring a Trinomial by the Trial-and-Error Method**

Factor. $-45x^2 - 3xy + 18y^2$

Solution:

$-45x^2 - 3xy + 18y^2$

$= -3(15x^2 + xy - 6y^2)$ **Step 1:** Factor out -3 to make the leading coefficient positive.

$= -3(\Box x \ \ \Box y)(\Box x \ \ \Box y)$ **Step 2:** List the factors of 15 and 6.

Factors of 15	**Factors of 6**
$1 \cdot 15$	$1 \cdot 6$
$3 \cdot 5$	$2 \cdot 3$
	$3 \cdot 2$
	$6 \cdot 1$

Step 3: We will construct all binomial combinations, without regard to signs first.

$-3(x \ \ y)(15x \ \ 6y)$ ⎫
$-3(x \ \ 2y)(15x \ \ 3y)$ ⎬ *Incorrect.* These combinations cannot work because
$-3(3x \ \ 3y)(5x \ \ 2y)$ ⎪ the binomials in red each contain a
$-3(3x \ \ 6y)(5x \ \ y)$ ⎭ common factor.

Test the remaining factorizations. The signs within parentheses must be opposite to produce a product of $-6y^2$. Also, the sum of the products of the inner terms and outer terms must be combined to form $1xy$.

$-3(x \ \ 3y)(15x \ \ 2y)$ *Incorrect.* Regardless of signs, $45xy$ and $2xy$ cannot be combined to equal xy.

$-3(x \ \ 6y)(15x \ \ y)$ *Incorrect.* Regardless of signs, $90xy$ and xy cannot be combined to equal xy.

$-3(3x \ \ y)(5x \ \ 6y)$ *Incorrect.* Regardless of signs, $5xy$ and $18xy$ cannot be combined to equal xy.

$-3(3x \ \ 2y)(5x \ \ 3y)$ *Correct.* The terms $10xy$ and $9xy$ can be combined to form xy provided that the signs are applied correctly. We require $10xy$ and $-9xy$.

$-3(3x + 2y)(5x - 3y)$ Factored form

Avoiding Mistakes

Do not forget to write the GCF in the final answer.

Skill Practice Factor.

4. $-4x^2 + 26xy - 40y^2$

Recall that a prime polynomial is a polynomial whose only factors are itself and 1. Not every trinomial is factorable by the methods presented in this text.

Answer

4. $-2(2x - 5y)(x - 4y)$

> **Example 5**   Factoring a Trinomial by the Trial-and-Error Method

Factor the trinomial by the trial-and-error method. $2p^2 - 8p + 3$

Solution:

$2p^2 - 8p + 3$ **Step 1:**   The GCF is 1.

$= (1p \quad \Box)(2p \quad \Box)$ **Step 2:**   List the factors of 2 and the factors of 3.

Factors of 2   **Factors of 3**   **Step 3:**   Construct all possible binomial factors
    $1 \cdot 2$ $1 \cdot 3$ using different combinations of the
                          $3 \cdot 1$ factors of 2 and 3. Because the third
                                                                        term in the trinomial is positive, both
                                                                        signs in the binomial must be the same.
                                                                        Because the middle term coefficient is
                                                                        negative, both signs will be negative.

$(p - 1)(2p - 3) = 2p^2 - 3p - 2p + 3$

$\qquad\qquad\qquad = 2p^2 - 5p + 3$ *Incorrect.*   Wrong middle term.

$(p - 3)(2p - 1) = 2p^2 - p - 6p + 3$

$\qquad\qquad\qquad = 2p^2 - 7p + 3$ *Incorrect.*   Wrong middle term.

None of the combinations of factors results in the correct product. Therefore, the polynomial $2p^2 - 8p + 3$ is prime and cannot be factored further.

Skill Practice   Factor.

5. $3a^2 + a + 4$

In Example 6, we use the trial-and-error method to factor a higher degree trinomial into two binomial factors.

> **Example 6**   Factoring a Higher Degree Trinomial

Factor the trinomial. $3x^4 + 8x^2 + 5$

Solution:

$3x^4 + 8x^2 + 5$ **Step 1:**   The GCF is 1.

$= (\Box x^2 + \Box)(\Box x^2 + \Box)$ **Step 2:**   To produce the product $3x^4$, we must use $3x^2$
                                                                        and $1x^2$. To produce a product of 5, we will
                                                                        try the factors $(1)(5)$ and $(5)(1)$.

                                                         Step 3:   Construct all possible binomial factors
                                                                        using the combinations of factors of
                                                                        $3x^4$ and 5.

$(3x^2 + 1)(x^2 + 5) = 3x^4 + 15x^2 + 1x^2 + 5 = 3x^4 + 16x^2 + 5$ Wrong middle term.

$(3x^2 + 5)(x^2 + 1) = 3x^4 + 3x^2 + 5x^2 + 5 = 3x^4 + 8x^2 + 5$ Correct!

Therefore, $3x^4 + 8x^2 + 5 = (3x^2 + 5)(x^2 + 1)$.

Skill Practice   Factor.

6. $2y^4 - y^2 - 15$

Answers

5. Prime   **6.** $(y^2 - 3)(2y^2 + 5)$

Section 6.3   Practice Exercises

Vocabulary and Key Concepts

1. **a.** Which is the correct factored form of $2x^2 - 5x - 12$, the product $(2x + 3)(x - 4)$ or $(x - 4)(2x + 3)$?

   b. Which is the complete factorization of $6x^2 - 4x - 10$, the product $(3x - 5)(2x + 2)$ or $2(3x - 5)(x + 1)$?

Review Exercises

For Exercises 2–6, factor completely.

2. $5uv^2 - 10u^2v + 25u^2v^2$

3. $mn - m - 2n + 2$

4. $5x - 10 - xy + 2y$

5. $6a^2 - 30a - 84$

6. $10b^2 + 20b - 240$

Concept 1: Factoring Trinomials by the Trial-and-Error Method

For Exercises 7–10, assume a, b, and c represent positive integers.

7. When factoring a polynomial of the form $ax^2 + bx + c$, pick an appropriate combination of signs.

   a. $(\ \ + \ \ )(\ \ + \ \ )$

   b. $(\ \ - \ \ )(\ \ - \ \ )$

   c. $(\ \ + \ \ )(\ \ - \ \ )$

8. When factoring a polynomial of the form $ax^2 - bx - c$, pick an appropriate combination of signs.

   a. $(\ \ + \ \ )(\ \ + \ \ )$

   b. $(\ \ - \ \ )(\ \ - \ \ )$

   c. $(\ \ + \ \ )(\ \ - \ \ )$

9. When factoring a polynomial of the form $ax^2 - bx + c$, pick an appropriate combination of signs.

   a. $(\ \ + \ \ )(\ \ + \ \ )$

   b. $(\ \ - \ \ )(\ \ - \ \ )$

   c. $(\ \ + \ \ )(\ \ - \ \ )$

10. When factoring a polynomial of the form $ax^2 + bx - c$, pick an appropriate combination of signs.

    a. $(\ \ + \ \ )(\ \ + \ \ )$

    b. $(\ \ - \ \ )(\ \ - \ \ )$

    c. $(\ \ + \ \ )(\ \ - \ \ )$

For Exercises 11–28, factor completely by using the trial-and-error method. **(See Examples 1, 2, and 5.)**

11. $3n^2 + 13n + 4$

12. $2w^2 + 5w - 3$

13. $2y^2 - 3y - 2$

14. $2a^2 + 7a + 6$

15. $5x^2 - 14x - 3$

16. $7y^2 + 9y - 10$

17. $12c^2 - 5c - 2$

18. $6z^2 + z - 12$

19. $-12 + 10w^2 + 37w$

20. $-10 + 10p^2 + 21p$

21. $-5q - 6 + 6q^2$

22. $17a - 2 + 3a^2$

23. $6b - 23 + 4b^2$

24. $8 + 7x^2 - 18x$

25. $-8 + 25m^2 - 10m$

26. $8q^2 + 31q - 4$

27. $6y^2 + 19xy - 20x^2$

28. $12y^2 - 73yz + 6z^2$

For Exercises 29–36, factor completely. Be sure to factor out the GCF first. **(See Examples 3–4.)**

29. $2m^2 - 12m - 80$

30. $3c^2 - 33c + 72$

31. $2y^5 + 13y^4 + 6y^3$

32. $3u^8 - 13u^7 + 4u^6$

33. $-a^2 - 15a + 34$

34. $-x^2 - 7x - 10$

35. $-80m^2 + 100mp + 30p^2$

36. $-60w^2 - 550wz + 500z^2$

For Exercises 37–42, factor the higher degree polynomial. **(See Example 6.)**

37. $x^4 + 10x^2 + 9$

38. $y^4 + 4y^2 - 21$

39. $w^4 + 2w^2 - 15$

40. $p^4 - 13p^2 + 40$

41. $2x^4 - 7x^2 - 15$

42. $5y^4 + 11y^2 + 2$

Mixed Exercises

For Exercises 43–82, factor each trinomial completely.

43. $20z - 18 - 2z^2$

44. $25t - 5t^2 - 30$

45. $42 - 13q + q^2$

46. $-5w - 24 + w^2$

47. $6t^2 + 7t - 3$

48. $4p^2 - 9p + 2$

49. $4m^2 - 20m + 25$

50. $16r^2 + 24r + 9$

51. $5c^2 - c + 2$

52. $7s^2 + 2s + 9$

53. $6x^2 - 19xy + 10y^2$

54. $15p^2 + pq - 2q^2$

55. $12m^2 + 11mn - 5n^2$

56. $4a^2 + 5ab - 6b^2$

57. $30r^2 + 5r - 10$

58. $36x^2 - 18x - 4$

59. $4s^2 - 8st + t^2$

60. $6u^2 - 10uv + 5v^2$

61. $10t^2 - 23t - 5$

62. $16n^2 + 14n + 3$

63. $14w^2 + 13w - 12$

64. $12x^2 - 16x + 5$

65. $a^2 - 10a - 24$

66. $b^2 + 6b - 7$

67. $x^2 + 9xy + 20y^2$

68. $p^2 - 13pq + 36q^2$

69. $a^2 + 21ab + 20b^2$

70. $x^2 - 17xy - 18y^2$

71. $t^2 - 10t + 21$

72. $z^2 - 15z + 36$

73. $5d^3 + 3d^2 - 10d$

74. $3y^3 - y^2 + 12y$

75. $4b^3 - 4b^2 - 80b$

76. $2w^2 + 20w + 42$

77. $x^2y^2 - 13xy^2 + 30y^2$

78. $p^2q^2 - 14pq^2 + 33q^2$

79. $-12u^3 - 22u^2 + 20u$

80. $-18z^4 + 15z^3 + 12z^2$

81. $8x^4 + 14x^2 + 3$

82. $6y^4 - 5y^2 - 4$

83. A rock is thrown straight upward from the top of a 40-ft building. Its height in feet after t seconds is given by the polynomial $-16t^2 + 12t + 40$.

   a. Calculate the height of the rock after 1 sec. ($t = 1$)

   b. Write $-16t^2 + 12t + 40$ in factored form. Then evaluate the factored form of the polynomial for $t = 1$. Is the result the same as from part (a)?

84. A baseball is thrown straight downward from the top of a 120-ft building. Its height in feet after t seconds is given by $-16t^2 - 8t + 120$.

   a. Calculate the height of the ball after 2 sec. ($t = 2$)

   b. Write $-16t^2 - 8t + 120$ in factored form. Then evaluate the factored form of the polynomial for $t = 2$. Is the result the same as from part (a)?

Expanding Your Skills

For Exercises 85–88, the two trinomials look similar but differ by one sign. Factor each trinomial and see how their factored forms differ.

85. **a.** $x^2 - 10x - 24$

   b. $x^2 - 10x + 24$

86. **a.** $x^2 - 13x - 30$

   b. $x^2 - 13x + 30$

87. **a.** $x^2 - 5x - 6$

   b. $x^2 - 5x + 6$

88. **a.** $x^2 - 10x + 9$

   b. $x^2 + 10x + 9$

Factoring Trinomials: AC-Method

We have already learned how to factor a trinomial of the form $ax^2 + bx + c = 0$ with a leading coefficient of 1. Then we learned the trial-and-error method to factor the more general case in which the leading coefficient is any integer. In this section, we provide an alternative method to factor trinomials, called the ac-method.

1. Factoring Trinomials by the AC-Method

1. Factoring Trinomials by the AC-Method

The product of two binomials results in a four-term expression that can sometimes be simplified to a trinomial. To factor the trinomial, we want to reverse the process.

Multiply:

Multiply the binomials.   Add the middle terms.

$$(2x + 3)(x + 2) = \longrightarrow 2x^2 + 4x + 3x + 6 = \longrightarrow 2x^2 + 7x + 6$$

Factor:

$$2x^2 + 7x + 6 = \longrightarrow 2x^2 + 4x + 3x + 6 = \longrightarrow (2x + 3)(x + 2)$$

Rewrite the middle term as   Factor by grouping.
a sum or difference of terms.

To factor a quadratic trinomial, $ax^2 + bx + c$, by the ac-method, we rewrite the middle term, bx, as a sum or difference of terms. The goal is to produce a four-term polynomial that can be factored by grouping. The process is outlined as follows.

AC-Method: Factoring $ax^2 + bx + c$ $(a \neq 0)$

Step 1 Factor out the GCF from all terms.

Step 2 Multiply the coefficients of the first and last terms (ac).

Step 3 Find two integers whose product is ac and whose sum is b. (If no pair of integers can be found, then the trinomial cannot be factored further and is a *prime polynomial*.)

Step 4 Rewrite the middle term, bx, as the sum of two terms whose coefficients are the integers found in step 3.

Step 5 Factor the polynomial by grouping.

The ac-method for factoring trinomials is illustrated in Example 1. However, before we begin, keep these two important guidelines in mind:

- For any factoring problem you encounter, always factor out the GCF from all terms first.
- To factor a trinomial, write the trinomial in the form $ax^2 + bx + c$.

Example 1   Factoring a Trinomial by the AC-Method

Factor the trinomial by the ac-method. $2x^2 + 7x + 6$

Solution:

$2x^2 + 7x + 6$ **Step 1:**   Factor out the GCF from all terms. In this case, the GCF is 1. The trinomial is written in the form $ax^2 + bx + c$.

$a = 2, b = 7, c = 6$ **Step 2:**   Find the product $ac = (2)(6) = 12$.

__12__	__12__
$1 \cdot 12$	$(-1)(-12)$
$2 \cdot 6$	$(-2)(-6)$
$3 \cdot 4$	$(-3)(-4)$

Step 3:   List all factors of ac and search for the pair whose sum equals the value of b. That is, list the factors of 12 and find the pair whose sum equals 7.

The numbers 3 and 4 satisfy both conditions: $3 \cdot 4 = 12$ and $3 + 4 = 7$.

$2x^2 + 7x + 6$

$= 2x^2 + 3x + 4x + 6$ **Step 4:**   Write the middle term of the trinomial as the sum of two terms whose coefficients are the selected pair of numbers: 3 and 4.

$= 2x^2 + 3x \mid + 4x + 6$ **Step 5:**   Factor by grouping.

$= x(2x + 3) + 2(2x + 3)$

$= (2x + 3)(x + 2)$

Check: $(2x + 3)(x + 2) = 2x^2 + 4x + 3x + 6$
                              $= 2x^2 + 7x + 6$ ✓

Skill Practice   Factor by the ac-method.

1. $2x^2 + 5x + 3$

TIP: One frequently asked question is whether the order matters when we rewrite the middle term of the trinomial as two terms (step 4). The answer is no. From the previous example, the two middle terms in step 4 could have been reversed to obtain the same result:

$$2x^2 + 7x + 6$$
$$= 2x^2 + 4x + 3x + 6$$
$$= 2x(x + 2) + 3(x + 2)$$
$$= (x + 2)(2x + 3)$$

This example also points out that the order in which two factors are written does not matter. The expression $(x + 2)(2x + 3)$ is equivalent to $(2x + 3)(x + 2)$ because multiplication is a commutative operation.

Answer

1. $(x + 1)(2x + 3)$

Example 2	**Factoring a Trinomial by the AC-Method**

Factor the trinomial by the ac-method. $-2x + 8x^2 - 3$

Solution:

$-2x + 8x^2 - 3$ First rewrite the polynomial in the form $ax^2 + bx + c$.

$= 8x^2 - 2x - 3$ **Step 1:** The GCF is 1.

$a = 8, b = -2, c = -3$ **Step 2:** Find the product $ac = (8)(-3) = -24$.

$\underline{-24}$	$\underline{-24}$
$-1 \cdot 24$	$-24 \cdot 1$
$-2 \cdot 12$	$-12 \cdot 2$
$-3 \cdot 8$	$-8 \cdot 3$
$-4 \cdot 6$	$-6 \cdot 4$

Step 3: List all the factors of -24 and find the pair of factors whose sum equals -2.

The numbers -6 and 4 satisfy both conditions: $(-6)(4) = -24$ and $-6 + 4 = -2$.

$= 8x^2 - 2x - 3$ **Step 4:** Write the middle term of the trinomial as two terms whose coefficients are the selected pair of numbers, -6 and 4.

$= 8x^2 - 6x + 4x - 3$

$= 8x^2 - 6x \mid + 4x - 3$ **Step 5:** Factor by grouping.

$= 2x(4x - 3) + 1(4x - 3)$

$= (4x - 3)(2x + 1)$

Check: $(4x - 3)(2x + 1) = 8x^2 + 4x - 6x - 3$
$= 8x^2 - 2x - 3 ✓$

Skill Practice Factor by the ac-method.

2. $13w + 6w^2 + 6$

Example 3	**Factoring a Trinomial by the AC-Method**

Factor the trinomial by the ac-method. $10x^3 - 85x^2 + 105x$

Solution:

$10x^3 - 85x^2 + 105x$ **Step 1:** Factor out the GCF of $5x$.

$= 5x(2x^2 - 17x + 21)$ The trinomial is in the form $ax^2 + bx + c$.

$a = 2, b = -17, c = 21$ **Step 2:** Find the product $ac = (2)(21) = 42$.

$\underline{42}$	$\underline{42}$
$1 \cdot 42$	$(-1)(-42)$
$2 \cdot 21$	$(-2)(-21)$
$3 \cdot 14$	$(-3)(-14)$
$6 \cdot 7$	$(-6)(-7)$

Step 3: List all the factors of 42 and find the pair whose sum equals -17.

The numbers -3 and -14 satisfy both conditions: $(-3)(-14) = 42$ and $-3 + (-14) = -17$.

Answer

2. $(2w + 3)(3w + 2)$

$$= 5x(2x^2 - 17x + 21)$$

Step 4:   Write the middle term of the trinomial as two terms whose coefficients are the selected pair of numbers, -3 and -14.

$$= 5x(2x^2 - 3x - 14x + 21)$$

$$= 5x(2x^2 - 3x \mid - 14x + 21)$$

Step 5:   Factor by grouping.

$$= 5x[x(2x - 3) - 7(2x - 3)]$$

$$= 5x(2x - 3)(x - 7)$$

Avoiding Mistakes

Be sure to bring down the GCF in each successive step as you factor.

TIP: Notice when the GCF is removed from the original trinomial, the new trinomial has smaller coefficients. This makes the factoring process simpler because the product ac is smaller. It is much easier to list the factors of 42 than the factors of 1050.

Original trinomial	**With the GCF factored out**
$10x^3 - 85x^2 + 105x$	$5x(2x^2 - 17x + 21)$
$ac = (10)(105) = 1050$	$ac = (2)(21) = 42$

Skill Practice   Factor by the ac-method.

3. $9y^3 - 30y^2 + 24y$

In most cases, it is easier to factor a trinomial with a positive leading coefficient.

Example 4   **Factoring a Trinomial by the AC-Method**

Factor the trinomial by the ac-method. $-18x^2 + 21xy + 15y^2$

Solution:

$-18x^2 + 21xy + 15y^2$

$= -3(6x^2 - 7xy - 5y^2)$

Step 1:   Factor out the GCF.

Factor out -3 to make the leading term positive.

Step 2:   The product $ac = (6)(-5) = -30$.

Step 3:   The numbers -10 and 3 have a product of -30 and a sum of -7.

$= -3[6x^2 - 10xy + 3xy - 5y^2]$

Step 4:   Rewrite the middle term, $-7xy$ as $-10xy + 3xy$.

$= -3[6x^2 - 10xy \mid + 3xy - 5y^2]$

$= -3[2x(3x - 5y) + y(3x - 5y)]$

Step 5:   Factor by grouping.

$= -3(3x - 5y)(2x + y)$

Factored form

Skill Practice   Factor.

4. $-8x^2 - 8xy + 30y^2$

Answers

3. $3y(3y - 4)(y - 2)$

4. $-2(2x - 3y)(2x + 5y)$

Recall that a prime polynomial is a polynomial whose only factors are itself and 1. It also should be noted that not every trinomial is factorable by the methods presented in this text.

Example 5 **Factoring a Trinomial by the AC-Method**

Factor the trinomial by the ac-method. $2p^2 - 8p + 3$

Solution:

$2p^2 - 8p + 3$

Step 1: The GCF is 1.

Step 2: The product $ac = 6$.

$\underline{6}$	$\underline{6}$
$1 \cdot 6$	$(-1)(-6)$
$2 \cdot 3$	$(-2)(-3)$

Step 3: List the factors of 6. Notice that no pair of factors has a sum of -8. Therefore, the trinomial cannot be factored.

The trinomial $2p^2 - 8p + 3$ is a prime polynomial.

Skill Practice Factor.

  5. $4x^2 + 5x + 2$

In Example 6, we use the ac-method to factor a higher degree trinomial.

Example 6 **Factoring a Higher Degree Trinomial**

Factor the trinomial by the ac-method. $2x^4 + 5x^2 + 2$

Solution:

$2x^4 + 5x^2 + 2$

Step 1: The GCF is 1.

$a = 2, b = 5, c = 2$

Step 2: Find the product $ac = (2)(2) = 4$.

Step 3: The numbers 1 and 4 have a product of 4 and a sum of 5.

$2x^4 + x^2 + 4x^2 + 2$

Step 4: Rewrite the middle term, $5x^2$, as $x^2 + 4x^2$.

$2x^4 + x^2 + 4x^2 + 2$

Step 5: Factor by grouping.

$x^2(2x^2 + 1) + 2(2x^2 + 1)$

$(2x^2 + 1)(x^2 + 2)$ Factored form

Skill Practice Factor.

  6. $3y^4 + 2y^2 - 8$

Section 6.4   Practice Exercises

Vocabulary and Key Concepts

1. **a.** Which is the correct factored form of $10x^2 - 13x - 3$? The product $(5x + 1)(2x - 3)$ or $(2x - 3)(5x + 1)$?

    b. Which is the complete factorization of $12x^2 - 15x - 18$? The product $(4x + 3)(3x - 6)$ or $3(4x + 3)(x - 2)$?

Review Exercises

For Exercises 2–4, factor completely.

2. $5x(x - 2) - 2(x - 2)$

3. $8(y + 5) + 9y(y + 5)$

4. $6ab + 24b - 12a - 48$

Concept 1: Factoring Trinomials by the AC-Method

For Exercises 5–12, find the pair of integers whose product and sum are given.

5. Product: 12   Sum: 13

6. Product: 12   Sum: 7

7. Product: 8   Sum: −9

8. Product: −4   Sum: −3

9. Product: −20   Sum: 1

10. Product: −6   Sum: −1

11. Product: −18   Sum: 7

12. Product: −72   Sum: −6

For Exercises 13–30, factor the trinomials using the ac-method. **(See Examples 1, 2, and 5.)**

13. $3x^2 + 13x + 4$

14. $2y^2 + 7y + 6$

15. $4w^2 - 9w + 2$

16. $2p^2 - 3p - 2$

17. $x^2 + 7x - 18$

18. $y^2 - 6y - 40$

19. $2m^2 + 5m - 3$

20. $6n^2 + 7n - 3$

21. $8k^2 - 6k - 9$

22. $9h^2 - 3h - 2$

23. $4k^2 - 20k + 25$

24. $16h^2 + 24h + 9$

25. $5x^2 + x + 7$

26. $4y^2 - y + 2$

27. $10 + 9z^2 - 21z$

28. $13x + 4x^2 - 12$

29. $12y^2 + 8yz - 15z^2$

30. $20a^2 + 3ab - 9b^2$

For Exercises 31–38, factor completely. Be sure to factor out the GCF first. **(See Examples 3–4.)**

31. $50y + 24 + 14y^2$

32. $-24 + 10w + 4w^2$

33. $-15w^2 + 22w + 5$

34. $-16z^2 + 34z + 15$

35. $-12x^2 + 20xy - 8y^2$

36. $-6p^2 - 21pq - 9q^2$

37. $18y^3 + 60y^2 + 42y$

38. $8t^3 - 4t^2 - 40t$

For Exercises 39–44, factor the higher degree polynomial. **(See Example 6.)**

39. $a^4 + 5a^2 + 6$

40. $y^4 - 2y^2 - 35$

41. $6x^4 - x^2 - 15$

42. $8t^4 + 2t^2 - 3$

43. $8p^4 + 37p^2 - 15$

44. $2a^4 + 11a^2 + 14$

Mixed Exercises

For Exercises 45–80, factor completely.

45. $20p^2 - 19p + 3$

46. $4p^2 + 5pq - 6q^2$

47. $6u^2 - 19uv + 10v^2$

48. $15m^2 + mn - 2n^2$

49. $12a^2 + 11ab - 5b^2$

50. $3r^2 - rs - 14s^2$

51. $3h^2 + 19hk - 14k^2$

52. $2u^2 + uv - 15v^2$

53. $2x^2 - 13xy + y^2$

54. $3p^2 + 20pq - q^2$

55. $3 - 14z + 16z^2$

56. $10w + 1 + 16w^2$

57. $b^2 + 16 - 8b$

58. $1 + q^2 - 2q$

59. $25x - 5x^2 - 30$

60. $20a - 18 - 2a^2$

61. $-6 - t + t^2$

62. $-6 + m + m^2$

63. $v^2 + 2v + 15$

64. $x^2 - x - 1$

65. $72x^2 + 18x - 2$

66. $20y^2 - 78y - 8$

67. $p^3 - 6p^2 - 27p$

68. $w^5 - 11w^4 + 28w^3$

69. $3x^3 + 10x^2 + 7x$

70. $4r^3 + 3r^2 - 10r$

71. $2p^3 - 38p^2 + 120p$

72. $4q^3 - 4q^2 - 80q$

73. $x^2y^2 + 14x^2y + 33x^2$

74. $a^2b^2 + 13ab^2 + 30b^2$

75. $-k^2 - 7k - 10$

76. $-m^2 - 15m + 34$

77. $-3n^2 - 3n + 90$

78. $-2h^2 + 28h - 90$

79. $x^4 - 7x^2 + 10$

80. $m^4 + 10m^2 + 21$

81. Is the expression $(2x + 4)(x - 7)$ factored completely? Explain why or why not.

82. Is the expression $(3x + 1)(5x - 10)$ factored completely? Explain why or why not.

83. Colleen noticed that the number of tables placed in her restaurant affects the number of customers who eat at the restaurant. The number of customers each night is given by $-2x^2 + 40x - 72$, where x is the number of tables set up in the room, and $2 \le x \le 18$.

  a. Calculate the number of customers when there are 10 tables set up. ($x = 10$)

  b. Write $-2x^2 + 40x - 72$ in factored form. Then evaluate the factored form of the polynomial for $x = 10$. Is the result the same as from part (a)?

84. Roland sells cases for smartphones online. He noticed that for every dollar he discounts the price, he sells two more cases per week. His income in dollars each week is given by $-2d^2 + 30d + 200$, where d is the dollar amount of the discount in price.

  a. Calculate his income if the discount is $2. ($d = 2$)

  b. Write $-2d^2 + 30d + 200$ in factored form. Then evaluate the factored form of the polynomial for $d = 2$. Is the result the same as from part (a)?

85. A formula for finding the sum of the first n even integers is given by $n^2 + n$.

  a. Find the sum of the first 6 even integers $(2 + 4 + 6 + 8 + 10 + 12)$ by evaluating the expression for $n = 6$.

  b. Write the polynomial in factored form. Then evaluate the factored form of the expression for $n = 6$. Is the result the same as part (a)?

86. A formula for finding the sum of the squares of the first n integers is given by $\dfrac{2n^3 + 3n^2 + n}{6}$.

  a. Find the sum of the squares of the first 4 integers $(1^2 + 2^2 + 3^2 + 4^2)$ by evaluating the expression for $n = 4$.

  b. Write the polynomial in the numerator of the expression in factored form. Then evaluate the factored form of the expression for $n = 4$. Is the result the same as part (a)?

Section 6.5 Difference of Squares and Perfect Square Trinomials

Concepts

1. Factoring a Difference of Squares
2. Factoring Perfect Square Trinomials

1. Factoring a Difference of Squares

Up to this point, we have learned several methods of factoring, including:

- Factoring out the greatest common factor from a polynomial
- Factoring a four-term polynomial by grouping
- Factoring trinomials by the ac-method or by the trial-and-error method

In this section, we will learn to factor polynomials that fit two special case patterns: a difference of squares, and a perfect square trinomial. First recall that the product of two conjugates results in a **difference of squares**:

$$(a + b)(a - b) = a^2 - b^2$$

Therefore, to factor a difference of squares, the process is reversed. Identify a and b and construct the conjugate factors.

> **Factored Form of a Difference of Squares**
>
> $$a^2 - b^2 = (a + b)(a - b)$$

To help recognize a difference of squares, we recommend that you become familiar with the first several perfect squares.

Perfect Squares	Perfect Squares	Perfect Squares
$1 = (1)^2$	$36 = (6)^2$	$121 = (11)^2$
$4 = (2)^2$	$49 = (7)^2$	$144 = (12)^2$
$9 = (3)^2$	$64 = (8)^2$	$169 = (13)^2$
$16 = (4)^2$	$81 = (9)^2$	$196 = (14)^2$
$25 = (5)^2$	$100 = (10)^2$	$225 = (15)^2$

It is also important to recognize that a variable expression is a perfect square if its exponent is a multiple of 2. For example:

Perfect Squares

$$x^2 = (x)^2$$
$$x^4 = (x^2)^2$$
$$x^6 = (x^3)^2$$
$$x^8 = (x^4)^2$$
$$x^{10} = (x^5)^2$$

Example 1	**Factoring Differences of Squares**

Factor the binomials.

a. $y^2 - 25$ **b.** $49s^2 - 4t^4$ **c.** $18w^2z - 2z$

Solution:

a. $y^2 - 25$ The binomial is a difference of squares.

$\quad = (y)^2 - (5)^2$ Write in the form: $a^2 - b^2$, where $a = y$, $b = 5$.

$\quad = (y + 5)(y - 5)$ Factor as $(a + b)(a - b)$.

b. $49s^2 - 4t^4$ The binomial is a difference of squares.

$\quad = (7s)^2 - (2t^2)^2$ Write in the form $a^2 - b^2$, where $a = 7s$ and $b = 2t^2$.

$\quad = (7s + 2t^2)(7s - 2t^2)$ Factor as $(a + b)(a - b)$.

c. $18w^2z - 2z$ The GCF is $2z$.

$\quad = 2z(9w^2 - 1)$ $(9w^2 - 1)$ is a difference of squares.

$\quad = 2z[(3w)^2 - (1)^2]$ Write in the form: $a^2 - b^2$, where $a = 3w$, $b = 1$.

$\quad = 2z(3w - 1)(3w + 1)$ Factor as $(a - b)(a + b)$.

> **TIP:** Recall that multiplication is commutative. Therefore,
> $$a^2 - b^2 = (a + b)(a - b)$$
> or $(a - b)(a + b)$.

Skill Practice Factor the binomials.

1. $a^2 - 64$ **2.** $25q^2 - 49w^2$ **3.** $98m^3n - 50mn$

The difference of squares $a^2 - b^2$ factors as $(a + b)(a - b)$. However, the *sum* of squares is not factorable.

Sum of Squares

Suppose a and b have no common factors. Then the **sum of squares** $a^2 + b^2$ is *not* factorable over the real numbers.

That is, $a^2 + b^2$ is prime over the real numbers.

To see why $a^2 + b^2$ is not factorable, consider the product of binomials:

$(a + b)(a - b) = a^2 - b^2$ Wrong sign

$(a + b)(a + b) = a^2 + 2ab + b^2$ Wrong middle term

$(a - b)(a - b) = a^2 - 2ab + b^2$ Wrong middle term

After exhausting all possibilities, we see that if a and b share no common factors, then the sum of squares $a^2 + b^2$ is a prime polynomial.

Example 2	**Factoring Binomials**

Factor the binomials, if possible.   **a.** $p^2 - 9$ **b.** $p^2 + 9$

Solution:

a. $p^2 - 9$ Difference of squares

$\quad = (p - 3)(p + 3)$ Factor as $a^2 - b^2 = (a - b)(a + b)$.

b. $p^2 + 9$ Sum of squares

$\quad$ Prime (cannot be factored)

Answers

1. $(a + 8)(a - 8)$
2. $(5q + 7w)(5q - 7w)$
3. $2mn(7m + 5)(7m - 5)$

Skill Practice   Factor the binomials, if possible.

4. $t^2 - 144$ **5.** $t^2 + 144$

Some factoring problems require several steps. Always be sure to factor completely.

Example 3   **Factoring a Difference of Squares**

Factor completely. $w^4 - 81$

Solution:

$w^4 - 81$ The GCF is 1. $w^4 - 81$ is a difference of squares.

$= (w^2)^2 - (9)^2$ Write in the form: $a^2 - b^2$, where $a = w^2$, $b = 9$.

$= (w^2 + 9)(w^2 - 9)$ Factor as $(a + b)(a - b)$.

$= (w^2 + 9)\overbrace{(w + 3)(w - 3)}$ Note that $w^2 - 9$ can be factored further as a difference of squares. (The binomial $w^2 + 9$ is a sum of squares and cannot be factored further.)

Skill Practice   Factor completely.

6. $y^4 - 1$

Example 4   **Factoring a Polynomial**

Factor completely. $y^3 - 5y^2 - 4y + 20$

Solution:

$y^3 - 5y^2 - 4y + 20$ The GCF is 1. The polynomial has four terms. Factor by grouping.

$= y^3 - 5y^2 \mid -4y + 20$

$= y^2(y - 5) - 4(y - 5)$

$= (y - 5)(y^2 - 4)$ The expression $y^2 - 4$ is a difference of squares and can be factored further as $(y - 2)(y + 2)$.

$= (y - 5)(y - 2)(y + 2)$

Check: $(y - 5)(y - 2)(y + 2) = (y - 5)(y^2 - 2y + 2y - 4)$

$ = (y - 5)(y^2 - 4)$

$ = (y^3 - 4y - 5y^2 + 20)$

$ = y^3 - 5y^2 - 4y + 20 \checkmark$

Skill Practice   Factor completely.

7. $p^3 + 7p^2 - 9p - 63$

2. Factoring Perfect Square Trinomials

Answers
4. $(t - 12)(t + 12)$
5. Prime
6. $(y + 1)(y - 1)(y^2 + 1)$
7. $(p - 3)(p + 3)(p + 7)$

Recall that the square of a binomial always results in a **perfect square trinomial**.

$(a + b)^2 = (a + b)(a + b) \xrightarrow{\text{Multiply.}} = a^2 + 2ab + b^2$

$(a - b)^2 = (a - b)(a - b) \xrightarrow{\text{Multiply.}} = a^2 - 2ab + b^2$

For example, $(3x + 5)^2 = (3x)^2 + 2(3x)(5) + (5)^2$

$$= 9x^2 + 30x + 25 \text{ (perfect square trinomial)}$$

We now want to reverse this process by factoring a perfect square trinomial. The trial-and-error method or the ac-method can always be used; however, if we recognize the pattern for a perfect square trinomial, we can use one of the following formulas to reach a quick solution.

Factored Form of a Perfect Square Trinomial

$$a^2 + 2ab + b^2 = (a + b)^2$$
$$a^2 - 2ab + b^2 = (a - b)^2$$

For example, $4x^2 + 36x + 81$ is a perfect square trinomial with $a = 2x$ and $b = 9$. Therefore, it factors as

$$4x^2 + 36x + 81 = (2x)^2 + 2(2x)(9) + (9)^2 = (2x + 9)^2$$
$$ a^2 \ + \ 2(a)(b) \ + \ (b)^2 = (a + b)^2$$

To apply the formula to factor a perfect square trinomial, we must first be sure that the trinomial is indeed a perfect square trinomial.

Checking for a Perfect Square Trinomial

Step 1   Determine whether the first and third terms are both perfect squares and have positive coefficients.

Step 2   If this is the case, identify a and b and determine if the middle term equals $2ab$ or $-2ab$.

Example 5   **Factoring Perfect Square Trinomials**

Factor the trinomials completely.

a. $x^2 + 14x + 49$ **b.** $25y^2 - 20y + 4$

Solution:

a. $x^2 + 14x + 49$ The GCF is 1.

- The first and third terms are positive.

- The first term is a perfect square: $x^2 = (x)^2$.

Perfect squares

$$x^2 + 14x + 49$$

- The third term is a perfect square: $49 = (7)^2$.

- The middle term is twice the product of x and 7: $14x = 2(x)(7)$.

$$= (x)^2 + 2(x)(7) + (7)^2 \qquad \text{The trinomial is in the form } a^2 + 2ab + b^2,$$
$$\text{where } a = x \text{ and } b = 7.$$

$$= (x + 7)^2 \qquad\qquad \text{Factor as } (a + b)^2.$$

> **TIP:** The sign of the middle term in a perfect square trinomial determines the sign within the binomial of the factored form.
>
> $$a^2 + 2ab + b^2 = (a + b)^2$$
> $$a^2 - 2ab + b^2 = (a - b)^2$$

b. $25y^2 - 20y + 4$

Perfect squares

$25y^2 - 20y + 4$

$= (5y)^2 - 2(5y)(2) + (2)^2$

$= (5y - 2)^2$

The GCF is 1.

- The first and third terms are positive.

- The first term is a perfect square: $25y^2 = (5y)^2$.

- The third term is a perfect square: $4 = (2)^2$.

- In the middle: $-20y = -2(5y)(2)$

Factor as $(a - b)^2$.

Skill Practice Factor completely.

8. $x^2 - 6x + 9$ **9.** $81w^2 + 72w + 16$

Example 6   **Factoring Perfect Square Trinomials**

Factor the trinomials completely.

  a. $18c^3 - 48c^2d + 32cd^2$ **b.** $5w^2 + 50w + 45$

Solution:

  a. $18c^3 - 48c^2d + 32cd^2$

$= 2c(9c^2 - 24cd + 16d^2)$

Perfect squares

$= 2c(9c^2 - 24cd + 16d^2)$

$= 2c[(3c)^2 - 2(3c)(4d) + (4d)^2]$

$= 2c(3c - 4d)^2$

The GCF is $2c$.

- The first and third terms are positive.

- The first term is a perfect square: $9c^2 = (3c)^2$.

- The third term is a perfect square: $16d^2 = (4d)^2$.

- In the middle: $-24cd = -2(3c)(4d)$

Factor as $(a - b)^2$.

  b. $5w^2 + 50w + 45$

$= 5(w^2 + 10w + 9)$

Perfect squares

$= 5(w^2 + 10w + 9)$

The GCF is 5.

The first and third terms are perfect squares.

$$w^2 = (w)^2 \qquad \text{and} \qquad 9 = (3)^2$$

However, the middle term is not 2 times the product of w and 3.

$$10w \neq 2(w)(3)$$

Therefore, this is not a perfect square trinomial.

To factor, use the trial-and-error method.

$= 5(w + 9)(w + 1)$

TIP: If you do not recognize that a trinomial is a perfect square trinomial, you can still use the trial-and-error method or ac-method to factor it.

Skill Practice Factor completely.

  10. $5z^3 + 20z^2w + 20zw^2$ **11.** $40x^2 + 130x + 90$

Answers

8. $(x - 3)^2$

9. $(9w + 4)^2$

10. $5z(z + 2w)^2$

11. $10(4x + 9)(x + 1)$

Section 6.5   Practice Exercises

Vocabulary and Key Concepts

1. **a.** The binomial $x^2 - 16$ is an example of a _____ of squares. After factoring out the GCF, we factor a difference of squares $a^2 - b^2$ as _____.

   b. The binomial $y^2 + 121$ is an example of a _____ of squares.

   c. A sum of squares with greatest common factor 1 (is/is not) factorable over the real numbers.

   d. The square of a binomial always results in a perfect _____ trinomial.

   e. A perfect square trinomial $a^2 + 2ab + b^2$ factors as _____.
   Likewise, $a^2 - 2ab + b^2$ factors as _____.

Review Exercises

For Exercises 2–10, factor completely.

2. $3x^2 + x - 10$

3. $6x^2 - 17x + 5$

4. $6a^2b + 3a^3b$

5. $15x^2y^5 - 10xy^6$

6. $5p^2q + 20p^2 - 3pq - 12p$

7. $ax + ab - 6x - 6b$

8. $-6x + 5 + x^2$

9. $6y - 40 + y^2$

10. $a^2 + 7a + 1$

Concept 1: Factoring a Difference of Squares

11. What binomial factors as $(x - 5)(x + 5)$?

12. What binomial factors as $(n - 3)(n + 3)$?

13. What binomial factors as $(2p - 3q)(2p + 3q)$?

14. What binomial factors as $(7x - 4y)(7x + 4y)$?

For Exercises 15–38, factor each binomial completely. **(See Examples 1–3.)**

15. $x^2 - 36$

16. $r^2 - 81$

17. $3w^2 - 300$

18. $t^3 - 49t$

19. $4a^2 - 121b^2$

20. $9x^2 - y^2$

21. $49m^2 - 16n^2$

22. $100a^2 - 49b^2$

23. $9q^2 + 16$

24. $36 + s^2$

25. $y^2 - 4z^2$

26. $b^2 - 144c^2$

27. $a^2 - b^4$

28. $y^4 - x^2$

29. $25p^2q^2 - 1$

30. $81s^2t^2 - 1$

31. $c^2 - \dfrac{1}{25}$

32. $z^2 - \dfrac{1}{4}$

33. $50 - 32t^2$

34. $63 - 7h^2$

35. $x^4 - 256$

36. $y^4 - 625$

37. $16 - z^4$

38. $81 - a^4$

For Exercises 39–46, factor each polynomial completely. **(See Example 4.)**

39. $x^3 + 5x^2 - 9x - 45$

40. $y^3 + 6y^2 - 4y - 24$

41. $c^3 - c^2 - 25c + 25$

42. $t^3 + 2t^2 - 16t - 32$

43. $2x^2 - 18 + x^2y - 9y$

44. $5a^2 - 5 + a^2b - b$

45. $x^2y^2 - 9x^2 - 4y^2 + 36$

46. $w^2z^2 - w^2 - 25z^2 + 25$

Concept 2: Factoring Perfect Square Trinomials

47. Multiply. $(3x + 5)^2$

48. Multiply. $(2y - 7)^2$

454   **Chapter 6**   Factoring Polynomials

49. a. Which trinomial is a perfect square trinomial?
$x^2 + 4x + 4$ or $x^2 + 5x + 4$

  b. Factor the trinomials from part (a).

50. a. Which trinomial is a perfect square trinomial?
$x^2 + 13x + 36$ or $x^2 + 12x + 36$

  b. Factor the trinomials from part (a).

For Exercises 51–68, factor completely. (*Hint:* Look for the pattern of a perfect square trinomial.) **(See Examples 5–6.)**

51. $x^2 + 18x + 81$

52. $y^2 - 8y + 16$

53. $25z^2 - 20z + 4$

54. $36p^2 + 60p + 25$

55. $49a^2 + 42ab + 9b^2$

56. $25m^2 - 30mn + 9n^2$

57. $-2y + y^2 + 1$

58. $4 + w^2 - 4w$

59. $80z^2 + 120zw + 45w^2$

60. $36p^2 - 24pq + 4q^2$

61. $9y^2 + 78y + 25$

62. $4y^2 + 20y + 9$

63. $2a^2 - 20a + 50$

64. $3t^2 + 18t + 27$

65. $4x^2 + x + 9$

66. $c^2 - 4c + 16$

67. $4x^2 + 4xy + y^2$

68. $100y^2 + 20yz + z^2$

69. The volume of the box shown is given as $3x^3 - 6x^2 + 3x$. Write the polynomial in factored form.

70. The volume of the box shown is given as $20y^3 + 20y^2 + 5y$. Write the polynomial in factored form.

Expanding Your Skills

For Exercises 71–78, factor the difference of squares.

71. $(y - 3)^2 - 9$

72. $(x - 2)^2 - 4$

73. $(2p + 1)^2 - 36$

74. $(4q + 3)^2 - 25$

75. $16 - (t + 2)^2$

76. $81 - (a + 5)^2$

77. $(2a - 5)^2 - 100b^2$

78. $(3k + 7)^2 - 49m^2$

79. a. Write a polynomial that represents the area of the shaded region in the figure.

  b. Factor the expression from part (a).

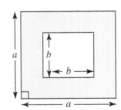

80. a. Write a polynomial that represents the area of the shaded region in the figure.

  b. Factor the expression from part (a).

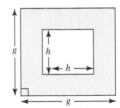

454   **Chapter 6**   Factoring Polynomials

Section 6.6   Sum and Difference of Cubes

1. Factoring a Sum or Difference of Cubes

A binomial $a^2 - b^2$ is a difference of squares and can be factored as $(a - b)(a + b)$. Furthermore, if a and b share no common factors, then a sum of squares $a^2 + b^2$ is not factorable over the real numbers. In this section, we will learn that both a difference of cubes, $a^3 - b^3$, and a sum of cubes, $a^3 + b^3$, are factorable.

> ### Factored Form of a Sum or Difference of Cubes
>
> **Sum of Cubes:** $\qquad a^3 + b^3 = (a + b)(a^2 - ab + b^2)$
>
> **Difference of Cubes:** $\quad a^3 - b^3 = (a - b)(a^2 + ab + b^2)$

Multiplication can be used to confirm the formulas for factoring a sum or difference of cubes:

$$(a + b)(a^2 - ab + b^2) = a^3 - \cancel{a^2 b} + \cancel{ab^2} + \cancel{a^2 b} - \cancel{ab^2} + b^3 = a^3 + b^3 \checkmark$$

$$(a - b)(a^2 + ab + b^2) = a^3 + \cancel{a^2 b} + \cancel{ab^2} - \cancel{a^2 b} - \cancel{ab^2} - b^3 = a^3 - b^3 \checkmark$$

To help you remember the formulas for factoring a sum or difference of cubes, keep the following guidelines in mind:

- The factored form is the product of a binomial and a trinomial.
- The first and third terms in the trinomial are the squares of the terms within the binomial factor.
- Without regard to signs, the middle term in the trinomial is the product of terms in the binomial factor.

Square the first term of the binomial.   Product of terms in the binomial

$$x^3 + 8 = (x)^3 + (2)^3 = (x + 2)[(x)^2 - (x)(2) + (2)^2]$$

Square the last term of the binomial.

- The sign within the binomial factor is the same as the sign of the original binomial.
- The first and third terms in the trinomial are always positive.
- The sign of the middle term in the trinomial is opposite the sign within the binomial.

Same sign   Positive

$$x^3 + 8 = (x)^3 + (2)^3 = (x + 2)[(x)^2 - (x)(2) + (2)^2]$$

Opposite signs

> **TIP:** To help remember the placement of the signs in factoring the sum or difference of cubes, remember SOAP: **S**ame sign, **O**pposite signs, **A**lways **P**ositive.

To help you recognize a sum or difference of cubes, we recommend that you familiarize yourself with the first several perfect cubes:

Perfect Cubes	**Perfect Cubes**
$1 = (1)^3$	$216 = (6)^3$
$8 = (2)^3$	$343 = (7)^3$
$27 = (3)^3$	$512 = (8)^3$
$64 = (4)^3$	$729 = (9)^3$
$125 = (5)^3$	$1000 = (10)^3$

It is also helpful to recognize that a variable expression is a perfect cube if its exponent is a multiple of 3. For example:

Perfect Cubes

$$x^3 = (x)^3$$
$$x^6 = (x^2)^3$$
$$x^9 = (x^3)^3$$
$$x^{12} = (x^4)^3$$

| Example 1 | **Factoring a Sum of Cubes** |

Factor. $w^3 + 64$

Solution:

$$w^3 + 64 \qquad\qquad w^3 \text{ and } 64 \text{ are perfect cubes.}$$

$$= (w)^3 + (4)^3 \qquad \text{Write as } a^3 + b^3, \text{ where } a = w, b = 4.$$

$$a^3 + b^3 = (a + b)(a^2 - ab + b^2) \qquad\qquad \text{Apply the formula for a sum of cubes.}$$

$$(w)^3 + (4)^3 = (w + 4)[(w)^2 - (w)(4) + (4)^2]$$

$$= (w + 4)(w^2 - 4w + 16) \qquad\qquad \text{Simplify.}$$

Skill Practice Factor.

1. $p^3 + 125$

| Example 2 | **Factoring a Difference of Cubes** |

Factor. $27p^3 - 1000q^3$

Solution:

$$27p^3 - 1000q^3 \qquad 27p^3 \text{ and } 1000q^3 \text{ are perfect cubes.}$$

$$= (3p)^3 - (10q)^3 \qquad \text{Write as } a^3 - b^3, \text{ where } a = 3p, b = 10q.$$

$$a^3 - b^3 = (a - b)(a^2 + ab + b^2) \qquad\qquad \text{Apply the formula for a difference of cubes.}$$

$$(3p)^3 - (10q)^3 = (3p - 10q)[(3p)^2 + (3p)(10q) + (10q)^2]$$

$$= (3p - 10q)(9p^2 + 30pq + 100q^2) \qquad\qquad \text{Simplify.}$$

Skill Practice Factor.

2. $8y^3 - 27z^3$

2. Factoring Binomials: A Summary

After removing the GCF, the next step in any factoring problem is to recognize what type of pattern it follows. Exponents that are divisible by 2 are perfect squares and those divisible by 3 are perfect cubes. The formulas for factoring binomials are summarized in the following box:

Factored Forms of Binomials

Difference of Squares: $a^2 - b^2 = (a + b)(a - b)$

Difference of Cubes: $a^3 - b^3 = (a - b)(a^2 + ab + b^2)$

Sum of Cubes: $a^3 + b^3 = (a + b)(a^2 - ab + b^2)$

| Example 3 | **Factoring Binomials** |

Factor completely.

a. $27y^3 + 1$ **b.** $\dfrac{1}{25}m^2 - \dfrac{1}{4}$ **c.** $z^6 - 8w^3$

Answers

1. $(p + 5)(p^2 - 5p + 25)$

2. $(2y - 3z)(4y^2 + 6yz + 9z^2)$

Solution:

a. $27y^3 + 1$ Sum of cubes: $27y^3 = (3y)^3$ and $1 = (1)^3$.

    $= (3y)^3 + (1)^3$ Write as $a^3 + b^3$, where $a = 3y$ and $b = 1$.

    $= (3y + 1)[(3y)^2 - (3y)(1) + (1)^2]$ Apply the formula
                                            $a^3 + b^3 = (a + b)(a^2 - ab + b^2)$.

    $= (3y + 1)(9y^2 - 3y + 1)$ Simplify.

b. $\dfrac{1}{25}m^2 - \dfrac{1}{4}$ Difference of squares

    $= \left(\dfrac{1}{5}m\right)^2 - \left(\dfrac{1}{2}\right)^2$ Write as $a^2 - b^2$, where $a = \frac{1}{5}m$ and $b = \frac{1}{2}$.

    $= \left(\dfrac{1}{5}m + \dfrac{1}{2}\right)\left(\dfrac{1}{5}m - \dfrac{1}{2}\right)$ Apply the formula $a^2 - b^2 = (a + b)(a - b)$.

c. $z^6 - 8w^3$ Difference of cubes: $z^6 = (z^2)^3$ and $8w^3 = (2w)^3$

    $= (z^2)^3 - (2w)^3$ Write as $a^3 - b^3$, where $a = z^2$ and $b = 2w$.

    $= (z^2 - 2w)[(z^2)^2 + (z^2)(2w) + (2w)^2]$ Apply the formula
                                             $a^3 - b^3 = (a - b)(a^2 + ab + b^2)$.

    $= (z^2 - 2w)(z^4 + 2z^2w + 4w^2)$ Simplify.

Each factorization in this example can be checked by multiplying.

Skill Practice Factor completely.

   3. $1000x^3 + 1$ **4.** $25p^2 - \dfrac{1}{9}$ **5.** $27a^6 - b^3$

Some factoring problems require more than one method of factoring. In general, when factoring a polynomial, be sure to factor completely.

Example 4   **Factoring a Polynomial**

Factor completely. $3y^4 - 48$

Solution:

   $3y^4 - 48$

   $= 3(y^4 - 16)$ Factor out the GCF. The binomial is a difference of squares.

   $= 3[(y^2)^2 - (4)^2]$ Write as $a^2 - b^2$, where $a = y^2$ and $b = 4$.

   $= 3(y^2 + 4)(y^2 - 4)$ Apply the formula
                                  $a^2 - b^2 = (a + b)(a - b)$.

                                  $y^2 + 4$ is a sum of squares and cannot be factored.

   $= 3(y^2 + 4)(y + 2)(y - 2)$ $y^2 - 4$ is a difference of squares and can be factored further.

Skill Practice Factor completely.

   6. $2x^4 - 2$

Answers

3. $(10x + 1)(100x^2 - 10x + 1)$

4. $\left(5p - \dfrac{1}{3}\right)\left(5p + \dfrac{1}{3}\right)$

5. $(3a^2 - b)(9a^4 + 3a^2b + b^2)$

6. $2(x^2 + 1)(x - 1)(x + 1)$

| Example 5 | **Factoring a Polynomial** |

Factor completely. $\quad 4x^3 + 4x^2 - 25x - 25$

Solution:

$4x^3 + 4x^2 - 25x - 25$ The GCF is 1.

$= 4x^3 + 4x^2 \mid - 25x - 25$ The polynomial has four terms. Factor by grouping.

$= 4x^2(x + 1) - 25(x + 1)$

$= (x + 1)(4x^2 - 25)$ $4x^2 - 25$ is a difference of squares.

$= (x + 1)\overbrace{(2x + 5)(2x - 5)}$

Skill Practice Factor completely.

7. $x^3 + 6x^2 - 4x - 24$

| Example 6 | **Factoring a Binomial** |

Factor the binomial $x^6 - y^6$ as

   a. A difference of cubes   **b.** A difference of squares

Notice that the expressions x^6 and y^6 are both perfect squares and perfect cubes because both exponents are multiples of 2 and of 3. Consequently, $x^6 - y^6$ can be factored initially as either the difference of squares or as the difference of cubes.

Solution:

  a. $x^6 - y^6$

$$= \overset{\text{Difference of cubes}}{(x^2)^3 - (y^2)^3}$$
     Write as $a^3 - b^3$, where $a = x^2$ and $b = y^2$.

$= (x^2 - y^2)[(x^2)^2 + (x^2)(y^2) + (y^2)^2]$
     Apply the formula $a^3 - b^3 = (a - b)(a^2 + ab + b^2)$.

$= (x^2 - y^2)(x^4 + x^2y^2 + y^4)$
     Factor $x^2 - y^2$ as a difference of squares.

$= \overbrace{(x + y)(x - y)}(x^4 + x^2y^2 + y^4)$

Avoiding Mistakes

The trinomial $x^4 + x^2y^2 + y^4$ cannot be factored further with the techniques presented in this chapter.

  b. $x^6 - y^6$

$$= \overset{\text{Difference of squares}}{(x^3)^2 - (y^3)^2}$$
     Write as $a^2 - b^2$, where $a = x^3$ and $b = y^3$.

$= (x^3 + y^3)(x^3 - y^3)$
     Apply the formula $a^2 - b^2 = (a + b)(a - b)$.

Sum of cubes   Difference of cubes

     Factor $x^3 + y^3$ as a sum of cubes.

     Factor $x^3 - y^3$ as a difference of cubes.

$= (x + y)(x^2 - xy + y^2)\ (x - y)(x^2 + xy + y^2)$

Answer

7. $(x + 6)(x + 2)(x - 2)$

In a case such as this, it is recommended that you factor the expression as a difference of squares first because it factors more completely into polynomials of lower degree.

$$x^6 - y^6 = (x + y)(x^2 - xy + y^2)(x - y)(x^2 + xy + y^2)$$

Skill Practice Factor completely.

8. $z^6 - 64$

Answer

8. $(z + 2)(z - 2)(z^2 + 2z + 4)$
$(z^2 - 2z + 4)$

Section 6.6   Practice Exercises

Vocabulary and Key Concepts

1. a. The binomial $x^3 + 27$ is an example of a _____ of _____.

  b. The binomial $c^3 - 8$ is an example of a _____ of _____.

  c. A difference of cubes $a^3 - b^3$ factors as (   )(   ).

  d. A sum of cubes $a^3 + b^3$ factors as (   )(   ).

Review Exercises

For Exercises 2–10, factor completely.

2. $600 - 6x^2$

3. $20 - 5t^2$

4. $ax + bx + 5a + 5b$

5. $2t + 2u + st + su$

6. $5y^2 + 13y - 6$

7. $3v^2 + 5v - 12$

8. $40a^3b^3 - 16a^2b^2 + 24a^3b$

9. $-c^2 - 10c - 25$

10. $-z^2 + 6z - 9$

Concept 1: Factoring a Sum or Difference of Cubes

11. Identify the expressions that are perfect cubes:
$x^3, 8, 9, y^6, a^4, b^2, 3p^3, 27q^3, w^{12}, r^3s^6$

12. Identify the expressions that are perfect cubes:
$z^9, -81, 30, 8, 6x^3, y^{15}, 27a^3, b^2, p^3q^2, -1$

13. Identify the expressions that are perfect cubes:
$36, t^3, -1, 27, a^3b^6, -9, 125, -8x^2, y^6, 25$

14. Identify the expressions that are perfect cubes:
$343, 15b^3, z^3, w^{12}, -p^9, -1000, a^2b^3, 3x^3, -8, 60$

For Exercises 15–30, factor the sums or differences of cubes. **(See Examples 1–2.)**

15. $y^3 - 8$

16. $x^3 + 27$

17. $1 - p^3$

18. $q^3 + 1$

19. $w^3 + 64$

20. $8 - t^3$

21. $x^3 - 1000y^3$

22. $8r^3 - 27t^3$

23. $64t^3 + 1$

24. $125r^3 + 1$

25. $1000a^3 + 27$

26. $216b^3 - 125$

27. $n^3 - \dfrac{1}{8}$

28. $\dfrac{8}{27} + m^3$

29. $125x^3 + 8y^3$

30. $27t^3 + 64u^3$

460   **Chapter 6** Factoring Polynomials

Concept 2: Factoring Binomials: A Summary

For Exercises 31–66, factor completely. **(See Examples 3–6.)**

31. $x^4 - 4$

32. $b^4 - 25$

33. $a^2 + 9$

34. $w^2 + 36$

35. $t^3 + 64$

36. $u^3 + 27$

37. $g^3 - 4$

38. $h^3 - 25$

39. $4b^3 + 108$

40. $3c^3 - 24$

41. $5p^2 - 125$

42. $2q^4 - 8$

43. $\dfrac{1}{64} - 8h^3$

44. $\dfrac{1}{125} + k^6$

45. $x^4 - 16$

46. $p^4 - 81$

47. $\dfrac{4}{9}x^2 - w^2$

48. $\dfrac{16}{25}y^2 - x^2$

49. $q^6 - 64$

50. $a^6 - 1$

(*Hint:* Factor using the difference of squares first.)

51. $x^9 + 64y^3$

52. $125w^3 - z^9$

53. $2x^3 + 3x^2 - 2x - 3$

54. $3x^3 + x^2 - 12x - 4$

55. $16x^4 - y^4$

56. $1 - t^4$

57. $81y^4 - 16$

58. $u^5 - 256u$

59. $a^3 + b^6$

60. $u^6 - v^3$

61. $x^4 - y^4$

62. $a^4 - b^4$

63. $k^3 + 4k^2 - 9k - 36$

64. $w^3 - 2w^2 - 4w + 8$

65. $2t^3 - 10t^2 - 2t + 10$

66. $9a^3 + 27a^2 - 4a - 12$

Expanding Your Skills

For Exercises 67–70, factor completely.

67. $\dfrac{64}{125}p^3 - \dfrac{1}{8}q^3$

68. $\dfrac{1}{1000}r^3 + \dfrac{8}{27}s^3$

69. $a^{12} + b^{12}$

70. $a^9 - b^9$

Use Exercises 71–72 to investigate the relationship between division and factoring.

71. **a.** Use long division to divide $x^3 - 8$ by $(x - 2)$.

 b. Factor $x^3 - 8$.

72. **a.** Use long division to divide $y^3 + 27$ by $(y + 3)$.

 b. Factor $y^3 + 27$.

73. What trinomial multiplied by $(x - 4)$ gives a difference of cubes?

74. What trinomial multiplied by $(p + 5)$ gives a sum of cubes?

75. Write a binomial that when multiplied by $(4x^2 - 2x + 1)$ produces a sum of cubes.

76. Write a binomial that when multiplied by $(9y^2 + 15y + 25)$ produces a difference of cubes.

Problem Recognition Exercises

Factoring Strategy

Factoring Strategy

Step 1 Factor out the GCF.

Step 2 Identify whether the polynomial has two terms, three terms, or more than three terms.

Step 3 If the polynomial has more than three terms, try factoring by grouping.

Step 4 If the polynomial has three terms, check first for a perfect square trinomial. Otherwise, factor the trinomial with the trial-and-error method or the ac-method.

Step 5 If the polynomial has two terms, determine if it fits the pattern for
- A difference of squares: $a^2 - b^2 = (a - b)(a + b)$
- A sum of squares: $a^2 + b^2$ is prime.
- A difference of cubes: $a^3 - b^3 = (a - b)(a^2 + ab + b^2)$
- A sum of cubes: $a^3 + b^3 = (a + b)(a^2 - ab + b^2)$

Step 6 Be sure to factor the polynomial completely.

Step 7 Check by multiplying.

1. What is meant by a prime polynomial?

2. What is the first step in factoring any polynomial?

3. When factoring a binomial, what patterns can you look for?

4. What technique should be considered when factoring a four-term polynomial?

For Exercises 5–73,

a. Factor out the GCF from each polynomial. Then identify the category in which the remaining polynomial best fits. Choose from
- difference of squares
- sum of squares
- difference of cubes
- sum of cubes
- trinomial (perfect square trinomial)
- trinomial (nonperfect square trinomial)
- four terms-grouping
- none of these

b. Factor the polynomial completely.

5. $2a^2 - 162$

6. $y^2 + 4y + 3$

7. $6w^2 - 6w$

8. $16z^4 - 81$

9. $3t^2 + 13t + 4$

10. $5r^3 + 5$

11. $3ac + ad - 3bc - bd$

12. $x^3 - 125$

13. $y^3 + 8$

14. $7p^2 - 29p + 4$

15. $3q^2 - 9q - 12$

16. $-2x^2 + 8x - 8$

462 **Chapter 6** Factoring Polynomials

17. $18a^2 + 12a$

18. $54 - 2y^3$

19. $4t^2 - 100$

20. $4t^2 - 31t - 8$

21. $10c^2 + 10c + 10$

22. $2xw - 10x + 3yw - 15y$

23. $x^3 + 0.001$

24. $4q^2 - 9$

25. $64 + 16k + k^2$

26. $s^2t + 5t + 6s^2 + 30$

27. $2x^2 + 2x - xy - y$

28. $w^3 + y^3$

29. $a^3 - c^3$

30. $3y^2 + y + 1$

31. $c^2 + 8c + 9$

32. $a^2 + 2a + 1$

33. $b^2 + 10b + 25$

34. $-t^2 - 4t + 32$

35. $-p^3 - 5p^2 - 4p$

36. $x^2y^2 - 49$

37. $6x^2 - 21x - 45$

38. $20y^2 - 14y + 2$

39. $5a^2bc^3 - 7abc^2$

40. $8a^2 - 50$

41. $t^2 + 2t - 63$

42. $b^2 + 2b - 80$

43. $ab + ay - b^2 - by$

44. $6x^3y^4 + 3x^2y^5$

45. $14u^2 - 11uv + 2v^2$

46. $9p^2 - 36pq + 4q^2$

47. $4q^2 - 8q - 6$

48. $9w^2 + 3w - 15$

49. $9m^2 + 16n^2$

50. $5b^2 - 30b + 45$

51. $6r^2 + 11r + 3$

52. $4s^2 + 4s - 15$

53. $16a^4 - 1$

54. $p^3 + p^2c - 9p - 9c$

55. $81u^2 - 90uv + 25v^2$

56. $4x^2 + 16$

57. $x^2 - 5x - 6$

58. $q^2 + q - 7$

59. $2ax - 6ay + 4bx - 12by$

60. $8m^3 - 10m^2 - 3m$

61. $21x^4y + 41x^3y + 10x^2y$

62. $2m^4 - 128$

63. $8uv - 6u + 12v - 9$

64. $4t^2 - 20t + st - 5s$

65. $12x^2 - 12x + 3$

66. $p^2 + 2pq + q^2$

67. $6n^3 + 5n^2 - 4n$

68. $4k^3 + 4k^2 - 3k$

69. $64 - y^2$

70. $36b - b^3$

71. $b^2 - 4b + 10$

72. $y^2 + 6y + 8$

73. $c^4 - 12c^2 + 20$

Section 6.7	Solving Equations Using the Zero Product Rule

Concepts

1. Definition of a Quadratic Equation
2. Zero Product Rule
3. Solving Equations by Factoring

1. Definition of a Quadratic Equation

We have already learned to solve linear equations in one variable. These are equations of the form $ax + b = c$ $(a \neq 0)$. A linear equation in one variable is sometimes called a first-degree polynomial equation because the highest degree of all its terms is 1. A second-degree polynomial equation in one variable is called a quadratic equation.

A Quadratic Equation in One Variable

If a, b, and c are real numbers such that $a \neq 0$, then a **quadratic equation** is an equation that can be written in the form

$$ax^2 + bx + c = 0$$

The following equations are quadratic because they can each be written in the form $ax^2 + bx + c = 0$, $(a \neq 0)$.

$$-4x^2 + 4x = 1 \qquad x(x-2) = 3 \qquad (x-4)(x+4) = 9$$
$$-4x^2 + 4x - 1 = 0 \qquad x^2 - 2x = 3 \qquad x^2 - 16 = 9$$
$$x^2 - 2x - 3 = 0 \qquad x^2 - 25 = 0$$
$$x^2 + 0x - 25 = 0$$

2. Zero Product Rule

One method for solving a quadratic equation is to factor and apply the zero product rule. The **zero product rule** states that if the product of two factors is zero, then one or both of its factors is zero.

Zero Product Rule

$$\text{If } ab = 0, \text{ then } a = 0 \text{ or } b = 0.$$

Example 1 **Applying the Zero Product Rule**

Solve the equation by using the zero product rule. $\qquad (x-4)(x+3) = 0$

Solution:

$(x-4)(x+3) = 0$	Apply the zero product rule.
$x - 4 = 0 \quad$ or $\quad x + 3 = 0$	Set each factor equal to zero.
$x = 4 \quad$ or $\quad x = -3$	Solve each equation for x.

$\underline{\text{Check}}$: $x = 4$ $\qquad\qquad\qquad$ $\underline{\text{Check}}$: $x = -3$

$(4-4)(4+3) \overset{?}{=} 0 \qquad\qquad (-3-4)(-3+3) \overset{?}{=} 0$

$\qquad\quad (0)(7) \overset{?}{=} 0 \checkmark \qquad\qquad\qquad (-7)(0) \overset{?}{=} 0 \checkmark$

The solution set is $\{4, -3\}$.

Skill Practice Solve.

1. $(x+1)(x-8) = 0$

Answer

1. $\{-1, 8\}$

Example 2   **Applying the Zero Product Rule**

Solve the equation by using the zero product rule. $(x + 8)(4x + 1) = 0$

Solution:

$(x + 8)(4x + 1) = 0$		Apply the zero product rule.
$x + 8 = 0$ or $4x + 1 = 0$		Set each factor equal to zero.
$x = -8$ or	$4x = -1$	Solve each equation for x.
$x = -8$ or	$x = -\dfrac{1}{4}$	The solutions check in the original equation.

The solution set is $\left\{ -8, -\dfrac{1}{4} \right\}$.

Skill Practice   Solve.

2. $(4x - 5)(x + 6) = 0$

Example 3   **Applying the Zero Product Rule**

Solve the equation using the zero product rule. $x(3x - 7) = 0$

Solution:

$x(3x - 7) = 0$		Apply the zero product rule.
$x = 0$ or $3x - 7 = 0$		Set each factor equal to zero.
$x = 0$ or	$3x = 7$	Solve each equation for x.
$x = 0$ or	$x = \dfrac{7}{3}$	The solutions check in the original equation.

The solution set is $\left\{ 0, \dfrac{7}{3} \right\}$.

Skill Practice   Solve.

3. $x(4x + 9) = 0$

---

3. Solving Equations by Factoring

Quadratic equations, like linear equations, arise in many applications in mathematics, science, and business. The following steps summarize the factoring method for solving a quadratic equation.

Solving a Quadratic Equation by Factoring

Step 1   Write the equation in the form: $ax^2 + bx + c = 0$.

Step 2   Factor the quadratic expression completely.

Step 3   Apply the zero product rule. That is, set each factor equal to zero and solve the resulting equations.

Note: The solution(s) found in step 3 may be checked by substitution in the original equation.

Answers

2. $\left\{ \dfrac{5}{4}, -6 \right\}$ **3.** $\left\{ 0, -\dfrac{9}{4} \right\}$

Example 4   **Solving a Quadratic Equation**

Solve the quadratic equation. $2x^2 - 9x = 5$

Solution:

$2x^2 - 9x = 5$

$2x^2 - 9x - 5 = 0$ Write the equation in the form $ax^2 + bx + c = 0$.

$(2x + 1)(x - 5) = 0$ Factor the polynomial completely.

$2x + 1 = 0$ or $x - 5 = 0$ Set each factor equal to zero.

$2x = -1$ or $x = 5$ Solve each equation.

$x = -\dfrac{1}{2}$ or $x = 5$

Check: $x = -\dfrac{1}{2}$ Check: $x = 5$

$2x^2 - 9x = 5$ $2x^2 - 9x = 5$

$2\left(-\dfrac{1}{2}\right)^2 - 9\left(-\dfrac{1}{2}\right) \overset{?}{=} 5$ $2(5)^2 - 9(5) \overset{?}{=} 5$

$2\left(\dfrac{1}{4}\right) + \dfrac{9}{2} \overset{?}{=} 5$ $2(25) - 45 \overset{?}{=} 5$

$\dfrac{1}{2} + \dfrac{9}{2} \overset{?}{=} 5$ $50 - 45 \overset{?}{=} 5 \checkmark$

$\dfrac{10}{2} \overset{?}{=} 5 \checkmark$

The solution set is $\left\{-\dfrac{1}{2}, 5\right\}$.

Skill Practice Solve the quadratic equation.

4. $2y^2 + 19y = -24$

Example 5   **Solving a Quadratic Equation**

Solve the quadratic equation. $4x^2 + 24x = 0$

Solution:

$4x^2 + 24x = 0$ The equation is already in the form $ax^2 + bx + c = 0$. (Note that $c = 0$.)

$4x(x + 6) = 0$ Factor completely.

$4x = 0$ or $x + 6 = 0$ Set each factor equal to zero.

$x = 0$ or $x = -6$ The solutions check in the original equation.

The solution set is $\{0, -6\}$.

Skill Practice Solve the quadratic equation.

5. $5s^2 = 45$

Answers

4. $\left\{-8, -\dfrac{3}{2}\right\}$ **5.** $\{3, -3\}$

Example 6 **Solving a Quadratic Equation**

Solve the quadratic equation. $5x(5x + 2) = 10x + 9$

Solution:

$$5x(5x + 2) = 10x + 9$$

$$25x^2 + 10x = 10x + 9$$ Clear parentheses.

$$25x^2 + 10x - 10x - 9 = 0$$ Set the equation equal to zero.

$$25x^2 - 9 = 0$$ The equation is in the form $ax^2 + bx + c = 0$. (Note that $b = 0$.)

$$(5x - 3)(5x + 3) = 0$$ Factor completely.

$$5x - 3 = 0 \quad \text{or} \quad 5x + 3 = 0$$ Set each factor equal to zero.

$$5x = 3 \quad \text{or} \quad 5x = -3$$ Solve each equation.

$$\frac{5x}{5} = \frac{3}{5} \quad \text{or} \quad \frac{5x}{5} = \frac{-3}{5}$$

$$x = \frac{3}{5} \quad \text{or} \quad x = -\frac{3}{5}$$ The solutions check in the original equation.

The solution set is $\left\{ \frac{3}{5}, -\frac{3}{5} \right\}$.

Skill Practice Solve the quadratic equation.

6. $4z(z + 3) = 4z + 5$

The zero product rule can be used to solve higher degree polynomial equations provided the equations can be set to zero and written in factored form.

Example 7 **Solving a Higher Degree Polynomial Equation**

Solve the equation. $-6(y + 3)(y - 5)(2y + 7) = 0$

Solution:

$$-6(y + 3)(y - 5)(2y + 7) = 0$$ The equation is already in factored form and equal to zero.

Set each factor equal to zero.

Solve each equation for y.

$$-6 \ne 0 \quad \text{or} \quad y + 3 = 0 \quad \text{or} \quad y - 5 = 0 \quad \text{or} \quad 2y + 7 = 0$$

No solution, $\quad y = -3 \quad \text{or} \quad y = 5 \quad \text{or} \quad y = -\frac{7}{2}$

Notice that when the constant factor is set equal to zero, the result is a contradiction, $-6 = 0$. The constant factor does not produce a solution to the equation. Therefore, the solution set is $\{-3, 5, -\frac{7}{2}\}$. Each solution can be checked in the original equation.

Answer

6. $\left\{ -\frac{5}{2}, \frac{1}{2} \right\}$

Skill Practice Solve the equation.

7. $5(p - 4)(p + 7)(2p - 9) = 0$

| **Example 8** | **Solving a Higher Degree Polynomial Equation** |

Solve the equation. $w^3 + 5w^2 - 9w - 45 = 0$

Solution:

$w^3 + 5w^2 - 9w - 45 = 0$ This is a higher degree polynomial equation.

$w^3 + 5w^2 \mid - 9w - 45 = 0$ The equation is already set equal to zero. Now factor.

$w^2(w + 5) - 9(w + 5) = 0$ Because there are four terms, try factoring
$(w + 5)(w^2 - 9) = 0$ by grouping.

$(w + 5)(w - 3)(w + 3) = 0$ $w^2 - 9$ is a difference of squares and can be factored further.

$w + 5 = 0$ or $w - 3 = 0$ or $w + 3 = 0$ Set each factor equal to zero.

$w = -5$ or $w = 3$ or $w = -3$ Solve each equation.

The solution set is $\{-5, 3, -3\}$. Each solution checks in the original equation.

Skill Practice Solve the equation.

8. $x^3 + 3x^2 - 4x - 12 = 0$

Answers

7. $\left\{ 4, -7, \dfrac{9}{2} \right\}$ **8.** $\{-2, -3, 2\}$

| **Section 6.7** | **Practice Exercises** |

Vocabulary and Key Concepts

1. a. An equation that can be written in the form $ax^2 + bx + c = 0$, $(a \neq 0)$, is called a _____ equation.

  b. The zero product rule states that if $ab = 0$, then $a = $ _____ or $b = $ _____.

Review Exercises

For Exercises 2–7, factor completely.

2. $6a - 8 - 3ab + 4b$ **3.** $4b^2 - 44b + 120$ **4.** $8u^2v^2 - 4uv$

5. $3x^2 + 10x - 8$ **6.** $3h^2 - 75$ **7.** $4x^2 + 16y^2$

Concept 1: Definition of a Quadratic Equation

For Exercises 8–13, identify the equations as linear, quadratic, or neither.

8. $4 - 5x = 0$

9. $5x^3 + 2 = 0$

10. $3x - 6x^2 = 0$

11. $1 - x + 2x^2 = 0$

12. $7x^4 + 8 = 0$

13. $3x + 2 = 0$

Concept 2: Zero Product Rule

For Exercises 14–22, solve each equation using the zero product rule. **(See Examples 1–3.)**

14. $(x - 5)(x + 1) = 0$

15. $(x + 3)(x - 1) = 0$

16. $(3x - 2)(3x + 2) = 0$

17. $(2x - 7)(2x + 7) = 0$

18. $2(x - 7)(x - 7) = 0$

19. $3(x + 5)(x + 5) = 0$

20. $(3x - 2)(2x - 3) = 0$

21. $x(5x - 1) = 0$

22. $x(3x + 8) = 0$

23. For a quadratic equation of the form $ax^2 + bx + c = 0$, what must be done before applying the zero product rule?

24. What are the requirements needed to use the zero product rule to solve a quadratic equation or higher degree polynomial equation?

Concept 3: Solving Equations by Factoring

For Exercises 25–72, solve each equation. **(See Examples 4–8.)**

25. $p^2 - 2p - 15 = 0$

26. $y^2 - 7y - 8 = 0$

27. $z^2 + 10z - 24 = 0$

28. $w^2 - 10w + 16 = 0$

29. $2q^2 - 7q = 4$

30. $4x^2 - 11x = 3$

31. $0 = 9x^2 - 4$

32. $4a^2 - 49 = 0$

33. $2k^2 - 28k + 96 = 0$

34. $0 = 2t^2 + 20t + 50$

35. $0 = 2m^3 - 5m^2 - 12m$

36. $3n^3 + 4n^2 + n = 0$

37. $5(3p + 1)(p - 3)(p + 6) = 0$

38. $4(2x - 1)(x - 10)(x + 7) = 0$

39. $x(x - 4)(2x + 3) = 0$

40. $x(3x + 1)(x + 1) = 0$

41. $-5x(2x + 9)(x - 11) = 0$

42. $-3x(x + 7)(3x - 5) = 0$

43. $x^3 - 16x = 0$

44. $t^3 - 36t = 0$

45. $3x^2 + 18x = 0$

46. $2y^2 - 20y = 0$

47. $16m^2 = 9$

48. $9n^2 = 1$

49. $2y^3 + 14y^2 = -20y$

50. $3d^3 - 6d^2 = 24d$

51. $5t - 2(t - 7) = 0$

52. $8h = 5(h - 9) + 6$

53. $2c(c - 8) = -30$

54. $3q(q - 3) = 12$

55. $b^3 = -4b^2 - 4b$

56. $x^3 + 36x = 12x^2$

57. $3(a^2 + 2a) = 2a^2 - 9$

58. $9(k - 1) = -4k^2$

59. $2n(n + 2) = 6$

60. $3p(p - 1) = 18$

61. $x(2x + 5) - 1 = 2x^2 + 3x + 2$

62. $3z(z - 2) - z = 3z^2 + 4$

63. $27q^2 = 9q$

64. $21w^2 = 14w$

65. $3(c^2 - 2c) = 0$

66. $2(4d^2 + d) = 0$

67. $y^3 - 3y^2 - 4y + 12 = 0$

68. $t^3 + 2t^2 - 16t - 32 = 0$

69. $(x - 1)(x + 2) = 18$

70. $(w + 5)(w - 3) = 20$

71. $(p + 2)(p + 3) = 1 - p$

72. $(k - 6)(k - 1) = -k - 2$

Problem Recognition Exercises

Polynomial Expressions Versus Polynomial Equations

For Exercises 1–36, factor the expressions and solve the equations.

1. a. $x^2 + 6x - 7$

   b. $x^2 + 6x - 7 = 0$

2. a. $c^2 + 8c + 12$

   b. $c^2 + 8c + 12 = 0$

3. a. $2y^2 + 7y + 3$

   b. $2y^2 + 7y + 3 = 0$

4. a. $3x^2 - 8x + 5$

   b. $3x^2 - 8x + 5 = 0$

5. a. $5q^2 + q - 4 = 0$

   b. $5q^2 + q - 4$

6. a. $6a^2 - 7a - 3 = 0$

   b. $6a^2 - 7a - 3$

7. a. $a^2 - 64 = 0$

   b. $a^2 - 64$

8. a. $v^2 - 100 = 0$

   b. $v^2 - 100$

9. a. $4b^2 - 81$

   b. $4b^2 - 81 = 0$

10. a. $36t^2 - 49$

    b. $36t^2 - 49 = 0$

11. a. $8x^2 + 16x + 6 = 0$

    b. $8x^2 + 16x + 6$

12. a. $12y^2 + 40y + 32 = 0$

    b. $12y^2 + 40y + 32$

13. a. $x^3 - 8x^2 - 20x$

    b. $x^3 - 8x^2 - 20x = 0$

14. a. $k^3 + 5k^2 - 14k$

    b. $k^3 + 5k^2 - 14k = 0$

15. a. $b^3 + b^2 - 9b - 9 = 0$

    b. $b^3 + b^2 - 9b - 9$

16. a. $x^3 - 8x^2 - 4x + 32 = 0$

    b. $x^3 - 8x^2 - 4x + 32$

17. $2s^2 - 6s + rs - 3r$

18. $6t^2 + 3t + 10tu + 5u$

19. $8x^3 - 2x = 0$

20. $2b^3 - 50b = 0$

21. $2x^3 - 4x^2 + 2x = 0$

22. $3t^3 + 18t^2 + 27t = 0$

23. $7c^2 - 2c + 3 = 7(c^2 + c)$

24. $3z(2z + 4) = -7 + 6z^2$

25. $8w^3 + 27$

26. $1000q^3 - 1$

27. $5z^2 + 2z = 7$

28. $4h^2 + 25h = -6$

29. $3b(b + 6) = b - 10$

30. $3y^2 + 1 = y(y - 3)$

31. $5(2x - 3) - 2(3x + 1) = 4 - 3x$

32. $11 - 6a = -4(2a - 3) - 1$

33. $4s^2 = 64$

34. $81v^2 = 36$

35. $(x - 3)(x - 4) = 6$

36. $(x + 5)(x + 9) = 21$

Section 6.8   Applications of Quadratic Equations

Concepts

1. Applications of Quadratic Equations
2. Pythagorean Theorem

1. Applications of Quadratic Equations

In this section we solve applications using the Problem-Solving Strategies for Word Problems.

Example 1   Translating to a Quadratic Equation

The product of two consecutive integers is 14 more than 6 times the smaller integer.

Solution:

Let x represent the first (smaller) integer.

Then $x + 1$ represents the second (larger) integer.   Label the variables.

(Smaller integer)(larger integer) $= 6 \cdot$ (smaller integer) $+ 14$ Verbal model

$$x(x + 1) = 6(x) + 14 \qquad \text{Algebraic equation}$$
$$x^2 + x = 6x + 14 \qquad \text{Simplify.}$$
$$x^2 + x - 6x - 14 = 0 \qquad \text{Set one side of the equation equal to zero.}$$
$$x^2 - 5x - 14 = 0$$
$$(x - 7)(x + 2) = 0 \qquad \text{Factor.}$$
$$x - 7 = 0 \quad \text{or} \quad x + 2 = 0 \qquad \text{Set each factor equal to zero.}$$
$$x = 7 \quad \text{or} \quad x = -2 \qquad \text{Solve for } x.$$

Recall that x represents the smaller integer. Therefore, there are two possibilities for the pairs of consecutive integers.

If $x = 7$, then the larger integer is $x + 1$ or $7 + 1 = 8$.

If $x = -2$, then the larger integer is $x + 1$ or $-2 + 1 = -1$.

The integers are 7 and 8, or -2 and -1.

Skill Practice

1. The product of two consecutive odd integers is 9 more than 10 times the smaller integer. Find the pair of integers.

Example 2   Using a Quadratic Equation in a Geometry Application

A rectangular sign has an area of 40 ft². If the width is 3 feet shorter than the length, what are the dimensions of the sign?

Solution:

Let x represent the length of the sign. Then $x - 3$ represents the width (Figure 6-1).

The problem gives information about the length of the sides and about the area. Therefore, we can form a relationship by using the formula for the area of a rectangle.

Label the variables.

$x - 3$

x

Figure 6-1
© McGraw-Hill Education/Jill Braaten

Answer

1. The integers are 9 and 11 or -1 and 1.

$A = l \cdot w$	Area equals length times width.
$40 = x(x - 3)$	Set up an algebraic equation.
$40 = x^2 - 3x$	Clear parentheses.
$0 = x^2 - 3x - 40$	Write the equation in the form, $ax^2 + bx + c = 0$.
$0 = (x - 8)(x + 5)$	Factor.
$0 = x - 8$ or $0 = x + 5$	Set each factor equal to zero.
$8 = x$ or $-5 \cancel{=} x$	Because x represents the length of a rectangle, reject the negative solution.

The variable x represents the length of the sign. The length is 8 ft.

The expression $x - 3$ represents the width. The width is 8 ft − 3 ft, or 5 ft.

Skill Practice

   2. The length of a rectangle is 5 ft more than the width. The area is 36 ft^2. Find the length and width.

> **Example 3**   **Using a Quadratic Equation in an Application**

A stone is dropped off a 64-ft cliff and falls into the ocean below. The height of the stone above sea level is given by the equation

$$h = -16t^2 + 64$$ where h is the stone's height in feet, and t is the time in seconds.

Find the time required for the stone to hit the water.

Solution:

When the stone hits the water, its height is zero. Therefore, substitute $h = 0$ into the equation.

$h = -16t^2 + 64$	The equation is quadratic.
$0 = -16t^2 + 64$	Substitute $h = 0$.
$0 = -16(t^2 - 4)$	Factor out the GCF.
$0 = -16(t - 2)(t + 2)$	Factor as a difference of squares.
$-16 \cancel{=} 0$ or $t - 2 = 0$ or $t + 2 = 0$	Set each factor to zero.
No solution, $t = 2$ or $t \cancel{=} -2$	Solve for t.

The negative value of t is rejected because the stone cannot fall for a negative time. Therefore, the stone hits the water after 2 sec.

Skill Practice

   3. An object is launched into the air from the ground and its height is given by $h = -16t^2 + 144t$, where h is the height in feet after t seconds. Find the time required for the object to hit the ground.

2. Pythagorean Theorem

Recall that a right triangle is a triangle that contains a 90° angle. Furthermore, the sum of the squares of the two legs (the shorter sides) of a right triangle equals the square of the hypotenuse (the longest side). This important fact is known as the Pythagorean theorem. The Pythagorean theorem is an enduring landmark of mathematical history from which many mathematical ideas have been built. Although the theorem is named after Pythagoras (sixth century B.C.E.), a Greek mathematician and philosopher, it is thought that the ancient Babylonians were familiar with the principle more than a thousand years earlier.

For the right triangle shown in Figure 6-2, the **Pythagorean theorem** is stated as:

$$a^2 + b^2 = c^2$$

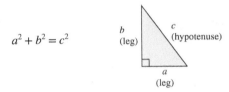

Figure 6-2

In this formula, a and b are the legs of the right triangle and c is the hypotenuse. Notice that the hypotenuse is the longest side of the right triangle and is opposite the 90° angle.

The triangle shown below is a right triangle. Notice that the lengths of the sides satisfy the Pythagorean theorem.

$a^2 + b^2 = c^2$	Apply the Pythagorean theorem.
$(4)^2 + (3)^2 = (5)^2$	Substitute $a = 4$, $b = 3$, and $c = 5$.
$16 + 9 = 25$	
$25 = 25$ ✓	

Example 4   **Applying the Pythagorean Theorem**

Find the length of the missing side of the right triangle.

Solution:

	Label the triangle.
$a^2 + b^2 = c^2$	Apply the Pythagorean theorem.
$a^2 + 6^2 = 10^2$	Substitute $b = 6$ and $c = 10$.
$a^2 + 36 = 100$	Simplify. The equation is quadratic.

$$a^2 + 36 - 100 = 100 - 100 \qquad \text{Subtract 100 from both sides.}$$

$$a^2 - 64 = 0 \qquad \text{One side is now equal to zero.}$$

$$(a + 8)(a - 8) = 0 \qquad \text{Factor.}$$

$$a + 8 = 0 \ \text{ or } \ a - 8 = 0 \qquad \text{Set each factor equal to zero.}$$

$$a = -8 \ \text{ or } \ a = 8 \qquad \text{Because } x \text{ represents the length of a side of a triangle, reject the negative solution.}$$

The third side is 8 ft.

Skill Practice

4. Find the length of the missing side.

| Example 5 | **Using a Quadratic Equation in an Application** |

A 13-ft board is used as a ramp to unload furniture off a loading platform. If the distance between the top of the board and the ground is 7 ft less than the distance between the bottom of the board and the base of the platform, find both distances.

Solution:

Let x represent the distance between the bottom of the board and the base of the platform. Then $x - 7$ represents the distance between the top of the board and the ground (Figure 6-3).

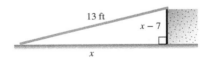

Figure 6-3

$$a^2 + b^2 = c^2 \qquad\qquad \text{Pythagorean theorem}$$

$$x^2 + (x - 7)^2 = (13)^2$$

$$x^2 + (x)^2 - 2(x)(7) + (7)^2 = 169$$

$$x^2 + x^2 - 14x + 49 = 169$$

$$2x^2 - 14x + 49 = 169 \qquad \text{Combine } like \text{ terms.}$$

$$2x^2 - 14x + 49 - 169 = 169 - 169 \qquad \text{Set the equation equal to zero.}$$

$$2x^2 - 14x - 120 = 0 \qquad \text{Write the equation in the form } ax^2 + bx + c = 0.$$

$$2(x^2 - 7x - 60) = 0 \qquad \text{Factor.}$$

$$2(x - 12)(x + 5) = 0$$

$$2 \neq 0 \ \text{ or } \ x - 12 = 0 \ \text{ or } \ x + 5 = 0 \qquad \text{Set each factor equal to zero.}$$

$$x = 12 \ \text{ or } \ x = -5 \qquad \text{Solve both equations for } x.$$

Avoiding Mistakes

Recall that the square of a binomial results in a perfect square trinomial.

$$(a - b)^2 = a^2 - 2ab + b^2$$
$$(x - 7)^2 = x^2 - 2(x)(7) + 7^2$$
$$= x^2 - 14x + 49$$

Don't forget the middle term.

Answer

4. The length of the third side is 12 m.

474   **Chapter 6** Factoring Polynomials

Recall that x represents the distance between the bottom of the board and the base of the platform. We reject the negative value of x because a distance cannot be negative. Therefore, the distance between the bottom of the board and the base of the platform is 12 ft. The distance between the top of the board and the ground is $x - 7 = 5$ ft.

Skill Practice

5. A 5-yd ladder leans against a wall. The distance from the bottom of the wall to the top of the ladder is 1 yd more than the distance from the bottom of the wall to the bottom of the ladder. Find both distances.

Answer

5. The distance along the wall to the top of the ladder is 4 yd. The distance on the ground from the ladder to the wall is 3 yd.

Section 6.8 Practice Exercises

Vocabulary and Key Concepts

1. **a.** If x is the smaller of two consecutive integers, then _____ represents the next greater integer.

   b. If x is the smaller of two consecutive odd integers, then _____ represents the next greater odd integer.

   c. If x is the smaller of two consecutive even integers, then _____ represents the next greater even integer.

   d. The area of a rectangle of length L and width W is given by $A =$ _____.

   e. The area of a triangle with base b and height h is given by the formula $A =$ _____.

   f. Given a right triangle with legs a and b and hypotenuse c, the Pythagorean theorem is stated as _____.

Review Exercises

For Exercises 2–7, solve the quadratic equations.

2. $(6x + 1)(x + 4) = 0$

3. $9x(3x + 2) = 0$

4. $4x^2 - 1 = 0$

5. $x^2 - 5x = 6$

6. $x(x - 20) = -100$

7. $6x^2 - 7x - 10 = 0$

8. Explain what is wrong with the following logic. $(x - 3)(x + 2) = 5$
   $$x - 3 = 5 \quad \text{or} \quad x + 2 = 5$$

Concept 1: Applications of Quadratic Equations

9. If eleven is added to the square of a number, the result is sixty. Find all such numbers.

10. If a number is added to two times its square, the result is thirty-six. Find all such numbers.

11. If twelve is added to six times a number, the result is twenty-eight less than the square of the number. Find all such numbers.

12. The square of a number is equal to twenty more than the number. Find all such numbers.

13. The product of two consecutive odd integers is sixty-three. Find all such integers. **(See Example 1.)**

14. The product of two consecutive even integers is forty-eight. Find all such integers.

15. The sum of the squares of two consecutive integers is sixty-one. Find all such integers.

16. The sum of the squares of two consecutive even integers is fifty-two. Find all such integers.

17. *Las Meninas* (Spanish for *The Maids of Honor*) is a famous painting by Spanish painter Diego Velázquez. This work is regarded as one of the most important paintings in Western art history. The height of the painting is approximately 2 ft more than its width. If the total area is 99 ft^2, determine the dimensions of the painting. **(See Example 2.)**

18. The width of a rectangular painting is 2 in. less than the length. The area is 120 in.^{2} Find the length and width.

© IT Stock Free/Alamy RF

19. The width of a rectangular slab of concrete is 3 m less than the length. The area is 28 m^2.

  a. What are the dimensions of the rectangle?

  b. What is the perimeter of the rectangle?

20. The width of a rectangular picture is 7 in. less than the length. The area of the picture is 78 in.^{2}

  a. What are the dimensions of the picture?

  b. What is the perimeter of the picture?

21. The base of a triangle is 3 ft more than the height. If the area is 14 ft^2, find the base and the height.

22. The height of a triangle is 15 cm more than the base. If the area is 125 cm^2, find the base and the height.

23. The height of a triangle is 7 cm less than 3 times the base. If the area is 20 cm^2, find the base and the height.

24. The base of a triangle is 2 ft less than 4 times the height. If the area is 6 ft^2, find the base and the height.

25. In a physics experiment, a ball is dropped off a 144-ft platform. The height of the ball above the ground is given by the equation

$h = -16t^2 + 144$ where h is the ball's height in feet, and t is the time in seconds after the ball is dropped ($t \geq 0$).

Find the time required for the ball to hit the ground. (*Hint:* Let $h = 0$.) **(See Example 3.)**

26. A stone is dropped off a 256-ft cliff. The height of the stone above the ground is given by the equation

$h = -16t^2 + 256$ where h is the stone's height in feet, and t is the time in seconds after the stone is dropped ($t \geq 0$).

Find the time required for the stone to hit the ground.

27. An object is shot straight up into the air from ground level with an initial speed of 24 ft/sec. The height of the object (in feet) is given by the equation

$h = -16t^2 + 24t$ where t is the time in seconds after launch ($t \geq 0$).

Find the time(s) when the object is at ground level.

28. A rocket is launched straight up into the air from the ground with initial speed of 64 ft/sec. The height of the rocket (in feet) is given by the equation

$h = -16t^2 + 64t$ where t is the time in seconds after launch ($t \geq 0$).

Find the time(s) when the rocket is at ground level.

Concept 2: Pythagorean Theorem

29. Sketch a right triangle and label the sides with the words *leg* and *hypotenuse*.

30. State the Pythagorean theorem.

476   Chapter 6 Factoring Polynomials

For Exercises 31–34, find the length of the missing side of the right triangle. **(See Example 4.)**

31.

c   24 cm
7 cm

32.

3 m   c
4 m

33.

a
17 in.   8 in.

34.

b   15 yd
9 yd

35. Find the length of the supporting brace.

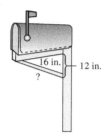
16 in.   12 in.
?

36. Find the height of the airplane above the ground.

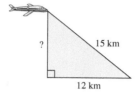
?   15 km
12 km

37. Darcy holds the end of a kite string 3 ft (1 yd) off the ground and wants to estimate the height of the kite. Her friend Jenna is 24 yd away from her, standing directly under the kite as shown in the figure. If Darcy has 30 yd of string out, find the height of the kite (ignore the sag in the string).

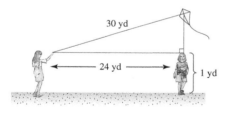
30 yd
← 24 yd →
1 yd

38. Two cars leave the same point at the same time, one traveling north and the other traveling east. After an hour, one car has traveled 48 mi and the other has traveled 64 mi. How many miles apart were they at that time?

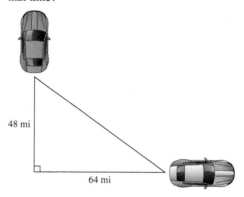
48 mi
64 mi

39. A 17-ft ladder rests against the side of a house. The distance between the top of the ladder and the ground is 7 ft more than the distance between the base of the ladder and the bottom of the house. Find both distances. **(See Example 5.)**

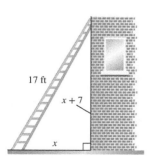
17 ft
x + 7
x

40. Two boats leave a marina. One travels east, and the other travels south. After 30 min, the second boat has traveled 1 mi farther than the first boat and the distance between the boats is 5 mi. Find the distance each boat traveled.

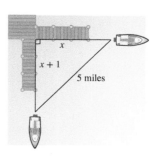
x
x + 1
5 miles

41. One leg of a right triangle is 4 m less than the hypotenuse. The other leg is 2 m less than the hypotenuse. Find the length of the hypotenuse.

42. The longer leg of a right triangle is 1 cm less than twice the shorter leg. The hypotenuse is 1 cm greater than twice the shorter leg. Find the length of the shorter leg.

Group Activity

Building a Factoring Test

Estimated Time: 30–45 minutes

Group Size: 3

In this activity, each group will make a test for this chapter. Then the groups will trade papers and take the test.

For Exercises 1–8, write a polynomial that has the given conditions. Do not use reference materials such as the textbook or your notes.

1. A trinomial with a GCF not equal to 1. The GCF should include a constant and at least one variable.

   1. _____

2. A four-term polynomial that is factorable by grouping.

   2. _____

3. A factorable trinomial with a leading coefficient of 1. (The trinomial should factor as a product of two binomials.)

   3. _____

4. A factorable trinomial with a leading coefficient not equal to 1. (The trinomial should factor as a product of two binomials.)

   4. _____

5. A trinomial that requires the GCF to be removed. The resulting trinomial should factor as a product of two binomials.

   5. _____

6. A difference of squares.

   6. _____

7. A difference of cubes.

   7. _____

8. A sum of cubes.

   8. _____

9. Write a quadratic *equation* that has solution set $\{4, -7\}$.

   9. _____

10. Write a quadratic *equation* that has solution set $\left\{0, -\dfrac{2}{3}\right\}$.

    10. _____

Chapter 6   Summary

Section 6.1   Greatest Common Factor and Factoring by Grouping

Key Concepts

The **greatest common factor** (GCF) is the greatest factor common to all terms of a polynomial. To factor out the GCF from a polynomial, use the distributive property.

A four-term polynomial may be factorable by grouping.

Steps to Factoring by Grouping

1. Identify and factor out the GCF from all four terms.
2. Factor out the GCF from the first pair of terms. Factor out the GCF or its opposite from the second pair of terms.
3. If the two terms share a common binomial factor, factor out the binomial factor.

Examples

Example 1

$3x(a + b) - 5(a + b)$ Greatest common factor is $(a + b)$.

$= (a + b)(3x - 5)$

Example 2

$60xa - 30xb - 80ya + 40yb$

$= 10[6xa - 3xb - 8ya + 4yb]$ Factor out the GCF.

$= 10[3x(2a - b) - 4y(2a - b)]$ Factor by grouping.

$= 10(2a - b)(3x - 4y)$

Section 6.2   Factoring Trinomials of the Form $x^2 + bx + c$

Key Concepts

Factoring a Trinomial with a Leading Coefficient of 1

A trinomial of the form $x^2 + bx + c$ factors as

$$x^2 + bx + c = (x \ \square)(x \ \square)$$

where the remaining terms are given by two integers whose product is c and whose sum is b.

Example

Example 1

$x^2 - 14x + 45$ The integers -5 and -9 have a product of 45 and a sum of -14.

$= (x \ \square)(x \ \square)$

$= (x - 5)(x - 9)$

Summary   **479**

| **Section 6.3** | Factoring Trinomials: Trial-and-Error Method |

Key Concepts

Trial-and-Error Method for Factoring Trinomials in the Form $ax^2 + bx + c$ (where $a \neq 0$)

1. Factor out the GCF from all terms.
2. List the pairs of factors of a and the pairs of factors of c. Consider the reverse order in one of the lists.
3. Construct two binomials of the form

Factors of a

$(\Box x \quad \Box)(\Box x \quad \Box)$

Factors of c

4. Test each combination of factors and signs until the product forms the correct trinomial.
5. If no combination of factors produces the correct product, then the trinomial is prime.

Example

Example 1

$10y^2 + 35y - 20$

$= 5(2y^2 + 7y - 4)$

The pairs of factors of 2 are: $2 \cdot 1$
The pairs of factors of -4 are:

$$-1(4) \qquad 1(-4)$$
$$-2(2) \qquad 2(-2)$$
$$-4(1) \qquad 4(-1)$$

$(2y - 2)(y + 2) = 2y^2 + 2y - 4$ No

$(2y - 4)(y + 1) = 2y^2 - 2y - 4$ No

$(2y + 1)(y - 4) = 2y^2 - 7y - 4$ No

$(2y + 2)(y - 2) = 2y^2 - 2y - 4$ No

$(2y + 4)(y - 1) = 2y^2 + 2y - 4$ No

$(2y - 1)(y + 4) = 2y^2 + 7y - 4$ Yes

$10y^2 + 35y - 20 = 5(2y - 1)(y + 4)$

| **Section 6.4** | Factoring Trinomials: AC-Method |

Key Concepts

AC-Method for Factoring Trinomials of the Form $ax^2 + bx + c$ (where $a \neq 0$)

1. Factor out the GCF from all terms.
2. Find the product ac.
3. Find two integers whose product is ac and whose sum is b. (If no pair of integers can be found, then the trinomial is prime.)
4. Rewrite the middle term (bx) as the sum of two terms whose coefficients are the integers found in step 3.
5. Factor the polynomial by grouping.

Example

Example 1

$10y^2 + 35y - 20$

$= 5(2y^2 + 7y - 4)$ First factor out the GCF.

Identify the product $ac = (2)(-4) = -8$.

Find two integers whose product is -8 and whose sum is 7. The numbers are 8 and -1.

$5[2y^2 + 8y - 1y - 4]$

$= 5[2y(y + 4) - 1(y + 4)]$

$= 5(y + 4)(2y - 1)$

Section 6.5   Difference of Squares and Perfect Square Trinomials

Key Concepts

Factoring a Difference of Squares

$a^2 - b^2 = (a + b)(a - b)$

Factoring a Perfect Square Trinomial

The factored form of a **perfect square trinomial** is the square of a binomial:

$a^2 + 2ab + b^2 = (a + b)^2$

$a^2 - 2ab + b^2 = (a - b)^2$

Examples

Example 1

$25z^2 - 4y^2$

$= (5z + 2y)(5z - 2y)$

Example 2

Factor: $25y^2 + 10y + 1$

$= (5y)^2 + 2(5y)(1) + (1)^2$

$= (5y + 1)^2$

Section 6.6   Sum and Difference of Cubes

Key Concepts

Factoring a Sum or Difference of Cubes

$a^3 + b^3 = (a + b)(a^2 - ab + b^2)$

$a^3 - b^3 = (a - b)(a^2 + ab + b^2)$

Examples

Example 1

$x^6 + 8y^3$

$= (x^2)^3 + (2y)^3$

$= (x^2 + 2y)(x^4 - 2x^2y + 4y^2)$

Example 2

$m^3 - 64$

$= (m)^3 - (4)^3$

$= (m - 4)(m^2 + 4m + 16)$

Section 6.7   Solving Equations Using the Zero Product Rule

Key Concepts

An equation of the form $ax^2 + bx + c = 0$, where $a \neq 0$, is a **quadratic equation**.

The zero product rule states that if $ab = 0$, then $a = 0$ or $b = 0$. The zero product rule can be used to solve a quadratic equation or a higher degree polynomial equation that is factored and set to zero.

Examples

Example 1

The equation $2x^2 - 17x + 30 = 0$ is a quadratic equation.

Example 2

$3w(w - 4)(2w + 1) = 0$

$3w = 0$ or $w - 4 = 0$ or $2w + 1 = 0$

$w = 0$ or $w = 4$ or $w = -\dfrac{1}{2}$

The solution set is $\left\{ 0, 4, -\dfrac{1}{2} \right\}$.

Example 3

$4x^2 = 34x - 60$

$4x^2 - 34x + 60 = 0$

$2(2x^2 - 17x + 30) = 0$

$2(2x - 5)(x - 6) = 0$

$2 \neq 0$ or $2x - 5 = 0$ or $x - 6 = 0$

$x = \dfrac{5}{2}$ or $x = 6$

The solution set is $\left\{ \dfrac{5}{2}, 6 \right\}$.

482   **Chapter 6**   Factoring Polynomials

Section 6.8   Applications of Quadratic Equations

Key Concepts

Use the zero product rule to solve applications.

Examples

Example 1

Find two consecutive integers such that the sum of their squares is 61.

Let x represent one integer.
Let $x + 1$ represent the next consecutive integer.

$$x^2 + (x + 1)^2 = 61$$
$$x^2 + x^2 + 2x + 1 = 61$$
$$2x^2 + 2x - 60 = 0$$
$$2(x^2 + x - 30) = 0$$
$$2(x - 5)(x + 6) = 0$$
$$x = 5 \quad \text{or} \quad x = -6$$

If $x = 5$, then the next consecutive integer is 6.
If $x = -6$, then the next consecutive integer is -5.

The integers are 5 and 6, or -6 and -5.

Some applications involve the Pythagorean theorem.

$$a^2 + b^2 = c^2$$

Example 2

Find the length of the missing side.

$$x^2 + (7)^2 = (25)^2$$
$$x^2 + 49 = 625$$
$$x^2 - 576 = 0$$
$$(x - 24)(x + 24) = 0$$
$$x = 24 \quad \text{or} \quad x = -24$$

The length of the side is 24 ft.

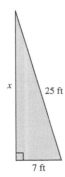

Chapter 6 Review Exercises

Section 6.1

For Exercises 1–4, identify the greatest common factor for each group of terms.

1. $15a^2b^4, 30a^3b, 9a^5b^3$ **2.** $3(x+5), x(x+5)$

3. $2c^3(3c-5), 4c(3c-5)$ **4.** $-2wyz, -4xyz$

For Exercises 5–10, factor out the greatest common factor.

5. $6x^2 + 2x^4 - 8x$ **6.** $11w^3y^3 - 44w^2y^5$

7. $-t^2 + 5t$ **8.** $-6u^2 - u$

9. $3b(b+2) - 7(b+2)$

10. $2(5x+9) + 8x(5x+9)$

For Exercises 11–14, factor by grouping.

11. $7w^2 + 14w + wb + 2b$

12. $b^2 - 2b + yb - 2y$

13. $60y^2 - 45y - 12y + 9$

14. $6a - 3a^2 - 2ab + a^2b$

Section 6.2

For Exercises 15–24, factor completely.

15. $x^2 - 10x + 21$ **16.** $y^2 - 19y + 88$

17. $-6z + z^2 - 72$ **18.** $-39 + q^2 - 10q$

19. $3p^2w + 36pw + 60w$ **20.** $2m^4 + 26m^3 + 80m^2$

21. $-t^2 + 10t - 16$ **22.** $-w^2 - w + 20$

23. $a^2 + 12ab + 11b^2$ **24.** $c^2 - 3cd - 18d^2$

Section 6.3

For Exercises 25–28, assume that a, b, and c represent positive integers.

25. When factoring a polynomial of the form $ax^2 - bx - c$, should the signs of the binomials be both positive, both negative, or different?

26. When factoring a polynomial of the form $ax^2 - bx + c$, should the signs of the binomials be both positive, both negative, or different?

27. When factoring a polynomial of the form $ax^2 + bx + c$, should the signs of the binomials be both positive, both negative, or different?

28. When factoring a polynomial of the form $ax^2 + bx - c$, should the signs of the binomials be both positive, both negative, or different?

For Exercises 29–42, factor each trinomial using the trial-and-error method.

29. $2y^2 - 5y - 12$ **30.** $4w^2 - 5w - 6$

31. $10z^2 + 29z + 10$ **32.** $8z^2 + 6z - 9$

33. $2p^2 - 5p + 1$ **34.** $5r^2 - 3r + 7$

35. $10w^2 - 60w - 270$ **36.** $-3y^2 + 18y + 48$

37. $9c^2 - 30cd + 25d^2$ **38.** $x^2 + 12x + 36$

39. $6g^2 + 7gh + 2h^2$ **40.** $12m^2 - 32mn + 5n^2$

41. $v^4 - 2v^2 - 3$ **42.** $x^4 + 7x^2 + 10$

Section 6.4

For Exercises 43–44, find a pair of integers whose product and sum are given.

43. Product: -5 sum: 4

44. Product: 15 sum: -8

For Exercises 45–58, factor each trinomial using the ac-method.

45. $3c^2 - 5c - 2$ **46.** $4y^2 + 13y + 3$

47. $t^2 + 13tw + 12w^2$ **48.** $4x^4 + 17x^2 - 15$

49. $w^4 + 7w^2 + 10$ **50.** $p^2 - 8pq + 15q^2$

51. $-40v^2 - 22v + 6$ **52.** $40s^2 + 30s - 100$

53. $a^3b - 10a^2b^2 + 24ab^3$ **54.** $2z^6 + 8z^5 - 42z^4$

484   **Chapter 6**   Factoring Polynomials

55. $m + 9m^2 - 2$

56. $2 + 6p^2 + 19p$

57. $49x^2 + 140x + 100$

58. $9w^2 - 6wz + z^2$

Section 6.5

For Exercises 59–60, write the formula to factor each binomial, if possible.

59. $a^2 - b^2$

60. $a^2 + b^2$

For Exercises 61–76, factor completely.

61. $a^2 - 49$

62. $d^2 - 64$

63. $100 - 81t^2$

64. $4 - 25k^2$

65. $x^2 + 16$

66. $y^2 + 121$

67. $y^2 + 12y + 36$

68. $t^2 + 16t + 64$

69. $9a^2 - 12a + 4$

70. $25x^2 - 40x + 16$

71. $-3v^2 - 12v - 12$

72. $-2x^2 + 20x - 50$

73. $2c^4 - 18$

74. $72x^2 - 2y^2$

75. $p^3 + 3p^2 - 16p - 48$

76. $4k - 8 - k^3 + 2k^2$

Section 6.6

For Exercises 77–78, write the formula to factor each binomial, if possible.

77. $a^3 + b^3$

78. $a^3 - b^3$

For Exercises 79–92, factor completely.

79. $64 + a^3$

80. $125 - b^3$

81. $p^6 + 8$

82. $q^6 - \dfrac{1}{27}$

83. $6x^3 - 48$

84. $7y^3 + 7$

85. $x^3 - 36x$

86. $q^4 - 64q$

87. $8h^2 + 20$

88. $m^2 - 8m$

89. $x^3 + 4x^2 - x - 4$

90. $5p^4q - 20q^3$

91. $8n + n^4$

92. $14m^3 - 14$

Section 6.7

93. For which of the following equations can the zero product rule be applied directly? Explain.
$(x - 3)(2x + 1) = 0$ or $(x - 3)(2x + 1) = 6$

For Exercises 94–109, solve each equation using the zero product rule.

94. $(4x - 1)(3x + 2) = 0$

95. $(a - 9)(2a - 1) = 0$

96. $3w(w + 3)(5w + 2) = 0$

97. $6u(u - 7)(4u - 9) = 0$

98. $7k^2 - 9k - 10 = 0$

99. $4h^2 - 23h - 6 = 0$

100. $q^2 - 144 = 0$

101. $r^2 = 25$

102. $5v^2 - v = 0$

103. $x(x - 6) = -8$

104. $36t^2 + 60t = -25$

105. $9s^2 + 12s = -4$

106. $3(y^2 + 4) = 20y$

107. $2(p^2 - 66) = -13p$

108. $2y^3 - 18y^2 = -28y$

109. $x^3 - 4x = 0$

Section 6.8

110. The base of a parallelogram is 1 ft longer than twice the height. If the area is 78 ft^2, find the base and height of the parallelogram.

111. A ball is tossed into the air from ground level with initial speed of 16 ft/sec. The height of the ball is given by the equation

$h = -16t^2 + 16t \quad (t \geq 0)$ where h is the ball's height in feet, and t is the time in seconds.

Find the time(s) when the ball is at ground level.

112. Find the length of the ramp.

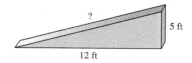

113. A right triangle has one leg that is 2 ft longer than the other leg. The hypotenuse is 2 ft less than twice the shorter leg. Find the lengths of all sides of the triangle.

114. If the square of a number is subtracted from 60, the result is -4. Find all such numbers.

115. The product of two consecutive integers is 44 more than 14 times their sum. Find all such integers.

116. The base of a triangle is 1 m longer than twice the height. If the area of the triangle is 18 m^2, find the base and height.

Chapter 6   Test

1. Factor out the GCF. $15x^4 - 3x + 6x^3$

2. Factor by grouping. $7a - 35 - a^2 + 5a$

3. Factor the trinomial. $6w^2 - 43w + 7$

4. Factor the difference of squares. $169 - p^2$

5. Factor the perfect square trinomial.
$q^2 - 16q + 64$

6. Factor the sum of cubes. $8 + t^3$

For Exercises 7–26, factor completely.

7. $a^2 + 12a + 32$

8. $x^2 + x - 42$

9. $2y^2 - 17y + 8$

10. $6z^2 + 19z + 8$

11. $9t^2 - 100$

12. $v^2 - 81$

13. $3a^2 + 27ab + 54b^2$

14. $c^4 - 1$

15. $xy - 7x + 3y - 21$

16. $49 + p^2$

17. $-10u^2 + 30u - 20$

18. $12t^2 - 75$

19. $5y^2 - 50y + 125$

20. $21q^2 + 14q$

21. $2x^3 + x^2 - 8x - 4$

22. $y^3 - 125$

23. $m^2n^2 - 81$

24. $16a^2 - 64b^2$

25. $64x^3 - 27y^6$

26. $3x^2y - 6xy - 24y$

For Exercises 27–31, solve the equation.

27. $(2x - 3)(x + 5) = 0$

28. $x^2 - 7x = 0$

29. $x^2 - 6x = 16$

30. $x(5x + 4) = 1$

31. $y^3 + 10y^2 - 9y - 90 = 0$

32. A tennis court has an area of 312 yd^2. If the length is 2 yd more than twice the width, find the dimensions of the court.

33. The product of two consecutive odd integers is 35. Find the integers.

34. The height of a triangle is 5 in. less than the length of the base. The area is 42 in^2. Find the base and the height of the triangle.

35. The hypotenuse of a right triangle is 2 ft less than three times the shorter leg. The longer leg is 3 ft less than three times the shorter leg. Find the length of the shorter leg.

36. A stone is dropped off a 64-ft cliff. The height of the stone above the ground is given in the equation

$h = -16t^2 + 64$ where h is the stone's height in feet, and t is the time in seconds after the stone is dropped ($t \geq 0$).

Find the time required for the stone to hit the ground.

Chapters 1–6   Cumulative Review Exercises

1. Simplify. $\dfrac{|4 - 25 \div (-5) \cdot 2|}{\sqrt{8^2 + 6^2}}$

2. Solve. $5 - 2(t + 4) = 3t + 12$

3. Solve for y. $3x - 2y = 8$

4. A child's piggy bank has 17 coins in quarters and dimes. The number of dimes is three less than the number of quarters. How many of each type of coin is in the piggy bank?

© Ryan McVay/Getty Images RF

5. Solve the inequality. Graph the solution on a number line and write the solution set in interval notation.

$$-\frac{5}{12}x \le \frac{5}{3}$$ ⟶

6. Given the equation $y = x + 4$,

   a. Is the equation linear?

   b. Identify the slope.

   c. Identify the y-intercept.

   d. Identify the x-intercept.

   e. Graph the line

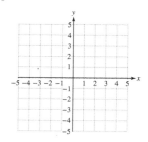

7. Consider the equation $x = 5$,

   a. Does the equation represent a horizontal or vertical line?

   b. Determine the slope of the line, if it exists.

   c. Identify the x-intercept, if it exists.

   d. Identify the y-intercept, if it exists.

8. Find an equation of the line passing through the point $(-3, 5)$ and having a slope of 3. Write the final answer in slope-intercept form.

9. Solve the system. $\begin{aligned} 2x - 3y &= 4 \\ 5x - 6y &= 13 \end{aligned}$

For Exercises 10–13, perform the indicated operations.

10. $2\left(\dfrac{1}{3}y^3 - \dfrac{3}{2}y^2 - 7\right) - \left(\dfrac{2}{3}y^3 + \dfrac{1}{2}y^2 + 5y\right)$

11. $(4p^2 - 5p - 1)(2p - 3)$

12. $(2w - 7)^2$

13. $(r^4 + 2r^3 - 5r + 1) \div (r - 3)$

14. Simplify. $\dfrac{c^{12}c^{-5}}{c^3}$

15. Simplify. $\left(\dfrac{6a^2b^{-4}}{2a^4b^{-5}}\right)^{-2}$

16. Divide. Write the final answer in scientific notation. $\dfrac{8 \times 10^{-3}}{5 \times 10^{-6}}$

For Exercises 17–19, factor completely.

17. $w^4 - 16$

18. $2ax + 10bx - 3ya - 15yb$

19. $4x^2 - 8x - 5$

20. Solve. $4x(2x - 1)(x + 5) = 0$

Rational Expressions and Equations

Rational Expressions and Equations

7

Mathematics in Purchasing Land

Suppose you want to purchase a parcel of land in a remote area. The current owner has a large amount of acreage that she plans to divide into *n* smaller lots for sale. Her total acreage is worth $120,000 and the smaller lots are of equal size. Thus, the cost (in dollars) of an individual lot is given by:

$$\frac{120{,}000}{n}$$

This fraction is called a **rational expression**, because it consists of a polynomial in the numerator and a nonzero polynomial in the denominator.

The cost to purchase an individual lot also includes closing costs. If closing costs are $5600, then the total cost (in dollars) to purchase one lot is given by:

$$\frac{120{,}000}{n} + 5600$$

© AlinaMD/Shutterstock RF

This expression can be simplified by combining the two terms into a single rational expression. In this chapter we will learn how to perform operations on rational expressions and see numerous applications of their use.

488   **Chapter 7**   Rational Expressions and Equations

Concepts

1. Definition of a Rational Expression
2. Evaluating Rational Expressions
3. Restricted Values of a Rational Expression
4. Simplifying Rational Expressions
5. Simplifying a Ratio of −1

1. Definition of a Rational Expression

We define a rational number as the ratio of two integers, $\frac{p}{q}$, where $q \neq 0$.

$$\text{Examples of rational numbers:} \quad \frac{2}{3}, -\frac{1}{5}, 9$$

In a similar way, we define a **rational expression** as the ratio of two polynomials, $\frac{p}{q}$, where $q \neq 0$.

$$\text{Examples of rational expressions:} \quad \frac{3x-6}{x^2-4}, \quad \frac{3}{4}, \quad \frac{6r^5+2r}{7r^3}$$

2. Evaluating Rational Expressions

Example 1   **Evaluating Rational Expressions**

Evaluate the rational expression (if possible) for the given values of x. $\dfrac{x}{x-3}$

a. $x = 6$ **b.** $x = -3$ **c.** $x = 0$ **d.** $x = 3$

Solution:

Substitute the given value for the variable. Use the order of operations to simplify.

a. $\dfrac{x}{x-3}$

$\dfrac{(6)}{(6)-3}$ Substitute $x = 6$.

$= \dfrac{6}{3}$

$= 2$

b. $\dfrac{x}{x-3}$

$\dfrac{(-3)}{(-3)-3}$ Substitute $x = -3$.

$= \dfrac{-3}{-6}$

$= \dfrac{1}{2}$

c. $\dfrac{x}{x-3}$

$\dfrac{(0)}{(0)-3}$ Substitute $x = 0$.

$= \dfrac{0}{-3}$

$= 0$

d. $\dfrac{x}{x-3}$

$\dfrac{(3)}{(3)-3}$ Substitute $x = 3$.

$= \dfrac{3}{0}$ Undefined.

Recall that division by zero is undefined.

Avoiding Mistakes

The numerator is 0 and the denominator is nonzero. Therefore, the fraction is equal to 0.

Avoiding Mistakes

The denominator is 0, therefore the fraction is undefined.

Skill Practice Evaluate the expression for the given values of x. $\dfrac{x-3}{x+5}$

1. $x = 2$ **2.** $x = 0$ **3.** $x = 3$ **4.** $x = -5$

Answers

1. $-\dfrac{1}{7}$ **2.** $-\dfrac{3}{5}$

3. 0   **4.** Undefined

3. Restricted Values of a Rational Expression

From Example 1 we see that not all values of x can be substituted into a rational expression. The values that make the denominator zero must be restricted.

The expression $\dfrac{x}{x-3}$ is undefined for $x = 3$, so we call $x = 3$ a restricted value.

Restricted values of a rational expression are all values that make the expression undefined, that is, make the denominator equal to zero.

> **Finding the Restricted Values of a Rational Expression**
> - Set the denominator equal to zero and solve the resulting equation.
> - The restricted values are the solutions to the equation.

Example 2 **Finding the Restricted Values of Rational Expressions**

Identify the restricted values for each expression.

   a. $\dfrac{y-3}{2y+7}$ **b.** $\dfrac{-5}{x}$

Solution:

a. $\dfrac{y-3}{2y+7}$

$2y + 7 = 0$	Set the denominator equal to zero.
$2y = -7$	Solve the equation.
$\dfrac{2y}{2} = \dfrac{-7}{2}$	
$y = -\dfrac{7}{2}$	The restricted value is $y = -\dfrac{7}{2}$.

b. $\dfrac{-5}{x}$

$x = 0$	Set the denominator equal to zero.
	The restricted value is $x = 0$.

Skill Practice Identify the restricted values.

   5. $\dfrac{a+2}{2a-8}$ **6.** $\dfrac{2}{t}$

Answers

5. $a = 4$ **6.** $t = 0$

> **Example 3**   **Finding the Restricted Values of Rational Expressions**
>
> Identify the restricted values for each expression.
>
> **a.** $\dfrac{a+10}{a^2-25}$ **b.** $\dfrac{2x^3+5}{x^2+9}$
>
> **Solution:**
>
> **a.** $\dfrac{a+10}{a^2-25}$
>
> $a^2-25=0$ Set the denominator equal to zero. The equation is quadratic.
>
> $(a-5)(a+5)=0$ Factor.
>
> $a-5=0$ or $a+5=0$ Set each factor equal to zero.
>
> $a=5$ or $a=-5$
>
> The restricted values are $a=5$ and $a=-5$.
>
> **b.** $\dfrac{2x^3+5}{x^2+9}$
>
> $x^2+9=0$
>
> $x^2=-9$
>
> The quantity x^2 cannot be negative for any real number, x. The denominator x^2+9 is the sum of two nonnegative values, and thus cannot equal zero. Therefore, there are no restricted values.
>
> **Skill Practice** Identify the restricted values.
>
> **7.** $\dfrac{w-4}{w^2-9}$ **8.** $\dfrac{8}{z^4+1}$

4. Simplifying Rational Expressions

In many cases, it is advantageous to simplify or reduce a fraction to lowest terms. The same is true for rational expressions.

The method for simplifying rational expressions mirrors the process for simplifying fractions. In each case, factor the numerator and denominator. Common factors in the numerator and denominator form a ratio of 1 and can be reduced.

Simplifying a fraction: $\dfrac{21}{35} \xrightarrow{\text{Factor}} \dfrac{3\cdot7}{5\cdot7}=\dfrac{3}{5}\cdot\dfrac{\overset{1}{7}}{7}=\dfrac{3}{5}\cdot(1)=\dfrac{3}{5}$

Simplifying a rational expression: $\dfrac{2x-6}{x^2-9}\xrightarrow{\text{Factor}}\dfrac{2(x-3)}{(x+3)(x-3)}=\dfrac{2}{(x+3)}\cdot\dfrac{\overset{1}{(x-3)}}{(x-3)}=\dfrac{2}{(x+3)}(1)$

$=\dfrac{2}{x+3}$

Informally, to simplify a rational expression, we simplify the ratio of common factors to 1. Formally, this is accomplished by applying the fundamental principle of rational expressions.

Answers

7. $w=3, w=-3$
8. There are no restricted values.

Fundamental Principle of Rational Expressions

Let p, q, and r represent polynomials where $q \neq 0$ and $r \neq 0$. Then

$$\frac{pr}{qr} = \frac{p}{q} \cdot \frac{r}{r} = \frac{p}{q} \cdot 1 = \frac{p}{q}$$

TIP: In practice we often shorten the process to reduce a rational expression by dividing out common factors.

$$\frac{p \cdot \overset{1}{r}}{q \cdot r} = \frac{p}{q}$$

Example 4   **Simplifying a Rational Expression**

Given the expression $\dfrac{2p - 14}{p^2 - 49}$

a. Factor the numerator and denominator.

b. Identify the restricted values.

c. Simplify the rational expression.

Solution:

a. $\dfrac{2p - 14}{p^2 - 49}$ | Factor out the GCF in the numerator.

$= \dfrac{2(p - 7)}{(p + 7)(p - 7)}$ | Factor the denominator as a difference of squares.

b. $(p + 7)(p - 7) = 0$ | To find the restricted values, set the denominator equal to zero. The equation is quadratic.

$p + 7 = 0$ or $p - 7 = 0$ | Set each factor equal to 0.

$p = -7$ or $p = 7$ | The restricted values are -7 and 7.

Avoiding Mistakes

The restricted values of a rational expression are always determined *before* simplifying the expression.

c. $\dfrac{2(p \overset{1}{- 7})}{(p + 7)(p - 7)}$ | Simplify the ratio of common factors to 1.

$= \dfrac{2}{p + 7}$ (provided $p \neq 7$ and $p \neq -7$)

Skill Practice   Given $\dfrac{5z + 25}{z^2 + 3z - 10}$

9. Factor the numerator and the denominator.

10. Identify the restricted values.   **11.** Simplify the rational expression.

In Example 4, it is important to note that the expressions

$$\frac{2p - 14}{p^2 - 49}   \text{ and }   \frac{2}{p + 7}$$

are equal for all values of p that make each expression a real number. Therefore,

$$\frac{2p - 14}{p^2 - 49} = \frac{2}{p + 7}$$

for all values of p except $p = 7$ and $p = -7$. (At $p = 7$ and $p = -7$, the original expression is undefined.) This is why the restricted values are determined before the expression is simplified.

Answers

9. $\dfrac{5(z + 5)}{(z + 5)(z - 2)}$

10. $z = -5, z = 2$

11. $\dfrac{5}{z - 2}$ $(z \neq 2, z \neq -5)$

From this point forward, we will write statements of equality between two rational expressions with the assumption that they are equal for all values of the variable for which each expression is defined.

Example 5   **Simplifying a Rational Expression**

Simplify the rational expression. $\dfrac{18a^4}{9a^5}$

Solution:

$$\dfrac{18a^4}{9a^5}$$

$$= \dfrac{2 \cdot 3 \cdot 3 \cdot a \cdot a \cdot a \cdot a}{3 \cdot 3 \cdot a \cdot a \cdot a \cdot a \cdot a} \qquad \text{Factor the numerator and denominator.}$$

$$= \dfrac{2 \cdot (\overset{1}{\cancel{3 \cdot 3 \cdot a \cdot a \cdot a \cdot a}})}{(\cancel{3 \cdot 3 \cdot a \cdot a \cdot a \cdot a}) \cdot a} \qquad \text{Simplify common factors.}$$

$$= \dfrac{2}{a}$$

> **TIP:** The expression $\dfrac{18a^4}{9a^5}$ can also be simplified using the properties of exponents.
>
> $$\dfrac{18a^4}{9a^5} = 2a^{4-5} = 2a^{-1} = \dfrac{2}{a}$$

Skill Practice   Simplify the rational expression.

12. $\dfrac{15q^3}{9q^2}$

Example 6   **Simplifying a Rational Expression**

Simplify the rational expression. $\dfrac{2c - 8}{10c^2 - 80c + 160}$

Solution:

$$\dfrac{2c - 8}{10c^2 - 80c + 160}$$

$$= \dfrac{2(c - 4)}{10(c^2 - 8c + 16)} \qquad \text{Factor out the GCF.}$$

$$= \dfrac{2(c - 4)}{10(c - 4)^2} \qquad \text{Factor the denominator.}$$

$$= \dfrac{2(\overset{1}{\cancel{c - 4}})}{2 \cdot 5(\cancel{c - 4})(c - 4)} \qquad \text{Simplify the ratio of common factors to 1.}$$

$$= \dfrac{1}{5(c - 4)}$$

> **Avoiding Mistakes**
>
> Given the expression
>
> $$\dfrac{2c - 8}{10c^2 - 80c + 160}$$
>
> do not be tempted to reduce before factoring. The terms $2c$ and $10c^2$ cannot be "canceled" because they are *terms* not factors.
>
> The numerator and denominator must be in factored form before simplifying.

Skill Practice   Simplify the rational expression.

13. $\dfrac{x^2 - 1}{2x^2 - x - 3}$

Answers

12. $\dfrac{5q}{3}$ 13. $\dfrac{x - 1}{2x - 3}$

The process to simplify a rational expression is based on the identity property of multiplication. Therefore, this process applies only to factors (remember that factors are multiplied). For example:

$$\frac{3x}{3y} = \frac{3 \cdot x}{3 \cdot y} = \frac{\overset{1}{\cancel{3}}}{\cancel{3}} \cdot \frac{x}{y} = 1 \cdot \frac{x}{y} = \frac{x}{y}$$

Simplify

Terms that are added or subtracted cannot be reduced to lowest terms. For example:

$$\frac{x+3}{y+3}$$

Cannot be simplified

The objective of simplifying a rational expression is to create an equivalent expression that is simpler to use. Consider the rational expression from Example 6 in its original form and in its reduced form. If we substitute a value c into each expression, we see that the reduced form is easier to evaluate. For example, substitute $c = 3$:

	Original Expression	**Simplified Expression**
	$\dfrac{2c-8}{10c^2 - 80c + 160}$	$\dfrac{1}{5(c-4)}$
Substitute $c = 3$	$= \dfrac{2(3) - 8}{10(3)^2 - 80(3) + 160}$	$= \dfrac{1}{5(3-4)}$
	$= \dfrac{6-8}{10(9) - 240 + 160}$	$= \dfrac{1}{5(-1)}$
	$= \dfrac{-2}{90 - 240 + 160}$	$= -\dfrac{1}{5}$
	$= \dfrac{-2}{10} \quad$ or $\quad -\dfrac{1}{5}$	

5. Simplifying a Ratio of −1

When two factors are identical in the numerator and denominator, they form a ratio of 1 and can be reduced. Sometimes we encounter two factors that are *opposites* and form a ratio of −1. For example:

Simplified Form   **Details/Notes**

$\dfrac{-5}{5} = -1$ The ratio of a number and its opposite is −1.

$\dfrac{100}{-100} = -1$ The ratio of a number and its opposite is −1.

$\dfrac{x+7}{-x-7} = -1$ $\dfrac{x+7}{-x-7} = \dfrac{x+7}{-1(x+7)} = \dfrac{\overset{1}{\cancel{x+7}}}{-1\cancel{(x+7)}} = \dfrac{1}{-1} = -1$

factor out −1

$\dfrac{2-x}{x-2} = -1$ $\dfrac{2-x}{x-2} = \dfrac{-1(-2+x)}{x-2} = \dfrac{-1\overset{1}{\cancel{(x-2)}}}{\cancel{x-2}} = \dfrac{-1}{1} = -1$

Recognizing factors that are opposites is useful when simplifying rational expressions.

> **Avoiding Mistakes**
>
> While the expression $2 - x$ and $x - 2$ are opposites, the expressions $2 - x$ and $2 + x$ are *not*.
>
> Therefore, $\dfrac{2-x}{2+x}$ does not simplify to −1.

| Example 7 | **Simplifying a Rational Expression** |

Simplify the rational expression. $\dfrac{3c - 3d}{d - c}$

Solution:

$\dfrac{3c - 3d}{d - c}$

$= \dfrac{3(c - d)}{d - c}$ Factor the numerator and denominator.

Notice that $(c - d)$ and $(d - c)$ are opposites and form a ratio of -1.

$= \dfrac{3(\overset{-1}{c - d})}{d - c}$ Details: $\dfrac{3(c - d)}{d - c} = \dfrac{3(-1)(-c + d)}{d - c} = \dfrac{-3(d - c)}{d - c)} = -3$

$= 3(-1)$

$= -3$

Skill Practice Simplify the rational expression.

14. $\dfrac{2t - 12}{6 - t}$

TIP: It is important to recognize that a rational expression can be written in several equivalent forms. In particular, two numbers with opposite signs form a negative quotient. Therefore, a number such as $-\frac{3}{4}$ can be written as:

$$-\dfrac{3}{4} \quad \text{or} \quad \dfrac{-3}{4} \quad \text{or} \quad \dfrac{3}{-4}$$

The negative sign can be written in the numerator, in the denominator, or out in front of the fraction. We demonstrate this concept in Example 8.

| Example 8 | **Simplifying a Rational Expression** |

Simplify the rational expression. $\dfrac{5 - y}{y^2 - 25}$

Solution:

$\dfrac{5 - y}{y^2 - 25}$

$= \dfrac{5 - y}{(y - 5)(y + 5)}$ Factor the numerator and denominator.

Notice that $5 - y$ and $y - 5$ are opposites and form a ratio of -1.

Answer

14. -2

$$= \frac{5 \overset{-1}{-} y}{(y - 5)(y + 5)} \qquad \text{Details:} \quad \frac{5 - y}{(y - 5)(y + 5)} = \frac{-1(-5 + y)}{(y - 5)(y + 5)}$$

$$= \frac{-1(y - 5)}{(y - 5)(y + 5)} = \frac{-1}{y + 5}$$

$$= \frac{-1}{y + 5} \qquad \text{or} \qquad \frac{1}{-(y + 5)} \qquad \text{or} \qquad -\frac{1}{y + 5}$$

Skill Practice Simplify the rational expression.

15. $\dfrac{b - a}{a^2 - b^2}$

Answer

15. $-\dfrac{1}{a + b}$

Section 7.1   Practice Exercises

Study Skills Exercise

Write an example of how to simplify (reduce) a fraction, multiply two fractions, divide two fractions, add two fractions, and subtract two fractions. Then as you learn about rational expressions, compare the operations on rational expressions with those on fractions. This is a great place to use 3×5 cards again. Write an example of an operation with fractions on one side and the same operation with rational expressions on the other side.

Vocabulary and Key Concepts

1. **a.** A _____ expression is the ratio of two polynomials, $\dfrac{p}{q}$, where $q \neq 0$.

    b. Restricted values of a rational expression are all values that make the _____ equal to _____.

    c. For polynomials p, q, and r, where ($q \neq 0$ and $r \neq 0$), $\dfrac{pr}{qr} = $ _____.

    d. The ratio $\dfrac{a - b}{a - b} = $ _____ whereas the ratio $\dfrac{a - b}{b - a} = $ _____ provided that $a \neq b$.

Concept 2: Evaluating Rational Expressions

For Exercises 2–10, substitute the given number into the expression and simplify (if possible). **(See Example 1.)**

2. $\dfrac{5}{y - 4}$; $y = 6$

3. $\dfrac{t - 2}{t^2 - 4t + 8}$; $t = 2$

4. $\dfrac{4x}{x - 7}$; $x = 8$

5. $\dfrac{1}{x - 6}$; $x = -2$

6. $\dfrac{w - 10}{w + 6}$; $w = 0$

7. $\dfrac{w - 4}{2w + 8}$; $w = 0$

8. $\dfrac{y - 8}{2y^2 + y - 1}$; $y = 8$

9. $\dfrac{(a - 7)(a + 1)}{(a - 2)(a + 5)}$; $a = 2$

10. $\dfrac{(a + 4)(a + 1)}{(a - 4)(a - 1)}$; $a = 1$

496   **Chapter 7** Rational Expressions and Equations

11. A bicyclist rides 24 mi against a wind and returns 24 mi with the same wind. His average speed for the return trip traveling with the wind is 8 mph faster than his speed going out against the wind. If x represents the bicyclist's speed going out against the wind, then the total time, t, required for the round trip is given by

$$t = \frac{24}{x} + \frac{24}{x+8}$$ where t is measured in hours.

© Royalty Free/Corbis RF

a. Find the time required for the round trip if the cyclist rides 12 mph against the wind.

b. Find the time required for the round trip if the cyclist rides 24 mph against the wind.

12. The manufacturer of mountain bikes has a fixed cost of $56,000, plus a variable cost of $140 per bike. The average cost per bike, y (in dollars), is given by the equation:

$$y = \frac{56{,}000 + 140x}{x}$$ where x represents the number of bikes produced.

© Jeff Maloney/Getty Images RF

a. Find the average cost per bike if the manufacturer produces 1000 bikes.

b. Find the average cost per bike if the manufacturer produces 2000 bikes.

c. Find the average cost per bike if the manufacturer produces 10,000 bikes.

Concept 3: Restricted Values of a Rational Expression

For Exercises 13–24, identify the restricted values. **(See Examples 2–3.)**

13. $\dfrac{5}{k+2}$

14. $\dfrac{-3}{h-4}$

15. $\dfrac{x+5}{(2x-5)(x+8)}$

16. $\dfrac{4y+1}{(3y+7)(y+3)}$

17. $\dfrac{m+12}{m^2+5m+6}$

18. $\dfrac{c-11}{c^2-5c-6}$

19. $\dfrac{x-4}{x^2+9}$

20. $\dfrac{x+1}{x^2+4}$

21. $\dfrac{y^2-y-12}{12}$

22. $\dfrac{z^2+10z+9}{9}$

23. $\dfrac{t-5}{t}$

24. $\dfrac{2w+7}{w}$

25. Construct a rational expression that is undefined for $x = 2$. (Answers will vary.)

26. Construct a rational expression that is undefined for $x = 5$. (Answers will vary.)

27. Construct a rational expression that is undefined for $x = -3$ and $x = 7$. (Answers will vary.)

28. Construct a rational expression that is undefined for $x = -1$ and $x = 4$. (Answers will vary.)

29. Evaluate the expressions for $x = -1$.

    a. $\dfrac{3x^2-2x-1}{6x^2-7x-3}$ **b.** $\dfrac{x-1}{2x-3}$

30. Evaluate the expressions for $x = 4$.

    a. $\dfrac{(x+5)^2}{x^2+6x+5}$ **b.** $\dfrac{x+5}{x+1}$

31. Evaluate the expressions for $x = 1$.

    a. $\dfrac{5x+5}{x^2-1}$ **b.** $\dfrac{5}{x-1}$

32. Evaluate the expressions for $x = -3$.

    a. $\dfrac{2x^2-4x-6}{2x^2-18}$ **b.** $\dfrac{x+1}{x+3}$

Concept 4: Simplifying Rational Expressions

For Exercises 33–42,

    a. Identify the restricted values.   **b.** Simplify the rational expression. **(See Example 4.)**

33. $\dfrac{3y + 6}{6y + 12}$

34. $\dfrac{8x - 8}{4x - 4}$

35. $\dfrac{t^2 - 1}{t + 1}$

36. $\dfrac{r^2 - 4}{r - 2}$

37. $\dfrac{7w}{21w^2 - 35w}$

38. $\dfrac{12a^2}{24a^2 - 18a}$

39. $\dfrac{9x^2 - 4}{6x + 4}$

40. $\dfrac{8n - 20}{4n^2 - 25}$

41. $\dfrac{a^2 + 3a - 10}{a^2 + a - 6}$

42. $\dfrac{t^2 + 3t - 10}{t^2 + t - 20}$

For Exercises 43–72, simplify the rational expression. **(See Examples 5–6.)**

43. $\dfrac{7b^2}{21b}$

44. $\dfrac{15c^3}{3c^5}$

45. $\dfrac{-24x^2y^5z}{8xy^4z^3}$

46. $\dfrac{60rs^4t^2}{-12r^4s^2t^3}$

47. $\dfrac{(p - 3)(p + 5)}{(p + 5)(p + 4)}$

48. $\dfrac{(c + 4)(c - 1)}{(c + 4)(c + 2)}$

49. $\dfrac{m + 11}{4(m + 11)(m - 11)}$

50. $\dfrac{n - 7}{9(n + 2)(n - 7)}$

51. $\dfrac{x(2x + 1)^2}{4x^3(2x + 1)}$

52. $\dfrac{(p + 2)(p - 3)^4}{(p + 2)^2(p - 3)^2}$

53. $\dfrac{5}{20a - 25}$

54. $\dfrac{7}{14c - 21}$

55. $\dfrac{3x^2 - 6x}{9xy + 18x}$

56. $\dfrac{6p^2 + 12p}{2pq - 4p}$

57. $\dfrac{2x + 4}{x^2 - 3x - 10}$

58. $\dfrac{5z + 15}{z^2 - 4z - 21}$

59. $\dfrac{a^2 - 49}{a - 7}$

60. $\dfrac{b^2 - 64}{b - 8}$

61. $\dfrac{q^2 + 25}{q + 5}$

62. $\dfrac{r^2 + 36}{r + 6}$

63. $\dfrac{y^2 + 6y + 9}{2y^2 + y - 15}$

64. $\dfrac{h^2 + h - 6}{h^2 + 2h - 8}$

65. $\dfrac{5q^2 + 5}{q^4 - 1}$

66. $\dfrac{4t^2 + 16}{t^4 - 16}$

67. $\dfrac{ac - ad + 2bc - 2bd}{2ac + ad + 4bc + 2bd}$ (*Hint*: Factor by grouping.)

68. $\dfrac{3pr - ps - 3qr + qs}{3pr - ps + 3qr - qs}$ (*Hint*: Factor by grouping.)

69. $\dfrac{5x^3 + 4x^2 - 45x - 36}{x^2 - 9}$

70. $\dfrac{x^2 - 1}{ax^3 - bx^2 - ax + b}$

71. $\dfrac{2x^2 - xy - 3y^2}{2x^2 - 11xy + 12y^2}$

72. $\dfrac{2c^2 + cd - d^2}{5c^2 + 3cd - 2d^2}$

Concept 5: Simplifying a Ratio of −1

73. What is the relationship between $x - 2$ and $2 - x$?

74. What is the relationship between $w + p$ and $-w - p$?

For Exercises 75–86, simplify the rational expressions. **(See Examples 7–8.)**

75. $\dfrac{x - 5}{5 - x}$

76. $\dfrac{8 - p}{p - 8}$

77. $\dfrac{-4 - y}{4 + y}$

78. $\dfrac{z + 10}{-z - 10}$

79. $\dfrac{3y - 6}{12 - 6y}$

80. $\dfrac{4q - 4}{12 - 12q}$

81. $\dfrac{k + 5}{5 - k}$

82. $\dfrac{2 + n}{2 - n}$

83. $\dfrac{10x - 12}{10x + 12}$

84. $\dfrac{4t - 16}{16 + 4t}$

85. $\dfrac{x^2 - x - 12}{16 - x^2}$

86. $\dfrac{49 - b^2}{b^2 - 10b + 21}$

498   **Chapter 7**   Rational Expressions and Equations

Mixed Exercises

For Exercises 87–100, simplify the rational expressions.

87. $\dfrac{3x^2 + 7x - 6}{x^2 + 7x + 12}$

88. $\dfrac{y^2 - 5y - 14}{2y^2 - y - 10}$

89. $\dfrac{3(m - 2)}{6(2 - m)}$

90. $\dfrac{8(1 - x)}{4(x - 1)}$

91. $\dfrac{w^2 - 4}{8 - 4w}$

92. $\dfrac{15 - 3x}{x^2 - 25}$

93. $\dfrac{18st^5}{12st^3}$

94. $\dfrac{20a^4b^2}{25ab^2}$

95. $\dfrac{4r^2 - 4rs + s^2}{s^2 - 4r^2}$

96. $\dfrac{y^2 - 9z^2}{3z^2 + 2yz - y^2}$

97. $\dfrac{3y - 3x}{2x^2 - 4xy + 2y^2}$

98. $\dfrac{49p^2 - 28pq + 4q^2}{4q - 14p}$

99. $\dfrac{2t^2 - 3t}{2t^4 - 13t^3 + 15t^2}$

100. $\dfrac{4m^3 + 3m^2}{4m^3 + 7m^2 + 3m}$

Expanding Your Skills

For Exercises 101–104, factor and simplify.

101. $\dfrac{w^3 - 8}{w^2 + 2w + 4}$

102. $\dfrac{y^3 + 27}{y^2 - 3y + 9}$

103. $\dfrac{z^2 - 16}{z^3 - 64}$

104. $\dfrac{x^2 - 25}{x^3 + 125}$

Section 7.2	Multiplication and Division of Rational Expressions

Concepts

1. Multiplication of Rational Expressions
2. Division of Rational Expressions

1. Multiplication of Rational Expressions

Recall that to multiply fractions, we multiply the numerators and multiply the denominators. The same is true for multiplying rational expressions.

> **Multiplication of Rational Expressions**
>
> Let p, q, r, and s represent polynomials, such that $q \neq 0$, $s \neq 0$. Then,
>
> $$\frac{p}{q} \cdot \frac{r}{s} = \frac{pr}{qs}$$

For example:

Multiply the Fractions

$$\frac{2}{3} \cdot \frac{5}{7} = \frac{10}{21}$$

Multiply the Rational Expressions

$$\frac{2x}{3y} \cdot \frac{5z}{7} = \frac{10xz}{21y}$$

Sometimes it is possible to simplify a ratio of common factors to 1 *before* multiplying. To do so, we must first factor the numerators and denominators of each fraction.

$$\frac{15}{14} \cdot \frac{21}{10} = \frac{3 \cdot \overset{1}{\cancel{5}}}{2 \cdot \cancel{7}} \cdot \frac{3 \cdot \overset{1}{\cancel{7}}}{2 \cdot \cancel{5}} = \frac{9}{4}$$

The same process is also used to multiply rational expressions.

Multiplying Rational Expressions

Step 1   Factor the numerators and denominators of all rational expressions.
Step 2   Simplify the ratios of common factors to 1 and opposite factors to -1.
Step 3   Multiply the remaining factors in the numerator, and multiply the remaining factors in the denominator.

Example 1   **Multiplying Rational Expressions**

Multiply. $\dfrac{5a^2b}{2} \cdot \dfrac{6a}{10b}$

Solution:

$\dfrac{5a^2b}{2} \cdot \dfrac{6a}{10b}$

$= \dfrac{5 \cdot a \cdot a \cdot b}{2} \cdot \dfrac{2 \cdot 3 \cdot a}{2 \cdot 5 \cdot b}$ Factor into prime factors.

$= \dfrac{\cancel{5} \cdot a \cdot a \cdot \cancel{b}}{2} \cdot \dfrac{\cancel{2} \cdot 3 \cdot a}{\cancel{2} \cdot \cancel{5} \cdot \cancel{b}}$ Simplify.

$= \dfrac{3a^3}{2}$ Multiply remaining factors.

Skill Practice   Multiply.

1. $\dfrac{7a}{3b} \cdot \dfrac{15b}{14a^2}$

Example 2   **Multiplying Rational Expressions**

Multiply. $\dfrac{3c - 3d}{6c} \cdot \dfrac{2}{c^2 - d^2}$

Solution:

$\dfrac{3c - 3d}{6c} \cdot \dfrac{2}{c^2 - d^2}$

$= \dfrac{3(c - d)}{2 \cdot 3 \cdot c} \cdot \dfrac{2}{(c - d)(c + d)}$ Factor.

$= \dfrac{\cancel{3}(\cancel{c - d})}{\cancel{2} \cdot \cancel{3} \cdot c} \cdot \dfrac{\cancel{2}}{(\cancel{c - d})(c + d)}$ Simplify.

$= \dfrac{1}{c(c + d)}$ Multiply remaining factors.

> **Avoiding Mistakes**
> If all the factors in the numerator reduce to a ratio of 1, a factor of 1 is left in the numerator.

Skill Practice   Multiply.

2. $\dfrac{4x - 8}{x + 6} \cdot \dfrac{x^2 + 6x}{2x}$

Answers

1. $\dfrac{5}{2a}$ **2.** $2(x - 2)$

> **Example 3**   **Multiplying Rational Expressions**
>
> Multiply. $\dfrac{35 - 5x}{5x + 5} \cdot \dfrac{x^2 + 5x + 4}{x^2 - 49}$
>
> **Solution:**
>
> $\dfrac{35 - 5x}{5x + 5} \cdot \dfrac{x^2 + 5x + 4}{x^2 - 49}$
>
> $= \dfrac{5(7 - x)}{5(x + 1)} \cdot \dfrac{(x + 4)(x + 1)}{(x - 7)(x + 7)}$ Factor the numerators and denominators completely.
>
> $= \dfrac{\overset{1}{\cancel{5}}\overset{-1}{\cancel{(7 - x)}}}{\cancel{5}\cancel{(x + 1)}} \cdot \dfrac{(x + 4)\overset{1}{\cancel{(x + 1)}}}{\cancel{(x - 7)}(x + 7)}$ Simplify the ratios of common factors to 1 or −1.
>
> $= \dfrac{-1(x + 4)}{x + 7}$ Multiply remaining factors.
>
> $= \dfrac{-(x + 4)}{x + 7}$ or $\dfrac{x + 4}{-(x + 7)}$ or $-\dfrac{x + 4}{x + 7}$

TIP: The ratio $\dfrac{7 - x}{x - 7} = -1$ because $7 - x$ and $x - 7$ are opposites.

Skill Practice Multiply.

3. $\dfrac{p^2 + 4p + 3}{5p + 10} \cdot \dfrac{p^2 - p - 6}{9 - p^2}$

---

2. Division of Rational Expressions

Recall that to divide two fractions, multiply the first fraction by the reciprocal of the second.

$$\dfrac{21}{10} \div \dfrac{49}{15} \xrightarrow[\text{of the second fraction}]{\text{multiply by the reciprocal}} \dfrac{21}{10} \cdot \dfrac{15}{49} \xrightarrow{\text{factor}} \dfrac{3 \cdot \overset{1}{\cancel{7}}}{2 \cdot \cancel{5}} \cdot \dfrac{3 \cdot \overset{1}{\cancel{5}}}{\cancel{7} \cdot 7} = \dfrac{9}{14}$$

The same process is used to divide rational expressions.

> **Division of Rational Expressions**
>
> Let p, q, r, and s represent polynomials, such that $q \neq 0$, $r \neq 0$, $s \neq 0$. Then,
>
> $$\dfrac{p}{q} \div \dfrac{r}{s} = \dfrac{p}{q} \cdot \dfrac{s}{r} = \dfrac{ps}{qr}$$

> **Example 4**   **Dividing Rational Expressions**
>
> Divide. $\dfrac{5t - 15}{2} \div \dfrac{t^2 - 9}{10}$
>
> **Solution:**
>
> $\dfrac{5t - 15}{2} \div \dfrac{t^2 - 9}{10}$
>
> $= \dfrac{5t - 15}{2} \cdot \dfrac{10}{t^2 - 9}$ Multiply the first fraction by the reciprocal of the second.

Avoiding Mistakes

When dividing rational expressions, take the reciprocal of the second fraction and change to multiplication *before* reducing like factors.

Answer

3. $\dfrac{-(p + 1)}{5}$ or $\dfrac{p + 1}{-5}$ or $-\dfrac{p + 1}{5}$

$$= \frac{5(t-3)}{2} \cdot \frac{2 \cdot 5}{(t-3)(t+3)} \qquad \text{Factor each polynomial.}$$

$$= \frac{5(t-3)}{2} \cdot \frac{2 \cdot 5}{(t-3)(t+3)} \qquad \text{Simplify the ratio of common factors to 1.}$$

$$= \frac{25}{t+3}$$

Skill Practice Divide.

4. $\dfrac{7y - 14}{y + 1} \div \dfrac{y^2 + 2y - 8}{2y + 2}$

> **Example 5**   **Dividing Rational Expressions**

Divide. $\dfrac{p^2 - 11p + 30}{10p^2 - 250} \div \dfrac{30p - 5p^2}{2p + 4}$

Solution:

$$\frac{p^2 - 11p + 30}{10p^2 - 250} \div \frac{30p - 5p^2}{2p + 4}$$

$$= \frac{p^2 - 11p + 30}{10p^2 - 250} \cdot \frac{2p + 4}{30p - 5p^2} \qquad \begin{array}{l}\text{Multiply the first fraction by the}\\ \text{reciprocal of the second.}\end{array}$$

$$\text{Factor the trinomial.}$$
$$p^2 - 11p + 30 = (p - 5)(p - 6)$$

$$= \frac{(p-5)(p-6)}{2 \cdot 5(p-5)(p+5)} \cdot \frac{2(p+2)}{5p(6-p)} \qquad \begin{array}{l}\text{Factor out the GCF.}\\ 2p + 4 = 2(p + 2)\end{array}$$

$$\begin{array}{l}\text{Factor out the GCF. Then factor}\\ \text{the difference of squares.}\end{array}$$
$$\begin{aligned} 10p^2 - 250 &= 10(p^2 - 25)\\ &= 2 \cdot 5(p - 5)(p + 5)\end{aligned}$$

$$\text{Factor out the GCF.}$$
$$30p - 5p^2 = 5p(6 - p)$$

$$= \frac{\overset{1}{(p-5)}\overset{-1}{(p-6)}}{2 \cdot 5(p-5)(p+5)} \cdot \frac{\overset{1}{2}(p+2)}{5p(6-p)} \qquad \begin{array}{l}\text{Simplify the ratio of common}\\ \text{factors to 1 or }-1.\end{array}$$

$$= -\frac{(p+2)}{25p(p+5)}$$

Skill Practice Divide.

5. $\dfrac{4x^2 - 9}{2x^2 - x - 3} \div \dfrac{20x + 30}{x^2 + 7x + 6}$

Answers

4. $\dfrac{14}{y+4}$ **5.** $\dfrac{x+6}{10}$

| **Example 6** | **Dividing Rational Expressions** |

Divide. $\dfrac{\dfrac{3x}{4y}}{\dfrac{5x}{6y}}$

Solution:

$\dfrac{\dfrac{3x}{4y}}{\dfrac{5x}{6y}}$ ⟵———————————— This fraction bar denotes division ($\div$).

$= \dfrac{3x}{4y} \div \dfrac{5x}{6y}$

$= \dfrac{3x}{4y} \cdot \dfrac{6y}{5x}$ Multiply by the reciprocal of the second fraction.

$= \dfrac{3 \cdot \overset{1}{\cancel{x}}}{\cancel{2} \cdot 2 \cdot \cancel{y}} \cdot \dfrac{\overset{1}{\cancel{2}} \cdot 3 \cdot \overset{1}{\cancel{y}}}{5 \cdot \cancel{x}}$ Simplify the ratio of common factors to 1.

$= \dfrac{9}{10}$

Skill Practice Divide.

6. $\dfrac{\dfrac{a^3b}{9c}}{\dfrac{4ab}{3c^3}}$

Sometimes multiplication and division of rational expressions appear in the same problem. In such a case, apply the order of operations by multiplying or dividing in order from left to right.

| **Example 7** | **Multiplying and Dividing Rational Expressions** |

Perform the indicated operations. $\dfrac{4}{c^2 - 9} \div \dfrac{6}{c - 3} \cdot \dfrac{3c}{8}$

Solution:
In this example, division occurs first, before multiplication. Parentheses may be inserted to reinforce the proper order.

$\left(\dfrac{4}{c^2 - 9} \div \dfrac{6}{c - 3} \right) \cdot \dfrac{3c}{8}$

$= \left(\dfrac{4}{c^2 - 9} \cdot \dfrac{c - 3}{6} \right) \cdot \dfrac{3c}{8}$ Multiply the first fraction by the reciprocal of the second.

$$= \left(\frac{2 \cdot 2}{(c-3)(c+3)} \cdot \frac{c-3}{2 \cdot 3} \right) \cdot \frac{3 \cdot c}{2 \cdot 2 \cdot 2}$$

Now that each operation is written as multiplication, factor the polynomials and reduce the common factors.

$$= \frac{\overset{1}{2} \cdot \overset{1}{2}}{(c-3)(c+3)} \cdot \frac{(c-3)}{2 \cdot 3} \cdot \frac{\overset{1}{3} \cdot c}{2 \cdot 2 \cdot 2}$$

$$= \frac{c}{4(c+3)}$$

Simplify.

Skill Practice Perform the indicated operations.

7. $\dfrac{v}{v+2} \div \dfrac{5v^2}{v^2-4} \cdot \dfrac{v}{10}$

Answer

7. $\dfrac{v-2}{50}$

Section 7.2   Practice Exercises

Review Exercises

For Exercises 1–8, multiply or divide the fractions.

1. $\dfrac{3}{5} \cdot \dfrac{1}{2}$

2. $\dfrac{6}{7} \cdot \dfrac{5}{12}$

3. $\dfrac{3}{4} \div \dfrac{3}{8}$

4. $\dfrac{18}{5} \div \dfrac{2}{5}$

5. $6 \cdot \dfrac{5}{12}$

6. $\dfrac{7}{25} \cdot 5$

7. $\dfrac{\frac{21}{4}}{\frac{7}{5}}$

8. $\dfrac{\frac{9}{2}}{\frac{3}{4}}$

Concept 1: Multiplication of Rational Expressions

For Exercises 9–24, multiply. **(See Examples 1–3.)**

9. $\dfrac{2xy}{5x^2} \cdot \dfrac{15}{4y}$

10. $\dfrac{7s}{t^2} \cdot \dfrac{t^2}{14s^2}$

11. $\dfrac{6x^3}{9x^6y^2} \cdot \dfrac{18x^4y^7}{4y}$

12. $\dfrac{10a^2b}{15b^2} \cdot \dfrac{30b}{2a^3}$

13. $\dfrac{4x-24}{20x} \cdot \dfrac{5x}{8}$

14. $\dfrac{5a+20}{a} \cdot \dfrac{3a}{10}$

15. $\dfrac{3y+18}{y^2} \cdot \dfrac{4y}{6y+36}$

16. $\dfrac{2p-4}{6p} \cdot \dfrac{4p^2}{8p-16}$

17. $\dfrac{10}{2-a} \cdot \dfrac{a-2}{16}$

18. $\dfrac{w-3}{6} \cdot \dfrac{20}{3-w}$

19. $\dfrac{b^2-a^2}{a-b} \cdot \dfrac{a}{a^2-ab}$

20. $\dfrac{(x-y)^2}{x^2+xy} \cdot \dfrac{x}{y-x}$

21. $\dfrac{y^2+2y+1}{5y-10} \cdot \dfrac{y^2-3y+2}{y^2-1}$

22. $\dfrac{6a^2-6}{a^2+6a+5} \cdot \dfrac{a^2+5a}{12a}$

23. $\dfrac{10x}{2x^2+3x+1} \cdot \dfrac{x^2+7x+6}{5x}$

24. $\dfrac{p-3}{p^2+p-12} \cdot \dfrac{4p+16}{p+1}$

Concept 2: Division of Rational Expressions

For Exercises 25–38, divide. **(See Examples 4–6.)**

25. $\dfrac{4x}{7y} \div \dfrac{2x^2}{21xy}$

26. $\dfrac{6cd}{5d^2} \div \dfrac{8c^3}{10d}$

27. $\dfrac{\dfrac{8m^4n^5}{5n^6}}{\dfrac{24mn}{15m^3}}$

28. $\dfrac{\dfrac{10a^3b}{3a}}{\dfrac{5b}{9ab}}$

29. $\dfrac{4a+12}{6a-18} \div \dfrac{3a+9}{5a-15}$

30. $\dfrac{8m-16}{3m+3} \div \dfrac{5m-10}{2m+2}$

31. $\dfrac{3x-21}{6x^2-42x} \div \dfrac{7}{12x}$

32. $\dfrac{4a^2-4a}{9a-9} \div \dfrac{5}{12a}$

33. $\dfrac{m^2-n^2}{9} \div \dfrac{3n-3m}{27m}$

34. $\dfrac{9-t^2}{15t+15} \div \dfrac{t-3}{5t}$

35. $\dfrac{3p+4q}{p^2+4pq+4q^2} \div \dfrac{4}{p+2q}$

36. $\dfrac{x^2+2xy+y^2}{2x-y} \div \dfrac{x+y}{5}$

37. $\dfrac{p^2-2p-3}{p^2-p-6} \div \dfrac{p^2-1}{p^2+2p}$

38. $\dfrac{4t^2-1}{t^2-5t} \div \dfrac{2t^2+5t+2}{t^2-3t-10}$

Mixed Exercises

For Exercises 39–64, multiply or divide as indicated.

39. $(w+3) \cdot \dfrac{w}{2w^2+5w-3}$

40. $\dfrac{5t+1}{5t^2-31t+6} \cdot (t-6)$

41. $(r-5) \cdot \dfrac{4r}{2r^2-7r-15}$

42. $\dfrac{q+1}{5q^2-28q-12} \cdot (5q+2)$

43. $\dfrac{\dfrac{5t-10}{12}}{\dfrac{4t-8}{8}}$

44. $\dfrac{\dfrac{6m+6}{5}}{\dfrac{3m+3}{10}}$

45. $\dfrac{2a^2+13a-24}{8a-12} \div (a+8)$

46. $\dfrac{3y^2+20y-7}{5y+35} \div (3y-1)$

47. $\dfrac{y^2+5y-36}{y^2-2y-8} \cdot \dfrac{y+2}{y-6}$

48. $\dfrac{z^2-11z+28}{z-1} \cdot \dfrac{z+1}{z^2-6z-7}$

49. $\dfrac{2t^2+t-1}{t^2+3t+2} \cdot \dfrac{t+2}{2t-1}$

50. $\dfrac{3p^2-2p-8}{3p^2-5p-12} \cdot \dfrac{p-3}{p-2}$

51. $(5t-1) \div \dfrac{5t^2+9t-2}{3t+8}$

52. $(2q-3) \div \dfrac{2q^2+5q-12}{q-7}$

53. $\dfrac{x^2+2x-3}{x^2-3x+2} \cdot \dfrac{x^2+2x-8}{x^2+4x+3}$

54. $\dfrac{y^2+y-12}{y^2-y-20} \cdot \dfrac{y^2+y-30}{y^2-2y-3}$

55. $\dfrac{\dfrac{w^2-6w+9}{8}}{\dfrac{9-w^2}{4w+12}}$

56. $\dfrac{\dfrac{p^2-6p+8}{24}}{\dfrac{16-p^2}{6p+6}}$

57. $\dfrac{5k^2+7k+2}{k^2+5k+4} \div \dfrac{5k^2+17k+6}{k^2+10k+24}$

58. $\dfrac{4h^2-5h+1}{h^2+h-2} \div \dfrac{6h^2-7h+2}{2h^2+3h-2}$

59. $\dfrac{ax+a+bx+b}{2x^2+4x+2} \cdot \dfrac{4x+4}{a^2+ab}$

60. $\dfrac{3my+9m+ny+3n}{9m^2+6mn+n^2} \cdot \dfrac{30m+10n}{5y^2+15y}$

61. $\dfrac{y^4 - 1}{2y^2 - 3y + 1} \div \dfrac{2y^2 + 2}{8y^2 - 4y}$

62. $\dfrac{x^4 - 16}{6x^2 + 24} \div \dfrac{x^2 - 2x}{3x}$

63. $\dfrac{x^2 - xy - 2y^2}{x + 2y} \div \dfrac{x^2 - 4xy + 4y^2}{x^2 - 4y^2}$

64. $\dfrac{4m^2 - 4mn - 3n^2}{8m^2 - 18n^2} \div \dfrac{3m + 3n}{6m^2 + 15mn + 9n^2}$

For Exercises 65–70, multiply or divide as indicated. **(See Example 7.)**

65. $\dfrac{y^3 - 3y^2 + 4y - 12}{y^4 - 16} \cdot \dfrac{3y^2 + 5y - 2}{3y^2 - 10y + 3} \div \dfrac{3}{6y - 12}$

66. $\dfrac{x^2 - 25}{3x^2 + 3xy} \cdot \dfrac{x^2 + 4x + xy + 4y}{x^2 + 9x + 20} \div \dfrac{x - 5}{x}$

67. $\dfrac{a^2 - 5a}{a^2 + 7a + 12} \div \dfrac{a^3 - 7a^2 + 10a}{a^2 + 9a + 18} \div \dfrac{a + 6}{a + 4}$

68. $\dfrac{t^2 + t - 2}{t^2 + 5t + 6} \div \dfrac{t - 1}{t} \div \dfrac{5t - 5}{t + 3}$

69. $\dfrac{p^3 - q^3}{p - q} \cdot \dfrac{p + q}{2p^2 + 2pq + 2q^2}$

70. $\dfrac{r^3 + s^3}{r - s} \div \dfrac{r^2 + 2rs + s^2}{r^2 - s^2}$

Least Common Denominator

1. Least Common Denominator

We have already learned how to simplify, multiply, and divide rational expressions. Our next goal is to add and subtract rational expressions. As with fractions, rational expressions may be added or subtracted only if they have the same denominator.

The **least common denominator (LCD)** of two or more rational expressions is defined as the least common multiple of the denominators. For example, consider the fractions $\frac{1}{20}$ and $\frac{1}{8}$. By inspection, you can probably see that the least common denominator is 40. To understand why, find the prime factorization of both denominators:

$$20 = 2^2 \cdot 5 \quad \text{and} \quad 8 = 2^3$$

A common multiple of 20 and 8 must be a multiple of 5, a multiple of 2^2, and a multiple of 2^3. However, any number that is a multiple of $2^3 = 8$ is automatically a multiple of $2^2 = 4$. Therefore, it is sufficient to construct the least common denominator as the product of unique prime factors, in which each factor is raised to its highest power.

The LCD of $\dfrac{1}{20}$ and $\dfrac{1}{8}$ is $2^3 \cdot 5 = 40$.

1. Least Common Denominator

2. Writing Rational Expressions with the Least Common Denominator

> **Finding the Least Common Denominator of Two or More Rational Expressions**
>
> **Step 1** Factor all denominators completely.
> **Step 2** The LCD is the product of unique prime factors from the denominators, in which each factor is raised to the highest power to which it appears in any denominator.

| Example 1 | **Finding the Least Common Denominator** |

Find the LCD of the rational expressions.

a. $\dfrac{5}{14}; \dfrac{3}{49}; \dfrac{1}{8}$ **b.** $\dfrac{5}{3x^2z}; \dfrac{7}{x^5y^3}$

Solution:

a. $\dfrac{5}{14}; \dfrac{3}{49}; \dfrac{1}{8}$

$= \dfrac{5}{2 \cdot 7}; \dfrac{3}{7^2}; \dfrac{1}{2^3}$ Factor the denominators.

The LCD is $7^2 \cdot 2^3 = 392$.   The LCD is the product of unique factors, each raised to its highest power.

b. $\dfrac{5}{3x^2z}; \dfrac{7}{x^5y^3}$

$= \dfrac{5}{3 \cdot x^2 \cdot z^1}; \dfrac{7}{x^5 \cdot y^3}$ The denominators are in factored form.

The LCD is the product of $3 \cdot x^5 \cdot y^3 \cdot z^1$ or simply $3x^5y^3z$.

Skill Practice Find the LCD for each set of expressions.

1. $\dfrac{3}{8}; \dfrac{7}{10}; \dfrac{1}{15}$ **2.** $\dfrac{1}{5a^3b^2}; \dfrac{1}{10a^4b}$

| Example 2 | **Finding the Least Common Denominator** |

Find the LCD for each pair of rational expressions.

a. $\dfrac{a+b}{a^2-25}; \dfrac{1}{2a-10}$ **b.** $\dfrac{x-5}{x^2-2x}; \dfrac{1}{x^2-4x+4}$

Solution:

a. $\dfrac{a+b}{a^2-25}; \dfrac{1}{2a-10}$

$= \dfrac{a+b}{(a-5)(a+5)}; \dfrac{1}{2(a-5)}$ Factor the denominators.

The LCD is $2(a-5)(a+5)$.   The LCD is the product of unique factors, each raised to its highest power.

b. $\dfrac{x-5}{x^2-2x}; \dfrac{1}{x^2-4x+4}$

$= \dfrac{x-5}{x(x-2)}; \dfrac{1}{(x-2)^2}$ Factor the denominators.

The LCD is $x(x-2)^2$.   The LCD is the product of unique factors, each raised to its highest power.

Answers
1. 120
2. $10a^4b^2$

Skill Practice Find the LCD.

3. $\dfrac{x}{x^2 - 16}; \dfrac{2}{3x + 12}$ **4.** $\dfrac{6}{t^2 + 5t - 14}; \dfrac{8}{t^2 - 3t + 2}$

2. Writing Rational Expressions with the Least Common Denominator

To add or subtract two rational expressions, the expressions must have the same denominator. Therefore, we must first practice the skill of converting each rational expression into an equivalent expression with the LCD as its denominator.

Writing Equivalent Fractions with Common Denominators

Step 1 Identify the LCD for the expressions.

Step 2 Multiply the numerator and denominator of each fraction by the factors from the LCD that are missing from the original denominators.

Example 3 **Converting to the Least Common Denominator**

Find the LCD of each pair of rational expressions. Then convert each expression to an equivalent fraction with the denominator equal to the LCD.

a. $\dfrac{3}{2ab}; \dfrac{6}{5a^2}$ **b.** $\dfrac{4}{x + 1}; \dfrac{7}{x - 4}$

Solution:

a. $\dfrac{3}{2ab}; \dfrac{6}{5a^2}$ The LCD is $10a^2b$.

$\dfrac{3}{2ab} = \dfrac{3 \cdot 5a}{2ab \cdot 5a} = \dfrac{15a}{10a^2b}$ The first expression is missing the factor $5a$ from the denominator.

$\dfrac{6}{5a^2} = \dfrac{6 \cdot 2b}{5a^2 \cdot 2b} = \dfrac{12b}{10a^2b}$ The second expression is missing the factor $2b$ from the denominator.

b. $\dfrac{4}{x + 1}; \dfrac{7}{x - 4}$ The LCD is $(x + 1)(x - 4)$.

$\dfrac{4}{x + 1} = \dfrac{4(x - 4)}{(x + 1)(x - 4)} = \dfrac{4x - 16}{(x + 1)(x - 4)}$ The first expression is missing the factor $(x - 4)$ from the denominator.

$\dfrac{7}{x - 4} = \dfrac{7(x + 1)}{(x - 4)(x + 1)} = \dfrac{7x + 7}{(x - 4)(x + 1)}$ The second expression is missing the factor $(x + 1)$ from the denominator.

Skill Practice For each pair of expressions, find the LCD, and then convert each expression to an equivalent fraction with the denominator equal to the LCD.

5. $\dfrac{2}{rs^2}; \dfrac{-1}{r^3s}$ **6.** $\dfrac{5}{x - 3}; \dfrac{x}{x + 1}$

Answers

3. $3(x - 4)(x + 4)$

4. $(t + 7)(t - 2)(t - 1)$

5. $\dfrac{2}{rs^2} = \dfrac{2r^2}{r^3s^2}; \dfrac{-1}{r^3s} = \dfrac{-s}{r^3s^2}$

6. $\dfrac{5}{x - 3} = \dfrac{5x + 5}{(x - 3)(x + 1)}$

$\dfrac{x}{x + 1} = \dfrac{x^2 - 3x}{(x + 1)(x - 3)}$

| Example 4 | **Converting to the Least Common Denominator** |

Find the LCD of the pair of rational expressions. Then convert each expression to an equivalent fraction with the denominator equal to the LCD.

$$\frac{w+2}{w^2-w-12}; \frac{1}{w^2-9}$$

Solution:

$$\frac{w+2}{w^2-w-12}; \frac{1}{w^2-9}$$

To find the LCD, factor each denominator.

$$\frac{w+2}{(w-4)(w+3)}; \frac{1}{(w-3)(w+3)}$$

The LCD is $(w-4)(w+3)(w-3)$.

$$\frac{w+2}{(w-4)(w+3)} = \frac{(w+2)(w-3)}{(w-4)(w+3)(w-3)}$$

The first expression is missing the factor $(w-3)$ from the denominator.

$$= \frac{w^2-w-6}{(w-4)(w+3)(w-3)}$$

$$\frac{1}{(w-3)(w+3)} = \frac{1(w-4)}{(w-3)(w+3)(w-4)}$$

The second expression is missing the factor $(w-4)$ from the denominator.

$$= \frac{w-4}{(w-3)(w+3)(w-4)}$$

Skill Practice Find the LCD. Then convert each expression to an equivalent expression with the denominator equal to the LCD.

7. $\dfrac{z}{z^2-4}; \dfrac{-3}{z^2-z-2}$

| Example 5 | **Converting to the Least Common Denominator** |

Convert each expression to an equivalent expression with the denominator equal to the LCD.

$$\frac{3}{x-7} \quad \text{and} \quad \frac{1}{7-x}$$

TIP: In Example 5, the expressions
$$\frac{3}{x-7} \quad \text{and} \quad \frac{1}{7-x}$$
have opposite factors in the denominators. In such a case, you do not need to include *both* factors in the LCD.

Solution:

Notice that the expressions $x-7$ and $7-x$ are opposites and differ by a factor of -1. Therefore, we may use either $x-7$ or $7-x$ as a common denominator. Each case is shown below.

Converting to the Denominator $x-7$

$$\frac{3}{x-7}; \frac{1}{7-x}$$

Leave the first fraction unchanged because it has the desired LCD.

$$\frac{1}{7-x} = \frac{(-1)1}{(-1)(7-x)}$$

Multiply the *second* rational expression by the ratio $\frac{-1}{-1}$ to change its denominator to $x-7$.

$$= \frac{-1}{-7+x}$$

Apply the distributive property.

$$= \frac{-1}{x-7}$$

Answer

7. $\dfrac{z^2+z}{(z-2)(z+2)(z+1)};$
$\dfrac{-3z-6}{(z-2)(z+2)(z+1)}$

Converting to the Denominator $7 - x$

$$\frac{3}{x-7}; \frac{1}{7-x}$$

Leave the second fraction unchanged because it has the desired LCD.

$$\frac{3}{x-7} = \frac{(-1)3}{(-1)(x-7)};$$

Multiply the *first* rational expression by the ratio $\frac{-1}{-1}$ to change its denominator to $7 - x$.

$$= \frac{-3}{-x+7}$$

Apply the distributive property.

$$= \frac{-3}{7-x}$$

Skill Practice

8. **a.** Find the LCD of the expressions. $\dfrac{9}{w-2}; \dfrac{11}{2-w}$

b. Convert each expression to an equivalent fraction with denominator equal to the LCD.

Answers

8. a. The LCD is $(w - 2)$ or $(2 - w)$.

b. $\dfrac{9}{w-2} = \dfrac{9}{w-2};$

$\dfrac{11}{2-w} = \dfrac{-11}{w-2}$

or

$\dfrac{9}{w-2} = \dfrac{-9}{2-w};$

$\dfrac{11}{2-w} = \dfrac{11}{2-w}$

Section 7.3   Practice Exercises

Vocabulary and Key Concepts

1. The least common denominator (LCD) of two rational expressions is defined as the least common _____ of the _____.

Review Exercises

2. Evaluate the expression for the given values of x. $\dfrac{2x}{x+5}$

a. $x = 1$ **b.** $x = 5$ **c.** $x = -5$

For Exercises 3–4, identify the restricted values. Then simplify the expression.

3. $\dfrac{3x+3}{5x^2-5}$

4. $\dfrac{x+2}{x^2-3x-10}$

For Exercises 5–8, multiply or divide as indicated.

5. $\dfrac{a+3}{a+7} \cdot \dfrac{a^2+3a-10}{a^2+a-6}$

6. $\dfrac{6(a+2b)}{2(a-3b)} \cdot \dfrac{4(a+3b)(a-3b)}{9(a+2b)(a-2b)}$

7. $\dfrac{16y^2}{9y+36} \div \dfrac{8y^3}{3y+12}$

8. $\dfrac{5w^2+6w+1}{w^2+5w+6} \div (5w+1)$

9. Which of the expressions are equivalent to $-\dfrac{5}{x-3}$? Circle all that apply.

a. $\dfrac{-5}{x-3}$ **b.** $\dfrac{5}{-x+3}$ **c.** $\dfrac{5}{3-x}$ **d.** $\dfrac{5}{-(x-3)}$

510   **Chapter 7**   Rational Expressions and Equations

10. Which of the expressions are equivalent to $\dfrac{4-a}{6}$? Circle all that apply.

a. $\dfrac{a-4}{-6}$ **b.** $\dfrac{a-4}{6}$ **c.** $\dfrac{-(4-a)}{-6}$ **d.** $-\dfrac{a-4}{6}$

Concept 1: Least Common Denominator

11. Explain why the least common denominator of $\frac{1}{x^3}$, $\frac{1}{x^5}$, and $\frac{1}{x^4}$ is x^5.

12. Explain why the least common denominator of $\frac{2}{y^3}$, $\frac{9}{y^6}$, and $\frac{4}{y^5}$ is y^6.

For Exercises 13–30, identify the LCD. **(See Examples 1–2.)**

13. $\dfrac{4}{15}; \dfrac{5}{9}$

14. $\dfrac{7}{12}; \dfrac{1}{18}$

15. $\dfrac{1}{16}, \dfrac{1}{4}, \dfrac{1}{6}$

16. $\dfrac{1}{2}, \dfrac{11}{12}, \dfrac{3}{8}$

17. $\dfrac{1}{7}, \dfrac{2}{9}$

18. $\dfrac{2}{3}; \dfrac{5}{8}$

19. $\dfrac{1}{3x^2y}; \dfrac{8}{9xy^3}$

20. $\dfrac{5}{2a^4b^2}; \dfrac{1}{8ab^3}$

21. $\dfrac{6}{w^2}; \dfrac{7}{y}$

22. $\dfrac{2}{r}; \dfrac{3}{s^2}$

23. $\dfrac{p}{(p+3)(p-1)}; \dfrac{2}{(p+3)(p+2)}$

24. $\dfrac{6}{(q+4)(q-4)}; \dfrac{q^2}{(q+1)(q+4)}$

25. $\dfrac{7}{3t(t+1)}; \dfrac{10t}{9(t+1)^2}$

26. $\dfrac{13x}{15(x-1)^2}; \dfrac{5}{3x(x-1)}$

27. $\dfrac{y}{y^2-4}; \dfrac{3y}{y^2+5y+6}$

28. $\dfrac{4}{w^2-3w+2}; \dfrac{w}{w^2-4}$

29. $\dfrac{5}{3-x}; \dfrac{7}{x-3}$

30. $\dfrac{4}{x-6}; \dfrac{9}{6-x}$

31. Explain why a common denominator of

$$\dfrac{b+1}{b-1} \quad \text{and} \quad \dfrac{b}{1-b}$$

could be either $(b-1)$ or $(1-b)$.

32. Explain why a common denominator of

$$\dfrac{1}{6-t} \quad \text{and} \quad \dfrac{t}{t-6}$$

could be either $(6-t)$ or $(t-6)$.

Concept 2: Writing Rational Expressions with the Least Common Denominator

For Exercises 33–56, find the LCD. Then convert each expression to an equivalent expression with the denominator equal to the LCD. **(See Examples 3–5.)**

33. $\dfrac{6}{5x^2}; \dfrac{1}{x}$

34. $\dfrac{3}{y}; \dfrac{7}{9y^2}$

35. $\dfrac{4}{5x^2}; \dfrac{y}{6x^3}$

36. $\dfrac{3}{15b^2}; \dfrac{c}{3b^2}$

37. $\dfrac{5}{6a^2b}; \dfrac{a}{12b}$

38. $\dfrac{x}{15y^2}; \dfrac{y}{5xy}$

39. $\dfrac{6}{m+4}; \dfrac{3}{m-1}$

40. $\dfrac{3}{n-5}; \dfrac{7}{n+2}$

41. $\dfrac{6}{2x-5}; \dfrac{1}{x+3}$

42. $\dfrac{4}{m+3}; \dfrac{-3}{5m+1}$

43. $\dfrac{6}{(w+3)(w-8)}; \dfrac{w}{(w-8)(w+1)}$

44. $\dfrac{t}{(t+2)(t+12)}; \dfrac{18}{(t-2)(t+2)}$

45. $\dfrac{6p}{p^2 - 4}; \dfrac{3}{p^2 + 4p + 4}$

46. $\dfrac{5}{t^2 - 6t + 9}; \dfrac{t}{t^2 - 9}$

47. $\dfrac{1}{a - 4}; \dfrac{a}{4 - a}$

48. $\dfrac{3b}{2b - 5}; \dfrac{2b}{5 - 2b}$

49. $\dfrac{4}{x - 7}; \dfrac{y}{14 - 2x}$

50. $\dfrac{4}{3x - 15}; \dfrac{z}{5 - x}$

51. $\dfrac{1}{a + b}; \dfrac{6}{-a - b}$

52. $\dfrac{p}{-q - 8}; \dfrac{1}{q + 8}$

53. $\dfrac{-3}{24y + 8}; \dfrac{5}{18y + 6}$

54. $\dfrac{r}{10r + 5}; \dfrac{2}{16r + 8}$

55. $\dfrac{3}{5z}; \dfrac{1}{z + 4}$

56. $\dfrac{-1}{4a - 8}; \dfrac{5}{4a}$

Expanding Your Skills

For Exercises 57–60, find the LCD. Then convert each expression to an equivalent expression with the denominator equal to the LCD.

57. $\dfrac{z}{z^2 + 9z + 14}; \dfrac{-3z}{z^2 + 10z + 21}; \dfrac{5}{z^2 + 5z + 6}$

58. $\dfrac{6}{w^2 - 3w - 4}; \dfrac{1}{w^2 + 6w + 5}; \dfrac{-9w}{w^2 + w - 20}$

59. $\dfrac{3}{p^3 - 8}; \dfrac{p}{p^2 - 4}; \dfrac{5p}{p^2 + 2p + 4}$

60. $\dfrac{7}{n^3 + 125}; \dfrac{n}{n^2 - 25}; \dfrac{12}{n^2 - 5n + 25}$

Addition and Subtraction of Rational Expressions

Section 7.4

1. Addition and Subtraction of Rational Expressions with the Same Denominator

To add or subtract rational expressions, the expressions must have the same denominator. As with fractions, we add or subtract rational expressions with the same denominator by combining the terms in the numerator and then writing the result over the common denominator. Then, if possible, simplify the expression.

> **Addition and Subtraction of Rational Expressions**
>
> Let p, q, and r represent polynomials where $q \neq 0$. Then,
>
> **1.** $\dfrac{p}{q} + \dfrac{r}{q} = \dfrac{p+r}{q}$ **2.** $\dfrac{p}{q} - \dfrac{r}{q} = \dfrac{p-r}{q}$

Concepts

1. Addition and Subtraction of Rational Expressions with the Same Denominator
2. Addition and Subtraction of Rational Expressions with Different Denominators
3. Using Rational Expressions in Translations

Example 1 **Adding and Subtracting Rational Expressions with the Same Denominator**

Add or subtract as indicated.   **a.** $\dfrac{1}{12} + \dfrac{7}{12}$ **b.** $\dfrac{2}{5p} - \dfrac{7}{5p}$

Solution:

a. $\dfrac{1}{12} + \dfrac{7}{12}$ The fractions have the same denominator.

$= \dfrac{1 + 7}{12}$ Add the terms in the numerators, and write the result over the common denominator.

$= \dfrac{\overset{2}{8}}{\underset{3}{12}}$

$= \dfrac{2}{3}$ Simplify.

b. $\dfrac{2}{5p} - \dfrac{7}{5p}$ The rational expressions have the same denominator.

$= \dfrac{2 - 7}{5p}$ Subtract the terms in the numerators, and write the result over the common denominator.

$= \dfrac{-5}{5p}$

$= \dfrac{\overset{-1}{-5}}{5p}$ Simplify.

$= -\dfrac{1}{p}$

Skill Practice Add or subtract as indicated.

1. $\dfrac{3}{14} + \dfrac{4}{14}$ **2.** $\dfrac{2}{7d} - \dfrac{9}{7d}$

Example 2 **Adding and Subtracting Rational Expressions with the Same Denominator**

Add or subtract as indicated.

a. $\dfrac{2}{3d + 5} + \dfrac{7d}{3d + 5}$ **b.** $\dfrac{x^2}{x - 3} - \dfrac{-5x + 24}{x - 3}$

Solution:

a. $\dfrac{2}{3d + 5} + \dfrac{7d}{3d + 5}$ The rational expressions have the same denominator.

$= \dfrac{2 + 7d}{3d + 5}$ Add the terms in the numerators, and write the result over the common denominator.

$= \dfrac{7d + 2}{3d + 5}$ Because the numerator and denominator share no common factors, the expression is in lowest terms.

Answers

1. $\dfrac{1}{2}$ **2.** $-\dfrac{1}{d}$

b. $\dfrac{x^2}{x-3} - \dfrac{-5x+24}{x-3}$ The rational expressions have the same denominator.

$= \dfrac{x^2 - (-5x+24)}{x-3}$ Subtract the terms in the numerators, and write the result over the common denominator.

$= \dfrac{x^2 + 5x - 24}{x-3}$ Simplify the numerator.

$= \dfrac{(x+8)(x-3)}{(x-3)}$ Factor the numerator and denominator to determine if the rational expression can be simplified.

$= \dfrac{(x+8)(\overset{1}{\cancel{x-3}})}{(\cancel{x-3})}$ Simplify.

$= x + 8$

> **Avoiding Mistakes**
>
> When subtracting rational expressions, use parentheses to group the terms in the numerator that follow the subtraction sign. This will help you remember to apply the distributive property.

Skill Practice   Add or subtract as indicated.

3. $\dfrac{x^2+2}{x+3} + \dfrac{4x+1}{x+3}$ **4.** $\dfrac{4t-9}{2t+1} - \dfrac{t-5}{2t+1}$

2. Addition and Subtraction of Rational Expressions with Different Denominators

To add or subtract two rational expressions with unlike denominators, we must convert the expressions to equivalent expressions with the same denominator. For example, consider adding

$$\frac{1}{10} + \frac{12}{5y}$$

The LCD is $10y$. For each expression, identify the factors from the LCD that are missing from the denominator. Then multiply the numerator and denominator of the expression by the missing factor(s).

$$\underset{\substack{\text{Missing} \\ y}}{\frac{1}{10}} \quad + \quad \underset{\substack{\text{Missing} \\ 2}}{\frac{12}{5y}}$$

$= \dfrac{1 \cdot y}{10 \cdot y} + \dfrac{12 \cdot 2}{5y \cdot 2}$

$= \dfrac{y}{10y} + \dfrac{24}{10y}$ The rational expressions now have the same denominators.

$= \dfrac{y+24}{10y}$ Add the numerators.

After successfully adding or subtracting two rational expressions, always check to see if the final answer is simplified. If necessary, factor the numerator and denominator, and reduce common factors. The expression

$$\frac{y+24}{10y}$$

is in lowest terms because the numerator and denominator do not share any common factors.

> **Avoiding Mistakes**
>
> In the expression $\frac{y+24}{10y}$, notice that you cannot reduce the 24 and 10 because 24 is not a factor in the numerator, it is a term. Only factors can be reduced—not terms.

Answers

3. $x+1$ **4.** $\dfrac{3t-4}{2t+1}$

> **Adding or Subtracting Rational Expressions**
> **Step 1** Factor the denominators of each rational expression.
> **Step 2** Identify the LCD.
> **Step 3** Rewrite each rational expression as an equivalent expression with the LCD as its denominator.
> **Step 4** Add or subtract the numerators, and write the result over the common denominator.
> **Step 5** Simplify.

Example 3   **Subtracting Rational Expressions with Different Denominators**

Subtract. $\dfrac{4}{7k} - \dfrac{3}{k^2}$

Solution:

$\dfrac{4}{7k} - \dfrac{3}{k^2}$ **Step 1:** The denominators are already factored.

    Step 2: The LCD is $7k^2$.

$= \dfrac{4 \cdot k}{7k \cdot k} - \dfrac{3 \cdot 7}{k^2 \cdot 7}$ **Step 3:** Write each expression with the LCD.

$= \dfrac{4k}{7k^2} - \dfrac{21}{7k^2}$

$= \dfrac{4k - 21}{7k^2}$ **Step 4:** Subtract the numerators, and write the result over the LCD.

    Step 5: The expression is in lowest terms because the numerator and denominator share no common factors.

Avoiding Mistakes

Do not reduce after rewriting the individual fractions with the LCD. You will revert back to the original expression.

Skill Practice Subtract.

5. $\dfrac{4}{3x} - \dfrac{1}{2x^2}$

Example 4   **Subtracting Rational Expressions with Different Denominators**

Subtract. $\dfrac{2q - 4}{3} - \dfrac{q + 1}{2}$

Solution:

$\dfrac{2q - 4}{3} - \dfrac{q + 1}{2}$ **Step 1:** The denominators are already factored.

    Step 2: The LCD is 6.

$= \dfrac{2(2q - 4)}{2 \cdot 3} - \dfrac{3(q + 1)}{3 \cdot 2}$ **Step 3:** Write each expression with the LCD.

Answer

5. $\dfrac{8x - 3}{6x^2}$

$$= \frac{2(2q-4) - 3(q+1)}{6}$$

Step 4:   Subtract the numerators, and write the result over the LCD.

$$= \frac{4q - 8 - 3q - 3}{6}$$

$$= \frac{q - 11}{6}$$

Step 5:   The expression is in lowest terms because the numerator and denominator share no common factors.

Skill Practice   Subtract.

6. $\dfrac{t}{12} - \dfrac{t-2}{4}$

Example 5	**Adding Rational Expressions with Different Denominators**

Add. $\dfrac{1}{x-5} + \dfrac{-10}{x^2 - 25}$

Solution:

$$\frac{1}{x-5} + \frac{-10}{x^2 - 25}$$

$$= \frac{1}{x-5} + \frac{-10}{(x-5)(x+5)}$$

Step 1:   Factor the denominators.

Step 2:   The LCD is $(x-5)(x+5)$.

$$= \frac{1(x+5)}{(x-5)(x+5)} + \frac{-10}{(x-5)(x+5)}$$

Step 3:   Write each expression with the LCD.

$$= \frac{1(x+5) + (-10)}{(x-5)(x+5)}$$

Step 4:   Add the numerators, and write the result over the LCD.

$$= \frac{x + 5 - 10}{(x-5)(x+5)}$$

$$= \frac{x \overset{1}{-} 5}{(x-5)(x+5)}$$

Step 5:   Simplify.

$$= \frac{1}{x+5}$$

Skill Practice   Add.

7. $\dfrac{1}{x-4} + \dfrac{-8}{x^2 - 16}$

Answers

6. $\dfrac{-t+3}{6}$ 7. $\dfrac{1}{x+4}$

| **Example 6** | **Subtracting Rational Expressions with Different Denominators** |

Subtract. $\dfrac{p+2}{p-1} - \dfrac{2}{p+6} - \dfrac{14}{p^2+5p-6}$

Solution:

$\dfrac{p+2}{p-1} - \dfrac{2}{p+6} - \dfrac{14}{p^2+5p-6}$

$= \dfrac{p+2}{p-1} - \dfrac{2}{p+6} - \dfrac{14}{(p-1)(p+6)}$ **Step 1:** Factor the denominators.

Step 2: The LCD is $(p-1)(p+6)$.

Step 3: Write each expression with the LCD.

$= \dfrac{(p+2)(p+6)}{(p-1)(p+6)} - \dfrac{2(p-1)}{(p+6)(p-1)} - \dfrac{14}{(p-1)(p+6)}$

$= \dfrac{(p+2)(p+6) - 2(p-1) - 14}{(p-1)(p+6)}$ **Step 4:** Combine the numerators, and write the result over the LCD.

$= \dfrac{p^2+6p+2p+12-2p+2-14}{(p-1)(p+6)}$ **Step 5:** Clear parentheses in the numerator.

$= \dfrac{p^2+6p}{(p-1)(p+6)}$ Combine *like* terms.

$= \dfrac{p(p+6)}{(p-1)(p+6)}$ Factor the numerator to determine if the expression is in lowest terms.

$= \dfrac{p(\cancel{p+6})}{(p-1)(\cancel{p+6})}$ Simplify.

$= \dfrac{p}{p-1}$

Skill Practice Subtract.

8. $\dfrac{2y}{y-1} - \dfrac{1}{y} - \dfrac{2y+1}{y^2-y}$

When the denominators of two rational expressions are opposites, we can produce identical denominators by multiplying one of the expressions by the ratio $\frac{-1}{-1}$. This is demonstrated in Example 7.

| **Example 7** | **Adding Rational Expressions with Different Denominators** |

Add the rational expressions. $\dfrac{1}{d-7} + \dfrac{5}{7-d}$

Answer

8. $\dfrac{2y-3}{y-1}$

Solution:

$$\frac{1}{d-7}+\frac{5}{7-d}$$

The expressions $d-7$ and $7-d$ are opposites and differ by a factor of -1. Therefore, multiply the numerator and denominator of *either* expression by -1 to obtain a common denominator.

$$=\frac{1}{d-7}+\frac{(-1)5}{(-1)(7-d)}$$

Note that $-1(7-d)=-7+d$ or $d-7$.

$$=\frac{1}{d-7}+\frac{-5}{d-7}$$

Simplify.

$$=\frac{1+(-5)}{d-7}$$

Add the terms in the numerators, and write the result over the common denominator.

$$=\frac{-4}{d-7}$$

Skill Practice Add.

9. $\dfrac{3}{p-8}+\dfrac{1}{8-p}$

---

3. Using Rational Expressions in Translations

Example 8   Using Rational Expressions in Translations

Write the English phrase as a mathematical expression. Then simplify by combining the rational expressions.

The difference of the reciprocal of n and the quotient of n and 3

Solution:

The difference of the reciprocal of n and the quotient of n and 3

The difference of

$$\left(\frac{1}{n}\right)-\left(\frac{n}{3}\right)$$

The reciprocal of n The quotient of n and 3

$$\frac{1}{n}-\frac{n}{3}$$

The LCD is $3n$.

$$=\frac{3\cdot1}{3\cdot n}-\frac{n\cdot n}{3\cdot n}$$

Write each expression with the LCD.

$$=\frac{3-n^2}{3n}$$

Subtract the numerators.

Skill Practice Write the English phrase as a mathematical expression. Then simplify by combining the rational expressions.

10. The sum of 1 and the quotient of 2 and a

Answers

9. $\dfrac{2}{p-8}$ or $\dfrac{-2}{8-p}$

10. $1+\dfrac{2}{a}$; $\dfrac{a+2}{a}$

Section 7.4   Practice Exercises

Review Exercises

1. For the rational expression $\dfrac{x^2 - 4x - 5}{x^2 - 7x + 10}$

   a. Find the value of the expression (if possible) when $x = 0, 1, -1, 2,$ and 5.

   b. Factor the denominator and identify the restricted values.

   c. Simplify the expression.

2. For the rational expression $\dfrac{a^2 + a - 2}{a^2 - 4a - 12}$

   a. Find the value of the expression (if possible) when $a = 0, 1, -2, 2,$ and 6.

   b. Factor the denominator, and identify the restricted values.

   c. Simplify the expression.

For Exercises 3–4, multiply or divide as indicated.

3. $\dfrac{2x^2 - x - 3}{2x^2 - 3x - 9} \div \dfrac{x^2 - 1}{4x + 6}$

4. $\dfrac{6t - 1}{5t - 30} \cdot \dfrac{10t - 25}{2t^2 - 3t - 5}$

Concept 1: Addition and Subtraction of Rational Expressions with the Same Denominator

For Exercises 5–26, add or subtract the expressions with the same denominators as indicated. **(See Examples 1–2.)**

5. $\dfrac{7}{8} + \dfrac{3}{8}$

6. $\dfrac{1}{3} + \dfrac{7}{3}$

7. $\dfrac{9}{16} - \dfrac{3}{16}$

8. $\dfrac{14}{15} - \dfrac{4}{15}$

9. $\dfrac{5a}{a + 2} - \dfrac{3a - 4}{a + 2}$

10. $\dfrac{2b}{b - 3} - \dfrac{b - 9}{b - 3}$

11. $\dfrac{5c}{c + 6} + \dfrac{30}{c + 6}$

12. $\dfrac{12}{2 + d} + \dfrac{6d}{2 + d}$

13. $\dfrac{5}{t - 8} - \dfrac{2t + 1}{t - 8}$

14. $\dfrac{7p + 1}{2p + 1} - \dfrac{p - 4}{2p + 1}$

15. $\dfrac{9x^2}{3x - 7} - \dfrac{49}{3x - 7}$

16. $\dfrac{4w^2}{2w - 1} - \dfrac{1}{2w - 1}$

17. $\dfrac{m^2}{m + 5} + \dfrac{10m + 25}{m + 5}$

18. $\dfrac{k^2}{k - 3} - \dfrac{6k - 9}{k - 3}$

19. $\dfrac{2a}{a + 2} + \dfrac{4}{a + 2}$

20. $\dfrac{5b}{b + 4} + \dfrac{20}{b + 4}$

21. $\dfrac{x^2}{x + 5} - \dfrac{25}{x + 5}$

22. $\dfrac{y^2}{y - 7} - \dfrac{49}{y - 7}$

23. $\dfrac{r}{r^2 + 3r + 2} + \dfrac{2}{r^2 + 3r + 2}$

24. $\dfrac{x}{x^2 - x - 12} - \dfrac{4}{x^2 - x - 12}$

25. $\dfrac{1}{3y^2 + 22y + 7} - \dfrac{-3y}{3y^2 + 22y + 7}$

26. $\dfrac{5}{2x^2 + 13x + 20} + \dfrac{2x}{2x^2 + 13x + 20}$

For Exercises 27–28, find an expression that represents the perimeter of the figure (assume that $x > 0$, $y > 0$, and $t > 0$).

27.
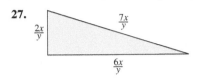

28.
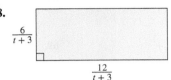

Concept 2: Addition and Subtraction of Rational Expressions with Different Denominators

For Exercises 29–70, add or subtract the expressions with different denominators as indicated. **(See Examples 3–7.)**

29. $\dfrac{5}{4} + \dfrac{3}{2a}$

30. $\dfrac{11}{6p} + \dfrac{-7}{4p}$

31. $\dfrac{4}{5xy^3} + \dfrac{2x}{15y^2}$

32. $\dfrac{5}{3a^2b} - \dfrac{7}{6b^2}$

33. $\dfrac{2}{s^3t^3} - \dfrac{3}{s^4t}$

34. $\dfrac{1}{p^2q} - \dfrac{2}{pq^3}$

35. $\dfrac{z}{3z - 9} - \dfrac{z - 2}{z - 3}$

36. $\dfrac{3w - 8}{2w - 4} - \dfrac{w - 3}{w - 2}$

37. $\dfrac{5}{a + 1} + \dfrac{4}{3a + 3}$

38. $\dfrac{2}{c - 4} + \dfrac{1}{5c - 20}$

39. $\dfrac{k}{k^2 - 9} - \dfrac{4}{k - 3}$

40. $\dfrac{7}{h + 2} + \dfrac{2h - 3}{h^2 - 4}$

41. $\dfrac{3a - 7}{6a + 10} - \dfrac{10}{3a^2 + 5a}$

42. $\dfrac{k + 2}{8k} - \dfrac{3 - k}{12k}$

43. $\dfrac{x}{x - 4} + \dfrac{3}{x + 1}$

44. $\dfrac{4}{y - 3} + \dfrac{y}{y - 5}$

45. $\dfrac{3x}{x^2 + 6x + 9} + \dfrac{x}{x^2 + 5x + 6}$

46. $\dfrac{7x}{x^2 + 2xy + y^2} + \dfrac{3x}{x^2 + xy}$

47. $\dfrac{p}{3} - \dfrac{4p - 1}{-3}$

48. $\dfrac{r}{7} - \dfrac{r - 5}{-7}$

49. $\dfrac{8}{x - 3} - \dfrac{1}{3 - x}$

50. $\dfrac{5y}{y - 1} - \dfrac{3y}{1 - y}$

51. $\dfrac{4n}{n - 8} - \dfrac{2n - 1}{8 - n}$

52. $\dfrac{m}{m - 2} - \dfrac{3m + 1}{2 - m}$

53. $\dfrac{5}{x} + \dfrac{3}{x + 2}$

54. $\dfrac{6}{y - 1} + \dfrac{9}{y}$

55. $\dfrac{y}{4y + 2} + \dfrac{3y}{6y + 3}$

56. $\dfrac{4}{q^2 - 2q} - \dfrac{5}{3q - 6}$

57. $\dfrac{4w}{w^2 + 2w - 3} + \dfrac{2}{1 - w}$

58. $\dfrac{z - 23}{z^2 - z - 20} - \dfrac{2}{5 - z}$

59. $\dfrac{3a - 8}{a^2 - 5a + 6} + \dfrac{a + 2}{a^2 - 6a + 8}$

60. $\dfrac{3b + 5}{b^2 + 4b + 3} + \dfrac{-b + 5}{b^2 + 2b - 3}$

61. $\dfrac{4x}{x^2 + 4x - 5} - \dfrac{x}{x^2 + 10x + 25}$

62. $\dfrac{x}{x^2 + 5x + 4} - \dfrac{2x}{x^2 + 8x + 16}$

63. $\dfrac{3y}{2y^2 - y - 1} - \dfrac{4y}{2y^2 - 7y - 4}$

64. $\dfrac{5}{6y^2 - 7y - 3} + \dfrac{4y}{3y^2 + 4y + 1}$

520   **Chapter 7**   Rational Expressions and Equations

65. $\dfrac{3}{2p-1} - \dfrac{4p+4}{4p^2-1}$

66. $\dfrac{1}{3q-2} - \dfrac{6q+4}{9q^2-4}$

67. $\dfrac{m}{m+n} - \dfrac{m}{m-n} + \dfrac{1}{m^2-n^2}$

68. $\dfrac{x}{x+y} - \dfrac{2xy}{x^2-y^2} + \dfrac{y}{x-y}$

69. $\dfrac{2}{a+b} + \dfrac{2}{a-b} - \dfrac{4a}{a^2-b^2}$

70. $\dfrac{-2x}{x^2-y^2} + \dfrac{1}{x+y} - \dfrac{1}{x-y}$

For Exercises 71–72, find an expression that represents the perimeter of the figure (assume that $x > 0$ and $t > 0$).

71.

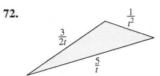

$\dfrac{2}{x+3}$

$\dfrac{1}{x+2}$

72.

$\dfrac{3}{2t}$ $\dfrac{1}{t^2}$ $\dfrac{5}{t}$

Concept 3: Using Rational Expressions in Translations

73. Let a number be represented by n. Write the reciprocal of n.

74. Write the reciprocal of the sum of a number and 6.

75. Write the quotient of 5 and the sum of a number and 2.

76. Write the quotient of 12 and p.

For Exercises 77–80, translate the English phrases into algebraic expressions. Then simplify by combining the rational expressions. **(See Example 8.)**

77. The sum of a number and the quantity seven times the reciprocal of the number.

78. The sum of a number and the quantity five times the reciprocal of the number.

79. The difference of the reciprocal of n and the quotient of 2 and n.

80. The difference of the reciprocal of m and the quotient of $3m$ and 7.

Expanding Your Skills

For Exercises 81–86, perform the indicated operations.

81. $\dfrac{-3}{w^3+27} - \dfrac{1}{w^2-9}$

82. $\dfrac{m}{m^3-1} + \dfrac{1}{(m-1)^2}$

83. $\dfrac{2p}{p^2+5p+6} - \dfrac{p+1}{p^2+2p-3} + \dfrac{3}{p^2+p-2}$

84. $\dfrac{3t}{8t^2+2t-1} - \dfrac{5t}{2t^2-9t-5} + \dfrac{2}{4t^2-21t+5}$

85. $\dfrac{3m}{m^2+3m-10} + \dfrac{5}{4-2m} - \dfrac{1}{m+5}$

86. $\dfrac{2n}{3n^2-8n-3} + \dfrac{1}{6-2n} - \dfrac{3}{3n+1}$

For Exercises 87–90, simplify by applying the order of operations.

87. $\left(\dfrac{2}{k+1} + 3\right)\left(\dfrac{k+1}{4k+7}\right)$

88. $\left(\dfrac{p+1}{3p+4}\right)\left(\dfrac{1}{p+1} + 2\right)$

89. $\left(\dfrac{1}{10a} - \dfrac{b}{10a^2}\right) \div \left(\dfrac{1}{10} - \dfrac{b}{10a}\right)$

90. $\left(\dfrac{1}{2m} + \dfrac{n}{2m^2}\right) \div \left(\dfrac{1}{4} + \dfrac{n}{4m}\right)$

Problem Recognition Exercises

Operations on Rational Expressions

We have learned how to simplify, add, subtract, multiply, and divide rational expressions. The procedure for each operation is different, and it takes considerable practice to determine the correct method to apply for a given problem. The following review exercises give you the opportunity to practice the specific techniques for simplifying rational expressions.

For Exercises 1–20, perform any indicated operations, and simplify the expression.

1. $\dfrac{5}{3x+1} - \dfrac{2x-4}{3x+1}$

2. $\dfrac{\dfrac{w+1}{w^2-16}}{\dfrac{w+1}{w+4}}$

3. $\dfrac{3}{y} \cdot \dfrac{y^2-5y}{6y-9}$

4. $\dfrac{-1}{x+3} + \dfrac{2}{2x-1}$

5. $\dfrac{x-9}{9x-x^2}$

6. $\dfrac{1}{p} - \dfrac{3}{p^2+3p} + \dfrac{p}{3p+9}$

7. $\dfrac{c^2+5c+6}{c^2+c-2} \div \dfrac{c}{c-1}$

8. $\dfrac{2x^2-5x-3}{x^2-9} \cdot \dfrac{x^2+6x+9}{10x+5}$

9. $\dfrac{6a^2b^3}{72ab^7c}$

10. $\dfrac{2a}{a+b} - \dfrac{b}{a-b} - \dfrac{-4ab}{a^2-b^2}$

11. $\dfrac{p^2+10pq+25q^2}{p^2+6pq+5q^2} \div \dfrac{10p+50q}{2p^2-2q^2}$

12. $\dfrac{3k-8}{k-5} + \dfrac{k-12}{k-5}$

13. $\dfrac{20x^2+10x}{4x^3+4x^2+x}$

14. $\dfrac{w^2-81}{w^2+10w+9} \cdot \dfrac{w^2+w+2zw+2z}{w^2-9w+zw-9z}$

15. $\dfrac{8x^2-18x-5}{4x^2-25} \div \dfrac{4x^2-11x-3}{3x-9}$

16. $\dfrac{xy+7x+5y+35}{x^2+ax+5x+5a}$

17. $\dfrac{a}{a^2-9} - \dfrac{3}{6a-18}$

18. $\dfrac{4}{y^2-36} + \dfrac{2}{y^2-4y-12}$

19. $(t^2+5t-24)\left(\dfrac{t+8}{t-3}\right)$

20. $\dfrac{6b^2-7b-10}{b-2}$

Section 7.5	Complex Fractions

1. Simplifying Complex Fractions (Method I)

A **complex fraction** is an expression containing one or more fractions in the numerator, denominator, or both. For example,

$$\frac{\dfrac{1}{ab}}{\dfrac{2}{b}} \quad \text{and} \quad \frac{1 + \dfrac{3}{4} - \dfrac{1}{6}}{\dfrac{1}{2} + \dfrac{1}{3}}$$

are complex fractions.

Two methods will be presented to simplify complex fractions. The first method (Method I) follows the order of operations to simplify the numerator and denominator separately before dividing. The process is summarized as follows.

Simplifying a Complex Fraction (Method I)

Step 1   Add or subtract expressions in the numerator to form a single fraction. Add or subtract expressions in the denominator to form a single fraction.

Step 2   Divide the rational expressions from step 1 by multiplying the numerator of the complex fraction by the reciprocal of the denominator of the complex fraction.

Step 3   Simplify to lowest terms if possible.

Example 1	Simplifying a Complex Fraction (Method I)

Simplify the expression. $\dfrac{\dfrac{1}{ab}}{\dfrac{2}{b}}$

Solution:

Step 1:   The numerator and denominator of the complex fraction are already single fractions.

$\dfrac{\dfrac{1}{ab}}{\dfrac{2}{b}} \longleftarrow$ This fraction bar denotes division ($\div$).

$= \dfrac{1}{ab} \div \dfrac{2}{b}$

$= \dfrac{1}{ab} \cdot \dfrac{b}{2}$ **Step 2:**   Multiply the numerator of the complex fraction by the reciprocal of $\frac{2}{b}$, which is $\frac{b}{2}$.

$= \dfrac{1}{a\cancel{b}} \cdot \dfrac{\overset{1}{\cancel{b}}}{2}$ **Step 3:**   Reduce common factors and simplify.

$= \dfrac{1}{2a}$

Skill Practice Simplify the expression.

1. $\dfrac{\dfrac{6x}{y}}{\dfrac{9}{2y}}$

Sometimes it is necessary to simplify the numerator and denominator of a complex fraction before the division can be performed. This is illustrated in Example 2.

Example 2 **Simplifying a Complex Fraction (Method I)**

Simplify the expression. $\dfrac{1 + \dfrac{3}{4} - \dfrac{1}{6}}{\dfrac{1}{2} + \dfrac{1}{3}}$

Solution:

$\dfrac{1 + \dfrac{3}{4} - \dfrac{1}{6}}{\dfrac{1}{2} + \dfrac{1}{3}}$

Step 1: Combine fractions in the numerator and denominator separately.

$= \dfrac{1 \cdot \dfrac{12}{12} + \dfrac{3}{4} \cdot \dfrac{3}{3} - \dfrac{1}{6} \cdot \dfrac{2}{2}}{\dfrac{1}{2} \cdot \dfrac{3}{3} + \dfrac{1}{3} \cdot \dfrac{2}{2}}$

The LCD in the numerator is 12.
The LCD in the denominator is 6.

$= \dfrac{\dfrac{12}{12} + \dfrac{9}{12} - \dfrac{2}{12}}{\dfrac{3}{6} + \dfrac{2}{6}}$

$= \dfrac{\dfrac{19}{12}}{\dfrac{5}{6}}$

Form a single fraction in the numerator and in the denominator.

$= \dfrac{19}{12} \cdot \dfrac{\overset{1}{\cancel{6}}}{5}$

Step 2: Multiply the numerator by the reciprocal of the denominator.

$= \dfrac{19}{10}$

Step 3: Simplify.

Skill Practice Simplify the expression.

2. $\dfrac{\dfrac{3}{4} - \dfrac{1}{6} + 2}{\dfrac{1}{3} + \dfrac{1}{2}}$

Answers

1. $\dfrac{4x}{3}$ 2. $\dfrac{31}{10}$

| **Example 3** | **Simplifying a Complex Fraction (Method I)** |

Simplify the expression.

$$\dfrac{\dfrac{1}{x} + \dfrac{1}{y}}{x - \dfrac{y^2}{x}}$$

Solution:

$$\dfrac{\dfrac{1}{x} + \dfrac{1}{y}}{x - \dfrac{y^2}{x}}$$

The LCD in the numerator is xy.
The LCD in the denominator is x.

$$= \dfrac{\dfrac{1 \cdot y}{x \cdot y} + \dfrac{1 \cdot x}{y \cdot x}}{\dfrac{x \cdot x}{1 \cdot x} - \dfrac{y^2}{x}}$$

Rewrite the expressions using common denominators.

$$= \dfrac{\dfrac{y}{xy} + \dfrac{x}{xy}}{\dfrac{x^2}{x} - \dfrac{y^2}{x}}$$

$$= \dfrac{\dfrac{y + x}{xy}}{\dfrac{x^2 - y^2}{x}}$$

Form single fractions in the numerator and denominator.

$$= \dfrac{y + x}{xy} \cdot \dfrac{x}{x^2 - y^2}$$

Multiply the numerator by the reciprocal of the denominator.

$$= \dfrac{\cancel{y + x}}{xy} \cdot \dfrac{\cancel{x}}{(x + y)(x - y)}$$

Factor and reduce. Note that $(y + x) = (x + y)$.

$$= \dfrac{1}{y(x - y)}$$

Simplify.

Skill Practice Simplify the expression.

3. $\dfrac{1 - \dfrac{1}{p}}{\dfrac{p}{w} + \dfrac{w}{p}}$

2. Simplifying Complex Fractions (Method II)

We will now simplify the expressions from Examples 2 and 3 again using a second method to simplify complex fractions (Method II). Recall that multiplying the numerator and denominator of a rational expression by the same quantity does not change the value of the expression because we are multiplying by a number equivalent to 1. This is the basis for Method II.

Answer

3. $\dfrac{w(p - 1)}{p^2 + w^2}$

Simplifying a Complex Fraction (Method II)

Step 1 Multiply the numerator and denominator of the complex fraction by the LCD of *all* individual fractions within the expression.

Step 2 Apply the distributive property, and simplify the numerator and denominator.

Step 3 Simplify to lowest terms if possible.

Example 4   **Simplifying a Complex Fraction (Method II)**

Simplify the expression.

$$\dfrac{1 + \dfrac{3}{4} - \dfrac{1}{6}}{\dfrac{1}{2} + \dfrac{1}{3}}$$

Solution:

$$\dfrac{1 + \dfrac{3}{4} - \dfrac{1}{6}}{\dfrac{1}{2} + \dfrac{1}{3}}$$

The LCD of the expressions $1, \frac{3}{4}, \frac{1}{6}, \frac{1}{2},$ and $\frac{1}{3}$ is 12.

$$= \dfrac{12\left(1 + \dfrac{3}{4} - \dfrac{1}{6}\right)}{12\left(\dfrac{1}{2} + \dfrac{1}{3}\right)}$$

Step 1: Multiply the numerator and denominator of the complex fraction by 12.

> **TIP:** In step 1, we multiply the original expression by $\frac{12}{12}$, which equals 1.

$$= \dfrac{12 \cdot 1 + 12 \cdot \dfrac{3}{4} - 12 \cdot \dfrac{1}{6}}{12 \cdot \dfrac{1}{2} + 12 \cdot \dfrac{1}{3}}$$

Step 2: Apply the distributive property.

$$= \dfrac{12 \cdot 1 + \overset{3}{\cancel{12}} \cdot \dfrac{3}{\cancel{4}} - \overset{2}{\cancel{12}} \cdot \dfrac{1}{\cancel{6}}}{\overset{6}{\cancel{12}} \cdot \dfrac{1}{\cancel{2}} + \overset{4}{\cancel{12}} \cdot \dfrac{1}{\cancel{3}}}$$

Simplify each term.

$$= \dfrac{12 + 9 - 2}{6 + 4}$$

$$= \dfrac{19}{10}$$

Step 3: Simplify. This is the same result as in Example 2.

Skill Practice Simplify the expression.

4. $\dfrac{1 - \dfrac{3}{5}}{\dfrac{1}{4} - \dfrac{7}{10} + 1}$

Answer

4. $\dfrac{8}{11}$

| Example 5 | **Simplifying a Complex Fraction (Method II)** |

Simplify the expression.

$$\dfrac{\dfrac{1}{x}+\dfrac{1}{y}}{x-\dfrac{y^2}{x}}$$

Solution:

$$\dfrac{\dfrac{1}{x}+\dfrac{1}{y}}{x-\dfrac{y^2}{x}}$$

The LCD of the expressions $\frac{1}{x}$, $\frac{1}{y}$, x, and $\frac{y^2}{x}$ is xy.

$$=\dfrac{xy\left(\dfrac{1}{x}+\dfrac{1}{y}\right)}{xy\left(x-\dfrac{y^2}{x}\right)}$$

Step 1: Multiply numerator and denominator of the complex fraction by xy.

$$=\dfrac{xy\cdot\dfrac{1}{x}+xy\cdot\dfrac{1}{y}}{xy\cdot x-xy\cdot\dfrac{y^2}{x}}$$

Step 2: Apply the distributive property, and simplify each term.

$$=\dfrac{y+x}{x^2y-y^3}$$

$$=\dfrac{y+x}{y(x^2-y^2)}$$

Step 3: Factor completely, and reduce common factors.

$$=\dfrac{\cancel{y+x}}{y\,(x+y)(x-y)}$$

Note that $(y+x)=(x+y)$.

$$=\dfrac{1}{y(x-y)}$$

This is the same result as in Example 3.

Skill Practice Simplify the expression.

5. $\dfrac{\dfrac{z}{3}-\dfrac{3}{z}}{1+\dfrac{3}{z}}$

Answer

5. $\dfrac{z-3}{3}$

| **Example 6** | **Simplifying a Complex Fraction (Method II)** |

Simplify the expression.

$$\dfrac{\dfrac{1}{k+1} - 1}{\dfrac{1}{k+1} + 1}$$

Solution:

$$\dfrac{\dfrac{1}{k+1} - 1}{\dfrac{1}{k+1} + 1}$$

The LCD of $\dfrac{1}{k+1}$ and 1 is $(k+1)$.

$$= \dfrac{(k+1)\left(\dfrac{1}{k+1} - 1\right)}{(k+1)\left(\dfrac{1}{k+1} + 1\right)}$$

Step 1: Multiply numerator and denominator of the complex fraction by $(k+1)$.

$$= \dfrac{(k+1) \cdot \dfrac{1}{(k+1)} - (k+1) \cdot 1}{(k+1) \cdot \dfrac{1}{(k+1)} + (k+1) \cdot 1}$$

Step 2: Apply the distributive property.

$$= \dfrac{1 - (k+1)}{1 + (k+1)}$$

Simplify.

$$= \dfrac{1 - k - 1}{1 + k + 1}$$

$$= \dfrac{-k}{k+2}$$

Step 3: The expression is already in lowest terms.

Skill Practice Simplify the expression.

6. $\dfrac{\dfrac{4}{p-3} + 1}{1 + \dfrac{2}{p-3}}$

Answer

6. $\dfrac{p+1}{p-1}$

| **Section 7.5** | **Practice Exercises** |

Vocabulary and Key Concepts

1. A _____ fraction is an expression containing one or more fractions in the numerator, denominator, or both.

Review Exercises

For Exercises 2–3, simplify the expression.

2. $\dfrac{y(2y+9)}{y^2(2y+9)}$

3. $\dfrac{a+5}{2a^2 + 7a - 15}$

For Exercises 4–6, perform the indicated operations.

4. $\dfrac{2}{w-2} + \dfrac{3}{w}$

5. $\dfrac{6}{5} - \dfrac{3}{5k-10}$

6. $\dfrac{x^2 - 2xy + y^2}{x^4 - y^4} \div \dfrac{3x^2y - 3xy^2}{x^2 + y^2}$

Concepts 1–2: Simplifying Complex Fractions (Methods I and II)

For Exercises 7–34, simplify the complex fractions using either method. **(See Examples 1–6.)**

7. $\dfrac{\dfrac{7}{18y}}{\dfrac{2}{9}}$

8. $\dfrac{\dfrac{a^2}{2a-3}}{\dfrac{5a}{8a-12}}$

9. $\dfrac{\dfrac{3x+2y}{2y}}{\dfrac{6x+4y}{2}}$

10. $\dfrac{\dfrac{2x-10}{4}}{\dfrac{x^2-5x}{3x}}$

11. $\dfrac{\dfrac{8a^4b^3}{3c}}{\dfrac{a^7b^2}{9c}}$

12. $\dfrac{\dfrac{12x^2}{5y}}{\dfrac{8x^6}{9y^2}}$

13. $\dfrac{\dfrac{4r^3s}{t^5}}{\dfrac{2s^7}{r^2t^9}}$

14. $\dfrac{\dfrac{5p^4q}{w^4}}{\dfrac{10p^2}{qw^2}}$

15. $\dfrac{\dfrac{1}{8} + \dfrac{4}{3}}{\dfrac{1}{2} - \dfrac{5}{12}}$

16. $\dfrac{\dfrac{8}{9} - \dfrac{1}{3}}{\dfrac{7}{6} + \dfrac{1}{9}}$

17. $\dfrac{\dfrac{1}{h} + \dfrac{1}{k}}{\dfrac{1}{hk}}$

18. $\dfrac{\dfrac{1}{b} + 1}{\dfrac{1}{b}}$

19. $\dfrac{\dfrac{n+1}{n^2-9}}{\dfrac{2}{n+3}}$

20. $\dfrac{\dfrac{5}{k-5}}{\dfrac{k+1}{k^2-25}}$

21. $\dfrac{2 + \dfrac{1}{x}}{4 + \dfrac{1}{x}}$

22. $\dfrac{6 + \dfrac{6}{k}}{1 + \dfrac{1}{k}}$

23. $\dfrac{\dfrac{m}{7} - \dfrac{7}{m}}{\dfrac{1}{7} + \dfrac{1}{m}}$

24. $\dfrac{\dfrac{2}{p} + \dfrac{p}{2}}{\dfrac{p}{3} - \dfrac{3}{p}}$

25. $\dfrac{\dfrac{1}{5} - \dfrac{1}{y}}{\dfrac{7}{10} + \dfrac{1}{y^2}}$

26. $\dfrac{\dfrac{1}{m^2} + \dfrac{2}{3}}{\dfrac{1}{m} - \dfrac{5}{6}}$

27. $\dfrac{\dfrac{8}{a+4} + 2}{\dfrac{12}{a+4} - 2}$

28. $\dfrac{\dfrac{2}{w+1} + 3}{\dfrac{3}{w+1} + 4}$

29. $\dfrac{1 - \dfrac{4}{t^2}}{1 - \dfrac{2}{t} - \dfrac{8}{t^2}}$

30. $\dfrac{1 - \dfrac{9}{p^2}}{1 - \dfrac{1}{p} - \dfrac{6}{p^2}}$

31. $\dfrac{t + 4 + \dfrac{3}{t}}{t - 4 - \dfrac{5}{t}}$

32. $\dfrac{\dfrac{9}{4m} + \dfrac{9}{2m^2}}{\dfrac{3}{2} + \dfrac{3}{m}}$

33. $\dfrac{\dfrac{1}{k-6} - 1}{\dfrac{2}{k-6} - 2}$

34. $\dfrac{\dfrac{3}{y-3} + 4}{8 + \dfrac{6}{y-3}}$

For Exercises 35–38, write the English phrases as algebraic expressions. Then simplify the expressions.

35. The sum of one-half and two-thirds, divided by five

36. The quotient of ten and the difference of two-fifths and one-fourth

37. The quotient of three and the sum of two-thirds and three-fourths

38. The difference of three-fifths and one-half, divided by four

39. In electronics, resistors oppose the flow of current. For two resistors in parallel, the total resistance is given by

$$R = \frac{1}{\dfrac{1}{R_1} + \dfrac{1}{R_2}}$$

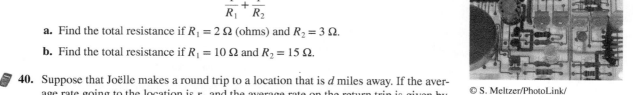

© S. Meltzer/PhotoLink/
Getty Images RF

a. Find the total resistance if $R_1 = 2\ \Omega$ (ohms) and $R_2 = 3\ \Omega$.

b. Find the total resistance if $R_1 = 10\ \Omega$ and $R_2 = 15\ \Omega$.

40. Suppose that Joëlle makes a round trip to a location that is d miles away. If the average rate going to the location is r_1 and the average rate on the return trip is given by r_2, the average rate of the entire trip, R, is given by

$$R = \frac{2d}{\dfrac{d}{r_1} + \dfrac{d}{r_2}}$$

a. Find the average rate of a trip to a destination 30 mi away when the average rate going there is 60 mph and the average rate returning home is 45 mph. (Round to the nearest tenth of a mile per hour.)

b. Find the average rate of a trip to a destination that is 50 mi away if the driver travels at the same rates as in part (a). (Round to the nearest tenth of a mile per hour.)

c. Compare your answers from parts (a) and (b) and explain the results in the context of the problem.

Expanding Your Skills

For Exercises 41–50, simplify the complex fractions using either method.

41. $\dfrac{x^{-1} - y^{-1}}{x^{-2} - y^{-2}}$

42. $\dfrac{a^{-2} - 1}{a^{-1} - 1}$

43. $\dfrac{2x^{-1} + 8y^{-1}}{4x^{-1}}$

$\left(Hint:\ 2x^{-1} = \dfrac{2}{x}\right)$

44. $\dfrac{6a^{-1} + 4b^{-1}}{8b^{-1}}$

45. $\dfrac{(mn)^{-2}}{m^{-2} + n^{-2}}$

46. $\dfrac{(xy)^{-1}}{2x^{-1} + 3y^{-1}}$

47. $\dfrac{\dfrac{1}{z^2 - 9} + \dfrac{2}{z + 3}}{\dfrac{3}{z - 3}}$

48. $\dfrac{\dfrac{5}{w^2 - 25} - \dfrac{3}{w + 5}}{\dfrac{4}{w - 5}}$

49. $\dfrac{\dfrac{2}{x - 1} + 2}{\dfrac{2}{x + 1} - 2}$

50. $\dfrac{\dfrac{1}{y - 3} + 1}{\dfrac{2}{y + 3} - 1}$

For Exercises 51–52, simplify the complex fractions. (*Hint:* Use the order of operations and begin with the fraction on the lower right.)

51. $1 + \dfrac{1}{1 + 1}$

52. $1 + \dfrac{1}{1 + \dfrac{1}{1 + 1}}$

Section 7.6   Rational Equations

1. Introduction to Rational Equations

Thus far we have studied two specific types of equations in one variable: linear equations and quadratic equations. Recall,

$$ax + b = c, \text{ where } a \neq 0, \text{ is a } \textbf{linear equation.}$$

$$ax^2 + bx + c = 0, \text{ where } a \neq 0, \text{ is a } \textbf{quadratic equation.}$$

We will now study another type of equation called a rational equation.

> **Definition of a Rational Equation**
>
> An equation with one or more rational expressions is called a **rational equation.**

The following equations are rational equations:

$$\frac{1}{x} + \frac{1}{3} = \frac{5}{6} \qquad \frac{6}{t^2 - 7t + 12} + \frac{2t}{t - 3} = \frac{3t}{t - 4}$$

To understand the process of solving a rational equation, first review the process of clearing fractions. We can clear the fractions in an equation by multiplying both sides of the equation by the LCD of all terms.

Example 1   **Solving an Equation Containing Fractions**

Solve. $\dfrac{y}{2} + \dfrac{y}{4} = 6$

Solution:

$$\frac{y}{2} + \frac{y}{4} = 6 \qquad \text{The LCD of all terms in the equation is } 4.$$

$$4\left(\frac{y}{2} + \frac{y}{4}\right) = 4(6) \qquad \text{Multiply both sides of the equation by 4 to clear fractions.}$$

$$\overset{2}{\cancel{4}} \cdot \frac{y}{2} + \overset{1}{\cancel{4}} \cdot \frac{y}{4} = 4(6) \qquad \text{Apply the distributive property.}$$

$$2y + y = 24 \qquad \text{Clear fractions.}$$

$$3y = 24 \qquad \text{Solve the resulting equation (linear).}$$

$$y = 8$$

Check: $\dfrac{y}{2} + \dfrac{y}{4} = 6$

$$\frac{(8)}{2} + \frac{(8)}{4} \overset{?}{=} 6$$

$$4 + 2 \overset{?}{=} 6$$

The solution set is $\{8\}$. $6 \overset{?}{=} 6 \checkmark \text{ (True)}$

Skill Practice Solve the equation.

1. $\dfrac{t}{5} - \dfrac{t}{4} = 2$

2. Solving Rational Equations

The same process of clearing fractions is used to solve rational equations when variables are present in the denominator. However, variables in the denominator make it necessary to take note of the restricted values.

Example 2   **Solving a Rational Equation**

Solve the equation. $\dfrac{x+1}{x} + \dfrac{1}{3} = \dfrac{5}{6}$

Solution:

$$\dfrac{x+1}{x} + \dfrac{1}{3} = \dfrac{5}{6}$$

The LCD of all the expressions is $6x$. The restricted value is $x = 0$.

> **TIP:** The restricted value tells us that $x = 0$ is *not* a possible solution to the equation.

$$6x \cdot \left(\dfrac{x+1}{x} + \dfrac{1}{3} \right) = 6x \cdot \left(\dfrac{5}{6} \right)$$

Multiply by the LCD.

$$\overset{1}{6x} \cdot \left(\dfrac{x+1}{x} \right) + \overset{2}{6x} \cdot \left(\dfrac{1}{3} \right) = \overset{1}{6x} \cdot \left(\dfrac{5}{6} \right)$$

Apply the distributive property.

$$6(x+1) + 2x = 5x$$

Clear fractions.

$$6x + 6 + 2x = 5x$$

Solve the resulting equation.

$$8x + 6 = 5x$$

$$3x = -6$$

$$x = -2$$

-2 is not a restricted value.

Check: $\dfrac{x+1}{x} + \dfrac{1}{3} = \dfrac{5}{6}$

$$\dfrac{(-2)+1}{(-2)} + \dfrac{1}{3} \overset{?}{=} \dfrac{5}{6}$$

$$\dfrac{-1}{-2} + \dfrac{1}{3} \overset{?}{=} \dfrac{5}{6}$$

$$\dfrac{1}{2} + \dfrac{1}{3} \overset{?}{=} \dfrac{5}{6}$$

$$\dfrac{3}{6} + \dfrac{2}{6} \overset{?}{=} \dfrac{5}{6}$$

The solution set is $\{-2\}$.

$$\dfrac{5}{6} \overset{?}{=} \dfrac{5}{6} \ \checkmark \ \text{(True)}$$

Skill Practice Solve the equation.

2. $\dfrac{3}{4} + \dfrac{5+a}{a} = \dfrac{1}{2}$

Answers

1. $\{-40\}$ **2.** $\{-4\}$

| **Example 3** | **Solving a Rational Equation** |

Solve the equation. $1 + \dfrac{3a}{a-2} = \dfrac{6}{a-2}$

Solution:

$$1 + \frac{3a}{a-2} = \frac{6}{a-2}$$

The LCD of all the expressions is $a-2$. The restricted value is $a=2$.

$$(a-2)\left(1 + \frac{3a}{a-2}\right) = (a-2)\left(\frac{6}{a-2}\right)$$

Multiply by the LCD.

$$(a-2)1 + (a-2)\left(\frac{3a}{a-2}\right) = (a-2)\left(\frac{6}{a-2}\right)$$

Apply the distributive property.

$$a - 2 + 3a = 6$$

Solve the resulting equation (linear).

$$4a - 2 = 6$$

$$4a = 8$$

$$a = 2$$

2 is a restricted value.

Check: $1 + \dfrac{3a}{a-2} = \dfrac{6}{a-2}$

$$1 + \frac{3(2)}{(2)-2} \stackrel{?}{=} \frac{6}{(2)-2}$$

$$1 + \frac{6}{0} \stackrel{?}{=} \frac{6}{0}$$

The denominator is 0 when $a = 2$.

Because the value $a = 2$ makes the denominator zero in one (or more) of the rational expressions within the equation, the equation is undefined for $a = 2$. No other potential solutions exist for the equation, therefore, the solution set is { }.

Skill Practice Solve the equation.

3. $\dfrac{x}{x+1} - 2 = \dfrac{-1}{x+1}$

Examples 1–3 show that the steps to solve a rational equation mirror the process of clearing fractions. However, there is one significant difference. The solutions of a rational equation must not make the denominator equal to zero for any expression within the equation.

Answer

3. { } (The value −1 does not check.)

The steps to solve a rational equation are summarized as follows.

Solving a Rational Equation

Step 1 Factor the denominators of all rational expressions. Identify the restricted values.

Step 2 Identify the LCD of all expressions in the equation.

Step 3 Multiply both sides of the equation by the LCD.

Step 4 Solve the resulting equation.

Step 5 Check potential solutions in the original equation.

After multiplying by the LCD and then simplifying, the rational equation will be either a linear equation or higher degree equation.

Example 4 **Solving a Rational Equation**

Solve the equation. $1 - \dfrac{4}{p} = -\dfrac{3}{p^2}$

Solution:

$$1 - \frac{4}{p} = -\frac{3}{p^2}$$

Step 1: The denominators are already factored. The restricted value is $p = 0$.

Step 2: The LCD of all expressions is p^2.

$$p^2\left(1 - \frac{4}{p}\right) = p^2\left(-\frac{3}{p^2}\right)$$

Step 3: Multiply by the LCD.

$$p^2(1) - \overset{p}{\cancel{p^2}}\left(\frac{4}{p}\right) = \overset{1}{\cancel{p^2}}\left(-\frac{3}{p^2}\right)$$

Apply the distributive property.

$$p^2 - 4p = -3$$

Step 4: Solve the resulting quadratic equation.

$$p^2 - 4p + 3 = 0$$

Set the equation equal to zero and factor.

$$(p - 3)(p - 1) = 0$$

$$p - 3 = 0 \quad \text{or} \quad p - 1 = 0$$

Set each factor equal to zero.

$$p = 3 \quad \text{or} \quad p = 1$$

Step 5: $\underline{\text{Check}: p = 3}$ $\underline{\text{Check}: p = 1}$

3 and 1 are not restricted values.

$$1 - \frac{4}{p} = -\frac{3}{p^2} \qquad 1 - \frac{4}{p} = -\frac{3}{p^2}$$

$$1 - \frac{4}{(3)} \overset{?}{=} -\frac{3}{(3)^2} \qquad 1 - \frac{4}{(1)} \overset{?}{=} -\frac{3}{(1)^2}$$

$$\frac{3}{3} - \frac{4}{3} \overset{?}{=} -\frac{3}{9} \qquad 1 - 4 \overset{?}{=} -3$$

The solution set is $\{3, 1\}$.

$$-\frac{1}{3} \overset{?}{=} -\frac{1}{3} \checkmark \qquad -3 \overset{?}{=} -3 \checkmark$$

Skill Practice Solve the equation.

4. $\dfrac{z}{2} - \dfrac{1}{2z} = \dfrac{12}{z}$

Answer

4. $\{5, -5\}$

| **Example 5** | **Solving a Rational Equation** |

Solve the equation. $\quad \dfrac{6}{t^2 - 7t + 12} + \dfrac{2t}{t - 3} = \dfrac{3t}{t - 4}$

Solution:

$$\dfrac{6}{t^2 - 7t + 12} + \dfrac{2t}{t - 3} = \dfrac{3t}{t - 4}$$

$$\dfrac{6}{(t - 3)(t - 4)} + \dfrac{2t}{t - 3} = \dfrac{3t}{t - 4}$$

Step 1: Factor the denominators. The restricted values are $t = 3$ and $t = 4$.

Step 2: The LCD is $(t - 3)(t - 4)$.

Step 3: Multiply by the LCD on both sides.

$$(t - 3)(t - 4)\left[\dfrac{6}{(t - 3)(t - 4)} + \dfrac{2t}{t - 3}\right] = (t - 3)(t - 4)\left(\dfrac{3t}{t - 4}\right)$$

$$(t - 3)(t - 4)\left[\dfrac{6}{(t - 3)(t - 4)}\right] + (t - 3)(t - 4)\left(\dfrac{2t}{t - 3}\right) = (t - 3)(t - 4)\left(\dfrac{3t}{t - 4}\right)$$

$$6 + 2t(t - 4) = 3t(t - 3)$$

$$6 + 2t^2 - 8t = 3t^2 - 9t$$

$$0 = 3t^2 - 2t^2 - 9t + 8t - 6$$

$$0 = t^2 - t - 6$$

$$0 = (t - 3)(t + 2)$$

$$t - 3 = 0 \quad \text{or} \quad t + 2 = 0$$

$$t = 3 \quad \text{or} \quad t = -2$$

3 is a restricted value, but -2 is not restricted.

Step 4: Solve the resulting equation.

Because the resulting equation is quadratic, set the equation equal to zero and factor.

Set each factor equal to zero.

Step 5: Check the potential solutions in the original equation.

Check: $t = 3$

3 cannot be a solution to the equation because it will make the denominator zero in the original equation.

$$\dfrac{6}{t^2 - 7t + 12} + \dfrac{2t}{t - 3} = \dfrac{3t}{t - 4}$$

$$\dfrac{6}{(3)^2 - 7(3) + 12} + \dfrac{2(3)}{(3) - 3} \stackrel{?}{=} \dfrac{3(3)}{(3) - 4}$$

$$\dfrac{6}{0} + \dfrac{6}{0} \stackrel{?}{=} \dfrac{9}{-1}$$

Zero in the denominator

The solution set is $\{-2\}$.

Check: $t = -2$

$$\dfrac{6}{t^2 - 7t + 12} + \dfrac{2t}{t - 3} = \dfrac{3t}{t - 4}$$

$$\dfrac{6}{(-2)^2 - 7(-2) + 12} + \dfrac{2(-2)}{(-2) - 3} \stackrel{?}{=} \dfrac{3(-2)}{(-2) - 4}$$

$$\dfrac{6}{4 + 14 + 12} + \dfrac{-4}{-5} \stackrel{?}{=} \dfrac{-6}{-6}$$

$$\dfrac{6}{30} + \dfrac{4}{5} \stackrel{?}{=} 1$$

$$\dfrac{1}{5} + \dfrac{4}{5} \stackrel{?}{=} 1 \checkmark \text{(True)}$$

$$t = -2 \text{ is a solution.}$$

Skill Practice Solve the equation.

5. $\dfrac{-8}{x^2 + 6x + 8} + \dfrac{x}{x + 4} = \dfrac{2}{x + 2}$

Answer

5. $\{4\}$ (The value -4 does not check.)

Example 6	**Translating to a Rational Equation**

Ten times the reciprocal of a number is added to four. The result is equal to the quotient of twenty-two and the number. Find the number.

Solution:

Let x represent the number.

$$\underset{\substack{\text{is added} \\ \text{to four}}}{4} \quad + \quad \underset{\substack{10 \text{ times} \\ \text{the reciprocal} \\ \text{of a number}}}{10\left(\frac{1}{x}\right)} \quad \underset{\substack{\text{the result} \\ \text{is equal to}}}{=} \quad \underset{\substack{\text{the quotient of} \\ 22 \text{ and the number}}}{\frac{22}{x}}$$

$4 + \dfrac{10}{x} = \dfrac{22}{x}$

Step 1: The denominators are already factored. The restricted value is $x = 0$.

Step 2: The LCD is x.

$x\left(4 + \dfrac{10}{x}\right) = x\left(\dfrac{22}{x}\right)$

Step 3: Multiply both sides by the LCD.

$4x + 10 = 22$

Apply the distributive property.

$4x = 12$

Step 4: Solve the resulting linear equation.

$x = 3$ is a potential solution.

Step 5: 3 is not a restricted value. Substituting $x = 3$ into the original equation verifies that it is a solution.

The number is 3.

Skill Practice

6. The quotient of ten and a number is two less than four times the reciprocal of the number. Find the number.

3. Solving Formulas Involving Rational Expressions

A rational equation may have more than one variable. To solve for a specific variable within a rational equation, we can still apply the principle of clearing fractions.

Answer

6. The number is −3.

| Example 7 | Solving Formulas Involving Rational Equations |

Solve for k. $F = \dfrac{ma}{k}$

Solution:

To solve for k, we must clear fractions so that k no longer appears in the denominator.

$$F = \frac{ma}{k}$$ The LCD is k.

$$k \cdot (F) = k \cdot \left(\frac{ma}{k}\right)$$ Multiply both sides of the equation by the LCD.

$$kF = ma$$ Clear fractions.

$$\frac{kF}{F} = \frac{ma}{F}$$ Divide both sides by F.

$$k = \frac{ma}{F}$$

Skill Practice

7. Solve for t. $C = \dfrac{rt}{d}$

| Example 8 | Solving Formulas Involving Rational Equations |

A formula to find the height of a trapezoid given its area and the lengths of the two parallel sides is $h = \dfrac{2A}{B + b}$. Solve for b, the length of one of the parallel sides.

Solution:

To solve for b, we must clear fractions so that b no longer appears in the denominator.

$$h = \frac{2A}{B + b}$$ The LCD is $(B + b)$.

$$h(B + b) = \left(\frac{2A}{B+b}\right) \cdot (B+b)$$ Multiply both sides of the equation by the LCD.

$$hB + hb = 2A$$ Apply the distributive property.

$$hb = 2A - hB$$ Subtract hB from both sides to isolate the b term.

$$\frac{hb}{h} = \frac{2A - hB}{h}$$ Divide by h.

$$b = \frac{2A - hB}{h}$$

Avoiding Mistakes

Algebra is case-sensitive. The variables B and b represent different values.

Skill Practice

8. Solve the formula for x. $y = \dfrac{3}{x - 2}$

Answers

7. $t = \dfrac{Cd}{r}$

8. $x = \dfrac{3 + 2y}{y}$ or $x = \dfrac{3}{y} + 2$

TIP: The solution to Example 8 can be written in several forms. The quantity

$$\frac{2A - hB}{h}$$

can be left as a single rational expression or can be split into two fractions and simplified.

$$b = \frac{2A - hB}{h} = \frac{2A}{h} - \frac{hB}{h} = \frac{2A}{h} - B$$

| **Example 9** | **Solving Formulas Involving Rational Equations** |

Solve for z. $y = \dfrac{x - z}{x + z}$

Solution:

To solve for z, we must clear fractions so that z no longer appears in the denominator.

$y = \dfrac{x - z}{x + z}$ LCD is $(x + z)$.

$y(x + z) = \left(\dfrac{x - z}{x + z}\right)(x + z)$ Multiply both sides of the equation by the LCD.

$yx + yz = x - z$ Apply the distributive property.

$yz + z = x - yx$ Collect z terms on one side of the equation and collect terms not containing z on the other side.

$z(y + 1) = x - yx$ Factor out z.

$z = \dfrac{x - yx}{y + 1}$ Divide by $y + 1$ to solve for z.

Skill Practice

9. Solve for h. $\dfrac{b}{x} = \dfrac{a}{h} + 1$

Answer

9. $h = \dfrac{ax}{b - x}$ or $\dfrac{-ax}{x - b}$

Section 7.6   Practice Exercises

Vocabulary and Key Concepts

1. a. The equation $4x + 7 = -18$ is an example of a _____ equation, whereas $3y^2 - 4y - 7 = 0$ is an example of a _____ equation.

b. The equation $\dfrac{6}{x + 2} + \dfrac{1}{4} = \dfrac{2}{3}$ is an example of a _____ equation.

c. After solving a rational equation, check each potential solution to determine if it makes the _____ equal to zero in one or more of the rational expressions. If so, that potential solution is not part of the solution set.

Review Exercises

For Exercises 2–7, perform the indicated operations.

2. $\dfrac{2}{x-3} - \dfrac{3}{x^2 - x - 6}$

3. $\dfrac{2x-6}{4x^2 + 7x - 2} \div \dfrac{x^2 - 5x + 6}{x^2 - 4}$

4. $\dfrac{2y}{y-3} + \dfrac{4}{y^2 - 9}$

5. $\dfrac{h - \dfrac{1}{h}}{\dfrac{1}{5} - \dfrac{1}{5h}}$

6. $\dfrac{w-4}{w^2 - 9} \cdot \dfrac{w-3}{w^2 - 8w + 16}$

7. $1 + \dfrac{1}{x} - \dfrac{12}{x^2}$

Concept 1: Introduction to Rational Equations

For Exercises 8–13, solve the equations by first clearing the fractions. **(See Example 1.)**

8. $\dfrac{1}{3}z + \dfrac{2}{3} = -2z + 10$

9. $\dfrac{5}{2} + \dfrac{1}{2}b = 5 - \dfrac{1}{3}b$

10. $\dfrac{3}{2}p + \dfrac{1}{3} = \dfrac{2p-3}{4}$

11. $\dfrac{5}{3} - \dfrac{1}{6}k = \dfrac{3k+5}{4}$

12. $\dfrac{2x-3}{4} + \dfrac{9}{10} = \dfrac{x}{5}$

13. $\dfrac{4y+2}{3} - \dfrac{7}{6} = -\dfrac{y}{6}$

Concept 2: Solving Rational Equations

14. For the equation

$$\dfrac{1}{w} - \dfrac{1}{2} = -\dfrac{1}{4}$$

    a. Identify the restricted values.

    b. Identify the LCD of the fractions in the equation.

    c. Solve the equation.

15. For the equation

$$\dfrac{3}{z} - \dfrac{4}{5} = \dfrac{1}{5}$$

    a. Identify the restricted values.

    b. Identify the LCD of the fractions in the equation.

    c. Solve the equation.

16. Identify the LCD of all the denominators in the equation.

$$\dfrac{x+1}{x^2 + 2x - 3} = \dfrac{1}{x+3} - \dfrac{1}{x-1}$$

For Exercises 17–46, solve the equations. **(See Examples 2–5.)**

17. $\dfrac{1}{8} = \dfrac{3}{5} + \dfrac{5}{y}$

18. $\dfrac{2}{7} - \dfrac{1}{x} = \dfrac{2}{3}$

19. $\dfrac{7}{4a} = \dfrac{3}{a-5}$

20. $\dfrac{2}{x+4} = \dfrac{5}{3x}$

21. $\dfrac{5}{6x} + \dfrac{7}{x} = 1$

22. $\dfrac{14}{3x} - \dfrac{5}{x} = 2$

23. $1 - \dfrac{2}{y} = \dfrac{3}{y^2}$

24. $1 - \dfrac{2}{m} = \dfrac{8}{m^2}$

25. $\dfrac{a+1}{a} = 1 + \dfrac{a-2}{2a}$

26. $\dfrac{7b-4}{5b} = \dfrac{9}{5} - \dfrac{4}{b}$

27. $\dfrac{w}{5} - \dfrac{w+3}{w} = -\dfrac{3}{w}$

28. $\dfrac{t}{12} + \dfrac{t+3}{3t} = \dfrac{1}{t}$

29. $\dfrac{2}{m+3} = \dfrac{5}{4m+12} - \dfrac{3}{8}$

30. $\dfrac{2}{4n-4} - \dfrac{7}{4} = \dfrac{-3}{n-1}$

31. $\dfrac{p}{p-4} - 5 = \dfrac{4}{p-4}$

32. $\dfrac{-5}{q+5} = \dfrac{q}{q+5} + 2$

33. $\dfrac{2t}{t+2} - 2 = \dfrac{t-8}{t+2}$

34. $\dfrac{4w}{w-3} - 3 = \dfrac{3w-1}{w-3}$

35. $\dfrac{x^2-x}{x-2} = \dfrac{12}{x-2}$

36. $\dfrac{x^2+9}{x+4} = \dfrac{-10x}{x+4}$

37. $\dfrac{x^2+3x}{x-1} = \dfrac{4}{x-1}$

38. $\dfrac{2x^2-21}{2x-3} = \dfrac{-11x}{2x-3}$

39. $\dfrac{2x}{x+4} - \dfrac{8}{x-4} = \dfrac{2x^2+32}{x^2-16}$

40. $\dfrac{4x}{x+3} - \dfrac{12}{x-3} = \dfrac{4x^2+36}{x^2-9}$

41. $\dfrac{x}{x+6} = \dfrac{72}{x^2-36} + 4$

42. $\dfrac{y}{y+4} = \dfrac{32}{y^2-16} + 3$

43. $\dfrac{5}{3x-3} - \dfrac{2}{x-2} = \dfrac{7}{x^2-3x+2}$

44. $\dfrac{6}{5a+10} - \dfrac{1}{a-5} = \dfrac{4}{a^2-3a-10}$

45. $\dfrac{w}{w-3} = \dfrac{17}{w^2-7w+12} + \dfrac{1}{w-4}$

46. $\dfrac{y}{y+6} = \dfrac{-6}{y^2+7y+6} + \dfrac{2}{y+1}$

For Exercises 47–50, translate to a rational equation and solve. **(See Example 6.)**

47. The reciprocal of a number is added to three. The result is the quotient of 25 and the number. Find the number.

48. The difference of three and the reciprocal of a number is equal to the quotient of 20 and the number. Find the number.

49. If a number added to five is divided by the difference of the number and two, the result is three-fourths. Find the number.

50. If twice a number added to three is divided by the number plus one, the result is three-halves. Find the number.

Concept 3: Solving Formulas Involving Rational Expressions

For Exercises 51–68, solve for the indicated variable. **(See Examples 7–9.)**

51. $K = \dfrac{ma}{F}$ for m

52. $K = \dfrac{ma}{F}$ for a

53. $K = \dfrac{IR}{E}$ for E

54. $K = \dfrac{IR}{E}$ for R

55. $I = \dfrac{E}{R+r}$ for R

56. $I = \dfrac{E}{R+r}$ for r

57. $h = \dfrac{2A}{B+b}$ for B

58. $\dfrac{C}{\pi r} = 2$ for r

59. $\dfrac{V}{\pi h} = r^2$ for h

60. $\dfrac{V}{lw} = h$ for w

61. $x = \dfrac{at+b}{t}$ for t

62. $\dfrac{T+mf}{m} = g$ for m

63. $\dfrac{x-y}{xy} = z$ for x

64. $\dfrac{w-n}{wn} = P$ for w

65. $a + b = \dfrac{2A}{h}$ for h

66. $1 + rt = \dfrac{A}{P}$ for P

67. $\dfrac{1}{R} = \dfrac{1}{R_1} + \dfrac{1}{R_2}$ for R

68. $\dfrac{b+a}{ab} = \dfrac{1}{f}$ for b

Problem Recognition Exercises

Comparing Rational Equations and Rational Expressions

Often adding or subtracting rational expressions is confused with solving rational equations. When adding rational expressions, we combine the terms to simplify the expression. When solving an equation, we clear the fractions and find numerical solutions, if possible. Both processes begin with finding the LCD, but the LCD is used differently in each process. Compare these two examples.

Example 1:

Add. $\dfrac{4}{x} + \dfrac{x}{3}$ (The LCD is $3x$.)

$$= \frac{3}{3} \cdot \left(\frac{4}{x}\right) + \left(\frac{x}{3}\right) \cdot \frac{x}{x}$$

$$= \frac{12}{3x} + \frac{x^2}{3x}$$

$$= \frac{12 + x^2}{3x} \quad \begin{array}{l}\text{The answer is a} \\ \text{rational expression.}\end{array}$$

Example 2:

Solve. $\dfrac{4}{x} + \dfrac{x}{3} = -\dfrac{8}{3}$ (The LCD is $3x$.)

$$\frac{3x}{1}\left(\frac{4}{x} + \frac{x}{3}\right) = \frac{3x}{1}\left(-\frac{8}{3}\right)$$

$$12 + x^2 = -8x$$

$$x^2 + 8x + 12 = 0$$

$$(x + 2)(x + 6) = 0$$

$$x + 2 = 0 \text{ or } x + 6 = 0$$

$$x = -2 \text{ or } x = -6 \quad \begin{array}{l}\text{The answer is} \\ \text{the set } \{-2, -6\}.\end{array}$$

For Exercises 1–20, solve the equations and simplify the expressions.

1. $\dfrac{y}{2y + 4} - \dfrac{2}{y^2 + 2y}$

2. $\dfrac{1}{x + 2} + 2 = \dfrac{x + 11}{x + 2}$

3. $\dfrac{5t}{2} - \dfrac{t - 2}{3} = 5$

4. $3 - \dfrac{2}{a - 5}$

5. $\dfrac{7}{6p^2} + \dfrac{2}{9p} + \dfrac{1}{3p^2}$

6. $\dfrac{3b}{b + 1} - \dfrac{2b}{b - 1}$

7. $4 + \dfrac{2}{h - 3} = 5$

8. $\dfrac{2}{w + 1} + \dfrac{3}{(w + 1)^2}$

9. $\dfrac{1}{x - 6} - \dfrac{3}{x^2 - 6x} = \dfrac{4}{x}$

10. $\dfrac{3}{m} - \dfrac{6}{5} = -\dfrac{3}{m}$

11. $\dfrac{7}{2x + 2} + \dfrac{3x}{4x + 4}$

12. $\dfrac{10}{2t - 1} - 1 = \dfrac{t}{2t - 1}$

13. $\dfrac{3}{5x} + \dfrac{7}{2x} = 1$

14. $\dfrac{7}{t^2 - 5t} - \dfrac{3}{t - 5}$

15. $\dfrac{5}{2a - 1} + 4$

16. $p - \dfrac{5p}{p - 2} = -\dfrac{10}{p - 2}$

17. $\dfrac{3}{u} + \dfrac{12}{u^2 - 3u} = \dfrac{u + 1}{u - 3}$

18. $\dfrac{5}{4k} - \dfrac{2}{6k}$

19. $\dfrac{-2h}{h^2 - 9} + \dfrac{3}{h - 3}$

20. $\dfrac{3y}{y^2 - 5y + 4} = \dfrac{2}{y - 4} + \dfrac{3}{y - 1}$

Applications of Rational Equations and Proportions

1. Solving Proportions

In this section, we look at how rational equations can be used to solve a variety of applications. The first type of rational equation that will be applied is called a proportion.

Concepts

1. Solving Proportions
2. Applications of Proportions and Similar Triangles
3. Distance, Rate, and Time Applications
4. Work Applications

Definition of Ratio and Proportion

1. The **ratio** of a to b is $\dfrac{a}{b}$ ($b \neq 0$) and can also be expressed as $a{:}b$ or $a \div b$.

2. An equation that equates two ratios or rates is called a **proportion**. Therefore, if $b \neq 0$ and $d \neq 0$, then $\dfrac{a}{b} = \dfrac{c}{d}$ is a proportion.

A proportion can be solved by multiplying both sides of the equation by the LCD and clearing fractions.

Example 1   **Solving a Proportion**

Solve the proportion. $\dfrac{3}{11} = \dfrac{123}{w}$

Solution:

$$\frac{3}{11} = \frac{123}{w} \qquad \text{The LCD is } 11w.$$

$$11w\left(\frac{3}{11}\right) = 11w\left(\frac{123}{w}\right) \qquad \text{Multiply by the LCD and clear fractions.}$$

$$3w = 11 \cdot 123 \qquad \text{Solve the resulting equation (linear).}$$

$$3w = 1353$$

$$\frac{3w}{3} = \frac{1353}{3}$$

$$w = 451$$

Check: $w = 451$

$$\frac{3}{11} = \frac{123}{w}$$

$$\frac{3}{11} \overset{?}{=} \frac{123}{(451)}$$

The solution set is $\{451\}$. $\dfrac{3}{11} \overset{?}{=} \dfrac{3}{11}$ ✓ (True)   Simplify to lowest terms.

Skill Practice Solve the proportion.

1. $\dfrac{10}{b} = \dfrac{2}{33}$

Answer

1. $\{165\}$

2. Applications of Proportions and Similar Triangles

Example 2   Using a Proportion in an Application

For a recent year, the population of Alabama was approximately 4.2 million. At that time, Alabama had seven representatives in the U.S. House of Representatives. In the same year, North Carolina had a population of approximately 7.2 million. If representation in the House is based on population in equal proportions for each state, how many representatives did North Carolina have?

© Brand X Pictures/
PunchStock RF

TIP: The equation from Example 2 could have been solved by first equating the cross products:

$$\frac{4.2}{7} = \frac{7.2}{x}$$

$$4.2x = (7.2)(7)$$

$$4.2x = 50.4$$

$$x = 12$$

Solution:

Let x represent the number of representatives for North Carolina.

Set up a proportion by writing two equivalent ratios.

$$\boxed{\frac{\text{Population of Alabama}}{\text{number of representatives}}} \rightarrow \frac{4.2}{7} = \frac{7.2}{x} \leftarrow \boxed{\frac{\text{Population of North Carolina}}{\text{number of representatives}}}$$

$$\frac{4.2}{7} = \frac{7.2}{x}$$

$$7x \cdot \frac{4.2}{7} = 7x \cdot \frac{7.2}{x} \qquad \text{Multiply by the LCD, } 7x.$$

$$4.2x = (7.2)(7) \qquad \text{Solve the resulting linear equation.}$$

$$4.2x = 50.4$$

$$\frac{4.2x}{4.2} = \frac{50.4}{4.2}$$

$$x = 12 \qquad \text{North Carolina had 12 representatives.}$$

Skill Practice

2. A university has a ratio of students to faculty of 105 to 2. If the student population at the university is 15,750, how many faculty members are needed?

Proportions are used in geometry with **similar triangles**. Two triangles are similar if their angles have equal measure. In such a case, the lengths of the corresponding sides are proportional. In Figure 7-1, triangle ABC is similar to triangle XYZ. Therefore, the following ratios are equivalent.

$$\frac{a}{x} = \frac{b}{y} = \frac{c}{z}$$

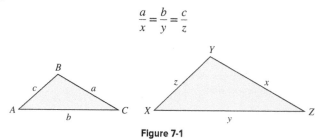

Figure 7-1

Answer

2. 300 faculty members are needed.

| **Example 3** | **Using Similar Triangles to Find an Unknown Side in a Triangle** |

In Figure 7-2, triangle *XYZ* is similar to triangle *ABC*.

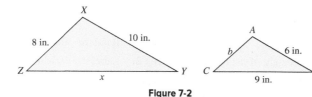

Figure 7-2

a. Solve for *x*.   **b.** Solve for *b*.

Solution:

a. The lengths of the upper right sides of the triangles are given. These form a known ratio of $\frac{10}{6}$. Because the triangles are similar, the ratio of the other corresponding sides must also be equal to $\frac{10}{6}$. To solve for *x*, we have

| Bottom side from large triangle | $\longrightarrow$ | $\dfrac{x}{9 \text{ in.}} = \dfrac{10 \text{ in.}}{6 \text{ in.}}$ | $\longleftarrow$ | Right side from large triangle |
| bottom side from small triangle | $\longrightarrow$ | | $\longleftarrow$ | right side from small triangle |

$$\frac{x}{9} = \frac{10}{6} \qquad \text{The LCD is 18.}$$

$$\overset{2}{\cancel{18}} \cdot \left(\frac{x}{9}\right) = \overset{3}{\cancel{18}} \cdot \left(\frac{10}{6}\right) \qquad \text{Multiply by the LCD.}$$

$$2x = 30 \qquad \text{Clear fractions.}$$

$$x = 15 \qquad \text{Divide by 2.}$$

The length of side *x* is 15 in.

b. To solve for *b*, the ratio of the upper left sides of the triangles must equal $\frac{10}{6}$.

| Left side from large triangle | $\longrightarrow$ | $\dfrac{8 \text{ in.}}{b} = \dfrac{10 \text{ in.}}{6 \text{ in.}}$ | $\longleftarrow$ | Right side from large triangle |
| left side from small triangle | $\longrightarrow$ | | $\longleftarrow$ | right side from small triangle |

$$\frac{8}{b} = \frac{10}{6} \qquad \text{The LCD is } 6b.$$

$$6\cancel{b} \cdot \left(\frac{8}{\cancel{b}}\right) = \cancel{6}b \cdot \left(\frac{10}{\cancel{6}}\right) \qquad \text{Multiply by the LCD.}$$

$$48 = 10b \qquad \text{Clear fractions.}$$

$$\frac{48}{10} = \frac{10b}{10}$$

$$4.8 = b$$

The length of side *b* is 4.8 in.

Skill Practice

3. Triangle *ABC* is similar to triangle *XYZ*.
   Solve for the lengths of the missing sides.

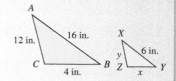

Answer

3. $x = 1.5$ in., and $y = 4.5$ in.

Example 4	**Using Similar Triangles in an Application**

A tree that is 20 ft from a house is to be cut down. Use the following information and similar triangles to find the height of the tree to determine if it will hit the house.

   The shadow cast by a yardstick is 2 ft long. The shadow cast by the tree is 11 ft long.

Solution:	**Step 1:** Read the problem.
Let x represent the height of the tree.	**Step 2:** Label the variables.

We will assume that the measurements were taken at the same time of day. Therefore, the angle of the Sun is the same on both objects, and we can set up similar triangles (Figure 7-3).

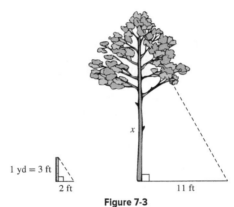

1 yd = 3 ft   2 ft   11 ft

Figure 7-3

Step 3: Create a verbal model.

Height of yardstick	→	3 ft	$=$	2 ft	←	Length of yardstick's shadow
height of tree	→	x		11 ft	←	length of tree's shadow

$$\frac{3}{x} = \frac{2}{11}$$

Step 4: Write a mathematical equation.

$$11x\left(\frac{3}{x}\right) = \left(\frac{2}{11}\right)11x$$

Step 5: Multiply by the LCD.

$$33 = 2x$$

Solve the equation.

$$\frac{33}{2} = \frac{2x}{2}$$

$$16.5 = x$$

Step 6: Interpret the results, and write the answer in words.

The tree is 16.5 ft high. The tree is less than 20 ft high so it will not hit the house.

Skill Practice

4. The Sun casts a 3.2-ft shadow of a 6-ft man. At the same time, the Sun casts an 80-ft shadow of a building. How tall is the building?

Answer

4. The building is 150 ft tall.

3. Distance, Rate, and Time Applications

In Examples 5 and 6, we use the familiar relationship among the variables distance, rate, and time. Recall that $d = rt$.

Example 5	**Using a Rational Equation in a Distance, Rate, and Time Application**

A small plane flies 440 mi with the wind from Memphis, TN, to Oklahoma City, OK. In the same amount of time, the plane flies 340 miles against the wind from Oklahoma City to Little Rock, AR (see Figure 7-4). If the wind speed is 30 mph, find the speed of the plane in still air.

Figure 7-4

Solution:

Let x represent the speed of the plane in still air.

Then $x + 30$ is the speed of the plane with the wind.

$x - 30$ is the speed of the plane against the wind.

Organize the given information in a chart.

	Distance	Rate	Time
With the wind	440	$x + 30$	$\dfrac{440}{x + 30}$
Against the wind	340	$x - 30$	$\dfrac{340}{x - 30}$

Because $d = rt$, then $t = \dfrac{d}{r}$

The plane travels with the wind for the same amount of time as it travels against the wind, so we can equate the two expressions for time.

$$\left(\begin{array}{c}\text{Time with}\\\text{the wind}\end{array}\right) = \left(\begin{array}{c}\text{time against}\\\text{the wind}\end{array}\right)$$

$$\frac{440}{x + 30} = \frac{340}{x - 30}$$

The LCD is $(x + 30)(x - 30)$.

$$(x+30)(x-30) \cdot \frac{440}{x+30} = (x+30)(x-30) \cdot \frac{340}{x-30}$$

$$440(x - 30) = 340(x + 30)$$

$$440x - 13{,}200 = 340x + 10{,}200 \qquad \text{Solve the resulting linear equation.}$$

$$100x = 23{,}400$$

$$x = 234$$

The plane's speed in still air is 234 mph.

TIP: The equation

$$\frac{440}{x + 30} = \frac{340}{x - 30}$$

is a proportion. The fractions can also be cleared by equating the cross products.

$$\frac{440}{x + 30} = \frac{340}{x - 30}$$

$$440(x - 30) = 340(x + 30)$$

Skill Practice

5. Alison paddles her kayak in a river where the current is 2 mph. She can paddle 20 mi with the current in the same amount of time that she can paddle 10 mi against the current. Find the speed of the kayak in still water.

Example 6	Using a Rational Equation in a Distance, Rate, and Time Application

A motorist drives 100 mi between two cities in a bad rainstorm. For the return trip in sunny weather, she averages 10 mph faster and takes $\frac{1}{2}$ hr less time. Find the average speed of the motorist in the rainstorm and in sunny weather.

Solution:

Let x represent the motorist's speed during the rain.

Then $x + 10$ represents the speed in sunny weather.

	Distance	Rate	Time
Trip during rainstorm	100	x	$\dfrac{100}{x}$
Trip during sunny weather	100	$x + 10$	$\dfrac{100}{x + 10}$

Because $d = rt$, then $t = \dfrac{d}{r}$

Because the same distance is traveled in $\frac{1}{2}$ hr less time, the difference between the time of the trip during the rainstorm and the time during sunny weather is $\frac{1}{2}$ hr.

$$\left(\begin{array}{c}\text{Time during}\\ \text{the rainstorm}\end{array}\right) - \left(\begin{array}{c}\text{time during}\\ \text{sunny weather}\end{array}\right) = \left(\frac{1}{2}\text{ hr}\right) \qquad \text{Verbal model}$$

$$\frac{100}{x} - \frac{100}{x + 10} = \frac{1}{2} \qquad \text{Mathematical equation}$$

$$2x(x + 10)\left(\frac{100}{x} - \frac{100}{x + 10}\right) = 2x(x + 10)\left(\frac{1}{2}\right) \qquad \text{Multiply by the LCD.}$$

$$2x(x + 10)\left(\frac{100}{x}\right) - 2x(x + 10)\left(\frac{100}{x + 10}\right) = 2x(x + 10)\left(\frac{1}{2}\right) \qquad \begin{array}{l}\text{Apply the}\\ \text{distributive}\\ \text{property.}\end{array}$$

$$200(x + 10) - 200x = x(x + 10) \qquad \text{Clear fractions.}$$

$$200x + 2000 - 200x = x^2 + 10x \qquad \begin{array}{l}\text{Solve the}\\ \text{resulting}\\ \text{equation}\\ \text{(quadratic).}\end{array}$$

$$2000 = x^2 + 10x$$

$$0 = x^2 + 10x - 2000 \qquad \begin{array}{l}\text{Set the}\\ \text{equation equal}\\ \text{to zero.}\end{array}$$

$$0 = (x - 40)(x + 50) \qquad \text{Factor.}$$

$$x = 40 \quad \text{or} \quad x = -50$$

Avoiding Mistakes

The equation
$$\frac{100}{x} - \frac{100}{x + 10} = \frac{1}{2}$$
is not a proportion because the left-hand side has more than one fraction. Do not try to multiply the cross products. Instead, multiply by the LCD to clear fractions.

Answer

5. The speed of the kayak is 6 mph.

Because a rate of speed cannot be negative, reject $x = -50$. Therefore, the speed of the motorist in the rainstorm is 40 mph. Because $x + 10 = 40 + 10 = 50$, the average speed for the return trip in sunny weather is 50 mph.

Skill Practice

> **6.** Harley rode his mountain bike 12 mi to the top of a mountain and the same distance back down. His speed going up was 8 mph slower than coming down. The ride up took 2 hr longer than the ride coming down. Find his speed in each direction.

4. Work Applications

Example 7 demonstrates how work rates are related to a portion of a job that can be completed in one unit of time.

> **Example 7** | **Using a Rational Equation in a Work Problem**
>
> A new printing press can print the morning edition in 2 hr, whereas the old printer requires 4 hr. How long would it take to print the morning edition if both printers work together?
>
> **Solution:**
>
> One method to solve this problem is to add rates.
>
> Let x represent the time required for both printers working together to complete the job.
>
> $$\left(\begin{array}{c}\text{Rate} \\ \text{of old printer}\end{array}\right) + \left(\begin{array}{c}\text{rate} \\ \text{of new printer}\end{array}\right) = \left(\begin{array}{c}\text{rate of} \\ \text{both working together}\end{array}\right)$$
>
> $$\frac{1 \text{ job}}{4 \text{ hr}} \quad + \quad \frac{1 \text{ job}}{2 \text{ hr}} \quad = \quad \frac{1 \text{ job}}{x \text{ hr}}$$
>
> $$\frac{1}{4} + \frac{1}{2} = \frac{1}{x}$$
>
> $$4x\left(\frac{1}{4} + \frac{1}{2}\right) = 4x\left(\frac{1}{x}\right) \qquad \text{The LCD is } 4x.$$
>
> $$\overset{1}{4x} \cdot \frac{1}{4} + \overset{2}{4x} \cdot \frac{1}{2} = \overset{1}{4x} \cdot \frac{1}{x} \qquad \text{Apply the distributive property.}$$
>
> $$x + 2x = 4 \qquad \text{Solve the resulting linear equation.}$$
>
> $$3x = 4$$
>
> $$x = \frac{4}{3} \qquad \begin{array}{l}\text{The time required to print the morning} \\ \text{edition using both printers is } 1\frac{1}{3} \text{ hr.}\end{array}$$

© Getty Images RF

Skill Practice

> **7.** The computer at a bank can process and prepare the bank statements in 30 hr. A new faster computer can do the job in 20 hr. If the bank uses both computers together, how long will it take to process the statements?

Answers

6. Uphill speed was 4 mph; downhill speed was 12 mph.

7. 12 hr

An alternative approach to Example 7 is to determine the portion of the job that each printer can complete in 1 hr and extend that rate to the portion of the job completed in x hours.

- The old printer can perform the job in 4 hr. Therefore, it completes $\frac{1}{4}$ of the job in 1 hr and $\frac{1}{4}x$ jobs in x hours.
- The new printer can perform the job in 2 hr. Therefore, it completes $\frac{1}{2}$ of the job in 1 hr and $\frac{1}{2}x$ jobs in x hours.

The sum of the portions of the job completed by each printer must equal one whole job.

$$\begin{pmatrix} \text{Portion of job} \\ \text{completed by} \\ \text{old printer} \end{pmatrix} + \begin{pmatrix} \text{portion of job} \\ \text{completed by} \\ \text{new printer} \end{pmatrix} = \begin{pmatrix} 1 \\ \text{whole} \\ \text{job} \end{pmatrix}$$

$$\frac{1}{4}x + \frac{1}{2}x = 1 \qquad \text{The LCD is 4.}$$

$$4\left(\frac{1}{4}x + \frac{1}{2}x\right) = 4(1) \qquad \text{Multiply by the LCD.}$$

$$x + 2x = 4 \qquad \text{Solve the resulting linear equation.}$$

$$3x = 4$$

$$x = \frac{4}{3} \qquad \text{The time required using both printers is } 1\frac{1}{3} \text{ hr.}$$

Section 7.7 Practice Exercises

Vocabulary and Key Concepts

1. **a.** An equation that equates two ratios is called a _____.

   b. Given similar triangles, the lengths of corresponding sides are _____.

Review Exercises

For Exercises 2–7, determine whether each of the following is an equation or an expression. If it is an equation, solve it. If it is an expression, perform the indicated operation.

2. $\dfrac{b}{5} + 3 = 9$

3. $\dfrac{m}{m-1} - \dfrac{2}{m+3}$

4. $\dfrac{2}{a+5} + \dfrac{5}{a^2-25}$

5. $\dfrac{3y+6}{20} \div \dfrac{4y+8}{8}$

6. $\dfrac{z^2+z}{24} \cdot \dfrac{8}{z+1}$

7. $\dfrac{3}{p+3} = \dfrac{12p+19}{p^2+7p+12} - \dfrac{5}{p+4}$

8. Determine whether 1 is a solution to the equation. $\dfrac{1}{x-1} + \dfrac{1}{2} = \dfrac{2}{x^2-1}$

Concept 1: Solving Proportions

For Exercises 9–22, solve the proportions. **(See Example 1.)**

9. $\dfrac{8}{5} = \dfrac{152}{p}$

10. $\dfrac{6}{7} = \dfrac{96}{y}$

11. $\dfrac{19}{76} = \dfrac{z}{4}$

12. $\dfrac{15}{135} = \dfrac{w}{9}$

13. $\dfrac{5}{3} = \dfrac{a}{8}$

14. $\dfrac{b}{14} = \dfrac{3}{8}$

15. $\dfrac{2}{1.9} = \dfrac{x}{38}$

16. $\dfrac{16}{1.3} = \dfrac{30}{p}$

17. $\dfrac{y+1}{2y} = \dfrac{2}{3}$

18. $\dfrac{w-2}{4w} = \dfrac{1}{6}$

19. $\dfrac{9}{2z-1} = \dfrac{3}{z}$

20. $\dfrac{1}{t} = \dfrac{1}{4-t}$

21. $\dfrac{8}{9a-1} = \dfrac{5}{3a+2}$

22. $\dfrac{4p+1}{3} = \dfrac{2p-5}{6}$

23. Charles' law describes the relationship between the initial and final temperature and volume of a gas held at a constant pressure.

$$\frac{V_i}{V_f} = \frac{T_i}{T_f}$$

  a. Solve the equation for V_f.

  b. Solve the equation for T_f.

24. The relationship between the area, height, and base of a triangle is given by the proportion

$$\frac{A}{b} = \frac{h}{2}$$

  a. Solve the equation for A.

  b. Solve the equation for b.

Concept 2: Applications of Proportions and Similar Triangles

For Exercises 25–32, solve using proportions.

25. Toni drives her car 132 mi on the highway on 4 gal of gas. At this rate how many miles can she drive on 9 gal of gas?
  (See Example 2.)

26. Tim takes his pulse for 10 sec and counts 12 beats. How many beats per minute is this?

27. It is recommended that 7.8 mL of Grow-It-Right plant food be mixed with 2 L of water for feeding house plants. How much plant food should be mixed with 1 gal of water to maintain the same concentration? (1 gal ≈ 3.8 L.) Express the answer in milliliters.

28. According to the website for the state of Virginia, 0.8 million tons of clothing is reused or recycled out of 7 million tons of clothing discarded. If 17.5 million tons of clothing is discarded, how many tons will be reused or recycled?

© Duncan Smith/Getty Images RF

29. Andrew is on a low-carbohydrate diet. If his diet book tells him that an 8-oz serving of pineapple contains 19.2 g of carbohydrate, how many grams of carbohydrate does a 5-oz serving contain?

30. Cooking oatmeal requires 1 cup of water for every $\frac{1}{2}$ cup of oats. How many cups of water will be required for $\frac{3}{4}$ cup of oats?

31. According to a building code, a wheelchair ramp must be at least 12 ft long for each foot of height. If the height of a newly constructed ramp is to be $1\frac{2}{3}$ ft, find the minimum acceptable length.

32. A map has a scale of 50 mi/in. If two cities measure 6.5 in. apart, how many miles does this represent?

For Exercises 33–36, triangle ABC is similar to triangle XYZ. Solve for x and y. **(See Example 3.)**

33.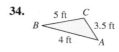

34.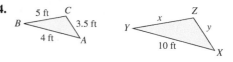

550 **Chapter 7** Rational Expressions and Equations

35.

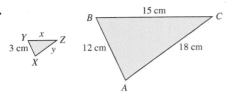

36.

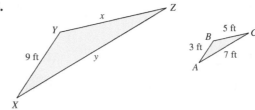

37. To estimate the height of a light pole, a mathematics student measures the length of a shadow cast by a meterstick and the length of the shadow cast by the light pole. Find the height of the light pole. **(See Example 4.)**

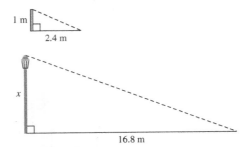

38. To estimate the height of a building, a student measures the length of a shadow cast by a yardstick and the length of the shadow cast by the building. Find the height of the building.

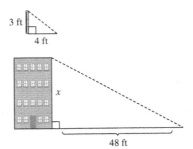

39. A 6-ft-tall man standing 54 ft from a light post casts an 18-ft shadow. What is the height of the light post?

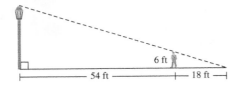

40. For a science project at school, a student must measure the height of a tree. The student measures the length of the shadow of the tree and then measures the length of the shadow cast by a yardstick. Find the height of the tree.

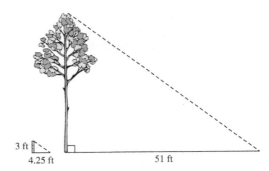

Concept 3: Distance, Rate, and Time Applications

41. A boat travels 54 mi upstream against the current in the same amount of time it takes to travel 66 mi downstream with the current. If the current is 2 mph, what is the speed of the boat in still water? (Use $t = \frac{d}{r}$ to complete the table.) **(See Example 5.)**

	Distance	Rate	Time
With the current (downstream)			
Against the current (upstream)			

42. A plane flies 630 mi with the wind in the same amount of time that it takes to fly 455 mi against the wind. If this plane flies at the rate of 217 mph in still air, what is the speed of the wind? (Use $t = \frac{d}{r}$ to complete the table.)

	Distance	Rate	Time
With the wind			
Against the wind			

43. The jet stream is a fast-flowing air current found in the atmosphere at around 36,000 ft above the surface of the Earth. During one summer day, the speed of the jet stream is 35 mph. A plane flying with the jet stream can fly 700 mi in the same amount of time that it would take to fly 500 mi against the jet stream. What is the speed of the plane in still air?

44. A fishing boat travels 9 mi downstream with the current in the same amount of time that it travels 3 mi upstream against the current. If the speed of the current is 6 mph, what is the speed at which the boat travels in still water?

45. An athlete in training rides his bike 20 mi and then immediately follows with a 10-mi run. The total workout takes him 2.5 hr. He also knows that he bikes about twice as fast as he runs. Determine his biking speed and his running speed.

46. Devon can cross-country ski 5 km/hr faster than his sister Shanelle. Devon skis 45 km in the same amount of time Shanelle skis 30 km. Find their speeds.

© PhotoLink/Getty Images RF

47. Floyd can walk 2 mph faster than his wife, Rachel. It takes Rachel 3 hr longer than Floyd to hike a 12-mi trail through a park. Find their speeds. **(See Example 6.)**

48. Janine bikes 3 mph faster than her sister, Jessica. Janine can ride 36 mi in 1 hr less time than Jessica can ride the same distance. Find each of their speeds.

49. Sergio rode his bike 4 mi. Then he got a flat tire and had to walk back 4 mi. It took him 1 hr longer to walk than it did to ride. If his rate walking was 9 mph less than his rate riding, find the two rates.

50. Amber jogs 10 km in $\frac{3}{4}$ hr less time than she can walk the same distance. If her walking rate is 3 km/hr less than her jogging rate, find her rates jogging and walking (in km/hr).

Concept 4: Work Applications

51. If the cold-water faucet is left on, the sink will fill in 10 min. If the hot-water faucet is left on, the sink will fill in 12 min. How long would it take to fill the sink if both faucets are left on? **(See Example 7.)**

Animation

52. The CUT-IT-OUT lawn mowing company consists of two people: Tina and Bill. If Tina cuts a lawn by herself, she can do it in 4 hr. If Bill cuts the same lawn himself, it takes him an hour longer than Tina. How long would it take them if they worked together?

53. A manuscript needs to be printed. One printer can do the job in 50 min, and another printer can do the job in 40 min. How long would it take if both printers were used?

54. A pump can empty a small pond in 4 hr. Another more efficient pump can do the job in 3 hr. How long would it take to empty the pond if both pumps were used?

55. A pipe can fill a reservoir in 16 hr. A drainage pipe can drain the reservoir in 24 hr. How long would it take to fill the reservoir if the drainage pipe were left open by mistake? (*Hint:* The rate at which water drains should be negative.)

56. A hole in the bottom of a child's plastic swimming pool can drain the pool in 60 min. If the pool had no hole, a hose could fill the pool in 40 min. How long would it take the hose to fill the pool with the hole?

57. Tim and Al are bricklayers. Tim can construct an outdoor grill in 5 days. If Al helps Tim, they can build it in only 2 days. How long would it take Al to build the grill alone?

58. Norma is a new and inexperienced secretary. It takes her 3 hr to prepare a mailing. If her boss helps her, the mailing can be completed in 1 hr. How long would it take the boss to do the job by herself?

Expanding Your Skills

For Exercises 59–62, solve using proportions.

59. The ratio of smokers to nonsmokers in a restaurant is 2 to 7. There are 100 more nonsmokers than smokers. How many smokers and nonsmokers are in the restaurant?

60. The ratio of fiction to nonfiction books sold in a bookstore is 5 to 3. One week there were 180 more fiction books sold than nonfiction. Find the number of fiction and nonfiction books sold during that week.

61. There are 440 students attending a biology lecture. The ratio of male to female students at the lecture is 6 to 5. How many men and women are attending the lecture?

62. The ratio of dogs to cats at the humane society is 5 to 8. The total number of dogs and cats is 650. How many dogs and how many cats are at the humane society?

552   **Chapter 7**   Rational Expressions and Equations

Computing Monthly Mortgage Payments

Materials: A calculator

Estimated Time: 15–20 minutes

Group Size: 3

When a person borrows money to buy a house, the bank usually requires a down payment of between 0% and 20% of the cost of the house. The bank then issues a loan for the remaining balance on the house. The loan to buy a house is called a *mortgage*. Monthly payments are made to pay off the mortgage over a period of years.

A formula to calculate the monthly payment, P, for a loan is given by:

$$P = \frac{\dfrac{Ar}{12}}{1 - \dfrac{1}{\left(1 + \dfrac{r}{12}\right)^{12t}}}$$ where

P is the monthly payment
A is the original amount of the mortgage
r is the annual interest rate written as a decimal
t is the term of the loan in years

Suppose a person wants to buy a $200,000 house. The bank requires a down payment of 20%, and the loan is issued for 30 years at 7.5% interest for 30 years.

1. Find the amount of the down payment. _____

2. Find the amount of the mortgage. _____

3. Find the monthly payment (to the nearest cent). _____

4. Multiply the monthly payment found in question 3 by the total number of months in a 30-year period. Interpret what this value means in the context of the problem.

5. How much total interest was paid on the loan for the house? _____

6. What was the total amount paid to the bank (include the down payment). _____

Chapter 7   Summary

Section 7.1   Introduction to Rational Expressions

Key Concepts

A **rational expression** is a ratio of the form $\frac{p}{q}$ where p and q are polynomials and $q \neq 0$.

Restricted values of a rational expression are those values that, when substituted for the variable, make the expression undefined. To find restricted values, set the denominator equal to 0 and solve the equation.

Simplifying a Rational Expression

Factor the numerator and denominator completely, and reduce factors whose ratio is equal to 1 or to -1. A rational expression written in lowest terms will still have the same restricted values as the original expression.

Examples

Example 1

$$\frac{x+2}{x^2 - 5x - 14} \quad \text{is a rational expression.}$$

Example 2

To find the restricted values of $\dfrac{x+2}{x^2 - 5x - 14}$ factor the

denominator: $\dfrac{x+2}{(x+2)(x-7)}$

The restricted values are $x = -2$ and $x = 7$.

Example 3

Simplify the rational expression. $\dfrac{x+2}{x^2 - 5x - 14}$

$\dfrac{\overset{1}{\cancel{x+2}}}{\cancel{(x+2)}(x-7)}$ Simplify.

$= \dfrac{1}{x-7}$ (provided $x \neq 7,\ x \neq -2$).

Section 7.2   Multiplication and Division of Rational Expressions

Key Concepts

Multiplying Rational Expressions

Multiply the numerators and multiply the denominators. That is, if $q \neq 0$ and $s \neq 0$, then

$$\frac{p}{q} \cdot \frac{r}{s} = \frac{pr}{qs}$$

Factor the numerator and denominator completely. Then reduce factors whose ratio is 1 or -1.

Examples

Example 1

Multiply. $\dfrac{b^2 - a^2}{a^2 - 2ab + b^2} \cdot \dfrac{a^2 - 3ab + 2b^2}{2a + 2b}$

$= \dfrac{\overset{-1}{\cancel{(b-a)}}\overset{1}{\cancel{(b+a)}}}{\cancel{(a-b)}\cancel{(a-b)}} \cdot \dfrac{(a-2b)\overset{1}{\cancel{(a-b)}}}{2\cancel{(a+b)}}$

$= -\dfrac{a-2b}{2} \quad \text{or} \quad \dfrac{2b-a}{2}$

554 Chapter 7 Rational Expressions and Equations

Dividing Rational Expressions

Multiply the first expression by the reciprocal of the second expression. That is, for $q \neq 0$, $r \neq 0$, and $s \neq 0$,

$$\frac{p}{q} \div \frac{r}{s} = \frac{p}{q} \cdot \frac{s}{r} = \frac{ps}{qr}$$

Example 2

Divide. $\quad \dfrac{x-2}{15} \div \dfrac{x^2 + 2x - 8}{20x}$

$$= \frac{x-2}{15} \cdot \frac{20x}{x^2 + 2x - 8}$$

$$= \frac{\overset{1}{(x-2)}}{\underset{3}{15}} \cdot \frac{\overset{4}{20x}}{\underset{1}{(x-2)(x+4)}}$$

$$= \frac{4x}{3(x+4)}$$

Section 7.3   Least Common Denominator

Key Concepts

Finding the Least Common Denominator (LCD) of Two or More Rational Expressions

1. Factor all denominators completely.
2. The LCD is the product of unique factors from the denominators, where each factor is raised to its highest power.

Examples

Example 1

Identify the LCD. $\quad \dfrac{1}{8x^3 y^2 z}; \dfrac{5}{6xy^4}$

1. Write the denominators as a product of prime factors:

   $$\frac{1}{2^3 x^3 y^2 z}; \frac{5}{2 \cdot 3xy^4}$$

2. The LCD is $2^3 \cdot 3x^3 y^4 z$ or $24x^3 y^4 z$

Converting a Rational Expression to an Equivalent Expression with a Different Denominator

Multiply numerator and denominator of the rational expression by the missing factors necessary to create the desired denominator.

Example 2

Convert $\dfrac{-3}{x-2}$ to an equivalent expression with the indicated denominator:

$$\frac{-3}{x-2} = \frac{}{5(x-2)(x+2)}$$

Multiply numerator and denominator by the missing factors from the denominator.

$$\frac{-3 \cdot 5(x+2)}{(x-2) \cdot 5(x+2)} = \frac{-15x - 30}{5(x-2)(x+2)}$$

Section 7.4   Addition and Subtraction of Rational Expressions

Key Concepts

To add or subtract rational expressions, the expressions must have the same denominator.

Steps to Add or Subtract Rational Expressions

1. Factor the denominators of each rational expression.
2. Identify the LCD.
3. Rewrite each rational expression as an equivalent expression with the LCD as its denominator.
4. Add or subtract the numerators, and write the result over the common denominator.
5. Simplify.

Example

Example 1

Add. $\dfrac{c-2}{c+1} + \dfrac{12c-3}{2c^2-c-3}$

$= \dfrac{c-2}{c+1} + \dfrac{12c-3}{(2c-3)(c+1)}$

The LCD is $(2c-3)(c+1)$.

$= \dfrac{(2c-3)(c-2)}{(2c-3)(c+1)} + \dfrac{12c-3}{(2c-3)(c+1)}$

$= \dfrac{2c^2-4c-3c+6+12c-3}{(2c-3)(c+1)}$

$= \dfrac{2c^2+5c+3}{(2c-3)(c+1)}$

$= \dfrac{(2c+3)(c+1)}{(2c-3)(c+1)} = \dfrac{2c+3}{2c-3}$

Section 7.5   Complex Fractions

Key Concepts

Complex fractions can be simplified by using Method I or Method II.

Method I

1. Add or subtract expressions in the numerator to form a single fraction. Add or subtract expressions in the denominator to form a single fraction.
2. Divide the rational expressions from step 1 by multiplying the numerator of the complex fraction by the reciprocal of the denominator of the complex fraction.
3. Simplify to lowest terms, if possible.

Examples

Example 1

Simplify. $\dfrac{1 - \dfrac{4}{w^2}}{1 - \dfrac{1}{w} - \dfrac{6}{w^2}} = \dfrac{1 \cdot \dfrac{w^2}{w^2} - \dfrac{4}{w^2}}{1 \cdot \dfrac{w^2}{w^2} - \dfrac{1}{w} \cdot \dfrac{w}{w} - \dfrac{6}{w^2}}$

$= \dfrac{\dfrac{w^2}{w^2} - \dfrac{4}{w^2}}{\dfrac{w^2}{w^2} - \dfrac{w}{w^2} - \dfrac{6}{w^2}} = \dfrac{\dfrac{w^2-4}{w^2}}{\dfrac{w^2-w-6}{w^2}}$

$= \dfrac{w^2-4}{w^2} \cdot \dfrac{w^2}{w^2-w-6}$

$= \dfrac{(w-2)(w+2)}{w^2} \cdot \dfrac{w^2}{(w-3)(w+2)}$

$= \dfrac{w-2}{w-3}$

556   **Chapter 7** Rational Expressions and Equations

Method II

1. Multiply the numerator and denominator of the complex fraction by the LCD of all individual fractions within the expression.
2. Apply the distributive property, and simplify the result.
3. Simplify to lowest terms, if possible.

Example 2

Simplify.

$$\frac{1 - \dfrac{4}{w^2}}{1 - \dfrac{1}{w} - \dfrac{6}{w^2}} = \frac{w^2\left(1 - \dfrac{4}{w^2}\right)}{w^2\left(1 - \dfrac{1}{w} - \dfrac{6}{w^2}\right)}$$

$$= \frac{w^2 - 4}{w^2 - w - 6} = \frac{(w - 2)(w + 2)}{(w - 3)(w + 2)}$$

$$= \frac{w - 2}{w - 3}$$

Section 7.6   Rational Equations

Key Concepts

An equation with one or more rational expressions is called a **rational equation**.

Steps to Solve a Rational Equation

1. Factor the denominators of all rational expressions. Identify the restricted values.
2. Identify the LCD of all expressions in the equation.
3. Multiply both sides of the equation by the LCD.
4. Solve the resulting equation.
5. Check each potential solution in the original equation.

Examples

Example 1

Solve. $\dfrac{1}{w} - \dfrac{1}{2w - 1} = \dfrac{-2w}{2w - 1}$ The restricted values are $w = 0$ and $w = \frac{1}{2}$.

The LCD is $w(2w - 1)$.

$$w(2w - 1)\frac{1}{w} - w(2w - 1)\frac{1}{2w - 1}$$

$$= w(2w - 1)\frac{-2w}{2w - 1}$$

$$(2w - 1)(1) - w(1) = w(-2w)$$

$$2w - 1 - w = -2w^2 \qquad \text{Quadratic equation}$$

$$2w^2 + w - 1 = 0$$

$$(2w - 1)(w + 1) = 0$$

$$w = \tfrac{1}{2} \qquad \text{or} \qquad w = -1$$
$$\text{Does not check.} \qquad\qquad \text{Checks.}$$

The solution set is $\{-1\}$.

Example 2

Solve for I. $q = \dfrac{VQ}{I}$

$$I \cdot q = \frac{VQ}{I} \cdot I$$

$$Iq = VQ$$

$$I = \frac{VQ}{q}$$

Section 7.7   Applications of Rational Equations and Proportions

Key Concepts and Examples

Solving Proportions

An equation that equates two rates or ratios is called a **proportion**:

$$\frac{a}{b} = \frac{c}{d} \quad (b \neq 0, d \neq 0)$$

To solve a proportion, multiply both sides of the equation by the LCD.

Examples

Example 1

A 90-g serving of a particular ice cream contains 10 g of fat. How much fat does 400 g of the same ice cream contain?

$$\frac{10 \text{ g fat}}{90 \text{ g ice cream}} = \frac{x \text{ grams fat}}{400 \text{ g ice cream}}$$

$$\frac{10}{90} = \frac{x}{400} \qquad \text{The LCD is 3600.}$$

$$\overset{40}{3600} \cdot \left(\frac{10}{90}\right) = \left(\frac{x}{400}\right) \cdot \overset{9}{3600}$$

$$400 = 9x$$

$$x = \frac{400}{9} \approx 44.4 \text{ g}$$

Examples 2 and 3 give applications of rational equations.

Example 2

Two cars travel from Los Angeles to Las Vegas. One car travels an average of 8 mph faster than the other car. If the faster car travels 189 mi in the same amount of time that the slower car travels 165 mi, what is the average speed of each car?

Let r represent the speed of the slower car.
Let $r + 8$ represent the speed of the faster car.

	Distance	Rate	Time
Slower car	165	r	$\frac{165}{r}$
Faster car	189	$r + 8$	$\frac{189}{r + 8}$

$$\frac{165}{r} = \frac{189}{r + 8}$$

$$165(r + 8) = 189r$$

$$165r + 1320 = 189r$$

$$1320 = 24r$$

$$55 = r$$

The slower car travels 55 mph, and the faster car travels $55 + 8 = 63$ mph.

Example 3

Beth and Cecelia have a house cleaning business. Beth can clean a particular house in 5 hr by herself. Cecelia can clean the same house in 4 hr. How long would it take if they cleaned the house together?

Let x be the number of hours it takes for both Beth and Cecelia to clean the house.

Beth's rate is $\frac{1 \text{ job}}{5 \text{ hr}}$. Cecelia's rate is $\frac{1 \text{ job}}{4 \text{ hr}}$.

The rate together is $\frac{1 \text{ job}}{x \text{ hr}}$.

$$\frac{1}{5} + \frac{1}{4} = \frac{1}{x} \qquad \text{Add the rates.}$$

$$20x\left(\frac{1}{5} + \frac{1}{4}\right) = 20x\left(\frac{1}{x}\right)$$

$$4x + 5x = 20$$

$$9x = 20$$

$$x = \frac{20}{9}$$

It takes $\frac{20}{9}$ hr or $2\frac{2}{9}$ hr working together.

558   **Chapter 7**   Rational Expressions and Equations

Chapter 7   Review Exercises

Section 7.1

1. For the rational expression $\dfrac{t-2}{t+9}$

   a. Evaluate the expression (if possible) for $t = 0, 1, 2, -3, -9$

   b. Identify the restricted values.

2. For the rational expression $\dfrac{k+1}{k-5}$

   a. Evaluate the expression for $k = 0, 1, 5, -1, -2$

   b. Identify the restricted values.

3. Which of the rational expressions are equal to -1?

   a. $\dfrac{2-x}{x-2}$ b. $\dfrac{x-5}{x+5}$

   c. $\dfrac{-x-7}{x+7}$ d. $\dfrac{x^2-4}{4-x^2}$

For Exercises 4–13, identify the restricted values. Then simplify the expressions.

4. $\dfrac{x-3}{(2x-5)(x-3)}$ 5. $\dfrac{h+7}{(3h+1)(h+7)}$

6. $\dfrac{4a^2+7a-2}{a^2-4}$ 7. $\dfrac{2w^2+11w+12}{w^2-16}$

8. $\dfrac{z^2-4z}{8-2z}$ 9. $\dfrac{15-3k}{2k^2-10k}$

10. $\dfrac{2b^2+4b-6}{4b+12}$ 11. $\dfrac{3m^2-12m-15}{9m+9}$

12. $\dfrac{n+3}{n^2+6n+9}$ 13. $\dfrac{p+7}{p^2+14p+49}$

Section 7.2

For Exercises 14–27, multiply or divide as indicated.

14. $\dfrac{3y^3}{3y-6} \cdot \dfrac{y-2}{y}$ 15. $\dfrac{2u+10}{u} \cdot \dfrac{u^3}{4u+20}$

16. $\dfrac{11}{v-2} \cdot \dfrac{2v^2-8}{22}$ 17. $\dfrac{8}{x^2-25} \cdot \dfrac{3x+15}{16}$

18. $\dfrac{4c^2+4c}{c^2-25} \div \dfrac{8c}{c^2-5c}$ 19. $\dfrac{q^2-5q+6}{2q+4} \div \dfrac{2q-6}{q+2}$

20. $\left(\dfrac{-2t}{t+1}\right)(t^2-4t-5)$ 21. $(s^2-6s+8)\left(\dfrac{4s}{s-2}\right)$

22. $\dfrac{\dfrac{a^2+5a+1}{7a-7}}{\dfrac{a^2+5a+1}{a-1}}$ 23. $\dfrac{\dfrac{n^2+n+1}{n^2-4}}{\dfrac{n^2+n+1}{n+2}}$

24. $\dfrac{5h^2-6h+1}{h^2-1} \div \dfrac{16h^2-9}{4h^2+7h+3} \cdot \dfrac{3-4h}{30h-6}$

25. $\dfrac{3m-3}{6m^2+18m+12} \cdot \dfrac{2m^2-8}{m^2-3m+2} \div \dfrac{m+3}{m+1}$

26. $\dfrac{x-2}{x^2-3x-18} \cdot \dfrac{6-x}{x^2-4}$

27. $\dfrac{4y^2-1}{1+2y} \div \dfrac{y^2-4y-5}{5-y}$

Section 7.3

28. Determine the LCD.

$$\dfrac{6}{n^2-9}; \dfrac{5}{n^2-n-6}$$

29. Determine the LCD.

$$\dfrac{8}{m^2-16}; \dfrac{7}{m^2-m-12}$$

30. State two possible LCDs that could be used to add the fractions.

$$\dfrac{7}{c-2}+\dfrac{4}{2-c}$$

31. State two possible LCDs that could be used to subtract the fractions.

$$\dfrac{10}{3-x}-\dfrac{5}{x-3}$$

For Exercises 32–37, write each fraction as an equivalent fraction with the LCD as its denominator.

32. $\dfrac{2}{5a}; \dfrac{3}{10b}$

33. $\dfrac{7}{4x}; \dfrac{11}{6y}$

34. $\dfrac{1}{x^2 y^4}; \dfrac{3}{xy^5}$

35. $\dfrac{5}{ab^3}; \dfrac{3}{ac^2}$

36. $\dfrac{5}{p+2}; \dfrac{p}{p-4}$

37. $\dfrac{6}{q}; \dfrac{1}{q+8}$

Section 7.4

For Exercises 38–49, add or subtract as indicated.

38. $\dfrac{h+3}{h+1} + \dfrac{h-1}{h+1}$

39. $\dfrac{b-6}{b-2} + \dfrac{b+2}{b-2}$

40. $\dfrac{a^2}{a-5} - \dfrac{25}{a-5}$

41. $\dfrac{x^2}{x+7} - \dfrac{49}{x+7}$

42. $\dfrac{y}{y^2-81} + \dfrac{2}{9-y}$

43. $\dfrac{3}{4-t^2} + \dfrac{t}{2-t}$

44. $\dfrac{4}{3m} - \dfrac{1}{m+2}$

45. $\dfrac{5}{2r+12} - \dfrac{1}{r}$

46. $\dfrac{4p}{p^2+6p+5} - \dfrac{3p}{p^2+5p+4}$

47. $\dfrac{3q}{q^2+7q+10} - \dfrac{2q}{q^2+6q+8}$

48. $\dfrac{1}{h} + \dfrac{h}{2h+4} - \dfrac{2}{h^2+2h}$

49. $\dfrac{x}{3x+9} - \dfrac{3}{x^2+3x} + \dfrac{1}{x}$

Section 7.5

For Exercises 50–57, simplify the complex fractions.

50. $\dfrac{\frac{a-4}{3}}{\frac{a-2}{3}}$

51. $\dfrac{\frac{z+5}{z}}{\frac{z-5}{3}}$

52. $\dfrac{\frac{2-3w}{2}}{\frac{2}{w}-3}$

53. $\dfrac{\frac{2}{y}+6}{\frac{3y+1}{4}}$

54. $\dfrac{\frac{y}{x}-\frac{x}{y}}{\frac{1}{x}+\frac{1}{y}}$

55. $\dfrac{\frac{b}{a}-\frac{a}{b}}{\frac{1}{b}-\frac{1}{a}}$

56. $\dfrac{\frac{6}{p+2}+4}{\frac{8}{p+2}-4}$

57. $\dfrac{\frac{25}{k+5}+5}{\frac{5}{k+5}-5}$

Section 7.6

For Exercises 58–65, solve the equations.

58. $\dfrac{2}{x} + \dfrac{1}{2} = \dfrac{1}{4}$

59. $\dfrac{1}{y} + \dfrac{3}{4} = \dfrac{1}{4}$

60. $\dfrac{2}{h-2} + 1 = \dfrac{h}{h+2}$

61. $\dfrac{w}{w-1} = \dfrac{3}{w+1} + 1$

62. $\dfrac{t+1}{3} - \dfrac{t-1}{6} = \dfrac{1}{6}$

63. $\dfrac{w+1}{w-3} - \dfrac{3}{w} = \dfrac{12}{w^2-3w}$

64. $\dfrac{1}{z+2} = \dfrac{4}{z^2-4} - \dfrac{1}{z-2}$

65. $\dfrac{y+1}{y+3} = \dfrac{y^2-11y}{y^2+y-6} - \dfrac{y-3}{y-2}$

66. Four times a number is added to 5. The sum is then divided by 6. The result is $\frac{7}{2}$. Find the number.

67. Solve the formula $\dfrac{V}{h} = \dfrac{\pi r^2}{3}$ for h.

68. Solve the formula $\dfrac{A}{b} = \dfrac{h}{2}$ for b.

Section 7.7

For Exercises 69–70, solve the proportions.

69. $\dfrac{m+2}{8} = \dfrac{m}{3}$

70. $\dfrac{12}{a} = \dfrac{5}{8}$

560   Chapter 7   Rational Expressions and Equations

71. A bag of popcorn states that it contains 4 g of fat per serving. If a serving is 2 oz, how many grams of fat are in a 5-oz bag?

72. Bud goes 10 mph faster on his motorcycle than Ed goes on his motorcycle. If Bud travels 105 mi in the same amount of time that Ed travels 90 mi, what are the rates of the two bikers?

© Glow Images RF

73. There are two pumps set up to fill a small swimming pool. One pump takes 24 min by itself to fill the pool, but the other takes 56 min by itself. How long would it take if both pumps work together?

74. Triangle *XYZ* is similar to triangle *ABC*. Find the values of *x* and *b*.

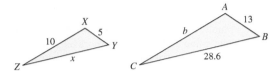

Chapter 7 Test

For Exercises 1–2,

a. Identify the restricted values.

b. Simplify the rational expression.

1. $\dfrac{5(x-2)(x+1)}{30(2-x)}$
     2. $\dfrac{7a^2 - 42a}{a^3 - 4a^2 - 12a}$

3. Identify the rational expressions that are equal to -1.

a. $\dfrac{x+4}{x-4}$
     b. $\dfrac{7-2x}{2x-7}$

c. $\dfrac{9x^2 + 16}{-9x^2 - 16}$
     d. $-\dfrac{x+5}{x+5}$

4. Find the LCD of the following pairs of rational expressions.

a. $\dfrac{x}{3(x+3)}; \dfrac{7}{5(x+3)}$
     b. $\dfrac{-2}{3x^2y}; \dfrac{4}{xy^2}$

For Exercises 5–11, perform the indicated operation.

5. $\dfrac{2}{y^2 + 4y + 3} + \dfrac{1}{3y + 9}$

6. $\dfrac{9 - b^2}{5b + 15} \div \dfrac{b-3}{b+3}$

7. $\dfrac{w^2 - 4w}{w^2 - 8w + 16} \cdot \dfrac{w-4}{w^2 + w}$

8. $\dfrac{t}{t-2} - \dfrac{8}{t^2 - 4}$

9. $\dfrac{1}{x+4} + \dfrac{2}{x^2 + 2x - 8} + \dfrac{x}{x-2}$

10. $\dfrac{2y}{y-6} - \dfrac{7}{6-y}$
     11. $\dfrac{1 - \dfrac{4}{m}}{m - \dfrac{16}{m}}$

For Exercises 12–16, solve the equation.

12. $\dfrac{3}{a} + \dfrac{5}{2} = \dfrac{7}{a}$

13. $\dfrac{p}{p-1} + \dfrac{1}{p} = \dfrac{p^2 + 1}{p^2 - p}$

14. $\dfrac{3}{c-2} - \dfrac{1}{c+1} = \dfrac{7}{c^2 - c - 2}$

15. $\dfrac{4x}{x-4} = 3 + \dfrac{16}{x-4}$

16. $\dfrac{y^2 + 7y}{y-2} - \dfrac{36}{2y-4} = 4$

17. Solve the formula $\dfrac{C}{2} = \dfrac{A}{r}$ for *r*.

18. Solve the proportion.

$$\frac{y+7}{-4} = \frac{1}{4}$$

19. A recipe for vegetable soup calls for $\frac{1}{2}$ cup of carrots for six servings. How many cups of carrots are needed to prepare 15 servings?

20. A motorboat can travel 28 mi downstream in the same amount of time as it can travel 18 mi upstream. Find the speed of the current if the boat can travel 23 mph in still water.

21. Two printers working together can complete a job in 2 hr. If one printer requires 6 hr to do the job alone, how many hours would the second printer need to complete the job alone?

22. Triangle *XYZ* is similar to triangle *ABC*. Find the values of *a* and *b*.

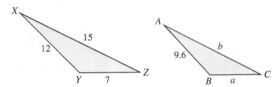

Chapters 1–7   Cumulative Review Exercises

For Exercises 1–2, simplify completely.

1. $\left(\frac{1}{2}\right)^{-4} + 2^4$

2. $|3 - 5| + |-2 + 7|$

3. Solve. $\frac{1}{2} - \frac{3}{4}(y - 1) = \frac{5}{12}$

4. Complete the table.

Set-Builder Notation	Graph	Interval Notation
$\{x \mid x \geq -1\}$		
		$(-\infty, 5)$

5. The perimeter of a rectangular swimming pool is 104 m. The length is 1 m more than twice the width. Find the length and width.

6. The height of a triangle is 2 in. less than the base. The area is 40 in.^{2} Find the base and height of the triangle.

7. Simplify. $\left(\frac{4x^{-1}y^{-2}}{z^4}\right)^{-2}(2y^{-1}z^3)^3$

8. The length and width of a rectangle are given in terms of *x*.

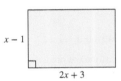

   a. Write a polynomial that represents the perimeter of the rectangle.

   b. Write a polynomial that represents the area of the rectangle.

9. Factor completely. $25x^2 - 30x + 9$

10. Factor completely. $10cd + 5d - 6c - 3$

11. Identify the restricted values of the expression.

$$\frac{x+3}{(x-5)(2x+1)}$$

12. Solve the system.

$$x + 2y = -7$$
$$6x + 3y = -6$$

13. Divide. $\frac{2x-6}{x^2-16} \div \frac{10x^2-90}{x^2-x-12}$

562   **Chapter 7**   Rational Expressions and Equations

14. Simplify.

$$\frac{\dfrac{3}{4} - \dfrac{1}{x}}{\dfrac{1}{3x} - \dfrac{1}{4}}$$

15. Solve. $\dfrac{7}{y^2 - 4} = \dfrac{3}{y - 2} + \dfrac{2}{y + 2}$

16. Solve the proportion.

$$\frac{2b - 5}{6} = \frac{4b}{7}$$

17. Determine the x- and y-intercepts.

    a. $-2x + 4y = 8$ **b.** $y = 5x$

18. Determine the slope

    a. of the line containing the points $(0, -6)$ and $(-5, 1)$.

    b. of the line $y = -\dfrac{2}{3}x - 6$.

    c. of a line parallel to a line having a slope of 4.

    d. of a line perpendicular to a line having a slope of 4.

19. Find an equation of a line passing through the point $(1, 2)$ and having a slope of 5. Write the answer in slope-intercept form.

20. A group of teenagers buys 2 large popcorns and 6 drinks at the movie theater for $27. A couple buys 1 large popcorn and 2 drinks for $10.50. Find the price for 1 large popcorn and the price for 1 drink.

© BananaStock/PunchStock RF

Relations and Functions

Relations and Functions

Mathematics in Communication

Imagine that every time you call your friend's cell phone your call is sent to a wrong device, and a different person answers the call. Suppose that one time you reach a single mother in Alabama, another time perhaps a small-business owner in Georgia, and the next time a person in Kansas.

This sort of haphazard relationship between a phone number and a target would create chaos and seriously compromise the future of your cell phone provider. Instead, when we dial 10 digits on our phone we know that the call will be routed to *only one* person's device—the person to whom the phone number is registered.

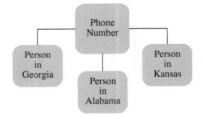

This example illustrates the importance of a **function**. That is, every item in a first set of items (in this case, a phone number being dialed) is associated with one and only one element in a second set of items (in this case, the phone of the proper recipient). Functions are relationships that take an input value and perform an operation on that value to produce a unique and predictable output value. The study of relations and functions begins this chapter and provides the springboard for mathematics at the next level.

564   Chapter 8   Relations and Functions

<table>
<tr><td>**Section 8.1**</td><td>**Introduction to Relations**</td></tr>
</table>

Concepts

1. Definition of a Relation
2. Domain and Range of a Relation
3. Applications Involving Relations

1. Definition of a Relation

In many naturally occurring phenomena, two variables may be linked by some other type of relationship. Table 8-1 shows a correspondence between the length of a woman's femur and her height. (The femur is the large bone in the thigh attached to the knee and hip.)

Table 8-1

Length of Femur (cm) x	Height (in.) y	Ordered Pair
45.5	65.5	⟶ (45.5, 65.5)
48.2	68.0	⟶ (48.2, 68.0)
41.8	62.2	⟶ (41.8, 62.2)
46.0	66.0	⟶ (46.0, 66.0)
50.4	70.0	⟶ (50.4, 70.0)

Each data point from Table 8-1 may be represented as an ordered pair. In this case, the first value represents the length of a woman's femur and the second, the woman's height. The set of ordered pairs {(45.5, 65.5), (48.2, 68.0), (41.8, 62.2), (46.0, 66.0), (50.4, 70.0)} defines a relation between femur length and height.

2. Domain and Range of a Relation

Definition of Relation in x and y

A set of ordered pairs (x, y) is called a **relation in x and y**. Furthermore,

- The set of first components in the ordered pairs is called the **domain of the relation**.
- The set of second components in the ordered pairs is called the **range of the relation**.

Example 1   **Finding the Domain and Range of a Relation**

Find the domain and range of the relation linking the length of a woman's femur to her height {(45.5, 65.5), (48.2, 68.0), (41.8, 62.2), (46.0, 66.0), (50.4, 70.0)}.

Solution:

Domain: {45.5, 48.2, 41.8, 46.0, 50.4}   Set of first components

Range: {65.5, 68.0, 62.2, 66.0, 70.0}   Set of second components

Skill Practice   Find the domain and range of the relation.

1. $\left\{ (0, 0), (-8, 4), \left(\dfrac{1}{2}, 1\right), (-3, 4), (-8, 0) \right\}$

The x and y components that constitute the ordered pairs in a relation do not need to be numerical. This is demonstrated in Example 2.

Answer

1. Domain: $\left\{ 0, -8, \dfrac{1}{2}, -3 \right\}$;
   range: {0, 4, 1}

| Example 2 | **Writing a Relation and Finding Its Domain and Range** |

Table 8-2 gives five states in the United States and the corresponding number of representatives in the House of Representatives for a recent year.

Table 8-2

State x	Number of Representatives y
Alabama	7
California	53
Colorado	7
Florida	27
Kansas	4

a. The data in the table define a relation. Write a list of ordered pairs for this relation.

b. Write the domain and range.

Solution:

a. {(Alabama, 7), (California, 53), (Colorado, 7), (Florida, 27), (Kansas, 4)}

b. Domain: {Alabama, California, Colorado, Florida, Kansas}

    Range: {7, 53, 27, 4}   (*Note:* The element 7 is not listed twice.)

Skill Practice The table depicts six types of animals and their average longevity.

2. Write the ordered pairs indicated by the relation in the table.

3. Find the domain and range of the relation.

Animal x	Longevity (Years) y
Bear	22.5
Cat	11
Cow	20.5
Deer	12.5
Dog	11
Elephant	35

A relation may consist of a finite number of ordered pairs or an infinite number of ordered pairs. Furthermore, a relation may be defined by several different methods.

- A relation may be defined as a set of ordered pairs.

    {(1, 2), (−3, 4), (1, −4), (3, 4)}

- A relation may be defined by a correspondence (Figure 8-1). The corresponding ordered pairs are {(1, 2), (1, −4), (−3, 4), (3, 4)}.

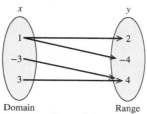

Figure 8-1

- A relation may be defined by a graph (Figure 8-2). The corresponding ordered pairs are {(1, 2), (−3, 4), (1, −4), (3, 4)}.

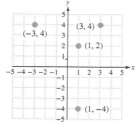

Figure 8-2

Answers

2. {(Bear, 22.5), (Cat, 11), (Cow, 20.5), (Deer, 12.5), (Dog, 11), (Elephant, 35)}

3. Domain: {Bear, Cat, Cow, Deer, Dog, Elephant}; range: {22.5, 11, 20.5, 12.5, 35}

566   **Chapter 8**   Relations and Functions

- A relation may be expressed by an equation such as $x = y^2$. The solutions to this equation define an infinite set of ordered pairs of the form $\{(x, y) \mid x = y^2\}$. The solutions can also be represented by a graph in a rectangular coordinate system (Figure 8-3).

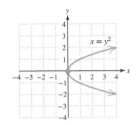

Figure 8-3

Example 3   **Finding the Domain and Range of a Relation**

Write the relation as a set of ordered pairs. Then find the domain and range.

a.

b.

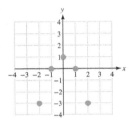

Solution:

a. From the figure, the relation defines the set of ordered pairs:
$\{(3, -9), (2, -9), (-7, -9)\}$

Domain: $\{3, 2, -7\}$

Range: $\{-9\}$

b. The points in the graph make up the set of ordered pairs:
$\{(-2, -3), (-1, 0), (0, 1), (1, 0), (2, -3)\}$

Domain: $\{-2, -1, 0, 1, 2\}$

Range: $\{-3, 0, 1\}$

Skill Practice Find the domain and range of the relations.

4.

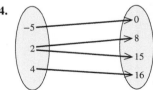

5.

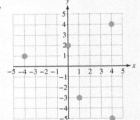

Answers

4. Domain: $\{-5, 2, 4\}$;
range: $\{0, 8, 15, 16\}$

5. Domain: $\{-4, 0, 1, 4\}$;
range: $\{-5, -3, 1, 2, 4\}$

Example 4   **Finding the Domain and Range of a Relation**

Use interval notation to express the domain and range of the relation.

a.

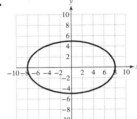

b.

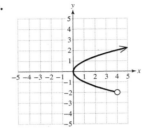

Solution:

a.

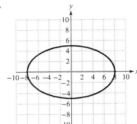

The domain consists of an infinite number of x values extending from -8 to 8 (shown in red). The range consists of all y values from -5 to 5 (shown in blue). Thus, the domain and range must be expressed in set-builder notation or in interval notation.

Domain: $[-8, 8]$

Range: $[-5, 5]$

b.

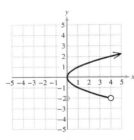

The arrow on the curve indicates that the graph extends infinitely far up and to the right. The open circle means that the graph will end at the point $(4, -2)$, but not include that point.

Domain: $[0, \infty)$

Range: $(-2, \infty)$

Skill Practice Use interval notation to express the domain and range of the relations.

6.

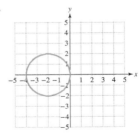

7.

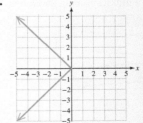

568   **Chapter 8**   Relations and Functions

3. Applications Involving Relations

| Example 5 | **Analyzing a Relation** |

The data in Table 8-3 depict the length of a woman's femur and her corresponding height. Based on these data, a forensics specialist can find a linear relationship between height y (in inches) and femur length x (in centimeters):

$$y = 0.91x + 24 \qquad 40 \le x \le 55$$

From this type of relationship, the height of a woman can be inferred based on skeletal remains.

Table 8-3

Length of Femur (cm) x	Height (in.) y
45.5	65.5
48.2	68.0
41.8	62.2
46.0	66.0
50.4	70.0

  a. Find the height of a woman whose femur is 46.0 cm.

  b. Find the height of a woman whose femur is 51.0 cm.

  c. Why is the domain restricted to $40 \le x \le 55$?

Solution:

  a. $y = 0.91x + 24$

      $= 0.91(46.0) + 24$ Substitute $x = 46.0$ cm.

      $= 65.86$ The woman is approximately 65.9 in. tall.

  b. $y = 0.91x + 24$

      $= 0.91(51.0) + 24$ Substitute $x = 51.0$ cm.

      $= 70.41$ The woman is approximately 70.4 in. tall.

  c. The domain restricts femur length to values between 40 cm and 55 cm inclusive. These values are within the normal lengths for an adult female and are in the proximity of the observed data (Figure 8-4).

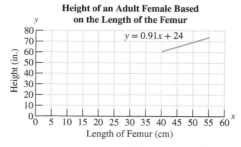

Figure 8-4

Skill Practice   The linear equation, $y = -0.014x + 64.5$, for $1500 \le x \le 4000$, relates the weight of a car, x (in pounds), to its gas mileage, y (in mpg).

  8. Find the gas mileage in miles per gallon for a car weighing 2550 lb.

  9. Find the gas mileage for a car weighing 2850 lb.

  10. Why is the domain restricted to $1500 \le x \le 4000$?

Answers

 8. 28.8 mpg   **9.** 24.6 mpg
10. The relation is valid only for cars weighing between 1500 lb and 4000 lb, inclusive.

Section 8.1   Practice Exercises

Vocabulary and Key Concepts

1. **a.** A set of ordered pairs (x, y) is called a _____ in x and y.

    b. The _____ of a relation is the set of first components in the ordered pairs.

    c. The _____ of a relation is the set of second components in the ordered pairs.

Concept 2: Domain and Range of a Relation

2. Explain how to determine the domain and range of a relation represented by a set of ordered pairs.

For Exercises 3–14,

    a. Write the relation as a set of ordered pairs.

    b. Determine the domain and range. **(See Examples 1–3.)**

3.

Region	Number living in poverty (thousands)
Northeast	54.1
Midwest	65.6
South	110.7
West	70.7

4.

x	y
0	3
−2	$\frac{1}{2}$
−7	1
−2	8
5	1

5.

Country	Year of First Man or Woman in Space
USSR	1961
USA	1962
Poland	1978
Vietnam	1980
Cuba	1980

6.

State, x	Year of Statehood, y
Maine	1820
Nebraska	1823
Utah	1847
Hawaii	1959
Alaska	1959

7.

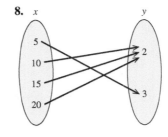

8.

570   **Chapter 8** Relations and Functions

9.
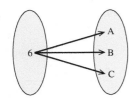

10.
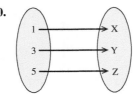

11.
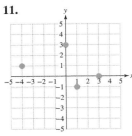

12.
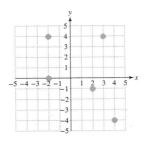

13.
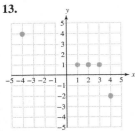

14.
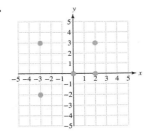

For Exercises 15–30, find the domain and range of the relations. Use interval notation where appropriate.
(See Example 4.)

15.
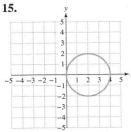

16.
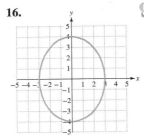

17.
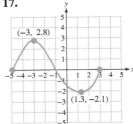

18.
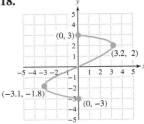

19.
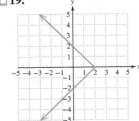

20.
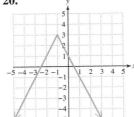

21.
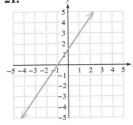

22.
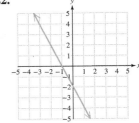

23.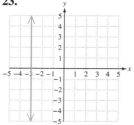

24.

25.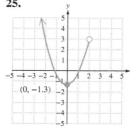

26.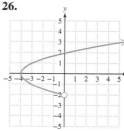

27.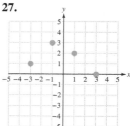

28.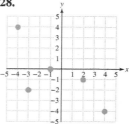

29.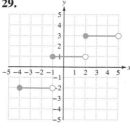

30.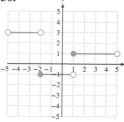

Concept 3: Applications Involving Relations

31. The table gives a relation between the month of the year and the average precipitation for that month for Miami, Florida. **(See Example 5.)**

   a. What is the range element corresponding to April?

   b. What is the range element corresponding to June?

   c. Which element in the domain corresponds to the least value in the range?

   d. Complete the ordered pair: (, 2.66)

   e. Complete the ordered pair: (Sept.,   )

   f. What is the domain of this relation?

Month x	Precipitation (in.) y	Month x	Precipitation (in.) y
Jan.	2.01	July	5.70
Feb.	2.08	Aug.	7.58
Mar.	2.39	Sept.	7.63
Apr.	2.85	Oct.	5.64
May	6.21	Nov.	2.66
June	9.33	Dec.	1.83

Source: U.S. National Oceanic and Atmospheric Administration

32. The table gives a relation between a person's age and the person's maximum recommended heart rate.

   a. What is the domain?

   b. What is the range?

   c. The range element 200 corresponds to what element in the domain?

   d. Complete the ordered pair: (50,   )

   e. Complete the ordered pair: (, 190)

Age (years) x	Maximum Recommended Heart Rate (Beats per Minute) y
20	200
30	190
40	180
50	170
60	160

33. The population of Canada y (in millions) can be approximated by the relation $y = 0.276x + 31$, where x represents the number of years since 2000.

   a. Approximate the population of Canada in the year 2009.

   b. In what year did the population of Canada reach approximately 35,140,000?

572   **Chapter 8** Relations and Functions

34. The world record times for women's track and field events are shown in the table. The women's world record time y (in seconds) required to run x meters can be approximated by the relation $y = 0.159x - 10.79$.

© Digital Vision/Getty Images RF

Distance (m)	Time (sec)	Winner's Name and Country
100	10.49	Florence Griffith Joyner (United States)
200	21.34	Florence Griffith Joyner (United States)
400	47.60	Marita Koch (East Germany)
800	113.28	Jarmila Kratochvilova (Czechoslovakia)
1000	148.98	Svetlana Masterkova (Russia)
1500	230.07	Genzebe Dibaba (Ethiopia)

a. Predict the time required for a 500-m race.

b. Use this model to predict the time for a 1000-m race. Is this value exactly the same as the data value given in the table? Explain.

Expanding Your Skills

35. a. Define a relation with four ordered pairs such that the first element of the ordered pair is the name of a friend and the second element is your friend's place of birth.

b. State the domain and range of this relation.

36. a. Define a relation with four ordered pairs such that the first element is a state and the second element is its capital.

b. State the domain and range of this relation.

37. Use a mathematical equation to define a relation whose second component y is 1 less than 2 times the first component x.

38. Use a mathematical equation to define a relation whose second component y is 3 more than the first component x.

39. Use a mathematical equation to define a relation whose second component y is the square of the first component x.

40. Use a mathematical equation to define a relation whose second component y is one-fourth the first component x.

Introduction to Functions

1. Definition of a Function

In this section, we introduce a special type of relation called a function.

Concepts

1. Definition of a Function
2. Vertical Line Test
3. Function Notation
4. Finding Function Values from a Graph
5. Domain of a Function

> **Definition of a Function**
>
> Given a relation in x and y, we say "y is a **function** of x" if, for each element x in the domain, there is exactly one value of y in the range.
>
> *Note:* This means that no two ordered pairs may have the same first coordinate and different second coordinates.

To understand the difference between a relation that is a function and a relation that is not a function, consider Example 1.

Example 1   **Determining Whether a Relation Is a Function**

Determine which of the relations define y as a function of x.

a.

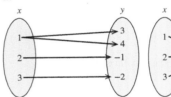

b.

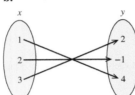

c.

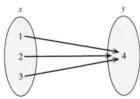

Solution:

a. This relation is defined by the set of ordered pairs

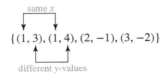

$$\{(1, 3), (1, 4), (2, -1), (3, -2)\}$$

When $x = 1$, there are *two* possible range elements: $y = 3$ and $y = 4$. Therefore, this relation is *not* a function.

b. This relation is defined by the set of ordered pairs $\{(1, 4), (2, -1), (3, 2)\}$.

Notice that no two ordered pairs have the same value of x but different values of y. Therefore, this relation *is* a function.

c. This relation is defined by the set of ordered pairs $\{(1, 4), (2, 4), (3, 4)\}$.

Notice that no two ordered pairs have the same value of x but different values of y. Therefore, this relation *is* a function.

574   **Chapter 8**   Relations and Functions

Skill Practice Determine if the relation defines y as a function of x.

1.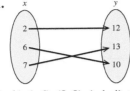

2. $\{(4, 2), (-5, 4), (0, 0), (8, 4)\}$

3. $\{(-1, 6), (8, 9), (-1, 4), (-3, 10)\}$

2. Vertical Line Test

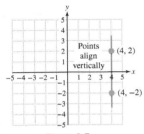

Figure 8-5

A relation that is not a function has at least one domain element x paired with more than one range value y. For example, the set $\{(4, 2), (4, -2)\}$ does not define a function because two different y values correspond to the same x. These two points are aligned vertically in the xy-plane, and a vertical line drawn through one point also intersects the other point (see Figure 8-5). If a vertical line drawn through a graph of a relation intersects the graph in more than one point, the relation cannot be a function. This idea is stated formally as the **vertical line test**.

> **The Vertical Line Test**
>
> Consider a relation defined by a set of points (x, y) in a rectangular coordinate system. The graph defines y as a function of x if no vertical line intersects the graph in more than one point.

The vertical line test can be demonstrated by graphing the ordered pairs from the relations in Example 1.

a. $\{(1, 3), (1, 4), (2, -1), (3, -2)\}$

b. $\{(1, 4), (2, -1), (3, 2)\}$

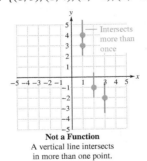

Not a Function
A vertical line intersects
in more than one point.

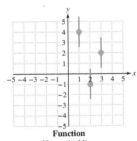

Function
No vertical line
intersects more than once.

Example 2   **Using the Vertical Line Test**

Use the vertical line test to determine whether the relations define y as a function of x.

a.

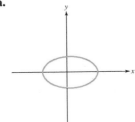

b.

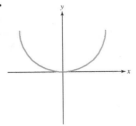

Answers
1. Yes   **2.** Yes   **3.** No

Solution:

a.

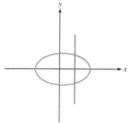

Not a Function
A vertical line intersects
in more than one point.

b.

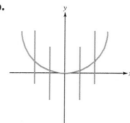

Function
No vertical line intersects
in more than one point.

Skill Practice Use the vertical line test to determine whether the relations define y as a function of x.

4.

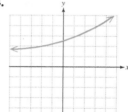

5.

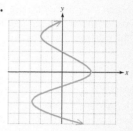

3. Function Notation

A function is defined as a relation with the added restriction that each value in the domain must have only one corresponding y value in the range. In mathematics, functions are often given by rules or equations to define the relationship between two or more variables. For example, the equation $y = 2x$ defines the set of ordered pairs such that the y value is twice the x value.

When a function is defined by an equation, we often use **function notation**. For example, the equation $y = 2x$ may be written in function notation as

$f(x) = 2x$ • f is the name of the function.
• x is an input value from the domain of the function.
• $f(x)$ is the function value (y value) corresponding to x.

The notation $f(x)$ is read as "f of x" or "the value of the function f at x."

A function may be evaluated at different values of x by substituting x values from the domain into the function. For example, to evaluate the function defined by $f(x) = 2x$ at $x = 5$, substitute $x = 5$ into the function.

$$f(x) = 2x$$

$$f(5) = 2(5)$$

$$f(5) = 10$$

TIP: $f(5) = 10$ can be interpreted as the ordered pair (5, 10).

Answers

4. Yes   **5.** No

576   **Chapter 8**   Relations and Functions

Thus, when $x = 5$, the corresponding function value is 10. We say:

- f of 5 is 10.
- f at 5 is 10.
- f evaluated at 5 is 10.

The names of functions are often given by either lowercase or uppercase letters, such as f, g, h, p, K, and M. The input variable may also be a letter other than x. For example, $y = P(t)$ might represent population as a function of time.

Example 3   **Evaluating a Function**

Given the function defined by $g(x) = \frac{1}{2}x - 1$, find the function values.

a. $g(0)$ **b.** $g(2)$ **c.** $g(4)$ **d.** $g(-2)$

Solution:

a. $g(x) = \frac{1}{2}x - 1$

$$g(0) = \frac{1}{2}(0) - 1$$
$$= 0 - 1$$
$$= -1$$

We say that "g of 0 is -1."
This is equivalent to the ordered pair $(0, -1)$.

b. $g(x) = \frac{1}{2}x - 1$

$$g(2) = \frac{1}{2}(2) - 1$$
$$= 1 - 1$$
$$= 0$$

We say that "g of 2 is 0."
This is equivalent to the ordered pair $(2, 0)$.

c. $g(x) = \frac{1}{2}x - 1$

$$g(4) = \frac{1}{2}(4) - 1$$
$$= 2 - 1$$
$$= 1$$

We say that "g of 4 is 1."
This is equivalent to the ordered pair $(4, 1)$.

d. $g(x) = \frac{1}{2}x - 1$

$$g(-2) = \frac{1}{2}(-2) - 1$$
$$= -1 - 1$$
$$= -2$$

We say that "g of -2 is -2."
This is equivalent to the ordered pair $(-2, -2)$.

Skill Practice   Given the function defined by $f(x) = -2x - 3$, find the function values.

6. $f(1)$ **7.** $f(0)$ **8.** $f(-3)$ **9.** $f\left(\dfrac{1}{2}\right)$

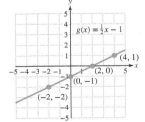

Figure 8-6

In Example 3, notice that $g(0)$, $g(2)$, $g(4)$, and $g(-2)$ correspond to the ordered pairs $(0, -1)$, $(2, 0)$, $(4, 1)$, and $(-2, -2)$. In the graph, these points "line up." The graph of *all* ordered pairs defined by this function is a line with a slope of $\frac{1}{2}$ and y-intercept of $(0, -1)$ (Figure 8-6). This should not be surprising because the function defined by $g(x) = \frac{1}{2}x - 1$ is equivalent to $y = \frac{1}{2}x - 1$.

Answers

6. -5 **7.** -3 **8.** 3   **9.** -4

Calculator Connections

Topic: Using the *Table* and *Value* Features

The values of $g(x)$ in Example 3 can be found using a *Table* feature. First enter the equation of the function as

$$Y_1 = \tfrac{1}{2}x - 1$$

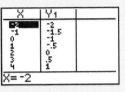

Function values can also be evaluated by using a *Value* feature. The value of $g(4)$ is shown here.

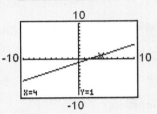

A function may be evaluated at numerical values or at algebraic expressions, as shown in Example 4.

Example 4   Evaluating Functions

Given the functions defined by $f(x) = x^2 - 2x$ and $g(x) = 3x + 5$, find the function values.

   a. $f(t)$ **b.** $g(w + 4)$ **c.** $f(-t)$

Solution:

   a. $f(x) = x^2 - 2x$

$\quad\quad f(t) = (t)^2 - 2(t)$ Substitute $x = t$ for all values of x in the function.

$\quad\quad\quad = t^2 - 2t$ Simplify.

   b. $\quad g(x) = 3x + 5$

$\quad\quad g(w + 4) = 3(w + 4) + 5$ Substitute $x = w + 4$ for all values of x in the function.

$\quad\quad\quad\quad = 3w + 12 + 5$

$\quad\quad\quad\quad = 3w + 17$ Simplify.

   c. $f(x) = x^2 - 2x$ Substitute $-t$ for x.

$\quad f(-t) = (-t)^2 - 2(-t)$

$\quad\quad\quad = t^2 + 2t$ Simplify.

Skill Practice   Given the function defined by $g(x) = 4x - 3$, find the function values.

   10. $g(a)$ **11.** $g(x + h)$ **12.** $g(-x)$

Answers

10. $4a - 3$ **11.** $4x + 4h - 3$

12. $-4x - 3$

4. Finding Function Values from a Graph

We can find function values by looking at the graph of a function. The value of $f(a)$ refers to the y-coordinate of a point with x-coordinate a.

| Example 5 | **Finding Function Values from a Graph** |

Consider the function pictured in Figure 8-7.

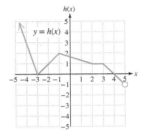

a. Find $h(-1)$.

b. Find $h(2)$.

c. Find $h(5)$.

d. For what value of x is $h(x) = 3$?

e. For what values of x is $h(x) = 0$?

Figure 8-7

Solution:

a. $h(-1) = 2$　　From the graph, when $x = -1$, the function value (y value) is 2. This corresponds to the ordered pair $(-1, 2)$.

b. $h(2) = 1$　　From the graph, when $x = 2$, the function value (y value) is 1. This corresponds to the ordered pair $(2, 1)$.

c. $h(5)$ is not defined.　　The open dot at $(5, -1)$ indicates that 5 is not in the domain.

d. $h(x) = 3$　for $x = -4$　　We want to find the x value(s) that correspond to a function value (y value) of 3. This corresponds to the ordered pair $(-4, 3)$.

e. $h(x) = 0$　for $x = -3$ and $x = 4$　　We want to find the x value(s) that correspond to a function value (y value) of 0. These correspond to the ordered pairs $(-3, 0)$ and $(4, 0)$.

Skill Practice　Refer to the function graphed here.

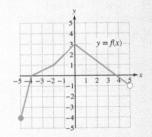

13. Find $f(0)$.

14. Find $f(-2)$.

15. Find $f(5)$.

16. For what value(s) of x is $f(x) = 0$?

17. For what value(s) of x is $f(x) = -4$?

5. Domain of a Function

A function is a relation, and it is often necessary to determine its domain and range. Consider a function defined by the equation $y = f(x)$. The **domain** of f is the set of all x values that when substituted into the function produce a real number. The **range** of f is the set of all y values corresponding to the values of x in the domain.

To find the domain of a function defined by $y = f(x)$, keep these guidelines in mind.

- Exclude values of x that make the denominator of a fraction zero.
- Exclude values of x that make the expression within a square root negative.

Answers

13. 3　　**14.** 1

15. not defined

16. $x = -4$ and $x = 4$

17. $x = -5$

> **Example 6** **Finding the Domain of a Function**
>
> Write the domain in interval notation.
>
> **a.** $f(x) = \dfrac{x+7}{2x-1}$ **b.** $h(x) = \dfrac{x-4}{x^2+9}$
>
> **c.** $k(t) = \sqrt{t+4}$ **d.** $g(t) = t^2 - 3t$
>
> **Solution:**
>
> **a.** $f(x) = \dfrac{x+7}{2x-1}$ will not be a real number when the denominator is zero, that is, when
>
> $$2x - 1 = 0$$
> $$2x = 1$$
> $$x = \frac{1}{2} \qquad \text{The value } x = \tfrac{1}{2} \text{ must be } excluded \text{ from the domain.}$$
>
>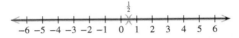
>
> The number line indicates that the domain consists of two intervals, $(-\infty, \frac{1}{2})$ and $(\frac{1}{2}, \infty)$. We use the notation $\cup$ to combine the two intervals. The symbol $\cup$ stands for union. The union of two intervals consists of all the numbers in the first interval, along with all the numbers in the second interval.
>
> Interval notation: $\left(-\infty, \dfrac{1}{2}\right) \cup \left(\dfrac{1}{2}, \infty\right)$
>
> **b.** For $h(x) = \dfrac{x-4}{x^2+9}$ the quantity x^2 is greater than or equal to 0 for all real numbers x, and the number 9 is positive. The sum $x^2 + 9$ must be *positive* for all real numbers x. The denominator will never be zero; therefore, the domain is the set of all real numbers.
>
> 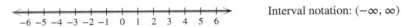   Interval notation: $(-\infty, \infty)$
>
> **c.** The value of the function defined by $k(t) = \sqrt{t+4}$ will not be a real number when the expression within the square root is negative. Therefore, the domain is the set of all t values that make $t + 4$ greater than or equal to zero.
>
> $$t + 4 \geq 0$$
> $$t \geq -4$$
>
> 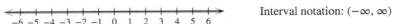   Interval notation: $[-4, \infty)$
>
> **d.** The function defined by $g(t) = t^2 - 3t$ has no restrictions on its domain because any real number substituted for t will produce a real number. The domain is the set of all real numbers.
>
> Interval notation: $(-\infty, \infty)$

Skill Practice Write the domain in interval notation.

18. $f(x) = \dfrac{2x+1}{x-9}$ **19.** $k(x) = \dfrac{-5}{4x^2+1}$

20. $g(x) = \sqrt{x-2}$ **21.** $h(x) = x + 6$

Answers

18. $(-\infty, 9) \cup (9, \infty)$ **19.** $(-\infty, \infty)$
20. $[2, \infty)$ **21.** $(-\infty, \infty)$

580   **Chapter 8** Relations and Functions

Section 8.2   Practice Exercises

Vocabulary and Key Concepts

1. a. Given a relation in x and y, we say that y is a _____ of x if for each element x in the domain, there is exactly one value of y in the range.

b. If a _____ line intersects the graph of a relation in more than one point, the relation is not a function.

c. Function notation for the equation $y = 2x + 1$ is $f(x) =$ _____.

d. Given a function defined by $y = f(x)$, the set of all _____ that produce a real number when substituted into a function is called the domain of the function.

e. The set of all _____ corresponding to x values in the domain is called the range of a function.

f. To find the domain of a function defined by $y = f(x)$, exclude any values of x that make the _____ of a fraction equal to zero.

g. To find the domain of a function defined by $y = f(x)$, exclude any values of x that make the expression within a square root _____.

Review Exercises

For Exercises 2–4, **a.** write the relation as a set of ordered pairs, **b.** identify the domain, and **c.** identify the range.

2.

Parent, x	Child, y
Kevin	Kayla
Kevin	Kira
Kathleen	Katie
Kathleen	Kira

3.

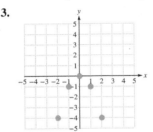

4.

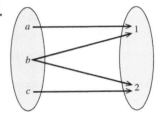

Concept 1: Definition of a Function

For Exercises 5–10, determine if the relation defines y as a function of x. **(See Example 1.)**

5.

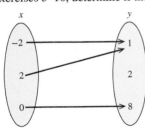

6.

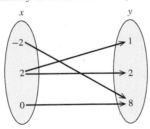

7.

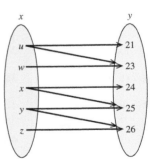

8.

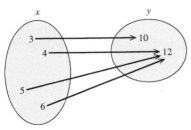

9. $\{(1, 2), (3, 4), (5, 4), (-9, 3)\}$

10. $\left\{ (0, -1.1), \left(\frac{1}{2}, 8\right), (1.1, 8), \left(4, \frac{1}{2}\right) \right\}$

Concept 2: Vertical Line Test

For Exercises 11–16, use the vertical line test to determine whether the relation defines y as a function of x. **(See Example 2.)**

11.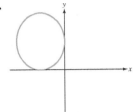

12.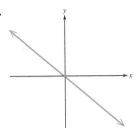

13.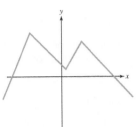

14.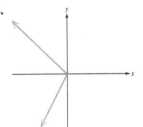

15.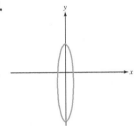

16.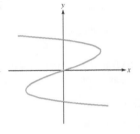

Concept 3: Function Notation

For Exercises 17–20, consider a function defined by $y = f(x)$.

17. Interpret the meaning of $f(2) = 5$.

18. Interpret the meaning of $f(-7) = 8$.

19. Write the ordered pair represented by $f(0) = -2$.

20. Write the ordered pair represented by $f(-10) = 11$.

Consider the functions defined by $f(x) = 6x - 2$, $g(x) = -x^2 - 4x + 1$, $h(x) = 7$, and $k(x) = |x - 2|$. For Exercises 21–52, find the following. **(See Examples 3–4.)**

21. $g(2)$

22. $k(2)$

23. $g(0)$

24. $h(0)$

25. $k(0)$

26. $f(0)$

27. $f(t)$

28. $g(a)$

29. $h(u)$

30. $k(v)$

31. $g(-3)$

32. $h(-5)$

33. $k(-2)$

34. $f(-6)$

35. $f(x + 1)$

36. $h(x + 1)$

37. $g(2x)$

38. $k(x - 3)$

39. $g(-\pi)$

40. $g(a^2)$

41. $h(a + b)$

42. $f(x + h)$

43. $f(-a)$

44. $g(-b)$

45. $k(-c)$

46. $h(-x)$

47. $f\left(\dfrac{1}{2}\right)$

48. $g\left(\dfrac{1}{4}\right)$

49. $h\left(\dfrac{1}{7}\right)$

50. $k\left(\dfrac{3}{2}\right)$

51. $f(-2.8)$

52. $k(-5.4)$

Consider the functions $p = \{(\tfrac{1}{2}, 6), (2, -7), (1, 0), (3, 2\pi)\}$ and $q = \{(6, 4), (2, -5), (\tfrac{3}{4}, \tfrac{1}{5}), (0, 9)\}$. For Exercises 53–60, find the function values.

53. $p(2)$

54. $p(1)$

55. $p(3)$

56. $p\left(\dfrac{1}{2}\right)$

57. $q(2)$

58. $q\left(\dfrac{3}{4}\right)$

59. $q(6)$

60. $q(0)$

582   **Chapter 8**   Relations and Functions

Concept 4: Finding Function Values from a Graph

61. The graph of $y = f(x)$ is given. **(See Example 5.)**

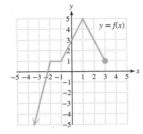

    a. Find $f(0)$.

    b. Find $f(3)$.

    c. Find $f(-2)$.

    d. For what value(s) of x is $f(x) = -3$?

    e. For what value(s) of x is $f(x) = 3$?

    f. Write the domain of f.

    g. Write the range of f.

62. The graph of $y = g(x)$ is given.

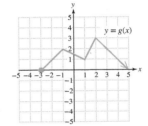

    a. Find $g(-1)$.

    b. Find $g(1)$.

    c. Find $g(4)$.

    d. For what value(s) of x is $g(x) = 3$?

    e. For what value(s) of x is $g(x) = 0$?

    f. Write the domain of g.

    g. Write the range of g.

63. The graph of $y = H(x)$ is given.

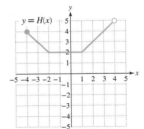

    a. Find $H(-3)$.

    b. Find $H(4)$.

    c. Find $H(3)$.

    d. For what value(s) of x is $H(x) = 3$?

    e. For what value(s) of x is $H(x) = 2$?

    f. Write the domain of H.

    g. Write the range of H.

64. The graph of $y = K(x)$ is given.

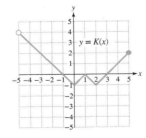

    a. Find $K(0)$.

    b. Find $K(-5)$.

    c. Find $K(1)$.

    d. For what value(s) of x is $K(x) = 0$?

    e. For what value(s) of x is $K(x) = 3$?

    f. Write the domain of K.

    g. Write the range of K.

65. The graph of $y = p(x)$ is given.

    a. Find $p(2)$.

    b. Find $p(-1)$.

    c. Find $p(1)$.

    d. For what value(s) of x is $p(x) = 0$?

    e. For what value(s) of x is $p(x) = -2$?

    f. Write the domain of p.

    g. Write the range of p.

66. The graph of $y = q(x)$ is given.

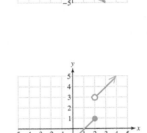

    a. Find $q(3)$.

    b. Find $q(-1)$.

    c. Find $q(2)$.

    d. For what value(s) of x is $q(x) = -4$?

    e. For what value(s) of x is $q(x) = 3$?

    f. Write the domain of q.

    g. Write the range of q.

For Exercises 67–76, refer to the functions $y = f(x)$ and $y = g(x)$, defined as follows:

$$f = \{(-3, 5), (-7, -3), (-\tfrac{3}{2}, 4), (1.2, 5)\}$$
$$g = \{(0, 6), (2, 6), (6, 0), (1, 0)\}$$

67. Identify the domain of f.

68. Identify the range of f.

69. Identify the range of g.

70. Identify the domain of g.

71. For what value(s) of x is $f(x) = 5$?

72. For what value(s) of x is $f(x) = -3$?

73. For what value(s) of x is $g(x) = 0$?

74. For what value(s) of x is $g(x) = 6$?

75. Find $f(-7)$.

76. Find $g(0)$.

Concept 5: Domain of a Function

77. Explain how to determine the domain of the function defined by $f(x) = \dfrac{x+6}{x-2}$.

78. Explain how to determine the domain of the function defined by $g(x) = \sqrt{x-3}$.

For Exercises 79–94, find the domain. Write the answer in interval notation. **(See Example 6.)**

79. $k(x) = \dfrac{x-3}{x+6}$

80. $m(x) = \dfrac{x-1}{x-4}$

81. $f(t) = \dfrac{5}{t}$

82. $g(t) = \dfrac{t-7}{t}$

83. $h(p) = \dfrac{p-4}{p^2+1}$

84. $n(p) = \dfrac{p+8}{p^2+2}$

85. $h(t) = \sqrt{t+7}$

86. $k(t) = \sqrt{t-5}$

584   **Chapter 8** Relations and Functions

87. $f(a) = \sqrt{a-3}$ **88.** $g(a) = \sqrt{a+2}$ **89.** $m(x) = \sqrt{1-2x}$ **90.** $n(x) = \sqrt{12-6x}$

91. $p(t) = 2t^2 + t - 1$ **92.** $q(t) = t^3 + t - 1$ **93.** $f(x) = x + 6$ **94.** $g(x) = 8x - \pi$

Mixed Exercises

95. The height (in feet) of a ball that is dropped from an 80-ft building is given by $h(t) = -16t^2 + 80$, where t is the time in seconds after the ball is dropped.

   a. Find $h(1)$ and $h(1.5)$.

   b. Interpret the meaning of the function values found in part (a).

96. A ball is dropped from a 50-m building. The height (in meters) after t sec is given by $h(t) = -4.9t^2 + 50$.

   a. Find $h(1)$ and $h(1.5)$.

   b. Interpret the meaning of the function values found in part (a).

97. If Alicia rides a bike at an average speed of 11.5 mph, the distance that she rides can be represented by $d(t) = 11.5t$, where t is the time in hours.

   a. Find $d(1)$ and $d(1.5)$.

   b. Interpret the meaning of the function values found in part (a).

98. Brian's score on an exam is a function of the number of hours he spends studying. The function defined by

$P(x) = \dfrac{100x^2}{50 + x^2}$ $(x \geq 0)$ indicates that he will achieve a score of $P\%$ if he studies for x hours.

Evaluate $P(0)$, $P(5)$, $P(10)$, $P(15)$, $P(20)$, and $P(25)$ and confirm the values on the graph. (Round to one decimal place.) Interpret $P(25)$ in the context of this problem.

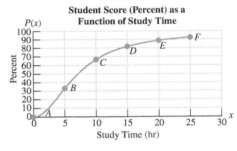

For Exercises 99–102, write a function defined by $y = f(x)$ subject to the conditions given.

99. The value of $f(x)$ is three more than two times x.

100. The value of $f(x)$ is four less than the square of x.

101. The value of $f(x)$ is ten less than the absolute value of x.

102. The value of $f(x)$ is sixteen times the square root of x.

Expanding Your Skills

For Exercises 103–104, write the domain in interval notation.

103. $q(x) = \dfrac{2}{\sqrt{x+2}}$

104. $p(x) = \dfrac{8}{\sqrt{x-4}}$

Graphing Calculator Exercises

105. Graph $k(t) = \sqrt{t-5}$. Use the graph to support your answer to Exercise 86.

106. Graph $h(t) = \sqrt{t+7}$. Use the graph to support your answer to Exercise 85.

Graphs of Functions

1. Linear and Constant Functions

A function may be expressed as a mathematical equation that relates two or more variables. In this section, we will look at several elementary functions.

Recall that the graph of an equation $y = k$, where k is a constant, is a horizontal line. In function notation, this can be written as $f(x) = k$. For example, the graph of the function defined by $f(x) = 3$ is a horizontal line, as shown in Figure 8-8.

We say that a function defined by $f(x) = k$ is a constant function because for any value of x, the function value is constant.

An equation of the form $y = mx + b$ is represented graphically by a line with slope m and y-intercept $(0, b)$. In function notation, this may be written as $f(x) = mx + b$. A function in this form is called a linear function. For example, the function defined by $f(x) = 2x - 3$ is a linear function with slope $m = 2$ and y-intercept $(0, -3)$ (Figure 8-9).

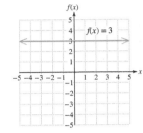

Figure 8-8

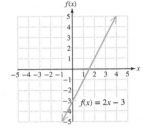

Figure 8-9

> **Linear Functions and Constant Functions**
>
> Let m and b represent real numbers such that $m \neq 0$. Then
>
> A function that can be written in the form $f(x) = mx + b$ is a **linear function**.
> A function that can be written in the form $f(x) = b$ is a **constant function**.
>
> *Note:* The graphs of linear and constant functions are lines.

2. Graphs of Basic Functions

At this point, we are able to recognize the equations and graphs of linear and constant functions. In addition to linear and constant functions, the following equations define six basic functions that will be encountered in the study of algebra:

Equation		Function Notation	Type of Function
$y = x$		$f(x) = x$	Identity function
$y = x^2$		$f(x) = x^2$	Quadratic function
$y = x^3$		$f(x) = x^3$	Cubic function
$y = |x|$	equivalent function notation	$f(x) = |x|$	Absolute value function
$y = \sqrt{x}$		$f(x) = \sqrt{x}$	Square root function
$y = \dfrac{1}{x}$		$f(x) = \dfrac{1}{x}$	Reciprocal function

586   **Chapter 8**   Relations and Functions

The graph of the function defined by $f(x) = x$ is linear, with slope $m = 1$ and y-intercept $(0, 0)$ (Figure 8-10).

To determine the shapes of the other basic functions, we can plot several points to establish the pattern of the graph. Analyzing the equation itself may also provide insight to the domain, range, and shape of the graph. To demonstrate this, we will graph $f(x) = x^2$ and $g(x) = \frac{1}{x}$.

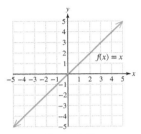

Figure 8-10

Example 1   **Graphing Basic Functions**

Graph the function defined by $f(x) = x^2$.

Solution:

The domain of the function given by $f(x) = x^2$ (or equivalently $y = x^2$) is all real numbers.

To graph the function, choose arbitrary values of x within the domain of the function. Be sure to choose values of x that are positive and values that are negative to determine the behavior of the function to the right and left of the origin (Table 8-4). The graph of $f(x) = x^2$ is shown in Figure 8-11.

The function values are equated to the square of x, so $f(x)$ will always be greater than or equal to zero. Hence, the y-coordinates on the graph will never be negative. The range of the function is $[0, \infty)$. The arrows on each branch of the graph imply that the pattern continues indefinitely.

Table 8-4

x	$f(x) = x^2$
0	0
1	1
2	4
3	9
−1	1
−2	4
−3	9

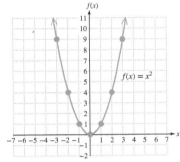

Figure 8-11

Skill Practice

1. Graph $f(x) = -x^2$ by first making a table of points.

Answer

1.

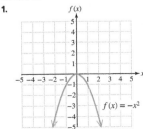

| Example 2 | **Graphing Basic Functions** |

Graph the function defined by $g(x) = \dfrac{1}{x}$.

Solution:

$g(x) = \dfrac{1}{x}$ Notice that $x = 0$ is not in the domain of the function. From the equation $y = \frac{1}{x}$, the y values will be the reciprocal of the x-values. The graph defined by $g(x) = \frac{1}{x}$ is shown in Figure 8-12.

x	$g(x) = \dfrac{1}{x}$
1	1
2	$\frac{1}{2}$
3	$\frac{1}{3}$
-1	-1
-2	$-\frac{1}{2}$
-3	$-\frac{1}{3}$

x	$g(x) = \dfrac{1}{x}$
$\frac{1}{2}$	2
$\frac{1}{3}$	3
$\frac{1}{4}$	4
$-\frac{1}{2}$	-2
$-\frac{1}{3}$	-3
$-\frac{1}{4}$	-4

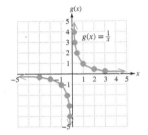

Figure 8-12

Notice that as x approaches ∞ and $-\infty$, the y values approach zero, and the graph approaches the x-axis. In this case, the x-axis is called a *horizontal asymptote*. Similarly, the graph of the function approaches the y-axis as x gets close to zero. In this case, the y-axis is called a *vertical asymptote*.

Skill Practice

2. Graph $h(x) = |x| - 1$ by first making a table of points.

| **Calculator Connections** |

Topic: Graphing Nonlinear Functions

To enter a function, let $f(x) = y$. That is, to graph $f(x) = x^2$, enter $Y_1 = x^2$.

To graph $g(x) = \dfrac{1}{x}$, enter $Y_1 = 1/x$.

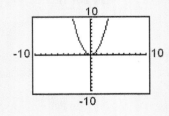

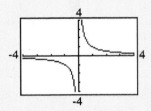

Answer

2.

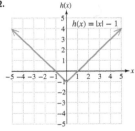

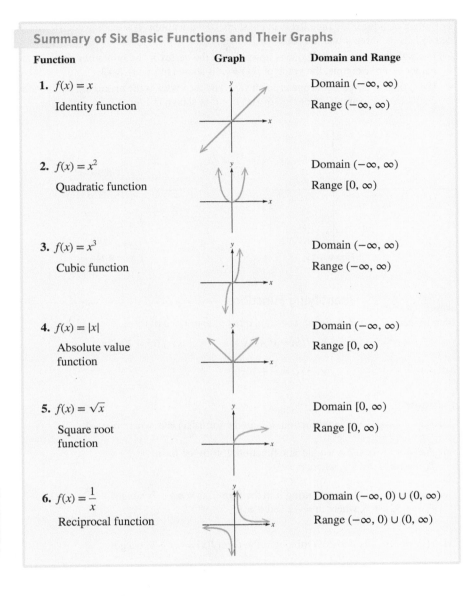

Summary of Six Basic Functions and Their Graphs

Function	Graph	Domain and Range
1. $f(x) = x$ Identity function		Domain $(-\infty, \infty)$ Range $(-\infty, \infty)$
2. $f(x) = x^2$ Quadratic function		Domain $(-\infty, \infty)$ Range $[0, \infty)$
3. $f(x) = x^3$ Cubic function		Domain $(-\infty, \infty)$ Range $(-\infty, \infty)$
4. $f(x) = |x|$ Absolute value function		Domain $(-\infty, \infty)$ Range $[0, \infty)$
5. $f(x) = \sqrt{x}$ Square root function		Domain $[0, \infty)$ Range $[0, \infty)$
6. $f(x) = \dfrac{1}{x}$ Reciprocal function		Domain $(-\infty, 0) \cup (0, \infty)$ Range $(-\infty, 0) \cup (0, \infty)$

TIP: Recall that the symbol ∪ means the combination (or union) of the two intervals.

The shapes of these six graphs will be developed in the homework exercises. These functions are used often in the study of algebra. Therefore, we recommend that you associate an equation with its graph and commit each to memory.

3. Definition of a Quadratic Function

In Example 1 we graphed the function defined by $f(x) = x^2$ by plotting points. This function belongs to a special category called quadratic functions.

Definition of a Quadratic Function

A **quadratic function** is a function defined by

$$f(x) = ax^2 + bx + c \qquad \text{where } a, b, \text{ and } c \text{ are real numbers and } a \neq 0.$$

The graph of a quadratic function is in the shape of a **parabola**. The leading coefficient, a, determines the direction of the parabola.

- If $a > 0$, then the parabola opens upward, and the vertex is the minimum point on the parabola. For example, the graph of $f(x) = x^2$ is shown in Figure 8-13.
- If $a < 0$, then the parabola opens downward, and the vertex is the maximum point on the parabola. For example, the graph of $f(x) = -x^2$ is shown in Figure 8-14.

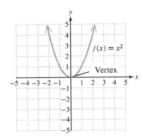

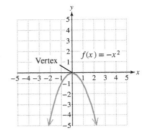

Figure 8-13   **Figure 8-14**

Example 3   **Identifying Functions**

Identify each function as linear, constant, quadratic, or none of these.

   a. $f(x) = -4$ **b.** $f(x) = x^2 + 3x + 2$ **c.** $f(x) = 7 - 2x$

   d. $f(x) = \dfrac{4x + 8}{8}$ **e.** $f(x) = \dfrac{6}{x} + 2$

Solution:

   a. $f(x) = -4$ is a constant function. It is in the form $f(x) = b$, where $b = -4$.

   b. $f(x) = x^2 + 3x + 2$ is a quadratic function. It is in the form $f(x) = ax^2 + bx + c$, where $a \neq 0$.

   c. $f(x) = 7 - 2x$ is linear. Writing it in the form $f(x) = mx + b$, we get $f(x) = -2x + 7$, where $m = -2$ and $b = 7$.

   d. $f(x) = \dfrac{4x + 8}{8}$ is linear. Writing it in the form $f(x) = mx + b$, we get

   $$f(x) = \frac{4x}{8} + \frac{8}{8}$$

   $$= \frac{1}{2}x + 1, \text{ where } m = \frac{1}{2} \text{ and } b = 1.$$

   e. $f(x) = \dfrac{6}{x} + 2$ fits none of these categories because the variable is in the denominator.

Skill Practice   Identify each function as constant, linear, quadratic, or none of these.

   3. $m(x) = -2x^2 - 3x + 7$ **4.** $n(x) = -6$

   5. $W(x) = \dfrac{4}{3}x - \dfrac{1}{2}$ **6.** $R(x) = \dfrac{4}{3x} - \dfrac{1}{2}$

Answers
3. Quadratic
4. Constant
5. Linear
6. None of these

4. Finding the *x*- and *y*-Intercepts of a Graph Defined by $y = f(x)$

We have already learned that to find an *x*-intercept, we substitute $y = 0$ and solve the equation for *x*. Using function notation, this is equivalent to finding the real solutions of the equation $f(x) = 0$. To find the *y*-intercept, substitute $x = 0$ and solve the equation for *y*. In function notation, this is equivalent to finding $f(0)$.

> ### Finding Intercepts Using Function Notation
>
> Given a function defined by $y = f(x)$,
>
> **Step 1**   The *x*-intercepts are the real solutions to the equation $f(x) = 0$.
> **Step 2**   The *y*-intercept is given by $f(0)$.

Example 4   Finding *x*- and *y*-Intercepts

Given the function defined by $f(x) = 2x - 4$:

a. Find the *x*-intercept(s).

b. Find the *y*-intercept.

c. Graph the function.

Solution:

a. To find the *x*-intercept(s), find the real solutions to the equation $f(x) = 0$.

$$f(x) = 2x - 4$$
$$0 = 2x - 4 \qquad \text{Substitute } f(x) = 0.$$
$$4 = 2x$$
$$2 = x \qquad \text{The } x\text{-intercept is } (2, 0).$$

b. To find the *y*-intercept, evaluate $f(0)$.

$$f(0) = 2(0) - 4 \qquad \text{Substitute } x = 0.$$
$$f(0) = -4 \qquad \text{The } y\text{-intercept is } (0, -4).$$

c. This function is linear, with a *y*-intercept of $(0, -4)$, an *x*-intercept of $(2, 0)$, and a slope of 2 (Figure 8-15).

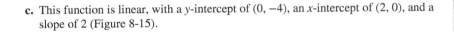

Figure 8-15

Skill Practice   Consider $f(x) = -5x + 1$.

7. Find the *x*-intercept.

8. Find the *y*-intercept.

9. Graph the function.

Answers

7. $(\frac{1}{5}, 0)$ **8.** $(0, 1)$
9.

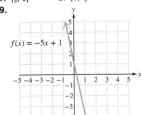

Calculator Connections

Topic: Finding *x*- and *y*-Intercepts

Refer to Example 4 with $f(x) = 2x - 4$. To find the *y*-intercept, let $x = 0$. We can do this using the *Value* key.

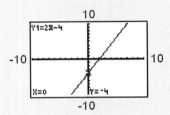

To find the *x*-intercept, use the *Zero* feature. To use this feature you must give bounds for the *x*-intercept. To find a left bound, place the curser to the left of the *x*-intercept and press Enter. For the right bound, place the curser to the right of the *x*-intercept and press Enter.

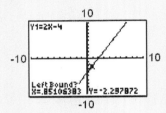   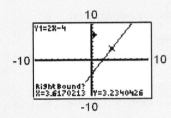

Then make a guess by placing the curser near the *x*-intercept. Press Enter and the *x*-intercept will be displayed.

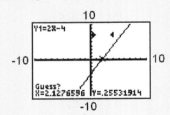   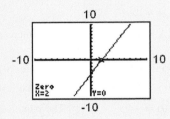

Example 5   **Finding *x*- and *y*-Intercepts**

For the function pictured in Figure 8-16, estimate

a. The real values of *x* for which $f(x) = 0$.

b. The value of $f(0)$.

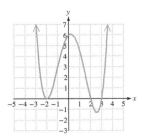

Figure 8-16

592   **Chapter 8**   Relations and Functions

Solution:

a. The real values of x for which $f(x) = 0$ are the x-intercepts of the function. For this graph, the x-intercepts are located at $x = -2$, $x = 2$, and $x = 3$.

b. The value of $f(0)$ is the value of y at $x = 0$. That is, $f(0)$ is the y-intercept, $f(0) = 6$.

Skill Practice Use the function pictured.

10. a. Estimate the real value(s) of x for which $f(x) = 0$.

b. Estimate the value of $f(0)$.

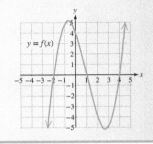

Answer

10. a. $x = -2$, $x = 1$, and $x = 4$

b. $f(0) = 4$

Section 8.3   Practice Exercises

Vocabulary and Key Concepts

1. a. A function that can be written in the form $f(x) = mx + b$, $m \neq 0$, is a _____ function.

b. A function that can be written in the form $f(x) = b$ is a _____ function.

c. A function that can be written in the form $f(x) = ax^2 + bx + c$, $a \neq 0$, is a _____ function.

d. The graph of a quadratic function is in the shape of a _____.

e. To find the x-intercept(s) of a graph defined by $y = f(x)$, find the real solutions to the equation $f(x) =$ _____.

f. To find the _____-intercept of a graph defined by $y = f(x)$, evaluate $f(0)$.

Review Exercises

2. Given: $g = \{(6, 1), (5, 2), (4, 3), (3, 4)\}$

a. Is this relation a function?

b. Write the domain.

c. Write the range.

3. Given: $f = \{(7, 3), (2, 3), (-5, 3)\}$

a. Is this relation a function?

b. Write the domain.

c. Write the range.

4. Given: $f(x) = \sqrt{x + 4}$

a. Evaluate $f(0), f(-3), f(-4)$, and $f(-5)$, if possible.

b. Write the domain of f in interval notation.

5. The force (measured in pounds) to stretch a certain spring x inches is given by $f(x) = 3x$. Evaluate $f(3)$ and $f(10)$, and interpret the results in the context of this problem.

6. The velocity (in feet per second) of a falling object is given by $V(t) = -32t$, where t is the time in seconds after the object was released. Evaluate $V(2)$ and interpret the results in the context of this problem.

Concept 1: Linear and Constant Functions

7. Fill in the blank with the word *vertical* or *horizontal*. The graph of a constant function is a _____ line.

8. For the linear function defined by $f(x) = mx + b$, identify the slope and y-intercept.

9. Graph the constant function $f(x) = 2$. Then use the graph to identify the domain and range of f.

10. Graph the linear function $g(x) = -2x + 1$. Then use the graph to identify the domain and range of g.

Concept 2: Graphs of Basic Functions

For Exercises 11–16, sketch a graph by completing the table and plotting the points. **(See Examples 1–2.)**

11. $f(x) = \dfrac{1}{x}$

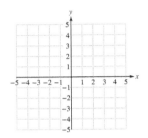

x	$f(x)$	x	$f(x)$
-2		$\frac{1}{4}$	
-1		$\frac{1}{2}$	
$-\frac{1}{2}$		1	
$-\frac{1}{4}$		2	

12. $g(x) = |x|$

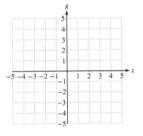

x	$g(x)$
-2	
-1	
0	
1	
2	

13. $h(x) = x^3$

x	$h(x)$
-2	
-1	
0	
1	
2	

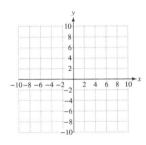

14. $k(x) = x$

x	$k(x)$
-2	
-1	
0	
1	
2	

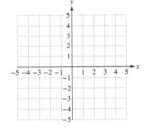

15. $q(x) = x^2$

x	$q(x)$
-2	
-1	
0	
1	
2	

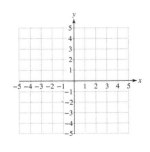

16. $p(x) = \sqrt{x}$

x	$p(x)$
0	
1	
4	
9	
16	

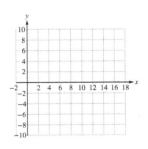

Concept 3: Definition of a Quadratic Function

For Exercises 17–28, determine if the function is constant, linear, quadratic, or none of these. **(See Example 3.)**

17. $f(x) = 2x^2 + 3x + 1$ 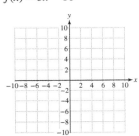   **18.** $g(x) = -x^2 + 4x + 12$

19. $k(x) = -3x - 7$

20. $h(x) = -x - 3$

21. $m(x) = \dfrac{4}{3}$

22. $n(x) = 0.8$

23. $p(x) = \dfrac{2}{3x} + \dfrac{1}{4}$

24. $Q(x) = \dfrac{1}{5x} - 3$

25. $t(x) = \dfrac{2}{3}x + \dfrac{1}{4}$

26. $r(x) = \dfrac{1}{5}x - 3$

27. $w(x) = \sqrt{4 - x}$

28. $T(x) = -|x + 10|$

Concept 4: Finding the *x*- and *y*-Intercepts of a Graph Defined by $y = f(x)$

For Exercises 29–36, find the *x*- and *y*-intercepts, and graph the function. **(See Example 4.)**

29. $f(x) = 5x - 10$

30. $f(x) = -3x + 12$

31. $g(x) = -6x + 5$

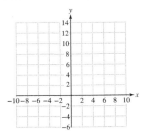
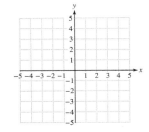

32. $h(x) = 2x + 9$

33. $f(x) = 18$

34. $g(x) = -7$

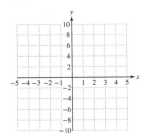
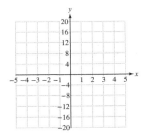
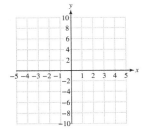

35. $g(x) = \dfrac{2}{3}x + 2$

36. $h(x) = -\dfrac{3}{5}x - 3$

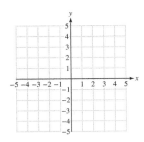
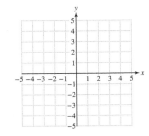

For Exercises 37–42, use the graph to estimate

    a. The real values of x for which $f(x) = 0$.   **b.** The value of $f(0)$. **(See Example 5.)**

37.
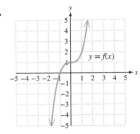

38.
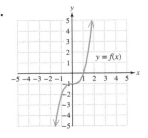

39.
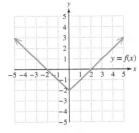

40.
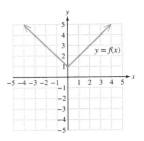

41.
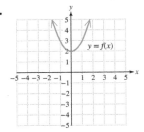

42.
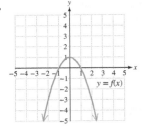

Mixed Exercises

For Exercises 43–52,

    a. Identify the domain of the function.

    b. Identify the y-intercept.

    c. Match the function with its graph by recognizing the basic shape of the graph and using the results from parts (a) and (b). Plot additional points if necessary.

43. $q(x) = 2x^2$ **44.** $p(x) = -2x^2 + 1$ **45.** $h(x) = x^3 + 1$

46. $k(x) = x^3 - 2$ **47.** $r(x) = \sqrt{x + 1}$ **48.** $s(x) = \sqrt{x + 4}$

49. $f(x) = \dfrac{1}{x - 3}$ **50.** $g(x) = \dfrac{1}{x + 1}$ **51.** $k(x) = |x + 2|$

52. $h(x) = |x - 1| + 2$

i.
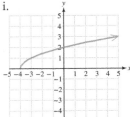

ii.
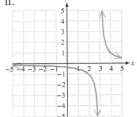

iii.
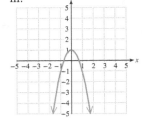

iv.
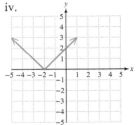

v.
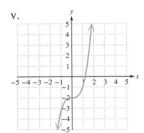

vi.
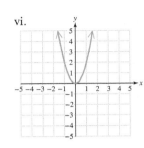

vii.
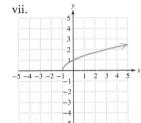

viii.
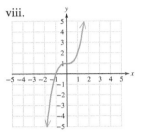

ix.
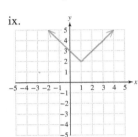

x.
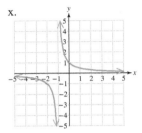

53. Suppose that a student has an 80% average on all of her chapter tests in her Intermediate Algebra class. This counts as $\frac{3}{4}$ of the student's overall grade. The final exam grade counts as the remaining $\frac{1}{4}$ of the student's overall grade. The student's overall course grade, $G(x)$, can be computed by

$$G(x) = \frac{3}{4}(80) + \frac{1}{4}x, \text{ where } x \text{ is the student's grade on the final exam.}$$

a. Is this function linear, quadratic, or neither?

b. Evaluate $G(90)$ and interpret its meaning in the context of the problem.

c. Evaluate $G(50)$ and interpret its meaning in the context of the problem.

54. The median weekly earnings, $E(x)$ in dollars, for women 16 yr and older working full time can be approximated by $E(x) = 0.14x^2 + 7.8x + 540$. For this function, x represents the number of years since 2000. (*Source:* U.S. Department of Labor)

a. Is this function linear, quadratic, or neither?

b. Evaluate $E(5)$ and interpret its meaning in the context of this problem.

c. Evaluate $E(10)$ and interpret its meaning in the context of this problem.

For Exercises 55–60, write a function defined by $y = f(x)$ under the given conditions.

55. The value of $f(x)$ is two more than the square of x.

56. The value of $f(x)$ is the square of the sum of two and x.

57. The function f is a constant function passing through the point $(4, 3)$.

58. The function f is a constant function with y-intercept $(0, 5)$.

59. The function f is a linear function with slope $\frac{1}{2}$ and y-intercept $(0, -2)$.

60. The function f is a linear function with slope -4 and y-intercept $(0, \frac{1}{3})$.

Graphing Calculator Exercises

For Exercises 61–66, use a graphing calculator to graph the basic functions. Verify your answers from the Summary of Six Basic Functions and Their Graphs.

61. $f(x) = x$

62. $f(x) = x^2$

63. $f(x) = x^3$

64. $f(x) = |x|$

65. $f(x) = \sqrt{x}$

66. $f(x) = \frac{1}{x}$

For Exercises 67–70, find the x- and y-intercepts using a graphing calculator and the *Value* and *Zero* features.

67. $y = -\dfrac{1}{8}x + 1$ **68.** $y = -\dfrac{1}{2}x - 3$ **69.** $y = \dfrac{4}{5}x + 4$ **70.** $y = \dfrac{7}{2}x - 7$

Problem Recognition Exercises

Characteristics of Relations

Exercises 1–15 refer to the sets of points (x, y) described in a–h.

a. $\{(0, 8), (1, 4), (\frac{1}{2}, 4), (-3, 5), (2, 1)\}$

b. $\{(-6, 4), (2, 3), (-9, 6), (2, 1), (0, 10)\}$

c. $c(x) = 3x^2 - 2x - 1$

d. $d(x) = 5x - 9$

e.

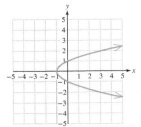

f.

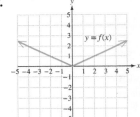

g.

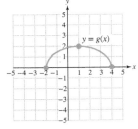

h.

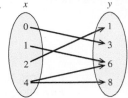

1. Which relations define y as a function of x?

2. Which relations contain the point $(2, 1)$?

3. Use relation (c) to find $c(-1)$.

4. Use relation (f) to find $f(-4)$.

5. Find the domain of relation (a).

6. Find the range of relation (b).

7. Find the domain of relation (g).

8. Find the range of relation (f).

9. Use relation (h) to complete the ordered pair (__, 3).

10. Find the x-intercept(s) of the graph of relation (d).

11. Find the y-intercept(s) of the graph shown in relation (e).

12. Use relation (g) to determine the value of x such that $g(x) = 2$.

13. Which relation describes a quadratic function?

14. Which relation describes a linear function?

15. Use relation (d) to find the value of x such that $d(x) = 6$.

Section 8.4   Algebra of Functions and Composition

Objectives

1. Algebra of Functions
2. Composition of Functions
3. Operations on Functions

1. Algebra of Functions

Addition, subtraction, multiplication, and division can be used to create a new function from two or more functions. The domain of the new function will be the intersection of the domains of the original functions.

> **Sum, Difference, Product, and Quotient of Functions**
>
> Given two functions f and g, the functions $f + g, f - g, f \cdot g$, and $\frac{f}{g}$ are defined as
>
> $$(f + g)(x) = f(x) + g(x)$$
> $$(f - g)(x) = f(x) - g(x)$$
> $$(f \cdot g)(x) = f(x) \cdot g(x)$$
> $$\left(\frac{f}{g}\right)(x) = \frac{f(x)}{g(x)} \qquad \text{provided } g(x) \neq 0$$

For example, suppose $f(x) = |x|$ and $g(x) = 3$. Taking the sum of the functions produces a new function denoted by $f + g$. In this case, $(f + g)(x) = |x| + 3$. Graphically, the y values of the function $f + g$ are given by the sum of the corresponding y values of f and g. This is depicted in Figure 8-17. The function $f + g$ appears in red. In particular, notice that $(f + g)(2) = f(2) + g(2) = 2 + 3 = 5$.

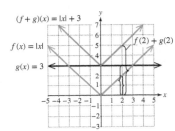

Figure 8-17

Example 1   **Adding, Subtracting, Multiplying and Dividing Functions**

Given: $g(x) = 4x \qquad h(x) = x^2 - 3x \qquad k(x) = x - 2$

a. Find $(g + h)(x)$.   **b.** Find $(h - g)(x)$.

c. Find $(g \cdot k)(x)$.   **d.** Find $\left(\dfrac{k}{h}\right)(x)$.

Solution:

a. $(g + h)(x) = g(x) + h(x)$

$\qquad\qquad = (4x) + (x^2 - 3x)$

$\qquad\qquad = 4x + x^2 - 3x$

$\qquad\qquad = x^2 + x \qquad\qquad$ Simplify.

b. $(h - g)(x) = h(x) - g(x)$

$\qquad\qquad = (x^2 - 3x) - (4x)$

$\qquad\qquad = x^2 - 3x - 4x$

$\qquad\qquad = x^2 - 7x \qquad\qquad$ Simplify.

c. $(g \cdot k)(x) = g(x) \cdot k(x)$

$\qquad = (4x)(x - 2)$

$\qquad = 4x^2 - 8x$ $\qquad$ Simplify.

d. $\left(\dfrac{k}{h}\right)(x) = \dfrac{k(x)}{h(x)}$

$\qquad = \dfrac{x - 2}{x^2 - 3x}$ $\qquad$ From the denominator we have $x^2 - 3x \neq 0$ or, equivalently, $x(x - 3) \neq 0$. Hence, $x \neq 3$ and $x \neq 0$.

Skill Practice   Given $f(x) = x - 1$, $g(x) = 5x^2 + x$, and $h(x) = x^2$, find

1. $(f + g)(x)$ $\qquad$ **2.** $(g - f)(x)$ $\qquad$ **3.** $(g \cdot h)(x)$ $\qquad$ **4.** $\left(\dfrac{f}{h}\right)(x)$

2. Composition of Functions

Composition of Functions

The **composition** of f and g, denoted $f \circ g$, is defined by the rule

$\qquad (f \circ g)(x) = f(g(x))$ $\qquad$ provided that $g(x)$ is in the domain of f

Note: $f \circ g$ is read as "f of g" or "f compose g."

For example, given $f(x) = 2x - 3$ and $g(x) = x + 5$, we have

$(f \circ g)(x) = f(g(x))$

$\qquad = f(x + 5)$ $\qquad$ Substitute $g(x) = x + 5$ into the function f.

$\qquad = 2(x + 5) - 3$

$\qquad = 2x + 10 - 3$

$\qquad = 2x + 7$

In this composition, the function g is the innermost operation and acts on x first. Then the output value of function g becomes the domain element of the function f, as shown in the figure.

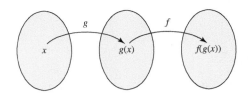

Example 2   **Composing Functions**

Given: $f(x) = x - 5$, $g(x) = x^2$, and $n(x) = \sqrt{x + 2}$, find

a. $(f \circ g)(x)$

b. $(g \circ f)(x)$

c. $(n \circ f)(x)$

Answers

1. $5x^2 + 2x - 1$ $\qquad$ **2.** $5x^2 + 1$

3. $5x^4 + x^3$ $\qquad$ **4.** $\dfrac{x - 1}{x^2}, x \neq 0$

Solution:

a. $(f \circ g)(x) = f(g(x))$

            $= f(x^2)$ Evaluate the function f at x^2.

            $= (x^2) - 5$ Replace x by x^2 in function f.

            $= x^2 - 5$

TIP: Examples 2(a) and 2(b) illustrate that the order in which two functions are composed may result in different functions. That is, $f \circ g$ does not necessarily equal $g \circ f$.

b. $(g \circ f)(x) = g(f(x))$

            $= g(x - 5)$ Evaluate the function g at $(x - 5)$.

            $= (x - 5)^2$ Replace x by $(x - 5)$ in function g.

            $= x^2 - 10x + 25$ Simplify.

c. $(n \circ f)(x) = n(f(x))$

            $= n(x - 5)$ Evaluate the function n at $x - 5$.

            $= \sqrt{(x - 5) + 2}$ Replace x by the quantity $(x - 5)$ in function n.

            $= \sqrt{x - 3}$

Skill Practice Given $f(x) = 2x^2$, $g(x) = x + 3$, and $h(x) = \sqrt{x - 1}$, find

  5. $(f \circ g)(x)$ **6.** $(g \circ f)(x)$ **7.** $(h \circ g)(x)$

3. Operations on Functions

Example 3   **Combining Functions**

Given the functions defined by $f(x) = x - 7$ and $h(x) = 2x^3$, find the function values, if possible.

  a. $(f \cdot h)(3)$ **b.** $\left(\dfrac{h}{f}\right)(7)$ **c.** $(h \circ f)(2)$

Solution:

a. $(f \cdot h)(3) = f(3) \cdot h(3)$ $(f \cdot h)(3)$ is a product (not a composition).

            $= (3 - 7) \cdot 2(3)^3$

            $= (-4) \cdot 2(27)$

            $= -216$

b. $\left(\dfrac{h}{f}\right)(7) = \dfrac{h(7)}{f(7)} = \dfrac{2(7)^3}{7 - 7}$

   The value $x = 7$ will make the denominator equal to 0. Therefore, $\left(\dfrac{h}{f}\right)(7)$ is undefined.

c. $(h \circ f)(2) = h(f(2))$ Evaluate $f(2)$ first. $f(2) = 2 - 7 = -5$

            $= h(-5)$ Substitute the result into function h.

            $= 2(-5)^3$

            $= 2(-125)$

            $= -250$

Answers

5. $2x^2 + 12x + 18$ **6.** $2x^2 + 3$

7. $\sqrt{x + 2}$

Skill Practice Given $h(x) = x + 4$ and $k(x) = x^2 - 3$, find

8. $(h \cdot k)(-2)$ **9.** $\left(\dfrac{k}{h}\right)(-4)$ **10.** $(k \circ h)(1)$

| Example 4 | **Finding Function Values from a Graph** |

For the functions f and g pictured, find the function values if possible.

a. $g(2)$

b. $(f - g)(-3)$

c. $\left(\dfrac{g}{f}\right)(5)$

d. $(f \circ g)(4)$

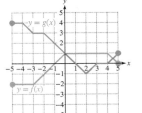

Solution:

a. $g(2) = -1$

The value $g(2)$ represents the y value of $y = g(x)$ (the red graph) when $x = 2$. Because the point $(2, -1)$ lies on the graph, $g(2) = -1$.

b. $(f - g)(-3) = f(-3) - g(-3)$ Evaluate the difference of $f(-3)$ and $g(-3)$.

$\qquad = -2 - (3)$ Estimate function values from the graph.

$\qquad = -5$

c. $\left(\dfrac{g}{f}\right)(5) = \dfrac{g(5)}{f(5)}$ Evaluate the quotient of $g(5)$ and $f(5)$.

$\qquad = \dfrac{1}{0}$ (undefined)

The function $\dfrac{g}{f}$ is undefined at 5 because the denominator is zero.

d. $(f \circ g)(4) = f(g(4))$ From the red graph, find the value of $g(4)$ first. We see that $g(4) = 0$.

$\qquad = f(0)$ From the blue graph, find the value of f at $x = 0$.

$\qquad = 1$

Skill Practice Find the values from the graph.

11. $g(3)$

12. $(f + g)(-4)$

13. $\left(\dfrac{f}{g}\right)(2)$

14. $(g \circ f)(-2)$

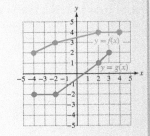

Answers

8. 2   **9.** undefined   **10.** 22
11. 2   **12.** 0   **13.** 4   **14.** 2

Section 8.4   Practice Exercises

Vocabulary and Key Concepts

1. **a.** Given the functions f and g, the function $(f + g)(x) =$ _____ + _____.

   b. Given the functions f and g, the function $\left(\dfrac{f}{g}\right)(x) = \dfrac{f(x)}{\square}$, provided _____ $\neq 0$.

   c. The composition of functions f and g is defined by the rule $(f \circ g)(x) =$ _____.

Concept 1: Algebra of Functions

2. Given $f(x) = x^2$ and $g(x) = 2x - 3$, find

   a. $f(-2)$ **b.** $g(-2)$ **c.** $(f + g)(-2)$

For Exercises 3–14, refer to the functions defined below.

$$f(x) = x + 4 \qquad g(x) = 2x^2 + 4x \qquad h(x) = x^2 + 1 \qquad k(x) = \frac{1}{x}$$

Find the indicated functions. **(See Example 1.)**

3. $(f + g)(x)$ 4. $(f - g)(x)$ 5. $(g - f)(x)$

6. $(f + h)(x)$ 7. $(f \cdot h)(x)$ 8. $(h \cdot k)(x)$

9. $(g \cdot f)(x)$ 10. $(f \cdot k)(x)$ 11. $\left(\dfrac{h}{f}\right)(x)$

12. $\left(\dfrac{g}{f}\right)(x)$ 13. $\left(\dfrac{f}{g}\right)(x)$ 14. $\left(\dfrac{f}{h}\right)(x)$

Concept 2: Composition of Functions

For Exercises 15–22, find the indicated functions. Use f, g, h, and k as defined in Exercises 3–14. **(See Example 2.)**

15. $(f \circ g)(x)$ 16. $(f \circ k)(x)$ 17. $(g \circ f)(x)$

18. $(k \circ f)(x)$ 19. $(k \circ h)(x)$ 20. $(h \circ k)(x)$

21. $(k \circ g)(x)$ 22. $(g \circ k)(x)$

23. Based on your answers to Exercises 15 and 17, is it true in general that $(f \circ g)(x) = (g \circ f)(x)$?

24. Based on your answers to Exercises 16 and 18, is it true in general that $(f \circ k)(x) = (k \circ f)(x)$?

For Exercises 25–28, find $(f \circ g)(x)$ and $(g \circ f)(x)$.

25. $f(x) = x^2 - 3x + 1$, $g(x) = 5x$

26. $f(x) = 3x^2 + 8$, $g(x) = 2x - 4$

27. $f(x) = |x|$, $g(x) = x^3 - 1$

28. $f(x) = \dfrac{1}{x + 2}$, $g(x) = |x + 2|$

29. For $h(x) = 5x - 4$,
find $(h \circ h)(x)$.

30. For $k(x) = -x^2 + 1$,
find $(k \circ k)(x)$.

Concept 3: Operations on Functions

For Exercises 31–46, refer to the functions defined below.

$$m(x) = x^3 \qquad n(x) = x - 3 \qquad r(x) = \sqrt{x + 4} \qquad p(x) = \dfrac{1}{x + 2}$$

Find each function value if possible. **(See Example 3.)**

31. $(m \cdot r)(0)$

32. $(n \cdot p)(0)$

33. $(m + r)(-4)$

34. $(n - m)(4)$

35. $(r \circ n)(3)$

36. $(n \circ r)(5)$

37. $(p \circ m)(-1)$

38. $(m \circ n)(5)$

39. $(m \circ p)(2)$

40. $(r \circ m)(2)$

41. $(r + p)(-3)$

42. $(n + p)(-2)$

43. $(m \circ p)(-2)$

44. $(r \circ m)(-2)$

45. $\left(\dfrac{r}{n}\right)(12)$

46. $\left(\dfrac{n}{m}\right)(2)$

For Exercises 47–64, approximate each function value from the graph, if possible. **(See Example 4.)**

47. $f(-4)$

48. $f(1)$

49. $g(-2)$

50. $g(3)$

51. $(f + g)(2)$

52. $(g - f)(3)$

53. $(f \cdot g)(-1)$

54. $(g \cdot f)(-4)$

55. $\left(\dfrac{g}{f}\right)(0)$

56. $\left(\dfrac{f}{g}\right)(-2)$

57. $\left(\dfrac{f}{g}\right)(0)$

58. $\left(\dfrac{g}{f}\right)(-2)$

59. $(g \circ f)(-1)$

60. $(f \circ g)(0)$

61. $(f \circ g)(-4)$

62. $(g \circ f)(-4)$

63. $(g \circ g)(2)$

64. $(f \circ f)(-2)$

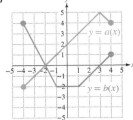

For Exercises 65–80, approximate each function value from the graph, if possible. **(See Example 4.)**

65. $a(-3)$

66. $a(1)$

67. $b(-1)$

68. $b(3)$

69. $(a - b)(-1)$

70. $(a + b)(0)$

71. $(b \cdot a)(1)$

72. $(a \cdot b)(2)$

73. $(b \circ a)(0)$

74. $(a \circ b)(-2)$

75. $(a \circ b)(-4)$

76. $(b \circ a)(-3)$

77. $\left(\dfrac{b}{a}\right)(3)$

78. $\left(\dfrac{a}{b}\right)(4)$

79. $(a \circ a)(-2)$

80. $(b \circ b)(1)$

81. The cost in dollars of producing x toy cars is $C(x) = 2.2x + 1$. The revenue for selling x toy cars is $R(x) = 5.98x$. To calculate profit, subtract the cost from the revenue.

a. Write and simplify a function P that represents profit in terms of x.

b. Find the profit of producing 50 toy cars.

82. The cost in dollars of producing x lawn chairs is $C(x) = 2.5x + 10.1$. The revenue for selling x lawn chairs is $R(x) = 6.99x$. To calculate profit, subtract the cost from the revenue.

a. Write and simplify a function P that represents profit in terms of x.

b. Find the profit in producing 100 lawn chairs.

83. The functions defined by $D(t) = 0.925t + 26.958$ and $R(t) = 0.725t + 20.558$ approximate the amount of child support (in billions of dollars) that was due $D(t)$ and the amount of child support actually received $R(t)$ in the United States for a selected number of years. In each case, $t = 0$ represents the first year of the study.

a. Find the function defined by $F(t) = D(t) - R(t)$. What does $F(t)$ represent in the context of this problem?

b. Find $F(4)$. What does this function value represent in the context of this problem?

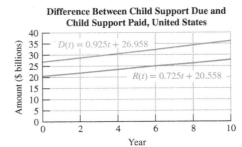

Difference Between Child Support Due and Child Support Paid, United States

Source: U.S. Bureau of the Census

84. The rural and urban populations in the South (in the United States) between the years 1900 and 1970 can be modeled by the following:

$$r(t) = -3.497t^2 + 266.2t + 20{,}220$$

$$u(t) = 0.0566t^3 + 0.952t^2 + 177.8t + 4593$$

The variable t represents the number of years since 1900, $r(t)$ represents the rural population in thousands, and $u(t)$ represents the urban population in thousands.

a. Find the function defined by $T(t) = r(t) + u(t)$. What does $T(t)$ represent in the context of this problem?

b. Use the function T to approximate the total population in the South for the year 1940.

Rural and Urban Populations in the South, United States, 1900–1970

Source: Historical Abstract of the United States

85. Joe rides a bicycle and his wheels revolve at 80 revolutions per minute (rpm). Therefore, the total number of revolutions, r, is given by $r(t) = 80t$, where t is the time in minutes. For each revolution of the wheels of the bike, he travels approximately 7 ft. Therefore, the total distance he travels $D(r)$ (in feet) depends on the total number of revolutions, r, according to the function $D(r) = 7r$.

a. Find $(D \circ r)(t)$ and interpret its meaning in the context of this problem.

b. Find Joe's total distance in feet after 10 min.

86. The area of a square is given by the function $a(x) = x^2$, where x is the length of the sides of the square. If carpeting costs \$9.95 per square yard, then the cost $C(a)$ (in dollars) to carpet a square room is given by $C(a) = 9.95a$, where a is the area of the room in square yards.

a. Find $(C \circ a)(x)$ and interpret its meaning in the context of this problem.

b. Find the cost to carpet a square room if its floor dimensions are 15 yd by 15 yd.

Variation

1. Definition of Direct and Inverse Variation

In this section, we introduce the concept of variation. Direct and inverse variation models can show how one quantity varies in proportion to another.

Definition of Direct and Inverse Variation

Let k be a nonzero constant real number. Then,

1. y varies **directly** as x.
   y is directly proportional to x. $\left.\right\}$ $y = kx$

2. y varies **inversely** as x.
   y is inversely proportional to x. $\left.\right\}$ $y = \dfrac{k}{x}$

Note: The value of k is called the constant of variation.

For a car traveling 30 mph, the equation $d = 30t$ indicates that the distance traveled is *directly proportional* to the time of travel. For positive values of k, when two variables are directly related, as one variable increases, the other variable will also increase. Likewise, if one variable decreases, the other will decrease. In the equation $d = 30t$, the longer the time of the trip, the greater the distance traveled. The shorter the time of the trip, the shorter the distance traveled.

For positive values of k, when two positive variables are *inversely related*, as one variable increases, the other will decrease, and vice versa. Consider a car traveling between Toronto and Montreal, a distance of 500 km. The time required to make the trip is inversely proportional to the speed of travel: $t = 500/r$. As the rate of speed, r, increases, the quotient $500/r$ will decrease. Thus, the time will decrease. Similarly, as the rate of speed decreases, the trip will take longer.

2. Translations Involving Variation

The first step in using a variation model is to write an English phrase as an equivalent mathematical equation.

Example 1 Translating to a Variation Model

Write each expression as an equivalent mathematical model.

a. The circumference of a circle varies directly as the radius.

b. At a constant temperature, the volume of a gas varies inversely as the pressure.

c. The length of time of a meeting is directly proportional to the *square* of the number of people present.

Solution:

a. Let C represent circumference and r represent radius. The variables are directly related, so use the model $C = kr$.

b. Let V represent volume and P represent pressure. Because the variables are inversely related, use the model $V = \frac{k}{P}$.

c. Let t represent time, and let N be the number of people present at a meeting. Because t is directly related to N^2, use the model $t = kN^2$.

Skill Practice Write each expression as an equivalent mathematical model.

1. The distance, d, driven in a particular time varies directly with the speed of the car, s.
2. The weight of an individual kitten, w, varies inversely with the number of kittens in the litter, n.
3. The value of v varies inversely as the square root of b.

Sometimes a variable varies directly as the product of two or more other variables. In this case, we have joint variation.

Definition of Joint Variation

Let k be a nonzero constant real number. Then the following statements are equivalent:

$$\left. \begin{array}{l} y \text{ varies } \textbf{jointly} \text{ as } w \text{ and } z. \\ y \text{ is jointly proportional to } w \text{ and } z. \end{array} \right\} \quad y = kwz$$

Example 2 **Translating to a Variation Model**

Write each expression as an equivalent mathematical model.

a. y varies jointly as u and the square root of v.

b. The gravitational force of attraction between two planets varies jointly as the product of their masses and inversely as the square of the distance between them.

Solution:

a. $y = ku\sqrt{v}$

b. Let m_1 and m_2 represent the masses of the two planets. Let F represent the gravitational force of attraction and d represent the distance between the planets.

The variation model is: $\quad F = \dfrac{km_1m_2}{d^2}$

Skill Practice Write each expression as an equivalent mathematical model.

4. The value of q varies jointly as u and v.
5. The value of x varies directly as the square of y and inversely as z.

Answers

1. $d = ks$
2. $w = \dfrac{k}{n}$
3. $v = \dfrac{k}{\sqrt{b}}$
4. $q = kuv$
5. $x = \dfrac{ky^2}{z}$

3. Applications of Variation

Consider the variation models $y = kx$ and $y = \frac{k}{x}$. In either case, if values for x and y are known, we can solve for k. Once k is known, we can use the variation equation to find y if x is known, or to find x if y is known. This concept is the basis for solving many applications involving variation.

Finding a Variation Model

Step 1   Write a general variation model that relates the variables given in the problem. Let k represent the constant of variation.

Step 2   Solve for k by substituting known values of the variables into the model from step 1.

Step 3   Substitute the value of k into the original variation model from step 1.

Example 3   **Solving an Application Involving Direct Variation**

The variable z varies directly as w. When w is 16, z is 56.

a. Write a variation model for this situation. Use k as the constant of variation.

b. Solve for the constant of variation.

c. Find the value of z when w is 84.

Solution:

a. $z = kw$

b. $z = kw$

$56 = k(16)$ Substitute known values for z and w. Then solve for the unknown value of k.

$\dfrac{56}{16} = \dfrac{k(16)}{16}$ To isolate k, divide both sides by 16.

$\dfrac{7}{2} = k$ Simplify $\dfrac{56}{16}$ to $\dfrac{7}{2}$.

c. With the value of k known, the variation model can now be written as:

$z = \dfrac{7}{2}w$

$z = \dfrac{7}{2}(84)$ To find z when $w = 84$, substitute $w = 84$ into the equation.

$z = 294$

Skill Practice   The variable t varies directly as the square of v. When v is 8, t is 32.

6. Write a variation model for this relationship.

7. Solve for the constant of variation.

8. Find t when $v = 10$.

Answers

6. $t = kv^2$ **7.** $\dfrac{1}{2}$ **8.** 50

| Example 4 | Solving an Application Involving Direct Variation |

The speed of a racing canoe in still water varies directly as the square root of the length of the canoe.

a. If a 16-ft canoe can travel 6.2 mph in still water, find a variation model that relates the speed of a canoe to its length.

b. Find the speed of a 25-ft canoe.

Solution:

a. Let s represent the speed of the canoe and L represent the length. The general variation model is $s = k\sqrt{L}$. To solve for k, substitute the known values for s and L.

$$s = k\sqrt{L}$$
$$6.2 = k\sqrt{16} \qquad \text{Substitute } s = 6.2 \text{ mph and } L = 16 \text{ ft.}$$
$$6.2 = k \cdot 4$$
$$\frac{6.2}{4} = \frac{4k}{4} \qquad \text{Solve for } k.$$
$$k = 1.55$$
$$s = 1.55\sqrt{L} \qquad \text{Substitute } k = 1.55 \text{ into the model } s = k\sqrt{L}.$$

b. $s = 1.55\sqrt{L}$
$$= 1.55\sqrt{25} \qquad \text{Find the speed when } L = 25 \text{ ft.}$$
$$= 7.75 \text{ mph} \qquad \text{The speed is 7.75 mph.}$$

Skill Practice

9. The amount of water needed by a mountain hiker varies directly as the time spent hiking. The hiker needs 2.4 L for a 4-hr hike. How much water will be needed for a 5-hr hike?

| Example 5 | Solving an Application Involving Inverse Variation |

The loudness of sound measured in decibels (dB) varies inversely as the square of the distance between the listener and the source of the sound. If the loudness of sound is 17.92 dB at a distance of 10 ft from a home theater speaker, what is the decibel level 20 ft from the speaker?

Solution:

Let L represent the loudness of sound in decibels and d represent the distance in feet. The inverse relationship between decibel level and the square of the distance is modeled by

$$L = \frac{k}{d^2}$$

$$17.92 = \frac{k}{(10)^2} \qquad \text{Substitute } L = 17.92 \text{ dB and } d = 10 \text{ ft.}$$

Answer

9. 3 L

$$17.92 = \frac{k}{100}$$

$$(17.92)100 = \frac{k}{100} \cdot 100 \qquad \text{Solve for } k \text{ (clear fractions).}$$

$$k = 1792$$

$$L = \frac{1792}{d^2} \qquad \text{Substitute } k = 1792 \text{ into the original}$$
$$\text{model } L = \frac{k}{d^2}.$$

With the value of k known, we can find L for any value of d.

$$L = \frac{1792}{(20)^2} \qquad \text{Find the loudness when } d = 20 \text{ ft.}$$

$$= 4.48 \text{ dB} \qquad \text{The loudness is 4.48 dB.}$$

Notice that the loudness of sound is 17.92 dB at a distance 10 ft from the speaker. When the distance from the speaker is increased to 20 ft, the decibel level decreases to 4.48 dB. This is consistent with an inverse relationship. For $k > 0$, as one variable is increased, the other is decreased. It also seems reasonable that the farther one moves away from the source of a sound, the softer the sound becomes.

Skill Practice

10. The yield on a bond varies inversely as the price. The yield on a particular bond is 5% when the price is $100. Find the yield when the price is $125.

Example 6   **Solving an Application Involving Joint Variation**

The kinetic energy of an object varies jointly as the weight of the object at sea level and as the square of its velocity. During a hurricane, a 0.5-lb stone traveling at 60 mph has 81 J (joules) of kinetic energy. Suppose the wind speed doubles to 120 mph. Find the kinetic energy.

Solution:

Let E represent the kinetic energy, let w represent the weight, and let v represent the velocity of the stone. The variation model is

$$E = kwv^2$$

$$81 = k(0.5)(60)^2 \qquad \text{Substitute } E = 81 \text{ J}, w = 0.5 \text{ lb, and } v = 60 \text{ mph.}$$

$$81 = k(0.5)(3600) \qquad \text{Simplify exponents.}$$

$$81 = k(1800)$$

$$\frac{81}{1800} = \frac{k(1800)}{1800} \qquad \text{Divide by 1800.}$$

$$0.045 = k \qquad \text{Solve for } k.$$

Answer

10. 4%

With the value of k known, the model $E = kwv^2$ can now be written as $E = 0.045wv^2$. We now find the kinetic energy of a 0.5-lb stone traveling at 120 mph.

$$E = 0.045(0.5)(120)^2$$

$$= 324$$

The kinetic energy of a 0.5-lb stone traveling 120 mph is 324 J.

Skill Practice

11. The amount of simple interest earned in an account varies jointly as the interest rate and time of the investment. An account earns \$72 in 4 years at 2% interest. How much interest would be earned in 3 years at a rate of 5%?

Answer

11. \$135

In Example 6, when the velocity increased by 2 times, the kinetic energy increased by 4 times (note that $324 \text{ J} = 4 \cdot 81 \text{ J}$). This factor of 4 occurs because the kinetic energy is proportional to the *square* of the velocity. When the velocity increased by 2 times, the kinetic energy increased by 2^2 times.

Section 8.5   Practice Exercises

Vocabulary and Key Concepts

1. **a.** Let k be a nonzero constant. If y varies directly as x, then $y =$ _____, where k is the constant of variation.

   b. Let k be a nonzero constant. If y varies inversely as x, then $y =$ _____, where k is the constant of variation.

   c. Let k be a nonzero constant. If y varies jointly as x and w, then $y =$ _____, where k is the constant of variation.

Review Exercises

For Exercises 2–7, refer to the functions defined below.

$$f(x) = x^2 \qquad g(x) = x - 2 \qquad h(x) = \sqrt{2 - x}$$

Find the indicated functions or function values.

2. $(f + g)(2)$

3. $(f \circ g)(x)$

4. $(g - f)(3)$

5. $(g \circ f)(x)$

6. $(f \cdot g)(x)$

7. $\left(\dfrac{g}{h}\right)(1)$

Concept 1: Definition of Direct and Inverse Variation

8. In the equation $r = kt$, does r vary directly or inversely as t?

9. In the equation $w = \dfrac{k}{v}$, does w vary directly or inversely as v?

10. In the equation $P = \dfrac{k \cdot c}{v}$, does P vary directly or inversely as v?

Concept 2: Translations Involving Variation

For Exercises 11–22, write a variation model. Use k as the constant of variation. **(See Examples 1–2.)**

11. T varies directly as q.

12. W varies directly as z.

13. b varies inversely as c.

14. m varies inversely as t.

15. Q is directly proportional to x and inversely proportional to y.

16. d is directly proportional to p and inversely proportional to n.

17. c varies jointly as s and t.

18. w varies jointly as p and f.

19. L varies jointly as w and the square root of v.

20. q varies jointly as v and the cube root of w.

21. x varies directly as the square of y and inversely as z.

22. a varies directly as n and inversely as the square of d.

Concept 3: Applications of Variation

For Exercises 23–28, find the constant of variation, k. **(See Example 3.)**

23. y varies directly as x and when x is 4, y is 18.

24. m varies directly as x and when x is 8, m is 22.

25. p varies inversely as q and when q is 16, p is 32.

26. T varies inversely as x and when x is 40, T is 200.

27. y varies jointly as w and v. When w is 50 and v is 0.1, y is 8.75.

28. N varies jointly as t and p. When t is 1 and p is 7.5, N is 330.

For Exercises 29–40, solve for the indicated variable. **(See Example 3.)**

29. x varies directly as p. If $x = 50$ when $p = 10$, find x when p is 14.

30. y is directly proportional to z. If $y = 12$ when $z = 36$, find y when z is 21.

31. b is inversely proportional to c. If b is 4 when c is 3, find b when $c = 2$.

32. q varies inversely as w. If q is 8 when w is 50, find q when w is 125.

33. Z varies directly as the square of w. If $Z = 14$ when $w = 4$, find Z when $w = 8$.

34. m varies directly as the square of x. If $m = 200$ when $x = 20$, find m when x is 32.

35. Q varies inversely as the square of p. If $Q = 4$ when $p = 3$, find Q when $p = 2$.

36. z is inversely proportional to the square of t. If $z = 15$ when $t = 4$, find z when $t = 10$.

37. L varies jointly as a and the square root of b. If $L = 72$ when $a = 8$ and $b = 9$, find L when $a = \frac{1}{2}$ and $b = 36$.

38. Y varies jointly as the cube of x and the square root of w. $Y = 128$ when $x = 2$ and $w = 16$. Find Y when $x = \frac{1}{2}$ and $w = 64$.

39. B varies directly as m and inversely as n. $B = 20$ when $m = 10$ and $n = 3$. Find B when $m = 15$ and $n = 12$.

40. R varies directly as s and inversely as t. $R = 14$ when $s = 2$ and $t = 9$. Find R when $s = 4$ and $t = 3$.

For Exercises 41–58, use a variation model to solve for the unknown value. **(See Examples 4–6.)**

41. The weight of a person's heart varies directly as the person's actual weight. For a 150-lb man, his heart would weigh 0.75 lb.

   a. Approximate the weight of a 184-lb man's heart.

   b. How much does your heart weigh?

42. The number of calories, *C,* in beer varies directly with the number of ounces, *n.* If 12 oz of beer contains 153 calories, how many calories are in 40 oz of beer?

43. The amount of medicine that a physician prescribes for a patient varies directly as the weight of the patient. A physician prescribes 3 g of a medicine for a 150-lb person.

   a. How many grams should be prescribed for a 180-lb person?

   b. How many grams should be prescribed for a 225-lb person?

   c. How many grams should be prescribed for a 120-lb person?

© Sean Justice/Corbis RF

44. The number of turkeys needed for a banquet is directly proportional to the number of guests that must be fed. Master Chef Rico knows that he needs to cook 3 turkeys to feed 42 guests.

   a. How many turkeys should he cook to feed 70 guests?

   b. How many turkeys should he cook to feed 140 guests?

   c. How many turkeys should be cooked to feed 700 guests at an inaugural ball?

   d. How many turkeys should be cooked for a wedding with 100 guests?

© BananaStock/PunchStock RF

45. The unit cost of producing CDs is inversely proportional to the number of CDs produced. If 5000 CDs are produced, the cost per CD is $0.48.

   a. What would be the unit cost if 6000 CDs were produced?

   b. What would be the unit cost if 8000 CDs were produced?

   c. What would be the unit cost if 2400 CDs were produced?

46. An author self-publishes a book and finds that the number of books she can sell per month varies inversely as the price of the book. The author can sell 1500 books per month when the price is set at $8 per book.

   a. How many books would she expect to sell if the price were $12?

   b. How many books would she expect to sell if the price were $15?

   c. How many books would she expect to sell if the price were $6?

47. The amount of pollution entering the atmosphere over a given time varies directly as the number of people living in an area. If 80,000 people create 56,800 tons of pollutants, how many tons enter the atmosphere in a city with a population of 500,000?

© Patrick Clark/Getty Images RF

48. The area of a picture projected on a wall varies directly as the square of the distance from the projector to the wall. If a 10-ft distance produces a 16-ft^2 picture, what is the area of a picture produced when the projection unit is moved to a distance 20 ft from the wall?

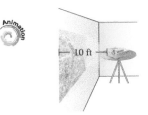

49. The stopping distance of a car varies directly as the square of the speed of the car. If a car traveling 40 mph has a stopping distance of 109 ft, find the stopping distance of a car that travels 25 mph. (Round the answer to one decimal place.)

50. The intensity of a light source varies inversely as the square of the distance from the source. If the intensity of a light bulb is 400 lumen/m^2 (lux) at a distance of 5 m, determine the intensity at 8 m.

51. The power in an electric circuit varies jointly as the current and the square of the resistance. If the power is 144 W (watts) when the current is 4 A (amperes) and the resistance is 6 Ω (ohms), find the power when the current is 3 A and the resistance is 10 Ω.

52. Some body-builders claim that, within safe limits, the number of repetitions that a person can complete on a given weight-lifting exercise is inversely proportional to the amount of weight lifted. Roxanne can bench press 45 lb for 15 repetitions.

   a. How many repetitions can Roxanne bench with 60 lb of weight?

   b. How many repetitions can Roxanne bench with 75 lb of weight?

   c. How many repetitions can Roxanne bench with 100 lb of weight?

53. The current in a wire varies directly as the voltage and inversely as the resistance. If the current is 9 A when the voltage is 90 V (volts) and the resistance is 10 Ω, find the current when the voltage is 185 V and the resistance is 10 Ω.

54. The resistance of a wire varies directly as its length and inversely as the square of its diameter. A 40-ft wire 0.1 in. in diameter has a resistance of 4 Ω. What is the resistance of a 50-ft wire with a diameter of 0.2 in.?

55. The weight of a medicine ball varies directly as the cube of its radius. A ball with a radius of 3 in. weighs 4.32 lb. How much would a medicine ball weigh if its radius is 5 in.?

56. The area of an equilateral triangle varies directly as the square of the length of the sides. For an equilateral triangle with 7-cm sides, the area is 21.22 cm^2. What is the area of an equilateral triangle with 17-cm sides? Round to the nearest whole unit.

57. The amount of simple interest earned in an account varies jointly as the amount of principal invested and the amount of time the money is invested. If $2500 in principal earns $500 in interest after 4 years, then how much interest will be earned on $7000 invested for 10 years?

58. The amount of simple interest earned in an account varies jointly as the amount of principal invested and the amount of time the money is invested. If $6000 in principal earns $840 in interest after 2 years, then how much interest will be earned on $4500 invested for 8 years?

Group Activity

Deciphering a Coded Message

Materials: A calculator

Estimated time: 20–25 minutes

Group Size: 4 (two pairs)

Cryptography is the study of coding and decoding messages. One type of coding process assigns a number to each letter of the alphabet and to the space character. For example:

A	B	C	D	E	F	G	H	I	J	K	L	M	N
1	2	3	4	5	6	7	8	9	10	11	12	13	14

O	P	Q	R	S	T	U	V	W	X	Y	Z	space
15	16	17	18	19	20	21	22	23	24	25	26	27

According to the numbers assigned to each letter, the message "*Decimals have a point*" would be coded as follows:

D	E	C	I	M	A	L	S	_	H	A	V	E	_	A	_	P	O	I	N	T
4	5	3	9	13	1	12	19	27	8	1	22	5	27	1	27	16	15	9	14	20

Now suppose each letter is encoded by applying a function such as $f(x) = 2x + 5$, where x is the numerical value of each letter. For example:

The letter "a" would be coded as: $f(1) = 2(1) + 5 = 7$

The letter "b" would be coded as: $f(2) = 2(2) + 5 = 9$

Using this encoding function, we have

Message:	D	E	C	I	M	A	L	S	_	H	A	V	E	_	A	_	P	O	I	N	T
Original:	4	5	3	9	13	1	12	19	27	8	1	22	5	27	1	27	16	15	9	14	20
Coded Form:	13	15	11	23	31	7	29	43	59	21	7	49	15	59	7	59	37	35	23	33	45

To decode this message, the receiver would need to reverse the operations assigned by $f(x) = 2x + 5$. Since the function f multiplies x by 2 and then adds 5, we can reverse this process by subtracting 5 and dividing by 2. This is represented by $g(x) = \frac{x-5}{2}$.

1. **a.** One pair of students will encode the follow message according to $f(x) = 4x + 2$.

    MATH IS THE KEY TO THE SCIENCES

    b. The second pair of students will encode the follow message according to $f(x) = 3x - 1$.

    MATH IS NOT A SPECTATOR SPORT

2. With each message encoded, the pairs will exchange papers. Each pair will then decode the message.

Summary   **615**

Chapter 8   Summary

Section 8.1   Introduction to Relations

Key Concepts

A set of ordered pairs (x, y) is called a **relation in x and y**.

The **domain** of a relation is the set of first components in the ordered pairs in the relation. The **range** of a relation is the set of second components in the ordered pairs.

Examples

Example 1

Let $A = \{(0, 0), (1, 1), (2, 4), (3, 9), (-1, 1), (-2, 4)\}$.

Domain of A: $\{0, 1, 2, 3, -1, -2\}$

Range of A: $\{0, 1, 4, 9\}$

Example 2

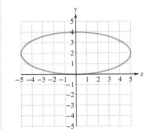

Domain: $[-5, 5]$
Range: $[0, 4]$

Section 8.2   Introduction to Functions

Key Concepts

Given a relation in x and y, we say "y is a **function** of x" if, for each element x in the domain, there is exactly one value of y in the range.

Note: This means that no two ordered pairs may have the same first coordinate and different second coordinates.

The Vertical Line Test for Functions

Consider a relation defined by a set of points (x, y) in a rectangular coordinate system. The graph defines y as a function of x if no vertical line intersects the graph in more than one point.

Examples

Example 1

Function $\{(1, 3), (2, 5), (6, 3)\}$

Not a function $\{(1, 3), (2, 5), (1, 4)\}$

Example 2

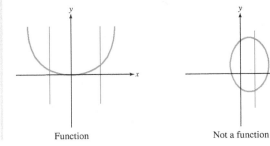

Function   Not a function

616 **Chapter 8** Relations and Functions

Function Notation

$f(x)$ is the value of the function f at x.

The domain of a function defined by $y = f(x)$ is the set of x values that when substituted into the function produce a real number. In particular,

- Exclude values of x that make the denominator of a fraction zero.
- Exclude values of x that make the expression within a square root negative.

Example 3

Given $f(x) = -3x^2 + 5x$, find $f(-2)$.

$$f(-2) = -3(-2)^2 + 5(-2)$$
$$= -12 - 10$$
$$= -22$$

Example 4

Find the domain.

1. $f(x) = \dfrac{x+4}{x-5}$; Domain: $(-\infty, 5) \cup (5, \infty)$

2. $f(x) = \sqrt{x-3}$; Domain: $[3, \infty)$

3. $f(x) = 3x^2 - 5$; Domain: $(-\infty, \infty)$

Section 8.3 Graphs of Functions

Key Concepts

A function defined by $f(x) = mx + b$ $(m \neq 0)$ is a **linear function**. Its graph is a line with slope m and y-intercept $(0, b)$.

A function defined by $f(x) = k$ is a **constant function**. Its graph is a horizontal line.

A function defined by $f(x) = ax^2 + bx + c$ $(a \neq 0)$ is a **quadratic function**. Its graph is a **parabola**.

Examples

Example 1

$f(x) = 2x - 3$ $\qquad\qquad$ $f(x) = 3$

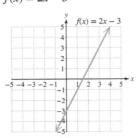
Linear function

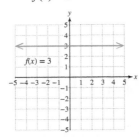
Constant function

Graphs of basic functions:

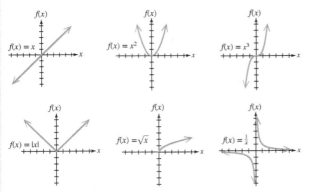

The x-intercepts of a function are determined by finding the real solutions to the equation $f(x) = 0$.

The y-intercept of a function is at $f(0)$.

Example 2

Find the x- and y-intercepts for the function pictured.

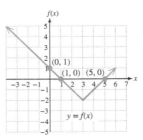

$f(x) = 0$, when $x = 1$ and $x = 5$.
The x-intercepts are $(1, 0)$ and $(5, 0)$.

$f(0) = 1$. The y-intercept is $(0, 1)$.

Section 8.4   Algebra of Functions and Composition

Key Concepts

The Algebra of Functions

Given two functions f and g, the functions

$f + g, f - g, f \cdot g$, and $\dfrac{f}{g}$ are defined as

$(f + g)(x) = f(x) + g(x)$

$(f - g)(x) = f(x) - g(x)$

$(f \cdot g)(x) = f(x) \cdot g(x)$

$\left(\dfrac{f}{g}\right)(x) = \dfrac{f(x)}{g(x)}$ provided $g(x) \neq 0$

Composition of Functions

The **composition** of f and g, denoted $f \circ g$, is defined by the rule

$(f \circ g)(x) = f(g(x))$ provided that $g(x)$ is in the domain of f

Examples

Example 1

Let $g(x) = 5x + 1$ and $h(x) = x^3$. Find:

1. $(g + h)(3) = g(3) + h(3) = 16 + 27 = 43$

2. $(g \cdot h)(-1) = g(-1) \cdot h(-1) = (-4) \cdot (-1) = 4$

3. $(g - h)(x) = 5x + 1 - x^3$

4. $\left(\dfrac{g}{h}\right)(x) = \dfrac{5x + 1}{x^3}, x \neq 0$

Example 2

Find $(f \circ g)(x)$ given the functions defined by $f(x) = 4x + 3$ and $g(x) = 7x$.

$(f \circ g)(x) = f(g(x))$

$\qquad\qquad = f(7x)$

$\qquad\qquad = 4(7x) + 3$

$\qquad\qquad = 28x + 3$

Section 8.5   Variation

Key Concepts

Direct Variation

$\left.\begin{array}{l} y \text{ varies directly as } x. \\ y \text{ is directly proportional to } x. \end{array}\right\}$ $y = kx$

Inverse Variation

$\left.\begin{array}{l} y \text{ varies inversely as } x. \\ y \text{ is inversely proportional to } x. \end{array}\right\}$ $y = \dfrac{k}{x}$

Examples

Example 1

t varies directly as the square root of x.

$t = k\sqrt{x}$

Example 2

W is inversely proportional to the cube of x.

$W = \dfrac{k}{x^3}$

Joint Variation

y varies jointly as w and z.
y is jointly proportional to w and z. $\left.\right\}$ $y = kwz$

Steps to Find a Variation Model

1. Write a general variation model that relates the variables given in the problem. Let k represent the constant of variation.
2. Solve for k by substituting known values of the variables into the model from step 1.
3. Substitute the value of k into the original variation model from step 1.

Example 3

y is jointly proportional to x and to the square of z.

$y = kxz^2$

Example 4

C varies directly as the square root of d and inversely as t. If $C = 12$ when d is 9 and t is 6, find C if d is 16 and t is 12.

Step 1. $C = \dfrac{k\sqrt{d}}{t}$

Step 2. $12 = \dfrac{k\sqrt{9}}{6} \Rightarrow 12 = \dfrac{k \cdot 3}{6} \Rightarrow k = 24$

Step 3. $C = \dfrac{24\sqrt{d}}{t} \Rightarrow C = \dfrac{24\sqrt{16}}{12} \Rightarrow C = 8$

Chapter 8   Review Exercises

Section 8.1

For Exercises 1–4, find the domain and range.

1. $\left\{ \left(\frac{1}{3}, 10 \right), \left(6, -\frac{1}{2} \right), \left(\frac{1}{4}, 4 \right), \left(7, \frac{2}{5} \right) \right\}$

2.

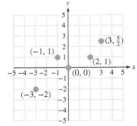

3.

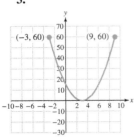

4.

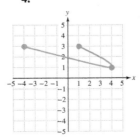

Section 8.2

5. Sketch a relation that is *not* a function. (Answers may vary.)

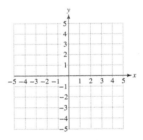

6. Sketch a relation that *is* a function. (Answers may vary.)

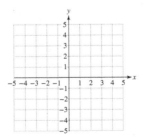

For Exercises 7–12:

a. Determine whether the relation defines y as a function of x.

b. Find the domain.

c. Find the range.

7.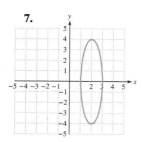

8.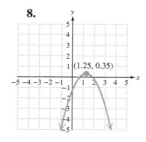

9. $\{(1, 3), (2, 3), (3, 3), (4, 3)\}$

10. $\{(0, 2), (0, 3), (4, 4), (0, 5)\}$

11.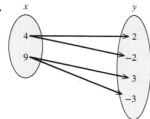

12.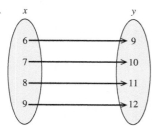

For Exercises 13–20, find the function values given $f(x) = 6x^2 - 4$.

13. $f(0)$ **14.** $f(1)$

15. $f(-1)$ **16.** $f(t)$

17. $f(b)$ **18.** $f(\pi)$

19. $f(a)$ **20.** $f(-2)$

For Exercises 21–24, write the domain of each function in interval notation.

21. $g(x) = 7x^3 + 1$ **22.** $h(x) = \dfrac{x + 10}{x - 11}$

23. $k(x) = \sqrt{x - 8}$ **24.** $w(x) = \sqrt{x + 2}$

25. Anita is a waitress and makes \$12.50 per hour plus tips. Her tips average \$5 per table. In one 8-hr shift, Anita's total pay $p(x)$ can be described by $p(x) = 100 + 5x$, where x represents the number of tables she waits on. Determine how much Anita will earn if she waits on

a. 10 tables   b. 15 tables   c. 20 tables

Section 8.3

For Exercises 26–31, sketch the functions from memory.

26. $h(x) = x$ **27.** $f(x) = x^2$

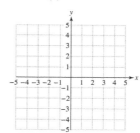   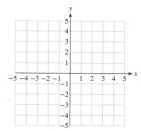

28. $g(x) = x^3$ **29.** $w(x) = |x|$

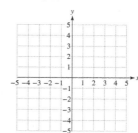   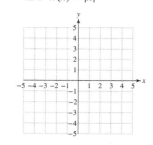

30. $s(x) = \sqrt{x}$ **31.** $r(x) = \dfrac{1}{x}$

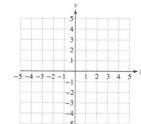   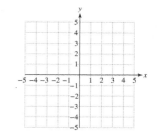

For Exercises 32–33, sketch the functions.

32. $q(x) = 3$

33. $k(x) = 2x + 1$

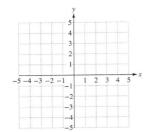 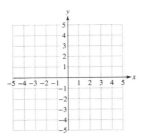

34. Given: $s(x) = (x - 2)^2$

    a. Find $s(4)$, $s(-3)$, $s(2)$, $s(1)$, and $s(0)$.

    b. What is the domain of s?

35. Given: $r(x) = 2\sqrt{x - 4}$

    a. Find $r(2)$, $r(4)$, $r(5)$, and $r(8)$.

    b. What is the domain of r?

36. Given: $h(x) = \dfrac{3}{x - 3}$

    a. Find $h(-3)$, $h(0)$, $h(2)$, and $h(5)$.

    b. What is the domain of h?

37. Given: $k(x) = -|x + 3|$

    a. Find $k(-5)$, $k(-4)$, $k(-3)$, and $k(2)$.

    b. What is the domain of k?

For Exercises 38–39, find the x- and y-intercepts.

38. $p(x) = 4x - 7$

39. $q(x) = -2x + 9$

 40. The function defined by $b(t) = 1.64t + 28.3$ represents the per capita consumption of bottled water in the United States since 2010. The values of $b(t)$ are measured in gallons, and $t = 0$ corresponds to the year 2010. (*Source:* U.S. Department of Agriculture)

    a. Evaluate $b(0)$ and $b(5)$ and interpret the results in the context of this problem.

    b. Determine the slope and interpret its meaning in the context of this problem.

For Exercises 41–46, refer to the graph.

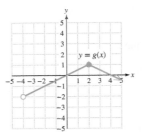

41. Find $g(-2)$.

42. Find $g(4)$.

43. For what value(s) of x is $g(x) = 0$?

44. For what value(s) of x is $g(x) = 4$?

45. Write the domain of g.

46. Write the range of g.

Section 8.4

For Exercises 47–54, refer to the functions defined here.

$$f(x) = x - 7 \qquad g(x) = -2x^3 - 8x$$

$$m(x) = x^2 \qquad n(x) = \frac{1}{x - 2}$$

Find the indicated functions.

47. $(f - g)(x)$

48. $(f + g)(x)$

49. $(f \cdot n)(x)$

50. $(f \cdot m)(x)$

51. $\left(\dfrac{f}{g}\right)(x)$

52. $\left(\dfrac{g}{f}\right)(x)$

53. $(m \circ f)(x)$

54. $(n \circ f)(x)$

For Exercises 55–58, refer to the functions defined for Exercises 47–54. Find the function values, if possible.

55. $(m \circ g)(-1)$

56. $(n \circ g)(-1)$

57. $(f \circ g)(4)$

58. $(g \circ f)(8)$

59. Given: $f(x) = 2x + 1$ and $g(x) = x^2$

    a. Find $(g \circ f)(x)$.

    b. Find $(f \circ g)(x)$.

    c. Based on your answers to part (a), is $f \circ g$ equal to $g \circ f$?

For Exercises 60–65, refer to the graph. Approximate the function values, if possible.

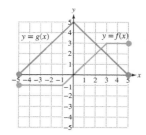

60. $\left(\dfrac{f}{g}\right)(1)$

61. $(f \cdot g)(-2)$

62. $(f + g)(-4)$

63. $(f - g)(2)$

64. $(g \circ f)(-3)$

65. $(f \circ g)(4)$

Section 8.5

66. The force F applied to a spring varies directly with the distance d that the spring is stretched.

   a. Write a variation model using k as the constant of variation.

   b. When 6 lb of force is applied, the spring stretches 2 ft. Find k.

   c. How much force is required to stretch the spring 4.2 ft?

67. Suppose y varies inversely with the cube of x, and $y = 9$ when $x = 2$. Find y when $x = 3$.

68. Suppose y varies jointly with x and the square root of z, and $y = 3$ when $x = 3$ and $z = 4$. Find y when $x = 8$ and $z = 9$.

69. The distance, d, that one can see to the horizon varies directly as the square root of the height above sea level. If a person 25 m above sea level can see 30 km, how far can a person see if she is 64 m above sea level?

© Royalty Free/Corbis RF

Chapter 8   Test

For Exercises 1–2, **a.** determine if the relation defines y as a function of x, **b.** identify the domain, and **c.** identify the range.

1.

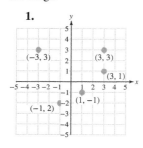

2.

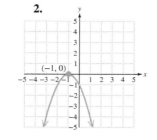

3. Explain how to find the x- and y-intercepts of the graph defined by $y = f(x)$.

For Exercises 4–7, graph the functions.

4. $f(x) = -3x - 1$

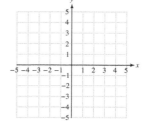

5. $k(x) = -2$

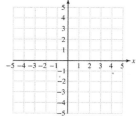

6. $p(x) = x^2$

7. $w(x) = |x|$

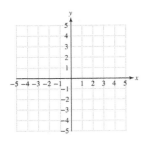

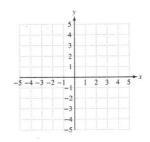

For Exercises 8–10, write the domain in interval notation.

8. $f(x) = \dfrac{x-5}{x+7}$

9. $f(x) = \sqrt{x+7}$

10. $h(x) = (x+7)(x-5)$

11. Given: $r(x) = x^2 - 2x + 1$

   a. Find $r(-2)$, $r(0)$, and $r(3)$.

   b. What is the domain of r?

 12. The function defined by $s(t) = -0.008t + 0.96$ approximates the per capita consumption of milk per day in the United States, t years after the study began. The values of $s(t)$ are measured in cups. (*Source:* U.S. Department of Agriculture) Evaluate $s(0)$ and $s(20)$ and interpret the results in the context of this problem.

For Exercises 13–20, refer to the graph.

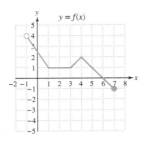

13. Find $f(1)$.

14. Find $f(4)$.

15. Write the domain of f.

16. Write the range of f.

17. Answer true or false. The value $y = 5$ is in the range of f.

18. Find the x-intercept.

19. For what value(s) of x is $f(x) = 0$?

20. For what value(s) of x is $f(x) = 1$?

For Exercises 21–24, determine if the function is constant, linear, quadratic, or none of these.

21. $f(x) = -3x^2$

22. $g(x) = -3x$

23. $h(x) = -3$

24. $k(x) = -\dfrac{3}{x}$

25. Find the x- and y-intercepts for $f(x) = \dfrac{3}{4}x + 9$.

For Exercises 26–34, refer to functions f, g, and h.

$$f(x) = x - 4 \qquad g(x) = x^2 + 2 \qquad h(x) = \dfrac{1}{x}$$

Find the indicated functions or function values.

26. $\left(\dfrac{f}{g}\right)(x)$

27. $(h \cdot g)(x)$

28. $(g \circ f)(x)$

29. $(h \circ f)(x)$

30. $(f - g)(7)$

31. $(h + f)(2)$

32. $(h \circ g)(4)$

33. $(g \circ f)(0)$

34. $\left(\dfrac{g}{f}\right)(x)$

35. The amount of medication prescribed for a patient varies directly as the patient's weight. If a 160-lb person is prescribed 6 mL of a medicine, how much medicine would be prescribed for a 220-lb person?

36. The number of drinks sold at a concession stand varies inversely as price. If the price is set at $1.25 per drink, then 400 drinks are sold. If the price is set at $2.50 per drink, then how many drinks are sold?

Chapters 1–8   Cumulative Review Exercises

For Exercises 1–2, simplify the expression.

1. $\dfrac{5 - 2^3 \div 4 + 7}{-1 - 3(4 - 1)}$

2. $4[-3x - 5(y - 2x) + 3] - 7(6y + x)$

For Exercises 3–4, solve the equation.

3. $\dfrac{2x - 3}{6} - \dfrac{x + 1}{4} = -2$

4. $w - (3 + 2w) + 5 = -w - 5$

5. Solve the inequality. $-3x + 2 \le 11$

6. Find the x- and y-intercepts of $3x - 5y = 10$. Then graph the line.

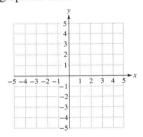

7. Find the slope of the line that passes through the point $(4, -5)$ and $(-6, -3)$.

8. Find the slope of the line $5x - 2y = -10$.

For Exercises 9–10, solve the system of equations.

9. $4x - y = 9$
$\ \ x + 2y = 0$

10. $x - 2y + \ z = 1$
$\ 3x + \ y - 2z = -22$
$\ 4x + \ z = -11$

11. Simplify. $\left(\dfrac{3x^2 y}{9x^3 y^{-2}}\right)^{-2}$

For Exercises 12–13, perform the indicated operations.

12. $(5x^2 - 6x) + (-2x + 7)$

13. $(5x^2 - 6x)(-2x + 7)$

For Exercises 14–15, factor completely.

14. $2x^2 + 7x + 3$

15. $5x^2 - 80$

16. Add. $\dfrac{5}{x - 5} + \dfrac{x}{x + 1}$

17. Divide. $\dfrac{x^2 + 3x}{x - 2} \div \dfrac{x^4 + 3x^3}{x^2 - 4}$

18. Determine the domain and range of the function.

$$\{(2, 4), (-1, 4), (9, 2), (-6, 8)\}$$

19. Determine the domain of $f(x) = \dfrac{x - 5}{x}$.

20. Find $(f \circ g)(x)$ for $f(x) = x^2 - 6$ and $g(x) = x + 1$.

More Equations and Inequalities

More Equations and Inequalities

9

Mathematics in Manufacturing

When a company manufactures a product, the goal is to obtain maximum profit at minimum cost. However, the production process is often limited by certain constraints such as the amount of labor available, the capacity of machinery, and the amount of money available for the company to invest in the process. To determine the optimal production parameters for a manufacturing process, mathematicians use **linear inequalities in two variables** and a process called linear programming.

© zhanglianxun/Getty Images RF

To understand the concept of a linear inequality in two variables, suppose that Morgan tutors algebra and physics and that he has exactly 15 hr of time available. Let x represent the amount of time he spends tutoring algebra, and let y represent the amount of time he spends tutoring physics. Then the inequality $x + y \leq 15$ represents the distribution of his time tutoring. Furthermore, since Morgan cannot tutor for a negative period of time, we also have $x \geq 0$ and $y \geq 0$. The solution set to the three inequalities is the set of points in the first quadrant on and below the line $x + y = 15$. For example, the point (5, 8) means that Morgan tutored 5 hr of algebra and 8 hr of physics.

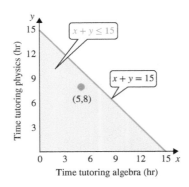

Section 9.1   Compound Inequalities

Concepts

1. Union and Intersection of Sets
2. Solving Compound Inequalities: And
3. Solving Inequalities of the Form $a < x < b$
4. Solving Compound Inequalities: Or
5. Applications of Compound Inequalities

1. Union and Intersection of Sets

We have already learned how to graph linear inequalities and to express the solution sets in interval notation and in set-builder notation. Now we will solve **compound inequalities** that involve the union or intersection of two or more inequalities.

> **Definition of A Union B and A Intersection B**
>
> The **union** of sets A and B, denoted $A \cup B$, is the set of elements that belong to set A or to set B or to both sets A and B.
>
> The **intersection** of two sets A and B, denoted $A \cap B$, is the set of elements common to both A and B.

The concepts of the union and intersection of two sets are illustrated in Figures 9-1 and 9-2.

$A \cup B$
A union B
The elements in A *or* B *or* both

Figure 9-1

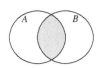

$A \cap B$
A intersection B
The elements in A *and* B

Figure 9-2

Example 1   **Finding the Union and Intersection of Sets**

Given the sets: $A = \{a, b, c, d, e, f\}$ $B = \{a, c, e, g, i, k\}$ $C = \{g, h, i, j, k\}$

Find: **a.** $A \cup B$ **b.** $A \cap B$ **c.** $A \cap C$

Solution:

a. $A \cup B = \{a, b, c, d, e, f, g, i, k\}$ The union of A and B includes all the elements of A along with all the elements of B. Notice that the elements a, c, and e are not listed twice.

b. $A \cap B = \{a, c, e\}$ The intersection of A and B includes only those elements that are common to both sets.

TIP: The empty set is denoted by the symbol $\{\ \}$ or by the symbol $\emptyset$.

c. $A \cap C = \{\ \}$ (the empty set)   Because A and C share no common elements, the intersection of A and C is the empty set (also called the null set).

Skill Practice Given: $A = \{r, s, t, u, v, w\}$ $B = \{s, v, w, y, z\}$ $C = \{x, y, z\}$

Find: **1.** $B \cup C$ **2.** $A \cap B$ **3.** $A \cap C$

Answers

1. $\{s, v, w, x, y, z\}$ **2.** $\{s, v, w\}$ **3.** $\{\ \}$

| Example 2 | **Finding the Union and Intersection of Sets** |

Given the sets: $A = \{x \mid x < 3\}$ $B = \{x \mid x \geq -2\}$ $C = \{x \mid x \geq 5\}$

Graph the following sets. Then express each set in interval notation.

a. $A \cap B$ **b.** $A \cup C$

Solution:

It is helpful to visualize the graphs of individual sets on the number line before taking the union or intersection.

a. Graph of $A = \{x \mid x < 3\}$

Graph of $B = \{x \mid x \geq -2\}$

Graph of $A \cap B$ (the "overlap")

Interval notation: $[-2, 3)$

Note that the set $A \cap B$ represents the real numbers greater than or equal to -2 and less than 3. This relationship can be written more concisely as a compound inequality: $-2 \leq x < 3$. We can interpret this inequality as "x is between -2 and 3, including $x = -2$."

b. Graph of $A = \{x \mid x < 3\}$

Graph of $C = \{x \mid x \geq 5\}$

Graph of $A \cup C$

Interval notation: $(-\infty, 3) \cup [5, \infty)$

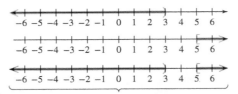

$A \cup C$ includes all elements from set A along with the elements from set C.

Skill Practice Given the sets: $A = \{x \mid x \geq -1\}$, $B = \{x \mid x < 4\}$, and $C = \{x \mid x \geq 9\}$, determine the union or intersection and express the answer in interval notation.

4. $A \cap B$ **5.** $B \cup C$

In Example 3, we find the union and intersection of sets expressed in interval notation.

| Example 3 | **Finding the Union and Intersection of Two Intervals** |

Find the union or intersection as indicated. Write the answer in interval notation.

a. $(-\infty, -2) \cup [-4, 3)$ **b.** $(-\infty, -2) \cap [-4, 3)$

Solution:

a. $(-\infty, -2) \cup [-4, 3)$ To find the union, graph each interval separately. The union is the collection of real numbers that lie in the first interval, the second interval, or both intervals.

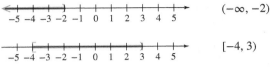

$(-\infty, -2)$

$[-4, 3)$

The union is $(-\infty, 3)$.

The union consists of all real numbers in the red interval along with the real numbers in the blue interval: $(-\infty, 3)$

b. $(-\infty, -2) \cap [-4, 3)$

$(-\infty, -2)$

$[-4, 3)$

The intersection is the "overlap" of the two intervals: $[-4, -2)$.

The intersection is $[-4, -2)$.

Skill Practice Find the union or intersection. Write the answer in interval notation.

6. $(-\infty, -5] \cup (-7, 0)$ **7.** $(-\infty, -5] \cap (-7, 0)$

2. Solving Compound Inequalities: And

The solution to two inequalities joined by the word *and* is the intersection of their solution sets. For example, to play in a golf tournament for juniors, a child's age x must be at least 8 yr and not more than 16 yr. This is translated as $x \geq 8$ and $x \leq 16$. The word "and" joins the two inequalities and implies that we want the intersection of the individual solution sets.

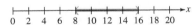

> **Solving a Compound Inequality: And**
> **Step 1**   Solve and graph each inequality separately.
> **Step 2**   If the inequalities are joined by the word *and*, find the intersection of the two solution sets.
> **Step 3**   Express the solution set in interval notation or in set-builder notation.

As you work through the examples in this section, remember that multiplying or dividing an inequality by a negative factor reverses the direction of the inequality sign.

Example 4   Solving a Compound Inequality: And

Solve the compound inequality.

$$-2x < 6 \quad \text{and} \quad x + 5 \leq 7$$

Solution:

$-2x < 6$	and	$x + 5 \leq 7$	Solve each inequality separately.
$\dfrac{-2x}{-2} > \dfrac{6}{-2}$	and	$x \leq 2$	Reverse the first inequality sign.
$x > -3$	and	$x \leq 2$	

Answers
6. $(-\infty, 0)$ **7.** $(-7, -5]$

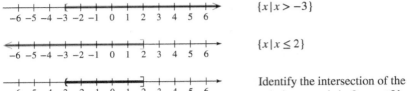

The solution is $\{x \mid -3 < x \le 2\}$, or equivalently in interval notation, $(-3, 2]$.

Skill Practice   Solve the compound inequality.

8. $5x + 2 \ge -8$ and $-4x > -24$

Example 5   **Solving a Compound Inequality: And**

Solve the compound inequality.

$$4.4a + 3.1 < -12.3 \quad \text{and} \quad -2.8a + 9.1 < -6.3$$

Solution:

$$4.4a + 3.1 < -12.3 \quad \text{and} \quad -2.8a + 9.1 < -6.3$$

$$4.4a < -15.4 \quad \text{and} \quad -2.8a < -15.4 \qquad \text{Solve each inequality separately.}$$

$$\frac{4.4a}{4.4} < \frac{-15.4}{4.4} \quad \text{and} \quad \frac{-2.8a}{-2.8} > \frac{-15.4}{-2.8} \qquad \text{Reverse the second inequality sign.}$$

$$a < -3.5 \quad \text{and} \quad a > 5.5$$

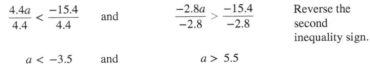

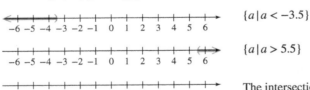

The intersection of the solution sets is the empty set: { }

There are no real numbers that are simultaneously less than -3.5 and greater than 5.5. There is no solution.

The solution set is { }.

Skill Practice   Solve the compound inequality.

9. $3.2y - 2.4 > 16.8$ and $-4.1y \ge 8.2$

630 Chapter 9 More Equations and Inequalities

| Example 6 | **Solving a Compound Inequality: And** |

Solve the compound inequality.

$$-\frac{2}{3}x \le 6 \quad \text{and} \quad -\frac{1}{2}x < 1$$

Solution:

$$-\frac{2}{3}x \le 6 \qquad \text{and} \qquad -\frac{1}{2}x < 1$$

$$-\frac{3}{2}\left(-\frac{2}{3}x\right) \ge -\frac{3}{2}(6) \quad \text{and} \quad -2\left(-\frac{1}{2}x\right) > -2(1) \qquad \begin{array}{l}\text{Solve each}\\\text{inequality}\\\text{separately.}\end{array}$$

$$x \ge -9 \qquad \text{and} \qquad x > -2$$

$\{x \mid x \ge -9\}$

$\{x \mid x > -2\}$

Identify the intersection
of the solution sets:
$\{x \mid x > -2\}$

The solution set is $\{x \mid x > -2\}$, or in interval notation, $(-2, \infty)$.

Skill Practice Solve the compound inequality.

10. $-\frac{1}{4}z < \frac{5}{8}$ and $\frac{1}{2}z + 1 \ge 3$

---

3. Solving Inequalities of the Form $a < x < b$

An inequality of the form $a < x < b$ is a type of compound inequality, one that defines two simultaneous conditions on x.

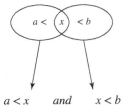

$$a < x \qquad and \qquad x < b$$

The solution set to the compound inequality $a < x < b$ is the *intersection* of the solution sets to the inequalities $a < x$ and $x < b$.

| Example 7 | **Solving an Inequality of the Form $a < x < b$** |

Solve the inequality. $\quad -4 < 3x + 5 \le 10$

Solution:

$$-4 < 3x + 5 \le 10$$

$$-4 < 3x + 5 \qquad \text{and} \qquad 3x + 5 \le 10 \qquad \begin{array}{l}\text{Set up the intersection of two}\\\text{inequalities.}\end{array}$$

Answer

10. $\{z \mid z \ge 4\}; [4, \infty)$

$-9 < 3x$	and	$3x \le 5$	Solve each inequality.

$$\frac{-9}{3} < \frac{3x}{3} \qquad \text{and} \qquad \frac{3x}{3} \le \frac{5}{3}$$

$$-3 < x \qquad \text{and} \qquad x \le \frac{5}{3} \qquad \text{Recall } -3 < x \text{ is the same as } x > -3.$$

$$-3 < x \le \frac{5}{3} \qquad \text{Identify the intersection of the solution sets.}$$

The solution is $\{x \mid -3 < x \le \frac{5}{3}\}$, or equivalently in interval notation, $(-3, \frac{5}{3}]$.

Skill Practice Solve the inequality.

11. $-6 \le 2x - 5 < 1$

To solve an inequality of the form $a < x < b$, we can also work with the inequality as a "three-part" inequality and isolate x. This is demonstrated in Example 8.

Example 8   **Solving an Inequality of the Form $a < x < b$**

Solve the inequality. $2 \ge \dfrac{p - 2}{-3} \ge -1$

Solution:

$$2 \ge \frac{p - 2}{-3} \ge -1 \qquad \text{Isolate the variable in the middle part.}$$

$$-3(2) \le -3\left(\frac{p - 2}{-3}\right) \le -3(-1) \qquad \begin{array}{l}\text{Multiply all three parts by } -3. \text{ Remember} \\ \text{to reverse the inequality signs.}\end{array}$$

$$-6 \le p - 2 \le 3 \qquad \text{Simplify.}$$

$$-6 + 2 \le p - 2 + 2 \le 3 + 2 \qquad \text{Add 2 to all three parts to isolate } p.$$

$$-4 \le p \le 5$$

The solution is $\{p \mid -4 \le p \le 5\}$, or equivalently in interval notation $[-4, 5]$.

Skill Practice Solve the inequality.

12. $8 > \dfrac{t + 4}{-2} > -5$

---

4. Solving Compound Inequalities: Or

In Examples 9 and 10, we solve compound inequalities that involve inequalities joined by the word "or." In such a case, the solution to the compound inequality is the union of the solution sets of the individual inequalities.

Answers

11. $\{x \mid -\frac{1}{2} \le x < 3\}$; $[-\frac{1}{2}, 3)$
12. $\{t \mid -20 < t < 6\}$; $(-20, 6)$

For example, a resting heart rate x is potentially abnormal if it is below 50 beats per minute or above 100 beats per minute.

0   10 20 30 40 50 60 70 80 90 100 110 120

Solving a Compound Inequality: Or

Step 1   Solve and graph each inequality separately.

Step 2   If the inequalities are joined by the word *or*, find the union of the two solution sets.

Step 3   Express the solution set in interval notation or in set-builder notation.

Example 9   **Solving a Compound Inequality: Or**

Solve the compound inequality. $-3y - 5 > 4$ or $4 - y \leq 6$

Solution:

$-3y - 5 > 4$	or	$4 - y \leq 6$
$-3y > 9$	or	$-y \leq 2$

Solve each inequality separately.

$$\frac{-3y}{-3} < \frac{9}{-3} \quad \text{or} \quad \frac{-y}{-1} \geq \frac{2}{-1}$$

Reverse the inequality signs.

$$y < -3 \quad \text{or} \quad y \geq -2$$

$\{y \mid y < -3\}$

$\{y \mid y \geq -2\}$

Identify the union of the solution sets:
$\{y \mid y < -3 \text{ or } y \geq -2\}$

The solution is $\{y \mid y < -3 \text{ or } y \geq -2\}$ or, equivalently in interval notation, $(-\infty, -3) \cup [-2, \infty)$.

Skill Practice   Solve the compound inequality.

13. $-10t - 8 \geq 12$ or $3t - 6 > 3$

Answer

13. $\{t \mid t \leq -2 \text{ or } t > 3\}$;
     $(-\infty, -2] \cup (3, \infty)$

Example 10	**Solving a Compound Inequality: Or**

Solve the compound inequality. $4x + 3 < 16$ or $-2x < 3$

Solution:

$4x + 3 < 16$ or $-2x < 3$

$\qquad 4x < 13$ or $x > -\dfrac{3}{2}$ Solve each inequality separately.

$\qquad x < \dfrac{13}{4}$ or $x > -\dfrac{3}{2}$

$\{x \mid x < \frac{13}{4}\}$

$\{x \mid x > -\frac{3}{2}\}$

Identify the union of the solution sets.

The union of the solution sets is $\{x \mid x$ is a real number$\}$, or equivalently, $(-\infty, \infty)$.

Skill Practice Solve the compound inequality.

14. $x - 7 > -2$ or $-6x > -48$

5. Applications of Compound Inequalities

Compound inequalities are used in many applications, as shown in Examples 11 and 12.

Example 11	**Translating Compound Inequalities**

The normal level of thyroid-stimulating hormone (TSH) for adults ranges from 0.4 to 4.8 microunits per milliliter (μU/mL), inclusive. Let x represent the amount of TSH measured in microunits per milliliter.

a. Write an inequality representing the normal range of TSH.

b. Write a compound inequality representing abnormal TSH levels.

Solution:

a. $0.4 \leq x \leq 4.8$ **b.** $x < 0.4$ or $x > 4.8$

Skill Practice The length of a normal human pregnancy, w, is from 37 to 41 weeks, inclusive.

15. Write an inequality representing the normal length of a pregnancy.

16. Write a compound inequality representing an abnormal length for a pregnancy.

Answers

14. $\{x \mid x$ is a real number$\}$; $(-\infty, \infty)$
15. $37 \leq w \leq 41$
16. $w < 37$ or $w > 41$

> **TIP:**
> - In mathematics, the word "between" means strictly between two values. That is, the endpoints are *excluded*.
>   <u>Example</u>: x is between 4 and 10 $\Rightarrow$ (4, 10).
>
> - If the word "inclusive" is added to the statement, then we *include* the endpoints.
>   <u>Example</u>: x is between 4 and 10, inclusive $\Rightarrow$ [4, 10].

| **Example 12** | **Translating and Solving a Compound Inequality** |

The sum of a number and 4 is between -5 and 12. Find all such numbers.

Solution:

Let x represent a number.

$$-5 < x + 4 < 12 \qquad \text{Translate the inequality.}$$

$$-5 - 4 < x + 4 - 4 < 12 - 4 \qquad \text{Subtract 4 from all three parts of the inequality.}$$

$$-9 < x < 8$$

The number may be any real number between -9 and 8: $\{x \,|\, -9 < x < 8\}$.

Skill Practice

17. The sum of twice a number and 11 is between 21 and 31. Find all such numbers.

Answer

17. Any real number between 5 and 10: $\{x \,|\, 5 < x < 10\}$

Section 9.1   Practice Exercises

Vocabulary and Key Concepts

1. a. The _____ of two sets A and B, denoted by _____, is the set of elements that belong to A or B or both A and B.

b. The _____ of two sets A and B, denoted by _____, is the set of elements common to both A and B.

c. The solution set to the compound inequality $x < c$ and $x > d$ is the (union/intersection) of the solution sets of the individual inequalities.

d. The compound inequality $a < x$ and $x < b$ can be written as the three-part inequality _____.

e. The solution set to the compound inequality $x < a$ or $x > b$ is the (union/intersection) of the solution sets of the individual inequalities.

Review Exercises

For Exercises 2–6, solve the linear inequality. Write the solution in interval notation.

2. $-6u + 8 > 2$

3. $2 - 3z \geq -4$

4. $-12 \leq \frac{3}{4}p$

5. $5 > \frac{1}{3}w$

6. $-3x + 5 < -2x + 1$

Concept 1: Union and Intersection of Sets

7. Given $M = \{-3, -1, 1, 3, 5\}$ and
$N = \{-4, -3, -2, -1, 0\}$, **(See Example 1.)**

List the elements of the following sets.

    a. $M \cap N$ **b.** $M \cup N$

8. Given $P = \{a, b, c, d, e, f, g, h, i\}$ and
$Q = \{a, e, i, o, u\}$,

List the elements of the following sets.

    a. $P \cap Q$ **b.** $P \cup Q$

For Exercises 9–20, refer to the sets A, B, C, and D. Determine the union or intersection as indicated. Express the answer in interval notation, if possible. **(See Example 2.)**

$$A = \{x \,|\, x < -4\}, \qquad B = \{x \,|\, x > 2\}, \qquad C = \{x \,|\, x \geq -7\}, \qquad D = \{x \,|\, 0 \leq x < 5\}$$

9. $A \cap C$

10. $B \cap C$

11. $A \cup B$

12. $A \cup D$

13. $A \cap B$

14. $A \cap D$

15. $B \cup C$

16. $B \cup D$

17. $C \cap D$

18. $B \cap D$

19. $C \cup D$

20. $A \cup C$

For Exercises 21–26, find the intersection and union of sets as indicated. Write the answers in interval notation.
(See Example 3.)

21. **a.** $(-2, 5) \cap [-1, \infty)$

    b. $(-2, 5) \cup [-1, \infty)$

22. **a.** $(-\infty, 4) \cap [-1, 5)$

    b. $(-\infty, 4) \cup [-1, 5)$

23. **a.** $\left(-\dfrac{5}{2}, 3\right) \cap \left(-1, \dfrac{9}{2}\right)$

    b. $\left(-\dfrac{5}{2}, 3\right) \cup \left(-1, \dfrac{9}{2}\right)$

24. **a.** $(-3.4, 1.6) \cap (-2.2, 4.1)$

    b. $(-3.4, 1.6) \cup (-2.2, 4.1)$

25. **a.** $(-4, 5] \cap (0, 2]$

    b. $(-4, 5] \cup (0, 2]$

26. **a.** $[-1, 5) \cap (0, 3)$

    b. $[-1, 5) \cup (0, 3)$

Concept 2: Solving Compound Inequalities: And

For Exercises 27–36, solve the compound inequality and graph the solution. Write the answer in interval notation. **(See Examples 4–6.)**

27. $y - 7 \geq -9$ and $y + 2 \leq 5$

28. $a + 6 > -2$ and $5a < 30$

29. $2t + 7 < 19$ and $5t + 13 > 28$

30. $5p + 2p \geq -21$ and $-9p + 3p \geq -24$

31. $2.1k - 1.1 \leq 0.6k + 1.9$ and
$0.3k - 1.1 < -0.1k + 0.9$

32. $0.6w + 0.1 > 0.3w - 1.1$ and
$2.3w + 1.5 \geq 0.3w + 6.5$

33. $\dfrac{2}{3}(2p - 1) \geq 10$ and $\dfrac{4}{5}(3p + 4) \geq 20$

34. $\dfrac{5}{2}(a + 2) < -6$ and $\dfrac{3}{4}(a - 2) < 1$

35. $-2 < -x - 12$ and $-14 < 5(x - 3) + 6x$

36. $-8 \geq -3y - 2$ and $3(y - 7) + 16 > 4y$

636 **Chapter 9** More Equations and Inequalities

Concept 3: Solving Inequalities of the Form $a < x < b$

37. Write $-4 \le t < \frac{3}{4}$ as two separate inequalities.

38. Write $-2.8 < y \le 15$ as two separate inequalities.

39. Explain why $6 < x < 2$ has no solution.

40. Explain why $4 < t < 1$ has no solution.

41. Explain why $-5 > y > -2$ has no solution.

42. Explain why $-3 > w > -1$ has no solution.

For Exercises 43–54, solve the compound inequality and graph the solution set. Write the answer in interval notation.
(See Examples 7–8.)

43. $0 \le 2b - 5 < 9$

44. $-6 < 3k - 9 \le 0$

45. $-1 < \frac{a}{6} \le 1$

46. $-3 \le \frac{1}{2}x < 0$

47. $-\frac{2}{3} < \frac{y-4}{-6} < \frac{1}{3}$

48. $\frac{1}{3} > \frac{t-4}{-3} > -2$

49. $5 \le -3x - 2 \le 8$

50. $-1 < -2x + 4 \le 5$

51. $12 > 6x + 3 \ge 0$

52. $-4 \ge 2x - 5 > -7$

53. $-0.2 < 2.6 + 7t < 4$

54. $-1.5 < 0.1x \le 8.1$

Concept 4: Solving Compound Inequalities: Or

For Exercises 55–64, solve the compound inequality and graph the solution set. Write the answer in interval notation.
(See Examples 9–10.)

55. $2y - 1 \ge 3$ or $y < -2$

56. $x < 0$ or $3x + 1 \ge 7$

57. $1 > 6z - 8$ or $8z - 6 \le 10$

58. $22 > 4t - 10$ or $7 > 2t - 5$

59. $5(x - 1) \ge -5$ or $5 - x \le 11$

60. $-p + 7 \ge 10$ or $3(p - 1) \le 12$

61. $\frac{5}{3}v \le 5$ or $-v - 6 < 1$

62. $\frac{3}{8}u + 1 > 0$ or $-2u \ge -4$

63. $0.5w + 5 < 2.5w - 4$ or $0.3w \le -0.1w - 1.6$

64. $1.25a + 3 \le 0.5a - 6$ or $2.5a - 1 \ge 9 - 1.5a$

Mixed Exercises

For Exercises 65–74, solve the compound inequality. Write the answer in interval notation.

65. a. $3x - 5 < 19$ and $-2x + 3 < 23$

66. a. $0.5(6x + 8) > 0.8x - 7$ and $4(x + 1) < 7.2$

b. $3x - 5 < 19$ or $-2x + 3 < 23$

b. $0.5(6x + 8) > 0.8x - 7$ or $4(x + 1) < 7.2$

67. a. $8x - 4 \ge 6.4$ or $0.3(x + 6) \le -0.6$

68. a. $-2r + 4 \le -8$ or $3r + 5 \le 8$

b. $8x - 4 \ge 6.4$ and $0.3(x + 6) \le -0.6$

b. $-2r + 4 \le -8$ and $3r + 5 \le 8$

69. $-4 \leq \dfrac{2 - 4x}{3} < 8$

70. $-1 < \dfrac{3 - x}{2} \leq 0$

71. $5 \geq -4(t - 3) + 3t$ or
$6 < 12t + 8(4 - t)$

72. $3 > -(w - 3) + 4w$ or
$-5 \geq -3(w - 5) + 6w$

73. $\dfrac{-x + 3}{2} > \dfrac{4 + x}{5}$ or $\dfrac{1 - x}{4} > \dfrac{2 - x}{3}$

74. $\dfrac{y - 7}{-3} < \dfrac{1}{4}$ or $\dfrac{y + 1}{-2} > -\dfrac{1}{3}$

Concept 5: Applications of Compound Inequalities

75. The normal number of white blood cells for human blood is between 4800 and 10,800 cells per cubic millimeter, inclusive. Let x represent the number of white blood cells per cubic millimeter. **(See Example 11.)**

   a. Write an inequality representing the normal range of white blood cells per cubic millimeter.

   b. Write a compound inequality representing abnormal levels of white blood cells per cubic millimeter.

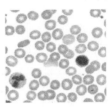

© McGraw-Hill Education/
Dr. Al Telser

76. Normal hemoglobin levels in human blood for adult males are between 13 and 16 grams per deciliter (g/dL), inclusive. Let x represent the level of hemoglobin measured in grams per deciliter.

   a. Write an inequality representing normal hemoglobin levels for adult males.

   b. Write a compound inequality representing abnormal levels of hemoglobin for adult males.

77. A polling company estimates that a certain candidate running for office will receive between 44% and 48% of the votes. Let x represent the percentage of votes for this candidate.

   a. Write a strict inequality representing the expected percentage of votes for this candidate.

   b. Write a compound inequality representing the percentage of votes that would fall outside the polling company's prediction.

78. A machine is calibrated to cut a piece of wood between 2.4 in. thick and 2.6 in. thick. Let x represent the thickness of the wood after it is cut.

   a. Write a strict inequality representing the expected range of thickness of the wood after it has been cut.

   b. Write a compound inequality representing the thickness of wood that would fall outside the normal range for this machine.

79. Twice a number is between -3 and 12. Find all such numbers. **(See Example 12.)**

80. The difference of a number and 6 is between 0 and 8. Find all such numbers.

81. One plus twice a number is either greater than 5 or less than -1. Find all such numbers.

82. One-third of a number is either less than -2 or greater than 5. Find all such numbers.

83. Amy knows from reading her syllabus in intermediate algebra that the average of her chapter tests accounts for 80% (0.8) of her overall course grade. She also knows that the final exam counts as 20% (0.2) of her grade. Suppose that the average of Amy's chapter tests is 92%.

a. Determine the range of grades that she would need on her final exam to get an "A" in the class. (Assume that a grade of "A" is obtained if Amy's overall average is 90% or better.)

b. Determine the range of grades that Amy would need on her final exam to get a "B" in the class. (Assume that a grade of "B" is obtained if Amy's overall average is at least 80% but less than 90%.)

84. Robert knows from reading his syllabus in intermediate algebra that the average of his chapter tests accounts for 60% (0.6) of his overall course grade. He also knows that the final exam counts as 40% (0.4) of his grade. Suppose that the average of Robert's chapter tests is 89%.

a. Determine the range of grades that he would need on his final exam to get an "A" in the class. (Assume that a grade of "A" is obtained if Robert's overall average is 90% or better.)

b. Determine the range of grades that Robert would need on his final exam to get a "B" in the class. (Assume that a grade of "B" is obtained if Robert's overall average is at least 80% but less than 90%.)

85. The average high and low temperatures for Vancouver, British Columbia, in January are 5.6°C and 0°C, respectively. The formula relating Celsius temperatures to Fahrenheit temperatures is given by $C = \frac{5}{9}(F - 32)$. Convert the inequality $0.0° \le C \le 5.6°$ to an equivalent inequality using Fahrenheit temperatures.

86. For a day in July, the temperature in Austin, Texas, ranged from 20°C to 29°C. The formula relating Celsius temperatures to Fahrenheit temperatures is given by $C = \frac{5}{9}(F - 32)$. Convert the inequality $20° \le C \le 29°$ to an equivalent inequality using Fahrenheit temperatures.

© BrandX/Punchstock/
Getty Images RF

Section 9.2 Polynomial and Rational Inequalities

Concepts

1. Solving Quadratic and Polynomial Inequalities
2. Solving Rational Inequalities

1. Solving Quadratic and Polynomial Inequalities

In this section, we will expand our study of solving inequalities.

Quadratic inequalities are inequalities that can be written in one of the following forms:

$$ax^2 + bx + c \geq 0 \qquad ax^2 + bx + c \leq 0$$
$$ax^2 + bx + c > 0 \qquad ax^2 + bx + c < 0 \qquad \text{where } a \neq 0$$

Recall that the graph of a quadratic function defined by $f(x) = ax^2 + bx + c$ is a parabola that opens upward or downward.

- The inequality $ax^2 + bx + c > 0$ is asking "For what values of x is the function positive (above the x-axis)?"
- The inequality $ax^2 + bx + c < 0$ is asking "For what values of x is the function negative (below the x-axis)?"

The graph of a quadratic function can be used to answer these questions.

Example 1 — **Using a Graph to Solve a Quadratic Inequality**

Use the graph of $f(x) = x^2 - 6x + 5$ in Figure 9-3 to solve the inequalities.

a. $x^2 - 6x + 5 < 0$ **b.** $x^2 - 6x + 5 > 0$

Solution:

From Figure 9-3, we see that the graph of $f(x) = x^2 - 6x + 5$ is a parabola opening upward. The function factors as $f(x) = (x - 1)(x - 5)$. The x-intercepts are $(1, 0)$ and $(5, 0)$, and the y-intercept is $(0, 5)$.

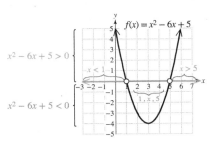

Figure 9-3

a. The solution to $x^2 - 6x + 5 < 0$ is the set of real numbers, x, for which $f(x) < 0$. Graphically, this is the set of all x values corresponding to the points where the parabola is below the x-axis (shown in red).

$$x^2 - 6x + 5 < 0 \quad \text{for } \{x \mid 1 < x < 5\} \text{ or in interval notation, } (1, 5)$$

b. The solution to $x^2 - 6x + 5 > 0$ is the set of real numbers, x, for which $f(x) > 0$. This is the set of x values where the parabola is above the x-axis (shown in blue).

$$x^2 - 6x + 5 > 0 \quad \text{for } \{x \mid x < 1 \text{ or } x > 5\} \quad \text{or} \quad (-\infty, 1) \cup (5, \infty)$$

Skill Practice Refer to the graph of $f(x) = x^2 + 3x - 4$ to solve the inequalities.

1. $x^2 + 3x - 4 > 0$

2. $x^2 + 3x - 4 < 0$

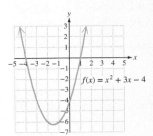

TIP: The inequalities in Example 1 are strict inequalities. Therefore, $x = 1$ and $x = 5$ (where $f(x) = 0$) are not included in the solution set. However, the corresponding inequalities using the symbols $\leq$ and $\geq$ *do* include the values where $f(x) = 0$.

The solution to $x^2 - 6x + 5 \leq 0$ is $\{x \mid 1 \leq x \leq 5\}$ or equivalently, $[1, 5]$.

The solution to $x^2 - 6x + 5 \geq 0$ is $\{x \mid x \leq 1 \text{ or } x \geq 5\}$ or $(-\infty, 1] \cup [5, \infty)$.

Answers

1. $\{x \mid x < -4 \text{ or } x > 1\}$; $(-\infty, -4) \cup (1, \infty)$

2. $\{x \mid -4 < x < 1\}$; $(-4, 1)$

Notice that $x = 1$ and $x = 5$ are the boundaries of the solution set to the inequalities in Example 1. These values are the solutions to the related equation $x^2 - 6x + 5 = 0$.

Definition of Boundary Points

The **boundary points** of an inequality consist of the real solutions to the related equation and the points where the inequality is undefined.

Testing points on intervals bounded by these points is the basis of the **test point method** to solve inequalities.

Solving Inequalities by Using the Test Point Method

Step 1   Find the boundary points of the inequality.

Step 2   Plot the boundary points on the number line. This divides the number line into intervals.

Step 3   Select a test point from each interval and substitute it into the original inequality.

- If a test point makes the original inequality true, then that interval is part of the solution set.

Step 4   Test the boundary points in the original inequality.

- If the original inequality is strict ($<$ or $>$), do not include the boundary points in the solution set.
- If the original inequality is defined using $\leq$ or $\geq$, then include the boundary points that are defined within the inequality.

Note: Any boundary point that makes an expression within the inequality undefined must *always* be excluded from the solution set.

Example 2   **Solving a Quadratic Inequality by Using the Test Point Method**

Solve the inequality by using the test point method. $2x^2 + 5x < 12$

Solution:

$$2x^2 + 5x < 12$$

Step 1:   Find the boundary points. Because polynomials are defined for all values of x, the only boundary points are the real solutions to the related equation.

$$2x^2 + 5x = 12$$

$$2x^2 + 5x - 12 = 0$$

$$(2x - 3)(x + 4) = 0$$

$$x = \frac{3}{2} \qquad x = -4$$

Solve the related equation.

The boundary points are $\frac{3}{2}$ and -4.

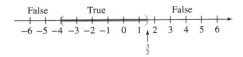

Step 2: Plot the boundary points.

Step 3: Select a test point from each interval.

Test $x = -5$
$$2x^2 + 5x < 12$$
$$2(-5)^2 + 5(-5) \overset{?}{<} 12$$
$$50 - 25 \overset{?}{<} 12$$
$$25 \overset{?}{<} 12 \quad \text{False}$$

Test $x = 0$
$$2x^2 + 5x < 12$$
$$2(0)^2 + 5(0) \overset{?}{<} 12$$
$$0 + 0 \overset{?}{<} 12$$
$$0 \overset{?}{<} 12 \quad \text{True}$$

Test $x = 2$
$$2x^2 + 5x < 12$$
$$2(2)^2 + 5(2) \overset{?}{<} 12$$
$$8 + 10 \overset{?}{<} 12$$
$$18 \overset{?}{<} 12 \quad \text{False}$$

Step 4: Test the boundary points. The strict inequality excludes values of x for which $2x^2 + 5x = 12$. Therefore, the boundary points are *not* included in the solution set.

The solution set is $\{x \mid -4 < x < \frac{3}{2}\}$ or equivalently in interval notation $(-4, \frac{3}{2})$.

Skill Practice Solve the inequality.

3. $x^2 + x > 6$

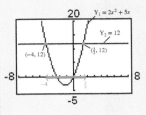

Example 3	**Solving a Polynomial Inequality by Using the Test Point Method**

Solve the inequality by using the test point method. $x(x + 4)^2(x - 4) \geq 0$

Solution:

$$x(x + 4)^2(x - 4) \geq 0$$
$$x(x + 4)^2(x - 4) = 0$$ **Step 1:** Find the boundary points.
$$x = 0 \qquad x = -4 \qquad x = 4$$

Step 2: Plot the boundary points.

Step 3: Select a test point from each interval.

Test $x = -5$: $-5(-5 + 4)^2(-5 - 4) \overset{?}{\geq} 0$ $45 \overset{?}{\geq} 0 \quad$ True

Test $x = -1$: $-1(-1 + 4)^2(-1 - 4) \overset{?}{\geq} 0$ $45 \overset{?}{\geq} 0 \quad$ True

Test $x = 1$: $1(1 + 4)^2(1 - 4) \overset{?}{\geq} 0$ $-75 \overset{?}{\geq} 0 \quad$ False

Test $x = 5$: $5(5 + 4)^2(5 - 4) \overset{?}{\geq} 0$ $405 \overset{?}{\geq} 0 \quad$ True

Answer

3. $(-\infty, -3) \cup (2, \infty)$

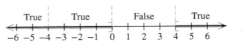

Step 4: The inequality symbol, $\geq$, includes equality. Therefore, include the boundary points in the solution set.

The solution set is $\{x \mid x \leq 0 \text{ and } x \geq 4\}$, or equivalently in interval notation, $(-\infty, 0] \cup [4, \infty)$.

Skill Practice Solve the inequality.

4. $t(t - 5)(t + 2)^2 > 0$

Calculator Connections

Topic: Analyzing a Polynomial Inequality Graphically

Graph $Y_1 = x(x + 4)^2(x - 4)$. Y_1 is positive (above the x-axis) for $\{x \mid x \leq 0 \text{ and } x \geq 4\}$ or equivalently $(-\infty, 0] \cup [4, \infty)$.

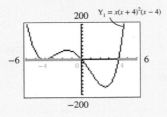

TIP: In Example 3, one side of the inequality is factored, and the other side is zero. For inequalities written in this form, we can use a sign chart to determine the sign of each factor. Then the sign of the product (bottom row) is easily determined.

Sign of x	$-$	$-$	$+$	$+$
Sign of $(x + 4)^2$	$+$	$+$	$+$	$+$
Sign of $(x - 4)$	$-$	$-$	$-$	$+$
Sign of $x(x + 4)^2(x - 4)$	$+$	$+$	$-$	$+$

$$-4 \qquad 0 \qquad 4$$

The solution to the inequality $x(x + 4)^2(x - 4) \geq 0$ includes the intervals for which the product is positive (shown in blue).

The solution is $(-\infty, 0] \cup [4, \infty)$.

2. Solving Rational Inequalities

The test point method can be used to solve rational inequalities. A **rational inequality** is an inequality in which one or more terms is a rational expression. The solution set to a rational inequality must exclude all values of the variable that make the inequality undefined. That is, exclude all values that make the denominator equal to zero for any rational expression in the inequality.

Answer

4. $(-\infty, -2) \cup (-2, 0) \cup (5, \infty)$

| Example 4 | **Solving a Rational Inequality by Using the Test Point Method** |

Solve the inequality. $\dfrac{3}{x-1} > 0$

Solution:

$$\dfrac{3}{x-1} > 0$$

Step 1: Find the boundary points. Note that the inequality is undefined for $x = 1$, so $x = 1$ is a boundary point. To find any other boundary points, solve the related equation.

$$\dfrac{3}{x-1} = 0$$

$$(x-1) \cdot \left(\dfrac{3}{x-1}\right) = (x-1) \cdot 0$$ Clear fractions.

$$3 = 0$$ There is no solution to the related equation.

The only boundary point is $x = 1$.

Step 2: Plot boundary points.

Test $x = 0$:   **Test $x = 2$:**   **Step 3:** Select test points.

$$\dfrac{3}{(0)-1} \overset{?}{>} 0 \qquad\qquad \dfrac{3}{(2)-1} \overset{?}{>} 0$$

$$\dfrac{3}{-1} \overset{?}{>} 0 \ \text{False} \qquad \dfrac{3}{1} > 0 \ \text{True}$$

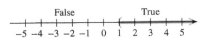

Step 4: The boundary point $x = 1$ cannot be included in the solution set because it is undefined in the original inequality.

The solution is $\{x \mid x > 1\}$ or equivalently in interval notation, $(1, \infty)$.

Skill Practice Solve the inequality.

5. $\dfrac{-5}{y+2} < 0$

TIP: Using a sign chart we see that the quotient of the factors 3 and $(x - 1)$ is positive on the interval $(1, \infty)$.

Therefore, the solution to the inequality $\dfrac{3}{x-1} > 0$ is $(1, \infty)$.

Sign of 3	+	+
Sign of $(x - 1)$	−	+
Sign of $\dfrac{3}{x-1}$	−	+

                                                     1
                                              (undefined)

Answer

5. $(-2, \infty)$

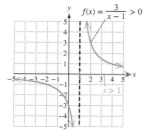

Figure 9-4

The solution to the inequality $\dfrac{3}{x-1} > 0$ can be confirmed from the graph of the related rational function, $f(x) = \dfrac{3}{x-1}$ (see Figure 9-4).

- The graph is above the x-axis where $f(x) = \dfrac{3}{x-1} > 0$ for $x > 1$ (shaded red).
- Also note that $x = 1$ cannot be included in the solution set because 1 is not in the domain of f.

Example 5   **Solving a Rational Inequality by Using the Test Point Method**

Solve the inequality by using the test point method. $\dfrac{x+2}{x-4} \le 3$

Solution:

$$\dfrac{x+2}{x-4} \le 3$$

Step 1: Find the boundary points. Note that the inequality is undefined for $x = 4$. Therefore, $x = 4$ is automatically a boundary point. To find any other boundary points, solve the related equation.

$$\dfrac{x+2}{x-4} = 3$$

$$(x-4)\left(\dfrac{x+2}{x-4}\right) = (x-4)(3) \qquad \text{Clear fractions.}$$

$$x + 2 = 3(x - 4) \qquad \text{Solve for } x.$$

$$x + 2 = 3x - 12$$

$$-2x = -14$$

$$x = 7$$

The solution to the related equation is $x = 7$, and the inequality is undefined for $x = 4$. Therefore, the boundary points are $x = 4$ and $x = 7$.

Step 2: Plot boundary points.

Step 3: Select test points.

Test $x = 0$

$$\dfrac{x+2}{x-4} \le 3$$

$$\dfrac{0+2}{0-4} \overset{?}{\le} 3$$

$$-\dfrac{1}{2} \overset{?}{\le} 3 \quad \text{True}$$

Test $x = 5$

$$\dfrac{x+2}{x-4} \le 3$$

$$\dfrac{5+2}{5-4} \overset{?}{\le} 3$$

$$\dfrac{7}{1} \overset{?}{\le} 3 \quad \text{False}$$

Test $x = 8$

$$\dfrac{x+2}{x-4} \le 3$$

$$\dfrac{8+2}{8-4} \overset{?}{\le} 3$$

$$\dfrac{10}{4} \overset{?}{\le} 3$$

$$\dfrac{5}{2} \overset{?}{\le} 3 \quad \text{True}$$

Test $x = 4$:

$$\frac{x+2}{x-4} \le 3$$

$$\frac{4+2}{4-4} \overset{?}{\le} 3$$

$$\frac{6}{0} \overset{?}{\le} 3 \quad \text{Undefined}$$

Test $x = 7$:

$$\frac{x+2}{x-4} \le 3$$

$$\frac{7+2}{7-4} \overset{?}{\le} 3$$

$$\frac{9}{3} \overset{?}{\le} 3 \quad \text{True}$$

Step 4: Test the boundary points.

The boundary point $x = 4$ cannot be included in the solution set, because it is undefined in the inequality. The boundary point $x = 7$ makes the original inequality true and must be included in the solution set.

The solution is $\{x \mid x < 4 \text{ or } x \ge 7\}$, or equivalently in interval notation, $(-\infty, 4) \cup [7, \infty)$.

Skill Practice Solve the inequality.

6. $\dfrac{x-5}{x+4} \le -1$

Answer

6. $\left(-4, \dfrac{1}{2}\right]$

Section 9.2 Practice Exercises

Vocabulary and Key Concepts

1. a. An inequality of the form $ax^2 + bx + c > 0$ or $ax^2 + bx + c < 0$ is an example of a _____ inequality.

b. The boundary points of an inequality consist of the real _____ to the related equation and the points where the inequality is _____.

c. In solving an inequality by using the _____ _____ method, a point is selected from each interval formed by the boundary points and substituted into the original inequality.

d. If a test point makes the original inequality _____, then that interval is part of the solution set.

e. The inequality $\dfrac{4}{x+7} > 0$ is an example of a _____ inequality.

f. The solution set to a rational inequality must exclude all values that make the denominator equal to _____ for any rational expression in the inequality.

Review Exercises

For Exercises 2–8, solve the compound inequalities. Write the solutions in interval notation.

2. $6x - 10 > 8$ or $8x + 2 < 5$

3. $3(a - 1) + 2 > 0$ or $2a > 5a + 12$

4. $5(k - 2) > -25$ and $7(1 - k) > 7$

5. $2y + 4 \ge 10$ and $5y - 3 \le 13$

6. $0 < 3(x + 1) \le 4$

7. $6 \ge 4 - 2x \ge -2$

8. $-4 > 5 - x > -6$

Concept 1: Solving Quadratic and Polynomial Inequalities

For Exercises 9–12, estimate from the graph the intervals for which the inequality is true. **(See Example 1.)**

 9.

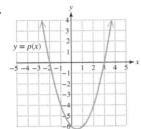

    a. $p(x) > 0$ **b.** $p(x) < 0$

    c. $p(x) \leq 0$ **d.** $p(x) \geq 0$

10.

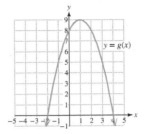

    a. $g(x) > 0$ **b.** $g(x) < 0$

    c. $g(x) \leq 0$ **d.** $g(x) \geq 0$

11.

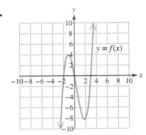

    a. $f(x) > 0$ **b.** $f(x) < 0$

    c. $f(x) \leq 0$ **d.** $f(x) \geq 0$

12.

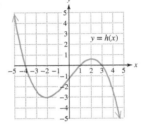

    a. $h(x) > 0$ **b.** $h(x) < 0$

    c. $h(x) \leq 0$ **d.** $h(x) \geq 0$

For Exercises 13–18, solve the equation and related inequalities. **(See Examples 2–3.)**

13. **a.** $3(4 - x)(2x + 1) = 0$

    b. $3(4 - x)(2x + 1) < 0$

    c. $3(4 - x)(2x + 1) > 0$

14. **a.** $5(y + 6)(3 - 5y) = 0$

    b. $5(y + 6)(3 - 5y) < 0$

    c. $5(y + 6)(3 - 5y) > 0$

15. **a.** $x^2 + 7x = 30$

    b. $x^2 + 7x < 30$

    c. $x^2 + 7x > 30$

16. **a.** $q^2 - 4q = 5$

    b. $q^2 - 4q \leq 5$

    c. $q^2 - 4q \geq 5$

17. **a.** $2p(p - 2) = p + 3$

    b. $2p(p - 2) \leq p + 3$

    c. $2p(p - 2) \geq p + 3$

18. **a.** $3w(w + 4) = 10 - w$

    b. $3w(w + 4) < 10 - w$

    c. $3w(w + 4) > 10 - w$

For Exercises 19–36, solve the polynomial inequality. Write the answer in interval notation. **(See Examples 2–3.)**

19. $(t - 7)(t - 1) < 0$

20. $(p - 4)(p - 2) > 0$

21. $-6(4 + 2x)(5 - x) > 0$

22. $-8(2t + 5)(6 - t) < 0$

23. $m(m + 1)^2(m + 5) \leq 0$

24. $w^2(3 - w)(w + 2) \geq 0$

25. $a^2 - 12a \leq -32$

26. $w^2 + 20w \geq -64$

27. $5x^2 - 4x - 1 > 0$

28. $x^2 + x \leq 6$

29. $b^2 - 121 < 0$

30. $c^2 - 25 < 0$

31. $3p(p-2) - 3 \geq 2p$　　　**32.** $2t(t+3) - t \leq 12$　　　**33.** $x^3 - x^2 \leq 12x$

34. $x^3 + 36 > 4x^2 + 9x$　　　**35.** $w^3 + w^2 > 4w + 4$　　　 **36.** $2p^3 - 5p^2 \leq 3p$

Concept 2: Solving Rational Inequalities

For Exercises 37–40, estimate from the graph the intervals for which the inequality is true.

37.

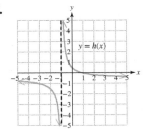

$y = h(x)$

a. $h(x) \geq 0$　　　**b.** $h(x) \leq 0$

c. $h(x) < 0$　　　**d.** $h(x) > 0$

38.

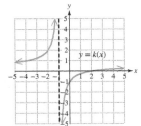

$y = k(x)$

a. $k(x) \leq 0$　　　**b.** $k(x) \geq 0$

c. $k(x) > 0$　　　**d.** $k(x) < 0$

39.

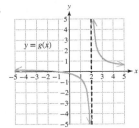

$y = g(x)$

a. $g(x) > 0$　　　**b.** $g(x) < 0$

c. $g(x) \leq 0$　　　**d.** $g(x) \geq 0$

40.

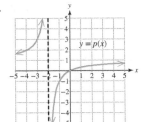

$y = p(x)$

a. $p(x) > 0$　　　**b.** $p(x) < 0$

c. $p(x) \leq 0$　　　**d.** $p(x) \geq 0$

For Exercises 41–44, solve the equation and related inequalities. **(See Examples 4–5.)**

41. a. $\dfrac{10}{x-5} = 5$　　**42. a.** $\dfrac{8}{a+1} = 4$　　**43. a.** $\dfrac{z+2}{z-6} = -3$　　**44. a.** $\dfrac{w-8}{w+6} = 2$

b. $\dfrac{10}{x-5} < 5$　　**b.** $\dfrac{8}{a+1} > 4$　　**b.** $\dfrac{z+2}{z-6} \leq -3$　　**b.** $\dfrac{w-8}{w+6} \leq 2$

c. $\dfrac{10}{x-5} > 5$　　**c.** $\dfrac{8}{a+1} < 4$　　**c.** $\dfrac{z+2}{z-6} \geq -3$　　**c.** $\dfrac{w-8}{w+6} \geq 2$

For Exercises 45–56, solve the rational inequality. Write the answer in interval notation. **(See Examples 4–5.)**

45. $\dfrac{2}{x-1} \geq 0$　　**46.** $\dfrac{-3}{x+2} \leq 0$　　**47.** $\dfrac{b+4}{b-4} > 0$　　 **48.** $\dfrac{a+1}{a-3} < 0$

49. $\dfrac{3}{2x-7} < -1$　　**50.** $\dfrac{8}{4x+9} > 1$　　**51.** $\dfrac{x+1}{x-5} \geq 4$　　**52.** $\dfrac{x-2}{x+6} \leq 5$

53. $\dfrac{1}{x} \leq 2$　　**54.** $\dfrac{1}{x} \geq 3$　　**55.** $\dfrac{(x+2)^2}{x} > 0$　　**56.** $\dfrac{(x-3)^2}{x} < 0$

Mixed Exercises

For Exercises 57–76, identify the inequality as one of the following types: linear, quadratic, rational, or polynomial (degree > 2). Then solve the inequality and write the answer in interval notation.

57. $2y^2 - 8 \leq 24$

58. $8p^2 - 18 > 0$

59. $(5x + 2)^2 > 4$

60. $(7x - 4)^2 < 9$

61. $4(x - 2) < 6x - 3$

62. $-7(3 - y) > 4 + 2y$

63. $\dfrac{2x + 3}{x + 1} \leq 2$

64. $\dfrac{5x - 1}{x + 3} \geq 5$

65. $4x^3 - 40x^2 + 100x > 0$

66. $2y^3 - 12y^2 + 18y < 0$

67. $2p^3 > 4p^2$

68. $w^3 \leq 5w^2$

69. $-3(x + 4)^2(x - 5) \geq 0$

70. $5x(x - 2)(x - 6)^2 \geq 0$

71. $x^2 - 4 < 0$

72. $y^2 - 9 > 0$

73. $\dfrac{a + 2}{a - 5} \geq 0$

74. $\dfrac{t + 1}{t - 2} \leq 0$

75. $2 \geq t - 3$

76. $-5p + 8 < p$

Expanding Your Skills

The solution to an inequality is often one or more intervals on the real number line. Sometimes, however, the solution to an inequality may be a single point on the number line, the empty set, or the set of all real numbers. We call these "special case" solution sets.

For Exercises 77–92, solve the inequalities involving "special case" solution sets.

77. $x^2 + 10x + 25 \geq 0$

78. $x^2 + 6x + 9 < 0$

79. $x^2 + 2x + 1 < 0$

80. $x^2 + 8x + 16 \geq 0$

81. $x^4 + 3x^2 \leq 0$

82. $x^4 + 2x^2 \leq 0$

83. $x^2 + 12x + 36 < 0$

84. $x^2 + 12x + 36 \geq 0$

85. $x^2 + 3x + 5 < 0$

86. $2x^2 + 3x + 3 > 0$

87. $-5x^2 + x < 1$

88. $-3x^2 - x > 6$

89. $x^2 + 22x + 121 > 0$

90. $y^2 - 24y + 144 > 0$

91. $4t^2 - 12t \leq -9$

92. $9y^2 - 30y \leq -25$

Graphing Calculator Exercises

93. To solve the inequality $\dfrac{x}{x - 2} > 0$ enter Y_1 as $x/(x - 2)$ and determine where the graph is above the x-axis. Write the solution in interval notation.

94. To solve the inequality $\dfrac{x}{x - 2} < 0$ enter Y_1 as $x/(x - 2)$ and determine where the graph is below the x-axis. Write the solution in interval notation.

95. To solve the inequality $x^2 - 1 < 0$, enter Y_1 as $x^2 - 1$ and determine where the graph is below the x-axis. Write the solution in interval notation.

96. To solve the inequality $x^2 - 1 > 0$, enter Y_1 as $x^2 - 1$ and determine where the graph is above the x-axis. Write the solution in interval notation.

For Exercises 97–100, determine the solution by graphing the inequalities.

97. $x^2 + 10x + 25 \leq 0$

98. $-x^2 + 10x - 25 \geq 0$

99. $\dfrac{8}{x^2 + 2} < 0$

100. $\dfrac{-6}{x^2 + 3} > 0$

Absolute Value Equations

1. Solving Absolute Value Equations

An equation of the form $|x| = a$ is called an **absolute value equation**. The solution includes all real numbers whose absolute value equals a. For example, the solutions to the equation $|x| = 4$ are 4 as well as −4, because $|4| = 4$ and $|-4| = 4$. A geometric interpretation of the absolute value of a number is its distance from zero on the number line (Figure 9-5). Therefore, the solutions to the equation $|x| = 4$ are the values of x that are 4 units away from zero.

Concepts

1. Solving Absolute Value Equations
2. Solving Equations Containing Two Absolute Values

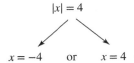

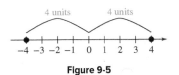

Figure 9-5

Solving Absolute Value Equations of the Form |x| = a

If a is a real number, then

- If $a \geq 0$, the solutions to the equation $|x| = a$ are $x = a$ and $x = -a$.
- If $a < 0$, there is no solution to the equation $|x| = a$.

To solve an absolute value equation of the form $|x| = a$ ($a \geq 0$), rewrite the equation as $x = a$ or $x = -a$.

Example 1   **Solving Absolute Value Equations**

Solve the absolute value equations.

 a. $|x| = 5$ **b.** $|w| - 2 = 12$ **c.** $|p| = 0$ **d.** $|x| = -6$

Solution:

a. $|x| = 5$ The equation is in the form $|x| = a$, where $a = 5$.

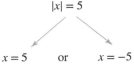

 $x = 5$ or $x = -5$ Rewrite the equation as $x = a$ or $x = -a$.

The solution set is $\{5, -5\}$.

 b. $|w| - 2 = 12$ Isolate the absolute value to write the equation in the form $|x| = a$.

          $|w| = 14$

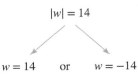

 $w = 14$ or $w = -14$ Rewrite the equation as $w = a$ or $w = -a$.

The solution set is $\{14, -14\}$.

c. $\qquad |p| = 0$

$p = 0 \qquad$ or $\qquad p = -0$

The solution set is $\{0\}$.

Rewrite as two equations. Notice that the second equation $p = -0$ is the same as the first equation. Intuitively, $p = 0$ is the only number whose absolute value equals 0.

d. $|x| = -6$

No solution, $\{\ \}$

The equation is of the form $|x| = a$, but a is negative. There is no number whose absolute value is negative.

Skill Practice Solve the absolute value equations.

1. $|y| = 7$ **2.** $|v| + 6 = 10$ **3.** $|w| + 3 = 3$ **4.** $|z| = -12$

We have solved absolute value equations of the form $|x| = a$. Notice that x can represent any algebraic quantity. For example, to solve the equation $|2w - 3| = 5$, we still rewrite the absolute value equation as two equations. In this case, we set the quantity $2w - 3$ equal to 5 and to -5, respectively.

$$|2w - 3| = 5$$

$$2w - 3 = 5 \qquad \text{or} \qquad 2w - 3 = -5$$

Solving an Absolute Value Equation

Step 1 Isolate the absolute value. That is, write the equation in the form $|x| = a$, where a is a real number.

Step 2 If $a < 0$, there is no solution.

Step 3 Otherwise, if $a \geq 0$, rewrite the absolute value equation as $x = a$ or $x = -a$.

Step 4 Solve the individual equations from step 3.

Step 5 Check the answers in the original absolute value equation.

| **Example 2** | **Solving an Absolute Value Equation** |

Solve the equation. $\qquad |2w - 3| = 5$

Solution:

$|2w - 3| = 5$ $\qquad$ The equation is already in the form $|x| = a$, where $x = 2w - 3$.

$2w - 3 = 5 \quad$ or $\quad 2w - 3 = -5$ $\qquad$ Rewrite as two equations.

$2w = 8 \quad$ or $\qquad 2w = -2$ $\qquad$ Solve each equation.

$w = 4 \quad$ or $\qquad w = -1$

Answers
1. $\{7, -7\}$
2. $\{4, -4\}$
3. $\{0\}$ **4.** $\{\ \}$

Check: $w = 4$	Check: $w = -1$	Check the solutions in the original
$\|2w - 3\| = 5$	$\|2w - 3\| = 5$	equation.
$\|2(4) - 3\| \stackrel{?}{=} 5$	$\|2(-1) - 3\| \stackrel{?}{=} 5$	
$\|8 - 3\| \stackrel{?}{=} 5$	$\|-2 - 3\| \stackrel{?}{=} 5$	
$\|5\| \stackrel{?}{=} 5 \checkmark$	$\|-5\| \stackrel{?}{=} 5 \checkmark$	

The solution set is $\{4, -1\}$.

Skill Practice Solve the equation.

5. $|4x + 1| = 9$

Calculator Connections

Topic: Analyzing an Absolute Value Equation Graphically

To confirm the answers to Example 2, graph $Y_1 = \text{abs}(2x - 3)$ and $Y_2 = 5$. The solutions to the equation $|2x - 3| = 5$ are the x-coordinates of the points of intersection $(4, 5)$ and $(-1, 5)$.

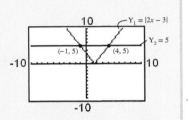

Example 3 **Solving an Absolute Value Equation**

Solve the equation. $|2c - 5| + 6 = 2$

Solution:

$|2c - 5| + 6 = 2$

$\quad |2c - 5| = -4$ Isolate the absolute value. The equation is in the form $|x| = a$, where $x = 2c - 5$ and $a = -4$. Because $a < 0$, there is no solution.

No solution, $\{\ \}$ There are no numbers c that will make an absolute value equal to a negative number.

Avoiding Mistakes

Always isolate the absolute value first. Otherwise you will get answers that do not check.

Skill Practice Solve the equation.

6. $|3z + 10| + 3 = 1$

Calculator Connections

Topic: Analyzing an Absolute Value Equation with No Solution

To confirm the answer in Example 3, note that the graphs of $Y_1 = \text{abs}(2x - 5) + 6$ and $Y_2 = 2$ do not intersect.

Therefore, there is no solution to the equation $|2x - 5| + 6 = 2$.

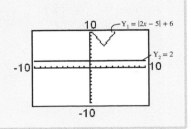

Answers

5. $\left\{2, -\dfrac{5}{2}\right\}$ **6.** $\{\ \}$

Example 4   **Solving an Absolute Value Equation**

Solve the equation. $-2\left|\dfrac{2}{5}p + 3\right| - 7 = -19$

Solution:

$$-2\left|\dfrac{2}{5}p + 3\right| - 7 = -19$$

$$-2\left|\dfrac{2}{5}p + 3\right| = -12 \qquad\qquad \text{Isolate the absolute value.}$$

$$\dfrac{-2\left|\dfrac{2}{5}p + 3\right|}{-2} = \dfrac{-12}{-2}$$

$$\left|\dfrac{2}{5}p + 3\right| = 6$$

$\dfrac{2}{5}p + 3 = 6$	or	$\dfrac{2}{5}p + 3 = -6$	Rewrite as two equations.
$2p + 15 = 30$	or	$2p + 15 = -30$	Multiply by 5 to clear fractions.
$2p = 15$	or	$2p = -45$	
$p = \dfrac{15}{2}$	or	$p = -\dfrac{45}{2}$	Both values check in the original equation.

The solution set is $\left\{\dfrac{15}{2}, -\dfrac{45}{2}\right\}$.

Skill Practice   Solve the equation.

7. $3\left|\dfrac{3}{2}a + 1\right| + 2 = 14$

Example 5   **Solving an Absolute Value Equation**

Solve the equation. $6.9 = |4.1 - p| + 6.9$

Solution:

$$6.9 = |4.1 - p| + 6.9$$

$$|4.1 - p| + 6.9 = 6.9 \qquad \text{First write the absolute value on the left.}$$
$$\text{Then subtract 6.9 from both sides to write}$$
$$\text{the equation in the form } |x| = a.$$

$$|4.1 - p| = 0 \qquad\qquad \text{Isolate the absolute value.}$$

$$4.1 - p = 0 \quad \text{or} \quad 4.1 - p = -0 \qquad \text{Rewrite as two equations. Notice that the}$$
$$\text{equations are the same.}$$

$$-p = -4.1 \qquad\qquad \text{Subtract 4.1 from both sides.}$$

$$p = 4.1$$

Answer

7. $\left\{2, -\dfrac{10}{3}\right\}$

Check $p = 4.1$ in the original equation.

Check: $p = 4.1$

$$|4.1 - p| + 6.9 = 6.9$$

$$|4.1 - 4.1| + 6.9 \overset{?}{=} 6.9$$

$$|0| + 6.9 \overset{?}{=} 6.9$$

The solution set is $\{4.1\}$.

$$6.9 \overset{?}{=} 6.9 \checkmark$$

Skill Practice Solve the equation.

8. $-3.5 = |1.2 + x| - 3.5$

2. Solving Equations Containing Two Absolute Values

Some equations have two absolute values such as $|x| = |y|$. If two quantities have the same absolute value, then the quantities are equal or the quantities are opposites.

Equality of Absolute Values

$$|x| = |y| \text{ implies that } x = y \text{ or } x = -y.$$

Example 6 **Solving an Equation Having Two Absolute Values**

Solve the equation. $|2w - 3| = |5w + 1|$

Solution:

$$|2w - 3| = |5w + 1|$$

$2w - 3 = 5w + 1$	or	$2w - 3 = -(5w + 1)$	Rewrite as two equations, $x = y$ or $x = -y$.
$2w - 3 = 5w + 1$	or	$2w - 3 = -5w - 1$	Solve for w.
$-3w - 3 = 1$	or	$7w - 3 = -1$	
$-3w = 4$	or	$7w = 2$	
$w = -\dfrac{4}{3}$	or	$w = \dfrac{2}{7}$	Both values check in the original equation.

The solution set is $\left\{ -\dfrac{4}{3}, \dfrac{2}{7} \right\}$.

Avoiding Mistakes

To take the opposite of the quantity $5w + 1$, use parentheses and apply the distributive property.

Skill Practice Solve the equation.

9. $|3 - 2x| = |3x - 1|$

Answers

8. $\{-1.2\}$ **9.** $\left\{ \dfrac{4}{5}, -2 \right\}$

Example 7   Solving an Equation Having Two Absolute Values

Solve the equation. $|x - 4| = |x + 8|$

Solution:

$$|x - 4| = |x + 8|$$

$x - 4 = x + 8$ or $x - 4 = -(x + 8)$ Rewrite as two equations, $x = y$ or $x = -y$.

$-4 = 8$ or $x - 4 = -x - 8$ Solve for x.

⤒ contradiction

$2x - 4 = -8$

$2x = -4$

$x = -2$ $x = -2$ checks in the original equation.

The solution set is $\{-2\}$.

Skill Practice   Solve the equation.

10. $|4t + 3| = |4t - 5|$

Calculator Connections

Topic: Analyzing an Absolute Value Equation Graphically

To confirm the answer in Example 7, graph $Y_1 = \text{abs}(x - 4)$ and $Y_2 = \text{abs}(x + 8)$. There is one point of intersection at $(-2, 6)$. Therefore, the solution to $|x - 4| = |x + 8|$ is -2.

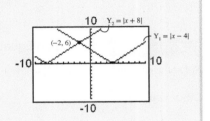

Answer

10. $\left\{ \dfrac{1}{4} \right\}$

Section 9.3   **Practice Exercises**

Vocabulary and Key Concepts

1. **a.** An _____ value equation is an equation of the form $|x| = a$. If a is a positive real number then the solution set is _____.

 b. What is the first step to solve the absolute value equation $|x| + 5 = 7$?

 c. The absolute value equation $|x| = |y|$ implies that $x =$ _____ or $x =$ _____.

 d. The solution set to the equation $|x + 4| = -2$ is _____. The solution set to the equation $|x + 4| = 0$ is _____.

Review Exercises

For Exercises 2–6, solve the inequalities. Write the answers in interval notation.

2. $x^2 - 3x - 10 \leq 0$

3. $x^2 - 1 \geq 0$

4. $\dfrac{4}{y - 4} \geq 3$

5. $\dfrac{3}{t + 1} \leq 2$

6. $x^3 - 7x^2 - 8x > 0$

Concept 1: Solving Absolute Value Equations

For Exercises 7–38, solve the absolute value equations. **(See Examples 1–5.)**

7. $|p| = 7$

8. $|q| = 10$

9. $|x| + 5 = 11$

10. $|x| - 3 = 20$

11. $|y| + 8 = 5$

12. $|x| + 12 = 6$

13. $|w| - 3 = -1$

14. $|z| - 14 = -10$

15. $|3q| = 0$

16. $|4p| = 0$

17. $|3x - 4| = 8$

18. $|4x + 1| = 6$

19. $5 = |2x - 4|$

20. $10 = |3x + 7|$

21. $\left|\frac{7z}{3} - \frac{1}{3}\right| + 3 = 6$

22. $\left|\frac{w}{2} + \frac{3}{2}\right| - 2 = 7$

23. $|0.2x - 3.5| = -5.6$

24. $|1.81 + 2x| = -2.2$

25. $1 = -4 + \left|2 - \frac{1}{4}w\right|$

26. $-12 = -6 - |6 - 2x|$

27. $10 = 4 + |2y + 1|$

28. $-1 = -|5x + 7|$

29. $-2|3b - 7| - 9 = -9$

30. $-3|5x + 1| + 4 = 4$

31. $-2|x + 3| = 5$

32. $-3|x - 5| = 7$

33. $0 = |6x - 9|$

34. $7 = |4k - 6| + 7$

35. $\left|-\frac{1}{5} - \frac{1}{2}k\right| = \frac{9}{5}$

36. $\left|-\frac{1}{6} - \frac{2}{9}h\right| = \frac{1}{2}$

37. $-3|2 - 6x| + 5 = -10$

38. $5|1 - 2x| - 7 = 3$

Concept 2: Solving Equations Containing Two Absolute Values

For Exercises 39–56, solve the absolute value equations. **(See Examples 6–7.)**

39. $|4x - 2| = |-8|$

40. $|3x + 5| = |-5|$

41. $|4w + 3| = |2w - 5|$

42. $|3y + 1| = |2y - 7|$

43. $|2y + 5| = |7 - 2y|$

44. $|9a + 5| = |9a - 1|$

45. $\left|\frac{4w - 1}{6}\right| = \left|\frac{2w}{3} + \frac{1}{4}\right|$

46. $\left|\frac{6p + 3}{8}\right| = \left|\frac{3}{4}p - 2\right|$

47. $|2h - 6| = |2h + 5|$

48. $|6n - 7| = |4 - 6n|$

49. $|3.5m - 1.2| = |8.5m + 6|$

50. $|11.2n + 9| = |7.2n - 2.1|$

51. $|4x - 3| = -|2x - 1|$

52. $-|3 - 6y| = |8 - 2y|$

53. $|8 - 7w| = |7w - 8|$

54. $|4 - 3z| = |3z - 4|$

55. $|x + 2| + |x - 4| = 0$

56. $|t + 6| + |t - 1| = 0$

Expanding Your Skills

57. Write an absolute value equation whose solution is the set of real numbers 6 units from zero on the number line.

58. Write an absolute value equation whose solution is the set of real numbers $\frac{7}{2}$ units from zero on the number line.

59. Write an absolute value equation whose solution is the set of real numbers $\frac{4}{3}$ units from zero on the number line.

60. Write an absolute value equation whose solution is the set of real numbers 9 units from zero on the number line.

Graphing Calculator Exercises

For Exercises 61–66, enter the left side of the equation as Y_1 and enter the right side of the equation as Y_2. Then use the *Intersect* feature to approximate the x-values where the two graphs intersect (if they intersect).

61. $|4x - 3| = 5$

62. $|x - 4| = 3$

63. $|8x + 1| + 8 = 1$

64. $|3x - 2| + 4 = 2$

65. $|x - 3| = |x + 2|$

66. $|x + 4| = |x - 2|$

Section 9.4   Absolute Value Inequalities

1. Solving Absolute Value Inequalities by Definition

In this section, we will solve absolute value *inequalities*. An inequality in any of the forms $|x| < a$, $|x| \leq a$, $|x| > a$, or $|x| \geq a$ is called an **absolute value inequality**.

    Recall that an absolute value represents distance from zero on the real number line. Consider the following absolute value equation and inequalities.

1. $|x| = 3$

     $x = 3$ or $x = -3$

Solution:

The set of all points 3 units from zero on the number line

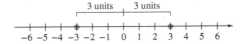

2. $|x| > 3$

     $x < -3$ or $x > 3$

Solution:

The set of all points more than 3 units from zero

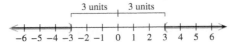

3. $|x| < 3$

     $-3 < x < 3$

Solution:

The set of all points less than 3 units from zero

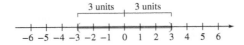

Solving Absolute Value Equations and Inequalities

Let a be a real number such that $a > 0$. Then

Equation/ Inequality	Solution (Equivalent Form)	Graph
$\|x\| = a$	$x = -a$ or $x = a$	
$\|x\| > a$	$x < -a$ or $x > a$	
$\|x\| < a$	$-a < x < a$	

To solve an absolute value inequality, first isolate the absolute value and then rewrite the absolute value inequality in its equivalent form.

Example 1	**Solving an Absolute Value Inequality**

Solve the inequality. $|3w + 1| - 4 < 7$

Solution:

$$|3w + 1| - 4 < 7$$

$$|3w + 1| < 11 \longleftarrow \text{Isolate the absolute value first.}$$

The inequality is in the form $|x| < a$, where $x = 3w + 1$.

$$-11 < 3w + 1 < 11 \qquad \text{Rewrite in the equivalent form } -a < x < a.$$

$$-12 < 3w < 10 \qquad \text{Solve for } w.$$

$$-4 < w < \frac{10}{3}$$

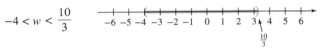

The solution is $\left\{ w \mid -4 < w < \frac{10}{3} \right\}$, or equivalently in interval notation, $\left(-4, \frac{10}{3}\right)$.

Skill Practice   Solve the inequality. Write the solution in interval notation.

1. $|2t + 5| + 2 \leq 11$

> **TIP:** Recall that a strict inequality (using the symbols > and <) will have parentheses at the endpoints of the interval form of the solution.

Calculator Connections

Topic: Analyzing an Absolute Value Inequality Graphically

To confirm the answer in Example 1, graph $Y_1 = \text{abs}(3x + 1) - 4$ and $Y_2 = 7$. On the given display window, $Y_1 < Y_2$ (Y_1 is below Y_2) for $-4 < x < \frac{10}{3}$.

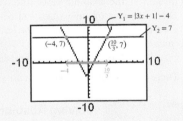

Example 2	**Solving an Absolute Value Inequality**

Solve the inequality. $3 \leq 1 + \left| \frac{1}{2}t - 5 \right|$

Solution:

$$3 \leq 1 + \left| \frac{1}{2}t - 5 \right|$$

$$1 + \left| \frac{1}{2}t - 5 \right| \geq 3 \qquad \text{Write the inequality with the absolute value on the left.}$$

$$\left| \frac{1}{2}t - 5 \right| \geq 2 \qquad \text{Isolate the absolute value.}$$

The inequality is in the form $|x| \geq a$, where $x = \frac{1}{2}t - 5$.

$$\frac{1}{2}t - 5 \leq -2 \qquad \text{or} \qquad \frac{1}{2}t - 5 \geq 2 \qquad \begin{array}{l}\text{Rewrite in the equivalent}\\ \text{form } x \leq -a \text{ or } x \geq a.\end{array}$$

> **TIP:** It is generally easier to solve an absolute value inequality if the absolute value appears on the left-hand side of the inequality.

Answer

1. $[-7, 2]$

658 Chapter 9 More Equations and Inequalities

$$\frac{1}{2}t \le 3 \qquad \text{or} \qquad \frac{1}{2}t \ge 7 \qquad \text{Solve the compound inequality.}$$

$$2\left(\frac{1}{2}t\right) \le 2(3) \qquad \text{or} \qquad 2\left(\frac{1}{2}t\right) \ge 2(7) \qquad \text{Clear fractions.}$$

$$t \le 6 \qquad \text{or} \qquad t \ge 14$$

The solution is $\{t \,|\, t \le 6 \text{ or } t \ge 14\}$ or, equivalently in interval notation, $(-\infty, 6] \cup [14, \infty)$.

Skill Practice Solve the inequality. Write the solution in interval notation.

2. $5 < 1 + \left|\frac{1}{3}c - 1\right|$

Calculator Connections

Topic: Analyzing an Absolute Value Inequality Graphically

To confirm the answer in Example 2, graph $Y_1 = \text{abs}((1/2)x - 5) + 1$ and $Y_2 = 3$. On the given display window, $Y_1 \ge Y_2$ for $x \le 6$ or $x \ge 14$.

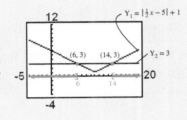

By definition, the absolute value of a real number will always be nonnegative. Therefore, the absolute value of any expression will always be greater than a negative number. Similarly, an absolute value can never be less than a negative number. If a represents a positive real number, then

- The solution to the inequality $|x| > -a$ is all real numbers, $(-\infty, \infty)$.
- There is no solution to the inequality $|x| < -a$.

Example 3 Solving Absolute Value Inequalities

Solve the inequalities.

a. $|3d - 5| + 7 < 4$ **b.** $|3d - 5| + 7 > 4$

Solution:

a. $|3d - 5| + 7 < 4$ Isolate the absolute value. An absolute value expression cannot be less than a negative number. Therefore, there is no solution.

$|3d - 5| < -3$

No solution, { }

b. $|3d - 5| + 7 > 4$ Isolate the absolute value. The inequality is in the form $|x| > a$, where a is negative. An absolute value of any real number is greater than a negative number. Therefore, the solution is all real numbers.

$|3d - 5| > -3$

All real numbers, $(-\infty, \infty)$

Skill Practice Solve the inequalities.

3. $|4p + 2| + 6 < 2$ **4.** $|4p + 2| + 6 > 2$

Answer

2. $(-\infty, -9) \cup (15, \infty)$
3. { }
4. All real numbers; $(-\infty, \infty)$

Topic: Analyzing an Absolute Value Inequality Graphically

By graphing $Y_1 = abs(3x - 5) + 7$ and $Y_2 = 4$ from Example 3, we see that $Y_1 > Y_2$ (Y_1 is above Y_2) for all real numbers x on the given display window.

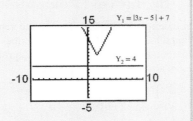

Example 4   **Solving Absolute Value Inequalities**

Solve the inequalities.

a. $|4x + 2| \geq 0$ **b.** $|4x + 2| > 0$ **c.** $|4x + 2| \leq 0$

Solution:

a. $|4x + 2| \geq 0$ ◄— The absolute value is already isolated.

The absolute value of any real number is nonnegative. Therefore, the solution is all real numbers, $(-\infty, \infty)$.

b. $|4x + 2| > 0$

An absolute value will be greater than zero at all points *except where it is equal to zero*. That is, the value(s) of x for which $|4x + 2| = 0$ must be excluded from the solution set.

$|4x + 2| = 0$

$4x + 2 = 0$ or $4x + 2 = -0$ The second equation is the same as the first.

$4x = -2$

$x = -\dfrac{1}{2}$ Therefore, exclude $x = -\dfrac{1}{2}$ from the solution.

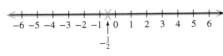

The solution is $\{x \mid x \neq -\frac{1}{2}\}$ or equivalently in interval notation, $(-\infty, -\frac{1}{2}) \cup (-\frac{1}{2}, \infty)$.

c. $|4x + 2| \leq 0$

An absolute value of a number cannot be less than zero. However, it can be *equal* to zero. Therefore, the only solutions to this inequality are the solutions to the related equation:

$|4x + 2| = 0$ From part (b), we see that the solution set is $\left\{ -\dfrac{1}{2} \right\}$.

Topic: Analyzing an Absolute Value Inequality Graphically

From Example 4, graph $Y_1 = abs(4x + 2)$. From the graph, $Y_1 = 0$ at $x = -\frac{1}{2}$ (the x-intercept). On the given display window, $Y_1 > 0$ for $x < -\frac{1}{2}$ or $x > -\frac{1}{2}$.

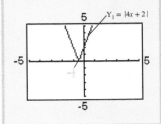

Skill Practice Solve the inequalities.

5. $|3x - 1| \geq 0$ **6.** $|3x - 1| > 0$ **7.** $|3x - 1| \leq 0$

Answers

5. $(-\infty, \infty)$

6. $\left\{ x \mid x \neq \dfrac{1}{3} \right\}$ or $\left(-\infty, \dfrac{1}{3} \right) \cup \left(\dfrac{1}{3}, \infty \right)$

7. $\left\{ \dfrac{1}{3} \right\}$

2. Solving Absolute Value Inequalities by the Test Point Method

In Examples 1 and 2, each absolute value inequality was converted to an equivalent compound inequality. However, sometimes students have difficulty setting up the appropriate compound inequality. To avoid this problem, you may want to use the test point method to solve absolute value inequalities.

Solving Inequalities by Using the Test Point Method

Step 1 Find the boundary points of the inequality. (Boundary points are the real solutions to the related equation and points where the inequality is undefined.)

Step 2 Plot the boundary points on the number line. This divides the number line into intervals.

Step 3 Select a test point from each interval and substitute it into the original inequality.
- If a test point makes the original inequality true, then that interval is part of the solution set.

Step 4 Test the boundary points in the original inequality.
- If the original inequality is strict (< or >), do not include the boundary points in the solution set.
- If the original inequality is defined using ≤ or ≥, then include the boundary points that are defined within the inequality.

Note: Any boundary point that makes an expression within the inequality undefined must *always* be excluded from the solution set.

To demonstrate the use of the test point method, we will repeat the absolute value inequalities from Examples 1 and 2. Notice that regardless of the method used, the absolute value is always isolated *first* before any further action is taken.

Example 5   **Solving an Absolute Value Inequality by the Test Point Method**

Solve the inequality by using the test point method. $|3w + 1| - 4 < 7$

Solution:

$|3w + 1| - 4 < 7$

$|3w + 1| < 11$ ⟵——————— Isolate the absolute value.

$|3w + 1| = 11$ **Step 1:** Solve the related equation.

$3w + 1 = 11$ or $3w + 1 = -11$ Write as an equivalent system of two equations.

$3w = 10$ or $3w = -12$

$w = \dfrac{10}{3}$ or $w = -4$ These are the only boundary points.

Step 2: Plot the boundary points.

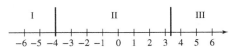

Step 3: Select a test point from each interval.

Test $w = -5$:

$|3(-5) + 1| - 4 \overset{?}{<} 7$

$|-14| - 4 \overset{?}{<} 7$

$14 - 4 \overset{?}{<} 7$

$10 \overset{?}{<} 7$ False

Test $w = 0$:

$|3(0) + 1| - 4 \overset{?}{<} 7$

$|1| - 4 \overset{?}{<} 7$

$-3 \overset{?}{<} 7$ True

Test $w = 4$:

$|3(4) + 1| - 4 \overset{?}{<} 7$

$|13| - 4 \overset{?}{<} 7$

$13 - 4 \overset{?}{<} 7$

$9 \overset{?}{<} 7$ False

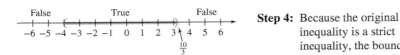

Step 4: Because the original inequality is a strict inequality, the boundary points (where equality occurs) are not included.

The solution is $\left\{ w \mid -4 < w < \frac{10}{3} \right\}$ or, equivalently in interval notation, $\left(-4, \frac{10}{3} \right)$.

Skill Practice Solve the inequality.

8. $6 + |3t - 4| \le 10$

Example 6	Solving an Absolute Value Inequality by the Test Point Method

Solve the inequality by using the test point method. $3 \le 1 + \left| \frac{1}{2}t - 5 \right|$

Solution:

$3 \le 1 + \left| \frac{1}{2}t - 5 \right|$

$1 + \left| \frac{1}{2}t - 5 \right| \ge 3$ Write the inequality with the absolute value on the left.

$\left| \frac{1}{2}t - 5 \right| \ge 2$ ⟵————————— Isolate the absolute value.

$\left| \frac{1}{2}t - 5 \right| = 2$ **Step 1:** Solve the related equation.

$\frac{1}{2}t - 5 = 2$ or $\frac{1}{2}t - 5 = -2$ Write as an equivalent system of two equations.

$\frac{1}{2}t = 7$ or $\frac{1}{2}t = 3$

$t = 14$ or $t = 6$ These are the boundary points.

Step 2: Plot the boundary points.

Step 3: Select a test point from each interval.

Answer

8. $\left[0, \frac{8}{3} \right]$

Test $t = 0$:

$3 \overset{?}{\leq} 1 + \left| \frac{1}{2}(0) - 5 \right|$

$3 \overset{?}{\leq} 1 + |0 - 5|$

$3 \overset{?}{\leq} 1 + |-5|$

$3 \overset{?}{\leq} 6$ True

Test $t = 10$:

$3 \overset{?}{\leq} 1 + \left| \frac{1}{2}(10) - 5 \right|$

$3 \overset{?}{\leq} 1 + |5 - 5|$

$3 \overset{?}{\leq} 1 + |0|$

$3 \overset{?}{\leq} 1$ False

Test $t = 16$:

$3 \overset{?}{\leq} 1 + \left| \frac{1}{2}(16) - 5 \right|$

$3 \overset{?}{\leq} 1 + |8 - 5|$

$3 \overset{?}{\leq} 1 + |3|$

$3 \overset{?}{\leq} 4$ True

Step 4: The original inequality uses the sign $\geq$. Therefore, the boundary points (where equality occurs) must be part of the solution set.

True ———┼——— False ———┤——— True
         6   14

The solution is $\{t \mid t \leq 6 \text{ or } t \geq 14\}$ or, equivalently in interval notation, $(-\infty, 6] \cup [14, \infty)$.

Skill Practice Solve the inequality.

9. $\left| \frac{1}{2}c + 4 \right| + 1 > 6$

3. Translating to an Absolute Value Expression

Absolute value expressions can be used to describe distances. The distance between c and d is given by $|c - d|$. For example, the distance between -2 and 3 on the number line is $|(-2) - 3| = 5$ as expected.

Example 7   Expressing Distances with Absolute Value

Write an absolute value inequality to represent the following phrases.

a. All real numbers x, whose distance from zero is greater than 5 units

b. All real numbers x, whose distance from -7 is less than 3 units

Solution:

a. All real numbers x, whose distance from zero is greater than 5 units

   $|x - 0| > 5$ or simply $|x| > 5$

b. All real numbers x, whose distance from -7 is less than 3 units

   $|x - (-7)| < 3$ or simply $|x + 7| < 3$

Skill Practice Write an absolute value inequality to represent the following phrases.

10. All real numbers whose distance from zero is greater than 10 units

11. All real numbers whose distance from 4 is less than 6 units

Answers

9. $(-\infty, -18) \cup (2, \infty)$
10. $|x| > 10$
11. $|x - 4| < 6$

Absolute value expressions can also be used to describe boundaries for measurement error.

Example 8 **Expressing Measurement Error with Absolute Value**

Latoya measured a certain compound on a scale in the chemistry lab at school. She measured 8 g of the compound, but the scale is only accurate to ±0.1 g. Write an absolute value inequality to express an interval for the true mass, x, of the compound she measured.

Solution:

Because the scale is only accurate to ±0.1 g, the true mass, x, of the compound may deviate by as much as 0.1 g above or below 8 g. This may be expressed as an absolute value inequality:

$|x - 8.0| \leq 0.1$ or equivalently $7.9 \leq x \leq 8.1$

Skill Practice

12. Vonzell molded a piece of metal in her machine shop. She measured the thickness at 12 mm. Her machine is accurate to ±0.05 mm. Write an absolute value inequality to express an interval for the true measurement of the thickness, t, of the metal.

Answer

12. $|t - 12| \leq 0.05$

Section 9.4 Practice Exercises

Vocabulary and Key Concepts

1. **a.** If a is a positive real number, then the inequality $|x| < a$ is equivalent to _____ $< x <$ _____.

    b. If a is a positive real number, then the inequality $|x| > a$ is equivalent to $x <$ _____ or x _____ a.

    c. The solution set to the inequality $|x + 2| < -6$ is _____, whereas the solution set to the inequality $|x + 2| > -6$ is _____.

    d. The solution set to the inequality $|x + 4| \leq 0$ (includes/excludes) -4, whereas the solution set to the inequality $|x + 4| < 0$ (includes/excludes) -4.

Review Exercises

For Exercises 2–4, solve the equations.

2. $|10x - 6| = -5$

3. $2 = |5 - 7x| + 1$

4. $|3x - 12| + 4 = 6 - 2$

For Exercises 5–8, solve the inequality and graph the solution set. Write the solution in interval notation.

5. $-15 < 3w - 6 \leq -9$

6. $5 - 2y \leq 1$ and $3y + 2 \geq 14$

7. $m - 7 \leq -5$ or $m - 7 \geq -10$

8. $3b - 2 < 7$ or $b - 2 > 4$

Concepts 1 and 2: Solving Absolute Value Inequalities

For Exercises 9–20, solve the equations and inequalities. For each inequality, graph the solution set and express the solution in interval notation. **(See Examples 1–6.)**

9. a. $|x| = 5$

  b. $|x| > 5$

  c. $|x| < 5$

10. a. $|a| = 4$

  b. $|a| > 4$

  c. $|a| < 4$

11. a. $|x - 3| = 7$

  b. $|x - 3| > 7$

  c. $|x - 3| < 7$

12. a. $|w + 2| = 6$

  b. $|w + 2| > 6$

  c. $|w + 2| < 6$

13. a. $|p| = -2$

  b. $|p| > -2$

  c. $|p| < -2$

14. a. $|x| = -14$

  b. $|x| > -14$

  c. $|x| < -14$

15. a. $|y + 1| = -6$

  b. $|y + 1| > -6$

  c. $|y + 1| < -6$

16. a. $|z - 4| = -3$

  b. $|z - 4| > -3$

  c. $|z - 4| < -3$

17. a. $|x| = 0$

  b. $|x| > 0$

  c. $|x| < 0$

18. a. $|p + 3| = 0$

  b. $|p + 3| > 0$

  c. $|p + 3| < 0$

19. a. $|k - 7| = 0$

  b. $|k - 7| > 0$

  c. $|k - 7| < 0$

20. a. $|2x + 4| + 3 = 2$

  b. $|2x + 4| + 3 > 2$

  c. $|2x + 4| + 3 < 2$

For Exercises 21–50, solve the absolute value inequality. Graph the solution set and write the solution in interval notation.
(See Examples 1–6.)

21. $|x| > 6$

22. $|x| \leq 6$

23. $|t| \leq 3$

24. $|p| > 3$

25. $|y + 2| \geq 0$

26. $0 \leq |7n + 2|$

27. $5 \leq |2x - 1|$

28. $|x - 2| \geq 7$

29. $|k - 7| < -3$

30. $|h + 2| < -9$

31. $\left| \dfrac{w - 2}{3} \right| - 3 \leq 1$

32. $\left| \dfrac{x + 3}{2} \right| - 2 \geq 4$

33. $12 \leq |9 - 4y| - 2$

34. $5 > |2m - 7| + 4$

35. $4 > -1 + \left| \dfrac{2x + 1}{4} \right|$

36. $9 \geq 2 + \left| \dfrac{x - 4}{5} \right|$

37. $8 < |4 - 3x| + 12$

38. $-16 < |5x - 1| - 1$

39. $5 - |2m + 1| > 5$

40. $3 - |5x + 3| > 3$

41. $|p + 5| \leq 0$

42. $|y + 1| - 4 \leq -4$

43. $|z - 6| + 5 > 5$

44. $|2c - 1| - 4 > -4$

45. $5|2y - 6| + 3 \geq 13$

46. $7|y + 1| - 3 \geq 11$

47. $-3|6 - t| + 1 > -5$

48. $-4|8 - x| + 2 > -14$

49. $|0.02x + 0.06| - 0.1 < 0.05$

50. $|0.05x - 0.04| - 0.01 < 0.11$

Concept 3: Translating to an Absolute Value Expression

For Exercises 51–54, write an absolute value inequality equivalent to the expression given. (See Example 7.)

51. All real numbers whose distance from 0 is greater than 7

52. All real numbers whose distance from −3 is less than 4

53. All real numbers whose distance from 2 is at most 13

54. All real numbers whose distance from 0 is at least 6

55. A 32-oz jug of orange juice may not contain exactly 32 oz of juice. The possibility of measurement error exists when the jug is filled in the factory. If the maximum measurement error is ±0.05 oz, write an absolute value inequality representing the range of volumes, x, in which the orange juice jug may be filled. (See Example 8.)

56. The length of a board is measured to be 32.3 in. The maximum measurement error is ±0.2 in. Write an absolute value inequality that represents the range for the length of the board, x.

57. A bag of potato chips states that its weight is $6\frac{3}{4}$ oz. The maximum measurement error is $\pm\frac{1}{8}$ oz. Write an absolute value inequality that represents the range for the weight, x, of the bag of chips.

58. A $\frac{7}{8}$-in. bolt varies in length by at most $\pm\frac{1}{16}$ in. Write an absolute value inequality that represents the range for the length, x, of the bolt.

59. The width, w, of a bolt is supposed to be 2 cm but may have a 0.01-cm margin of error. Solve $|w - 2| \leq 0.01$, and interpret the solution to the inequality in the context of this problem.

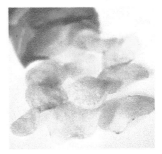

© BananaStock/Punchstock RF

60. In a political poll, the front-runner was projected to receive 53% of the votes with a margin of error of 3%. Solve $|p - 0.53| \leq 0.03$ and interpret the solution in the context of this problem.

Expanding Your Skills

For Exercises 61–64, match the graph with the inequality.

61.

62.

63.

64.

a. $|x - 2| < 4$ **b.** $|x - 1| > 4$ **c.** $|x - 3| < 2$ **d.** $|x - 5| > 1$

Graphing Calculator Exercises

To solve an absolute value inequality by using a graphing calculator, let Y_1 equal the left side of the inequality and let Y_2 equal the right side of the inequality. Graph both Y_1 and Y_2 on a standard viewing window and use an *Intersect* feature to approximate the intersection of the graphs. To solve $Y_1 > Y_2$, determine all x-values where the graph of Y_1 is above the graph of Y_2. To solve $Y_1 < Y_2$, determine all x-values where the graph of Y_1 is below the graph of Y_2.

For Exercises 65–74, solve the inequalities using a graphing calculator.

65. $|x + 2| > 4$

66. $|3 - x| > 6$

67. $\left|\dfrac{x + 1}{3}\right| < 2$

68. $\left|\dfrac{x - 1}{4}\right| < 1$

69. $|x - 5| < -3$

70. $|x + 2| < -2$

71. $|2x + 5| > -4$

72. $|1 - 2x| > -4$

73. $|6x + 1| \leq 0$

74. $|3x - 4| \leq 0$

666   **Chapter 9**   More Equations and Inequalities

Problem Recognition Exercises

Equations and Inequalities

For Exercises 1–24, identify the category for each equation or inequality (choose from the list here). Then solve the equation or inequality. Express the solution in interval notation where appropriate.

- Linear
- Quadratic
- Polynomial (degree greater than 2)
- Rational
- Absolute value

1. $z^2 + 10z + 9 > 0$

2. $5a - 2 = 6(a + 4)$

3. $\dfrac{x - 4}{2x + 4} \geq 1$

4. $4x^2 - 7x = 2$

5. $|3x - 1| + 4 < 6$

6. $2t^2 - t + 1 < 0$

7. $\dfrac{1}{2}p - \dfrac{2}{3} < \dfrac{1}{6}p - 4$

8. $p^2 + 3p \leq 4$

9. $3y^2 + y - 2 \geq 0$

10. $\dfrac{x + 6}{x + 4} = 7$

11. $3(2x - 4) \geq 1 - (x - 3)$

12. $|6x + 5| + 3 = 2$

13. $(x - 3)(2x + 1)(x + 5) \geq 0$

14. $-x^2 - x - 3 \leq 0$

15. $\dfrac{-6}{y - 2} < 2$

16. $x^2 - 5 = 4x$

17. $\left|\dfrac{x}{4} + 2\right| + 6 > 6$

18. $x^2 - 36 < 0$

19. $3y^3 + 5y^2 - 12y - 20 = 0$

20. $|8 - 2x| = 16$

21. $5b - 10 - 3b = 3(b - 2) - 4$

22. $\dfrac{x}{x - 5} \geq 0$

23. $|6x + 1| = |5 + 6x|$

24. $4x(x - 5)^2(2x + 3) < 0$

Linear Inequalities and Systems of Linear Inequalities in Two Variables

1. Graphing Linear Inequalities in Two Variables

A **linear inequality in two variables** x and y is an inequality that can be written in one of the following forms: $Ax + By < C$, $Ax + By > C$, $Ax + By \leq C$, or $Ax + By \geq C$, provided A and B are not both zero.

A solution to a linear inequality in two variables is an ordered pair that makes the inequality true. For example, solutions to the inequality $x + y < 6$ are ordered pairs (x, y) such that the sum of the x- and y-coordinates is less than 6. This inequality has an infinite number of solutions, and therefore it is convenient to express the solution set as a graph.

To graph a linear inequality in two variables, we will follow these steps.

> ### Graphing a Linear Inequality in Two Variables
>
> **Step 1** Write the inequality with the y variable isolated, if possible.
>
> **Step 2** Graph the related equation. Draw a dashed line if the inequality is strict, $<$ or $>$. Otherwise, draw a solid line.
>
> **Step 3** Shade above or below the line as follows:
> - Shade *above* the line if the inequality is of the form $y > mx + b$ or $y \geq mx + b$.
> - Shade *below* the line if the inequality is of the form $y < mx + b$ or $y \leq mx + b$.
>
> *Note:* A dashed line indicates that the line is *not* included in the solution set. A solid line implies that the line *is* included in the solution set.

This process is demonstrated in Example 1.

Concepts

1. Graphing Linear Inequalities in Two Variables
2. Systems of Linear Inequalities in Two Variables
3. Graphing a Feasible Region

Example 1   Graphing a Linear Inequality in Two Variables

Graph the solution set. $-3x + y \leq 1$

Solution:

$$-3x + y \leq 1$$
$$y \leq 3x + 1 \qquad \text{Solve for } y.$$

Next graph the line defined by the related equation $y = 3x + 1$.

Because the inequality is of the form $y \leq mx + b$, the solution to the inequality is the region *below* the line $y = 3x + 1$. So to indicate the solution set, shade the region on and below the line. See Figure 9-6.

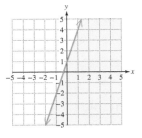

Figure 9-6

Answer

1.

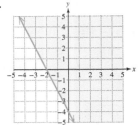

Skill Practice Graph the solution set.

1. $2x + y \geq -4$

668   **Chapter 9**   More Equations and Inequalities

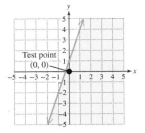

Figure 9-7

After graphing the solution to a linear inequality, we can verify that we have shaded the correct side of the line by using test points. In Example 1, we can pick an arbitrary ordered pair within the shaded region. Then substitute the x- and y-coordinates in the original inequality. If the result is a true statement, then that ordered pair is a solution to the inequality and suggests that other points from the same region are also solutions.

For example, the point $(0, 0)$ lies within the shaded region (Figure 9-7).

$$-3x + y \leq 1 \qquad \text{Substitute } (0, 0) \text{ in the original inequality.}$$

$$-3(0) + (0) \overset{?}{\leq} 1$$

$$0 + 0 \overset{?}{\leq} 1 \checkmark \text{ True} \qquad \text{The point } (0, 0) \text{ from the shaded region is a solution.}$$

In Example 2, we will graph the solution set to a strict inequality. A strict inequality does not include equality and therefore, is expressed with the symbols $<$ or $>$. In such a case, the boundary line will be drawn as a dashed line. This indicates that the boundary itself is *not* part of the solution set.

Example 2   **Graphing a Linear Inequality in Two Variables**

Graph the solution set. $-4y < 5x$

Solution:

$$-4y < 5x$$

$$\frac{-4y}{-4} > \frac{5x}{-4} \qquad \text{Solve for } y. \text{ Recall that when we divide both sides by a negative number, reverse the inequality sign.}$$

$$y > -\frac{5}{4}x$$

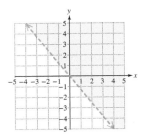

Figure 9-8

Graph the line defined by the related equation, $y = -\frac{5}{4}x$. The boundary line is drawn as a dashed line because the inequality is strict. Also note that the line passes through the origin.

Because the inequality is of the form $y > mx + b$, the solution to the inequality is the region *above* the line. See Figure 9-8.

Skill Practice   Graph the solution set.

2. $-3y < x$

Answer

2.

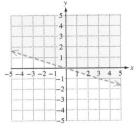

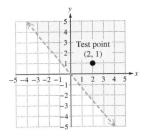

Figure 9-9

In Example 2, we cannot use the origin as a test point, because the point $(0, 0)$ is on the boundary line. Be sure to select a test point strictly within the shaded region. In this case, we choose $(2, 1)$. See Figure 9-9.

$$-4y < 5x \qquad \text{The test point } (2, 1) \text{ is}$$

$$-4(1) \overset{?}{<} 5(2) \qquad \text{indeed a solution to the}$$

$$\qquad\qquad\qquad \text{original inequality.}$$

$$-4 \overset{?}{<} 10 \checkmark \text{ True}$$

In Example 3, we encounter a situation in which we cannot solve for the *y*-variable.

| Example 3 | **Graphing a Linear Inequality in Two Variables** |

Graph the solution set. $4x \geq -12$

Solution:

$$4x \geq -12$$
$$x \geq -3$$

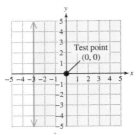

Figure 9-10

In this inequality, there is no *y*-variable. However, we can simplify the inequality by solving for *x*.

Graph the related equation $x = -3$. This is a vertical line. The boundary is drawn as a solid line, because the inequality is not strict, $\geq$.

To shade the appropriate region, refer to the inequality, $x \geq -3$. The points for which *x* is greater than -3 are to the right of $x = -3$. Therefore, shade the region to the *right* of the line (Figure 9-10).

Selecting a test point such as (0, 0) from the shaded region indicates that we have shaded the correct side of the line.

$$4x \geq -12 \qquad \text{Substitute } x = 0.$$
$$4(0) \overset{?}{\geq} -12 \checkmark \qquad \text{True}$$

Skill Practice Graph the solution set.

3. $-2x \geq 2$

2. Systems of Linear Inequalities in Two Variables

Some applications require us to find the solutions to a system of linear inequalities.

| Example 4 | **Graphing a System of Linear Inequalities** |

Graph the solution set. $y > \frac{1}{2}x + 1$
$$x + y < 1$$

Solution:

Solve each inequality for *y*.

<u>First inequality</u>

$y > \frac{1}{2}x + 1$

The inequality is of the form $y > mx + b$. Shade *above* the boundary line. See Figure 9-11.

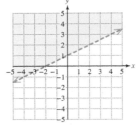

Figure 9-11

Answer

3.

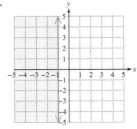

<u>Second inequality</u>

$x + y < 1$

$y < -x + 1$

The inequality is of the form
$y < mx + b$. Shade *below* the
boundary line. See Figure 9-12.

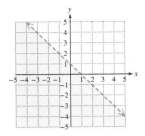

Figure 9-12

The region bounded by the inequalities is
the region above the line $y = \frac{1}{2}x + 1$ and
below the line $y = -x + 1$. This is the
intersection or "overlap" of the two shaded
regions (shown in purple in Figure 9-13).

The intersection is the solution
set to the system of inequalities.
See Figure 9-14.

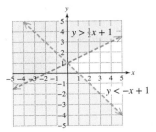

Figure 9-13

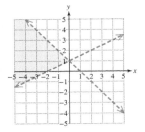

Figure 9-14

Skill Practice Graph the solution set.

4. $x - 3y > 3$

$\quad y < -2x + 4$

| **Example 5** | **Graphing a System of Linear Inequalities** |

Graph the solution set. $3y \le 6$

$\qquad\qquad\qquad\qquad\quad y - x \le 0$

Solution:

<u>First inequality</u>

$3y \le 6$

$\ y \le 2$

The graph of $y \le 2$ is the region
on and below the horizontal
line $y = 2$. See Figure 9-15.

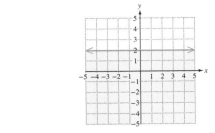

Figure 9-15

Answer

4.

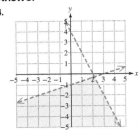

Second inequality

$y - x \leq 0$

$y \leq x$

The inequality $y \leq x$ is of the form $y \leq mx + b$. Graph a solid line and shade the region below the line. See Figure 9-16.

The solution to the system of inequalities is the intersection of the shaded regions. Notice that the portions of the lines not bounding the solution are dashed. See Figure 9-17.

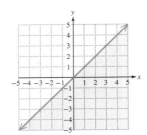

Figure 9-16

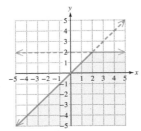

Figure 9-17

Skill Practice Graph the solution set.

5. $2y \leq 4$

$y \leq x + 1$

Example 6 **Graphing a System of Linear Inequalities**

Describe the region of the plane defined by the system of inequalities.

$$x \leq 0$$
$$y \geq 0$$

Solution:

$x \leq 0$ $\quad$ $x \leq 0$ for points on the y-axis and in the second and third quadrants.

$y \geq 0$ $\quad$ $y \geq 0$ for points on the x-axis and in the first and second quadrants.

The intersection of these regions is the set of points in the second quadrant (with the boundaries included).

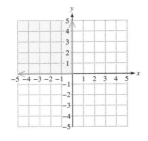

Skill Practice Graph the region defined by the system of inequalities.

6. $x \leq 0$

$y \leq 0$

---

3. Graphing a Feasible Region

When two variables are related under certain constraints, a system of linear inequalities can be used to show a region of feasible values for the variables.

The feasible region represents the ordered pairs that are true for each inequality in the system.

Answers

5.

6.

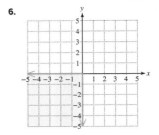

672   **Chapter 9**   More Equations and Inequalities

Example 7

Graphing a Feasible Region

Susan has two tests on Friday: one in chemistry and one in psychology. Because the two classes meet in consecutive hours, she has no study time between tests. Susan estimates that she has a maximum of 12 hr of study time before the tests, and she must divide her time between chemistry and psychology.

Let x represent the number of hours Susan spends studying chemistry.

Let y represent the number of hours Susan spends studying psychology.

a. Find a set of inequalities to describe the constraints on Susan's study time.

b. Graph the constraints to find the feasible region defining Susan's study time.

Solution:

a. Because Susan cannot study chemistry or psychology for a negative period of time, we have $x \geq 0$ and $y \geq 0$. Furthermore, her total time studying cannot exceed 12 hr: $x + y \leq 12$.

A system of inequalities that defines the constraints on Susan's study time is:

$$x \geq 0$$
$$y \geq 0$$
$$x + y \leq 12$$

b. The first two conditions $x \geq 0$ and $y \geq 0$ represent the set of points in the first quadrant. The third condition $x + y \leq 12$ represents the set of points below and including the line $x + y = 12$ (Figure 9-18).

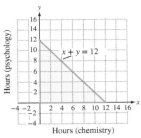

Figure 9-18

Discussion:

1. Refer to the feasible region drawn in Example 7(b). Is the ordered pair $(8, 5)$ part of the feasible region?

No. The ordered pair $(8, 5)$ indicates that Susan spent 8 hr studying chemistry and 5 hr studying psychology. This is a total of 13 hr, which exceeds the constraint that Susan only had 12 hr to study. The point $(8, 5)$ lies outside the feasible region, above the line $x + y = 12$ (Figure 9-19).

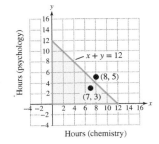

Figure 9-19

2. Is the ordered pair $(7, 3)$ part of the feasible region?

Yes. The ordered pair $(7, 3)$ indicates that Susan spent 7 hr studying chemistry and 3 hr studying psychology.

This point lies within the feasible region and satisfies all three constraints.

$$x \geq 0 \longrightarrow \quad 7 \geq 0 \quad \text{True}$$
$$y \geq 0 \longrightarrow \quad 3 \geq 0 \quad \text{True}$$
$$x + y \leq 12 \longrightarrow (7) + (3) \leq 12 \quad \text{True}$$

Notice that the ordered pair $(7, 3)$ corresponds to a point where Susan is not making full use of the 12 hr of study time.

3. Suppose there was one additional constraint imposed on Susan's study time. She knows she needs to spend at least twice as much time studying chemistry as she does studying psychology. Graph the feasible region with this additional constraint.

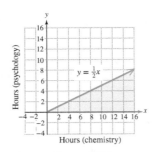

Because the time studying chemistry must be at least twice the time studying psychology, we have $x \geq 2y$.

This inequality may also be written as $y \leq \frac{1}{2}x$.

Figure 9-20 shows the first quadrant with the constraint $y \leq \frac{1}{2}x$.

Figure 9-20

4. At what point in the feasible region is Susan making the most efficient use of her time for both classes?

First and foremost, Susan must make use of *all* 12 hr. This occurs for points along the line $x + y = 12$. Susan will also want to study for both classes with approximately twice as much time devoted to chemistry. Therefore, Susan will be deriving the maximum benefit at the point of intersection of the line

$x + y = 12$ and the line $y = \frac{1}{2}x$.

Using the substitution method, replace $y = \frac{1}{2}x$ into the equation $x + y = 12$.

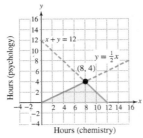

$x + \frac{1}{2}x = 12$

$2x + x = 24$ Clear fractions.

$3x = 24$

$x = 8$ Solve for x.

$y = \frac{(8)}{2}$ To solve for y, substitute $x = 8$ into the equation $y = \frac{1}{2}x$.

$y = 4$

Therefore, Susan should spend 8 hr studying chemistry and 4 hr studying psychology.

Skill Practice

7. A local pet rescue group has a total of 30 cages that can be used to hold cats and dogs. Let x represent the number of cages used for cats, and let y represent the number used for dogs.

  a. Write a set of inequalities to express the fact that the number of cat and dog cages cannot be negative.

  b. Write an inequality to describe the constraint on the total number of cages for cats and dogs.

  c. Graph the system of inequalities to find the feasible region describing the available cages.

Answer

7 a. $x \geq 0$ and $y \geq 0$

  b. $x + y \leq 30$

  c.

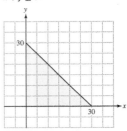

674   **Chapter 9** More Equations and Inequalities

Section 9.5   Practice Exercises

Vocabulary and Key Concepts

1. a. An inequality that can be written in the form $Ax + By > C$ is called a _____ inequality in two variables.

   b. Given the inequality $3x - 4y < 6$, the boundary line $3x - 4y = 6$ (is/is not) included in the solution set. However, given $3x - 4y \leq 6$, then the boundary line (is/is not) included in the solution set.

   c. Given the inequality $5x + y > 5$, the boundary line $5x + y = 5$ should be drawn as a (solid/dashed) line to indicate that the line (is/is not) part of the solution set.

   d. Given the inequality $y \geq -x + 4$, the boundary line $y = -x + 4$ should be drawn as a (solid/dashed) line to indicate that the line (is/is not) part of the solution set.

Review Exercises

For Exercises 2–5, solve the inequality. Write the solution set in interval notation.

2. $5 < x + 1$ and $-2x + 6 \geq -6$

3. $5 - x \leq 4$ and $6 > 3x - 3$

4. $4 - y < 3y + 12$ or $-2(y + 3) \geq 12$

5. $-2x < 4$ or $3x - 1 \leq -13$

Concept 1: Graphing Linear Inequalities in Two Variables

For Exercises 6–9, determine if the given point is a solution to the inequality.

6. $2x - y > 8$

   a. $(3, -5)$ **c.** $(4, -2)$

   b. $(-1, -10)$ **d.** $(0, 0)$

7. $3y + x < 5$

   a. $(-1, 7)$ **c.** $(0, 0)$

   b. $(5, 0)$ **d.** $(2, -3)$

8. $y \leq -2$

   a. $(5, -3)$ **c.** $(0, 0)$

   b. $(-4, -2)$ **d.** $(3, 2)$

9. $x \geq 5$

   a. $(4, 5)$ **c.** $(8, 8)$

   b. $(5, -1)$ **d.** $(0, 0)$

10. When should you use a dashed line to graph the solution to a linear inequality?

For Exercises 11–16, decide which inequality symbol should be used ($<, >, \geq, \leq$) by looking at the graph.

11.

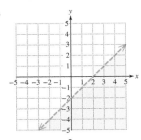

$x - y$ _____ 2

12.

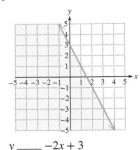

y _____ $-2x + 3$

13.

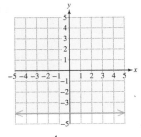

y _____ -4

14.

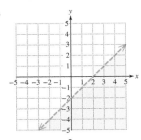

x _____ 3

15.

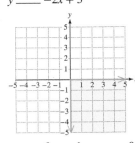

x _____ 0 and y _____ 0

16.

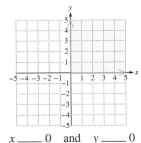

x _____ 0 and y _____ 0

For Exercises 17–40, graph the solution set. **(See Examples 1–3.)**

17. $x - 2y > 4$

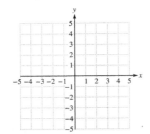

18. $x - 3y \geq 6$

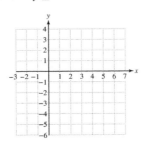

19. $5x - 2y < 10$

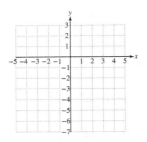

20. $x - 3y < 8$

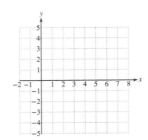

21. $2x \leq -6y + 12$

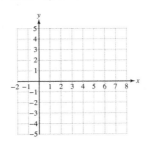

22. $4x < 3y + 12$

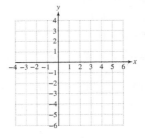

23. $2y \leq 4x$

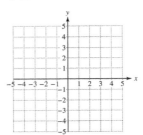

24. $-6x < 2y$

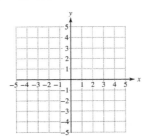

25. $y \geq -2$

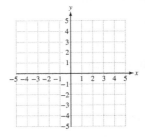

26. $y \geq 5$

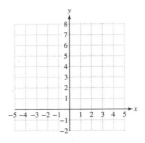

27. $4x < 5$

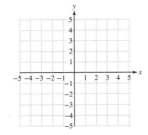

28. $x + 6 < 7$

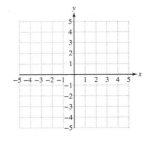

676   **Chapter 9**   More Equations and Inequalities

29. $y \geq \dfrac{2}{5}x - 4$

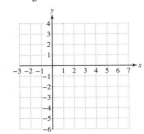

30. $y \geq -\dfrac{5}{2}x - 4$

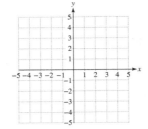

31. $y \leq \dfrac{1}{3}x + 6$

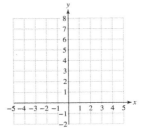

32. $y \leq -\dfrac{1}{4}x + 2$

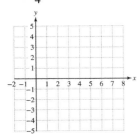

33. $y - 5x > 0$

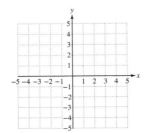

34. $y - \dfrac{1}{2}x > 0$

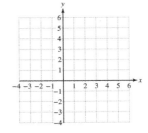

35. $\dfrac{x}{5} + \dfrac{y}{4} < 1$

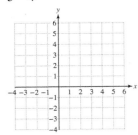

36. $x + \dfrac{y}{2} \geq 2$

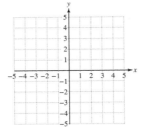

37. $0.1x + 0.2y \leq 0.6$

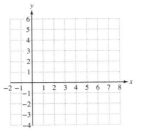

38. $0.3x - 0.2y < 0.6$

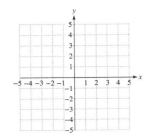

39. $x \leq -\dfrac{2}{3}y$

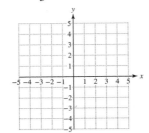

40. $x \geq -\dfrac{5}{4}y$

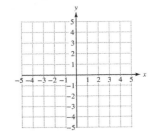

Concept 2: Systems of Linear Inequalities in Two Variables

For Exercises 41–55, graph the solution set. **(See Examples 4–6.)**

41. $y < 4$
$y > -x + 2$

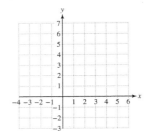

42. $y < 3$
$x + 2y < 6$

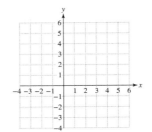

43. $2x + y \leq 5$
$x \geq 3$

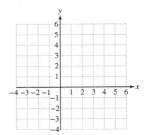

44. $x + 3y \geq 3$
$x \leq -2$

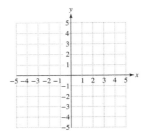

45. $x + y < 3$
$4x + y < 6$

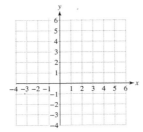

46. $x + y < 4$
$3x + y < 9$

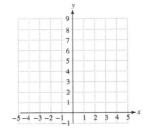

47. $2x - y \leq 2$
$2x + 3y \geq 6$

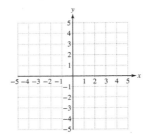

48. $3x + 2y \geq 4$
$x - y \leq 3$

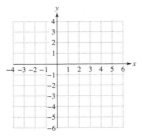

49. $x > 4$
$y < 2$

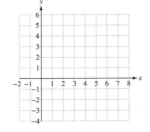

50. $x < 3$
$y > 4$

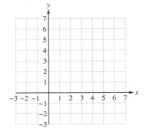

51. $x \leq -2$
$y \leq 0$

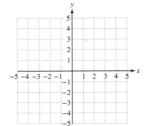

52. $x \geq 0$
$y \geq -3$

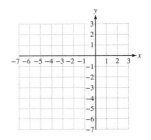

678   **Chapter 9**   More Equations and Inequalities

53. $x > 0$
 $x + y < 6$

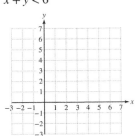

54. $x < 0$
 $x + y < 2$

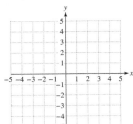

55. $y \geq 0$
 $-2x + y \leq -4$

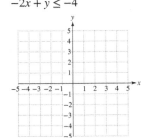

Concept 3: Graphing a Feasible Region

For Exercises 56–59, graph the feasible regions.

56. $x + y \leq 3$ and
 $x \geq 0, y \geq 0$

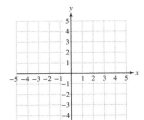

57. $x - y \leq 2$ and
 $x \geq 0, y \geq 0$

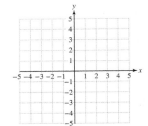

58. $x \geq 0, y \geq 0$
 $x + y \leq 8$ and
 $3x + 5y \leq 30$

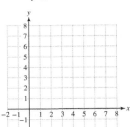

59. $x \geq 0, y \geq 0$
 $x + y \leq 5$ and
 $x + 2y \leq 6$

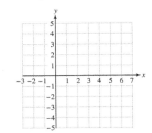

60. Suppose Sue has 50 ft of fencing with which she can build a rectangular dog run. Let x represent the length of the dog run and let y represent the width.

    a. Write an inequality representing the fact that the total perimeter of the dog run is at most 50 ft.

    b. Sketch part of the solution set for this inequality that represents all possible values for the length and width of the dog run. (*Hint:* Note that both the length and the width must be positive.)

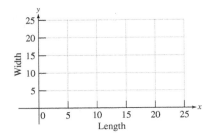

61. Suppose Rick has 40 ft of fencing with which he can build a rectangular garden. Let x represent the length of the garden and let y represent the width.

    a. Write an inequality representing the fact that the total perimeter of the garden is at most 40 ft.

    b. Sketch part of the solution set for this inequality that represents all possible values for the length and width of the garden. (*Hint:* Note that both the length and the width must be positive.)

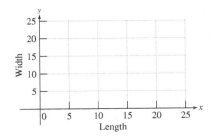

62. A manufacturer produces two models of desks. Model A requires 4 hr to stain and finish and 3 hr to assemble. Model B requires 3 hr to stain and finish and 1 hr to assemble. The total amount of time available for staining and finishing is 24 hr and for assembling is 12 hr. Let x represent the number of Model A desks produced, and let y represent the number of Model B desks produced.

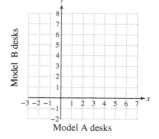

a. Write two inequalities that express the fact that the number of desks to be produced cannot be negative.

b. Write an inequality in terms of the number of Model A and Model B desks that can be produced if the total time for staining and finishing is at most 24 hr.

c. Write an inequality in terms of the number of Model A and Model B desks that can be produced if the total time for assembly is no more than 12 hr.

d. Graph the feasible region formed by graphing the preceding inequalities.

e. Is the point (3, 1) in the feasible region? What does the point (3, 1) represent in the context of this problem?

f. Is the point (5, 4) in the feasible region? What does the point (5, 4) represent in the context of this problem?

63. In scheduling two drivers for delivering pizza, James needs to have at least 65 hr scheduled this week. His two drivers, Karen and Todd, are not allowed to get overtime, so each one can work at most 40 hr. Let x represent the number of hours that Karen can be scheduled, and let y represent the number of hours Todd can be scheduled. **(See Example 7.)**

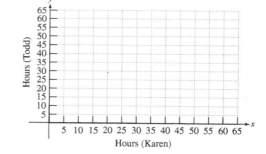

a. Write two inequalities that express the fact that Karen and Todd cannot work a negative number of hours.

b. Write two inequalities that express the fact that neither Karen nor Todd is allowed overtime (i.e., each driver can have at most 40 hr).

c. Write an inequality that expresses the fact that the total number of hours from both Karen and Todd needs to be at least 65 hr.

d. Graph the feasible region formed by graphing the inequalities.

e. Is the point (35, 40) in the feasible region? What does the point (35, 40) represent in the context of this problem?

f. Is the point (20, 40) in the feasible region? What does the point (20, 40) represent in the context of this problem?

680   **Chapter 9** More Equations and Inequalities

Group Activity

Recognizing Inequality Types

Estimated time: 20–25 minutes

Group Size: 3

For each exercise, solve the equation in part (a). Then determine how the solution sets differ for parts (b)–(e). Use interval notation to express your answers to the inequalities.

1. a. $2x - 3 = 15$

   b. $2x - 3 > 15$

   c. $2x - 3 < 15$

   d. $2x - 3 \leq 15$

   e. $2x - 3 \geq 15$

2. a. $|2x - 3| = 15$

   b. $|2x - 3| > 15$

   c. $|2x - 3| < 15$

   d. $|2x - 3| \leq 15$

   e. $|2x - 3| \geq 15$

3. a. $2x^2 - 3 = 15$

   b. $2x^2 - 3 > 15$

   c. $2x^2 - 3 < 15$

   d. $2x^2 - 3 \leq 15$

   e. $2x^2 - 3 \geq 15$

4. a. $\dfrac{3}{x - 6} = 3$

   b. $\dfrac{3}{x - 6} > 3$

   c. $\dfrac{3}{x - 6} < 3$

   d. $\dfrac{3}{x - 6} \leq 3$

   e. $\dfrac{3}{x - 6} \geq 3$

5. a. $x^2 + 12x + 36 = 0$

   b. $x^2 + 12x + 36 > 0$

   c. $x^2 + 12x + 36 < 0$

   d. $x^2 + 12x + 36 \leq 0$

   e. $x^2 + 12x + 36 \geq 0$

6. a. $|x - 3| = -6$

   b. $|x - 3| > -6$

   c. $|x - 3| < -6$

   d. $|x - 3| \leq -6$

   e. $|x - 3| \geq -6$

Chapter 9   Summary

Key Concepts

$A \cup B$ is the **union** of A and B. This is the set of elements that belong to set A or set B or both sets A and B.

$A \cap B$ is the **intersection** of A and B. This is the set of elements common to both A and B.

- Solve two or more inequalities joined by *and* by finding the intersection of their solution sets.
- Solve two or more inequalities joined by *or* by finding the union of their solution sets.

Example 2

$$-7x + 3 \geq -11 \quad \text{and} \quad 1 - x < 4.5$$
$$-7x \geq -14 \quad \text{and} \quad -x < 3.5$$
$$x \leq 2 \quad \text{and} \quad x > -3.5$$

$x \leq 2$

$x > -3.5$

The solution is $\{x \mid -3.5 < x \leq 2\}$ or equivalently $(-3.5, 2]$.

Inequalities of the form $a < x < b$:

The inequality $a < x < b$ is equivalent to the compound inequality $a < x$ and $x < b$.

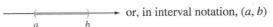 or, in interval notation, (a, b)

Examples

Example 1

Union   Intersection

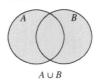

$A \cup B$ $A \cap B$

Example 3

$$5y + 1 \geq 6 \quad \text{or} \quad 2y - 5 \leq -11$$
$$5y \geq 5 \quad \text{or} \quad 2y \leq -6$$
$$y \geq 1 \quad \text{or} \quad y \leq -3$$

$y \geq 1$

$y \leq -3$

The solution is $\{y \mid y \leq -3 \text{ or } y \geq 1\}$ or equivalently $(-\infty, -3] \cup [1, \infty)$.

Example 4

Solve.

$$-13 \leq 3x - 1 < 5$$
$$-13 + 1 \leq 3x - 1 + 1 < 5 + 1$$
$$-12 \leq 3x < 6$$
$$\frac{-12}{3} \leq \frac{3x}{3} < \frac{6}{3}$$
$$-4 \leq x < 2$$

Interval notation: $[-4, 2)$

682   **Chapter 9**   More Equations and Inequalities

Section 9.2   Polynomial and Rational Inequalities

Key Concepts

The Test Point Method to Solve Polynomial and

Rational Inequalities

1. Find the boundary points of the inequality. (Boundary points are the real solutions to the related equation and points where the inequality is undefined.)
2. Plot the boundary points on the number line. This divides the number line into intervals.
3. Select a test point from each interval and substitute it into the original inequality.
   - If a test point makes the original inequality true, then that interval is part of the solution set.
4. Test the boundary points in the original inequality.
   - If the original inequality is strict ($<$ or $>$), do not include the boundary points in the solution set.
   - If the original inequality is defined using $\le$ or $\ge$, then include the boundary points that are defined within the inequality.

Note: Any boundary point that makes an expression within the inequality undefined must *always* be excluded from the solution set.

Example 1

$4x^2 - 7x - 2 < 0$

$(4x + 1)(x - 2) = 0$ Related equation

$4x + 1 = 0 \quad x - 2 = 0$

$x = -\dfrac{1}{4} \qquad x = 2$ The boundaries are $-\dfrac{1}{4}$ and 2.

Interval I: Test $x = -1$: $4(-1)^2 - 7(-1) - 2 \overset{?}{<} 0$ False

Interval II: Test $x = 0$: $4(0)^2 - 7(0) - 2 \overset{?}{<} 0$ True

Interval III: Test $x = 3$: $4(3)^2 - 7(3) - 2 \overset{?}{<} 0$ False

The strict inequality excludes the boundary points as solutions.

 The solution is $\left(-\dfrac{1}{4}, 2\right)$.

Examples

Example 2

$\dfrac{28}{2x - 3} \le 4$ The inequality is undefined for $x = \frac{3}{2}$. Find other possible boundary points by solving the related equation.

$\dfrac{28}{2x - 3} = 4$ Related equation

$(2x - 3) \cdot \dfrac{28}{2x - 3} = (2x - 3) \cdot 4$

$28 = 8x - 12$

$40 = 8x$

$x = 5$

The boundaries are $x = \dfrac{3}{2}$ and $x = 5$.

Interval I: Test $x = 1$: $\dfrac{28}{2(1) - 3} \overset{?}{\le} 4$ True

Interval II: Test $x = 2$: $\dfrac{28}{2(2) - 3} \overset{?}{\le} 4$ False

Interval III: Test $x = 6$: $\dfrac{28}{2(6) - 3} \overset{?}{\le} 4$ True

The boundary point $x = \frac{3}{2}$ is not included because $\dfrac{28}{2x - 3}$ is undefined there. The boundary $x = 5$ does check in the original inequality.

The solution is $(-\infty, \frac{3}{2}) \cup [5, \infty)$.

Section 9.3   Absolute Value Equations

Key Concepts

The equation $|x| = a$ is an absolute value equation. For $a \geq 0$, the solution to the equation $|x| = a$ is $x = a$ or $x = -a$.

Steps to Solve an Absolute Value Equation

1. Isolate the absolute value to write the equation in the form $|x| = a$.
2. If $a < 0$, there is no solution.
3. Otherwise, rewrite the equation $|x| = a$ as $x = a$ or $x = -a$.
4. Solve the equations from step 3.
5. Check answers in the original equation.

The equation $|x| = |y|$ implies $x = y$ or $x = -y$.

Examples

Example 1

$|2x - 3| + 5 = 10$

$\quad |2x - 3| = 5 \qquad$ Isolate the absolute value.

$2x - 3 = 5 \quad$ or $\quad 2x - 3 = -5$

$\quad 2x = 8 \quad$ or $\qquad 2x = -2$

$\qquad x = 4 \quad$ or $\qquad x = -1$

The solution set is $\{4, -1\}$.

Example 2

$|x + 2| + 5 = 1$

$\quad |x + 2| = -4 \quad$ There is no solution, $\{\ \}$.

Example 3

$|2x - 1| = |x + 4|$

$2x - 1 = x + 4 \quad$ or $\quad 2x - 1 = -(x + 4)$

$\qquad x = 5 \qquad$ or $\quad 2x - 1 = -x - 4$

$\qquad\qquad\qquad$ or $\qquad 3x = -3$

$\qquad\qquad\qquad$ or $\qquad\quad x = -1$

The solution set is $\{5, -1\}$.

684   **Chapter 9**   More Equations and Inequalities

Section 9.4   Absolute Value Inequalities

Key Concepts

Solutions to Absolute Value Inequalities

For $a > 0$, we have:

$|x| > a \Rightarrow x < -a$ or $x > a$

$|x| < a \Rightarrow -a < x < a$

Examples

Example 1

$$|5x - 2| < 12$$

$$-12 < 5x - 2 < 12$$

$$-10 < 5x < 14$$

$$-2 < x < \frac{14}{5}$$

The solution is $\left(-2, \frac{14}{5}\right)$.

Test Point Method to Solve Inequalities

1. Find the boundary points of the inequality. (Boundary points are the real solutions to the related equation and points where the inequality is undefined.)
2. Plot the boundary points on the number line. This divides the number line into intervals.
3. Select a test point from each interval and substitute it into the original inequality.
   - If a test point makes the original inequality true, then that interval is part of the solution set.
4. Test the boundary points in the original inequality.
   - If the original inequality is strict ($<$ or $>$), do not include the boundary in the solution set.
   - If the original inequality is defined using $\leq$ or $\geq$, then include the boundary points that are defined within the inequality.

Note: Any boundary point that makes an expression within the inequality undefined must *always* be excluded from the solution set.

If *a* is *negative* (*a* < 0), then

1. $|x| < a$ has no solution.
2. $|x| > a$ is true for all real numbers.

Example 2

$|x - 3| + 2 \geq 7$

$|x - 3| \geq 5$ Isolate the absolute value.

$|x - 3| = 5$ Solve the related equation.

$x - 3 = 5$ or $x - 3 = -5$

$x = 8$ or $x = -2$ Boundary points

Interval I: Test $x = -3$: $|(-3) - 3| + 2 \overset{?}{\geq} 7$ True

Interval II: Test $x = 0$: $|(0) - 3| + 2 \overset{?}{\geq} 7$ False

Interval III: Test $x = 9$: $|(9) - 3| + 2 \overset{?}{\geq} 7$ True

The solution is $(-\infty, -2] \cup [8, \infty)$.

Example 3

$|x + 5| > -2$

The solution is all real numbers because an absolute value will always be greater than a negative number.

$(-\infty, \infty)$

Example 4

$|x + 5| < -2$

There is no solution because an absolute value cannot be less than a negative number.

The solution set is { }.

Section 9.5   Linear Inequalities and Systems of Linear Inequalities in Two Variables

Key Concepts

A **linear inequality in two variables** is an inequality of the form $Ax + By < C$, $Ax + By > C$, $Ax + By \leq C$, or $Ax + By \geq C$.

Graphing a Linear Inequality in Two Variables

1. Write the inequality with the y variable isolated, if possible.
2. Graph the related equation. Draw a dashed line if the inequality is strict, $<$ or $>$. Otherwise, draw a solid line.
3. Shade above or below the line according to the following convention.

   - Shade *above* the line if the inequality is of the form $y > mx + b$ or $y \geq mx + b$.
   - Shade *below* the line if the inequality is of the form $y < mx + b$ or $y \leq mx + b$.

You can use test points to check that you have shaded the correct region. Select an ordered pair from the proposed solution set and substitute the values of x and y in the original inequality. If the test point produces a true statement, then you have shaded the correct region.

Graphing a System of Linear Inequalities in Two Variables

Graph each linear inequality in the system. The solution to the system is the intersection of the shaded regions.

Examples

Example 1

Graph the solution to the inequality $2x - y < 4$.

Graph the related equation, $y = 2x - 4$, with a dashed line.

Solve for y: $2x - y < 4$

$$-y < -2x + 4$$

$$y > 2x - 4$$

Shade above the line.

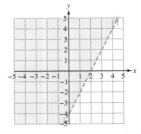

Example 2

Graph.

$x < 0$

$y > 2$

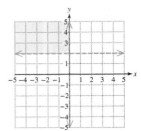

686   **Chapter 9**   More Equations and Inequalities

Chapter 9   Review Exercises

Section 9.1

1. Explain the difference between the union and intersection of two sets. You may use the sets C and D in the following diagram to provide an example.

$$C \quad D$$

Let $X = \{x \mid x \geq -10\}$, $Y = \{x \mid x < 1\}$, $Z = \{x \mid x > -1\}$, and $W = \{x \mid x \leq -3\}$. For Exercises 2–7, find the intersection or union of the sets X, Y, Z, and W. Write the answers in interval notation.

2. $X \cap Y$ **3.** $X \cup Y$

4. $Y \cup Z$ **5.** $Y \cap Z$

6. $Z \cup W$ **7.** $Z \cap W$

For Exercises 8–13, solve the compound inequalities. Write the solutions in interval notation.

8. $4m > -11$ and $4m - 3 \leq 13$

9. $4n - 7 < 1$ and $7 + 3n \geq -8$

10. $\frac{2}{3}t - 3 \leq 1$ or $\frac{3}{4}t - 2 > 7$

11. $2(3x + 1) < -10$ or $3(2x - 4) \geq 0$

12. $2 \geq -(b - 2) - 5b \geq -6$

13. $-4 \leq \frac{1}{2}(x - 1) < -\frac{3}{2}$

14. Normal levels of total cholesterol vary according to age. For adults between 25 and 40 yr old, the normal range is generally accepted to be between 140 and 225 mg/dL (milligrams per deciliter), inclusive. Let x represent cholesterol level.

   a. Write an inequality representing the normal range for total cholesterol for adults between 25 and 40 yr old.

   b. Write a compound inequality representing abnormal ranges for total cholesterol for adults between 25 and 40 yr old.

15. Normal levels of total cholesterol vary according to age. For adults younger than 25 yr old, the normal range is generally accepted to be between 125 and 200 mg/dL, inclusive. Let x represent cholesterol level.

   a. Write an inequality representing the normal range for total cholesterol for adults younger than 25 yr old.

   b. Write a compound inequality representing abnormal ranges for total cholesterol for adults younger than 25 yr old.

Section 9.2

16. Solve the equation and inequalities. How do your answers to parts (a), (b), and (c) relate to the graph of $g(x) = x^2 - 4$?

   a. $x^2 - 4 = 0$

   b. $x^2 - 4 < 0$

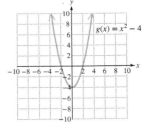

   c. $x^2 - 4 > 0$

17. Solve the equation and inequalities. How do your answers to parts (a), (b), (c), and (d) relate to the graph of $k(x) = \dfrac{4x}{(x - 2)}$?

   a. $\dfrac{4x}{x - 2} = 0$

   b. For which values is $k(x)$ undefined?

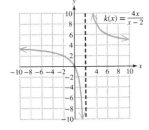

   c. $\dfrac{4x}{x - 2} \geq 0$

   d. $\dfrac{4x}{x - 2} \leq 0$

For Exercises 18–29, solve the inequalities. Write the answers in interval notation.

18. $w^2 - 4w - 12 < 0$

19. $t^2 + 6t + 9 \geq 0$

20. $\dfrac{12}{x+2} \leq 6$

21. $\dfrac{8}{p-1} \geq -4$

22. $3y(y-5)(y+2) > 0$

23. $-3c(c+2)(2c-5) < 0$

24. $-x^2 - 4x \geq 3$

25. $y^2 + 4y > 5$

26. $\dfrac{w+1}{w-3} > 1$

27. $\dfrac{2a}{a+3} \leq 2$

28. $t^2 + 10t + 25 \leq 0$

29. $-x^2 - 4x < 4$

Section 9.3

For Exercises 30–41, solve the absolute value equations.

30. $|x| = 10$

31. $|x| = 17$

32. $|8.7 - 2x| = 6.1$

33. $|5.25 - 5x| = 7.45$

34. $16 = |x+2| + 9$

35. $5 = |x-2| + 4$

36. $|4x - 1| + 6 = 4$

37. $|3x - 1| + 7 = 3$

38. $\left|\dfrac{7x-3}{5}\right| + 4 = 4$

39. $\left|\dfrac{4x+5}{-2}\right| - 3 = -3$

40. $|3x - 5| = |2x + 1|$

41. $|8x + 9| = |8x - 1|$

42. Which absolute value expression represents the distance between 3 and −2 on the number line?

$$|3 - (-2)| \qquad |-2 - 3|$$

Section 9.4

43. Write the compound inequality $x < -5$ or $x > 5$ as an absolute value inequality.

44. Write the compound inequality $-4 < x < 4$ as an absolute value inequality.

For Exercises 45–46, write an absolute value inequality that represents the solution set graphed here.

45.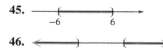

46.

For Exercises 47–60, solve the absolute value inequalities. Graph each solution set and write the solution in interval notation.

47. $|x + 6| \geq 8$

48. $|x + 8| \leq 3$

49. $2|7x - 1| + 4 > 4$

50. $4|5x + 1| - 3 > -3$

51. $|3x + 4| - 6 \leq -4$

52. $|5x - 3| + 3 \leq 6$

53. $\left|\dfrac{x}{2} - 6\right| < 5$

54. $\left|\dfrac{x}{3} + 2\right| < 2$

55. $|4 - 2x| + 8 \geq 8$

56. $|9 + 3x| + 1 \geq 1$

57. $-2|5.2x - 7.8| < 13$

58. $-|2.5x + 15| < 7$

59. $|3x - 8| < -1$

60. $|x + 5| < -4$

61. State one possible situation in which an absolute value inequality will have no solution.

62. State one possible situation in which an absolute value inequality will have a solution of all real numbers.

63. The Neilsen ratings estimated that the percent, p, of the television viewing audience watching a popular reality show was 20% with a 3% margin of error. Solve the inequality $|p - 0.20| \leq 0.03$ and interpret the answer in the context of this problem.

688   **Chapter 9**   More Equations and Inequalities

64. The length, L, of a screw is supposed to be $3\frac{3}{8}$ in. Due to variation in the production equipment, there is a $\frac{1}{4}$-in. margin of error. Solve the inequality $|L - 3\frac{3}{8}| \leq \frac{1}{4}$ and interpret the answer in the context of this problem.

Section 9.5

For Exercises 65–72, solve the inequalities by graphing.

65. $2x > -y + 5$

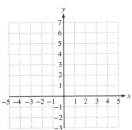

66. $2x \leq -8 - 3y$

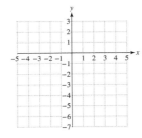

67. $y \geq -\frac{2}{3}x + 3$

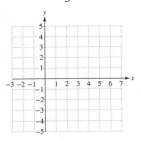

68. $y > \frac{3}{4}x - 2$

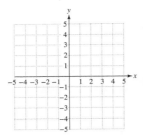

69. $x > -3$

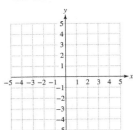

70. $x \leq 2$

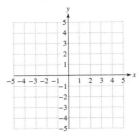

71. $x \geq \frac{1}{2}y$

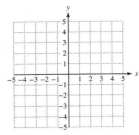

72. $x < \frac{2}{5}y$

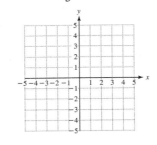

For Exercises 73–76 graph the system of inequalities.

73. $2x - y > -2$
 $2x - y \leq 2$

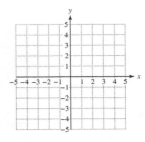

74. $3x + y < 6$
 $-3x + y < -2$

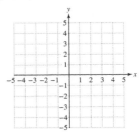

75. $y \geq x$
 $y \leq -x$

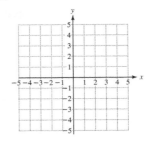

76. $x \geq 0$
 $y \geq 0$
 $y \leq -\frac{2}{3}x + 4$

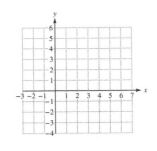

77. Suppose a farmer has 100 acres of land on which to grow oranges and grapefruit. Furthermore, because of demand from his customers, he wants to plant at least 4 times as many acres of orange trees as grapefruit trees.

© Adalberto Rios Lanz/Sexto Sol/Getty Images RF

Let x represent the number of acres of orange trees.

Let y represent the number of acres of grapefruit trees.

a. Write two inequalities that express the fact that the farmer cannot use a negative number of acres to plant orange and grapefruit trees.

b. Write an inequality that expresses the fact that the total number of acres used for growing orange and grapefruit trees is at most 100.

c. Write an inequality that expresses the fact that the farmer wants to plant at least 4 times as many orange trees as grapefruit trees.

d. Sketch the inequalities in parts (a)–(c) to find the feasible region for the farmer's distribution of orange and grapefruit trees.

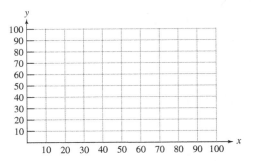

Chapter 9   Test

For Exercises 1–5, solve the compound inequalities. Write the answers in interval notation.

1. $-2 \le 3x - 1 \le 5$

2. $-\dfrac{3}{5}x - 1 \le 8$ or $-\dfrac{2}{3}x \ge 16$

3. $-2x - 3 > -3$ and $x + 3 \ge 0$

4. $5x + 1 \le 6$ or $2x + 4 > -6$

5. $2x - 3 > 1$ and $x + 4 < -1$

6. The normal range in humans of the enzyme adenosine deaminase (ADA), is between 9 and 33 IU (international units), inclusive. Let x represent the ADA level in international units.

a. Write an inequality representing the normal range for ADA.

b. Write a compound inequality representing abnormal ranges for ADA.

For Exercises 7–12, solve the polynomial and rational inequalities.

7. $50 - 2a^2 > 0$

8. $y^3 + 3y^2 - 4y - 12 < 0$

9. $5x^2 - 2x + 2 < 0$

10. $t^2 + 22t + 121 \le 0$

11. $\dfrac{2x - 1}{x - 6} \le 0$

12. $\dfrac{3}{w + 3} > 2$

For Exercises 13–14, solve the absolute value equations.

13. $\left| \dfrac{1}{2}x + 3 \right| - 4 = 4$

14. $|3x + 4| = |x - 12|$

For Exercises 15–18, solve the absolute value inequalities. Write the answers in interval notation.

15. $|3 - 2x| + 6 < 2$

16. $|3x - 8| > 9$

690   **Chapter 9**   More Equations and Inequalities

17. $|0.4x + 0.3| - 0.2 < 7$

18. $|7 - 3x| + 1 > -3$

19. The mass of a small piece of metal is measured to be 15.41 g. If the measurement error is at most ±0.01 g, write an absolute value inequality that represents the possible mass, x, of the piece of metal.

20. Graph the solution to the inequality $2x - 5y \geq 10$.

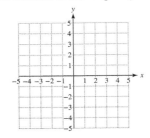

For Exercises 21–22, graph the solution to the system.

21. $x + y < 3$
$3x - 2y > -6$

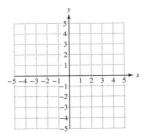

22. $5x \leq 5$
$x + y \leq 0$

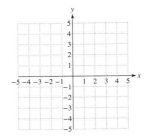

23. After menopause, women are at higher risk for hip fractures as a result of low calcium. As early as their teen years, women need at least 1200 mg of calcium per day (the USDA recommended daily allowance). One 8-oz glass of skim milk contains 300 mg of calcium, and one Antacid (regular strength) contains 400 mg of calcium. Let x represent the number of 8-oz glasses of milk that a woman drinks per day. Let y represent the number of Antacid tablets (regular strength) that a woman takes per day.

a. Write two inequalities that express the fact that the number of glasses of milk and the number of Antacid taken each day cannot be negative.

b. Write a linear inequality in terms of x and y for which the daily calcium intake is at least 1200 mg.

c. Graph the inequalities.

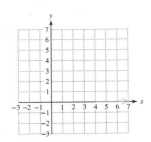

Chapters 1–9   Cumulative Review Exercises

1. Perform the indicated operations.

$$(2x - 3)(x - 4) - (x - 5)^2$$

2. Solve. $-9m + 3 = 2m(m - 4)$

For Exercises 3–4, solve the equation and inequalities. Write the solutions to the inequalities in interval notation.

3. a. $2|3 - p| - 4 = 2$

b. $2|3 - p| - 4 < 2$

c. $2|3 - p| - 4 > 2$

4. a. $\left|\dfrac{y-2}{4}\right| - 6 = -3$

b. $\left|\dfrac{y-2}{4}\right| - 6 < -3$

c. $\left|\dfrac{y-2}{4}\right| - 6 > -3$

5. Graph the inequality. $4x - y > 12$

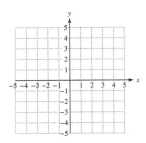

6. The time in minutes required for a rat to run through a maze depends on the number of trials, n, that the rat has practiced.

$$t(n) = \dfrac{3n+15}{n+1} \qquad n \geq 1$$

a. Find $t(1)$, $t(50)$, and $t(500)$, and interpret the results in the context of this problem. Round to 2 decimal places, if necessary.

b. Does there appear to be a limiting time in which the rat can complete the maze?

c. How many trials are required so that the rat is able to finish the maze in under 5 min?

7. a. Solve the inequality. $2x^2 + x - 10 \geq 0$

b. How does the answer in part (a) relate to the graph of the function $f(x) = 2x^2 + x - 10$?

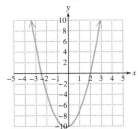

8. Graph the solution to the system of inequalities.

$$3x + y \leq -2$$

$$y \geq 1$$

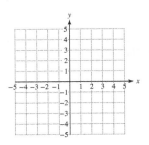

9. Simplify the expression.

$$2 - 3(x - 5) + 2[4 - (2x + 6)]$$

10. a. Divide the polynomials.

$$\dfrac{2x^4 - x^3 + 5x - 7}{x^2 + 2x - 1}$$

Identify the quotient and remainder.

b. Check your answer by multiplying.

11. The area of a trapezoid is given by $A = \frac{1}{2}h(b_1 + b_2)$.

a. Solve for b_1.

b. Find b_1 when $h = 4$ cm, $b_2 = 6$ cm, and $A = 32$ cm^2.

12. The speed of a car varies inversely as the time to travel a fixed distance. A car traveling the speed limit of 60 mph travels between two points in 10 sec. How fast is a car moving if it takes only 8 sec to cover the same distance?

13. Two angles are supplementary. One angle measures 9° more than twice the other angle. Find the measures of the angles.

14. Chemique invests $3000 less in an account earning 5% simple interest than she does in an account earning 6.5% simple interest. At the end of one year, she earns a total $770 in interest. Find the amount invested in each account.

15. Determine algebraically whether the lines are parallel, perpendicular, or neither.

$$4x - 2y = 5$$

$$-3x + 6y = 10$$

692   **Chapter 9** More Equations and Inequalities

16. Find the x- and y-intercepts and slope (if they exist) of the lines. Then graph the lines.

   a. $3x + 5 = 8$ **b.** $\frac{1}{2}x + y = 4$

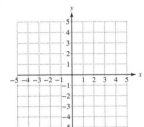 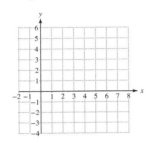

17. Find an equation of the line with slope $-\frac{2}{3}$ passing through the point $(4, -7)$. Write the final answer in slope-intercept form.

18. Solve the system of equations.

$$3x + y = z + 2$$
$$y = 1 - 2x$$
$$3z = -2y$$

19. Simplify. $\left(\dfrac{5x^2y^5}{30x^{-2}y^0} \right)^{-1}$

20. Against the wind, a plane can travel 6240 mi in 13 hr. On the return trip flying with the same wind, the plane can fly 6240 mi in 12 hr. Find the wind speed and the speed of the plane in still air.

21. The profit that a company makes manufacturing computer desks is given by

$$P(x) = -\tfrac{1}{5}(x - 20)(x - 650) \qquad x \geq 0$$

where x is the number of desks produced and $P(x)$ is the profit in dollars.

   a. Is this function constant, linear, or quadratic?

   b. Find $P(0)$ and interpret the result in the context of this problem.

   c. Find the values of x where $P(x) = 0$. Interpret the results in the context of this problem.

22. Factor the expression. $3x^3 - 6x^2 - 12x + 24$

23. Simplify completely. $\dfrac{x^{-1} - y^{-1}}{y^{-2} - x^{-2}}$

24. Divide. $\dfrac{a^3 + 64}{16 - a^2} \div \dfrac{a^3 - 4a^2 + 16a}{a^2 - 3a - 4}$

25. Perform the indicated operations.

$$\frac{1}{x^2 - 7x + 10} + \frac{1}{x^2 + 8x - 20}$$

Radicals and Complex Numbers

Radicals and Complex Numbers

10

Mathematics in Architecture

The area *A* of a triangle can be found if the length of one side (the base *b*) and the corresponding height *h* of the triangle are known. $A = \frac{1}{2}bh$

   However, if the base and height are not known, but the lengths of the three sides *a*, *b*, and *c* are known, then we can use Heron's formula to find the area of the triangle. Let *s* represent the semi-perimeter of the triangle.

That is, $s = \frac{1}{2}(a + b + c)$.

Then Heron's formula gives the area *A* as

  $A = \sqrt{s(s - a)(s - b)(s - c)}$

© Photov.com/AGE Fotostock RF

The Louvre pyramid, designed by architect I.M. Pei, is a glass structure that serves as the entrance to the Louvre Museum in Paris, France. Each triangular face is made of glass with sides of lengths 108.5 ft, 108.5 ft, and 116 ft. To determine the surface area of glass for each face, we can apply Heron's formula.

  $s = \frac{1}{2}(a + b + c) = \frac{1}{2}(108.5 + 108.5 + 116) = 166.5$

  $A = \sqrt{s(s - a)(s - b)(s - c)} = \sqrt{166.5(166.5 - 108.5)(166.5 - 108.5)(166.5 - 116)}$

      $\approx 5318 \text{ ft}^2$ Each face is approximately 5318 ft² of glass.

Heron's formula is one application of radicals. In this chapter, we will simplify radical expressions and solve equations containing radicals.

694   **Chapter 10**   Radicals and Complex Numbers

Section 10.1   Definition of an *n*th Root

Section 10.1   Definition of an *n*th Root

Concepts

1. Definition of a Square Root
2. Definition of an *n*th Root
3. Roots of Variable Expressions
4. Pythagorean Theorem
5. Radical Functions

1. Definition of a Square Root

The reverse operation to squaring a number is to find its square roots. For example, finding a square root of 36 is equivalent to asking, "when squared, what number equals 36?"

One obvious answer to this question is 6 because $(6)^2 = 36$, but -6 will also work, because $(-6)^2 = 36$.

Definition of a Square Root

b is a **square root** of a if $b^2 = a$.

Example 1   **Identifying Square Roots**

Identify the square roots of the real numbers.

a. 25   **b.** 49   **c.** 0   **d.** -9

Solution:

a. 5 is a square root of 25 because $(5)^2 = 25$.

-5 is a square root of 25 because $(-5)^2 = 25$.

b. 7 is a square root of 49 because $(7)^2 = 49$.

-7 is a square root of 49 because $(-7)^2 = 49$.

c. 0 is a square root of 0 because $(0)^2 = 0$.

d. There are no real numbers that when squared will equal a negative number; therefore, there are no real-valued square roots of -9.

Skill Practice   Identify the square roots of the real numbers.

1. 64   **2.** 16   **3.** 1   **4.** -100

TIP:

- All positive real numbers have two real-valued square roots (one positive and one negative).
- Zero has only one square root, which is zero itself.
- A negative number has no real-valued square roots.

Recall that the positive square root of a real number can be denoted with a **radical sign** $\sqrt{}$.

Positive and Negative Square Roots

Let a represent a positive real number. Then

1. $\sqrt{a}$ is the *positive* square root of a. The positive square root is also called the **principal square root**.
2. $-\sqrt{a}$ is the *negative* square root of a.
3. $\sqrt{0} = 0$

Answers

1. -8 and 8
2. -4 and 4
3. -1 and 1
4. No real-valued square roots

Example 2	**Simplifying Square Roots**

Simplify the square roots.

a. $\sqrt{36}$ **b.** $\sqrt{\dfrac{4}{9}}$ **c.** $\sqrt{0.04}$

Solution:

a. $\sqrt{36}$ denotes the positive square root of 36.

    $\sqrt{36} = 6$ because $(6)^2 = 36$

b. $\sqrt{\dfrac{4}{9}}$ denotes the positive square root of $\dfrac{4}{9}$.

    $\sqrt{\dfrac{4}{9}} = \dfrac{2}{3}$ because $\left(\dfrac{2}{3}\right)^2 = \dfrac{4}{9}$

c. $\sqrt{0.04}$ denotes the positive square root of 0.04.

    $\sqrt{0.04} = 0.2$ because $(0.2)^2 = 0.04$

Skill Practice Simplify the square roots.

5. $\sqrt{81}$ **6.** $\sqrt{\dfrac{36}{49}}$ **7.** $\sqrt{0.09}$

The numbers 36, $\frac{4}{9}$, and 0.04 are **perfect squares** because their square roots are rational numbers.

Radicals that cannot be simplified to rational numbers are irrational numbers. Recall that an irrational number cannot be written as a terminating or repeating decimal. For example, the symbol $\sqrt{13}$ is used to represent the *exact* value of the square root of 13. The symbol $\sqrt{42}$ is used to represent the *exact* value of the square root of 42. These values can be approximated by a rational number by using a calculator.

$$\sqrt{13} \approx 3.605551275 \qquad \sqrt{42} \approx 6.480740698$$

TIP: Before using a calculator to evaluate a square root, try estimating the value first.
$\sqrt{13}$ must be a number between 3 and 4 because $\sqrt{9} < \sqrt{13} < \sqrt{16}$.
$\sqrt{42}$ must be a number between 6 and 7 because $\sqrt{36} < \sqrt{42} < \sqrt{49}$.

Calculator Connections

Topic: Approximating Square Roots

Use a calculator to approximate the values of $\sqrt{13}$ and $\sqrt{42}$.

```
√(13)
          3.605551275
√(42)
          6.480740698
```

A negative number cannot have a real number as a square root because no real number when squared is negative. For example, $\sqrt{-25}$ is *not* a real number because there is no real number b for which $(b)^2 = -25$.

Answers

5. 9   **6.** $\dfrac{6}{7}$ **7.** 0.3

> | **Example 3** | **Simplifying Square Roots** |
>
> Simplify the square roots, if possible.
>
> **a.** $\sqrt{-144}$ **b.** $-\sqrt{144}$ **c.** $\sqrt{-0.01}$ **d.** $-\sqrt{\dfrac{1}{9}}$
>
> **Solution:**
>
> **a.** $\sqrt{-144}$ is *not* a real number. No real number when squared equals -144.
>
> **b.** $-\sqrt{144}$
>
> $$= -1 \cdot \sqrt{144}$$
> $$= -1 \cdot \quad 12$$
> $$= -12$$
>
> > **TIP:** For the expression $-\sqrt{144}$, the factor of -1 is *outside* the radical.
>
> **c.** $\sqrt{-0.01}$ is *not* a real number. No real number when squared equals -0.01.
>
> **d.** $-\sqrt{\dfrac{1}{9}}$
>
> $$= -1 \cdot \sqrt{\frac{1}{9}}$$
> $$= -1 \cdot \frac{1}{3}$$
> $$= -\frac{1}{3}$$

Skill Practice Simplify the square roots, if possible.

8. $\sqrt{-81}$ **9.** $-\sqrt{64}$ **10.** $-\sqrt{0.25}$ **11.** $\sqrt{-\dfrac{1}{4}}$

2. Definition of an *n*th Root

Finding a square root of a number is the reverse process of squaring a number. This concept can be extended to finding a third root (called a cube root), a fourth root, and in general an ***n*th root**.

> **Definition of an *n*th Root**
>
> b is an *n*th root of a if $b^n = a$.
>
> Example: 2 is a square root of 4 because 2^2 is 4.
>
> Example: 2 is a third root of 8 because 2^3 is 8.
>
> Example: 2 is a fourth root of 16 because 2^4 is 16.

The radical sign $\sqrt{}$ is used to denote the principal square root of a number. The symbol $\sqrt[n]{}$ is used to denote the principal *n*th root of a number. In the expression $\sqrt[n]{a}$, n is called the **index** of the radical, and a is called the **radicand**. For a square root, the index is 2, but it is usually not written ($\sqrt[2]{a}$ is denoted simply as $\sqrt{a}$). A radical with an index of 3 is called a **cube root**, denoted by $\sqrt[3]{a}$.

Answers

8. Not a real number   **9.** -8

10. -0.5 **11.** Not a real number

Evaluating $\sqrt[n]{a}$

1. If $n > 1$ is an *even* integer and $a > 0$, then $\sqrt[n]{a}$ is the principal (positive) nth root of a. Example: $\sqrt[4]{625} = 5$

2. If $n > 1$ is an *odd* integer, then $\sqrt[n]{a}$ is the nth root of a.
   Example: $\sqrt[3]{8} = 2$, $\sqrt[3]{-8} = -2$

3. If $n > 1$ is an integer, then $\sqrt[n]{0} = 0$.

For the purpose of simplifying nth roots, it is helpful to know numbers that are perfect squares as well as the following common perfect cubes, fourth powers, and fifth powers.

Perfect Cubes	Perfect Fourth Powers	Perfect Fifth Powers
$1^3 = 1$	$1^4 = 1$	$1^5 = 1$
$2^3 = 8$	$2^4 = 16$	$2^5 = 32$
$3^3 = 27$	$3^4 = 81$	$3^5 = 243$
$4^3 = 64$	$4^4 = 256$	$4^5 = 1024$
$5^3 = 125$	$5^4 = 625$	$5^5 = 3125$

Example 4   **Identifying the nth Root of a Real Number**

Simplify the expressions, if possible.

a. $\sqrt{4}$ b. $\sqrt[3]{64}$ c. $\sqrt[5]{-32}$ d. $\sqrt[4]{81}$

e. $\sqrt[6]{1,000,000}$ f. $\sqrt{-100}$ g. $\sqrt[4]{-16}$

Solution:

a. $\sqrt{4} = 2$ because $(2)^2 = 4$

b. $\sqrt[3]{64} = 4$ because $(4)^3 = 64$

c. $\sqrt[5]{-32} = -2$ because $(-2)^5 = -32$

d. $\sqrt[4]{81} = 3$ because $(3)^4 = 81$

e. $\sqrt[6]{1,000,000} = 10$ because $(10)^6 = 1,000,000$

f. $\sqrt{-100}$ is not a real number.   No real number when squared equals -100.

g. $\sqrt[4]{-16}$ is not a real number. No real number when raised to the fourth power equals -16.

Skill Practice Simplify if possible.

12. $\sqrt[4]{16}$ 13. $\sqrt[3]{1000}$ 14. $\sqrt[5]{-1}$ 15. $\sqrt[5]{32}$

16. $\sqrt[5]{100,000}$ 17. $\sqrt{-36}$ 18. $\sqrt[3]{-27}$

Calculator Connections

Topic: Approximating nth Roots

A calculator can be used to approximate nth roots by using the $\boxed{\sqrt[x]{}}$ function. On most calculators, the index is entered first.

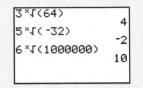

Examples 4(f) and 4(g) illustrate that an nth root of a negative quantity is not a real number if the index is even. This is because no real number raised to an even power is negative.

3. Roots of Variable Expressions

Finding an nth root of a variable expression is similar to finding an nth root of a numerical expression. For roots with an even index, however, particular care must be taken to obtain a nonnegative result.

Answers
12. 2   13. 10   14. −1
15. 2   16. 10
17. Not a real number   18. −3

698   Chapter 10   Radicals and Complex Numbers

> **Evaluating $\sqrt[n]{a^n}$**
> 1. If n is a positive *odd* integer, then $\sqrt[n]{a^n} = a$.
> 2. If n is a positive *even* integer, then $\sqrt[n]{a^n} = |a|$.

The absolute value bars are necessary for roots with an even index because the variable a may represent a positive quantity or a negative quantity. By using absolute value bars, $\sqrt[n]{a^n} = |a|$ is nonnegative and represents the principal nth root of a^n.

Example 5   **Simplifying Expressions of the Form $\sqrt[n]{a^n}$**

Simplify the expressions.

 a. $\sqrt[4]{(-3)^4}$ **b.** $\sqrt[5]{(-3)^5}$ **c.** $\sqrt{(x+2)^2}$ **d.** $\sqrt[6]{(a+b)^3}$ **e.** $\sqrt{y^4}$

Solution:

a. $\sqrt[4]{(-3)^4} = |-3| = 3$ Because this is an *even*-indexed root, absolute value bars are necessary to make the answer positive.

b. $\sqrt[5]{(-3)^5} = -3$ This is an *odd*-indexed root, so absolute value bars are not necessary.

c. $\sqrt{(x+2)^2} = |x+2|$ Because this is an *even*-indexed root, absolute value bars are necessary. The sign of the quantity $x+2$ is unknown; however, $|x+2| \geq 0$ regardless of the value of x.

d. $\sqrt[3]{(a+b)^3} = a+b$ This is an *odd*-indexed root, so absolute value bars are not necessary.

e. $\sqrt{y^4} = \sqrt{(y^2)^2}$

   $= |y^2|$ Because this is an even-indexed root, use absolute value bars.

   $= y^2$ However, because y^2 is nonnegative, the absolute value bars are not necessary.

Skill Practice Simplify the expressions.

19. $\sqrt{(-4)^2}$ **20.** $\sqrt[3]{(-4)^3}$ **21.** $\sqrt{(y+9)^2}$ **22.** $\sqrt[3]{(t+1)^3}$ **23.** $\sqrt[4]{v^8}$

If n is an even integer, then $\sqrt[n]{a^n} = |a|$; however, if the variable a is assumed to be *nonnegative*, then the absolute value bars may be dropped. That is, $\sqrt[n]{a^n} = a$ provided $a \geq 0$. In many examples and exercises, we will make the assumption that the variables within a radical expression are positive real numbers. In such a case, the absolute value bars are not needed to evaluate $\sqrt[n]{a^n}$.

Take a minute to examine the following patterns associated with perfect squares and perfect cubes. In general, any expression raised to an even power is a perfect square. An expression raised to a power that is a multiple of three is a perfect cube.

Perfect Squares	**Perfect Cubes**
$(x^1)^2 = x^2$	$(x^1)^3 = x^3$
$(x^2)^2 = x^4$	$(x^2)^3 = x^6$
$(x^3)^2 = x^6$	$(x^3)^3 = x^9$
$(x^4)^2 = x^8$	$(x^4)^3 = x^{12}$

These patterns may be extended to higher powers.

Answers
19. 4   **20.** -4 **21.** $|y+9|$
22. $t+1$ **23.** v^2

Example 6	**Simplifying *n*th Roots**

Simplify the expressions. Assume that all variables are positive real numbers.

   a. $\sqrt{y^8}$ **b.** $\sqrt[3]{27a^3}$ **c.** $\sqrt[5]{\dfrac{a^5}{b^5}}$ **d.** $-\sqrt[4]{\dfrac{81x^4y^8}{16}}$

Solution:

  a. $\sqrt{y^8} = \sqrt{(y^4)^2}$ **b.** $\sqrt[3]{27a^3} = \sqrt[3]{(3a)^3}$

            $= y^4$ $= 3a$

  c. $\sqrt[5]{\dfrac{a^5}{b^5}} = \sqrt[5]{\left(\dfrac{a}{b}\right)^5}$ **d.** $-\sqrt[4]{\dfrac{81x^4y^8}{16}} = -\sqrt[4]{\left(\dfrac{3xy^2}{2}\right)^4}$

            $= \dfrac{a}{b}$ $= -\dfrac{3xy^2}{2}$

> **TIP:** In Example 6, the variables are assumed to represent positive numbers. Therefore, absolute value bars are not necessary in the simplified form.

Skill Practice Simplify the expressions. Assume all variables represent positive real numbers.

  24. $\sqrt{t^6}$ **25.** $\sqrt[3]{64y^{12}}$ **26.** $\sqrt[4]{\dfrac{x^4}{y^4}}$ **27.** $-\sqrt[5]{\dfrac{32a^5}{b^{10}}}$

4. Pythagorean Theorem

Given a right triangle with legs of lengths a and b and hypotenuse of length c, the **Pythagorean theorem** can be stated as $a^2 + b^2 = c^2$. See Figure 10-1.

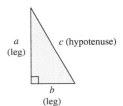

Figure 10-1

Example 7	**Applying the Pythagorean Theorem**

Use the Pythagorean theorem and the definition of the principal square root to find the length of the unknown side.

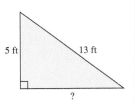

Solution:

Label the sides of the triangle.

  $a^2 + b^2 = c^2$ Apply the

  $(5)^2 + b^2 = (13)^2$ Pythagorean

                    theorem.

   $25 + b^2 = 169$ Simplify.

        $b^2 = 169 - 25$ Isolate b^2.

        $b^2 = 144$ By definition, b must be one of the square roots of 144. Because b represents the length of a side of a

         $b = 12$ triangle, choose the positive square root of 144.

The third side is 12 ft long.

Skill Practice

28. Use the Pythagorean theorem and the definition of the principal square root to find the length of the unknown side of the right triangle.

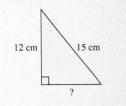

Answers

24. t^3 **25.** $4y^4$ **26.** $\dfrac{x}{y}$

27. $-\dfrac{2a}{b^2}$ **28.** 9 cm

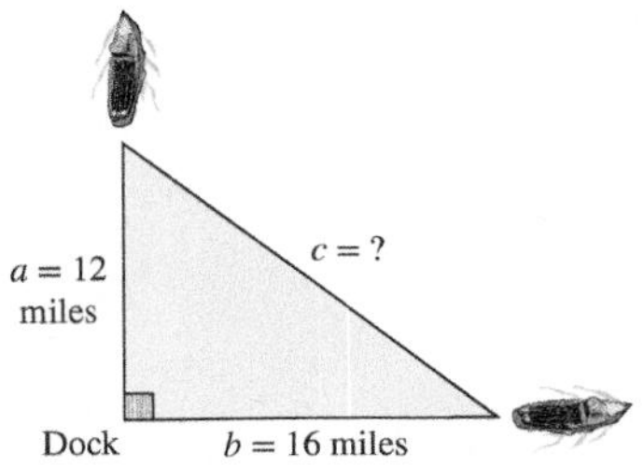

$a = 12$ miles

$c = ?$

Dock $b = 16$ miles

Figure 10-2

| Example 8 | **Applying the Pythagorean Theorem** |

Two boats leave a dock at 12:00 noon. One travels due north at 6 mph, and the other travels due east at 8 mph (Figure 10-2). How far apart are the two boats after 2 hr?

Solution:

The boat traveling north travels a distance of (6 mph)(2 hr) = 12 mi. The boat traveling east travels a distance of (8 mph)(2 hr) = 16 mi. The course of the boats forms a right triangle where the hypotenuse represents the distance between them.

$$a^2 + b^2 = c^2$$

$$(12)^2 + (16)^2 = c^2 \qquad \text{Apply the Pythagorean theorem.}$$

$$144 + 256 = c^2 \qquad \text{Simplify.}$$

$$400 = c^2$$

$$\sqrt{400} = c \qquad \text{By definition, } c \text{ must be one of the square roots of } 400. \text{ Choose the positive square root of } 400 \text{ to}$$

$$20 = c \qquad \text{represent the distance between the two boats.}$$

The boats are 20 mi apart.

Skill Practice

29. Two cars leave from the same place at the same time. One travels west at 40 mph, and the other travels north at 30 mph. How far apart are they after 2 hr?

5. Radical Functions

If n is an integer greater than 1, then a function written in the form $f(x) = \sqrt[n]{x}$ is called a **radical function**. Note that if n is an even integer, then the function will be a real number only if the radicand is nonnegative. Therefore, the domain is restricted to nonnegative real numbers, or equivalently, $[0, \infty)$. If n is an odd integer, then the domain is all real numbers.

| Example 9 | **Determining the Domain of Radical Functions** |

For each function, write the domain in interval notation.

a. $g(t) = \sqrt[4]{t - 2}$ **b.** $h(a) = \sqrt[3]{a - 3}$ **c.** $k(x) = \sqrt{3 - 5x} + 2$

Solution:

a. $g(t) = \sqrt[4]{t - 2}$ The index is even. The radicand must be nonnegative.

$$t - 2 \geq 0 \qquad \text{Set the radicand greater than or equal to zero.}$$

$$t \geq 2 \qquad \text{Solve for } t.$$

The domain is $[2, \infty)$.

b. $h(a) = \sqrt[3]{a - 3}$ The index is odd; therefore, the domain is all real numbers.

The domain is $(-\infty, \infty)$.

Answer

29. 100 mi

c. $\quad k(x) = \sqrt{3 - 5x} + 2$ The index is even; therefore, the radicand must be nonnegative.

$\quad 3 - 5x \geq 0$ Set the radicand greater than or equal to zero.

$\quad\quad -5x \geq -3$ Solve for x.

$\quad\quad \dfrac{-5x}{-5} \leq \dfrac{-3}{-5}$ Reverse the inequality sign.

$\quad\quad\quad x \leq \dfrac{3}{5}$

The domain is $\left(-\infty, \frac{3}{5}\right]$.

Skill Practice For each function, write the domain in interval notation.

30. $f(x) = \sqrt{x + 5}$ **31.** $g(t) = \sqrt[3]{t - 9}$ **32.** $h(a) = \sqrt{1 - 2a}$

Calculator Connections

Topic: Graphing Radical Functions

We can graph the functions defined in Example 9. The graphs support the answers we obtained for the domain of each function.

$\quad g(t) = \sqrt[4]{t - 2}$ $h(a) = \sqrt[3]{a - 3}$ $k(x) = \sqrt{3 - 5x} + 2$

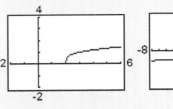   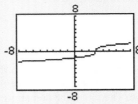   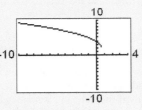

Domain: $[2, \infty)$ Domain: $(-\infty, \infty)$ Domain: $\left(-\infty, \frac{3}{5}\right]$

Example 10   **Graphing a Radical Function**

Given $f(x) = \sqrt{3 - x}$

a. Write the domain of f in interval notation.

b. Graph f by making a table of ordered pairs.

Solution:

a. $\quad f(x) = \sqrt{3 - x}$

$\quad\quad 3 - x \geq 0$ The index is even. The radicand must be greater than or equal to zero.

$\quad\quad\quad -x \geq -3$

$\quad\quad\quad\quad x \leq 3$ Reverse the inequality sign.

The domain is $(-\infty, 3]$.

Answers

30. $[-5, \infty)$ **31.** $(-\infty, \infty)$

32. $\left(-\infty, \frac{1}{2}\right]$

702   **Chapter 10**   Radicals and Complex Numbers

b. Create a table of ordered pairs where x values are taken to be less than or equal to 3.

x	$f(x)$
3	0
2	1
-1	2
-6	3

$f(3) = \sqrt{3-3} = \sqrt{0} = 0$
$f(2) = \sqrt{3-2} = \sqrt{1} = 1$
$f(-1) = \sqrt{3-(-1)} = \sqrt{4} = 2$
$f(-6) = \sqrt{3-(-6)} = \sqrt{9} = 3$

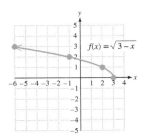

Answers

33. a. $[-4, \infty)$

b.

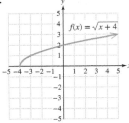

Skill Practice

33. Given $f(x) = \sqrt{x+4}$
  a. Write the domain of f in interval notation.
  b. Graph f by making a table of ordered pairs.

Section 10.1   Practice Exercises

Vocabulary and Key Concepts

1. a. If $b^2 = a$, then _____ is a square root of _____.

  b. Given $a > 0$, the symbol $\sqrt{a}$ denotes the positive or _____ square root of a.

  c. b is an nth root of a if _____ = _____.

  d. Given the symbol $\sqrt[n]{a}$, the value n is called the _____ and a is called the _____.

  e. The symbol $\sqrt[3]{a}$ denotes the _____ root of a.

  f. The expression $\sqrt{-4}$ (is/is not) a real number. The expression $-\sqrt{4}$ (is/is not) a real number.

  g. The expression $\sqrt[n]{a^n} = |a|$ if n is (even/odd). The expression $\sqrt[n]{a^n} = a$ if n is (even/odd).

  h. Given a right triangle with legs a and b and hypotenuse c, the _____ theorem is stated as $a^2 + b^2 =$ _____.

  i. In interval notation, the domain of $f(x) = \sqrt{x}$ is _____, whereas the domain of $g(x) = \sqrt[3]{x}$ is _____.

  j. Which of the following values of x are *not* in the domain of $h(x) = \sqrt{x+3}$: $x = -5, x = -4, x = -3, x = -2,$ $x = -1, x = 0$?

Concept 1: Definition of a Square Root

2. Simplify the expression $\sqrt[3]{8}$. Explain how you can check your answer.

3. a. Find the square roots of 64. **(See Example 1.)**

  b. Find $\sqrt{64}$.

  c. Explain the difference between the answers in part (a) and part (b).

4. a. Find the square roots of 121.

  b. Find $\sqrt{121}$.

  c. Explain the difference between the answers in part (a) and part (b).

5. a. What is the principal square root of 81?

  b. What is the negative square root of 81?

6. a. What is the principal square root of 100?

  b. What is the negative square root of 100?

7. Using the definition of a square root, explain why $\sqrt{-36}$ is not a real number.

For Exercises 8–19, evaluate the roots without using a calculator. Identify those that are not real numbers.
(See Examples 2–3.)

8. $\sqrt{25}$

9. $\sqrt{49}$

10. $-\sqrt{25}$

11. $-\sqrt{49}$

12. $\sqrt{-25}$

13. $\sqrt{-49}$

14. $\sqrt{\dfrac{100}{121}}$

15. $\sqrt{\dfrac{64}{9}}$

16. $\sqrt{0.64}$

17. $\sqrt{0.81}$

18. $-\sqrt{0.0144}$

19. $-\sqrt{0.16}$

Concept 2: Definition of an *n*th Root

20. Using the definition of an *n*th root, explain why $\sqrt[4]{-16}$ is not a real number.

For Exercises 21–38, evaluate the roots without using a calculator. Identify those that are not real numbers.
(See Example 4.)

21. a. $\sqrt{64}$ **b.** $\sqrt[3]{64}$ **c.** $-\sqrt{64}$

   d. $-\sqrt[3]{64}$ **e.** $\sqrt{-64}$ **f.** $\sqrt[3]{-64}$

22. a. $\sqrt{16}$ **b.** $\sqrt[4]{16}$ **c.** $-\sqrt{16}$

   d. $-\sqrt[4]{16}$ **e.** $\sqrt{-16}$ **f.** $\sqrt[4]{-16}$

23. $\sqrt[3]{-27}$

24. $\sqrt[3]{-125}$

25. $\sqrt[3]{\dfrac{1}{8}}$

26. $\sqrt[5]{\dfrac{1}{32}}$

27. $\sqrt[5]{32}$

28. $\sqrt[4]{1}$

29. $\sqrt[3]{-\dfrac{125}{64}}$

30. $\sqrt[3]{-\dfrac{8}{27}}$

31. $\sqrt[4]{-1}$

32. $\sqrt[6]{-1}$

33. $\sqrt[6]{1,000,000}$

34. $\sqrt[4]{10,000}$

35. $-\sqrt[3]{0.008}$

36. $-\sqrt[4]{0.0016}$

37. $\sqrt[4]{0.0625}$

38. $\sqrt[3]{0.064}$

Concept 3: Roots of Variable Expressions

For Exercises 39–58, simplify the radical expressions. **(See Example 5.)**

39. $\sqrt{a^2}$

40. $\sqrt[4]{a^4}$

41. $\sqrt[3]{a^3}$

42. $\sqrt[5]{a^5}$

43. $\sqrt[6]{a^6}$

44. $\sqrt[7]{a^7}$

45. $\sqrt{(x+1)^2}$

46. $\sqrt[3]{(y+3)^3}$

47. $\sqrt{x^2 y^4}$

48. $\sqrt[3]{(u+v)^3}$

49. $-\sqrt[3]{\dfrac{x^3}{y^3}}, \quad y \neq 0$

50. $\sqrt[4]{\dfrac{a^4}{b^8}}, \quad b \neq 0$

51. $\dfrac{2}{\sqrt[4]{x^4}}, \quad x \neq 0$

52. $\sqrt{(-5)^2}$

53. $\sqrt[3]{(-92)^3}$

54. $\sqrt[6]{(50)^6}$

55. $\sqrt[10]{(-2)^{10}}$

56. $\sqrt[5]{(-2)^5}$

57. $\sqrt[7]{(-923)^7}$

58. $\sqrt[6]{(-417)^6}$

For Exercises 59–74, simplify the expressions. Assume all variables are positive real numbers. **(See Example 6.)**

59. $\sqrt{y^8}$

60. $\sqrt{x^4}$

61. $\sqrt{\dfrac{a^6}{b^2}}$

62. $\sqrt{\dfrac{w^2}{z^4}}$

63. $-\sqrt{\dfrac{25}{q^2}}$

64. $-\sqrt{\dfrac{p^6}{81}}$

65. $\sqrt{9x^2 y^4 z^2}$

66. $\sqrt{4a^4 b^2 c^6}$

704   **Chapter 10**   Radicals and Complex Numbers

67. $\sqrt{\dfrac{h^2 k^4}{16}}$

68. $\sqrt{\dfrac{4x^2}{y^8}}$

69. $-\sqrt[3]{\dfrac{t^3}{27}}$

70. $\sqrt[4]{\dfrac{16}{w^4}}$

71. $\sqrt[5]{32y^{10}}$

72. $\sqrt[3]{64x^6 y^3}$

 73. $\sqrt[6]{64p^{12} q^{18}}$

74. $\sqrt[4]{16r^{12} s^8}$

Concept 4: Pythagorean Theorem

For Exercises 75–78, find the length of the third side of each triangle by using the Pythagorean theorem. **(See Example 7.)**

75.

76.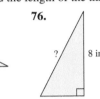

77.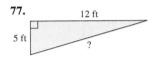

78.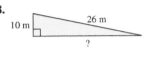

For Exercises 79–82, use the Pythagorean theorem.

79. Roberto and Sherona began running from the same place at the same time. They ran along two different paths that formed right angles with each other. Roberto ran 4 mi and stopped, while Sherona ran 3 mi and stopped. How far apart were they when they stopped? **(See Example 8.)**

80. Leine and Laura began hiking from their campground. Laura headed south while Leine headed east. Laura walked 12 mi and Leine walked 5 mi. How far apart were they when they stopped walking?

81. Two mountain bikers take off from the same place at the same time. One travels north at 4 mph, and the other travels east at 3 mph. How far apart are they after 5 hr?

82. Professor Ortiz leaves campus on her bike, heading west at 12 ft/sec. Professor Wilson leaves campus at the same time and walks south at 5 ft/sec. How far apart are they after 40 sec?

Concept 5: Radical Functions

For Exercises 83–86, evaluate the function for the given values of x. Then write the domain of the function in interval notation. **(See Example 9.)**

83. $h(x) = \sqrt{x - 2}$

   a. $h(0)$

   b. $h(1)$

   c. $h(2)$

   d. $h(3)$

   e. $h(6)$

84. $k(x) = \sqrt{x + 1}$

   a. $k(-3)$

   b. $k(-2)$

   c. $k(-1)$

   d. $k(0)$

   e. $k(3)$

85. $g(x) = \sqrt[3]{x - 2}$

   a. $g(-6)$

   b. $g(1)$

   c. $g(2)$

   d. $g(3)$

86. $f(x) = \sqrt[3]{x + 1}$

   a. $f(-9)$

   b. $f(-2)$

   c. $f(0)$

   d. $f(7)$

For each function defined in Exercises 87–94, write the domain in interval notation. **(See Example 9.)**

87. $f(x) = \sqrt{5 - 2x}$

88. $g(x) = \sqrt{3 - 4x}$

89. $k(x) = \sqrt[3]{4x - 7}$

90. $R(x) = \sqrt[3]{x + 1}$

91. $M(x) = \sqrt{x - 5} + 3$

92. $N(x) = \sqrt{x + 3} - 1$

93. $F(x) = \sqrt[3]{x + 7} - 2$

94. $G(x) = \sqrt[3]{x - 10} + 4$

For Exercises 95–102,

a. Write the domain of *f* in interval notation.

b. Graph *f* by making a table of ordered pairs. **(See Example 10.)**

95. $f(x) = \sqrt{1 - x}$ **96.** $f(x) = \sqrt{2 - x}$ **97.** $f(x) = \sqrt{x + 3}$ **98.** $f(x) = \sqrt{x + 1}$

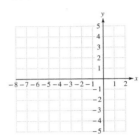 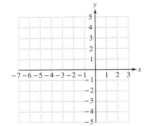 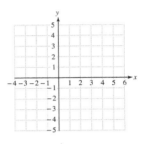 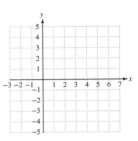

99. $f(x) = \sqrt{x} + 2$ **100.** $f(x) = \sqrt{x} - 1$ **101.** $f(x) = \sqrt[3]{x - 1}$ **102.** $f(x) = \sqrt[3]{x + 2}$

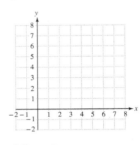 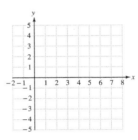 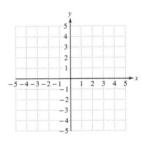 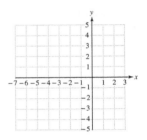

Mixed Exercises

For Exercises 103–106, write the English phrase as an algebraic expression.

103. The sum of *q* and the square of *p*

104. The product of 11 and the cube root of *x*

105. The quotient of 6 and the cube root of *x*

106. The difference of *y* and the principal square root of *x*

107. If a square has an area of 64 in.^{2}, then what are the lengths of the sides?

108. If a square has an area of 121 m^2, then what are the lengths of the sides?

Graphing Calculator Exercises

For Exercises 109–116, use a calculator to evaluate the expressions to four decimal places.

109. $\sqrt{69}$ **110.** $\sqrt{5798}$ **111.** $2 + \sqrt[3]{5}$ **112.** $3 - 2\sqrt[4]{10}$

113. $7\sqrt[4]{25}$ **114.** $-3\sqrt[3]{9}$ **115.** $\dfrac{3 - \sqrt{19}}{11}$ **116.** $\dfrac{5 + 2\sqrt{15}}{12}$

117. Graph $h(x) = \sqrt{x - 2}$. Use the graph to confirm the domain found in Exercise 83.

118. Graph $k(x) = \sqrt{x + 1}$. Use the graph to confirm the domain found in Exercise 84.

119. Graph $g(x) = \sqrt[3]{x - 2}$. Use the graph to confirm the domain found in Exercise 85.

120. Graph $f(x) = \sqrt[3]{x + 1}$. Use the graph to confirm the domain found in Exercise 86.

706   **Chapter 10**   Radicals and Complex Numbers

Section 10.2 Rational Exponents

1. Definition of $a^{1/n}$ and $a^{m/n}$

In this section, the properties for simplifying expressions with integer exponents are expanded to include expressions with rational exponents. We begin by defining expressions of the form $a^{1/n}$.

> ### Definition of $a^{1/n}$
> Let a be a real number, and let n be an integer such that $n > 1$. If $\sqrt[n]{a}$ is a real number, then
> $$a^{1/n} = \sqrt[n]{a}$$

Example 1   **Evaluating Expressions of the Form $a^{1/n}$**

Convert the expression to radical form and simplify, if possible.

  a. $(-8)^{1/3}$ **b.** $81^{1/4}$ **c.** $-100^{1/2}$ **d.** $(-100)^{1/2}$ **e.** $16^{-1/2}$

Solution:

  a. $(-8)^{1/3} = \sqrt[3]{-8} = -2$

  b. $81^{1/4} = \sqrt[4]{81} = 3$

  c. $-100^{1/2} = -1 \cdot 100^{1/2}$ The exponent applies only to the base of 100.

            $= -1\sqrt{100}$

            $= -10$

  d. $(-100)^{1/2}$ is not a real number because $\sqrt{-100}$ is not a real number.

  e. $16^{-1/2} = \dfrac{1}{16^{1/2}}$ Write the expression with a positive exponent.

                    Recall that $b^{-n} = \dfrac{1}{b^n}$.

       $= \dfrac{1}{\sqrt{16}}$

       $= \dfrac{1}{4}$

Skill Practice Convert the expression to radical form and simplify, if possible.

  1. $(-64)^{1/3}$ **2.** $16^{1/4}$ **3.** $-36^{1/2}$ **4.** $(-36)^{1/2}$ **5.** $64^{-1/3}$

If $\sqrt[n]{a}$ is a real number, then we can define an expression of the form $a^{m/n}$ in such a way that the multiplication property of exponents still holds true. For example:

$$16^{3/4} \begin{cases} (16^{1/4})^3 = (\sqrt[4]{16})^3 = (2)^3 = 8 \\ (16^3)^{1/4} = \sqrt[4]{16^3} = \sqrt[4]{4096} = 8 \end{cases}$$

Answers

1. -4 **2.** 2   **3.** -6

4. Not a real number   **5.** $\dfrac{1}{4}$

Definition of $a^{m/n}$

Let a be a real number, and let m and n be positive integers such that m and n share no common factors and $n > 1$. If $\sqrt[n]{a}$ is a real number, then

$$a^{m/n} = (a^{1/n})^m = (\sqrt[n]{a})^m \quad \text{and} \quad a^{m/n} = (a^m)^{1/n} = \sqrt[n]{a^m}$$

The rational exponent in the expression $a^{m/n}$ is essentially performing two operations. The numerator of the exponent raises the base to the mth power. The denominator takes the nth root.

Example 2   **Evaluating Expressions of the Form $a^{m/n}$**

Convert each expression to radical form and simplify.

a. $8^{2/3}$ **b.** $100^{5/2}$ **c.** $\left(\dfrac{1}{25}\right)^{3/2}$ **d.** $4^{-3/2}$ **e.** $(-81)^{3/4}$

Solution:

a. $8^{2/3} = (\sqrt[3]{8})^2$ Take the cube root of 8 and square the result.

$= (2)^2$ Simplify.

$= 4$

b. $100^{5/2} = (\sqrt{100})^5$ Take the square root of 100 and raise the result to the fifth power.

$= (10)^5$ Simplify.

$= 100{,}000$

c. $\left(\dfrac{1}{25}\right)^{3/2} = \left(\sqrt{\dfrac{1}{25}}\right)^3$ Take the square root of $\dfrac{1}{25}$ and cube the result.

$= \left(\dfrac{1}{5}\right)^3$ Simplify.

$= \dfrac{1}{125}$

d. $4^{-3/2} = \left(\dfrac{1}{4}\right)^{3/2} = \dfrac{1}{4^{3/2}}$ Write the expression with positive exponents.

$= \dfrac{1}{(\sqrt{4})^3}$ Take the square root of 4 and cube the result.

$= \dfrac{1}{2^3}$ Simplify.

$= \dfrac{1}{8}$

e. $(-81)^{3/4}$ is not a real number because $\sqrt[4]{-81}$ is not a real number.

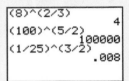

Skill Practice Convert each expression to radical form and simplify.

6. $9^{3/2}$ **7.** $8^{5/3}$ **8.** $\left(\dfrac{1}{27}\right)^{4/3}$ **9.** $32^{-4/5}$ **10.** $(-4)^{3/2}$

2. Converting Between Rational Exponents and Radical Notation

Example 3   **Using Radical Notation and Rational Exponents**

Convert each expression to radical notation. Assume all variables represent positive real numbers.

 a. $a^{3/5}$ **b.** $5^{1/3}x^{2/3}$ **c.** $3y^{1/4}$ **d.** $9z^{-3/4}$

Solution:

 a. $a^{3/5} = \sqrt[5]{a^3}$ or $\left(\sqrt[5]{a}\right)^3$

 b. $5^{1/3}x^{2/3} = (5x^2)^{1/3} = \sqrt[3]{5x^2}$

 c. $3y^{1/4} = 3\sqrt[4]{y}$ Note that the coefficient 3 is not raised to the $\frac{1}{4}$ power.

 d. $9z^{-3/4} = 9 \cdot \dfrac{1}{z^{3/4}} = \dfrac{9}{\sqrt[4]{z^3}}$ Note that the coefficient 9 has an implied exponent of 1, not $-\frac{3}{4}$.

Skill Practice Convert each expression to radical notation. Assume all variables represent positive real numbers.

 11. $t^{4/5}$ **12.** $2^{1/4}y^{3/4}$ **13.** $10p^{1/2}$ **14.** $11q^{-2/3}$

Example 4   **Using Radical Notation and Rational Exponents**

Convert each expression to an equivalent expression by using rational exponents. Assume that all variables represent positive real numbers.

 a. $\sqrt[4]{b^3}$ **b.** $\sqrt{7a}$ **c.** $7\sqrt{a}$

Solution:

 a. $\sqrt[4]{b^3} = b^{3/4}$ **b.** $\sqrt{7a} = (7a)^{1/2}$ **c.** $7\sqrt{a} = 7a^{1/2}$

Skill Practice Convert to an equivalent expression using rational exponents. Assume all variables represent positive real numbers.
 15. $\sqrt[3]{x^2}$ **16.** $\sqrt{5y}$ **17.** $5\sqrt{y}$

Answers

6. 27   **7.** 32   **8.** $\dfrac{1}{81}$

9. $\dfrac{1}{16}$ **10.** Not a real number

11. $\sqrt[5]{t^4}$ **12.** $\sqrt[4]{2y^3}$ **13.** $10\sqrt{p}$

14. $\dfrac{11}{\sqrt[3]{q^2}}$ **15.** $x^{2/3}$ **16.** $(5y)^{1/2}$

17. $5y^{1/2}$

3. Properties of Rational Exponents

The properties and definitions for simplifying expressions with integer exponents also apply to rational exponents.

Definitions and Properties of Exponents

Let a and b be nonzero real numbers. Let m and n be rational numbers such that a^m, a^n, and b^m are real numbers.

Description	Property	Example
1. Multiplying like bases	$a^m a^n = a^{m+n}$	$x^{1/3} x^{4/3} = x^{5/3}$
2. Dividing like bases	$\dfrac{a^m}{a^n} = a^{m-n}$	$\dfrac{x^{3/5}}{x^{1/5}} = x^{2/5}$
3. The power rule	$(a^m)^n = a^{mn}$	$(2^{1/3})^{1/2} = 2^{1/6}$
4. Power of a product	$(ab)^m = a^m b^m$	$(9y)^{1/2} = 9^{1/2} y^{1/2} = 3y^{1/2}$
5. Power of a quotient	$\left(\dfrac{a}{b}\right)^m = \dfrac{a^m}{b^m}$	$\left(\dfrac{4}{25}\right)^{1/2} = \dfrac{4^{1/2}}{25^{1/2}} = \dfrac{2}{5}$

Description	Definition	Example
1. Negative exponents	$a^{-m} = \left(\dfrac{1}{a}\right)^m = \dfrac{1}{a^m}$	$(8)^{-1/3} = \left(\dfrac{1}{8}\right)^{1/3} = \dfrac{1}{2}$
2. Zero exponent	$a^0 = 1$	$5^0 = 1$

Example 5   Simplifying Expressions with Rational Exponents

Use the properties of exponents to simplify the expressions. Assume all variables represent positive real numbers.

a. $y^{2/5} y^{3/5}$ **b.** $\dfrac{6a^{-1/2}}{a^{3/2}}$ **c.** $\left(\dfrac{s^{1/2} t^{1/3}}{w^{3/4}}\right)^4$

Solution:

a. $y^{2/5} y^{3/5} = y^{(2/5)+(3/5)}$ Multiply like bases by adding exponents.

$\quad\quad = y^{5/5}$ Simplify.

$\quad\quad = y$

b. $\dfrac{6a^{-1/2}}{a^{3/2}}$

$\quad = 6a^{(-1/2)-(3/2)}$ Divide like bases by subtracting exponents.

$\quad = 6a^{-2}$ Simplify: $-\dfrac{1}{2} - \left(\dfrac{3}{2}\right) = -\dfrac{4}{2} = -2$

$\quad = \dfrac{6}{a^2}$ Simplify the negative exponent.

c. $\left(\dfrac{s^{1/2} t^{1/3}}{w^{3/4}}\right)^4 = \dfrac{s^{(1/2)\cdot 4} t^{(1/3)\cdot 4}}{w^{(3/4)\cdot 4}}$ Apply the power rule. Multiply exponents.

$\quad\quad = \dfrac{s^2 t^{4/3}}{w^3}$ Simplify.

Skill Practice Use the properties of exponents to simplify the expressions. Assume all variables represent positive real numbers.

18. $x^{1/2} \cdot x^{3/4}$ **19.** $\dfrac{4k^{-2/3}}{k^{1/3}}$ **20.** $\left(\dfrac{a^{1/3} b^{1/2}}{c^{5/8}}\right)^6$

Answers

18. $x^{5/4}$ **19.** $\dfrac{4}{k}$ **20.** $\dfrac{a^2 b^3}{c^{15/4}}$

710   Chapter 10   Radicals and Complex Numbers

4. Applications Involving Rational Exponents

Example 6   **Applying Rational Exponents**

Suppose P dollars in principal is invested in an account that earns interest annually. If after t years the investment grows to A dollars, then the annual rate of return r on the investment is given by

$$r = \left(\frac{A}{P}\right)^{1/t} - 1$$

Find the annual rate of return on $5000 which grew to $6894.21 after 6 yr.

Solution:

$$r = \left(\frac{A}{P}\right)^{1/t} - 1$$

$$= \left(\frac{6894.21}{5000}\right)^{1/6} - 1 \quad \text{where } A = \$6894.21, P = \$5000, \text{ and } t = 6$$

$$\approx 0.055 \text{ or } 5.5\%$$

The annual rate of return is 5.5%.

Skill Practice

21. The formula for the radius of a sphere is

$$r = \left(\frac{3V}{4\pi}\right)^{1/3}$$

where V is the volume. Find the radius of a sphere whose volume is 113.04 in.^{3} (Use 3.14 for π.)

Answer

21. 3 in.

Section 10.2   Practice Exercises

For the exercises in this set, assume that all variables represent positive real numbers unless otherwise stated.

Vocabulary and Key Concepts

1. a. If n is an integer greater than 1, then radical notation for $a^{1/n}$ is _____.

   b. Assume that m and n are positive integers that share no common factors and $n > 1$. If $\sqrt[n]{a}$ exists, then in radical notation $a^{m/n} = $ _____.

   c. The radical notation for $x^{-1/2}$ is _____.

   d. $8^{1/3} = $ _____ and $8^{-1/3} = $ _____.

Review Exercises

2. Given $\sqrt[3]{27}$, identify the index and radicand.

For Exercises 3–6, evaluate the radicals.

3. $\sqrt{25}$　　　　**4.** $\sqrt[3]{8}$　　　　**5.** $\sqrt[4]{81}$　　　　**6.** $(\sqrt[4]{16})^3$

Concept 1: Definition of $a^{1/n}$ and $a^{m/n}$

For Exercises 7–18, convert the expressions to radical form and simplify. **(See Example 1.)**

7. $144^{1/2}$　　　**8.** $16^{1/4}$　　　**9.** $-144^{1/2}$　　　**10.** $-16^{1/4}$

11. $(-144)^{1/2}$　　**12.** $(-16)^{1/4}$　　**13.** $(-64)^{1/3}$　　**14.** $(-32)^{1/5}$

15. $25^{-1/2}$　　**16.** $27^{-1/3}$　　**17.** $-49^{-1/2}$　　**18.** $-64^{-1/2}$

19. Explain how to interpret the expression $a^{m/n}$ as a radical.

20. Explain why $(\sqrt[3]{8})^4$ is easier to evaluate than $\sqrt[3]{8^4}$.

For Exercises 21–24, simplify the expression, if possible. **(See Example 2.)**

21. **a.** $16^{3/4}$　　　　**22.** **a.** $81^{3/4}$　　　　**23.** **a.** $25^{3/2}$　　　　**24.** **a.** $4^{3/2}$

　　b. $-16^{3/4}$　　　　　**b.** $-81^{3/4}$　　　　　**b.** $-25^{3/2}$　　　　　**b.** $-4^{3/2}$

　　c. $(-16)^{3/4}$　　　　**c.** $(-81)^{3/4}$　　　　**c.** $(-25)^{3/2}$　　　　**c.** $(-4)^{3/2}$

　　d. $16^{-3/4}$　　　　　**d.** $81^{-3/4}$　　　　　**d.** $25^{-3/2}$　　　　　**d.** $4^{-3/2}$

　　e. $-16^{-3/4}$　　　　**e.** $-81^{-3/4}$　　　　**e.** $-25^{-3/2}$　　　　**e.** $-4^{-3/2}$

　　f. $(-16)^{-3/4}$　　　**f.** $(-81)^{-3/4}$　　　**f.** $(-25)^{-3/2}$　　　**f.** $(-4)^{-3/2}$

For Exercises 25–48, simplify the expression. **(See Example 2.)**

25. $64^{-3/2}$　　　**26.** $81^{-3/2}$　　　**27.** $243^{3/5}$　　　**28.** $1^{5/3}$

29. $-27^{-4/3}$　　**30.** $-16^{-5/4}$　　**31.** $\left(\dfrac{100}{9}\right)^{-3/2}$　　**32.** $\left(\dfrac{49}{100}\right)^{-1/2}$

33. $(-4)^{-3/2}$　　**34.** $(-49)^{-3/2}$　　**35.** $(-8)^{1/3}$　　**36.** $(-9)^{1/2}$

37. $-8^{1/3}$　　　**38.** $-9^{1/2}$　　　**39.** $\dfrac{1}{36^{-1/2}}$　　**40.** $\dfrac{1}{16^{-1/2}}$

41. $\dfrac{1}{1000^{-1/3}}$　　**42.** $\dfrac{1}{81^{-3/4}}$　　**43.** $\left(\dfrac{1}{8}\right)^{2/3} + \left(\dfrac{1}{4}\right)^{1/2}$　　**44.** $\left(\dfrac{1}{8}\right)^{-2/3} + \left(\dfrac{1}{4}\right)^{-1/2}$

45. $\left(\dfrac{1}{16}\right)^{-3/4} - \left(\dfrac{1}{49}\right)^{-1/2}$　　**46.** $\left(\dfrac{1}{16}\right)^{1/4} - \left(\dfrac{1}{49}\right)^{1/2}$　　**47.** $\left(\dfrac{1}{4}\right)^{1/2} + \left(\dfrac{1}{64}\right)^{-1/3}$　　**48.** $\left(\dfrac{1}{36}\right)^{1/2} + \left(\dfrac{1}{64}\right)^{-5/6}$

Concept 2: Converting Between Rational Exponents and Radical Notation

For Exercises 49–56, convert each expression to radical notation. **(See Example 3.)**

49. $q^{2/3}$　　　**50.** $t^{3/5}$　　　**51.** $6y^{3/4}$　　　**52.** $8b^{4/9}$

53. $x^{2/3}y^{1/3}$　　**54.** $c^{2/5}d^{3/5}$　　**55.** $6r^{-2/5}$　　**56.** $7x^{-3/4}$

712   **Chapter 10** Radicals and Complex Numbers

For Exercises 57–64, write each expression by using rational exponents rather than radical notation. **(See Example 4.)**

57. $\sqrt[3]{x}$ 　　　　　**58.** $\sqrt[4]{a}$ 　　　　　**59.** $10\sqrt{b}$ 　　　　　**60.** $-2\sqrt[3]{t}$

61. $\sqrt[3]{y^2}$ 　　　　**62.** $\sqrt[6]{z^5}$ 　　　　**63.** $\sqrt[4]{a^2b^3}$ 　　　　**64.** $\sqrt{abc}$

Concept 3: Properties of Rational Exponents

For Exercises 65–88, simplify the expressions by using the properties of rational exponents. Write the final answers using positive exponents only. **(See Example 5.)**

65. $x^{1/4}x^{-5/4}$ 　　　**66.** $2^{2/3}2^{-5/3}$ 　　　**67.** $\dfrac{p^{5/3}}{p^{2/3}}$ 　　　**68.** $\dfrac{q^{5/4}}{q^{1/4}}$

69. $(y^{1/5})^{10}$ 　　　**70.** $(x^{1/2})^8$ 　　　**71.** $6^{-1/5}6^{3/5}$ 　　　**72.** $a^{-1/3}a^{2/3}$

73. $\dfrac{4t^{-1/3}}{t^{4/3}}$ 　　　**74.** $\dfrac{5s^{-1/3}}{s^{5/3}}$ 　　　**75.** $(a^{1/3}a^{1/4})^{12}$ 　　　**76.** $(x^{2/3}x^{1/2})^6$

77. $(5a^2c^{-1/2}d^{1/2})^2$ 　**78.** $(2x^{-1/3}y^2z^{5/3})^3$ 　**79.** $\left(\dfrac{x^{-2/3}}{y^{-3/4}}\right)^{12}$ 　**80.** $\left(\dfrac{m^{-1/4}}{n^{-1/2}}\right)^{-4}$

81. $\left(\dfrac{16w^{-2}z}{2wz^{-8}}\right)^{1/3}$ 　**82.** $\left(\dfrac{50p^{-1}q}{2pq^{-3}}\right)^{1/2}$ 　**83.** $(25x^2y^4z^6)^{1/2}$ 　**84.** $(8a^6b^3c^9)^{2/3}$

85. $(x^2y^{-1/3})^6(x^{1/2}yz^{2/3})^2$ 　**86.** $(a^{-1/3}b^{1/2})^4(a^{-1/2}b^{3/5})^{10}$ 　**87.** $\left(\dfrac{x^{3m}y^{2m}}{z^{5m}}\right)^{1/m}$ 　**88.** $\left(\dfrac{a^{4n}b^{3n}}{c^n}\right)^{1/n}$

Concept 4: Applications Involving Rational Exponents

89. If P dollars in principal grows to A dollars after t years with annual interest, then the interest rate r is given by $r = \left(\dfrac{A}{P}\right)^{1/t} - 1$. **(See Example 6.)**

　　a. In one account, $10,000 grows to $16,802 after 5 yr. Compute the interest rate. Round your answer to a tenth of a percent.

　　b. In another account $10,000 grows to $18,000 after 7 yr. Compute the interest rate. Round your answer to a tenth of a percent.

　　c. Which account produced a higher average yearly return?

90. If the area A of a square is known, then the length of its sides, s, can be computed by the formula $s = A^{1/2}$.

　　a. Compute the length of the sides of a square having an area of 100 in.^{2}

　　b. Compute the length of the sides of a square having an area of 72 in.^{2} Round your answer to the nearest 0.1 in.

91. The radius r of a sphere of volume V is given by $r = \left(\dfrac{3V}{4\pi}\right)^{1/3}$. Find the radius of a sphere having a volume of 85 in.^{3} Round your answer to the nearest 0.1 in.

92. Is $(a+b)^{1/2}$ the same as $a^{1/2} + b^{1/2}$? If not, give a counterexample.

Expanding Your Skills

For Exercises 93–104, write the expression using rational exponents. Then simplify and convert back to radical notation.

Example: $\sqrt[15]{x^{10}}$ $\xrightarrow[\text{exponents}]{\text{Rational}}$ $x^{10/15}$ $\xrightarrow{\text{Simplify}}$ $x^{2/3}$ $\xrightarrow[\text{notation}]{\text{Radical}}$ $\sqrt[3]{x^2}$

93. $\sqrt[6]{y^3}$

94. $\sqrt[4]{w^2}$

95. $\sqrt[12]{z^3}$

96. $\sqrt[18]{t^3}$

97. $\sqrt[9]{x^6}$

98. $\sqrt[12]{p^9}$

99. $\sqrt[6]{x^3y^6}$

100. $\sqrt[8]{m^2p^8}$

101. $\sqrt{16x^8y^6}$

102. $\sqrt{81a^{12}b^{20}}$

103. $\sqrt[3]{8x^3y^2z}$

104. $\sqrt[3]{64m^2n^3p}$

For Exercises 105–108, write the expression as a single radical.

105. $\sqrt{\sqrt[3]{x}}$

106. $\sqrt[3]{\sqrt{x}}$

107. $\sqrt[5]{\sqrt[3]{w}}$

108. $\sqrt[3]{\sqrt[4]{w}}$

For Exercises 109–116, use a calculator to approximate the expressions. Round to four decimal places, if necessary.

109. $9^{1/2}$

110. $125^{-1/3}$

111. $50^{-1/4}$

112. $(172)^{3/5}$

113. $\sqrt[3]{5^2}$

114. $\sqrt[4]{6^3}$

115. $\sqrt{10^3}$

116. $\sqrt[3]{16}$

Simplifying Radical Expressions

Section 10.3

1. Multiplication Property of Radicals

Concepts

You may have already noticed certain properties of radicals involving a product or quotient.

> **Multiplication Property of Radicals**
>
> Let a and b represent real numbers such that $\sqrt[n]{a}$ and $\sqrt[n]{b}$ are both real. Then
>
> $$\sqrt[n]{ab} = \sqrt[n]{a} \cdot \sqrt[n]{b}$$

1. Multiplication Property of Radicals

2. Simplifying Radicals by Using the Multiplication Property of Radicals

3. Simplifying Radicals by Using the Order of Operations

The multiplication property of radicals follows from the property of rational exponents.

$$\sqrt[n]{ab} = (ab)^{1/n} = a^{1/n}b^{1/n} = \sqrt[n]{a} \cdot \sqrt[n]{b}$$

The multiplication property of radicals indicates that a product within a radicand can be written as a product of radicals, provided the roots are real numbers. For example:

$$\sqrt{144} = \sqrt{16} \cdot \sqrt{9}$$

The reverse process is also true. A product of radicals can be written as a single radical provided the roots are real numbers and they have the same indices.

$$\sqrt{3} \cdot \sqrt{12} = \sqrt{36}$$

2. Simplifying Radicals by Using the Multiplication Property of Radicals

In algebra, it is customary to simplify radical expressions.

> **Simplified Form of a Radical**
>
> Consider any radical expression where the radicand is written as a product of prime factors. The expression is in *simplified form* if all the following conditions are met:
>
> 1. The radicand has no factor raised to a power greater than or equal to the index.
> 2. The radicand does not contain a fraction.
> 3. There are no radicals in the denominator of a fraction.

For example, the following radicals are not simplified.

1. The expression $\sqrt[3]{x^5}$ fails condition 1.

2. The expression $\sqrt{\dfrac{1}{4}}$ fails condition 2.

3. The expression $\dfrac{1}{\sqrt[3]{8}}$ fails condition 3.

The expressions $\sqrt{x^2}$, $\sqrt{x^4}$, $\sqrt{x^6}$, and $\sqrt{x^8}$ are not simplified because they fail condition 1 (the exponents are not less than the index). However, each radicand is a perfect square and is easily simplified for $x \geq 0$.

$$\sqrt{x^2} = x$$
$$\sqrt{x^4} = x^2$$
$$\sqrt{x^6} = x^3$$
$$\sqrt{x^8} = x^4$$

However, how is an expression such as $\sqrt{x^9}$ simplified? This and many other radical expressions are simplified by using the multiplication property of radicals. We demonstrate the process in Examples 1–4.

Example 1 **Using the Multiplication Property to Simplify a Radical Expression**

Simplify the expression assuming that $x \geq 0$. $\sqrt{x^9}$

Solution:

The expression $\sqrt{x^9}$ is equivalent to $\sqrt{x^8 \cdot x}$.

$$\sqrt{x^9} = \sqrt{x^8 \cdot x}$$

$$= \sqrt{x^8} \cdot \sqrt{x} \qquad \text{Apply the multiplication property of radicals.}$$

$$\qquad\qquad \text{Note that } x^8 \text{ is a perfect square because } x^8 = (x^4)^2.$$

$$= x^4 \sqrt{x} \qquad \text{Simplify.}$$

Skill Practice Simplify the expression. Assume $a \geq 0$.

1. $\sqrt{a^{11}}$

Answer

1. $a^5 \sqrt{a}$

In Example 1, the expression x^9 is not a perfect square. Therefore, to simplify $\sqrt{x^9}$, it was necessary to write the expression as the product of the largest perfect square and a remaining or "left-over" factor: $\sqrt{x^9} = \sqrt{x^8 \cdot x}$. This process also applies to simplifying nth roots, as shown in Example 2.

> ### Example 2 Using the Multiplication Property to Simplify Radical Expressions

Simplify each expression. Assume all variables represent positive real numbers.

   a. $\sqrt[4]{b^7}$ **b.** $\sqrt[3]{w^7 z^9}$

Solution:

The goal is to rewrite each radicand as the product of the greatest perfect square (perfect cube, perfect fourth power, and so on) and a leftover factor.

a. $\sqrt[4]{b^7} = \sqrt[4]{b^4 \cdot b^3}$ b^4 is the greatest perfect fourth power in the radicand.

   $\qquad = \sqrt[4]{b^4} \cdot \sqrt[4]{b^3}$ Apply the multiplication property of radicals.

   $\qquad = b\sqrt[4]{b^3}$ Simplify.

b. $\sqrt[3]{w^7 z^9} = \sqrt[3]{(w^6 z^9) \cdot (w)}$ $w^6 z^9$ is the greatest perfect cube in the radicand.

   $\qquad = \sqrt[3]{w^6 z^9} \cdot \sqrt[3]{w}$ Apply the multiplication property of radicals.

   $\qquad = w^2 z^3 \sqrt[3]{w}$ Simplify.

Skill Practice Simplify the expressions. Assume all variables represent positive real numbers.

   2. $\sqrt[4]{v^{25}}$ **3.** $\sqrt[3]{p^{17} q^{10}}$

Each expression in Example 2 involves a radicand that is a product of variable factors. If a numerical factor is present, sometimes it is necessary to factor the coefficient before simplifying the radical.

> ### Example 3 Using the Multiplication Property to Simplify a Radical

Simplify the expression. $\sqrt{56}$

Solution:

   $\sqrt{56} = \sqrt{2^3 \cdot 7}$ Factor the radicand.

   $\qquad = \sqrt{(2^2) \cdot (2 \cdot 7)}$ 2^2 is the greatest perfect square in the radicand.

   $\qquad = \sqrt{2^2} \cdot \sqrt{2 \cdot 7}$ Apply the multiplication property of radicals.

   $\qquad = 2\sqrt{14}$ Simplify.

$$\begin{array}{r} 2\,\underline{|\,56} \\ 2\,\underline{|\,28} \\ 2\,\underline{|\,14} \\ 7 \end{array}$$

TIP: It may be easier to visualize the greatest perfect square factor within the radicand as follows:

$$\sqrt{56} = \sqrt{4 \cdot 14}$$
$$= \sqrt{4} \cdot \sqrt{14}$$
$$= 2\sqrt{14}$$

Skill Practice Simplify.

   4. $\sqrt{24}$

Answers

2. $v^6\sqrt[4]{v}$ **3.** $p^5 q^3 \sqrt[3]{p^2 q}$ **4.** $2\sqrt{6}$

Calculator Connections

Topic: Verifying a Simplified Radical

A calculator can be used to support the solution to Example 3. The decimal approximation for $\sqrt{56}$ and $2\sqrt{14}$ agree for the first 10 digits. This in itself does not make $\sqrt{56} = 2\sqrt{14}$. It is the multiplication property of radicals that guarantees that the expressions are equal.

```
√(56)
          7.483314774
2*√(14)
          7.483314774
```

Example 4   **Using the Multiplication Property to Simplify Radicals**

Simplify. $6\sqrt{50}$

Solution:

$$6\sqrt{50} = 6\sqrt{5^2 \cdot 2} \qquad\qquad \text{Factor the radicand.}$$
$$= 6 \cdot \sqrt{5^2} \cdot \sqrt{2} \qquad \text{Apply the multiplication property of radicals.}$$
$$= 6 \cdot 5 \cdot \sqrt{2} \qquad\quad \text{Simplify.}$$
$$= 30\sqrt{2} \qquad\qquad \text{Simplify.}$$

TIP: The radical can also be simplified as:

$$6\sqrt{50} = 6\sqrt{25 \cdot 2}$$
$$= 6\sqrt{25} \cdot \sqrt{2}$$
$$= 6 \cdot 5\sqrt{2}$$
$$= 30\sqrt{2}$$

Skill Practice Simplify.

5. $5\sqrt{18}$

Example 5   **Using the Multiplication Property to Simplify Radicals**

Simplify the expression. Assume that x, y, and z represent positive real numbers.

$$\sqrt[3]{40x^3y^5z^7}$$

TIP: In Example 5, the numerical coefficient within the radicand can be written $8 \cdot 5$ because 8 is the greatest perfect cube factor of 40:

$$\sqrt[3]{40x^3y^5z^7} = \sqrt[3]{8 \cdot 5x^3y^5z^7}$$
$$= \sqrt[3]{(8x^3y^3z^6)(5y^2z)}$$
$$= \sqrt[3]{8x^3y^3z^6} \cdot \sqrt[3]{5y^2z}$$
$$= 2xyz^2 \cdot \sqrt[3]{5y^2z}$$

Solution:

$$\sqrt[3]{40x^3y^5z^7}$$
$$= \sqrt[3]{2^3 5x^3y^5z^7} \qquad\qquad\qquad \text{Factor the radicand.}$$
$$= \sqrt[3]{(2^3x^3y^3z^6) \cdot (5y^2z)} \qquad 2^3x^3y^3z^6 \text{ is the greatest perfect cube.}$$
$$= \sqrt[3]{2^3x^3y^3z^6} \cdot \sqrt[3]{5y^2z} \qquad \text{Apply the multiplication property of radicals.}$$
$$= \quad 2xyz^2\sqrt[3]{5y^2z} \qquad\qquad\quad \text{Simplify.}$$

$$
\begin{array}{r}
2\lfloor 40 \\
2\lfloor 20 \\
2\lfloor 10 \\
5
\end{array}
$$

Skill Practice Simplify. Assume that $a > 0$ and $b > 0$.

6. $\sqrt[4]{32a^{10}b^{19}}$

---

3. Simplifying Radicals by Using the Order of Operations

Often a radical can be simplified by applying the order of operations. In Example 6, the first step will be to simplify the expression within the radicand.

Answers

5. $15\sqrt{2}$ **6.** $2a^2b^4\sqrt[4]{2a^2b^3}$

| **Example 6** | **Using the Order of Operations to Simplify Radicals** |

Use the order of operations to simplify the expressions. Assume $a > 0$.

a. $\sqrt{\dfrac{a^7}{a^3}}$ **b.** $\sqrt[3]{\dfrac{3}{81}}$

Solution:

a. $\sqrt{\dfrac{a^7}{a^3}}$ The radicand contains a fraction. However, the fraction can be reduced to lowest terms.

$= \sqrt{a^4}$

$= a^2$ Simplify the radical.

b. $\sqrt[3]{\dfrac{3}{81}}$ The radical contains a fraction that can be simplified.

$= \sqrt[3]{\dfrac{1}{27}}$ Reduce to lowest terms.

$= \dfrac{1}{3}$ Simplify.

Skill Practice Use the order of operations to simplify the expressions. Assume $v > 0$.

7. $\sqrt{\dfrac{v^{21}}{v^5}}$ **8.** $\sqrt[5]{\dfrac{64}{2}}$

| **Example 7** | **Simplifying a Radical Expression** |

Simplify. $\dfrac{7\sqrt{50}}{10}$

Solution:

$\dfrac{7\sqrt{50}}{10} = \dfrac{7\sqrt{25 \cdot 2}}{10}$ 25 is the greatest perfect square in the radicand.

$= \dfrac{7 \cdot 5\sqrt{2}}{10}$ Simplify the radical.

$= \dfrac{7 \cdot \overset{1}{5}\sqrt{2}}{\underset{2}{10}}$ Simplify the fraction to lowest terms.

$= \dfrac{7\sqrt{2}}{2}$

Avoiding Mistakes

The expression $\frac{7\sqrt{2}}{2}$ cannot be simplified further because one factor of 2 is in the radicand and the other is outside the radical.

Skill Practice Simplify.

9. $\dfrac{2\sqrt{300}}{30}$

Answers
7. v^8 **8.** 2   **9.** $\dfrac{2\sqrt{3}}{3}$

Section 10.3   Practice Exercises

Study Skills Exercise

The final exam is just around the corner. Your old tests and quizzes provide good material to study for the final exam. Use your old tests to make a list of the concepts on which you need to concentrate. Ask your professor for help if there are still concepts that you do not understand.

For the exercises in this set, assume that all variables represent positive real numbers unless otherwise stated.

Vocabulary and Key Concepts

1. a. The multiplication property of radicals indicates that if $\sqrt[n]{a}$ and $\sqrt[n]{b}$ are real numbers, then $\sqrt[n]{ab} = $ _____ · _____.

   b. Explain why the following radical is not in simplified form. $\sqrt{x^3}$

   c. The radical expression $\sqrt[3]{x^{10}}$ (is/is not) in simplified form.

   d. The radical expression $\sqrt{18}$ simplifies to __ $\sqrt{2}$.

   e. To simplify the radical expression $\sqrt[3]{t^{14}}$ the radicand is rewritten as $\sqrt[3]{\_\_ \cdot t^2}$.

   f. On a calculator, $\sqrt{2}$ is given as 1.414213562. Is this decimal number the exact value of $\sqrt{2}$?

Review Exercises

For Exercises 2–4, simplify the expression. Write the answer with positive exponents only.

2. $(a^2b^{-4})^{1/2}\left(\dfrac{a}{b^{-3}}\right)$

3. $\left(\dfrac{p^4}{q^{-6}}\right)^{-1/2} \cdot (p^3q^{-2})$

4. $(x^{1/3}y^{5/6})^{-6}$

5. Write $x^{4/7}$ in radical notation.

6. Write $y^{2/5}$ in radical notation.

7. Write $\sqrt{y^9}$ by using rational exponents.

8. Write $\sqrt[3]{x^2}$ by using rational exponents.

Concept 2: Simplifying Radicals by Using the Multiplication Property of Radicals

For Exercises 9–32, simplify the radicals. **(See Examples 1–5.)**

9. $\sqrt{x^5}$

10. $\sqrt{p^{15}}$

11. $\sqrt[3]{q^7}$

12. $\sqrt[3]{r^{17}}$

13. $\sqrt{a^5b^4}$

14. $\sqrt{c^9d^6}$

15. $-\sqrt[4]{x^8y^{13}}$

16. $-\sqrt[4]{p^{16}q^{17}}$

17. $\sqrt{28}$

18. $\sqrt{63}$

19. $\sqrt{20}$

20. $\sqrt{50}$

21. $5\sqrt{18}$

22. $2\sqrt{24}$

23. $\sqrt[3]{54}$

24. $\sqrt[3]{250}$

25. $\sqrt{25ab^3}$

26. $\sqrt{64m^5n^{20}}$

27. $\sqrt[3]{40x^7}$

28. $\sqrt[3]{81y^{17}}$

29. $\sqrt[3]{-16x^6yz^3}$

30. $\sqrt[3]{-192a^6bc^2}$

31. $\sqrt[4]{80w^4z^7}$

32. $\sqrt[4]{32p^8qr^5}$

Concept 3: Simplifying Radicals by Using the Order of Operations

For Exercises 33–44, simplify the radical expressions. **(See Examples 6–7.)**

33. $\sqrt{\dfrac{x^3}{x}}$

34. $\sqrt{\dfrac{y^5}{y}}$

35. $\sqrt{\dfrac{p^7}{p^3}}$

36. $\sqrt{\dfrac{q^{11}}{q^5}}$

37. $\sqrt{\dfrac{50}{2}}$

38. $\sqrt{\dfrac{98}{2}}$

39. $\sqrt[3]{\dfrac{3}{24}}$

40. $\sqrt[3]{\dfrac{2}{250}}$

41. $\dfrac{5\sqrt[3]{16}}{6}$

42. $\dfrac{7\sqrt{18}}{9}$

43. $\dfrac{5\sqrt[3]{72}}{12}$

44. $\dfrac{3\sqrt[3]{250}}{10}$

Mixed Exercises

For Exercises 45–72, simplify the radical expressions.

45. $\sqrt{80}$

46. $\sqrt{108}$

47. $-6\sqrt{75}$

48. $-8\sqrt{8}$

49. $\sqrt{25x^4y^3}$

50. $\sqrt{125p^3q^2}$

51. $\sqrt[3]{27x^2y^3z^4}$

52. $\sqrt[3]{108a^3bc^2}$

53. $\sqrt{\dfrac{12w^5}{3w}}$

54. $\sqrt{\dfrac{64x^9}{4x^3}}$

55. $\sqrt{\dfrac{3y^3}{300y^{15}}}$

56. $\sqrt{\dfrac{4h}{100h^5}}$

57. $\sqrt[3]{\dfrac{16a^2b}{2a^2b^4}}$

58. $\sqrt[3]{\dfrac{-27a^4}{8a}}$

59. $\sqrt{2^3a^{14}b^8c^{31}d^{22}}$

60. $\sqrt{7^5u^{12}v^{20}w^{65}x^{80}}$

61. $\sqrt[3]{54a^6b^4}$

62. $\sqrt[3]{72m^5n^3}$

63. $-5a\sqrt{12a^3b^4c}$

64. $-7y\sqrt{75xy^5z^6}$

65. $\sqrt[4]{7x^5y}$

66. $\sqrt[4]{10cd^7}$

67. $\sqrt{54a^4b^2}$

68. $\sqrt{48r^6s^2}$

69. $\dfrac{2\sqrt{27}}{3}$

70. $\dfrac{7\sqrt{24}}{2}$

71. $\dfrac{3\sqrt{125}}{20}$

72. $\dfrac{10\sqrt{63}}{12}$

For Exercises 73–76, write a mathematical expression for the English phrase and simplify.

73. The quotient of 1 and the cube root of w^6

74. The principal square root of the quotient of h^2 and 49

75. The principal square root of the quantity k raised to the third power

76. The cube root of $2x^4$

For Exercises 77–80, determine the length of the third side of the right triangle. Write the answer as a simplified radical.

77.
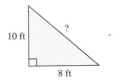
10 ft · ? · 8 ft

78.

? · 4 in. · 12 in.

79.
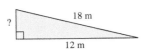
? · 18 m · 12 m

80.
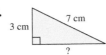
3 cm · 7 cm · ?

720 **Chapter 10** Radicals and Complex Numbers

81. On a baseball diamond, the bases are 90 ft apart. Find the exact distance from home plate to second base. Then round to the nearest tenth of a foot.

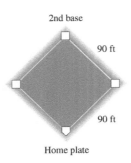

2nd base

90 ft

90 ft

Home plate

82. Linda is at the beach flying a kite. The kite is directly over a sand castle 60 ft away from Linda. If 100 ft of kite string is out (ignoring any sag in the string), how high is the kite? (Assume that Linda is 5 ft tall.) See figure.

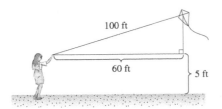

100 ft

60 ft

5 ft

Expanding Your Skills

83. Tom has to travel from town A to town C across a small mountain range. He can travel one of two routes. He can travel on a four-lane highway from A to B and then from B to C at an average speed of 55 mph. Or he can travel on a two-lane road directly from town A to town C, but his average speed will be only 35 mph. If Tom is in a hurry, which route will take him to town C faster?

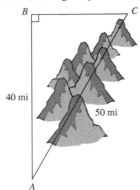

B

C

40 mi

50 mi

A

84. One side of a rectangular pasture is 80 ft in length. The diagonal distance is 110 yd. If fencing costs $3.29 per foot, how much will it cost to fence the pasture?

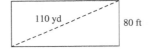

110 yd

80 ft

720   **Chapter 10**   Radicals and Complex Numbers

| **Section 10.4** | **Addition and Subtraction of Radicals** |

Concept

1. Addition and Subtraction of Radicals

1. Addition and Subtraction of Radicals

> **Definition of *Like* Radicals**
>
> Two radical terms are called ***like* radicals** if they have the same index and same radicand.

Like radicals can be added or subtracted by using the distributive property.

$$\overset{\text{Same index}}{3\sqrt{x}} + 7\sqrt{x} = \overset{\text{Distributive property}}{(3+7)\sqrt{x}} = 10\sqrt{x}$$

Same radicand

Example 1   **Adding and Subtracting Radicals**

Add or subtract as indicated.

a. $6\sqrt{11} - 2\sqrt{11}$ **b.** $\sqrt{3} + \sqrt{3}$

Solution:

a. $6\sqrt{11} - 2\sqrt{11}$

$= (6 - 2)\sqrt{11}$ Apply the distributive property.

$= 4\sqrt{11}$ Simplify.

b. $\sqrt{3} + \sqrt{3}$

$= 1\sqrt{3} + 1\sqrt{3}$ Note that $\sqrt{3} = 1\sqrt{3}$.

$= (1 + 1)\sqrt{3}$ Apply the distributive property.

$= 2\sqrt{3}$ Simplify.

Avoiding Mistakes

The process of adding *like* radicals with the distributive property is similar to adding *like* terms. The end result is that the numerical coefficients are added and the radical factor is unchanged.

$$\sqrt{3} + \sqrt{3} = 1\sqrt{3} + 1\sqrt{3} = 2\sqrt{3}$$

Be careful: $\sqrt{3} + \sqrt{3} \neq \sqrt{6}$

In general: $\sqrt{x} + \sqrt{y} \neq \sqrt{x + y}$

Skill Practice Add or subtract as indicated.

1. $5\sqrt{6} - 8\sqrt{6}$ **2.** $\sqrt{10} + \sqrt{10}$

Example 2   **Adding and Subtracting Radicals**

Add or subtract as indicated.

a. $-2\sqrt[3]{ab} + 7\sqrt[3]{ab} - \sqrt[3]{ab}$ **b.** $\frac{1}{4}x\sqrt{3y} - \frac{3}{2}x\sqrt{3y}$

Solution:

a. $-2\sqrt[3]{ab} + 7\sqrt[3]{ab} - \sqrt[3]{ab}$

$= (-2 + 7 - 1)\sqrt[3]{ab}$ Apply the distributive property.

$= 4\sqrt[3]{ab}$ Simplify.

b. $\frac{1}{4}x\sqrt{3y} - \frac{3}{2}x\sqrt{3y}$

$= \left(\frac{1}{4} - \frac{3}{2}\right)x\sqrt{3y}$ Apply the distributive property.

$= \left(\frac{1}{4} - \frac{6}{4}\right)x\sqrt{3y}$ Get a common denominator.

$= -\frac{5}{4}x\sqrt{3y}$ Simplify.

Answers

1. $-3\sqrt{6}$ **2.** $2\sqrt{10}$

Skill Practice Add or subtract as indicated.

3. $5\sqrt[3]{xy} - 3\sqrt[3]{xy} + 7\sqrt[3]{xy}$

4. $\dfrac{5}{6}y\sqrt{2} + \dfrac{1}{4}y\sqrt{2}$

Example 3 shows that it is often necessary to simplify radicals before adding or subtracting.

Example 3 **Adding and Subtracting Radicals**

Simplify the radicals and add or subtract as indicated. Assume all variables represent positive real numbers.

a. $3\sqrt{8} + \sqrt{2}$ **b.** $8\sqrt{x^3y^2} - 3y\sqrt{x^3}$

c. $\sqrt{50x^2y^5} - 13y\sqrt{2x^2y^3} + xy\sqrt{98y^3}$

Solution:

a. $3\sqrt{8} + \sqrt{2}$ The radicands are different. Try simplifying the radicals first.

$\quad = 3 \cdot 2\sqrt{2} + \sqrt{2}$ Simplify: $\sqrt{8} = \sqrt{2^3} = 2\sqrt{2}$

$\quad = 6\sqrt{2} + \sqrt{2}$

$\quad = (6 + 1)\sqrt{2}$ Apply the distributive property.

$\quad = 7\sqrt{2}$ Simplify.

b. $8\sqrt{x^3y^2} - 3y\sqrt{x^3}$ The radicands are different. Simplify the radicals first.

$\quad = 8xy\sqrt{x} - 3xy\sqrt{x}$ Simplify $\sqrt{x^3y^2} = xy\sqrt{x}$ and $\sqrt{x^3} = x\sqrt{x}$.

$\quad = (8 - 3)xy\sqrt{x}$ Apply the distributive property.

$\quad = 5xy\sqrt{x}$ Simplify.

c. $\sqrt{50x^2y^5} - 13y\sqrt{2x^2y^3} + xy\sqrt{98y^3}$ Simplify each radical.

$\quad = 5xy^2\sqrt{2y} - 13xy^2\sqrt{2y} + 7xy^2\sqrt{2y}$

$\left\{ \begin{array}{l} \sqrt{50x^2y^5} = \sqrt{25 \cdot 2x^2y^5} \\ \qquad\qquad = 5xy^2\sqrt{2y} \\ -13y\sqrt{2x^2y^3} = -13xy^2\sqrt{2y} \\ xy\sqrt{98y^3} = xy\sqrt{49 \cdot 2y^3} \\ \qquad\qquad = 7xy^2\sqrt{2y} \end{array} \right.$

Apply the distributive property.

$\quad = (5 - 13 + 7)xy^2\sqrt{2y}$

$\quad = -xy^2\sqrt{2y}$

Skill Practice Simplify the radicals and add or subtract as indicated. Assume all variables represent positive real numbers.

5. $\sqrt{75} + 2\sqrt{3}$

6. $4\sqrt{a^2b} - 6a\sqrt{b}$

7. $-3\sqrt{2y^3} + 5y\sqrt{18y} - 2\sqrt{50y^3}$

Answers

3. $9\sqrt[3]{xy}$ **4.** $\dfrac{13}{12}y\sqrt{2}$

5. $7\sqrt{3}$ **6.** $-2a\sqrt{b}$

7. $2y\sqrt{2y}$

In some cases, when two radicals are added, the resulting sum is written in factored form. This is demonstrated in Example 4.

| **Example 4** | **Adding Radical Expressions** |

Add the radicals. Assume that $x \geq 0$. $3\sqrt{2x^2} + \sqrt{8}$

Solution:

$3\sqrt{2x^2} + \sqrt{8}$

$= 3x\sqrt{2} + 2\sqrt{2}$ Simplify each radical. Notice that the radicands are the same, but the terms are not *like* terms. The first term has a factor of x and the second does not.

$= (3x + 2)\sqrt{2}$ Apply the distributive property. The expression cannot be simplified further because $3x$ and 2 are not *like* terms.

Skill Practice   Add the radicals. Assume that $y \geq 0$.

8. $4\sqrt{45} - \sqrt{5y^4}$

Answer

8. $(12 - y^2)\sqrt{5}$

| **Section 10.4** | **Practice Exercises** |

For the exercises in this set, assume that all variables represent positive real numbers, unless otherwise stated.

Vocabulary and Key Concepts

1. **a.** Two radical terms are called *like* radicals if they have the same _____ and the same _____.

   b. The expression $\sqrt{3x} + \sqrt{3x}$ simplifies to _____.

   c. The expression $\sqrt{2} + \sqrt{3}$ (can/cannot) be simplified further whereas the expression $\sqrt{2} \cdot \sqrt{3}$ (can/cannot) be simplified further.

   d. The expression $\sqrt{2} + \sqrt{18}$ simplifies to _____.

Review Exercises

For Exercises 2–5, simplify the radicals.

2. $\sqrt[3]{-16s^4t^9}$ **3.** $-\sqrt[4]{x^7y^4}$ **4.** $\sqrt{36a^2b^3}$ **5.** $\sqrt[3]{\dfrac{7b^8}{56b^2}}$

6. Write $(4x^2)^{1/3}$ in radical notation.   **7.** Write $\sqrt[4]{x^3y}$ using rational exponents.

8. Simplify. $32^{-1/5}$

For Exercises 9–10, simplify the expressions. Write the answer with positive exponents only.

9. $y^{2/3}y^{1/4}$ **10.** $(x^{1/2}y^{-3/4})^{-4}$

724 **Chapter 10** Radicals and Complex Numbers

Concept 1: Addition and Subtraction of Radicals

For Exercises 11–12, determine if the radical terms are *like*.

11. a. $\sqrt{2}$ and $\sqrt[3]{2}$

   b. $\sqrt{2}$ and $3\sqrt{2}$

   c. $\sqrt{2}$ and $\sqrt{5}$

12. a. $7\sqrt[3]{x}$ and $\sqrt[3]{x}$

   b. $\sqrt[3]{x}$ and $\sqrt[4]{x}$

   c. $2\sqrt[4]{x}$ and $x\sqrt[4]{2}$

13. Explain the similarities between the pairs of expressions.

   a. $7\sqrt{5} + 4\sqrt{5}$ and $7x + 4x$

   b. $-2\sqrt{6} - 9\sqrt{3}$ and $-2x - 9y$

14. Explain the similarities between the pairs of expressions.

   a. $-4\sqrt{3} + 5\sqrt{3}$ and $-4z + 5z$

   b. $13\sqrt{7} - 18$ and $13a - 18$

For Exercises 15–32, add or subtract the radical expressions, if possible. **(See Examples 1–2.)**

15. $3\sqrt{5} + 6\sqrt{5}$

16. $5\sqrt{a} + 3\sqrt{a}$

17. $3\sqrt[3]{tw} - 2\sqrt[3]{tw} + \sqrt[3]{tw}$

18. $6\sqrt[3]{7} - 2\sqrt[3]{7} + \sqrt[3]{7}$

19. $6\sqrt{10} - \sqrt{10}$

20. $13\sqrt{11} - \sqrt{11}$

21. $\sqrt[4]{3} + 7\sqrt[4]{3} - \sqrt[4]{14}$

22. $2\sqrt{11} + 3\sqrt{13} + 5\sqrt{11}$

23. $8\sqrt{x} + 2\sqrt{y} - 6\sqrt{x}$

24. $10\sqrt{10} - 8\sqrt{10} + \sqrt{2}$

25. $\sqrt[3]{ab} + a\sqrt[3]{b}$

26. $x\sqrt[4]{y} - y\sqrt[4]{x}$

27. $\sqrt{2t} + \sqrt[3]{2t}$

28. $\sqrt[4]{5c} + \sqrt[3]{5c}$

29. $\frac{5}{6}z\sqrt[3]{6} + \frac{7}{9}z\sqrt[3]{6}$

30. $\frac{3}{4}a\sqrt[4]{b} + \frac{1}{6}a\sqrt[4]{b}$

31. $0.81x\sqrt{y} - 0.11x\sqrt{y}$

32. $7.5\sqrt{pq} - 6.3\sqrt{pq}$

33. Explain the process for adding the two radicals. Then find the sum. $3\sqrt{2} + 7\sqrt{50}$

34. Explain the process for subtracting two radicals. Then find the difference. $\sqrt{12x} - \sqrt{75x}$

For Exercises 35–64, add or subtract the radical expressions as indicated. **(See Examples 3–4.)**

35. $\sqrt{36} + \sqrt{81}$

36. $3\sqrt{80} - 5\sqrt{45}$

37. $2\sqrt{12} + \sqrt{48}$

38. $5\sqrt{32} + 2\sqrt{50}$

39. $4\sqrt{7} + \sqrt{63} - 2\sqrt{28}$

40. $8\sqrt{3} - 2\sqrt{27} + \sqrt{75}$

41. $5\sqrt{18} + \sqrt{27} - 4\sqrt{50}$

42. $7\sqrt{40} - \sqrt{8} + 4\sqrt{50}$

43. $\sqrt[3]{81} - \sqrt[3]{24}$

44. $17\sqrt[3]{81} - 2\sqrt[3]{24}$

45. $3\sqrt{2a} - \sqrt{8a} - \sqrt{72a}$

46. $\sqrt{12t} - \sqrt{27t} + 5\sqrt{3t}$

47. $2s^2\sqrt[3]{s^2t^6} + 3t^2\sqrt[3]{8s^8}$

48. $4\sqrt[3]{x^4} - 2x\sqrt[3]{x}$

49. $7\sqrt[3]{x^4} - x\sqrt[3]{x}$

50. $6\sqrt[3]{y^{10}} - 3y^2\sqrt[3]{y^4}$

51. $5p\sqrt{20p^2} + p^2\sqrt{80}$

52. $2q\sqrt{48q^2} - \sqrt{27q^4}$

53. $\sqrt[3]{a^2b} - \sqrt[3]{8a^2b}$

54. $w\sqrt{80} - 3\sqrt{125w^2}$

55. $5x\sqrt{x} + 6\sqrt{x}$

56. $9y^2\sqrt{2} + 4\sqrt{2}$

57. $\sqrt{50x^2} - 3\sqrt{8}$

58. $\sqrt{9x^3} - \sqrt{25x}$

59. $11\sqrt[3]{54cd^3} - 2\sqrt[3]{2cd^3} + d\sqrt[3]{16c}$

60. $x\sqrt[3]{64x^5y^2} - x^2\sqrt[3]{x^2y^2} + 5\sqrt[3]{x^8y^2}$

61. $\dfrac{3}{2}ab\sqrt{24a^3} + \dfrac{4}{3}\sqrt{54a^5b^2} - a^2b\sqrt{150a}$

62. $mn\sqrt{72n} + \dfrac{2}{3}n\sqrt{8m^2n} - \dfrac{5}{6}\sqrt{50m^2n^3}$

63. $x\sqrt[3]{16} - 2\sqrt[3]{27x} + \sqrt[3]{54x^3}$

64. $5\sqrt[4]{y^5} - 2y\sqrt[4]{y} + \sqrt[4]{16y^7}$

Mixed Exercises

For Exercises 65–72, answer true or false. If an answer is false, explain why or give a counterexample.

65. $\sqrt{x} + \sqrt{y} = \sqrt{x+y}$

66. $\sqrt{x} + \sqrt{x} = 2\sqrt{x}$

67. $5\sqrt[3]{x} + 2\sqrt[3]{x} = 7\sqrt[3]{x}$

68. $6\sqrt{x} + 5\sqrt[3]{x} = 11\sqrt{x}$

69. $\sqrt{y} + \sqrt{y} = \sqrt{2y}$

70. $\sqrt{c^2 + d^2} = c + d$

71. $2w\sqrt{5} + 4w\sqrt{5} = 6w^2\sqrt{5}$

72. $7x\sqrt{3} - 2\sqrt{3} = (7x - 2)\sqrt{3}$

For Exercises 73–76, write the English phrase as an algebraic expression. Simplify each expression.

73. The sum of the principal square root of 48 and the principal square root of 12

74. The sum of the cube root of 16 and the cube root of 2

75. The difference of 5 times the cube root of x^6 and the square of x

76. The sum of the cube of y and the principal fourth root of y^{12}

For Exercises 77–80, write an English phrase that translates the mathematical expression. (Answers may vary.)

77. $\sqrt{18} - 5^2$

78. $4^3 - \sqrt[3]{4}$

79. $\sqrt[4]{x} + y^3$

80. $a^4 + \sqrt{a}$

For Exercises 81–82, find the exact value of the perimeter, and then approximate the value to one decimal place.

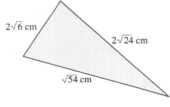 **81.**

2√6 cm, 2√24 cm, √54 cm

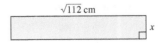 **82.**

√75 ft, √3 ft, √27 ft

83. The figure has perimeter $14\sqrt{2}$ ft. Find the value of x.

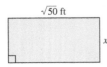

√50 ft, x

84. The figure has perimeter $12\sqrt{7}$ cm. Find the value of x.

√112 cm, x

Expanding Your Skills

85. **a.** An irregularly shaped garden is shown in the figure. All distances are expressed in yards. Find the perimeter. (*Hint:* Use the Pythagorean theorem to find the length of each side.) Write the final answer in radical form.

   b. Approximate your answer to two decimal places.

   c. If edging costs $1.49 per foot and sales tax is 6%, find the total cost of edging the garden.

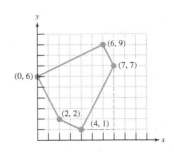

(6, 9), (7, 7), (0, 6), (2, 2), (4, 1)

Section 10.5   Multiplication of Radicals

Concepts

1. Multiplication Property of Radicals
2. Expressions of the Form $(\sqrt[n]{a})^n$
3. Special Case Products
4. Multiplying Radicals with Different Indices

1. Multiplication Property of Radicals

In this section, we will learn how to multiply radicals by using the multiplication property of radicals.

> **The Multiplication Property of Radicals**
>
> Let a and b represent real numbers such that $\sqrt[n]{a}$ and $\sqrt[n]{b}$ are both real. Then
>
> $$\sqrt[n]{ab} = \sqrt[n]{a} \cdot \sqrt[n]{b}$$

To multiply two radical expressions, we use the multiplication property of radicals along with the commutative and associative properties of multiplication.

Example 1   **Multiplying Radical Expressions**

Multiply each expression and simplify the result. Assume all variables represent positive real numbers.

a. $(3\sqrt{2})(5\sqrt{6})$ **b.** $(2x\sqrt{y})(-7\sqrt{xy})$ **c.** $(15c\sqrt[3]{cd})\left(\frac{1}{3}\sqrt[3]{cd^2}\right)$

Solution:

a. $(3\sqrt{2})(5\sqrt{6})$

$\qquad = (3 \cdot 5)(\sqrt{2} \cdot \sqrt{6})$ Commutative and associative properties of multiplication

$\qquad = 15\sqrt{12}$ Multiplication property of radicals

$\qquad = 15\sqrt{2^2 3}$

$\qquad = 15 \cdot 2\sqrt{3}$ Simplify the radical.

$\qquad = 30\sqrt{3}$

b. $(2x\sqrt{y})(-7\sqrt{xy})$

$\qquad = (2x)(-7)(\sqrt{y} \cdot \sqrt{xy})$ Commutative and associative properties of multiplication

$\qquad = -14x\sqrt{xy^2}$ Multiplication property of radicals

$\qquad = -14xy\sqrt{x}$ Simplify the radical.

c. $(15c\sqrt[3]{cd})\left(\frac{1}{3}\sqrt[3]{cd^2}\right)$

$\qquad = \left(15c \cdot \frac{1}{3}\right)(\sqrt[3]{cd} \cdot \sqrt[3]{cd^2})$ Commutative and associative properties of multiplication

$\qquad = 5c\sqrt[3]{c^2d^3}$ Multiplication property of radicals

$\qquad = 5cd\sqrt[3]{c^2}$ Simplify the radical.

Skill Practice Multiply the expressions and simplify the results. Assume all variables represent positive real numbers.

1. $(4\sqrt{6})(-2\sqrt{3})$
2. $(3ab\sqrt{b})(-2\sqrt{ab})$
3. $(2\sqrt[3]{4ab})(5\sqrt[3]{2a^2b})$

When multiplying radical expressions with more than one term, we use the distributive property.

Example 2   **Multiplying Radical Expressions**

Multiply. $3\sqrt{11}(2 + \sqrt{11})$

Solution:

$3\sqrt{11}(2 + \sqrt{11})$

$= 3\sqrt{11} \cdot (2) + 3\sqrt{11} \cdot \sqrt{11}$ Apply the distributive property.

$= 6\sqrt{11} + 3\sqrt{11^2}$ Multiplication property of radicals

$= 6\sqrt{11} + 3 \cdot 11$ Simplify the radical.

$= 6\sqrt{11} + 33$

Skill Practice Multiply.

4. $5\sqrt{5}(2\sqrt{5} - 2)$

Example 3   **Multiplying Radical Expressions**

Multiply.

a. $(\sqrt{5} + 3\sqrt{2})(2\sqrt{5} - \sqrt{2})$ b. $(-10a\sqrt{b} + 7b)(a\sqrt{b} + 2b)$

Solution:

a. $(\sqrt{5} + 3\sqrt{2})(2\sqrt{5} - \sqrt{2})$

$= 2\sqrt{5^2} - \sqrt{10} + 6\sqrt{10} - 3\sqrt{2^2}$ Apply the distributive property.

$= 2 \cdot 5 + 5\sqrt{10} - 3 \cdot 2$ Simplify radicals and combine *like* radicals.

$= 10 + 5\sqrt{10} - 6$

$= 4 + 5\sqrt{10}$ Combine *like* terms.

b. $(-10a\sqrt{b} + 7b)(a\sqrt{b} + 2b)$

$= -10a^2\sqrt{b^2} - 20ab\sqrt{b} + 7ab\sqrt{b} + 14b^2$ Apply the distributive property.

$= -10a^2b - 13ab\sqrt{b} + 14b^2$ Simplify and combine *like* terms.

Answers

1. $-24\sqrt{2}$ 2. $-6ab^2\sqrt{a}$
3. $20a\sqrt[3]{b^2}$ 4. $50 - 10\sqrt{5}$

Skill Practice　Multiply.

5. $(2\sqrt{3} - 3\sqrt{10})(\sqrt{3} + 2\sqrt{10})$　　　**6.** $(x\sqrt{y} + y)(3x\sqrt{y} - 2y)$

Example 4　**Multiplying Radical Expressions**

Multiply.　　　$(2\sqrt{x} + \sqrt{y})(6 - \sqrt{x} + 8\sqrt{y})$

Solution:

$(2\sqrt{x} + \sqrt{y})(6 - \sqrt{x} + 8\sqrt{y})$

$= 12\sqrt{x} - 2\sqrt{x^2} + 16\sqrt{xy} + 6\sqrt{y} - \sqrt{xy} + 8\sqrt{y^2}$　　Apply the distributive property.

$= 12\sqrt{x} - 2x + 16\sqrt{xy} + 6\sqrt{y} - \sqrt{xy} + 8y$　　Simplify the radicals.

$= 12\sqrt{x} - 2x + 15\sqrt{xy} + 6\sqrt{y} + 8y$　　Combine *like* terms.

Skill Practice　Multiply.

7. $(\sqrt{t} + 3\sqrt{w})(4 - \sqrt{t} - \sqrt{w})$

---

2. Expressions of the Form $\left(\sqrt[n]{a}\right)^n$

The multiplication property of radicals can be used to simplify an expression of the form $(\sqrt{a})^2$, where $a \geq 0$.

$$\left(\sqrt{a}\right)^2 = \sqrt{a} \cdot \sqrt{a} = \sqrt{a^2} = a \qquad \text{where } a \geq 0$$

This logic can be applied to nth roots.

- If $\sqrt[n]{a}$ is a real number, then $(\sqrt[n]{a})^n = a$.

Example 5　**Simplifying Radical Expressions**

Simplify the expressions. Assume all variables represent positive real numbers.

a. $(\sqrt{11})^2$　　**b.** $(\sqrt[5]{z})^5$　　**c.** $(\sqrt[3]{pq})^3$

Solution:

a. $(\sqrt{11})^2 = 11$　　　**b.** $(\sqrt[5]{z})^5 = z$　　　**c.** $(\sqrt[3]{pq})^3 = pq$

Skill Practice　Simplify.

8. $(\sqrt{14})^2$　　**9.** $(\sqrt[7]{q})^7$　　**10.** $(\sqrt[5]{3z})^5$

Answers

5. $-54 + \sqrt{30}$
6. $3x^2y + xy\sqrt{y} - 2y^2$
7. $4\sqrt{t} - t - 4\sqrt{tw} + 12\sqrt{w} - 3w$
8. 14　　**9.** q　　**10.** $3z$

3. Special Case Products

From Examples 2–4, you may have noticed a similarity between multiplying radical expressions and multiplying polynomials.

   Recall that the square of a binomial results in a perfect square trinomial:

$$(a + b)^2 = a^2 + 2ab + b^2$$
$$(a - b)^2 = a^2 - 2ab + b^2$$

The same patterns occur when squaring a radical expression with two terms.

Example 6   Squaring a Two-Term Radical Expression

Square the radical expressions. Assume all variables represent positive real numbers.

   a. $(\sqrt{d} + 3)^2$ **b.** $(5\sqrt{y} - \sqrt{2})^2$

Solution:

   a. $(\sqrt{d} + 3)^2$

$a^2 + 2ab + b^2$

$= (\sqrt{d})^2 + 2(\sqrt{d})(3) + (3)^2$

$= d + 6\sqrt{d} + 9$

This expression is in the form $(a + b)^2$, where $a = \sqrt{d}$ and $b = 3$.

Apply the formula

$(a + b)^2 = a^2 + 2ab + b^2$.

Simplify.

   b. $(5\sqrt{y} - \sqrt{2})^2$

$a^2 - 2ab + b^2$

$= (5\sqrt{y})^2 - 2(5\sqrt{y})(\sqrt{2}) + (\sqrt{2})^2$

$= 25y - 10\sqrt{2y} + 2$

This expression is in the form $(a - b)^2$, where $a = 5\sqrt{y}$ and $b = \sqrt{2}$.

Apply the formula

$(a - b)^2 = a^2 - 2ab + b^2$.

Simplify.

> **TIP:** The product $(\sqrt{d} + 3)^2$ can also be found by using the distributive property.
>
> $(\sqrt{d} + 3)^2 = (\sqrt{d} + 3)(\sqrt{d} + 3)$

Skill Practice Square the radical expressions. Assume all variables represent positive real numbers.

   11. $(\sqrt{a} - 5)^2$ **12.** $(4\sqrt{x} + \sqrt{3})^2$

Recall that the product of two conjugate binomials results in a difference of squares.

$$(a + b)(a - b) = a^2 - b^2$$

The same pattern occurs when multiplying two conjugate radical expressions.

Example 7   Multiplying Conjugate Radical Expressions

Multiply the radical expressions. Assume all variables represent positive real numbers.

   a. $(\sqrt{3} + 2)(\sqrt{3} - 2)$ **b.** $\left(\frac{1}{3}\sqrt{s} - \frac{3}{4}\sqrt{t}\right)\left(\frac{1}{3}\sqrt{s} + \frac{3}{4}\sqrt{t}\right)$

Answers
11. $a - 10\sqrt{a} + 25$
12. $16x + 8\sqrt{3x} + 3$

TIP: The product $(\sqrt{3}+2)(\sqrt{3}-2)$ can also be found by using the distributive property.

$(\sqrt{3}+2)(\sqrt{3}-2)$

Solution:

a. $(\sqrt{3}+2)(\sqrt{3}-2)$ — The expression is in the form $(a+b)(a-b)$, where $a=\sqrt{3}$ and $b=2$.

$$a^2 - b^2$$

$$=(\sqrt{3})^2 - (2)^2 \quad \text{Apply the formula } (a+b)(a-b)=a^2-b^2.$$

$$=3-4 \quad \text{Simplify.}$$

$$=-1$$

b. $\left(\frac{1}{3}\sqrt{s}-\frac{3}{4}\sqrt{t}\right)\left(\frac{1}{3}\sqrt{s}+\frac{3}{4}\sqrt{t}\right)$ — This expression is in the form $(a-b)(a+b)$, where $a=\frac{1}{3}\sqrt{s}$ and $b=\frac{3}{4}\sqrt{t}$.

$$a^2 - b^2$$

$$=\left(\frac{1}{3}\sqrt{s}\right)^2 - \left(\frac{3}{4}\sqrt{t}\right)^2 \quad \text{Apply the formula } (a+b)(a-b)=a^2-b^2.$$

$$=\frac{1}{9}s - \frac{9}{16}t \quad \text{Simplify.}$$

Skill Practice Multiply the conjugates. Assume all variables represent positive real numbers.

13. $(\sqrt{5}+3)(\sqrt{5}-3)$ **14.** $\left(\frac{1}{2}\sqrt{a}+\frac{2}{5}\sqrt{b}\right)\cdot\left(\frac{1}{2}\sqrt{a}-\frac{2}{5}\sqrt{b}\right)$

4. Multiplying Radicals with Different Indices

The product of two radicals can be simplified provided the radicals have the same index. If the radicals have different indices, then we can use the properties of rational exponents to obtain a common index.

Example 8   **Multiplying Radicals with Different Indices**

Multiply the expressions. Write the answers in radical form.

a. $\sqrt[3]{5}\cdot\sqrt[4]{5}$ **b.** $\sqrt[3]{7}\cdot\sqrt{2}$

Solution:

a. $\sqrt[3]{5}\cdot\sqrt[4]{5}$

$$=5^{1/3}5^{1/4} \quad \text{Rewrite each expression with rational exponents.}$$

$$=5^{(1/3)+(1/4)} \quad \text{Because the bases are equal, we can add the exponents.}$$

$$=5^{(4/12)+(3/12)} \quad \text{Write the fractions with a common denominator.}$$

$$=5^{7/12} \quad \text{Simplify the exponent.}$$

$$=\sqrt[12]{5^7} \quad \text{Rewrite the expression as a radical.}$$

Answers

13. -4 **14.** $\frac{1}{4}a - \frac{4}{25}b$

b. $\sqrt[3]{7} \cdot \sqrt{2}$

$= 7^{1/3} 2^{1/2}$	Rewrite each expression with rational exponents.
$= 7^{2/6} 2^{3/6}$	Write the rational exponents with a common denominator.
$= (7^2 2^3)^{1/6}$	Apply the power rule of exponents.
$= \sqrt[6]{7^2 2^3}$	Rewrite the expression as a single radical.
$= \sqrt[6]{392}$	Simplify.

Skill Practice Multiply the expressions. Write the answers in radical form. Assume all variables represent positive real numbers.

15. $\sqrt{x} \cdot \sqrt[3]{x}$ **16.** $\sqrt[4]{a^3} \cdot \sqrt[3]{b}$

Answers
15. $\sqrt[6]{x^5}$ **16.** $\sqrt[12]{a^9 b^4}$

Section 10.5   Practice Exercises

For the exercises in this set, assume that all variables represent positive real numbers, unless otherwise stated.

Vocabulary and Key Concepts

1. **a.** If $\sqrt[n]{a}$ and $\sqrt[n]{b}$ are real numbers, then $\sqrt[n]{a} \cdot \sqrt[n]{b} = $ _____.

   b. If $x \geq 0$, then $\sqrt{x} \cdot \sqrt{x} = $ _____.

   c. If $\sqrt[n]{a}$ is a real number, then $(\sqrt[n]{a})^n = $ _____.

   d. Two binomials $(x + \sqrt{2})$ and $(x - \sqrt{2})$ are called _____ of each other, and their product is $(x)^2 - (\sqrt{2})^2$.

   e. If $m \geq 0$ and $n \geq 0$, then $(\sqrt{m} + \sqrt{n})(\sqrt{m} - \sqrt{n}) = $ _____.

   f. Which is the correct simplification of $(\sqrt{c} + 4)^2$?

   $c + 16$ or $c + 8\sqrt{c} + 16$

Review Exercises

For Exercises 2–4, simplify the radicals.

2. $\sqrt[3]{-16x^5 y^6 z^7}$ **3.** $-\sqrt{20a^2 b^3 c}$ **4.** $\sqrt{\dfrac{8y^3 z^5}{y}}$

For Exercises 5–6, simplify the expressions. Write the answer with positive exponents only.

5. $x^{1/3} y^{1/4} x^{-1/6} y^{1/3}$ **6.** $\dfrac{b^{1/4}}{b^{3/2}}$

For Exercises 7–8, add or subtract as indicated.

7. $-2\sqrt[3]{7} + 4\sqrt[3]{7}$ **8.** $4\sqrt{8x^3} - x\sqrt{50x}$

732   **Chapter 10** Radicals and Complex Numbers

Concept 1: Multiplication Property of Radicals

For Exercises 9–44, multiply the radical expressions. **(See Examples 1–4.)**

9. $\sqrt[3]{7} \cdot \sqrt[3]{3}$

10. $\sqrt[4]{6} \cdot \sqrt[4]{2}$

11. $\sqrt{2} \cdot \sqrt{10}$

12. $\sqrt[3]{4} \cdot \sqrt[3]{12}$

13. $\sqrt[4]{16} \cdot \sqrt[4]{64}$

14. $\sqrt{5x^3} \cdot \sqrt{10x^4}$

15. $(4\sqrt[3]{4})(2\sqrt[3]{5})$

16. $(2\sqrt{5})(3\sqrt{7})$

17. $(8a\sqrt{b})(-3\sqrt{ab})$

18. $(p\sqrt[4]{q^3})(\sqrt[4]{pq})$

19. $\sqrt{30} \cdot \sqrt{12}$

20. $\sqrt{20} \cdot \sqrt{54}$

21. $\sqrt{6x} \cdot \sqrt{12x}$

22. $(\sqrt{3ab^2})(\sqrt{21a^2b})$

23. $\sqrt{5a^3b^2} \cdot \sqrt{20a^3b^3}$

24. $\sqrt[3]{m^2n^2} \cdot \sqrt[3]{48m^4n^2}$

25. $(4\sqrt{3xy^3})(-2\sqrt{6x^3y^2})$

26. $(2\sqrt[4]{3x})(4\sqrt[4]{27x^6})$

27. $(\sqrt[3]{4a^2b})(\sqrt[3]{2ab^3})(\sqrt[3]{54a^2b})$

28. $(\sqrt[3]{9x^3y})(\sqrt[3]{6xy})(\sqrt[3]{8x^2y^5})$

29. $\sqrt{3}(4\sqrt{3} - 6)$

30. $3\sqrt{5}(2\sqrt{5} + 4)$

31. $\sqrt{2}(\sqrt{6} - \sqrt{3})$

32. $\sqrt{5}(\sqrt{3} + \sqrt{7})$

33. $-\frac{1}{3}\sqrt{x}(6\sqrt{x} + 7)$

34. $-\frac{1}{2}\sqrt{y}(8 - 3\sqrt{y})$

35. $(\sqrt{3} + 2\sqrt{10})(4\sqrt{3} - \sqrt{10})$

36. $(8\sqrt{7} - \sqrt{5})(\sqrt{7} + 3\sqrt{5})$

37. $(\sqrt{x} + 4)(\sqrt{x} - 9)$

38. $(\sqrt{w} - 2)(\sqrt{w} - 9)$

39. $(\sqrt[3]{y} + 2)(\sqrt[3]{y} - 3)$

40. $(4 + \sqrt[5]{p})(5 + \sqrt[5]{p})$

41. $(\sqrt{a} - 3\sqrt{b})(9\sqrt{a} - \sqrt{b})$

42. $(11\sqrt{m} + 4\sqrt{n})(\sqrt{m} + \sqrt{n})$

43. $(\sqrt{p} + 2\sqrt{q})(8 + 3\sqrt{p} - \sqrt{q})$

44. $(5\sqrt{s} - \sqrt{t})(\sqrt{s} + 5 + 6\sqrt{t})$

Concept 2: Expressions of the Form $(\sqrt[n]{a})^n$

For Exercises 45–52, simplify the expressions. Assume all variables represent positive real numbers. **(See Example 5.)**

45. $(\sqrt{15})^2$

46. $(\sqrt{58})^2$

47. $(\sqrt{3y})^2$

48. $(\sqrt{19yz})^2$

49. $(\sqrt[3]{6})^3$

50. $(\sqrt[5]{24})^5$

51. $\sqrt{709} \cdot \sqrt{709}$

52. $\sqrt{401} \cdot \sqrt{401}$

Concept 3: Special Case Products

53. a. Write the formula for the product of two conjugates. $(x + y)(x - y) =$

  b. Multiply. $(x + 5)(x - 5)$

54. a. Write the formula for squaring a binomial. $(x + y)^2 =$

  b. Multiply. $(x + 5)^2$

For Exercises 55–66, multiply the radical expressions. **(See Examples 6–7.)**

55. $(\sqrt{13} + 4)^2$

56. $(6 - \sqrt{11})^2$

57. $(\sqrt{p} - \sqrt{7})^2$

58. $(\sqrt{q} + \sqrt{2})^2$

59. $(\sqrt{2a} - 3\sqrt{b})^2$

60. $(\sqrt{3w} + 4\sqrt{z})^2$

61. $(\sqrt{3} + x)(\sqrt{3} - x)$

62. $(y + \sqrt{6})(y - \sqrt{6})$

63. $(\sqrt{6} + \sqrt{2})(\sqrt{6} - \sqrt{2})$

64. $(\sqrt{15} + \sqrt{5})(\sqrt{15} - \sqrt{5})$

65. $\left(\frac{2}{3}\sqrt{x} + \frac{1}{2}\sqrt{y}\right)\left(\frac{2}{3}\sqrt{x} - \frac{1}{2}\sqrt{y}\right)$

66. $\left(\frac{1}{4}\sqrt{s} + \frac{1}{5}\sqrt{t}\right)\left(\frac{1}{4}\sqrt{s} - \frac{1}{5}\sqrt{t}\right)$

For Exercises 67–68, multiply the expressions.

67. **a.** $(\sqrt{3} + \sqrt{x})(\sqrt{3} - \sqrt{x})$

  b. $(\sqrt{3} + \sqrt{x})(\sqrt{3} + \sqrt{x})$

  c. $(\sqrt{3} - \sqrt{x})(\sqrt{3} - \sqrt{x})$

68. **a.** $(\sqrt{5} + \sqrt{y})(\sqrt{5} - \sqrt{y})$

  b. $(\sqrt{5} + \sqrt{y})(\sqrt{5} + \sqrt{y})$

  c. $(\sqrt{5} - \sqrt{y})(\sqrt{5} - \sqrt{y})$

Mixed Exercises

For Exercises 69–76, identify each statement as true or false. If an answer is false, explain why.

69. $\sqrt{3} \cdot \sqrt{2} = \sqrt{6}$

70. $\sqrt{5} \cdot \sqrt[3]{2} = \sqrt{10}$

71. $(x - \sqrt{5})^2 = x - 5$

72. $3(2\sqrt{5x}) = 6\sqrt{5x}$

73. $5(3\sqrt{4x}) = 15\sqrt{20x}$

74. $\dfrac{\sqrt{5x}}{5} = \sqrt{x}$

75. $\dfrac{3\sqrt{x}}{3} = \sqrt{x}$

76. $(\sqrt{t} - 1)(\sqrt{t} + 1) = t - 1$

For Exercises 77–84, perform the indicated operations.

77. $(-\sqrt{6x})^2$

78. $(-\sqrt{8a})^2$

79. $(\sqrt{3x + 1})^2$

80. $(\sqrt{x - 1})^2$

81. $(\sqrt{x + 3} - 4)^2$

82. $(\sqrt{x + 1} + 3)^2$

83. $(\sqrt{2t - 3} + 5)^2$

84. $(\sqrt{3w - 2} - 4)^2$

For Exercises 85–88, find the exact area.

85.

$\sqrt{40}$ ft

$3\sqrt{2}$ ft

86.

$6\sqrt{2}$ m

$10\sqrt{12}$ m

87.

$3\sqrt{5}$ in.

$6\sqrt{12}$ in.

88.

$2\sqrt{18}$ yd

$7\sqrt{6}$ yd

Concept 4: Multiplying Radicals with Different Indices

For Exercises 89–100, multiply or divide the radicals with different indices. Write the answers in radical form and simplify. **(See Example 8.)**

89. $\sqrt{x} \cdot \sqrt[4]{x}$

90. $\sqrt[3]{y} \cdot \sqrt{y}$

91. $\sqrt[5]{2z} \cdot \sqrt[3]{2z}$

92. $\sqrt[3]{5w} \cdot \sqrt[4]{5w}$

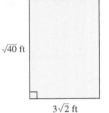 **93.** $\sqrt[3]{p^2} \cdot \sqrt{p^3}$

94. $\sqrt[4]{q^3} \cdot \sqrt[3]{q^2}$

95. $\dfrac{\sqrt{u^3}}{\sqrt[3]{u}}$

96. $\dfrac{\sqrt{v^5}}{\sqrt[4]{v}}$

97. $\sqrt[3]{x} \cdot \sqrt[6]{y}$

98. $\sqrt{a} \cdot \sqrt[6]{b}$

99. $\sqrt[4]{8} \cdot \sqrt{3}$

100. $\sqrt{11} \cdot \sqrt[6]{2}$

Expanding Your Skills

For Exercises 101–106, multiply.

101. $\sqrt[3]{2xy} \cdot \sqrt[4]{5xy}$

102. $\sqrt{6ab} \cdot \sqrt[3]{7ab}$

103. $\sqrt[3]{4m^2n} \cdot \sqrt{6mn}$

104. $\sqrt[4]{5xy^3} \cdot \sqrt[3]{10x^2y}$

105. $(\sqrt[3]{a} + \sqrt[3]{b})(\sqrt[3]{a^2} - \sqrt[3]{ab} + \sqrt[3]{b^2})$

106. $(\sqrt[3]{a} - \sqrt[3]{b})(\sqrt[3]{a^2} + \sqrt[3]{ab} + \sqrt[3]{b^2})$

734   **Chapter 10**   Radicals and Complex Numbers

Problem Recognition Exercises

Simplifying Radical Expressions

For Exercises 1–20, simplify the expressions.

1. a. $\sqrt{24}$
   b. $\sqrt[3]{24}$

2. a. $\sqrt{54}$
   b. $\sqrt[3]{54}$

3. a. $\sqrt{200y^6}$
   b. $\sqrt[3]{200y^6}$

4. a. $\sqrt{32z^{15}}$
   b. $\sqrt[3]{32z^{15}}$

5. a. $\sqrt{80}$
   b. $\sqrt[3]{80}$
   c. $\sqrt[4]{80}$

6. a. $\sqrt{48}$
   b. $\sqrt[3]{48}$
   c. $\sqrt[4]{48}$

7. a. $\sqrt{x^5y^6}$
   b. $\sqrt[3]{x^5y^6}$
   c. $\sqrt[4]{x^5y^6}$

8. a. $\sqrt{a^{10}b^9}$
   b. $\sqrt[3]{a^{10}b^9}$
   c. $\sqrt[4]{a^{10}b^9}$

9. a. $\sqrt[3]{32s^5t^6}$
   b. $\sqrt[4]{32s^5t^6}$
   c. $\sqrt[5]{32s^5t^6}$

10. a. $\sqrt[3]{96v^7w^{20}}$
   b. $\sqrt[4]{96v^7w^{20}}$
   c. $\sqrt[5]{96v^7w^{20}}$

11. a. $\sqrt{5} + \sqrt{5}$
   b. $\sqrt{5} \cdot \sqrt{5}$

12. a. $\sqrt{10} + \sqrt{10}$
   b. $\sqrt{10} \cdot \sqrt{10}$

13. a. $2\sqrt{6} - 5\sqrt{6}$
   b. $2\sqrt{6} \cdot 5\sqrt{6}$

14. a. $3\sqrt{7} - 10\sqrt{7}$
   b. $3\sqrt{7} \cdot 10\sqrt{7}$

15. a. $\sqrt{8} + \sqrt{2}$
   b. $\sqrt{8} \cdot \sqrt{2}$

16. a. $\sqrt{12} + \sqrt{3}$
   b. $\sqrt{12} \cdot \sqrt{3}$

17. a. $5\sqrt{18} - 4\sqrt{8}$
   b. $5\sqrt{18} \cdot 4\sqrt{8}$

18. a. $\sqrt{50} - \sqrt{72}$
   b. $\sqrt{50} \cdot \sqrt{72}$

19. a. $4\sqrt[3]{24} + 6\sqrt[3]{3}$
   b. $4\sqrt[3]{24} \cdot 6\sqrt[3]{3}$

20. a. $2\sqrt[3]{54} - 5\sqrt[3]{2}$
   b. $2\sqrt[3]{54} \cdot 5\sqrt[3]{2}$

Section 10.6   Division of Radicals and Rationalization

Concepts

1. Simplified Form of a Radical
2. Division Property of Radicals
3. Rationalizing the Denominator—One Term
4. Rationalizing the Denominator—Two Terms

1. Simplified Form of a Radical

Recall that for a radical expression to be in simplified form the following three conditions must be met.

Simplified Form of a Radical

Consider any radical expression in which the radicand is written as a product of prime factors. The expression is in simplified form if all the following conditions are met:

1. The radicand has no factor raised to a power greater than or equal to the index.
2. The radicand does not contain a fraction.
3. No radicals are in the denominator of a fraction.

In the previous sections, we have concentrated on the first condition in the simplification process. Next, we will demonstrate how to satisfy the second and third conditions involving radicals and fractions.

2. Division Property of Radicals

The multiplication property of radicals makes it possible to write a product within a radical to be separated as a product of radicals. We now state a similar property for radicals involving quotients.

> ### Division Property of Radicals
> Let a and b represent real numbers such that $\sqrt[n]{a}$ and $\sqrt[n]{b}$ are both real. Then,
>
> $$\sqrt[n]{\frac{a}{b}} = \frac{\sqrt[n]{a}}{\sqrt[n]{b}} \quad b \neq 0$$

The division property of radicals indicates that a quotient within a radicand can be written as a quotient of radicals provided the roots are real numbers. For example:

$$\sqrt{\frac{25}{36}} = \frac{\sqrt{25}}{\sqrt{36}}$$

The reverse process is also true. A quotient of radicals can be written as a single radical provided that the roots are real numbers and that they have the same index.

$$\text{Same index} \longrightarrow \frac{\sqrt[3]{125}}{\sqrt[3]{8}} = \sqrt[3]{\frac{125}{8}}$$

In Examples 1 and 2, we will apply the division property of radicals to simplify radical expressions.

Example 1   Using the Division Property to Simplify Radicals

Use the division property of radicals to simplify the expressions. Assume the variables represent positive real numbers.

a. $\sqrt{\dfrac{a^6}{b^4}}$ **b.** $\sqrt[3]{\dfrac{81y^5}{x^3}}$

Solution:

a. $\sqrt{\dfrac{a^6}{b^4}}$ The radicand contains an irreducible fraction.

$= \dfrac{\sqrt{a^6}}{\sqrt{b^4}}$ Apply the division property to rewrite as a quotient of radicals.

$= \dfrac{a^3}{b^2}$ Simplify the radicals.

b. $\sqrt[3]{\dfrac{81y^5}{x^3}}$ The radicand contains an irreducible fraction.

$= \dfrac{\sqrt[3]{81y^5}}{\sqrt[3]{x^3}}$ Apply the division property to rewrite as a quotient of radicals.

$= \dfrac{\sqrt[3]{3^4 \cdot y^5}}{\sqrt[3]{x^3}}$ Factor the radicand in the numerator to simplify the radical.

$= \dfrac{3y\sqrt[3]{3y^2}}{x}$ Simplify the radicals in the numerator and the denominator. The expression is simplified because it now satisfies all conditions.

Skill Practice Simplify the expressions.

1. $\sqrt{\dfrac{x^4}{y^{10}}}$ 2. $\sqrt[3]{\dfrac{w^7}{64}}$

Example 2   **Using the Division Property to Simplify a Radical**

Use the division property of radicals to simplify the expressions. Assume the variables represent positive real numbers.

$$\dfrac{\sqrt[4]{8p^7}}{\sqrt[4]{p^3}}$$

Solution:

$\dfrac{\sqrt[4]{8p^7}}{\sqrt[4]{p^3}}$ There is a radical in the denominator of the fraction.

$= \sqrt[4]{\dfrac{8p^7}{p^3}}$ Apply the division property to write the quotient under a single radical.

$= \sqrt[4]{8p^4}$ Simplify the fraction.

$= p\sqrt[4]{8}$ Simplify the radical.

Skill Practice Simplify the expression.

3. $\dfrac{\sqrt[3]{16y^4}}{\sqrt[3]{y}}$

---

3. Rationalizing the Denominator—One Term

The third condition restricts radicals from the denominator of an expression. The process to remove a radical from the denominator is called **rationalizing the denominator**. In many cases, rationalizing the denominator creates an expression that is computationally simpler. For example,

$$\dfrac{6}{\sqrt{3}} = 2\sqrt{3} \qquad \text{and} \qquad \dfrac{-2}{2 + \sqrt{6}} = 2 - \sqrt{6}$$

Answers

1. $\dfrac{x^2}{y^5}$ 2. $\dfrac{w^2\sqrt[3]{w}}{4}$ 3. $2y\sqrt[3]{2}$

We will demonstrate the process to rationalize the denominator as two separate cases:

- Rationalizing the denominator (one term)
- Rationalizing the denominator (two terms involving square roots)

To begin the first case, recall that the nth root of a perfect nth power simplifies completely.

$$\sqrt{x^2} = x \qquad x \geq 0$$
$$\sqrt[3]{x^3} = x$$
$$\sqrt[4]{x^4} = x \qquad x \geq 0$$
$$\sqrt[5]{x^5} = x$$
$$\cdots$$

Therefore, to rationalize a radical expression, use the multiplication property of radicals to create an nth root of an nth power.

Example 3   **Rationalizing Radical Expressions**

Fill in the missing radicand to rationalize the radical expressions. Assume all variables represent positive real numbers.

a. $\sqrt{a} \cdot \sqrt{?} = \sqrt{a^2} = a$ **b.** $\sqrt[3]{y} \cdot \sqrt[3]{?} = \sqrt[3]{y^3} = y$

c. $\sqrt[4]{2z^3} \cdot \sqrt[4]{?} = \sqrt[4]{2^4 z^4} = 2z$

Solution:

a. $\sqrt{a} \cdot \sqrt{?} = \sqrt{a^2} = a$ What multiplied by $\sqrt{a}$ will equal $\sqrt{a^2}$?

     $\sqrt{a} \cdot \sqrt{a} = \sqrt{a^2} = a$

b. $\sqrt[3]{y} \cdot \sqrt[3]{?} = \sqrt[3]{y^3} = y$ What multiplied by $\sqrt[3]{y}$ will equal $\sqrt[3]{y^3}$?

     $\sqrt[3]{y} \cdot \sqrt[3]{y^2} = \sqrt[3]{y^3} = y$

c. $\sqrt[4]{2z^3} \cdot \sqrt[4]{?} = \sqrt[4]{2^4 z^4} = 2z$ What multiplied by $\sqrt[4]{2z^3}$ will equal $\sqrt[4]{2^4 z^4}$?

     $\sqrt[4]{2z^3} \cdot \sqrt[4]{2^3 z} = \sqrt[4]{2^4 z^4} = 2z$

Skill Practice   Fill in the missing radicand to rationalize the radical expression.

4. $\sqrt{7} \cdot \sqrt{?}$ **5.** $\sqrt[5]{t^2} \cdot \sqrt[5]{?}$ **6.** $\sqrt[3]{5x^2} \cdot \sqrt[3]{?}$

To rationalize the denominator of an expression with a single radical term in the denominator, we have the following strategy. Multiply the numerator and denominator by an appropriate expression to create an nth root of an nth power in the denominator.

Answers

4. 7   **5.** t^3 **6.** $5^2 x$

| **Example 4** | **Rationalizing the Denominator—One Term** |

Simplify the expression. $\dfrac{5}{\sqrt[3]{a}}$ $\quad a \neq 0$

Solution:

To remove the radical from the denominator, a cube root of a perfect cube is needed in the denominator. Multiply numerator and denominator by $\sqrt[3]{a^2}$ because $\sqrt[3]{a} \cdot \sqrt[3]{a^2} = \sqrt[3]{a^3} = a$.

$$\dfrac{5}{\sqrt[3]{a}} = \dfrac{5}{\sqrt[3]{a}} \cdot \dfrac{\sqrt[3]{a^2}}{\sqrt[3]{a^2}}$$

$$= \dfrac{5\sqrt[3]{a^2}}{\sqrt[3]{a^3}} \qquad \text{Multiply the radicals.}$$

$$= \dfrac{5\sqrt[3]{a^2}}{a} \qquad \text{Simplify.}$$

Skill Practice Simplify the expression. Assume $y > 0$.

7. $\dfrac{2}{\sqrt[4]{y}}$

Note that for $a \neq 0$, the expression $\dfrac{\sqrt[3]{a^2}}{\sqrt[3]{a^2}} = 1$. In Example 4, multiplying the expression $\dfrac{5}{\sqrt[3]{a}}$ by this ratio does not change its value.

| **Example 5** | **Rationalizing the Denominator—One Term** |

Simplify the expression. $\sqrt{\dfrac{y^5}{7}}$

Solution:

$$\sqrt{\dfrac{y^5}{7}} \qquad \text{The radical contains an irreducible fraction.}$$

$$= \dfrac{\sqrt{y^5}}{\sqrt{7}} \qquad \text{Apply the division property of radicals.}$$

$$= \dfrac{y^2\sqrt{y}}{\sqrt{7}} \qquad \text{Simplify the radical in the numerator.}$$

$$= \dfrac{y^2\sqrt{y}}{\sqrt{7}} \cdot \dfrac{\sqrt{7}}{\sqrt{7}} \qquad \text{Rationalize the denominator.}$$
$$\qquad\qquad\qquad Note: \sqrt{7} \cdot \sqrt{7} = \sqrt{7^2} = 7$$

$$= \dfrac{y^2\sqrt{7y}}{\sqrt{7^2}}$$

$$= \dfrac{y^2\sqrt{7y}}{7} \qquad \text{Simplify.}$$

> **Avoiding Mistakes**
> A factor within a radicand cannot be simplified with a factor outside the radicand. For example, $\dfrac{\sqrt{7y}}{7}$ cannot be simplified.

Answer

7. $\dfrac{2\sqrt[4]{y^3}}{y}$

Skill Practice Simplify the expression.

8. $\sqrt{\dfrac{8}{3}}$

| **Example 6** | **Rationalizing the Denominator—One Term** |

Simplify the expression. $\dfrac{15}{\sqrt[3]{25s}}$

Solution:

$\dfrac{15}{\sqrt[3]{25s}}$

$= \dfrac{15}{\sqrt[3]{5^2 s}} \cdot \dfrac{\sqrt[3]{5s^2}}{\sqrt[3]{5s^2}}$ Because $25 = 5^2$, one additional factor of 5 is needed to form a perfect cube. Two additional factors of s are needed to make a perfect cube. Multiply numerator and denominator by $\sqrt[3]{5s^2}$.

$= \dfrac{15\sqrt[3]{5s^2}}{\sqrt[3]{5^3 s^3}}$

$= \dfrac{15\sqrt[3]{5s^2}}{5s}$ Simplify the perfect cube.

$= \dfrac{\overset{3}{\cancel{15}}\sqrt[3]{5s^2}}{\underset{1}{\cancel{5}s}}$ Reduce to lowest terms.

$= \dfrac{3\sqrt[3]{5s^2}}{s}$

> **TIP:** In the expression $\dfrac{15\sqrt[3]{5s^2}}{5s}$, the factor of 15 and the factor of 5 may be reduced because both are outside the radical.
>
> $\dfrac{15\sqrt[3]{5s^2}}{5s} = \dfrac{15}{5} \cdot \dfrac{\sqrt[3]{5s^2}}{s}$
>
> $= \dfrac{3\sqrt[3]{5s^2}}{s}$

Skill Practice Simplify the expression.

9. $\dfrac{18}{\sqrt[3]{3y^2}}$

---

4. Rationalizing the Denominator—Two Terms

Example 7 demonstrates how to rationalize a two-term denominator involving square roots.
First recall from the multiplication of polynomials that the product of two conjugates results in a difference of squares.

$$(a + b)(a - b) = a^2 - b^2$$

If either a or b has a square root factor, the expression will simplify without a radical. That is, the expression is *rationalized*. For example:

$$(2 + \sqrt{6})(2 - \sqrt{6}) = (2)^2 - (\sqrt{6})^2$$
$$= 4 - 6$$
$$= -2$$

Answers

8. $\dfrac{2\sqrt{6}}{3}$ **9.** $\dfrac{6\sqrt[3]{9y}}{y}$

Example 7   **Rationalizing the Denominator—Two Terms**

Simplify the expression by rationalizing the denominator. $\dfrac{-2}{2+\sqrt{6}}$

Solution:

$\dfrac{-2}{2+\sqrt{6}}$

$= \dfrac{(-2)}{(2+\sqrt{6})} \cdot \dfrac{(2-\sqrt{6})}{(2-\sqrt{6})}$ Multiply the numerator and denominator by the conjugate of the denominator.

conjugates

$= \dfrac{-2(2-\sqrt{6})}{(2)^2-(\sqrt{6})^2}$ In the denominator, apply the formula $(a+b)(a-b)=a^2-b^2$.

$= \dfrac{-2(2-\sqrt{6})}{4-6}$ Simplify.

$= \dfrac{-2(2-\sqrt{6})}{-2}$

$= \dfrac{\not{-2}(2-\sqrt{6})}{\not{-2}}$

$= 2-\sqrt{6}$

> **Avoiding Mistakes**
>
> When constructing the conjugate of an expression, change only the sign between the terms (not the sign of the leading term).

Skill Practice   Simplify by rationalizing the denominator.

10. $\dfrac{8}{3+\sqrt{5}}$

Example 8   **Rationalizing the Denominator—Two Terms**

Rationalize the denominator. $\dfrac{4+\sqrt{x}}{\sqrt{x}-7}$

Solution:

$\dfrac{(4+\sqrt{x})}{(\sqrt{x}-7)} \cdot \dfrac{(\sqrt{x}+7)}{(\sqrt{x}+7)}$ Multiply numerator and denominator by the conjugate of the denominator.

$= \dfrac{(4)(\sqrt{x})+(4)(7)+(\sqrt{x})(\sqrt{x})+(\sqrt{x})(7)}{(\sqrt{x})^2-(7)^2}$ Apply the distributive property.

$= \dfrac{4\sqrt{x}+28+x+7\sqrt{x}}{x-49}$ Multiply the radicals.

$= \dfrac{x+11\sqrt{x}+28}{x-49}$ Simplify.

Skill Practice   Rationalize the denominator.

11. $\dfrac{\sqrt{y}-4}{8-\sqrt{y}}$

Answers

10. $6-2\sqrt{5}$

11. $\dfrac{y+4\sqrt{y}-32}{64-y}$

Example 9 **Rationalizing the Denominator—Two Terms**

Rationalize the denominator. $\dfrac{3\sqrt{2}+2\sqrt{5}}{\sqrt{2}-4\sqrt{5}}$

Solution:

$\dfrac{(3\sqrt{2}+2\sqrt{5})}{(\sqrt{2}-4\sqrt{5})}\cdot\dfrac{(\sqrt{2}+4\sqrt{5})}{(\sqrt{2}+4\sqrt{5})}$ Multiply numerator and denominator by the conjugate of the denominator.

$=\dfrac{(3\sqrt{2})\cdot(\sqrt{2})+(3\sqrt{2})(4\sqrt{5})+(2\sqrt{5})(\sqrt{2})+(2\sqrt{5})(4\sqrt{5})}{(\sqrt{2})^2-(4\sqrt{5})^2}$ Apply the distributive property.

$=\dfrac{6+12\sqrt{10}+2\sqrt{10}+40}{2-80}$ Multiply the radicals.

$=\dfrac{46+14\sqrt{10}}{-78}$ or $-\dfrac{46+14\sqrt{10}}{78}$

$=-\dfrac{\overset{1}{2}(23+7\sqrt{10})}{\underset{39}{78}}$ Factor and simplify.

$=-\dfrac{23+7\sqrt{10}}{39}$

Skill Practice Rationalize the denominator.

12. $\dfrac{5\sqrt{2}-2\sqrt{5}}{\sqrt{2}-\sqrt{5}}$

Answer

12. $-\sqrt{10}$

Section 10.6 **Practice Exercises**

For the exercises in this set, assume that all variables represent positive real numbers unless otherwise stated.

Vocabulary and Key Concepts

1. **a.** In the simplified form of a radical expression, no _____ may appear in the denominator of a fraction.

   b. The division property of radicals indicates that if $\sqrt[n]{a}$ and $\sqrt[n]{b}$ are real numbers, then $\sqrt[n]{\dfrac{a}{b}}=\dfrac{\square}{\square}$ provided that $b\neq 0$.

   c. The simplified form of the expression $\sqrt[3]{\dfrac{64}{x^6}}$ is _____.

   d. The process of removing a radical from the denominator of a fraction is called _____ the denominator.

   e. The expression $\dfrac{\sqrt{3}}{3}$ (is/is not) in simplified form whereas $\dfrac{3}{\sqrt{3}}$ (is/is not) in simplified form.

   f. To rationalize the denominator for the expression $\dfrac{\sqrt{x}+3}{\sqrt{x}-2}$, multiply numerator and denominator by the conjugate of the _____.

Review Exercises

2. Simplify. $(4x^2y^4)^{1/2}(64y^{-3})^{1/3}$

For Exercises 3–10, perform the indicated operations.

3. $2y\sqrt{45} + 3\sqrt{20y^2}$ **4.** $3x\sqrt{72x} - 9\sqrt{50x^3}$ **5.** $(-6\sqrt{y} + 3)(3\sqrt{y} + 1)$ **6.** $(\sqrt{w} + 12)(2\sqrt{w} - 4)$

7. $(8 - \sqrt{t})^2$ **8.** $(\sqrt{p} + 4)^2$ **9.** $(\sqrt{2} + \sqrt{7})(\sqrt{2} - \sqrt{7})$ **10.** $(\sqrt{3} + 5)(\sqrt{3} - 5)$

Concept 2: Division Property of Radicals

For Exercises 11–22, simplify using the division property of radicals. Assume all variables represent positive real numbers.
(See Examples 1–2.)

11. $\sqrt{\dfrac{49x^4}{y^6}}$ **12.** $\sqrt{\dfrac{100p^2}{q^8}}$ **13.** $\sqrt{\dfrac{8a^2}{x^6}}$ **14.** $\sqrt{\dfrac{4w^3}{25y^4}}$

15. $\sqrt[3]{\dfrac{-16j^3}{k^3}}$ **16.** $\sqrt[5]{\dfrac{32x}{y^{10}}}$ **17.** $\dfrac{\sqrt{72ab^5}}{\sqrt{8ab}}$ **18.** $\dfrac{\sqrt{6x^3}}{\sqrt{24x}}$

19. $\dfrac{\sqrt[4]{3b^3}}{\sqrt[4]{48b^{11}}}$ **20.** $\dfrac{\sqrt[3]{128wz^8}}{\sqrt[3]{2wz^2}}$ **21.** $\dfrac{\sqrt{3yz^2}}{\sqrt{w^4}}$ **22.** $\dfrac{\sqrt{50x^3z}}{\sqrt{9y^4}}$

Concept 3: Rationalizing the Denominator—One Term

The radical expressions in Exercises 23–30 have radicals in the denominator. Fill in the missing radicands to rationalize the denominators. **(See Example 3.)**

23. $\dfrac{x}{\sqrt{5}} = \dfrac{x}{\sqrt{5}} \cdot \dfrac{\sqrt{?}}{\sqrt{?}}$ **24.** $\dfrac{2}{\sqrt{x}} = \dfrac{2}{\sqrt{x}} \cdot \dfrac{\sqrt{?}}{\sqrt{?}}$ **25.** $\dfrac{7}{\sqrt[3]{x}} = \dfrac{7}{\sqrt[3]{x}} \cdot \dfrac{\sqrt[3]{?}}{\sqrt[3]{?}}$ **26.** $\dfrac{5}{\sqrt[4]{y}} = \dfrac{5}{\sqrt[4]{y}} \cdot \dfrac{\sqrt[4]{?}}{\sqrt[4]{?}}$

27. $\dfrac{8}{\sqrt{3z}} = \dfrac{8}{\sqrt{3z}} \cdot \dfrac{\sqrt{??}}{\sqrt{??}}$ **28.** $\dfrac{10}{\sqrt{7w}} = \dfrac{10}{\sqrt{7w}} \cdot \dfrac{\sqrt{??}}{\sqrt{??}}$ **29.** $\dfrac{1}{\sqrt[4]{8a^2}} = \dfrac{1}{\sqrt[4]{8a^2}} \cdot \dfrac{\sqrt[4]{??}}{\sqrt[4]{??}}$ **30.** $\dfrac{1}{\sqrt[3]{9b^2}} = \dfrac{1}{\sqrt[3]{9b^2}} \cdot \dfrac{\sqrt[3]{??}}{\sqrt[3]{??}}$

For Exercises 31–58, rationalize the denominator. **(See Examples 4–6.)**

31. $\dfrac{1}{\sqrt{3}}$ **32.** $\dfrac{1}{\sqrt{7}}$ **33.** $\sqrt{\dfrac{1}{x}}$ **34.** $\sqrt{\dfrac{1}{z}}$

35. $\dfrac{6}{\sqrt{2y}}$ **36.** $\dfrac{9}{\sqrt{3t}}$ **37.** $\sqrt{\dfrac{a^3}{2}}$ **38.** $\sqrt{\dfrac{b^3}{3}}$

39. $\dfrac{6}{\sqrt{8}}$ **40.** $\dfrac{2}{\sqrt{48}}$ **41.** $\dfrac{3}{\sqrt[3]{2}}$ **42.** $\dfrac{2}{\sqrt[3]{7}}$

43. $\dfrac{-6}{\sqrt[4]{x}}$ **44.** $\dfrac{-2}{\sqrt[5]{y}}$ **45.** $\dfrac{7}{\sqrt[3]{4}}$ **46.** $\dfrac{1}{\sqrt[3]{9}}$

47. $\sqrt[3]{\dfrac{4}{w^2}}$ **48.** $\sqrt[3]{\dfrac{5}{z^2}}$ **49.** $\sqrt[4]{\dfrac{16}{3}}$ **50.** $\sqrt[4]{\dfrac{81}{8}}$

51. $\dfrac{2}{\sqrt[3]{4x^2}}$ **52.** $\dfrac{6}{\sqrt[3]{3y^2}}$ **53.** $\dfrac{8}{7\sqrt{24}}$ **54.** $\dfrac{5}{3\sqrt{50}}$

55. $\dfrac{1}{\sqrt{x^7}}$ **56.** $\dfrac{1}{\sqrt{y^5}}$ **57.** $\dfrac{2}{\sqrt{8x^5}}$ **58.** $\dfrac{6}{\sqrt{27t^7}}$

Concept 4: Rationalizing the Denominator—Two Terms

59. What is the conjugate of $\sqrt{2} - \sqrt{6}$?

60. What is the conjugate of $\sqrt{11} + \sqrt{5}$?

61. What is the conjugate of $\sqrt{x} + 23$?

62. What is the conjugate of $17 - \sqrt{y}$?

For Exercises 63–82, rationalize the denominator. **(See Examples 7–9.)**

 63. $\dfrac{4}{\sqrt{2} + 3}$ **64.** $\dfrac{6}{4 - \sqrt{3}}$ **65.** $\dfrac{8}{\sqrt{6} - 2}$ **66.** $\dfrac{-12}{\sqrt{5} - 3}$

67. $\dfrac{\sqrt{7}}{\sqrt{3} + 2}$ **68.** $\dfrac{\sqrt{8}}{\sqrt{3} + 1}$ **69.** $\dfrac{-1}{\sqrt{p} + \sqrt{q}}$ **70.** $\dfrac{6}{\sqrt{a} - \sqrt{b}}$

71. $\dfrac{x - 5}{\sqrt{x} + \sqrt{5}}$ **72.** $\dfrac{y - 2}{\sqrt{y} - \sqrt{2}}$ **73.** $\dfrac{\sqrt{w} + 2}{9 - \sqrt{w}}$ **74.** $\dfrac{10 - \sqrt{t}}{\sqrt{t} - 6}$

75. $\dfrac{3\sqrt{x} - \sqrt{y}}{\sqrt{y} + \sqrt{x}}$ **76.** $\dfrac{2\sqrt{a} + \sqrt{b}}{\sqrt{b} - \sqrt{a}}$ **77.** $\dfrac{3\sqrt{10}}{2 + \sqrt{10}}$ **78.** $\dfrac{4\sqrt{7}}{3 + \sqrt{7}}$

 79. $\dfrac{2\sqrt{3} + \sqrt{7}}{3\sqrt{3} - \sqrt{7}}$ **80.** $\dfrac{5\sqrt{2} - \sqrt{5}}{5\sqrt{2} + \sqrt{5}}$ **81.** $\dfrac{\sqrt{5} + 4}{2 - \sqrt{5}}$ **82.** $\dfrac{3 + \sqrt{2}}{\sqrt{2} - 5}$

Mixed Exercises

For Exercises 83–86, write the English phrase as an algebraic expression. Then simplify the expression.

83. 16 divided by the cube root of 4

84. 21 divided by the principal fourth root of 27

85. 4 divided by the difference of x and the principal square root of 2

86. 8 divided by the sum of y and the principal square root of 3

87. The time $T(x)$ (in seconds) for a pendulum to make one complete swing back and forth is approximated by

$$T(x) = 2\pi\sqrt{\dfrac{x}{32}}$$

where x is the length of the pendulum in feet.

Determine the exact time required for one swing for a pendulum that is 1 ft long. Then approximate the time to the nearest hundredth of a second.

© Jonnie Miles/Getty Images RF

88. An object is dropped off a building x meters tall. The time $T(x)$ (in seconds) required for the object to hit the ground is given by

$$T(x) = \sqrt{\dfrac{10x}{49}}$$

Find the exact time required for the object to hit the ground if it is dropped off Three First National Plaza in Chicago, a height of 230 m. Then round the time to the nearest hundredth of a second.

For Exercises 89–92, rationalize the denominator.

89. a. $\dfrac{1}{\sqrt{2}}$

b. $\dfrac{1}{\sqrt[3]{2}}$

90. a. $\dfrac{1}{\sqrt[3]{x}}$

b. $\dfrac{1}{\sqrt[3]{x^2}}$

91. a. $\dfrac{1}{\sqrt{5a}}$

b. $\dfrac{1}{\sqrt{5}+a}$

92. a. $\dfrac{4}{\sqrt{2x}}$

b. $\dfrac{4}{2-\sqrt{x}}$

Expanding Your Skills

For Exercises 93–98, simplify each term of the expression. Then add or subtract as indicated.

93. $\dfrac{\sqrt{6}}{2}+\dfrac{1}{\sqrt{6}}$

94. $\dfrac{1}{\sqrt{7}}+\sqrt{7}$

95. $\sqrt{15}-\sqrt{\dfrac{3}{5}}+\sqrt{\dfrac{5}{3}}$

96. $\sqrt{\dfrac{6}{2}}-\sqrt{12}+\sqrt{\dfrac{2}{6}}$

97. $\sqrt[3]{25}+\dfrac{3}{\sqrt[3]{5}}$

98. $\dfrac{1}{\sqrt[3]{4}}+\sqrt[3]{54}$

For Exercises 99–106, rationalize the numerator by multiplying both numerator and denominator by the conjugate of the numerator.

99. $\dfrac{\sqrt{3}+6}{2}$

100. $\dfrac{\sqrt{7}-2}{5}$

101. $\dfrac{\sqrt{a}-\sqrt{b}}{\sqrt{a}+\sqrt{b}}$

102. $\dfrac{\sqrt{p}+\sqrt{q}}{\sqrt{p}-\sqrt{q}}$

103. $\dfrac{\sqrt{5+3h}-\sqrt{5}}{h}$

104. $\dfrac{\sqrt{7+2h}-\sqrt{7}}{h}$

105. $\dfrac{\sqrt{4+5h}-2}{h}$

106. $\dfrac{\sqrt{9+4h}-3}{h}$

Concepts

1. Solutions to Radical Equations
2. Solving Radical Equations Involving One Radical
3. Solving Radical Equations Involving More than One Radical
4. Applications of Radical Equations and Functions

1. Solutions to Radical Equations

An equation with one or more radicals containing a variable is called a **radical equation**. For example, $\sqrt[3]{x} = 5$ is a radical equation. Recall that $(\sqrt[n]{a})^n = a$, provided $\sqrt[n]{a}$ is a real number. The basis of solving a radical equation is to eliminate the radical by raising both sides of the equation to a power equal to the index of the radical.

To solve the equation $\sqrt[3]{x} = 5$, cube both sides of the equation.

$$\sqrt[3]{x} = 5$$

$$(\sqrt[3]{x})^3 = (5)^3$$

$$x = 125$$

By raising each side of a radical equation to a power equal to the index of the radical, a new equation is produced. Note, however, that some of (or all) the solutions to the new equation may *not* be solutions to the original radical equation. For this reason, it is necessary to *check all potential solutions* in the original equation. For example, consider the equation $\sqrt{x} = -7$. This equation has no solution because by definition, the principal square root of x must be a nonnegative number. However, if we square both sides of the equation, it appears as though a solution exists.

$$(\sqrt{x})^2 = (-7)^2$$

$$x = 49 \qquad \text{The value 49 does not check in the original equation } \sqrt{x} = -7.$$

Therefore, 49 is an **extraneous solution**.

> **Solving a Radical Equation**
>
> **Step 1**   Isolate the radical. If an equation has more than one radical, choose one of the radicals to isolate.
>
> **Step 2**   Raise each side of the equation to a power equal to the index of the radical.
>
> **Step 3**   Solve the resulting equation. If the equation still has a radical, repeat steps 1 and 2.
>
> ***Step 4**   Check the potential solutions in the original equation.
>
> *In solving radical equations, extraneous solutions *potentially occur* only when each side of the equation is raised to an even power.

2. Solving Radical Equations Involving One Radical

Example 1   **Solving an Equation Containing One Radical**

Solve the equation. $\sqrt{p} + 5 = 9$

Solution:

$$\sqrt{p} + 5 = 9$$

$$\sqrt{p} = 4 \qquad \text{Isolate the radical.}$$

$$(\sqrt{p})^2 = 4^2 \qquad \text{Because the index is 2, square both sides.}$$

$$p = 16$$

$$\underline{\text{Check: }} p = 16 \qquad \text{Check } p = 16 \text{ as a potential solution.}$$

$$\sqrt{p} + 5 = 9$$

$$\sqrt{16} + 5 \overset{?}{=} 9$$

$$4 + 5 \overset{?}{=} 9 \checkmark \qquad \text{True, 16 is a solution to the original equation.}$$

The solution set is $\{16\}$.

Skill Practice Solve.

1. $\sqrt{x} - 3 = 2$

Example 2   **Solving an Equation Containing One Radical**

Solve the equation. $\sqrt[3]{w - 1} - 2 = 2$

Solution:

$$\sqrt[3]{w - 1} - 2 = 2$$

$$\sqrt[3]{w - 1} = 4 \qquad \text{Isolate the radical.}$$

$$(\sqrt[3]{w - 1})^3 = (4)^3 \qquad \text{Because the index is 3, cube both sides.}$$

$$w - 1 = 64 \qquad \text{Simplify.}$$

$$w = 65$$

Answer

1. $\{25\}$

Check: $w = 65$

$\sqrt[3]{65 - 1} - 2 \overset{?}{=} 2$ Check $w = 65$ as a potential solution.

$\sqrt[3]{64} - 2 \overset{?}{=} 2$

$4 - 2 \overset{?}{=} 2 \checkmark$ True, 65 is a solution to the original equation.

The solution set is $\{65\}$.

Skill Practice Solve.

2. $\sqrt[3]{t + 2} + 5 = 3$

Example 3   **Solving an Equation Containing One Radical**

Solve the equation. $7 = (x + 3)^{1/4} + 9$

Solution:

$7 = (x + 3)^{1/4} + 9$

$7 = \sqrt[4]{x + 3} + 9$ Note that $(x + 3)^{1/4} = \sqrt[4]{x + 3}$.

$-2 = \sqrt[4]{x + 3}$ Isolate the radical.

$(-2)^4 = (\sqrt[4]{x + 3})^4$ Because the index is 4, raise both sides to the fourth power.

$16 = x + 3$

$x = 13$ Solve for x.

Check: $x = 13$

$7 = \sqrt[4]{x + 3} + 9$

$7 \overset{?}{=} \sqrt[4]{(13) + 3} + 9$

$7 \overset{?}{=} \sqrt[4]{16} + 9$

$7 \overset{?}{=} 2 + 9$ (false)   13 is *not* a solution to the original equation.

The equation $7 = \sqrt[4]{x + 3} + 9$ has no solution.

The solution set is the empty set, $\{\ \}$.

TIP: After isolating the radical in Example 3, the equation shows a fourth root equated to a negative number:

$$-2 = \sqrt[4]{x + 3}$$

By definition, a principal fourth root of any real number must be nonnegative. Therefore, there can be no real solution to this equation.

Skill Practice Solve.

3. $3 = 6 + (x - 1)^{1/4}$

Example 4   **Solving an Equation Containing One Radical**

Solve the equation. $y + 2\sqrt{4y - 3} = 3$

Solution:

$y + 2\sqrt{4y - 3} = 3$

$2\sqrt{4y - 3} = 3 - y$ Isolate the radical term.

$(2\sqrt{4y - 3})^2 = (3 - y)^2$ Because the index is 2, square both sides.

$4(4y - 3) = 9 - 6y + y^2$ Note that $(2\sqrt{4y - 3})^2 = 2^2(\sqrt{4y - 3})^2$ and $(3 - y)^2 = (3 - y)(3 - y) = 9 - 6y + y^2$.

Answers

2. $\{-10\}$

3. $\{\ \}$ (The value 82 does not check.)

$$16y - 12 = 9 - 6y + y^2$$

$$0 = y^2 - 22y + 21$$

The equation is quadratic. Set one side equal to zero. Write the other side in descending order.

$$0 = (y - 21)(y - 1)$$

Factor.

$$y - 21 = 0 \qquad \text{or} \qquad y - 1 = 0$$

Set each factor equal to zero.

$$y = 21 \qquad \text{or} \qquad y = 1$$

Solve.

Check: $y = 21$

$$y + 2\sqrt{4y - 3} = 3$$

$$21 + 2\sqrt{4(21) - 3} \overset{?}{=} 3$$

$$21 + 2\sqrt{81} \overset{?}{=} 3$$

$$21 + 18 \overset{?}{=} 3$$

$$39 \overset{?}{=} 3 \text{ False}$$

Check: $y = 1$

$$y + 2\sqrt{4y - 3} = 3$$

$$1 + 2\sqrt{4(1) - 3} \overset{?}{=} 3$$

$$1 + 2\sqrt{1} \overset{?}{=} 3$$

$$1 + 2 \overset{?}{=} 3$$

$$3 \overset{?}{=} 3 \checkmark$$

The solution set is $\{1\}$. (The value 21 does not check.)

Skill Practice Solve.

4. $2\sqrt{m + 3} - m = 3$

3. Solving Radical Equations Involving More than One Radical

Example 5   **Solving an Equation with Two Radicals**

Solve the equation. $\sqrt[3]{2x - 4} = \sqrt[3]{1 - 8x}$

Solution:

$$\sqrt[3]{2x - 4} = \sqrt[3]{1 - 8x}$$

$$\left(\sqrt[3]{2x - 4}\right)^3 = \left(\sqrt[3]{1 - 8x}\right)^3$$

Because the index is 3, cube both sides.

$$2x - 4 = 1 - 8x$$

Simplify.

$$10x - 4 = 1$$

Solve the resulting equation.

$$10x = 5$$

$$x = \frac{1}{2}$$

Solve for x.

Check: $x = \frac{1}{2}$

$$\sqrt[3]{2x - 4} = \sqrt[3]{1 - 8x}$$

$$\sqrt[3]{2\left(\frac{1}{2}\right) - 4} \overset{?}{=} \sqrt[3]{1 - 8\left(\frac{1}{2}\right)}$$

$$\sqrt[3]{1 - 4} \overset{?}{=} \sqrt[3]{1 - 4}$$

$$\sqrt[3]{-3} \overset{?}{=} \sqrt[3]{-3} \checkmark \text{ (True)}$$

Therefore, $\frac{1}{2}$ is a solution to the original equation.

The solution set is $\left\{\frac{1}{2}\right\}$.

Answer

4. $\{-3, 1\}$

Skill Practice Solve.

5. $\sqrt[5]{2y - 1} = \sqrt[5]{10y + 3}$

| Example 6 | **Solving an Equation with Two Radicals** |

Solve the equation. $\sqrt{3m + 1} - \sqrt{m + 4} = 1$

Solution:

$$\sqrt{3m + 1} - \sqrt{m + 4} = 1$$

$$\sqrt{3m + 1} = \sqrt{m + 4} + 1 \qquad \text{Isolate one of the radicals.}$$

$$(\sqrt{3m + 1})^2 = (\sqrt{m + 4} + 1)^2 \qquad \text{Square both sides.}$$

$$3m + 1 = m + 4 + 2\sqrt{m + 4} + 1$$

$$\textit{Note}: (\sqrt{m + 4} + 1)^2$$
$$= (\sqrt{m + 4})^2 + 2(1)\sqrt{m + 4} + (1)^2$$
$$= m + 4 + 2\sqrt{m + 4} + 1$$

TIP: In Example 6, we divided the equation by 2 because all coefficients were divisible by 2. This makes the coefficients smaller before we square both sides of the equation a second time.

$$3m + 1 = m + 5 + 2\sqrt{m + 4} \qquad \text{Combine } \textit{like} \text{ terms.}$$

$$2m - 4 = 2\sqrt{m + 4} \qquad \text{Isolate the radical again.}$$

$$m - 2 = \sqrt{m + 4} \qquad \text{Divide both sides by 2.}$$

$$(m - 2)^2 = (\sqrt{m + 4})^2 \qquad \text{Square both sides again.}$$

$$m^2 - 4m + 4 = m + 4 \qquad \text{The resulting equation is quadratic.}$$

$$m^2 - 5m = 0 \qquad \text{Set one side equal to zero.}$$

$$m(m - 5) = 0 \qquad \text{Factor.}$$

$$m = 0 \qquad \text{or} \qquad m = 5$$

Check: $m = 0$

$$\sqrt{3(0) + 1} - \sqrt{(0) + 4} \stackrel{?}{=} 1$$

$$\sqrt{1} - \sqrt{4} \stackrel{?}{=} 1$$

$$1 - 2 \stackrel{?}{=} 1 \quad \text{(False)}$$

Check: $m = 5$

$$\sqrt{3(5) + 1} - \sqrt{(5) + 4} = 1$$

$$\sqrt{16} - \sqrt{9} \stackrel{?}{=} 1$$

$$4 - 3 \stackrel{?}{=} 1 \checkmark$$

The solution set is $\{5\}$. (The value 0 does not check.)

Skill Practice Solve.

6. $\sqrt{3c + 1} - \sqrt{c - 1} = 2$

Answers

5. $\left\{ -\dfrac{1}{2} \right\}$ **6.** $\{1, 5\}$

Example 7 **Solving an Equation with Two Radicals**

Solve the equation. $\sqrt{5x+4} = 1 + \sqrt{5x-3}$

Solution:

$$\sqrt{5x+4} = 1 + \sqrt{5x-3}$$ One radical is already isolated.

$$(\sqrt{5x+4})^2 = (1 + \sqrt{5x-3})^2$$ Square both sides.

$$5x+4 = 1 + 2\sqrt{5x-3} + 5x-3$$ *Note*: $(1 + \sqrt{5x-3})^2 =$
$(1)^2 + 2(1)\sqrt{5x-3} + (\sqrt{5x-3})^2$

$$5x+4 = 2\sqrt{5x-3} + 5x - 2$$ Combine *like* terms.

$$4 = 2\sqrt{5x-3} - 2$$ Subtract $5x$ from both sides.

$$6 = 2\sqrt{5x-3}$$ Isolate the radical.

$$3 = \sqrt{5x-3}$$ Divide both sides by 2.

$$(3)^2 = (\sqrt{5x-3})^2$$ Square both sides again.

$$9 = 5x - 3$$ The resulting equation is linear.

$$12 = 5x$$ Solve for x.

$$\frac{12}{5} = x$$ Check: $x = \dfrac{12}{5}$

$$\sqrt{5\left(\frac{12}{5}\right) + 4} \overset{?}{=} 1 + \sqrt{5\left(\frac{12}{5}\right) - 3}$$

$$\sqrt{16} \overset{?}{=} 1 + \sqrt{9}$$

$$4 \overset{?}{=} 1 + 3 \quad \checkmark \text{ True}$$

The solution set is $\left\{ \dfrac{12}{5} \right\}$.

Skill Practice Solve.

7. $\sqrt{4x-3} = 2 - \sqrt{4x+1}$

4. Applications of Radical Equations and Functions

Example 8 **Applying a Radical Equation in Geometry**

For a pyramid with a square base, the length of a side of the base b is given by

$$b = \sqrt{\frac{3V}{h}}$$

where V is the volume and h is the height.

The Pyramid of the Pharaoh Khufu (known as the Great Pyramid) at Giza has a square base (Figure 10-3). If the distance around the bottom of the pyramid is 921.6 m and the height is 146.6 m, what is the volume of the pyramid?

© Royalty Free/Corbis RF

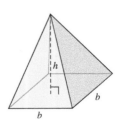

Figure 10-3

Answer

7. $\left\{ \dfrac{3}{4} \right\}$

750   **Chapter 10**   Radicals and Complex Numbers

Solution:

$$b = \sqrt{\frac{3V}{h}}$$

$$b^2 = \left(\sqrt{\frac{3V}{h}}\right)^2 \qquad \text{Because the index is 2, square both sides.}$$

$$b^2 = \frac{3V}{h} \qquad \text{Simplify.}$$

$$b^2 \cdot h = \frac{3V}{\cancel{h}} \cdot \cancel{h} \qquad \text{Multiply both sides by } h.$$

$$b^2 h = 3V$$

$$\frac{b^2 h}{3} = \frac{3V}{3} \qquad \text{Divide both sides by 3.}$$

$$\frac{b^2 h}{3} = V$$

The length of a side b (in meters) is given by $\dfrac{921.6}{4} = 230.4$ m.

$$\frac{(230.4)^2(146.6)}{3} = V \qquad \text{Substitute } b = 230.4 \text{ and } h = 146.6.$$

$$2{,}594{,}046 \approx V$$

The volume of the Great Pyramid at Giza is approximately 2,594,046 m³.

Skill Practice

8. The length of the legs, s, of an isosceles right triangle is $s = \sqrt{2A}$, where A is the area. If the legs of the triangle are 9 in., find the area.

| **Example 9** | **Applying a Radical Function** |

On a certain surface, the speed $s(x)$ (in miles per hour) of a car before the brakes were applied can be approximated from the length of its skid marks x (in feet) by

$$s(x) = 3.8\sqrt{x} \qquad x \geq 0 \quad \text{See Figure 10-4.}$$

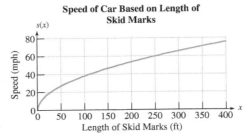

Speed of Car Based on Length of Skid Marks

Figure 10-4

a. Find the speed of a car before the brakes were applied if its skid marks are 361 ft long.

b. How long would you expect the skid marks to be if the car had been traveling the speed limit of 50 mph? (Round to the nearest foot.)

Answer

8. 40.5 in.²

Solution:

a. $s(x) = 3.8\sqrt{x}$

$s(361) = 3.8\sqrt{361}$ Substitute $x = 361$.

$= 3.8(19)$

$= 72.2$

If the skid marks are 361 ft, the car was traveling approximately 72.2 mph before the brakes were applied.

b. $s(x) = 3.8\sqrt{x}$

$50 = 3.8\sqrt{x}$ Substitute $s(x) = 50$ and solve for x.

$\dfrac{50}{3.8} = \sqrt{x}$ Isolate the radical.

$\left(\dfrac{50}{3.8}\right)^2 = x$

$x \approx 173$

If the car had been going the speed limit (50 mph), then the length of the skid marks would have been approximately 173 ft.

Skill Practice   When an object is dropped from a height of 64 ft, the time $t(x)$ (in seconds) it takes to reach a height x (in feet) is given by

$$t(x) = \frac{1}{4}\sqrt{64 - x}$$

9. Find the time to reach a height of 28 ft from the ground.

10. What is the height after 1 sec?

Answers

9. $\dfrac{3}{2}$ sec   **10.** 48 ft

Section 10.7   Practice Exercises

Vocabulary and Key Concepts

1.   **a.** The equation $\sqrt{x + 5} + 7 = 11$ is an example of a _____ equation.

b. The first step to solve the equation $\sqrt{x + 5} + 7 = 11$ is to _____ the radical by subtracting _____ from both sides of the equation.

c. When solving a radical equation some potential solutions may not check in the original equation. These are called _____ solutions.

d. To solve the equation $\sqrt[3]{w - 1} = 5$, raise both sides of the equation to the _____ power.

Review Exercises

2.   Identify the equation as linear or quadratic. Then solve the equation.

   a. $2x + 3 = 23$ **b.** $2x^2 - 9x = 5$

For Exercises 3–6, simplify the radical expressions. Assume all variables represent positive real numbers.

3. $\sqrt{\dfrac{9w^3}{16}}$
  4. $\sqrt{\dfrac{a^2}{3}}$
  5. $\sqrt[3]{54c^4}$
  6. $\sqrt{\dfrac{49}{5t^3}}$

For Exercises 7–10, simplify each expression. Assume all radicands represent positive real numbers.

7. $(\sqrt{4x-6})^2$
  8. $(\sqrt{5y+2})^2$
  9. $(\sqrt[3]{9p+7})^3$
  10. $(\sqrt[3]{4t+13})^3$

Concept 2: Solving Radical Equations Involving One Radical

For Exercises 11–30, solve the equations. **(See Examples 1–3.)**

11. $\sqrt{x}=10$
  12. $\sqrt{y}=7$
  13. $\sqrt{x}+4=6$
  14. $\sqrt{x}+2=8$

15. $\sqrt{5y+1}=4$
  16. $\sqrt{9z-5}-2=9$
  17. $6=\sqrt{2z-3}-3$
  18. $4=\sqrt{8+3a}-1$

19. $\sqrt{x^2+5}=x+1$
  20. $\sqrt{y^2-8}=y-2$
  21. $\sqrt[3]{x-2}-1=2$
  22. $\sqrt[3]{2x-5}-1=1$

23. $(15-w)^{1/3}+7=2$
  24. $(k+18)^{1/3}+5=3$
  25. $3+\sqrt{x-16}=0$
  26. $12+\sqrt{2x+1}=0$

27. $2\sqrt{6a+7}-2a=0$
  28. $2\sqrt{3-w}-w=0$
  29. $(2x-5)^{1/4}=-1$
  30. $(x+16)^{1/4}=-4$

For Exercises 31–34, assume all variables represent positive real numbers.

31. Solve for V: $r=\sqrt[3]{\dfrac{3V}{4\pi}}$
    32. Solve for V: $r=\sqrt{\dfrac{V}{h\pi}}$

33. Solve for h^2: $r=\pi\sqrt{r^2+h^2}$
    34. Solve for d: $s=1.3\sqrt{d}$

For Exercises 35–40, square the expression as indicated.

35. $(a+5)^2$
    36. $(b+7)^2$
    37. $(\sqrt{5a}-3)^2$

38. $(2+\sqrt{b})^2$
    39. $(\sqrt{r-3}+5)^2$
    40. $(2-\sqrt{2t-4})^2$

For Exercises 41–46, solve the radical equations, if possible. **(See Example 4.)**

41. $\sqrt{a^2+2a+1}=a+5$
    42. $\sqrt{b^2-5b-8}=b+7$
    43. $\sqrt{25w^2-2w-3}=5w-4$

44. $\sqrt{4p^2-2p+1}=2p-3$
    45. $4\sqrt{p-2}-2=-p$
    46. $x-3\sqrt{x-5}=5$

Concept 3: Solving Radical Equations Involving More than One Radical

For Exercises 47–70, solve the radical equations, if possible. **(See Examples 5–7.)**

47. $\sqrt[4]{h+4}=\sqrt[4]{2h-5}$
    48. $\sqrt[4]{3b+6}=\sqrt[4]{7b-6}$
    49. $\sqrt[3]{5a+3}-\sqrt[3]{a-13}=0$

50. $\sqrt[3]{k-8}-\sqrt[3]{4k+1}=0$
    51. $\sqrt{5a-9}=\sqrt{5a}-3$
    52. $\sqrt{8+b}=2+\sqrt{b}$

53. $\sqrt{2h+5}-\sqrt{2h}=1$
    54. $\sqrt{3k-5}-\sqrt{3k}=-1$
    55. $(t-9)^{1/2}-t^{1/2}=3$

56. $(y-16)^{1/2}-y^{1/2}=4$
    57. $6=\sqrt{x^2+3}-x$
    58. $2=\sqrt{y^2+5}-y$

59. $\sqrt{3t-7}=2-\sqrt{3t+1}$
    60. $\sqrt{p-6}=\sqrt{p+2}-4$
    61. $\sqrt{z+1}+\sqrt{2z+3}=1$

62. $\sqrt{2y+6}=\sqrt{7-2y}+1$
    63. $\sqrt{6m+7}-\sqrt{3m+3}=1$
    64. $\sqrt{5w+1}-\sqrt{3w}=1$

65. $2 + 2\sqrt{2t + 3} + 2\sqrt{3t - 5} = 0$ **66.** $6 + 3\sqrt{3x + 1} + 3\sqrt{x - 1} = 0$ **67.** $3\sqrt{y - 3} = \sqrt{4y + 3}$

68. $\sqrt{5x - 8} = 2\sqrt{x - 1}$ **69.** $\sqrt{p + 7} = \sqrt{2p} + 1$ **70.** $\sqrt{t} = \sqrt{t - 12} + 2$

Concept 4: Applications of Radical Equations and Functions

71. If an object is dropped from an initial height h, its velocity at impact with the ground is given by

$$v = \sqrt{2gh}$$

where g is the acceleration due to gravity and h is the initial height. **(See Example 8.)**

   a. Find the initial height (in feet) of an object if its velocity at impact is 44 ft/sec. (Assume that the acceleration due to gravity is $g = 32$ ft/sec².)

   b. Find the initial height (in meters) of an object if its velocity at impact is 26 m/sec. (Assume that the acceleration due to gravity is $g = 9.8$ m/sec².) Round to the nearest tenth of a meter.

72. The time T (in seconds) required for a pendulum to make one complete swing back and forth is approximated by

$$T = 2\pi\sqrt{\frac{L}{g}}$$

where g is the acceleration due to gravity and L is the length of the pendulum (in feet).

   a. Find the length of a pendulum that requires 1.36 sec to make one complete swing back and forth. (Assume that the acceleration due to gravity is $g = 32$ ft/sec².) Round to the nearest tenth of a foot.

   b. Find the time required for a pendulum to complete one swing back and forth if the length of the pendulum is 4 ft. (Assume that the acceleration due to gravity is $g = 32$ ft/sec².) Round to the nearest tenth of a second.

73. The airline cost for x thousand passengers to travel round trip from New York to Atlanta is given by

$$C(x) = \sqrt{0.3x + 1}$$

where $C(x)$ is measured in millions of dollars and $x \geq 0$. **(See Example 9.)**

   a. Find the airline's cost for 10,000 passengers ($x = 10$) to travel from New York to Atlanta.

   b. If the airline charges $320 per passenger, find the profit made by the airline for flying 10,000 passengers from New York to Atlanta.

   c. Approximate the number of passengers who traveled from New York to Atlanta if the total cost for the airline was $4 million.

74. The time $t(d)$ in seconds it takes an object to drop d meters is given by

$$t(d) = \sqrt{\frac{d}{4.9}}$$

   a. Approximate the height of the JP Morgan Chase Tower in Houston if it takes an object 7.89 sec to drop from the top. Round to the nearest meter.

   b. Approximate the height of the Willis Tower in Chicago if it takes an object 9.51 sec to drop from the top. Round to the nearest meter.

© Image Source RF

754   **Chapter 10**   Radicals and Complex Numbers

Expanding Your Skills

 75. The number of hours needed to cook a turkey that weighs x pounds can be approximated by

$$t(x) = 0.90\sqrt[5]{x^3}$$

where $t(x)$ is the time in hours and x is the weight of the turkey in pounds.

   a. Find the weight of a turkey that cooked for 4 hr. Round to the nearest pound.

   b. Find $t(18)$ and interpret the result. Round to the nearest tenth of an hour.

For Exercises 76–79, use the Pythagorean theorem to find a, b, or c.

76. Find b when $a = 2$ and $c = y$.

77. Find b when $a = h$ and $c = 5$.

78. Find a when $b = x$ and $c = 8$.

79. Find a when $b = 14$ and $c = k$.

Graphing Calculator Exercises

80. Graph Y_1 and Y_2 on a viewing window defined by $-10 \le x \le 40$ and $-5 \le y \le 10$.

$$Y_1 = \sqrt{2x} \qquad \text{and} \qquad Y_2 = 8$$

Use an *Intersect* feature to approximate the x-coordinate of the point of intersection of the two graphs. How does the point of intersection relate to the solution to the equation $\sqrt{2x} = 8$?

81. Graph Y_1 and Y_2 on a viewing window defined by $-10 \le x \le 20$ and $-5 \le y \le 10$.

$$Y_1 = \sqrt{4x} \qquad \text{and} \qquad Y_2 = 6$$

Use an *Intersect* feature to approximate the x-coordinate of the point of intersection of the two graphs. How does the point of intersection relate to the solution to the equation $\sqrt{4x} = 6$?

82. Refer to Exercise 48. Graph Y_1 and Y_2 on a viewing window defined by $-5 \le x \le 20$ and $-1 \le y \le 4$.

$$Y_1 = \sqrt[4]{3x + 6} \qquad \text{and} \qquad Y_2 = \sqrt[4]{7x - 6}$$

Use an *Intersect* feature to approximate the x-coordinate of the point of intersection of the two graphs to support your solution to Exercise 48.

83. Refer to Exercise 47. Graph Y_1 and Y_2 on a viewing window defined by $-5 \le x \le 20$ and $-1 \le y \le 4$.

$$Y_1 = \sqrt[4]{x + 4} \qquad \text{and} \qquad Y_2 = \sqrt[4]{2x - 5}$$

Use an *Intersect* feature to approximate the x-coordinate of the point of intersection of the two graphs to support your solution to Exercise 47.

Section 10.8   Complex Numbers

1. Definition of i

We have already learned that there are no real-valued square roots of a negative number. For example, $\sqrt{-9}$ is not a real number because no real number when squared equals -9. However, the square roots of a negative number are defined over another set of numbers called the **imaginary numbers**. The foundation of the set of imaginary numbers is the definition of the imaginary number i.

> **Definition of the Imaginary Number i**
> $$i = \sqrt{-1}$$
> *Note:* From the definition of i, it follows that $i^2 = -1$.

Using the imaginary number i, we can define the square root of any negative real number.

> ### Definition of $\sqrt{-b}$ for $b > 0$
> Let b be a positive real number. Then $\sqrt{-b} = i\sqrt{b}$.

Example 1 Simplifying Expressions in Terms of i

Simplify the expressions in terms of i.

a. $\sqrt{-64}$ b. $\sqrt{-50}$ c. $-\sqrt{-4}$ d. $\sqrt{-29}$

Solution:

a. $\sqrt{-64} = i\sqrt{64}$
$= 8i$

b. $\sqrt{-50} = i\sqrt{50}$
$= i\sqrt{5^2 \cdot 2}$
$= 5i\sqrt{2}$

c. $-\sqrt{-4} = -1 \cdot \sqrt{-4}$
$= -1 \cdot i\sqrt{4}$
$= -1 \cdot 2i$
$= -2i$

d. $\sqrt{-29} = i\sqrt{29}$

> **Avoiding Mistakes**
>
> In an expression such as $i\sqrt{29}$, the i is often written in front of the square root. The expression $\sqrt{29}i$ is also correct, but may be misinterpreted as $\sqrt{29i}$ (with i incorrectly placed under the radical).

Skill Practice Simplify the expressions in terms of i.

1. $\sqrt{-81}$ 2. $\sqrt{-20}$ 3. $-\sqrt{-36}$ 4. $\sqrt{-7}$

If a and b represent real numbers such that $\sqrt[n]{a}$ and $\sqrt[n]{b}$ are both real, then

$$\sqrt[n]{ab} = \sqrt[n]{a} \cdot \sqrt[n]{b} \quad \text{and} \quad \sqrt[n]{\frac{a}{b}} = \frac{\sqrt[n]{a}}{\sqrt[n]{b}} \quad b \neq 0$$

The conditions that $\sqrt[n]{a}$ and $\sqrt[n]{b}$ must both be real numbers prevent us from applying the multiplication and division properties of radicals for square roots with a negative radicand. Therefore, to multiply or divide radicals with a negative radicand, first write the radical in terms of the imaginary number i. This is demonstrated in Example 2.

Example 2 Simplifying a Product or Quotient in Terms of i

Simplify the expressions.

a. $\dfrac{\sqrt{-100}}{\sqrt{-25}}$ b. $\sqrt{-25} \cdot \sqrt{-9}$ c. $\sqrt{-5} \cdot \sqrt{-5}$

Answers

1. $9i$ **2.** $2i\sqrt{5}$ **3.** $-6i$ **4.** $i\sqrt{7}$

Solution:

a. $\dfrac{\sqrt{-100}}{\sqrt{-25}}$

$= \dfrac{10i}{5i}$ Simplify each radical in terms of *i before* dividing.

$= 2$

b. $\sqrt{-25} \cdot \sqrt{-9}$

$= 5i \cdot 3i$ Simplify each radical in terms of *i* first *before* multiplying.

$= 15i^2$ Multiply.

$= 15(-1)$ Recall that $i^2 = -1$.

$= -15$ Simplify.

c. $\sqrt{-5} \cdot \sqrt{-5}$

$= i\sqrt{5} \cdot i\sqrt{5}$

$= i^2 \cdot (\sqrt{5})^2$

$= -1 \cdot 5$

$= -5$

Skill Practice Simplify the expressions.

5. $\dfrac{\sqrt{-36}}{\sqrt{-9}}$ **6.** $\sqrt{-16} \cdot \sqrt{-49}$ **7.** $\sqrt{-2} \cdot \sqrt{-2}$

Avoiding Mistakes

In Example 2, we wrote the radical expressions in terms of *i* first, before multiplying or dividing. If we had mistakenly applied the multiplication or division property first, we would have obtained an incorrect answer.

Correct: $\sqrt{-25} \cdot \sqrt{-9}$

$= (5i)(3i) = 15i^2$

$= 15(-1) = -15$

↑ correct

Be careful: $\sqrt{-25} \cdot \sqrt{-9}$ $\sqrt{-25}$ and $\sqrt{-9}$ are not real numbers. Therefore, the multiplication property of radicals cannot be applied.

$\neq \sqrt{225} = 15$

↑ (incorrect answer)

2. Powers of *i*

From the definition of $i = \sqrt{-1}$, it follows that

$$i = i$$
$$i^2 = -1$$
$$i^3 = -i \qquad \text{because } i^3 = i^2 \cdot i = (-1)i = -i$$
$$i^4 = 1 \qquad \text{because } i^4 = i^2 \cdot i^2 = (-1)(-1) = 1$$
$$i^5 = i \qquad \text{because } i^5 = i^4 \cdot i = (1)i = i$$
$$i^6 = -1 \qquad \text{because } i^6 = i^4 \cdot i^2 = (1)(-1) = -1$$

Answers

5. 2   **6.** −28   **7.** −2

This pattern of values i, -1, $-i$, 1, i, -1, $-i$, 1, . . . continues for all subsequent powers of i. Table 10-1 lists several powers of i.

Table 10-1   **Powers of i**

$i^1 = i$	$i^5 = i$	$i^9 = i$
$i^2 = -1$	$i^6 = -1$	$i^{10} = -1$
$i^3 = -i$	$i^7 = -i$	$i^{11} = -i$
$i^4 = 1$	$i^8 = 1$	$i^{12} = 1$

To simplify higher powers of i, we can decompose the expression into multiples of i^4 ($i^4 = 1$) and write the remaining factors as i, i^2, or i^3.

Example 3   **Simplifying Powers of i**

Simplify the powers of i.

a. i^{13} **b.** i^{18} **c.** i^{107} **d.** i^{32}

Solution:

a. $i^{13} = (i^{12}) \cdot (i)$ Write the exponent as a multiple of 4 and a remainder.

$= (i^4)^3 \cdot (i)$

$= (1)^3(i)$ Recall that $i^4 = 1$.

$= i$ Simplify.

b. $i^{18} = (i^{16}) \cdot (i^2)$ Write the exponent as a multiple of 4 and a remainder.

$= (i^4)^4 \cdot (i^2)$

$= (1)^4 \cdot (-1)$ $i^4 = 1$ and $i^2 = -1$

$= -1$ Simplify.

c. $i^{107} = (i^{104}) \cdot (i^3)$ Write the exponent as a multiple of 4 and a remainder.

$= (i^4)^{26}(i^3)$

$= (1)^{26}(-i)$ $i^4 = 1$ and $i^3 = -i$

$= -i$ Simplify.

d. $i^{32} = (i^4)^8$

$= (1)^8$ $i^4 = 1$

$= 1$ Simplify.

Skill Practice Simplify the powers of i.

8. i^{45} **9.** i^{22} **10.** i^{31} **11.** i^{80}

3. Definition of a Complex Number

We have already learned the definitions of the integers, rational numbers, irrational numbers, and real numbers. In this section, we define the complex numbers.

Answers
8. i **9.** -1
10. $-i$ **11.** 1

> ### Definition of a Complex Number
>
> A **complex number** is a number of the form $a + bi$, where a and b are real numbers and $i = \sqrt{-1}$.
>
> *Notes:*
>
> - If $b = 0$, then the complex number $a + bi$ is a real number.
> - If $b \neq 0$, then we say that $a + bi$ is an imaginary number.
> - The complex number $a + bi$ is said to be written in standard form. The quantities a and b are called the real and imaginary parts (respectively) of the complex number.
> - The complex numbers $a - bi$ and $a + bi$ are called **complex conjugates**.

From the definition of a complex number, it follows that all real numbers are complex numbers and all imaginary numbers are complex numbers. Figure 10-5 illustrates the relationship among the sets of numbers we have learned so far.

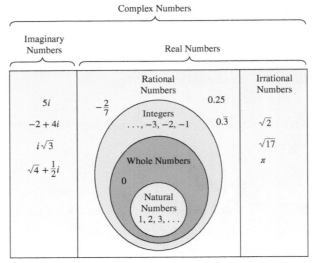

Figure 10-5

Example 4   Identifying the Real and Imaginary Parts of a Complex Number

Identify the real and imaginary parts of the complex numbers.

a. $-8 + 2i$ **b.** $\dfrac{3}{2}$ **c.** $-1.75i$

Solution:

a. $-8 + 2i$ -8 is the real part, and 2 is the imaginary part.

b. $\dfrac{3}{2} = \dfrac{3}{2} + 0i$ Rewrite $\frac{3}{2}$ in the form $a + bi$. $\frac{3}{2}$ is the real part, and 0 is the imaginary part.

c. $-1.75i$
$\quad = 0 + -1.75i$ Rewrite $-1.75i$ in the form $a + bi$. 0 is the real part, and -1.75 is the imaginary part.

12. $22 - 14i$ **13.** -50 **14.** $15i$

> **TIP:** Example 4(b) illustrates that a real number is also a complex number.
>
> $$\frac{3}{2} = \frac{3}{2} + 0i$$
>
> Example 4(c) illustrates that an imaginary number is also a complex number.
>
> $$-1.75i = 0 + -1.75i$$

4. Addition, Subtraction, and Multiplication of Complex Numbers

The operations of addition, subtraction, and multiplication of real numbers also apply to imaginary numbers. To add or subtract complex numbers, combine the real parts and combine the imaginary parts. The commutative, associative, and distributive properties that apply to real numbers also apply to complex numbers.

Example 5   Adding and Subtracting Complex Numbers

Add or subtract as indicated. Write the answers in the form $a + bi$.

a. $(1 - 5i) + (-3 + 7i)$ **b.** $\left(-\frac{1}{4} + \frac{3}{5}i\right) - \left(\frac{1}{2} - \frac{1}{10}i\right)$

c. $\sqrt{-8} + \sqrt{-18}$

Solution:

a. $(1 - 5i) + (-3 + 7i) = (1 + -3) + (-5 + 7)i$ Add the real parts.

(real parts / imaginary parts)

               Add the imaginary parts.

$$= -2 + 2i \qquad \text{Simplify.}$$

b. $\left(-\frac{1}{4} + \frac{3}{5}i\right) - \left(\frac{1}{2} - \frac{1}{10}i\right) = -\frac{1}{4} + \frac{3}{5}i - \frac{1}{2} + \frac{1}{10}i$ Apply the distributive property.

$$= \left(-\frac{1}{4} - \frac{1}{2}\right) + \left(\frac{3}{5} + \frac{1}{10}\right)i \qquad \text{Add real parts. Add imaginary parts.}$$

$$= \left(-\frac{1}{4} - \frac{2}{4}\right) + \left(\frac{6}{10} + \frac{1}{10}\right)i \qquad \text{Get common denominators.}$$

$$= -\frac{3}{4} + \frac{7}{10}i \qquad \text{Simplify.}$$

c. $\sqrt{-8} + \sqrt{-18} = 2i\sqrt{2} + 3i\sqrt{2}$ Simplify each radical in terms of i.

$$= 5i\sqrt{2} \qquad \text{Combine } like \text{ radicals.}$$

15. $\left(\frac{1}{2} - \frac{1}{4}i\right) + \left(\frac{3}{5} + \frac{2}{3}i\right)$ **16.** $(-6 + 11i) - (-9 - 12i)$ **17.** $\sqrt{-45} - \sqrt{-20}$

Answers

12. real: 22; imaginary: -14
13. real: -50; imaginary: 0
14. real: 0; imaginary: 15
15. $\frac{11}{10} + \frac{5}{12}i$ **16.** $3 + 23i$
17. $i\sqrt{5}$

> **Example 6**   **Multiplying Complex Numbers**
>
> Multiply the complex numbers. Write the answers in the form $a + bi$.
>
>   **a.** $(10 - 5i)(2 + 3i)$ **b.** $(1.2 + 0.5i)(1.2 - 0.5i)$
>
> **Solution:**
>
>   **a.** $(10 - 5i)(2 + 3i)$
>
> $$= (10)(2) + (10)(3i) + (-5i)(2) + (-5i)(3i) \qquad \text{Apply the distributive property.}$$
> $$= 20 + 30i - 10i - 15i^2$$
> $$= 20 + 20i - (15)(-1) \qquad \text{Recall } i^2 = -1.$$
> $$= 20 + 20i + 15$$
> $$= 35 + 20i \qquad \text{Write in the form } a + bi.$$
>
>   **b.** $(1.2 + 0.5i)(1.2 - 0.5i)$
>
> The expressions $(1.2 + 0.5i)$ and $(1.2 - 0.5i)$ are complex conjugates. The product is a difference of squares.
>
> $$(a + b)(a - b) = a^2 - b^2 \qquad \text{Apply the formula, where } a = 1.2 \text{ and } b = 0.5i.$$
>
> $$(1.2 + 0.5i)(1.2 - 0.5i) = (1.2)^2 - (0.5i)^2$$
> $$= 1.44 - 0.25i^2$$
> $$= 1.44 - 0.25(-1) \qquad \text{Recall } i^2 = -1.$$
> $$= 1.44 + 0.25$$
> $$= 1.69 + 0i$$
>
> ---
>
> **Skill Practice** Multiply.
>
> **18.** $(4 - 6i)(2 - 3i)$ **19.** $(1.5 + 0.8i)(1.5 - 0.8i)$

5. Division and Simplification of Complex Numbers

The product of a complex number and its complex conjugate is a real number. For example:

$$(5 + 3i)(5 - 3i) = 25 - 9i^2$$
$$= 25 - 9(-1)$$
$$= 25 + 9$$
$$= 34$$

To divide by a complex number, multiply the numerator and denominator by the complex conjugate of the denominator. This produces a real number in the denominator so that the resulting expression can be written in the form $a + bi$.

Answers

18. $-10 - 24i$ **19.** $2.89 + 0i$

Example 7   **Dividing by a Complex Number**

Divide the complex numbers and write the answer in the form $a + bi$.

$$\frac{4 - 3i}{5 + 2i}$$

Solution:

$\dfrac{4 - 3i}{5 + 2i}$ Multiply the numerator and denominator by the complex conjugate of the denominator:

$\dfrac{(4 - 3i)}{(5 + 2i)} \cdot \dfrac{(5 - 2i)}{(5 - 2i)} = \dfrac{(4)(5) + (4)(-2i) + (-3i)(5) + (-3i)(-2i)}{(5)^2 - (2i)^2}$

$= \dfrac{20 - 8i - 15i + 6i^2}{25 - 4i^2}$ Simplify numerator and denominator.

$= \dfrac{20 - 23i + 6(-1)}{25 - 4(-1)}$ Recall $i^2 = -1$.

$= \dfrac{20 - 23i - 6}{25 + 4}$

$= \dfrac{14 - 23i}{29}$ Simplify.

$= \dfrac{14}{29} - \dfrac{23}{29}i$ Write in the form $a + bi$.

> **TIP:** In Example 7, we asked for the answer in the form $a + bi$. However, if the second term is negative, we often leave an answer in terms of subtraction: $\frac{14}{29} - \frac{23}{29}i$. This is the same as $\frac{14}{29} + \left(-\frac{23}{29}i\right)$.

Skill Practice Divide the complex numbers. Write the answer in the form $a + bi$.

20. $\dfrac{2 + i}{3 - 2i}$

Example 8   **Simplifying a Complex Number**

Simplify the complex number. $\dfrac{6 + \sqrt{-18}}{9}$

Solution:

$\dfrac{6 + \sqrt{-18}}{9} = \dfrac{6 + i\sqrt{18}}{9}$ Write the radical in terms of i.

$= \dfrac{6 + 3i\sqrt{2}}{9}$ Simplify $\sqrt{18} = 3\sqrt{2}$.

$= \dfrac{3(2 + i\sqrt{2})}{9}$ Factor the numerator.

$= \dfrac{\overset{1}{3}(2 + i\sqrt{2})}{\underset{3}{9}}$ Simplify.

$= \dfrac{2 + i\sqrt{2}}{3}$ or $\dfrac{2}{3} + \dfrac{\sqrt{2}}{3}i$ Write in the form $a + bi$.

> **TIP:** As an alternative approach in Example 8, the expression $\dfrac{6 + i\sqrt{18}}{9}$ can be written in the form $a + bi$ and then simplified.
> $\dfrac{6 + i\sqrt{18}}{9} = \dfrac{6}{9} + \dfrac{3\sqrt{2}}{9}i$
> $= \dfrac{2}{3} + \dfrac{\sqrt{2}}{3}i$

Skill Practice Simplify the complex number.

21. $\dfrac{8 - \sqrt{-24}}{6}$

Answers

20. $\dfrac{4}{13} + \dfrac{7}{13}i$

21. $\dfrac{4 - i\sqrt{6}}{3}$ or $\dfrac{4}{3} - \dfrac{\sqrt{6}}{3}i$

Section 10.8 Practice Exercises

Vocabulary and Key Concepts

1. **a.** A square root of a negative number is not a real number, but rather is an _____ number.

   b. $i =$ _____, and $i^2 =$ _____.

   c. For a positive number b, the value $\sqrt{-b} =$ _____.

   d. A complex number is a number in the form _____, where a and b are real numbers and $i =$ _____.

   e. Given a complex number $a + bi$, the value a is called the _____ part, and _____ is called the imaginary part.

   f. The complex conjugate of $a - bi$ is _____.

   g. Answer true or false. All real numbers are complex numbers.

   h. Answer true or false. All imaginary numbers are complex numbers.

Review Exercises

For Exercises 2–4, perform the indicated operations.

2. $-2\sqrt{5} - 3\sqrt{50} + \sqrt{125}$

3. $(3 - \sqrt{x})(3 + \sqrt{x})$

4. $(\sqrt{5} + \sqrt{2})^2$

For Exercises 5–7, solve the equations.

5. $\sqrt[3]{3p + 7} - \sqrt[3]{2p - 1} = 0$

6. $\sqrt{9t + 10} + 18 = 10$

7. $\sqrt{4a + 29} = 2\sqrt{a} + 5$

8. Rationalize the denominator. $\dfrac{2}{\sqrt{x} - 3}$

Concept 1: Definition of i

9. Simplify the expressions $\sqrt{-1}$ and $-\sqrt{1}$.

10. Simplify i^2.

For Exercises 11–30, simplify the expressions. **(See Examples 1–2.)**

11. $\sqrt{-144}$

12. $\sqrt{-81}$

13. $\sqrt{-3}$

14. $\sqrt{-17}$

15. $-\sqrt{-20}$

16. $-\sqrt{-75}$

17. $(2\sqrt{-25})(3\sqrt{-4})$

18. $(-4\sqrt{-9})(-3\sqrt{-1})$

19. $7\sqrt{-63} - 4\sqrt{-28}$

20. $7\sqrt{-3} - 4\sqrt{-27}$

21. $\sqrt{-7} \cdot \sqrt{-7}$

22. $\sqrt{-11} \cdot \sqrt{-11}$

23. $\sqrt{-9} \cdot \sqrt{-16}$

24. $\sqrt{-25} \cdot \sqrt{-36}$

25. $\sqrt{-15} \cdot \sqrt{-6}$

26. $\sqrt{-12} \cdot \sqrt{-50}$

27. $\dfrac{\sqrt{-50}}{\sqrt{25}}$

28. $\dfrac{\sqrt{-27}}{\sqrt{9}}$

29. $\dfrac{\sqrt{-90}}{\sqrt{-10}}$

30. $\dfrac{\sqrt{-125}}{\sqrt{-45}}$

Concept 2: Powers of i

For Exercises 31–42, simplify the powers of i. **(See Example 3.)**

31. i^7

32. i^{38}

33. i^{64}

34. i^{75}

35. i^{41}

36. i^{25}

37. i^{52}

38. i^0

39. i^{23}

40. i^{103}

41. i^6

42. i^{82}

Concept 3: Definition of a Complex Number

43. What is the complex conjugate of a complex number $a + bi$?

44. True or false?

    a. Every real number is a complex number.   **b.** Every complex number is a real number.

For Exercises 45–52, identify the real and imaginary parts of the complex number. **(See Example 4.)**

45. $-5 + 12i$ **46.** $22 - 16i$ **47.** $-6i$ **48.** $10i$

49. 35 **50.** -1 **51.** $\dfrac{3}{5} + i$ **52.** $-\dfrac{1}{2} - \dfrac{1}{4}i$

Concept 4: Addition, Subtraction, and Multiplication of Complex Numbers

For Exercises 53–76, perform the indicated operations. Write the answer in the form $a + bi$. **(See Examples 5–6.)**

53. $(2 - i) + (5 + 7i)$ **54.** $(5 - 2i) + (3 + 4i)$ **55.** $\left(\dfrac{1}{2} + \dfrac{2}{3}i\right) - \left(\dfrac{1}{5} - \dfrac{5}{6}i\right)$

56. $\left(\dfrac{11}{10} - \dfrac{7}{5}i\right) - \left(-\dfrac{2}{5} + \dfrac{3}{5}i\right)$ **57.** $\sqrt{-98} - \sqrt{-8}$ **58.** $\sqrt{-75} + \sqrt{-12}$

59. $(2 + 3i) - (1 - 4i) + (-2 + 3i)$ **60.** $(2 + 5i) - (7 - 2i) + (-3 + 4i)$

61. $(8i)(3i)$ **62.** $(2i)(4i)$ **63.** $6i(1 - 3i)$ **64.** $-i(3 + 4i)$

65. $(2 - 10i)(3 + 2i)$ **66.** $(4 + 7i)(2 - 3i)$ **67.** $(-5 + 2i)(5 + 2i)$ **68.** $(4 - 11i)(4 + 11i)$

69. $(4 + 5i)^2$ **70.** $(3 - 2i)^2$ **71.** $(2 + i)(3 - 2i)(4 + 3i)$ **72.** $(3 - i)(3 + i)(4 - i)$

73. $(-4 - 6i)^2$ **74.** $(-3 - 5i)^2$ **75.** $\left(-\dfrac{1}{2} - \dfrac{3}{4}i\right)\left(-\dfrac{1}{2} + \dfrac{3}{4}i\right)$ **76.** $\left(-\dfrac{2}{3} + \dfrac{1}{6}i\right)\left(-\dfrac{2}{3} - \dfrac{1}{6}i\right)$

Concept 5: Division and Simplification of Complex Numbers

For Exercises 77–90, divide the complex numbers. Write the answer in the form $a + bi$. **(See Example 7.)**

77. $\dfrac{2}{1 + 3i}$ **78.** $\dfrac{-2}{3 + i}$ **79.** $\dfrac{-i}{4 - 3i}$ **80.** $\dfrac{3 - 3i}{1 - i}$

81. $\dfrac{5 + 2i}{5 - 2i}$ **82.** $\dfrac{7 + 3i}{4 - 2i}$ **83.** $\dfrac{3 + 7i}{-2 - 4i}$ **84.** $\dfrac{-2 + 9i}{-1 - 4i}$

85. $\dfrac{13i}{-5 - i}$ **86.** $\dfrac{15i}{-2 - i}$ **87.** $\dfrac{2 + 3i}{6i}$ (*Hint:* Consider multiplying numerator and denominator by i or by $-i$. This will make the denominator a real number.)

88. $\dfrac{4 - i}{2i}$ **89.** $\dfrac{-10 + i}{i}$ **90.** $\dfrac{-6 - i}{-i}$

For Exercises 91–98, simplify the complex numbers. Write the answer in the form $a + bi$. **(See Example 8.)**

91. $\dfrac{2 + \sqrt{-16}}{8}$ **92.** $\dfrac{6 - \sqrt{-4}}{4}$ **93.** $\dfrac{-6 + \sqrt{-72}}{6}$ **94.** $\dfrac{-20 + \sqrt{-500}}{10}$

95. $\dfrac{-8 - \sqrt{-48}}{4}$

96. $\dfrac{-18 - \sqrt{-72}}{3}$

97. $\dfrac{-5 + \sqrt{-50}}{10}$

98. $\dfrac{14 + \sqrt{-98}}{7}$

Expanding Your Skills

For Exercises 99–102, determine if the complex number is a solution to the equation.

99. $x^2 - 4x + 5 = 0$; $2 + i$

100. $x^2 - 6x + 25 = 0$; $3 - 4i$

101. $x^2 + 12 = 0$; $-2i\sqrt{3}$

102. $x^2 + 18 = 0$; $3i\sqrt{2}$

764   **Chapter 10** Radicals and Complex Numbers

Margin of Error of Survey Results

Materials: Calculator

Estimated time: 20 minutes

Group Size: 3

The members of the class will conduct a survey to estimate the percentage of the college population that answers "yes" to several survey questions.

1. The members of the class will decide on three "Yes or No" questions that they will use to perform a survey. For example, here are some possible questions.

   "Do you study more than 10 hr a week?"

   "Do you work more than 25 hr a week?"

   "Are you taking more than 10 credit hours?"

   List the questions here:

   a. _____

   b. _____

   c. _____

2. Each student in the class will survey 20 people and record the number of "yes" responses in the table.

Question	Number of "Yes" Responses
1	
2	
3	

3. The instructor will then pool the results obtained from each student to get the total number of people surveyed by the whole class. Record the number of people surveyed (sample size) and the number of "yes" responses for each question in the table. Once the data are entered into the table, compute the percent, p, of

"yes" responses in the fourth column. Write this value in decimal form. Round the values of p to three decimal places. (*Note:* For now, leave the last column blank.)

Question	Sample Size	Number of "Yes" Responses	Percent "Yes" Responses, p	Margin of Error, E
1				
2				
3				

4. The value of p represents the percent (written in decimal form) of people in the *sample* who answered "yes." However, the percentage of people in the entire college population who would answer "yes" is unknown. The value of p is only an *estimate*. Statisticians often compute a margin of error associated with such an estimate by using the following formula.

$$E = 1.96\sqrt{\frac{p(1-p)}{n}}$$

where E is the margin of error.

n is the sample size.

p is the percent (in decimal form) of "yes" responses.

Compute the margin of error for each of the three questions. Round the values of E to three decimal places. Record the results in the table.

5. The margin of error computed in step 4 is associated with what statisticians call a 95% level of confidence. To interpret the results, a statistician would say "With 95% confidence, the researcher estimates the percentage of 'yes' responses from the entire college population to be between $p \pm E$."

Interpret the results from each of the three questions.

766   Chapter 10   Radicals and Complex Numbers

Chapter 10   Summary

Section 10.1   Definition of an *n*th Root

Key Concepts

b is an **nth root** of a if $b^n = a$.

The expression $\sqrt{a}$ represents the **principal square root** of a.
The expression $\sqrt[n]{a}$ represents the principal nth root of a.

$\sqrt[n]{a^n} = |a|$ if n is even.

$\sqrt[n]{a^n} = a$ if n is odd.

$\sqrt[n]{a}$ is not a real number if $a < 0$ and n is even.

$f(x) = \sqrt[n]{x}$ defines a **radical function**.

The Pythagorean Theorem

$a^2 + b^2 = c^2$

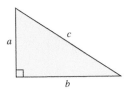

Examples

Example 1

2 is a square root of 4.

−2 is a square root of 4.

−3 is a cube root of −27.

Example 2

$\sqrt{36} = 6 \qquad \sqrt[3]{-64} = -4$

Example 3

$\sqrt[4]{(x+3)^4} = |x+3| \qquad \sqrt[5]{(x+3)^5} = x+3$

Example 4

$\sqrt[4]{-16}$ is not a real number.

Example 5

For $g(x) = \sqrt{x}$ the domain is $[0, \infty)$.
For $h(x) = \sqrt[3]{x}$ the domain is $(-\infty, \infty)$.

Example 6

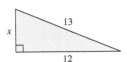

$x^2 + 12^2 = 13^2$

$x^2 + 144 = 169$

$x^2 = 25$

$x = \sqrt{25}$

$x = 5$

Section 10.2   **Rational Exponents**

Key Concepts

Let a be a real number and n be an integer such that $n > 1$. If $\sqrt[n]{a}$ exists, then

$$a^{1/n} = \sqrt[n]{a}$$

$$a^{m/n} = \left(\sqrt[n]{a}\right)^m = \sqrt[n]{a^m}$$

All properties of integer exponents hold for rational exponents, provided the roots are real-valued.

Examples

Example 1

$$121^{1/2} = \sqrt{121} = 11$$

Example 2

$$27^{2/3} = \left(\sqrt[3]{27}\right)^2 = (3)^2 = 9$$

Example 3

a. $p^{1/3} \, p^{1/4} = p^{1/3 + 1/4} = p^{4/12 + 3/12} = p^{7/12}$

b. $\dfrac{4^{4/3}}{4^{1/3}} = 4^{4/3 - 1/3} = 4^{3/3} = 4$

c. $\left(y^{-1/2}\right)^6 = y^{(-1/2)(6)} = y^{-3} = \dfrac{1}{y^3}$

Section 10.3   **Simplifying Radical Expressions**

Key Concepts

Let a and b represent real numbers such that $\sqrt[n]{a}$ and $\sqrt[n]{b}$ are both real. Then,

$$\sqrt[n]{ab} = \sqrt[n]{a} \cdot \sqrt[n]{b} \qquad \text{Multiplication property}$$

A radical expression whose radicand is written as a product of prime factors is in simplified form if all the following conditions are met:

1. The radicand has no factor raised to a power greater than or equal to the index.
2. The radicand does not contain a fraction.
3. No radicals are in the denominator of a fraction.

Examples

Example 1

$$\sqrt{12} = \sqrt{4 \cdot 3}$$
$$= \sqrt{4} \cdot \sqrt{3}$$
$$= 2\sqrt{3}$$

Example 2

$$\sqrt[3]{16x^5y^7}$$
$$= \sqrt[3]{2^4 x^5 y^7}$$
$$= \sqrt[3]{2^3 x^3 y^6 \cdot 2x^2 y}$$
$$= \sqrt[3]{2^3 x^3 y^6} \cdot \sqrt[3]{2x^2 y}$$
$$= 2xy^2 \sqrt[3]{2x^2 y}$$

Section 10.4   Addition and Subtraction of Radicals

Key Concepts

Like **radicals** have radical factors with the same index and the same radicand.

Use the distributive property to add and subtract *like* radicals.

Examples

Example 1

$2x\sqrt{7} - 5x\sqrt{7} + x\sqrt{7}$

$= (2 - 5 + 1)x\sqrt{7}$

$= -2x\sqrt{7}$

Example 2

$x\sqrt[4]{16x} - 3\sqrt[4]{x^5}$

$= 2x\sqrt[4]{x} - 3x\sqrt[4]{x}$

$= (2 - 3)x\sqrt[4]{x}$

$= -x\sqrt[4]{x}$

Section 10.5   Multiplication of Radicals

Key Concepts

The Multiplication Property of Radicals

If $\sqrt[n]{a}$ and $\sqrt[n]{b}$ are real numbers, then

$\sqrt[n]{a} \cdot \sqrt[n]{b} = \sqrt[n]{ab}$

To multiply or divide radicals with different indices, convert to rational exponents and use the properties of exponents.

Examples

Example 1

$3\sqrt{2}(\sqrt{2} + 5\sqrt{7} - \sqrt{6})$

$= 3\sqrt{4} + 15\sqrt{14} - 3\sqrt{12}$

$= 3 \cdot 2 + 15\sqrt{14} - 3 \cdot 2\sqrt{3}$

$= 6 + 15\sqrt{14} - 6\sqrt{3}$

Example 2

$\sqrt{p} \cdot \sqrt[5]{p^2}$

$= p^{1/2} \cdot p^{2/5}$

$= p^{5/10} \cdot p^{4/10}$

$= p^{9/10}$

$= \sqrt[10]{p^9}$

Section 10.6	Division of Radicals and Rationalization

Key Concepts

The Division Property of Radicals

If $\sqrt[n]{a}$ and $\sqrt[n]{b}$ are real numbers, then

$$\sqrt[n]{\frac{a}{b}} = \frac{\sqrt[n]{a}}{\sqrt[n]{b}} \quad b \neq 0$$

The process of removing a radical from the denominator of an expression is called **rationalizing the denominator**.

- Rationalizing a denominator with one term

- Rationalizing a denominator with two terms involving square roots

Examples

Example 1

Simplify.

$$\sqrt{\frac{4x^5}{y^4}}$$

$$= \frac{\sqrt{4x^5}}{\sqrt{y^4}}$$

$$= \frac{2x^2\sqrt{x}}{y^2}$$

Example 2

Rationalize the denominator.

$$\frac{4}{\sqrt[3]{t}}$$

$$= \frac{4}{\sqrt[3]{t}} \cdot \frac{\sqrt[3]{t^2}}{\sqrt[3]{t^2}}$$

$$= \frac{4\sqrt[3]{t^2}}{\sqrt[3]{t^3}} = \frac{4\sqrt[3]{t^2}}{t}$$

Example 3

Rationalize the denominator.

$$\frac{\sqrt{2} - 3\sqrt{x}}{\sqrt{x} - \sqrt{2}}$$

$$= \frac{\left(\sqrt{2} - 3\sqrt{x}\right)}{\left(\sqrt{x} - \sqrt{2}\right)} \cdot \frac{\left(\sqrt{x} + \sqrt{2}\right)}{\left(\sqrt{x} + \sqrt{2}\right)}$$

$$= \frac{\sqrt{2} \cdot \sqrt{x} + \sqrt{2} \cdot \sqrt{2} - 3\sqrt{x} \cdot \sqrt{x} - 3\sqrt{x} \cdot \sqrt{2}}{\left(\sqrt{x}\right)^2 - \left(\sqrt{2}\right)^2}$$

$$= \frac{\sqrt{2x} + 2 - 3x - 3\sqrt{2x}}{x - 2}$$

$$= \frac{-3x - 2\sqrt{2x} + 2}{x - 2}$$

770   **Chapter 10**   Radicals and Complex Numbers

Section 10.7   Solving Radical Equations

Key Concepts

Steps to Solve a Radical Equation

1. Isolate the radical. If an equation has more than one radical, choose one of the radicals to isolate.
2. Raise each side of the equation to a power equal to the index of the radical.
3. Solve the resulting equation. If the equation still has a radical, repeat steps 1 and 2.
4. Check the potential solutions in the original equation.

Example 1

Solve.

$$\sqrt[3]{2x+5} + 7 = 12$$
$$\sqrt[3]{2x+5} = 5$$
$$(\sqrt[3]{2x+5})^3 = (5)^3$$
$$2x + 5 = 125$$
$$2x = 120$$
$$x = 60$$

Check:

$$\sqrt[3]{2(60)+5} + 7 \overset{?}{=} 12$$
$$\sqrt[3]{125} + 7 \overset{?}{=} 12$$
$$5 + 7 \overset{?}{=} 12 \quad \text{(true)}$$

The solution set is $\{60\}$.

Examples

Example 2

Solve.

$$\sqrt{b-5} - \sqrt{b+3} = 2$$
$$\sqrt{b-5} = \sqrt{b+3} + 2$$
$$(\sqrt{b-5})^2 = (\sqrt{b+3} + 2)^2$$
$$b - 5 = b + 3 + 4\sqrt{b+3} + 4$$
$$b - 5 = b + 7 + 4\sqrt{b+3}$$
$$-12 = 4\sqrt{b+3}$$
$$-3 = \sqrt{b+3}$$
$$(-3)^2 = (\sqrt{b+3})^2$$
$$9 = b + 3$$
$$6 = b$$

Check:

$$\sqrt{6-5} - \sqrt{6+3} \overset{?}{=} 2$$
$$\sqrt{1} - \sqrt{9} \overset{?}{=} 2$$
$$1 - 3 \overset{?}{=} 2 \quad \text{(false)}$$

No solution, $\{\ \}$

Section 10.8	Complex Numbers

Key Concepts

$i = \sqrt{-1}$ and $i^2 = -1$

For a real number $b > 0$, $\sqrt{-b} = i\sqrt{b}$

A **complex number** is in the form $a + bi$, where a and b are real numbers. The value a is called the real part, and b is called the imaginary part.

To add or subtract complex numbers, combine the real parts and combine the imaginary parts.

Multiply complex numbers by using the distributive property.

Divide complex numbers by multiplying the numerator and denominator by the **complex conjugate** of the denominator.

Examples

Example 1

$\sqrt{-4} \cdot \sqrt{-9}$

$= (2i)(3i)$

$= 6i^2$

$= -6$

Example 2

$(3 - 5i) - (2 + i) + (3 - 2i)$

$= 3 - 5i - 2 - i + 3 - 2i$

$= 4 - 8i$

Example 3

$(1 + 6i)(2 + 4i)$

$= 2 + 4i + 12i + 24i^2$

$= 2 + 16i + 24(-1)$

$= -22 + 16i$

Example 4

$\dfrac{3}{2 - 5i}$

$= \dfrac{3}{(2 - 5i)} \cdot \dfrac{(2 + 5i)}{(2 + 5i)}$

$= \dfrac{6 + 15i}{4 - 25i^2}$

$= \dfrac{6 + 15i}{4 + 25}$

$= \dfrac{6 + 15i}{29}$

$= \dfrac{6}{29} + \dfrac{15}{29}i$

Chapter 10   Review Exercises

For the exercises in this set, assume that all variables represent positive real numbers unless otherwise stated.

Section 10.1

1. True or false?

   a. The principal nth root of an even-indexed root is always positive

   b. The principal nth root of an odd-indexed root is always positive.

2. Explain why $\sqrt{(-3)^2} \neq -3$.

3. For $a > 0$ and $b > 0$, are the following statements true or false?

   a. $\sqrt{a^2 + b^2} = a + b$

   b. $\sqrt{(a+b)^2} = a + b$

For Exercises 4–6, simplify the radicals.

4. $\sqrt{\dfrac{50}{32}}$ 5. $\sqrt[4]{625}$ 6. $\sqrt{(-6)^2}$

7. Evaluate the function values for $f(x) = \sqrt{x-1}$.

   a. $f(10)$ b. $f(1)$ c. $f(8)$

   d. Write the domain of f in interval notation.

8. Evaluate the function values for $g(t) = \sqrt{5+t}$.

   a. $g(-5)$ b. $g(-4)$ c. $g(4)$

   d. Write the domain of g in interval notation

9. Write the English expression as an algebraic expression: Four more than the quotient of the cube root of $2x$ and the principal fourth root of $2x$.

For Exercises 10–11, simplify the expression. Assume that x and y represent *any* real number.

10. a. $\sqrt{x^2}$ b. $\sqrt[3]{x^3}$

    c. $\sqrt[4]{x^4}$ d. $\sqrt[5]{(x+1)^5}$

11. a. $\sqrt{4y^2}$ b. $\sqrt[3]{27y^3}$

    c. $\sqrt[100]{y^{100}}$ d. $\sqrt[101]{y^{101}}$

12. Use the Pythagorean theorem to find the length of the third side of the triangle.

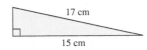

Section 10.2

13. Are the properties of exponents the same for rational exponents and integer exponents? Give an example. (Answers may vary.)

14. In the expression $x^{m/n}$ what does n represent?

15. Explain the process of eliminating a negative exponent from an algebraic expression.

For Exercises 16–21, simplify the expressions. Write the answers with positive exponents only.

16. $(-125)^{1/3}$ 17. $16^{-1/4}$

18. $\left(\dfrac{1}{16}\right)^{-3/4} - \left(\dfrac{1}{8}\right)^{-2/3}$ 19. $\left(b^{1/2} \cdot b^{1/3}\right)^{12}$

20. $\left(\dfrac{x^{-1/4}y^{-1/3}z^{3/4}}{2^{1/3}x^{-1/3}y^{2/3}}\right)^{-12}$ 21. $\left(\dfrac{a^{12}b^{-4}c^7}{a^3b^2c^4}\right)^{1/3}$

For Exercises 22–23, rewrite the expressions by using rational exponents.

22. $\sqrt[4]{x^3}$ 23. $\sqrt[3]{2y^2}$

For Exercises 24–26, use a calculator to approximate the expressions to four decimal places.

24. $10^{1/3}$ 25. $17.8^{2/3}$ 26. $\sqrt[5]{147^4}$

Section 10.3

27. List the criteria for a radical expression to be simplified.

For Exercises 28–31, simplify the radicals.

28. $\sqrt{108}$ 29. $\sqrt[4]{x^5yz^4}$

30. $-2\sqrt[3]{250a^3b^{10}}$ 31. $\sqrt[3]{\dfrac{-16a^4}{2ab^3}}$

32. Write an English phrase that describes the following mathematical expressions: (Answers may vary.)

    a. $\sqrt{\dfrac{2}{x}}$ **b.** $(x+1)^3$

33. An engineering firm made a mistake when building a $\frac{1}{4}$-mi bridge in the Florida Keys. The bridge was made without adequate expansion joints to prevent buckling during the heat of summer. During mid-June, the bridge expanded 1.5 ft, causing a vertical bulge in the middle. Calculate the height of the bulge h in feet. (*Note:* 1 mi = 5280 ft.) Round to the nearest foot.

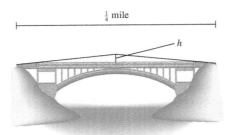

$\frac{1}{4}$ mile

Section 10.4

34. Complete the following statement: Radicals may be added or subtracted if . . .

For Exercises 35–38, determine whether the radicals may be combined, and explain your answer.

  35. $\sqrt[3]{2x} - 2\sqrt{2x}$ **36.** $2 + \sqrt{x}$

  37. $\sqrt[4]{3xy} + 2\sqrt[4]{3xy}$ **38.** $-4\sqrt{32} + 7\sqrt{50}$

For Exercises 39–42, add or subtract as indicated.

  39. $4\sqrt{7} - 2\sqrt{7} + 3\sqrt{7}$

  40. $2\sqrt[3]{64} + 3\sqrt[3]{54} - 16$

  41. $\sqrt{50} + 7\sqrt{2} - \sqrt{8}$

  42. $x\sqrt[3]{16x^2} - 4\sqrt[3]{2x^5} + 5x\sqrt[3]{54x^2}$

For Exercises 43–44, answer true or false. If an answer is false, explain why. Assume all variables represent positive real numbers.

  43. $5 + 3\sqrt{x} = 8\sqrt{x}$

  44. $\sqrt{y} + \sqrt{y} = \sqrt{2y}$

Section 10.5

For Exercises 45–56, multiply the radicals and simplify the answer.

  45. $\sqrt{3} \cdot \sqrt{12}$ **46.** $\sqrt[4]{4} \cdot \sqrt[4]{8}$

  47. $-2\sqrt{3}(\sqrt{7} - 3\sqrt{11})$ **48.** $-3\sqrt{5}(2\sqrt{3} - \sqrt{5})$

  49. $(2\sqrt{x} - 3)(2\sqrt{x} + 3)$ **50.** $(\sqrt{y} + 4)(\sqrt{y} - 4)$

  51. $(\sqrt{7y} - \sqrt{3x})^2$ **52.** $(2\sqrt{3w} + 5)^2$

  53. $(-\sqrt{z} - \sqrt{6})(2\sqrt{z} + 7\sqrt{6})$

  54. $(3\sqrt{a} - \sqrt{5})(\sqrt{a} + 2\sqrt{5})$

  55. $\sqrt[3]{u} \cdot \sqrt{u^5}$ **56.** $\sqrt{2} \cdot \sqrt[4]{w^3}$

Section 10.6

For Exercises 57–60, simplify the radicals.

  57. $\sqrt{\dfrac{3y^5}{25x^6}}$ **58.** $\sqrt[3]{\dfrac{-16x^7y^6}{z^9}}$

  59. $\dfrac{\sqrt{324\,w^7}}{\sqrt{4\,w^3}}$ **60.** $\dfrac{\sqrt[3]{3t^{14}}}{\sqrt[3]{192t^2}}$

For Exercises 61–68, rationalize the denominator.

  61. $\sqrt{\dfrac{7}{2y}}$ **62.** $\sqrt{\dfrac{5}{3w}}$

  63. $\dfrac{4}{\sqrt[3]{9p^2}}$ **64.** $\dfrac{-2}{\sqrt[3]{2x}}$

  65. $\dfrac{-5}{\sqrt{15} + \sqrt{10}}$ **66.** $\dfrac{-6}{\sqrt{7} + \sqrt{5}}$

  67. $\dfrac{t - 3}{\sqrt{t} - \sqrt{3}}$ **68.** $\dfrac{w - 7}{\sqrt{w} - \sqrt{7}}$

69. Write the mathematical expression as an English phrase. (Answers may vary.)

$$\dfrac{\sqrt{2}}{x^2}$$

Section 10.7

Solve the radical equations in Exercises 70–77, if possible.

  70. $\sqrt{2y} = 7$ **71.** $\sqrt{a - 6} - 5 = 0$

  72. $\sqrt[3]{2w - 3} + 5 = 2$

774   **Chapter 10** Radicals and Complex Numbers

73. $\sqrt[4]{p + 12} - \sqrt[4]{5p - 16} = 0$

74. $\sqrt{t} + \sqrt{t - 5} = 5$

75. $\sqrt{8x + 1} = -\sqrt{x - 13}$

76. $\sqrt{2m^2 + 4} - \sqrt{9m} = 0$

77. $\sqrt{x + 2} = 1 - \sqrt{2x + 5}$

78. A tower is supported by stabilizing wires. Find the exact length of each wire, and then round to the nearest tenth of a meter.

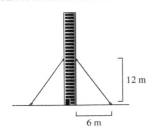

12 m

6 m

79. The velocity, $v(d)$, of an ocean wave depends on the water depth d as the wave approaches land.

$$v(d) = \sqrt{32d}$$

where $v(d)$ is in feet per second and d is in feet.

   a. Find $v(20)$ and interpret its value Round to one decimal place.

   b. Find the depth of the water at a point where a wave is traveling at 16 ft/sec.

Section 10.8

80. Define a complex number.

81. Define an imaginary number.

82. Describe the first step in the process to simplify the expression.

$$\frac{3}{4 + 6i}$$

For Exercises 83–86, rewrite the expressions in terms of i.

83. $\sqrt{-16}$

84. $-\sqrt{-5}$

85. $\sqrt{-75} \cdot \sqrt{-3}$

86. $\dfrac{-\sqrt{-24}}{\sqrt{6}}$

For Exercises 87–90, simplify the powers of i.

87. i^{38}

88. i^{101}

89. i^{19}

90. $i^{1000} + i^{1002}$

For Exercises 91–94, perform the indicated operations. Write the final answer in the form $a + bi$.

91. $(-3 + i) - (2 - 4i)$ **92.** $(1 + 6i)(3 - i)$

93. $(4 - 3i)(4 + 3i)$ **94.** $(5 - i)^2$

For Exercises 95–96, write the expressions in the form $a + bi$, and determine the real and imaginary parts.

95. $\dfrac{17 - 4i}{-4}$

96. $\dfrac{-16 - 8i}{8}$

For Exercises 97–100, divide and simplify. Write the final answer in the form $a + bi$.

97. $\dfrac{2 - i}{3 + 2i}$

98. $\dfrac{10 + 5i}{2 - i}$

99. $\dfrac{5 + 3i}{-2i}$

100. $\dfrac{4i}{4 - i}$

For Exercises 101–102, simplify the expression.

101. $\dfrac{-8 + \sqrt{-40}}{12}$

102. $\dfrac{6 - \sqrt{-144}}{3}$

Chapter 10   Test

1. a. What is the principal square root of 36?

   b. What is the negative square root of 36?

2. Which of the following are real numbers?

   a. $-\sqrt{100}$ **b.** $\sqrt{-100}$

   c. $-\sqrt[3]{1000}$ **d.** $\sqrt[3]{-1000}$

3. Simplify.

   a. $\sqrt[3]{y^3}$ **b.** $\sqrt[4]{y^4}$

For Exercises 4–11, simplify the radicals. Assume that all variables represent positive numbers.

4. $\sqrt[4]{81}$ **5.** $\sqrt{\dfrac{16}{9}}$

6. $\sqrt[3]{32}$ **7.** $\sqrt{a^4 b^3 c^5}$

8. $\sqrt{18x^5 y^3 z^4}$ **9.** $\sqrt{\dfrac{32w^6}{2w}}$

10. $\sqrt[3]{\dfrac{x^6}{125y^3}}$ **11.** $\dfrac{2\sqrt{72}}{8}$

12. a. Evaluate the function values $f(-8)$, $f(-6)$, $f(-4)$, and $f(-2)$ for $f(x) = \sqrt{-2x - 4}$.

   b. Write the domain of f in interval notation.

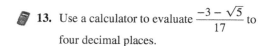 **13.** Use a calculator to evaluate $\dfrac{-3 - \sqrt{5}}{17}$ to four decimal places.

For Exercises 14–15, simplify the expressions. Assume that all variables represent positive numbers.

14. $-27^{1/3}$ **15.** $8^{2/3} \cdot \left(\dfrac{25x^4 y^6}{z^2}\right)^{1/2}$

For Exercises 16–17, use rational exponents to multiply or divide. Write the final answer in radical form.

16. $\sqrt[6]{7} \cdot \sqrt{y}$ **17.** $\dfrac{\sqrt[3]{10}}{\sqrt[4]{10}}$

18. Add or subtract as indicated.

$$3\sqrt{5} + 4\sqrt{5} - 2\sqrt{20}$$

For Exercises 19–20, multiply the radicals.

19. $3\sqrt{x}\left(\sqrt{2} - \sqrt{5}\right)$

20. $\left(2\sqrt{5} - 3\sqrt{x}\right)\left(4\sqrt{5} + \sqrt{x}\right)$

For Exercises 21–22, rationalize the denominator. Assume $x > 0$.

21. $\dfrac{-2}{\sqrt[3]{x}}$ **22.** $\dfrac{\sqrt{x} + 2}{3 - \sqrt{x}}$

23. Rewrite the expressions in terms of i.

   a. $\sqrt{-8}$ **b.** $2\sqrt{-16}$ **c.** $\dfrac{2 + \sqrt{-8}}{4}$

For Exercises 24–30, perform the indicated operations and simplify completely. Write the final answer in the form $a + bi$.

24. $(3 - 5i) - (2 + 6i)$ **25.** $(4 + i)(8 + 2i)$

26. $\sqrt{-16} \cdot \sqrt{-49}$ **27.** $(4 - 7i)^2$

28. $(2 - 10i)(2 + 10i)$ **29.** $\dfrac{3 - 2i}{3 - 4i}$

30. $\dfrac{6i}{3 - 5i}$

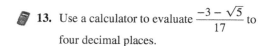 **31.** If the volume V of a sphere is known, the radius of the sphere can be computed by

$$r(V) = \sqrt[3]{\dfrac{3V}{4\pi}}$$

Find $r(10)$ to two decimal places. Interpret the meaning in the context of the problem.

776   **Chapter 10** Radicals and Complex Numbers

32. A patio 20 ft wide has a slanted roof, as shown in the figure. Find the length of the roof if there is an 8-in. overhang. Round the answer to the nearest foot.

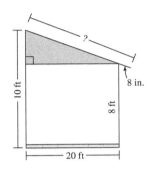

For Exercises 33–35, solve the radical equation.

33. $\sqrt[3]{2x + 5} = -3$

34. $\sqrt{5x + 8} = \sqrt{5x - 1} + 1$

35. $\sqrt{t + 7} - \sqrt{2t - 3} = 2$

Chapters 1–10 Cumulative Review Exercises

1. Simplify the expression.
$6^2 - 2[5 - 8(3 - 1) + 4 \div 2]$

2. Simplify the expression.
$3x - 3(-2x + 5) - 4y + 2(3x + 5) - y$

3. Solve. $9(2y + 8) = 20 - (y + 5)$

For Exercises 4–6, solve the inequalities. Write the answers in interval notation, if possible.

4. $2a - 4 < -14$ **5.** $11 \ge -x + 2 > 5$

6. $|9 - 4x| + 4 < 2$

7. Write an equation of the line that is parallel to the line $2x + y = 9$ and passes through the point $(3, -1)$. Write the answer in slope-intercept form.

8. Write an equation of a line parallel to the y-axis passing through the point $(-5, 8)$.

9. Solve the system of equations by using the addition method.
$$2x - 3y = 0$$
$$-4x + 3y = -1$$

10. Determine if $\left(2, -2, \dfrac{1}{2}\right)$ is a solution to the system.
$$2x + y - 4z = 0$$
$$x - y + 2z = 5$$
$$3x + 2y + 2z = 4$$

11. Bennette and Pepe are landscapers and have to dig a ditch in which to put underground piping for a sprinkler system. Bennette can dig 40 yd of ditch in 3 hr and Pepe can dig 40 yd of ditch in 5 hr. How long will it take them to dig 40 yd together?

12. Given the function defined by $f(x) = 4x - 2$.

   a. Find $f(-2), f(0), f(4)$, and $f(\frac{1}{2})$.

   b. Write the ordered pairs that correspond to the function values in part (a)

   c. Graph $y = f(x)$.

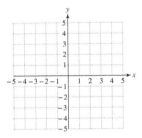

13. Simplify the expression. Write the final answer with positive exponents only.
$$\left(\frac{a^{3/2}b^{-1/4}c^{1/3}}{ab^{-5/4}c^0}\right)^{12}$$

14. Multiply or divide as indicated, and write the answer in scientific notation.

    a. $(3.5 \times 10^7)(4 \times 10^{-12})$

    b. $\dfrac{6.28 \times 10^5}{2 \times 10^{-4}}$

15. Multiply the polynomials $(2x + 5)(x - 3)$. What is the degree of the product?

16. Perform the indicated operations and simplify.
$$\sqrt{3}\left(\sqrt{5} + \sqrt{6} + \sqrt{3}\right)$$

17. Divide. $(x^2 - x - 12) \div (x + 3)$

18. Simplify and subtract. $\sqrt[4]{\dfrac{1}{16}} - \sqrt[3]{\dfrac{8}{27}}$

19. Simplify. $\sqrt[3]{\dfrac{54c^4}{cd^3}}$

20. Add. $4\sqrt{45b^3} + 5b\sqrt{80b}$

21. Divide. $\dfrac{13i}{3 + 2i}$ Write the answer in the form $a + bi$.

22. Solve. $\dfrac{5}{y - 2} - \dfrac{3}{y - 4} = \dfrac{6}{y^2 - 6y + 8}$

23. Add. $\dfrac{3}{x^2 + 5x} + \dfrac{-2}{x^2 - 25}$

24. Divide. $\dfrac{a + 10}{2a^2 - 11a - 6} \div \dfrac{a^2 + 12a + 20}{6 - a}$

25. Perform the indicated operations.
$(-5x^2 - 4x + 8) - (3x - 5)^2$

26. Simplify. $\dfrac{-4}{\sqrt{3} - \sqrt{5}}$

27. Divide. $\dfrac{4}{3 - 5i}$

28. Solve. $12x^2 + 4x - 21 = 0$

29. Factor. $x^2 + 6x + 9 - y^2$

30. Factor. $x^6 + 8$

Quadratic Equations and Functions

Quadratic Equations and Functions

11

Mathematics in Art

A **golden rectangle** is a rectangle in which the ratio of its length L to its width W is equal to the ratio of the sum of its length and width to its length.

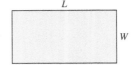

$$\frac{L}{W} = \frac{L + W}{L}$$

The values of L and W that meet this condition are said to be in the **golden ratio**. The golden ratio has been studied by artists and art historians for generations because the golden ratio represents an aesthetically pleasing ratio between the length and width of a figure. For example, the face of the Parthenon built in ancient Greece has the dimensions of a golden rectangle.

We can show that the length of a golden rectangle is approximately 1.62 times the width. Substituting 1 for the width, we have the proportion $\frac{L}{1} = \frac{L + 1}{L}$.

Then, clearing fractions and writing the quadratic equation in standard form gives $L^2 - L - 1 = 0$. The expression on the left is not factorable, but fortunately in this chapter, we will learn two techniques to solve a quadratic equation when factoring fails. The positive solution for L in this equation is the golden ratio, $\frac{1 + \sqrt{5}}{2} \approx 1.62$.

© Purestock/SuperStock RF

Section 11.1	Square Root Property and Completing the Square

Concepts

1. Solving Quadratic Equations by Using the Square Root Property
2. Solving Quadratic Equations by Completing the Square
3. Literal Equations

1. Solving Quadratic Equations by Using the Square Root Property

We have already learned how to solve a quadratic equation by factoring and applying the zero product rule. For example:

$$x^2 = 81$$
$$x^2 - 81 = 0 \qquad \text{Set one side equal to zero.}$$
$$(x - 9)(x + 9) = 0 \qquad \text{Factor.}$$
$$x - 9 = 0 \quad \text{or} \quad x + 9 = 0 \qquad \text{Set each factor equal to zero.}$$
$$x = 9 \quad \text{or} \qquad x = -9$$

The solution set is $\{9, -9\}$.

It is important to note that the zero product rule can only be used if the equation is factorable. In this section, we will learn a method to solve quadratic equations containing expressions that are both factorable and nonfactorable.

Consider a quadratic equation of the form $x^2 = k$. The solutions are all numbers (real or imaginary) that when squared equal k, so for any nonzero constant k, there will be two solutions, $\sqrt{k}$ or $-\sqrt{k}$. For example:

$$x^2 = 25 \qquad \text{The solutions are 5 and } -5.$$
$$x^2 = -25 \qquad \text{The solutions are } 5i \text{ and } -5i.$$

This principle is stated formally as the **square root property**.

> **The Square Root Property**
> For any real number, k, if $x^2 = k$, then $x = \sqrt{k}$ or $x = -\sqrt{k}$.
>
> *Note:* The solution may also be written as $\pm\sqrt{k}$, read "plus or minus the square root of k."

Example 1	Solving a Quadratic Equation by Using the Square Root Property

Use the square root property to solve the equation. $4p^2 = 9$

Solution:

$$4p^2 = 9$$

$$p^2 = \frac{9}{4} \qquad \text{Isolate } p^2 \text{ by dividing both sides by 4.}$$

$$p = \pm\sqrt{\frac{9}{4}} \qquad \text{Apply the square root property.}$$

$$p = \pm\frac{3}{2} \qquad \text{Simplify the radical.}$$

The solution set is $\left\{\frac{3}{2}, -\frac{3}{2}\right\}$.

Skill Practice Solve using the square root property.

1. $25a^2 = 16$

For a quadratic equation, $ax^2 + bx + c = 0$, if $b = 0$, then the equation is easily solved by using the square root property. This is demonstrated in Example 2.

Example 2   **Solving a Quadratic Equation by Using the Square Root Property**

Use the square root property to solve the equation. $3x^2 + 75 = 0$

Solution:

$$3x^2 + 75 = 0 \qquad \text{Rewrite the equation to fit the form } x^2 = k.$$

$$3x^2 = -75$$

$$x^2 = -25 \qquad \text{The equation is now in the form } x^2 = k.$$

$$x = \pm\sqrt{-25} \qquad \text{Apply the square root property.}$$

$$= \pm 5i$$

Check: $x = 5i$	Check: $x = -5i$
$3x^2 + 75 = 0$	$3x^2 + 75 = 0$
$3(5i)^2 + 75 \stackrel{?}{=} 0$	$3(-5i)^2 + 75 \stackrel{?}{=} 0$
$3(25i^2) + 75 \stackrel{?}{=} 0$	$3(25i^2) + 75 \stackrel{?}{=} 0$
$3(-25) + 75 \stackrel{?}{=} 0$	$3(-25) + 75 \stackrel{?}{=} 0$
$-75 + 75 \stackrel{?}{=} 0 \checkmark$	$-75 + 75 \stackrel{?}{=} 0 \checkmark$

The solution set is $\{\pm 5i\}$.

Avoiding Mistakes

A common mistake is to forget the $\pm$ symbol when solving the equation $x^2 = k$:

$$x = \pm\sqrt{k}$$

Skill Practice Solve using the square root property.

2. $8x^2 + 72 = 0$

Example 3   **Solving a Quadratic Equation by Using the Square Root Property**

Use the square root property to solve the equation. $(w + 3)^2 = 20$

Solution:

$$(w + 3)^2 = 20 \qquad \text{The equation is in the form } x^2 = k, \text{ where } x = (w + 3).$$

$$w + 3 = \pm\sqrt{20} \qquad \text{Apply the square root property.}$$

$$w + 3 = \pm\sqrt{4 \cdot 5} \qquad \text{Simplify the radical.}$$

$$w + 3 = \pm 2\sqrt{5}$$

$$w = -3 \pm 2\sqrt{5} \qquad \text{Solve for } w.$$

The solution set is $\{-3 \pm 2\sqrt{5}\}$.

TIP: Recall that $-3 \pm 2\sqrt{5}$ represents two solutions:

$$-3 + 2\sqrt{5} \text{ and } -3 - 2\sqrt{5}$$

Skill Practice Solve using the square root property.

3. $(t - 5)^2 = 18$

Answers

1. $\left\{\dfrac{4}{5}, -\dfrac{4}{5}\right\}$ **2.** $\{\pm 3i\}$

3. $\{5 \pm 3\sqrt{2}\}$

2. Solving Quadratic Equations by Completing the Square

In Example 3 we used the square root property to solve an equation where the square of a binomial was equal to a constant.

$$\underbrace{(w+3)^2}_{\substack{\text{Square of a} \\ \text{binomial}}} = \overset{\substack{\uparrow \\ \text{Constant}}}{20}$$

The square of a binomial is the factored form of a perfect square trinomial. For example:

Perfect Square Trinomial	**Factored Form**
$x^2 + 10x + 25$ $\longrightarrow$	$(x+5)^2$
$t^2 - 6t + 9$ $\longrightarrow$	$(t-3)^2$
$p^2 - 14p + 49$ $\longrightarrow$	$(p-7)^2$

For a perfect square trinomial with a leading coefficient of 1, the constant term is the square of one-half the linear term coefficient. For example:

$$x^2 + \underset{\big\downarrow}{10x} + \underset{\big\uparrow}{25}$$
$$\left[\tfrac{1}{2}(10)\right]^2$$

In general an expression of the form $x^2 + bx + n$ is a perfect square trinomial if $n = \left(\tfrac{1}{2}b\right)^2$. The process to create a perfect square trinomial is called **completing the square**.

Example 4   **Completing the Square**

Determine the value of n that makes the polynomial a perfect square trinomial. Then factor the expression as the square of a binomial.

a. $x^2 + 12x + n$ **b.** $x^2 - 26x + n$

c. $x^2 + 11x + n$ **d.** $x^2 - \dfrac{4}{7}x + n$

Solution:

The expressions are in the form $x^2 + bx + n$. The value of n equals the square of one-half the linear term coefficient $\left(\tfrac{1}{2}b\right)^2$.

a. $x^2 + 12x + n$

$\quad x^2 + 12x + 36 \qquad n = \left[\tfrac{1}{2}(12)\right]^2 = (6)^2 = 36$

$\quad (x+6)^2 \qquad\qquad$ Factored form

b. $x^2 - 26x + n$

$\quad x^2 - 26x + 169 \qquad n = \left[\tfrac{1}{2}(-26)\right]^2 = (-13)^2 = 169$

$\quad (x-13)^2 \qquad\qquad$ Factored form

c. $x^2 + 11x + n$

$\quad x^2 + 11x + \dfrac{121}{4} \qquad n = \left[\tfrac{1}{2}(11)\right]^2 = \left(\tfrac{11}{2}\right)^2 = \tfrac{121}{4}$

$\quad \left(x + \dfrac{11}{2}\right)^2 \qquad\qquad$ Factored form

d. $x^2 - \frac{4}{7}x + n$

$x^2 - \frac{4}{7}x + \frac{4}{49}$ $n = \left[\frac{1}{2}\left(-\frac{4}{7}\right)\right]^2 = \left(-\frac{2}{7}\right)^2 = \frac{4}{49}$

$\left(x - \frac{2}{7}\right)^2$ Factored form

Skill Practice Determine the value of n that makes the polynomial a perfect square trinomial. Then factor.

4. $x^2 + 20x + n$ **5.** $y^2 - 16y + n$

6. $a^2 - 15a + n$ **7.** $w^2 + \frac{7}{3}w + n$

The process of completing the square can be used to write a quadratic equation $ax^2 + bx + c = 0$ ($a \neq 0$) in the form $(x - h)^2 = k$. Then the square root property can be used to solve the equation. The following steps outline the procedure.

> **Solving a Quadratic Equation $ax^2 + bx + c = 0$ by Completing the Square and Applying the Square Root Property**
>
> **Step 1** Divide both sides by a to make the leading coefficient 1.
> **Step 2** Isolate the variable terms on one side of the equation.
> **Step 3** Complete the square.
> - Add the square of one-half the linear term coefficient to both sides, $\left(\frac{1}{2}b\right)^2$.
> - Factor the resulting perfect square trinomial.
> **Step 4** Apply the square root property and solve for x.

Example 5 **Solving a Quadratic Equation by Completing the Square and Applying the Square Root Property**

Solve by completing the square and applying the square root property.

$$x^2 - 6x + 13 = 0$$

Solution:

$x^2 - 6x + 13 = 0$ **Step 1:** Since the leading coefficient a is equal to 1, we do not have to divide by a. We can proceed to step 2.

$x^2 - 6x = -13$ **Step 2:** Isolate the variable terms on one side.

$x^2 - 6x + 9 = -13 + 9$ **Step 3:** To complete the square, add $\left[\frac{1}{2}(-6)\right]^2 = 9$ to both sides of the equation.

$(x - 3)^2 = -4$ Factor the perfect square trinomial.

Answers

4. $n = 100;\ (x + 10)^2$
5. $n = 64;\ (y - 8)^2$
6. $n = \frac{225}{4};\ \left(a - \frac{15}{2}\right)^2$
7. $n = \frac{49}{36};\ \left(w + \frac{7}{6}\right)^2$

784 Chapter 11 Quadratic Equations and Functions

$$x - 3 = \pm\sqrt{-4}$$ **Step 4:** Apply the square root property.

$$x - 3 = \pm 2i$$ Simplify the radical.

$$x = 3 \pm 2i$$ Solve for x.

The solutions are imaginary numbers and can be written as $3 + 2i$ and $3 - 2i$.

The solution set is $\{3 \pm 2i\}$.

Skill Practice Solve by completing the square and applying the square root property.

8. $z^2 - 4z + 26 = 0$

Example 6   **Solving a Quadratic Equation by Completing the Square and Applying the Square Root Property**

Solve by completing the square and applying the square root property.

$$2m^2 + 10m = 3$$

Solution:

$$2m^2 + 10m = 3$$ The variable terms are already isolated on one side of the equation.

$$\frac{2m^2}{2} + \frac{10m}{2} = \frac{3}{2}$$ Divide by the leading coefficient, 2.

$$m^2 + 5m = \frac{3}{2}$$

$$m^2 + 5m + \frac{25}{4} = \frac{3}{2} + \frac{25}{4}$$ Add $\left[\frac{1}{2}(5)\right]^2 = \left(\frac{5}{2}\right)^2 = \frac{25}{4}$ to both sides.

$$\left(m + \frac{5}{2}\right)^2 = \frac{6}{4} + \frac{25}{4}$$ Factor the left side and write the terms on the right with a common denominator.

$$\left(m + \frac{5}{2}\right)^2 = \frac{31}{4}$$

$$m + \frac{5}{2} = \pm\sqrt{\frac{31}{4}}$$ Apply the square root property.

$$m = -\frac{5}{2} \pm \frac{\sqrt{31}}{2}$$ Subtract $\frac{5}{2}$ from both sides and simplify the radical.

TIP: The solutions to Example 6 can also be written as: $\dfrac{-5 \pm \sqrt{31}}{2}$

The solution set is $\left\{-\frac{5}{2} \pm \frac{\sqrt{31}}{2}\right\}$.   The solutions are irrational numbers.

Skill Practice Solve by completing the square and applying the square root property.

9. $4x^2 + 12x = 5$

Answers

8. $\{2 \pm i\sqrt{22}\}$

9. $\left\{-\frac{3}{2} \pm \frac{\sqrt{14}}{2}\right\}$

Example 7	**Solving a Quadratic Equation by Completing the Square and Applying the Square Root Property**

Solve by completing the square and applying the square root property.

$$2x(2x - 10) = -30 + 6x$$

Solution:

$$2x(2x - 10) = -30 + 6x$$

$$4x^2 - 20x = -30 + 6x \qquad \text{Clear parentheses.}$$

$$4x^2 - 26x + 30 = 0 \qquad \text{Write the equation in the form } ax^2 + bx + c = 0.$$

$$\frac{4x^2}{4} - \frac{26x}{4} + \frac{30}{4} = \frac{0}{4} \qquad \textbf{Step 1:} \quad \text{Divide both sides by the leading coefficient, 4.}$$

$$x^2 - \frac{13}{2}x + \frac{15}{2} = 0$$

$$x^2 - \frac{13}{2}x = -\frac{15}{2} \qquad \textbf{Step 2:} \quad \text{Isolate the variable terms on one side.}$$

$$x^2 - \frac{13}{2}x + \frac{169}{16} = -\frac{15}{2} + \frac{169}{16} \qquad \textbf{Step 3:} \quad \text{Add } \left[\frac{1}{2}\left(-\frac{13}{2}\right)\right]^2 = \left(-\frac{13}{4}\right)^2 = \frac{169}{16} \text{ to both sides.}$$

$$\left(x - \frac{13}{4}\right)^2 = -\frac{120}{16} + \frac{169}{16} \qquad \text{Factor the perfect square trinomial. Rewrite the right-hand side with a common denominator.}$$

$$\left(x - \frac{13}{4}\right)^2 = \frac{49}{16}$$

$$x - \frac{13}{4} = \pm\sqrt{\frac{49}{16}} \qquad \textbf{Step 4:} \quad \text{Apply the square root property.}$$

$$x - \frac{13}{4} = \pm\frac{7}{4} \qquad \text{Simplify the radical.}$$

$$x = \frac{13}{4} + \frac{7}{4} = \frac{20}{4} = 5$$

$$x = \frac{13}{4} \pm \frac{7}{4}$$

$$x = \frac{13}{4} - \frac{7}{4} = \frac{6}{4} = \frac{3}{2}$$

The solution set is $\left\{5, \dfrac{3}{2}\right\}$.   The solutions are rational numbers.

TIP: In general, if the solutions to a quadratic equation are rational numbers, the equation can be solved by factoring and using the zero product rule. Consider the equation from Example 7.

$$2x(2x - 10) = -30 + 6x$$
$$4x^2 - 20x = -30 + 6x$$
$$4x^2 - 26x + 30 = 0$$
$$2(2x^2 - 13x + 15) = 0$$
$$2(x - 5)(2x - 3) = 0$$
$$x = 5 \quad \text{or} \quad x = \frac{3}{2}$$

Avoiding Mistakes

When the solutions are rational, combine the *like* terms. That is, do not leave the solution with the $\pm$ sign.

Skill Practice Solve by completing the square and applying the square root property.

10. $2y(y - 1) = 3 - y$

3. Literal Equations

Example 8   **Solving a Literal Equation**

Ignoring air resistance, the distance d (in meters) that an object falls in t sec is given by the equation

$$d = 4.9t^2 \qquad \text{where } t \geq 0$$

   a. Solve the equation for t. Do not rationalize the denominator.

   b. Using the equation from part (a), determine the amount of time required for an object to fall 500 m. Round to the nearest second.

Solution:

   a. $d = 4.9t^2$

   $\dfrac{d}{4.9} = t^2$ Isolate the quadratic term. The equation is in the form $t^2 = k$.

   $t = \pm\sqrt{\dfrac{d}{4.9}}$ Apply the square root property.

   $= \sqrt{\dfrac{d}{4.9}}$ Because t represents time, $t \geq 0$. We reject the negative solution.

   b. $t = \sqrt{\dfrac{d}{4.9}}$

   $= \sqrt{\dfrac{500}{4.9}}$ Substitute $d = 500$.

   $t \approx 10.1$

   The object will require approximately 10.1 sec to fall 500 m.

Skill Practice

Answers

11. $z = \sqrt{\dfrac{x}{2y}}$

12. $z = 3$

11. Given $x = 2yz^2$, solve for z where $z > 0$. Do not rationalize the denominator.

12. Use the equation from the previous exercise to find z when $x = 54$ and $y = 3$.

Section 11.1   **Practice Exercises**

Vocabulary and Key Concepts

   1. a. The zero product rule states that if $ab = 0$, then $a =$ _____ or $b =$ _____.

   b. To apply the zero product rule, one side of the equation must be equal to _____ and the other side must be written in factored form.

   c. The square root property states that for any real number k, if $x^2 = k$, then $x =$ _____ or $x =$ _____.

   d. To apply the square root property to the equation $t^2 + 2 = 11$, first subtract _____ from both sides. The solution set is _____.

   e. The process to create a perfect square trinomial is called _____ the square.

f. Fill in the blank to complete the square for the trinomial $x^2 + 20x +$ _____.

g. To use completing the square to solve the equation $4x^2 + 3x + 5 = 0$, the first step is to divide by _____ so that the coefficient of the x^2 term is _____.

h. Given the trinomial $y^2 + 8y + 16$, the coefficient of the linear term is _____.

Concept 1: Solving Quadratic Equations by Using the Square Root Property

For Exercises 2–21, solve the equations by using the square root property. Write imaginary solutions in the form $a + bi$.
(See Examples 1–3.)

2. $x^2 = 100$

3. $y^2 = 4$

4. $a^2 = 5$

5. $k^2 - 7 = 0$

6. $4t^2 = 81$

7. $36u^2 = 121$

8. $3v^2 + 33 = 0$

9. $-2m^2 = 50$

10. $(p - 5)^2 = 9$

11. $(q + 3)^2 = 4$

12. $(3x - 2)^2 - 5 = 0$

13. $(2y + 3)^2 - 7 = 0$

14. $(h - 4)^2 = -8$

15. $(t + 5)^2 = -18$

16. $6p^2 - 3 = 2$

17. $15 = 4 + 3w^2$

18. $\left(x - \dfrac{3}{2}\right)^2 + \dfrac{7}{4} = 0$

19. $\left(m + \dfrac{4}{5}\right)^2 + \dfrac{3}{25} = 0$

20. $-x^2 + 4 = 13$

21. $-y^2 - 2 = 14$

22. Given the equation $x^2 = k$, match the following statements.

    a. If $k > 0$, then _____

    b. If $k < 0$, then _____

    c. If $k = 0$, then _____

    i. there will be one real solution.

    ii. there will be two real solutions.

    iii. there will be two imaginary solutions.

23. State two methods that can be used to solve the equation $x^2 - 36 = 0$. Then solve the equation by using both methods.

24. Explain the difference between solving the equations: $x = \sqrt{16}$ and $x^2 = 16$.

For Exercises 25–26, solve the equations.

25. **a.** $\sqrt{x} = 4$

    b. $x^2 = 4$

26. **a.** $\sqrt{y} = 9$

    b. $y^2 = 9$

Concept 2: Solving Quadratic Equations by Completing the Square

For Exercises 27–38, find the value of n so that the expression is a perfect square trinomial. Then factor the trinomial.
(See Example 4.)

27. $x^2 - 6x + n$

28. $x^2 + 24x + n$

29. $t^2 + 8t + n$

30. $v^2 - 18v + n$

31. $c^2 - c + n$

32. $x^2 + 9x + n$

33. $y^2 + 5y + n$

34. $a^2 - 7a + n$

35. $b^2 + \dfrac{2}{5}b + n$

36. $m^2 - \dfrac{2}{7}m + n$

37. $p^2 - \dfrac{2}{3}p + n$

38. $w^2 + \dfrac{3}{4}w + n$

39. Summarize the steps used in solving a quadratic equation of the form $ax^2 + bx + c = 0$ by completing the square and applying the square root property.

40. What types of quadratic equations can be solved by completing the square and applying the square root property?

For Exercises 41–60, solve the quadratic equation by completing the square and applying the square root property. Write imaginary solutions in the form $a + bi$. **(See Examples 5–7.)**

41. $t^2 + 8t + 15 = 0$

42. $m^2 + 6m + 8 = 0$

43. $x^2 + 6x = -16$

44. $x^2 - 4x = -15$

45. $p^2 + 4p + 6 = 0$

46. $q^2 + 2q + 2 = 0$

47. $-3y - 10 = -y^2$

48. $-24 = -2y^2 + 2y$

49. $2a^2 + 4a + 5 = 0$

50. $3a^2 + 6a - 7 = 0$

51. $9x^2 - 36x + 40 = 0$

52. $9y^2 - 12y + 5 = 0$

53. $25p^2 - 10p = 2$

54. $9n^2 - 6n = 1$

55. $(2w + 5)(w - 1) = 2$

56. $(3p - 5)(p + 1) = -3$

57. $n(n - 4) = 7$

58. $m(m + 10) = 2$

59. $2x(x + 6) = 14$

60. $3x(x - 2) = 24$

Concept 3: Literal Equations

61. The distance d (in feet) that an object falls in t sec is given by the equation $d = 16t^2$, where $t \geq 0$.

    a. Solve the equation for t. **(See Example 8.)**

    b. Using the equation from part (a), determine the amount of time required for an object to fall 1024 ft.

62. The volume V (in cubic inches) of a can that is 4 in. tall is given by the equation $V = 4\pi r^2$, where r is the radius of the can, measured in inches.

    a. Solve the equation for r. Do not rationalize the denominator.

    b. Using the equation from part (a), determine the radius of a can with a volume of 12.56 in.^{3} Use 3.14 for π.

For Exercises 63–68, solve for the indicated variable.

63. $A = \pi r^2$ for r $(r > 0)$

64. $E = mc^2$ for c $(c > 0)$

65. $a^2 + b^2 + c^2 = d^2$ for a $(a > 0)$

66. $a^2 + b^2 = c^2$ for b $(b > 0)$

67. $V = \frac{1}{3}\pi r^2 h$ for r $(r > 0)$

68. $V = \frac{1}{3}s^2 h$ for s $(s > 0)$

69. A corner shelf is to be made from a triangular piece of plywood, as shown in the diagram. Find the distance x that the shelf will extend along the walls. Assume that the walls are at right angles. Round the answer to a tenth of a foot.

70. The volume $V(x)$ (in cubic inches) of a box with a square bottom and a height of 4 in. is given by $V(x) = 4x^2$, where x is the length (in inches) of the sides of the bottom of the box.

    a. If the volume of the box is 289 in.^{3}, find the dimensions of the box.

    b. Are there two possible answers to part (a)? Why or why not?

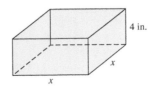

71. A square has an area of 50 in.^{2} What are the lengths of the sides? (Round to one decimal place.)

72. The amount of money A in an account with an interest rate r compounded annually is given by

$$A = P(1 + r)^t$$

where P is the initial principal and t is the number of years the money is invested.

a. If a \$10,000 investment grows to \$11,664 after 2 yr, find the interest rate.

b. If a \$6000 investment grows to \$7392.60 after 2 yr, find the interest rate.

c. Jamal wants to invest \$5000. He wants the money to grow to at least \$6500 in 2 yr to cover the cost of his son's first year at college. What interest rate does Jamal need for his investment to grow to \$6500 in 2 yr? Round to the nearest hundredth of a percent.

73. A textbook company has discovered that the profit for selling its books is given by

$$P(x) = -\frac{1}{8}x^2 + 5x$$

where x is the number of textbooks produced (in thousands) and $P(x)$ is the corresponding profit (in thousands of dollars).

a. Approximate the number of books required to make a profit of \$20,000. [*Hint:* Let $P(x) = 20$. Then complete the square to solve for x.] Round to one decimal place.

b. Why are there two answers to part (a)?

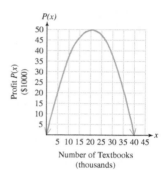

74. If we ignore air resistance, the distance $d(t)$ (in feet) that an object travels in free fall can be approximated by $d(t) = 16t^2$, where t is the time in seconds after the object was dropped.

a. If the CN Tower in Toronto is 1815 ft high, how long will it take an object to fall from the top of the building? Round to one decimal place.

b. If the Renaissance Tower in Dallas is 886 ft high, how long will it take an object to fall from the top of the building? Round to one decimal place.

© Songquan Deng/Shutterstock RF

© Digital Vision RF

Section 11.2	Quadratic Formula

Concepts

1. Derivation of the Quadratic Formula
2. Solving Quadratic Equations by Using the Quadratic Formula
3. Using the Quadratic Formula in Applications
4. Discriminant
5. Mixed Review: Methods to Solve a Quadratic Equation

1. Derivation of the Quadratic Formula

If we solve a quadratic equation in standard form $ax^2 + bx + c = 0, a > 0$, by completing the square and using the square root property, the result is a formula that gives the solutions for x in terms of a, b, and c.

$$ax^2 + bx + c = 0 \ (a \neq 0)$$
Begin with a quadratic equation in standard form.

$$\frac{ax^2}{a} + \frac{bx}{a} + \frac{c}{a} = \frac{0}{a}$$
Divide by the leading coefficient.

$$x^2 + \frac{b}{a}x + \frac{c}{a} = 0$$

$$x^2 + \frac{b}{a}x = -\frac{c}{a}$$
Isolate the terms containing x.

$$x^2 + \frac{b}{a}x + \left(\frac{1}{2} \cdot \frac{b}{a}\right)^2 = \left(\frac{1}{2} \cdot \frac{b}{a}\right)^2 - \frac{c}{a}$$
Add the square of $\frac{1}{2}$ the linear term coefficient to both sides of the equation.

$$\left(x + \frac{b}{2a}\right)^2 = \frac{b^2}{4a^2} - \frac{c}{a}$$
Factor the left side as a perfect square.

$$\left(x + \frac{b}{2a}\right)^2 = \frac{b^2 - 4ac}{4a^2}$$
Combine fractions on the right side by getting a common denominator.

$$x + \frac{b}{2a} = \pm\sqrt{\frac{b^2 - 4ac}{4a^2}}$$
Apply the square root property.

$$x + \frac{b}{2a} = \frac{\pm\sqrt{b^2 - 4ac}}{2a}$$
Simplify the denominator.

$$x = -\frac{b}{2a} \pm \frac{\sqrt{b^2 - 4ac}}{2a}$$
Subtract $\frac{b}{2a}$ from both sides.

$$= \frac{-b \pm \sqrt{b^2 - 4ac}}{2a}$$
Combine fractions.

The solutions to the equation $ax^2 + bx + c = 0$ in terms of the coefficients a, b, and c are given by the **quadratic formula**.

> **The Quadratic Formula**
>
> For a quadratic equation of the form $ax^2 + bx + c = 0 \ (a \neq 0)$ the solutions are
>
> $$x = \frac{-b \pm \sqrt{b^2 - 4ac}}{2a}$$

TIP: When applying the quadratic formula, note that a, b, and c are constants. The variable is x.

The quadratic formula gives us another technique to solve a quadratic equation. This method will work regardless of whether the equation is factorable or not factorable.

Beginning and Intermediate Algebra

2. Solving Quadratic Equations by Using the Quadratic Formula

| Example 1 | Solving a Quadratic Equation by Using the Quadratic Formula |

Solve the quadratic equation by using the quadratic formula. $2x^2 - 3x = 5$

Solution:

$$2x^2 - 3x = 5$$

$$2x^2 - 3x - 5 = 0$$ Write the equation in the form $ax^2 + bx + c = 0$.

$$a = 2, \quad b = -3, \quad c = -5$$ Identify a, b, and c.

$$x = \frac{-b \pm \sqrt{b^2 - 4ac}}{2a}$$ Apply the quadratic formula.

$$= \frac{-(-3) \pm \sqrt{(-3)^2 - 4(2)(-5)}}{2(2)}$$ Substitute $a = 2$, $b = -3$, and $c = -5$.

$$= \frac{3 \pm \sqrt{9 + 40}}{4}$$ Simplify.

$$= \frac{3 \pm \sqrt{49}}{4}$$

$$= \frac{3 \pm 7}{4}$$

$$x = \frac{3 + 7}{4} = \frac{10}{4} = \frac{5}{2}$$

$$x = \frac{3 - 7}{4} = \frac{-4}{4} = -1$$

Avoiding Mistakes

- The term, $-b$, represents the *opposite* of b.
- Remember to write the *entire* numerator over $2a$.

The solution set is $\left\{ \frac{5}{2}, -1 \right\}$. Both solutions check in the original equation.

Skill Practice Solve the equation by using the quadratic formula.

1. $6x^2 - 5x = 4$

| Example 2 | Solving a Quadratic Equation by Using the Quadratic Formula |

Solve the quadratic equation by using the quadratic formula. $-x(x - 6) = 11$

Solution:

$$-x(x - 6) = 11$$

$$-x^2 + 6x - 11 = 0$$ Write the equation in the form $ax^2 + bx + c = 0$.

$$-1(-x^2 + 6x - 11) = -1(0)$$ If the leading coefficient of the quadratic polynomial is negative, we suggest multiplying both sides of the equation by -1. Although this is not mandatory, it is generally easier to simplify the quadratic formula when the value of a is positive.

$$x^2 - 6x + 11 = 0$$

Answer

1. $\left\{ -\frac{1}{2}, \frac{4}{3} \right\}$

$$a = 1, b = -6, \text{ and } c = 11 \qquad \text{Identify } a, b, \text{ and } c.$$

$$x = \frac{-b \pm \sqrt{b^2 - 4ac}}{2a} \qquad \text{Apply the quadratic formula.}$$

Avoiding Mistakes

When identifying a, b, and c, use the coefficients only, not the variable. For example, the value of b is -6 not $-6x$.

$$= \frac{-(-6) \pm \sqrt{(-6)^2 - 4(1)(11)}}{2(1)} \qquad \text{Substitute } a = 1, b = -6, \text{ and } c = 11.$$

$$= \frac{6 \pm \sqrt{36 - 44}}{2} \qquad \text{Simplify.}$$

$$= \frac{6 \pm \sqrt{-8}}{2}$$

Avoiding Mistakes

Always simplify the radical completely before trying to reduce the fraction to lowest terms.

$$= \frac{6 \pm 2i\sqrt{2}}{2} \qquad \text{Simplify the radical.}$$

$$= \frac{2(3 \pm i\sqrt{2})}{2} \qquad \text{Factor the numerator.}$$

$$= \frac{2(3 \pm i\sqrt{2})}{2} \qquad \text{Simplify the fraction to lowest terms.}$$

$$= 3 \pm i\sqrt{2} \quad \begin{array}{l} \longrightarrow x = 3 + i\sqrt{2} \\ \\ \longrightarrow x = 3 - i\sqrt{2} \end{array} \quad \begin{array}{l} \text{The solutions are} \\ \text{imaginary numbers.} \end{array}$$

The solution set is $\{3 \pm i\sqrt{2}\}$.

Skill Practice Solve the equation by using the quadratic formula.

  2. $-y(y + 4) = 12$

3. Using the Quadratic Formula in Applications

Example 3   **Using the Quadratic Formula in an Application**

A delivery truck travels south from Hartselle, Alabama, to Birmingham, Alabama, along Interstate 65. The truck then heads east to Atlanta, Georgia, along Interstate 20. The distance from Birmingham to Atlanta is 8 mi less than twice the distance from Hartselle to Birmingham. If the straight-line distance from Hartselle to Atlanta is 165 mi, find the distance from Hartselle to Birmingham and from Birmingham to Atlanta. (Round the answers to the nearest mile.)

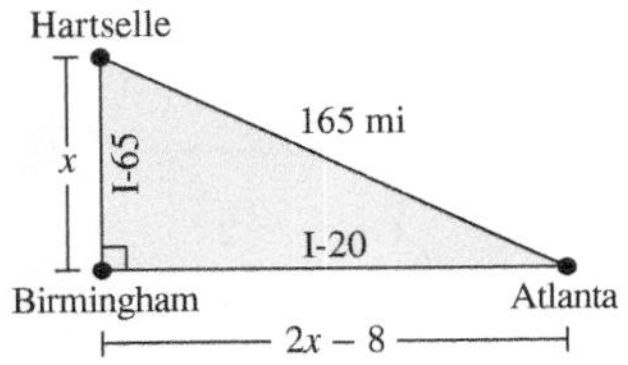

Solution:

The motorist travels due south and then due east. Therefore, the three cities form the vertices of a right triangle (Figure 11-1).

Let x represent the distance between Hartselle and Birmingham.

Then $2x - 8$ represents the distance between Birmingham and Atlanta.

Use the Pythagorean theorem to establish a relationship among the three sides of the triangle.

Figure 11-1

Answer

2. $\{-2 \pm 2i\sqrt{2}\}$

$$(x)^2 + (2x - 8)^2 = (165)^2$$

$$x^2 + 4x^2 - 32x + 64 = 27{,}225$$

$$5x^2 - 32x - 27{,}161 = 0 \qquad \text{Write the equation in the form } ax^2 + bx + c = 0.$$

$$a = 5 \qquad b = -32 \qquad c = -27{,}161 \qquad \text{Identify } a, b, \text{ and } c.$$

$$x = \frac{-(-32) \pm \sqrt{(-32)^2 - 4(5)(-27{,}161)}}{2(5)} \qquad \text{Apply the quadratic formula.}$$

$$= \frac{32 \pm \sqrt{1024 + 543{,}220}}{10} \qquad \text{Simplify.}$$

$$= \frac{32 \pm \sqrt{544{,}244}}{10}$$

$$x = \frac{32 + \sqrt{544{,}244}}{10} \approx 76.97$$

$$x = \frac{32 - \sqrt{544{,}244}}{10} \approx -70.57$$

We reject the negative solution because distance cannot be negative. Rounding to the nearest whole unit, we have $x = 77$. Therefore, $2x - 8 = 2(77) - 8 = 146$.

The distance between Hartselle and Birmingham is 77 mi, and the distance between Birmingham and Atlanta is 146 mi.

Skill Practice

3. Steve and Tammy leave a campground, hiking on two different trails. Steve heads south and Tammy heads east. By lunchtime they are 9 mi apart. Steve walked 3 mi more than twice as many miles as Tammy. Find the distance each person hiked. (Round to the nearest tenth of a mile.)

Example 4   **Analyzing a Quadratic Function**

A model rocket is launched straight upward from the side of a 144-ft cliff (Figure 11-2). The initial velocity is 112 ft/sec. The height of the rocket $h(t)$ is given by

$$h(t) = -16t^2 + 112t + 144$$

where $h(t)$ is measured in feet and t is the time in seconds after launch. Find the time(s) at which the rocket is 208 ft above the ground.

Solution:

$$h(t) = -16t^2 + 112t + 144$$

$$208 = -16t^2 + 112t + 144 \qquad \text{Substitute 208 for } h(t).$$

$$16t^2 - 112t + 64 = 0 \qquad \text{Write the equation in the form } at^2 + bt + c = 0.$$

$$\frac{16t^2}{16} - \frac{112t}{16} + \frac{64}{16} = \frac{0}{16} \qquad \text{Divide by 16. This makes the coefficients smaller, and it is less cumbersome to solve.}$$

$$t^2 - 7t + 4 = 0 \qquad \text{The equation is not factorable. Apply the quadratic formula.}$$

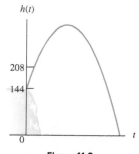

Figure 11-2

Answer

3. Tammy hiked 2.8 mi, and Steve hiked 8.6 mi.

$$t = \frac{-(-7) \pm \sqrt{(-7)^2 - 4(1)(4)}}{2(1)} \qquad \text{Let } a = 1, b = -7, \text{ and } c = 4.$$

$$= \frac{7 \pm \sqrt{33}}{2}$$

$$t = \frac{7 + \sqrt{33}}{2} \approx 6.37$$

$$t = \frac{7 - \sqrt{33}}{2} \approx 0.63$$

The rocket will reach a height of 208 ft after approximately 0.63 sec (on the way up) and after 6.37 sec (on the way down).

Skill Practice

4. A rocket is launched from the top of a 96-ft building with an initial velocity of 64 ft/sec. The height $h(t)$ of the rocket is given by $h(t) = -16t^2 + 64t + 96$. Find the time it takes for the rocket to hit the ground. [*Hint:* $h(t) = 0$ when the object hits the ground.]

4. Discriminant

The radicand within the quadratic formula is the expression $b^2 - 4ac$. This is called the **discriminant**. The discriminant can be used to determine the number of solutions to a quadratic equation as well as whether the solutions are rational, irrational, or imaginary numbers.

> ### Using the Discriminant to Determine the Number and Type of Solutions to a Quadratic Equation
>
> Consider the equation $ax^2 + bx + c = 0$, where a, b, and c are rational numbers and $a \neq 0$. The expression $b^2 - 4ac$ is called the *discriminant*. Furthermore,
>
> - If $b^2 - 4ac > 0$, then there will be two real solutions.
>   - **a.** If $b^2 - 4ac$ is a perfect square, the solutions will be rational numbers.
>   - **b.** If $b^2 - 4ac$ is not a perfect square, the solutions will be irrational numbers.
> - If $b^2 - 4ac < 0$, then there will be two imaginary solutions.
> - If $b^2 - 4ac = 0$, then there will be one rational solution.

Example 5   **Using the Discriminant**

Use the discriminant to determine the type and number of solutions for each equation.

a. $2x^2 - 5x + 9 = 0$ b. $3x^2 = -x + 2$

c. $-2x(2x - 3) = -1$ d. $3.6x^2 = -1.2x - 0.1$

Solution:

For each equation, first write the equation in standard form $ax^2 + bx + c = 0$. Then determine the discriminant.

Equation	Discriminant	Solution Type and Number
a. $2x^2 - 5x + 9 = 0$	$b^2 - 4ac$ $= (-5)^2 - 4(2)(9)$ $= 25 - 72$ $= -47$	Because $-47 < 0$, there will be two imaginary solutions.

Answer

4. $2 + \sqrt{10} \approx 5.16$ sec

b. $3x^2 = -x + 2$

$3x^2 + x - 2 = 0$

$b^2 - 4ac$
$= (1)^2 - 4(3)(-2)$
$= 1 - (-24)$
$= 25$

25 > 0 and 25 is a perfect square. There will be two rational solutions.

c. $-2x(2x - 3) = -1$

$-4x^2 + 6x = -1$

$-4x^2 + 6x + 1 = 0$

$b^2 - 4ac$
$= (6)^2 - 4(-4)(1)$
$= 36 - (-16)$
$= 52$

52 > 0, but 52 is *not* a perfect square. There will be two irrational solutions.

d. $3.6x^2 = -1.2x - 0.1$

$3.6x^2 + 1.2x + 0.1 = 0$

$b^2 - 4ac$
$= (1.2)^2 - 4(3.6)(0.1)$
$= 1.44 - 1.44$
$= 0$

Because the discriminant equals 0, there will be only one rational solution.

Skill Practice Use the discriminant to determine the type and number of solutions for the equation.

5. $3y^2 + y + 3 = 0$

6. $4t^2 = 6t - 2$

7. $3t(t + 1) = 9$

8. $\frac{2}{3}x^2 - \frac{2}{3}x + \frac{1}{6} = 0$

With the discriminant we can determine the number of real-valued solutions to the equation $ax^2 + bx + c = 0$, and thus the number of x-intercepts to the graph of $f(x) = ax^2 + bx + c$. The following illustrations show the graphical interpretation of the three cases of the discriminant.

$f(x) = x^2 - 4x + 3$

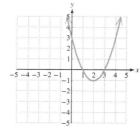

Use $x^2 - 4x + 3 = 0$ to find the value of the discriminant.

$$b^2 - 4ac = (-4)^2 - 4(1)(3)$$
$$= 4$$

Since the discriminant is positive, there are two real solutions to the quadratic equation. Therefore, there are two x-intercepts to the corresponding quadratic function, $(1, 0)$ and $(3, 0)$.

$f(x) = x^2 - x + 1$

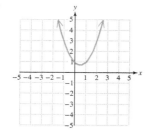

Use $x^2 - x + 1 = 0$ to find the value of the discriminant.

$$b^2 - 4ac = (-1)^2 - 4(1)(1)$$
$$= -3$$

Since the discriminant is negative, there are no real solutions to the quadratic equation. Therefore, there are no x-intercepts to the corresponding quadratic function.

Answers

5. -35; two imaginary solutions
6. 4; two rational solutions
7. 117; two irrational solutions
8. 0; one rational solution

796   **Chapter 11**   Quadratic Equations and Functions

$$f(x) = x^2 - 2x + 1$$

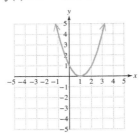

Use $x^2 - 2x + 1 = 0$ to find the value of the discriminant.

$$b^2 - 4ac = (-2)^2 - 4(1)(1)$$
$$= 0$$

Since the discriminant is zero, there is one real solution to the quadratic equation. Therefore, there is one x-intercept to the corresponding quadratic function, $(1, 0)$.

Example 6   **Finding *x*- and *y*-Intercepts of a Quadratic Function**

Given $f(x) = x^2 - 3x + 1$

a. Find the discriminant and use it to determine if there are any x-intercepts.

b. Find the x-intercept(s), if they exist.

c. Find the y-intercept.

Solution:

a. $a = 1$, $b = -3$, and $c = 1$.

The discriminant is $b^2 - 4ac = (-3)^2 - 4(1)(1)$
$$= 9 - 4$$
$$= 5$$

Since $5 > 0$, there are two x-intercepts.

TIP: Recall that an x-intercept is a point $(a, 0)$ where the graph of a function intersects the x-axis. A y-intercept is a point $(0, b)$ where the graph intersects the y-axis.

b. The x-intercepts are given by the real solutions to the equation $f(x) = 0$. In this case, we have

$$f(x) = x^2 - 3x + 1 = 0$$

$$x^2 - 3x + 1 = 0 \qquad \text{The equation is in the form } ax^2 + bx + c = 0.$$

$$x = \frac{-(-3) \pm \sqrt{(-3)^2 - (4)(1)(1)}}{2(1)} \qquad \text{Apply the quadratic formula.}$$

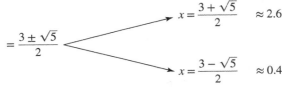

$$x = \frac{3 + \sqrt{5}}{2} \qquad \approx 2.6$$

$$= \frac{3 \pm \sqrt{5}}{2}$$

$$x = \frac{3 - \sqrt{5}}{2} \qquad \approx 0.4$$

The solutions are $\dfrac{3 + \sqrt{5}}{2}$ and $\dfrac{3 - \sqrt{5}}{2}$. Therefore, the x-intercepts are

$$\left(\frac{3 + \sqrt{5}}{2}, 0 \right) \text{ and } \left(\frac{3 - \sqrt{5}}{2}, 0 \right).$$

c. To find the y-intercept, evaluate $f(0)$.

$$f(0) = (0)^2 - 3(0) + 1 = 1$$

The y-intercept is located at $(0, 1)$.

The parabola is shown in the graph with the x- and y-intercepts labeled.

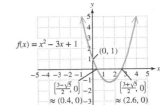

Answers

9. Discriminant: 17; there are two x-intercepts.

10. x-intercepts: $\left(\dfrac{-5 + \sqrt{17}}{2}, 0 \right)$,

$\left(\dfrac{-5 - \sqrt{17}}{2}, 0 \right)$

y-intercept: $(0, 2)$

Skill Practice   Given $f(x) = x^2 + 5x + 2$,

9. Find the discriminant and use it to determine if there are any x-intercepts.

10. Find the x- and y-intercepts.

Example 7	**Finding *x*- and *y*-Intercepts of a Quadratic Function**

Given $f(x) = x^2 + x + 2$

a. Find the discriminant and use it to determine if there are any *x*-intercepts.

b. Find the *x*-intercept(s), if they exist.

c. Find the *y*-intercept.

Solution:

a. $a = 1$, $b = 1$, and $c = 2$.

The discriminant is $b^2 - 4ac = (1)^2 - 4(1)(2)$

$$= 1 - 8$$

$$= -7$$

Since $-7 < 0$, there are no *x*-intercepts.

b. There are no *x*-intercepts.

c. $f(0) = (0)^2 + (0) + 2$

$$= 2$$

The *y*-intercept is located at $(0, 2)$.

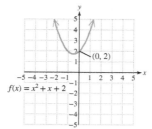

The parabola is shown. *Note:* The graph does not intersect the *x*-axis.

Skill Practice Given $f(x) = 2x^2 - 3x + 5$,

11. Find the discriminant and use it to determine if there are any *x*-intercepts.

12. Find the *y*-intercept.

---

5. Mixed Review: Methods to Solve a Quadratic Equation

Three methods have been presented to solve quadratic equations.

Methods to Solve a Quadratic Equation

Factor and use the zero product rule. • This method works well if you can factor the equation easily.	Example: $x^2 + 8x + 15 = 0$ factors as $(x + 3)(x + 5) = 0$
Use the square root property. Complete the square if necessary. This method is particularly good if • the equation is of the form $ax^2 + c = 0$ or • the equation is of the form $x^2 + bx + c = 0$, where *b* is even.	Examples: $4x^2 + 9 = 0$ $x^2 + 10x - 3 = 0$
Quadratic Formula • This method works in all cases—just be sure to write the equation in the form $ax^2 + bx + c = 0$ before applying the formula.	Example: $7x^2 - 3x + 11 = 0$

Answers

11. Discriminant: -31; there are no *x*-intercepts.

12. $(0, 5)$

Before solving a quadratic equation, take a minute to analyze it first. Each problem must be evaluated individually before choosing the most efficient method to find its solutions.

| Example 8 | **Solving a Quadratic Equation by Using Any Method** |

Solve the equation by using any method. $(x + 3)^2 + x^2 - 9x = 8$

Solution:

$$(x + 3)^2 + x^2 - 9x = 8$$

$$x^2 + 6x + 9 + x^2 - 9x - 8 = 0 \qquad \text{Clear parentheses and write the equation in the form } ax^2 + bx + c = 0.$$

$$2x^2 - 3x + 1 = 0 \qquad \text{This equation is factorable.}$$

$$(2x - 1)(x - 1) = 0 \qquad \text{Factor.}$$

$$2x - 1 = 0 \quad \text{or} \quad x - 1 = 0 \qquad \text{Apply the zero product rule.}$$

$$x = \tfrac{1}{2} \quad \text{or} \quad x = 1 \qquad \text{Solve for } x.$$

The solution set is $\{\tfrac{1}{2}, 1\}$.

This equation could have been solved by using any of the three methods, but factoring was the most efficient method.

Skill Practice Solve using any method.

13. $2t(t - 1) + t^2 = 5$

| Example 9 | **Solving a Quadratic Equation by Using Any Method** |

Solve the equation by using any method. $x^2 + 5 = -2x$

Solution:

$$x^2 + 2x + 5 = 0 \qquad \text{The equation does not factor.}$$

$$x^2 + 2x = -5 \qquad \text{Because } a = 1 \text{ and } b \text{ is even, we can easily complete the square.}$$

$$x^2 + 2x + 1 = -5 + 1 \qquad \text{Add } \left[\tfrac{1}{2}(2)\right]^2 = 1^2 = 1 \text{ to both sides.}$$

$$(x + 1)^2 = -4$$

$$x + 1 = \pm\sqrt{-4} \qquad \text{Apply the square root property.}$$

$$x = -1 \pm 2i \qquad \text{Solve for } x.$$

The solution set is $\{-1 \pm 2i\}$.

This equation could also have been solved by using the quadratic formula.

Skill Practice Solve using any method.

14. $x^2 - 4x = -7$

Answers

13. $\left\{-1, \tfrac{5}{3}\right\}$

14. $\{2 \pm i\sqrt{3}\}$

Example 10   Solving a Quadratic Equation by Using Any Method

Solve the equation by using any method. $\dfrac{1}{4}x^2 - \dfrac{1}{2}x + \dfrac{1}{3} = 0$

Solution:

$12 \cdot \left(\dfrac{1}{4}x^2 - \dfrac{1}{2}x + \dfrac{1}{3}\right) = 12 \cdot (0)$ Clear fractions.

$3x^2 - 6x + 4 = 0$ The equation is in the form $ax^2 + bx + c = 0$.
The left-hand side does not factor.

$a = 3, b = -6,$ and $c = 4$

$x = \dfrac{-(-6) \pm \sqrt{(-6)^2 - 4(3)(4)}}{2(3)}$ Apply the quadratic formula.

$= \dfrac{6 \pm \sqrt{-12}}{6}$ Simplify.

$= \dfrac{6 \pm 2i\sqrt{3}}{6}$ Simplify the radical.

$= \dfrac{\overset{1}{2}(3 \pm i\sqrt{3})}{\underset{3}{6}}$ Factor and simplify.

$= \dfrac{3 \pm i\sqrt{3}}{3}$

$= \dfrac{3}{3} \pm \dfrac{\sqrt{3}}{3}i$ Write in the form $a \pm bi$.

$= 1 \pm \dfrac{\sqrt{3}}{3}i$ Simplify.

The solution set is $\left\{1 \pm \dfrac{\sqrt{3}}{3}i\right\}$.

Skill Practice Solve using any method.

15. $\dfrac{1}{5}x^2 - \dfrac{4}{5}x + \dfrac{1}{2} = 0$

Answer

15. $\left\{\dfrac{4 \pm \sqrt{6}}{2}\right\}$

Example 11	Solving a Quadratic Equation by Using Any Method

Solve the equation by using any method. $9p^2 - 11 = 0$

Solution:

$$9p^2 - 11 = 0 \qquad \text{Because } b = 0, \text{ use the square root property.}$$

$$9p^2 = 11 \qquad \text{Isolate the variable term.}$$

$$p^2 = \frac{11}{9} \qquad \text{The equation is in the form } x^2 = k.$$

$$p = \pm\sqrt{\frac{11}{9}} \qquad \text{Apply the square root property.}$$

$$p = \pm\frac{\sqrt{11}}{3} \qquad \text{Simplify the radical.}$$

The solution set is $\left\{ \pm\dfrac{\sqrt{11}}{3} \right\}$.

Answer

16. $\left\{ \pm\dfrac{\sqrt{13}}{2} \right\}$

Skill Practice Solve using any method.

16. $4y^2 - 13 = 0$

Section 11.2 Practice Exercises

Vocabulary and Key Concepts

1. **a.** For the equation $ax^2 + bx + c = 0$ $(a \neq 0)$, the _____ formula gives the solutions as $x =$ _____.

    b. To apply the quadratic formula, a quadratic equation must be written in the form _____ where $a \neq 0$.

    c. To apply the quadratic formula to solve the equation $8x^2 - 42x - 27 = 0$, the value of a is _____, the value of b is _____, and the value of c is _____.

    d. To apply the quadratic formula to solve the equation $3x^2 - 7x - 4 = 0$, the value of $-b$ is _____ and the value of the radicand is _____.

    e. The radicand within the quadratic formula is _____ and is called the _____.

    f. If the discriminant is negative, then the solutions to a quadratic equation will be (real/imaginary) numbers.

    g. If the discriminant is positive, then the solutions to a quadratic equation will be (real/imaginary) numbers.

    h. Given a quadratic function $f(x) = ax^2 + bx + c = 0$, the function will have no x-intercepts if the discriminant is (less than, greater than, equal to) zero.

Review Exercises

2. Use substitution to determine if $x = -3 + \sqrt{5}$ is a solution to $x^2 + 6x + 4 = 0$.

For Exercises 3–6, simplify the expression.

3. $\dfrac{16 - \sqrt{320}}{4}$

4. $\dfrac{18 + \sqrt{180}}{3}$

5. $\dfrac{14 - \sqrt{-147}}{7}$

6. $\dfrac{10 - \sqrt{-175}}{5}$

Concept 2: Solving Quadratic Equations by Using the Quadratic Formula

For Exercises 7–8, determine whether the equation is linear or quadratic.

7. $2(x - 5) + x^2 = 3x(x - 4) - 2x^2$

8. $5x(x + 3) - 9 = 4x^2 - 3(x + 1)$

For Exercises 9–34, solve the equation by using the quadratic formula. Write imaginary solutions in the form $a + bi$.
(See Examples 1–2.)

9. $x^2 + 11x - 12 = 0$

10. $5x^2 - 14x - 3 = 0$

11. $9y^2 - 2y + 5 = 0$

12. $2t^2 + 3t - 7 = 0$

13. $12p^2 - 4p + 5 = 0$

14. $-5n^2 + 4n - 6 = 0$

15. $-z^2 = -2z - 35$

16. $12x^2 - 5x = 2$

17. $y^2 + 3y = 8$

18. $k^2 + 4 = 6k$

19. $25x^2 - 20x + 4 = 0$

20. $9y^2 = -12y - 4$

21. $w(w - 6) = -14$

22. $m(m + 6) = -11$

23. $(x + 2)(x - 3) = 1$

24. $3y(y + 1) - 7y(y + 2) = 6$

25. $-4a^2 - 2a + 3 = 0$

26. $-2m^2 - 5m + 3 = 0$

27. $\frac{1}{2}y^2 + \frac{2}{3} = -\frac{2}{3}y$
(*Hint:* Clear fractions first.)

28. $\frac{2}{3}p^2 - \frac{1}{6}p + \frac{1}{2} = 0$

29. $\frac{1}{5}h^2 + h + \frac{3}{5} = 0$

30. $\frac{1}{4}w^2 + \frac{7}{4}w + 1 = 0$

31. $0.01x^2 + 0.06x + 0.08 = 0$
(*Hint:* Clear decimals first.)

32. $0.5y^2 - 0.7y + 0.2 = 0$

33. $0.3t^2 + 0.7t - 0.5 = 0$

34. $0.01x^2 + 0.04x - 0.07 = 0$

For Exercises 35–38, factor the expression. Then use the zero product rule and the quadratic formula to solve the equation. There should be three solutions to each equation. Write imaginary solutions in the form $a + bi$.

35. a. Factor. $x^3 - 27$

    b. Solve. $x^3 - 27 = 0$

36. a. Factor. $64x^3 + 1$

    b. Solve. $64x^3 + 1 = 0$

37. a. Factor. $3x^3 - 6x^2 + 6x$

    b. Solve. $3x^3 - 6x^2 + 6x = 0$

38. a. Factor. $5x^3 + 5x^2 + 10x$

    b. Solve. $5x^3 + 5x^2 + 10x = 0$

Concept 3: Using the Quadratic Formula in Applications

39. The volume of a cube is 27 ft³. Find the lengths of the sides.

40. The volume of a rectangular box is 64 ft³. If the width is 3 times longer than the height, and the length is 9 times longer than the height, find the dimensions of the box.

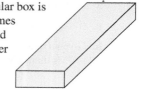

41. The hypotenuse of a right triangle measures 4 in. One leg of the triangle is 2 in. longer than the other leg. Find the lengths of the legs of the triangle. Round to one decimal place. **(See Example 3.)**

42. The length of one leg of a right triangle is 1 cm more than twice the length of the other leg. The hypotenuse measures 6 cm. Find the lengths of the legs. Round to one decimal place.

43. The hypotenuse of a right triangle is 10.2 m long. One leg is 2.1 m shorter than the other leg. Find the lengths of the legs. Round to one decimal place.

44. The hypotenuse of a right triangle is 17 ft long. One leg is 3.4 ft longer than the other leg. Find the lengths of the legs.

45. The fatality rate (in fatalities per 100 million vehicle miles driven) can be approximated for drivers x years old according to the function, $F(x) = 0.0036x^2 - 0.35x + 9.2$. (*Source:* U.S. Department of Transportation)

    a. Approximate the fatality rate for drivers 16 yr old.

    b. Approximate the fatality rate for drivers 40 yr old.

    c. Approximate the fatality rate for drivers 80 yr old.

    d. For what age(s) is the fatality rate approximately 2.5?

46. The braking distance (in feet) of a car going v mph is given by

$$d(v) = \frac{v^2}{20} + v \qquad v \geq 0$$

    a. Find the speed for a braking distance of 150 ft. Round to the nearest mile per hour.

    b. Find the speed for a braking distance of 100 ft. Round to the nearest mile per hour.

47. Mitch throws a baseball straight up in the air from a cliff that is 48 ft high. The initial velocity is 48 ft/sec. The height (in feet) of the object after t sec is given by $h(t) = -16t^2 + 48t + 48$. Find the time at which the height of the object is 64 ft. **(See Example 4.)**

48. An astronaut on the moon throws a rock into the air from the deck of a spacecraft that is 8 m high. The initial velocity of the rock is 2.4 m/sec. The height (in meters) of the rock after t sec is given by $h(t) = -0.8t^2 + 2.4t + 8$. Find the time at which the height of the rock is 6 m.

Concept 4: Discriminant

For Exercises 49–56,

    a. Write the equation in the form $ax^2 + bx + c = 0, a > 0$.

    b. Find the value of the discriminant.

    c. Use the discriminant to determine the number and type of solutions. Choose from imaginary, rational, and irrational. **(See Example 5.)**

49. $x^2 + 2x = -1$

50. $12y - 9 = 4y^2$

 51. $19m^2 = 8m$

52. $2n - 5n^2 = 0$

53. $5p^2 - 21 = 0$

54. $3k^2 = 7$

55. $4n(n-2) - 5n(n-1) = 4$

56. $(2x+1)(x-3) = -9$

For Exercises 57–62, determine the discriminant. Then use the discriminant to determine the number of x-intercepts for the function.

57. $f(x) = x^2 - 6x + 5$

58. $g(x) = -x^2 - 4x - 3$

59. $h(x) = 4x^2 + 12x + 9$

60. $k(x) = 25x^2 - 10x + 1$

61. $p(x) = 2x^2 + 3x + 6$

62. $m(x) = 3x^2 + 4x + 7$

For Exercises 63–68, find the x- and y-intercepts of the quadratic function. **(See Examples 6–7.)**

63. $f(x) = x^2 - 5x + 3$

64. $g(x) = 2x^2 + 7x + 2$

65. $g(x) = -x^2 + x - 1$

66. $f(x) = 2x^2 + x + 5$

67. $p(x) = 2x^2 + 5x - 2$

68. $h(x) = 3x^2 + 2x - 2$

Concept 5: Mixed Review: Methods to Solve a Quadratic Equation

For Exercises 69–86, solve the quadratic equation by using any method. Write imaginary solutions in the form $a + bi$.
(See Examples 8–11.)

69. $a^2 + 2a + 10 = 0$

70. $4z^2 + 7z = 0$

71. $(x - 2)^2 + 2x^2 - 13x = 10$

72. $(x - 3)^2 + 3x^2 - 5x = 12$

73. $4y^2 - 20y + 43 = 0$

74. $k^2 + 18 = 4k$

75. $\left(x + \dfrac{1}{2}\right)^2 + 4 = 0$

76. $(2y + 3)^2 = 9$

77. $2y(y - 3) = -1$

78. $w(w - 5) = 4$

79. $(2t + 5)(t - 1) = (t - 3)(t + 8)$

80. $(b - 1)(b + 4) = (3b + 2)(b + 1)$

81. $\dfrac{1}{8}x^2 - \dfrac{1}{2}x + \dfrac{1}{4} = 0$

82. $\dfrac{1}{6}x^2 - \dfrac{1}{2}x + \dfrac{1}{4} = 0$

83. $32z^2 - 20z - 3 = 0$

84. $8k^2 - 14k + 3 = 0$

85. $4p^2 - 21 = 0$

86. $5h^2 - 120 = 0$

Sometimes students shy away from completing the square and using the square root property to solve a quadratic equation. However, sometimes this process leads to a simple solution. For Exercises 87–88, solve the equations two ways.

  a. Solve the equation by completing the square and applying the square root property.

  b. Solve the equation by applying the quadratic formula.

  c. Which technique was easier for you?

87. $x^2 + 6x = 5$

88. $x^2 - 10x = -27$

Graphing Calculator Exercises

89. Graph $Y_1 = x^3 - 27$. Compare the x-intercepts with the solutions to the equation $x^3 - 27 = 0$ found in Exercise 35.

90. Graph $Y_1 = 64x^3 + 1$. Compare the x-intercepts with the solutions to the equation $64x^3 + 1 = 0$ found in Exercise 36.

91. Graph $Y_1 = 3x^3 - 6x^2 + 6x$. Compare the x-intercepts with the solutions to the equation $3x^3 - 6x^2 + 6x = 0$ found in Exercise 37.

92. Graph $Y_1 = 5x^3 + 5x^2 + 10x$. Compare the x-intercepts with the solutions to the equation $5x^3 + 5x^2 + 10x = 0$ found in Exercise 38.

Section 11.3   Equations in Quadratic Form

Concepts

1. Solving Equations by Using Substitution
2. Solving Equations Reducible to a Quadratic

1. Solving Equations by Using Substitution

We have learned to solve a variety of different types of equations, including linear, radical, rational, and polynomial equations. Sometimes, however, it is necessary to use a quadratic equation as a tool to solve other types of equations.

In Example 1, we will solve the equation $(2x^2 - 5)^2 - 16(2x^2 - 5) + 39 = 0$. Notice that the terms in the equation are written in descending order by degree. Furthermore, the first two terms have the same base, $2x^2 - 5$, and the exponent on the first term is exactly double the exponent on the second term. The third term is a constant. An equation in this pattern is called **quadratic in form**.

$$\overset{\text{exponent is double}}{\overbrace{\qquad}} \quad \overset{\text{third term is constant}}{\downarrow}$$

$$(2x^2 - 5)^2 - 16(2x^2 - 5)^1 + 39 = 0.$$

To solve this equation we will use substitution as demonstrated in Example 1.

Example 1   Solving an Equation in Quadratic Form

Solve the equation. $(2x^2 - 5)^2 - 16(2x^2 - 5) + 39 = 0$

Solution:

$(2x^2 - 5)^2 - 16(2x^2 - 5) + 39 = 0$ Once the substitution is made, the equation becomes quadratic in the variable u.

Substitute $u = (2x^2 - 5)$.

$u^2 - 16u + 39 = 0$ The equation is in the form $au^2 + bu + c = 0$.

$(u - 13)(u - 3) = 0$ Factor.

$u = 13$ or $u = 3$ Apply the zero product rule.

Reverse substitute.

$2x^2 - 5 = 13$ or $2x^2 - 5 = 3$ Reverse substitute.

$2x^2 = 18$ or $2x^2 = 8$

$x^2 = 9$ or $x^2 = 4$ Write the equations in the form $x^2 = k$.

$x = \pm\sqrt{9}$ or $x = \pm\sqrt{4}$ Apply the square root property.

$= \pm 3$ or $= \pm 2$

The solution set is $\{3, -3, 2, -2\}$.   All solutions check in the original equation.

Avoiding Mistakes

When using substitution, it is critical to reverse substitute to solve the equation in terms of the original variable.

Skill Practice   Solve the equation.

1. $(3t^2 - 10)^2 + 5(3t^2 - 10) - 14 = 0$

Answer

1. $\{1, -1, 2, -2\}$

For an equation written in descending order, notice that u was set equal to the variable factor on the middle term. This is generally the case.

Example 2 **Solving an Equation in Quadratic Form**

Solve the equation. $\quad p^{2/3} - 2p^{1/3} = 8$

Solution:

$$p^{2/3} - 2p^{1/3} = 8$$

$$p^{2/3} - 2p^{1/3} - 8 = 0 \qquad\qquad \text{Set the equation equal to zero.}$$

$$(p^{1/3})^2 - 2(p^{1/3})^1 - 8 = 0 \qquad\qquad \text{Make the substitution } u = p^{1/3}.$$

Substitute $u = p^{1/3}$.

$$u^2 \quad - \quad 2u \quad - \; 8 = 0 \qquad\qquad \begin{array}{l}\text{Then the equation is in the form}\\ au^2 + bu + c = 0.\end{array}$$

$$(u - 4)(u + 2) = 0 \qquad\qquad \text{Factor.}$$

$$u = 4 \qquad\text{or}\qquad u = -2 \qquad\qquad \text{Apply the zero product rule.}$$

Reverse substitute.

$$p^{1/3} = 4 \qquad\text{or}\qquad p^{1/3} = -2$$

$$\sqrt[3]{p} = 4 \qquad\text{or}\qquad \sqrt[3]{p} = -2 \qquad\qquad \begin{array}{l}\text{The equations are radical}\\ \text{equations.}\end{array}$$

$$(\sqrt[3]{p})^3 = (4)^3 \qquad\text{or}\qquad (\sqrt[3]{p})^3 = (-2)^3 \qquad\qquad \text{Cube both sides.}$$

$$p = 64 \qquad\text{or}\qquad p = -8$$

The solution set is $\{64, -8\}$. $\qquad\qquad\qquad\qquad \begin{array}{l}\text{All solutions check in the}\\ \text{original equation.}\end{array}$

Skill Practice Solve the equation.

2. $y^{2/3} - y^{1/3} = 12$

Example 3 **Solving an Equation in Quadratic Form**

Solve the equation. $\quad x - \sqrt{x} - 12 = 0$

Solution:

The equation can be solved by first isolating the radical and then squaring both sides (this is left as an exercise—see Exercise 25). However, this equation is also quadratic in form. By writing $\sqrt{x}$ as $x^{1/2}$, we see that the exponent on the first term is exactly double the exponent on the middle term.

$$x^1 - x^{1/2} - 12 = 0$$

$$(x^{1/2})^2 - (x^{1/2})^1 - 12 = 0 \qquad\qquad \text{Let } u = x^{1/2}.$$

$$u^2 - u - 12 = 0$$

$$(u - 4)(u + 3) = 0 \qquad\qquad \text{Factor.}$$

$$u = 4 \;\text{ or }\; u = -3 \qquad\qquad \text{Solve for } u.$$

$$x^{1/2} = 4 \;\text{ or }\; x^{1/2} = -3 \qquad\qquad \text{Reverse substitute.}$$

Answer

2. $\{64, -27\}$

806   **Chapter 11**   Quadratic Equations and Functions

$\sqrt{x} = 4$ or $\sqrt{x} = -3$ Solve each equation for x. Recall that the
                                          principal square root of a number cannot be
$\quad\quad x = 16$ negative.

The solution set is $\{16\}$.   The value 16 checks in the original equation.

Skill Practice Solve the equation.

3. $z - \sqrt{z} - 2 = 0$

2. Solving Equations Reducible to a Quadratic

Some equations are reducible to a quadratic equation. In Example 4, we solve a polynomial
equation by factoring. The resulting factors are quadratic.

Example 4   **Solving a Polynomial Equation**

Solve the equation. $4x^4 + 7x^2 - 2 = 0$

Solution:

$\quad\quad 4x^4 + 7x^2 - 2 = 0$ This is a polynomial equation.

$\quad\quad (4x^2 - 1)(x^2 + 2) = 0$ Factor.

$4x^2 - 1 = 0$ or $x^2 + 2 = 0$ Set each factor equal to zero. Notice
                                          that the two equations are quadratic.
$\quad\quad x^2 = \dfrac{1}{4}$ or $x^2 = -2$ Each can be solved by the square
                                          root property.

$\quad\quad x = \pm\sqrt{\dfrac{1}{4}}$ or $x = \pm\sqrt{-2}$ Apply the square root property.

$\quad\quad x = \pm\dfrac{1}{2}$ or $x = \pm i\sqrt{2}$ Simplify the radicals.

The solution set is $\left\{\dfrac{1}{2}, -\dfrac{1}{2}, i\sqrt{2}, -i\sqrt{2}\right\}$.

Skill Practice Solve the equation.

4. $9x^4 + 35x^2 - 4 = 0$

Example 5   **Solving a Rational Equation**

Solve the equation. $\dfrac{3y}{y+2} - \dfrac{2}{y-1} = 1$

Solution:

$\dfrac{3y}{y+2} - \dfrac{2}{y-1} = 1$ This is a rational equation. The LCD is $(y+2)(y-1)$.
                                              Also note that the restrictions on y are $y \neq -2$ and $y \neq 1$.

$\left(\dfrac{3y}{y+2} - \dfrac{2}{y-1}\right) \cdot (y+2)(y-1) = 1 \cdot (y+2)(y-1)$ Multiply both sides
                                                                                             by the LCD.

$\dfrac{3y}{y+2} \cdot (y+2)(y-1) - \dfrac{2}{y-1} \cdot (y+2)(y-1) = 1 \cdot (y+2)(y-1)$

Answers

3. $\{4\}$ (The value 1 does not check.)

4. $\left\{\pm\dfrac{1}{3}, \pm 2i\right\}$

$3y(y-1) - 2(y+2) = (y+2)(y-1)$	Clear fractions.
$3y^2 - 3y - 2y - 4 = y^2 - y + 2y - 2$	Apply the distributive property.
$3y^2 - 5y - 4 = y^2 + y - 2$	The equation is quadratic.
$2y^2 - 6y - 2 = 0$	Write the equation in descending order.

$$\frac{2y^2}{2} - \frac{6y}{2} - \frac{2}{2} = \frac{0}{2}$$

$$y^2 - 3y - 1 = 0$$

Each coefficient in the equation is divisible by 2. Therefore, if we divide both sides by 2, the coefficients in the equation are smaller. This will make it easier to apply the quadratic formula.

$$y = \frac{-(-3) \pm \sqrt{(-3)^2 - 4(1)(-1)}}{2(1)}$$ Apply the quadratic formula.

$$= \frac{3 \pm \sqrt{9+4}}{2}$$

$$= \frac{3 \pm \sqrt{13}}{2} \begin{cases} y = \dfrac{3 + \sqrt{13}}{2} \\ y = \dfrac{3 - \sqrt{13}}{2} \end{cases}$$

The solution set is $\left\{ \dfrac{3 + \sqrt{13}}{2}, \dfrac{3 - \sqrt{13}}{2} \right\}$.

Skill Practice Solve the equation.

5. $\dfrac{t}{2t-1} - \dfrac{1}{t+4} = 1$

Answer

5. $\left\{ \dfrac{-5 \pm 3\sqrt{5}}{2} \right\}$

Section 11.3   Practice Exercises

Vocabulary and Key Concepts

1. **a.** An equation that can be written in the form $au^2 + bu + c = 0$ where u represents an algebraic expression is said to be in _____ form.

  b. To use the method of substitution to solve the equation $(3x-1)^2 + 2(3x-1) - 8 = 0$, let $u = $ _____.

  c. To use the method of substitution to solve the equation $p^{2/3} - 2p^{1/3} - 15 = 0$, let $u = $ _____.

Review Exercises

For Exercises 2–7, solve the quadratic equations.

2. $16 = (2x-3)^2$

3. $\left(x - \dfrac{3}{2}\right)^2 = \dfrac{7}{4}$

4. $n(n-6) = -13$

5. $x(x+8) = -16$

6. $6k^2 + 7k = 6$

7. $2x^2 - 8x - 44 = 0$

Concept 1: Solving Equations by Using Substitution

8. **a.** Solve the quadratic equation by factoring. $u^2 - 2u - 24 = 0$

  b. Solve the equation by using substitution. $(x-5)^2 - 2(x-5) - 24 = 0$

9. a. Solve the quadratic equation by factoring. $u^2 + 10u + 24 = 0$

    b. Solve the equation by using substitution. $(y^2 + 5y)^2 + 10(y^2 + 5y) + 24 = 0$

10. a. Solve the quadratic equation by factoring. $u^2 - 2u - 35 = 0$

    b. Solve the equation by using substitution. $(w^2 - 6w)^2 - 2(w^2 - 6w) - 35 = 0$

For Exercises 11–24, solve the equation by using substitution. **(See Examples 1–3.)**

11. $(x^2 - 2x)^2 + 2(x^2 - 2x) = 3$ **12.** $(x^2 + x)^2 - 8(x^2 + x) = -12$

13. $(y^2 - 4y)^2 - (y^2 - 4y) = 20$ **14.** $(w^2 - 2w)^2 - 11(w^2 - 2w) = -24$

15. $m^{2/3} - m^{1/3} - 6 = 0$ **16.** $2n^{2/3} + 7n^{1/3} - 15 = 0$

17. $2t^{2/5} + 7t^{1/5} + 3 = 0$ **18.** $p^{2/5} + p^{1/5} - 2 = 0$

19. $y + 6\sqrt{y} = 16$ **20.** $p - 8\sqrt{p} = -15$

21. $2x + 3\sqrt{x} - 2 = 0$ **22.** $3t + 5\sqrt{t} - 2 = 0$

23. $16\left(\dfrac{x+6}{4}\right)^2 + 8\left(\dfrac{x+6}{4}\right) + 1 = 0$ **24.** $9\left(\dfrac{x+3}{2}\right)^2 - 6\left(\dfrac{x+3}{2}\right) + 1 = 0$

25. In Example 3, we solved the equation $x - \sqrt{x} - 12 = 0$ by using substitution. Now solve this equation by first isolating the radical and then squaring both sides. Don't forget to check the potential solutions in the original equation. Do you obtain the same solution as in Example 3?

Concept 2: Solving Equations Reducible to a Quadratic

For Exercises 26–36, solve the equations. **(See Examples 4–5.)**

26. $t^4 + t^2 - 12 = 0$ **27.** $w^4 + 4w^2 - 45 = 0$ **28.** $x^2(9x^2 + 7) = 2$

29. $y^2(4y^2 + 17) = 15$ **30.** $\dfrac{y}{10} - 1 = -\dfrac{12}{5y}$ **31.** $1 + \dfrac{5}{x} = -\dfrac{3}{x^2}$

32. $\dfrac{x+5}{x} + \dfrac{x}{2} = \dfrac{x+19}{4x}$ **33.** $\dfrac{3x}{x+1} - \dfrac{2}{x-3} = 1$ **34.** $\dfrac{2t}{t-3} - \dfrac{1}{t+4} = 1$

35. $\dfrac{x}{2x-1} = \dfrac{1}{x-2}$ **36.** $\dfrac{z}{3z+2} = \dfrac{2}{z+1}$

Mixed Exercises

For Exercises 37–60, solve the equations.

37. $x^4 - 16 = 0$ **38.** $t^4 - 625 = 0$ **39.** $(4x + 5)^2 + 3(4x + 5) + 2 = 0$

40. $2(5x + 3)^2 - (5x + 3) - 28 = 0$ **41.** $4m^4 - 9m^2 + 2 = 0$ **42.** $x^4 - 7x^2 + 12 = 0$

43. $x^6 - 9x^3 + 8 = 0$ **44.** $x^6 - 26x^3 - 27 = 0$ **45.** $\sqrt{x^2 + 20} = 3\sqrt{x}$

46. $\sqrt{x^2 + 60} = 4\sqrt{x}$ **47.** $\sqrt{4t + 1} = t + 1$ **48.** $\sqrt{t + 10} = t + 4$

49. $2\left(\dfrac{t-4}{3}\right)^2 - \left(\dfrac{t-4}{3}\right) - 3 = 0$

50. $\left(\dfrac{x+1}{5}\right)^2 - 3\left(\dfrac{x+1}{5}\right) - 10 = 0$

51. $x^{2/3} + x^{1/3} = 20$

52. $x^{2/5} - 3x^{1/5} = -2$

53. $m^4 + 2m^2 - 8 = 0$

54. $2c^4 + c^2 - 1 = 0$

55. $a^3 + 16a - a^2 - 16 = 0$
(*Hint:* Factor by grouping first.)

56. $b^3 + 9b - b^2 - 9 = 0$

57. $x^3 + 5x - 4x^2 - 20 = 0$

58. $y^3 + 8y - 3y^2 - 24 = 0$

59. $\left(\dfrac{2}{x-3}\right)^2 + 8\left(\dfrac{2}{x-3}\right) + 12 = 0$

60. $\left(\dfrac{5}{x+1}\right)^2 - 6\left(\dfrac{5}{x+1}\right) - 16 = 0$

Graphing Calculator Exercises

61. a. Solve the equation $x^4 + 4x^2 + 4 = 0$.

  b. How many solutions are real and how many solutions are imaginary?

  c. How many x-intercepts do you anticipate for the function defined by $y = x^4 + 4x^2 + 4$?

  d. Graph $Y_1 = x^4 + 4x^2 + 4$ on a standard viewing window.

62. a. Solve the equation $x^4 - 2x^2 + 1 = 0$.

  b. How many solutions are real and how many solutions are imaginary?

  c. How many x-intercepts do you anticipate for the function defined by $y = x^4 - 2x^2 + 1$?

  d. Graph $Y_1 = x^4 - 2x^2 + 1$ on a standard viewing window.

63. a. Solve the equation $x^4 - x^3 - 6x^2 = 0$.

  b. How many solutions are real and how many solutions are imaginary?

  c. How many x-intercepts do you anticipate for the function defined by $y = x^4 - x^3 - 6x^2$?

  d. Graph $Y_1 = x^4 - x^3 - 6x^2$ on a standard viewing window.

64. a. Solve the equation $x^4 - 10x^2 + 9 = 0$.

  b. How many solutions are real and how many solutions are imaginary?

  c. How many x-intercepts do you anticipate for the function defined by $y = x^4 - 10x^2 + 9$?

  d. Graph $Y_1 = x^4 - 10x^2 + 9$ on a standard viewing window.

Problem Recognition Exercises

Quadratic and Quadratic Type Equations

For Exercises 1–4, solve each equation by

a. Completing the square and applying the square root property.

b. Using the quadratic formula.

1. $x^2 + 10x + 3 = 0$ **2.** $v^2 - 16v + 5 = 0$ **3.** $3t^2 + t + 4 = 0$ **4.** $4y^2 + 3y + 5 = 0$

In Exercises 5–24, we have presented all types of equations that you have learned up to this point. For each equation,

a. First determine the type of equation that is presented. Choose from: linear equation, quadratic equation, quadratic in form, rational equation, or radical equation.

b. Solve the equation by using a suitable method.

5. $t^2 + 5t - 14 = 0$

6. $a^2 - 9a + 20 = 0$

7. $a^4 - 10a^2 + 9 = 0$

8. $x^4 - 3x^2 - 4 = 0$

9. $x - 3x^{1/2} - 4 = 0$

10. $x^2 - 9x - 2 = 0$

11. $8b(b + 1) + 2(3b - 4) = 4b(2b + 3)$

12. $6x(x + 1) - 3(x + 4) = 3x(2x + 5)$

13. $5a(a + 6) = 10(3a - 1)$

14. $4x(x + 3) = 6(2x - 4)$

15. $\dfrac{t}{t + 5} + \dfrac{3}{t - 4} = \dfrac{17}{t^2 + t - 20}$

16. $\dfrac{v}{v + 4} + \dfrac{12}{v^2 + 7v + 12} = \dfrac{5}{v + 3}$

17. $c^2 - 20c - 1 = 0$

18. $d^2 + 18d + 4 = 0$

19. $2u(u - 3) = 4(2 - u)$

20. $3y(y + 2) = 9(y + 1)$

21. $\sqrt{2b + 3} = b$

22. $\sqrt{5t + 6} = t$

23. $x^{2/3} + 2x^{1/3} - 15 = 0$

24. $y^{2/3} + 5y^{1/3} + 4 = 0$

Section 11.4	**Graphs of Quadratic Functions**

Concepts

1. Quadratic Functions of the Form $f(x) = x^2 + k$
2. Quadratic Functions of the Form $f(x) = (x - h)^2$
3. Quadratic Functions of the Form $f(x) = ax^2$
4. Quadratic Functions of the Form $f(x) = a(x - h)^2 + k$

A quadratic function is defined as a function of the form $f(x) = ax^2 + bx + c$ $(a \neq 0)$. The graph of a quadratic function is a **parabola**. In this section, we will learn how to graph parabolas.

A parabola opens upward if $a > 0$ (Figure 11-3) and opens downward if $a < 0$ (Figure 11-4). If a parabola opens upward, the **vertex** is the lowest point on the graph. If a parabola opens downward, the **vertex** is the highest point on the graph. The **axis of symmetry** is the vertical line that passes through the vertex.

$a > 0$

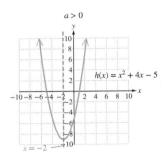

$h(x) = x^2 + 4x - 5$

$x = -2$

Figure 11-3

$a < 0$

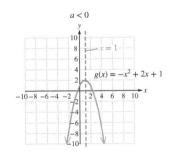

$x = 1$

$g(x) = -x^2 + 2x + 1$

Figure 11-4

1. Quadratic Functions of the Form $f(x) = x^2 + k$

One technique for graphing a function is to plot a sufficient number of points on the graph until the general shape and defining characteristics can be determined. Then sketch a curve through the points.

Example 1   **Graphing Quadratic Functions of the Form $f(x) = x^2 + k$**

Graph the functions f, g, and h on the same coordinate system.

$$f(x) = x^2 \qquad g(x) = x^2 + 1 \qquad h(x) = x^2 - 2$$

Solution:

Several function values for f, g, and h are shown in Table 11-1 for selected values of x. The corresponding graphs are pictured in Figure 11-5.

Table 11-1

x	$f(x) = x^2$	$g(x) = x^2 + 1$	$h(x) = x^2 - 2$
-3	9	10	7
-2	4	5	2
-1	1	2	-1
0	0	1	-2
1	1	2	-1
2	4	5	2
3	9	10	7

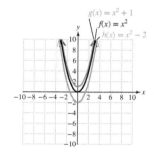

Figure 11-5

Skill Practice   Refer to the graph of $f(x) = x^2 + k$ to determine the value of k.

1.

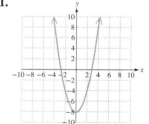

Notice that the graphs of $g(x) = x^2 + 1$ and $h(x) = x^2 - 2$ take on the same shape as $f(x) = x^2$. However, the y values of g are 1 greater than the y values of f. Hence, the graph of $g(x) = x^2 + 1$ is the same as the graph of $f(x) = x^2$ shifted *up* 1 unit. Likewise the y-values of h are 2 less than those of f. The graph of $h(x) = x^2 - 2$ is the same as the graph of $f(x) = x^2$ shifted *down* 2 units.

A function of the type $f(x) = x^2 + k$ represents a vertical shift of the graph of $f(x) = x^2$. The functions in Example 1 illustrate the following properties of quadratic functions of the form $f(x) = x^2 + k$.

Answer

1. $k = -8$

> ### Graphs of $f(x) = x^2 + k$
>
> A function of the type $f(x) = x^2 + k$ represents a vertical shift of the graph of $f(x) = x^2$.
>
> - If $k > 0$, then the graph of $f(x) = x^2 + k$ is the same as the graph of $f(x) = x^2$ shifted *up k* units.
> - If $k < 0$, then the graph of $f(x) = x^2 + k$ is the same as the graph of $f(x) = x^2$ shifted *down |k|* units.

Calculator Connections

Topic: Investigating Vertical Shifts of a Function

Try experimenting with a graphing calculator by graphing functions of the form $y = x^2 + k$ for several values of k.

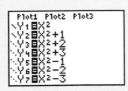 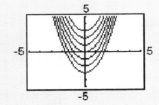

Example 2   ### Graphing Quadratic Functions of the Form $f(x) = x^2 + k$

Sketch the functions defined by

a. $m(x) = x^2 - 4$ **b.** $n(x) = x^2 + \dfrac{7}{2}$

Solution:

a. $m(x) = x^2 - 4$

   $m(x) = x^2 + (-4)$

   Because $k = -4$ (negative), the graph is obtained by shifting the graph of $f(x) = x^2$ down $|-4|$ units (Figure 11-6).

b. $n(x) = x^2 + \dfrac{7}{2}$

   Because $k = \frac{7}{2}$ (positive), the graph is obtained by shifting the graph of $f(x) = x^2$ up $\frac{7}{2}$ units (Figure 11-7).

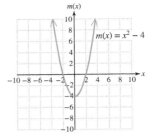

Figure 11-6

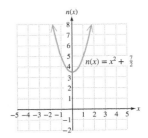

Figure 11-7

TIP: For more accuracy in the graph, plot one or two points near the vertex and use the symmetry of the curve to find additional points on the graph.

Answer

2.

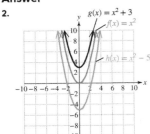

Skill Practice

2. Graph the functions f, g, and h on the same coordinate system.

   $f(x) = x^2$ $g(x) = x^2 + 3$ $h(x) = x^2 - 5$

2. Quadratic Functions of the Form $f(x) = (x - h)^2$

The graph of $f(x) = x^2 + k$ represents a vertical shift (up or down) of the graph of $f(x) = x^2$. Example 3 shows that functions of the form $f(x) = (x - h)^2$ represent a horizontal shift (left or right) of the graph of $f(x) = x^2$.

| Example 3 | **Graphing Quadratic Functions of the Form** $f(x) = (x - h)^2$ |

Graph the functions f, g, and h on the same coordinate system.

$$f(x) = x^2 \qquad g(x) = (x + 1)^2 \qquad h(x) = (x - 2)^2$$

Solution:

Several function values for f, g, and h are shown in Table 11-2 for selected values of x. The corresponding graphs are pictured in Figure 11-8.

Table 11-2

x	$f(x) = x^2$	$g(x) = (x + 1)^2$	$h(x) = (x - 2)^2$
−4	16	9	36
−3	9	4	25
−2	4	1	16
−1	1	0	9
0	0	1	4
1	1	4	1
2	4	9	0
3	9	16	1
4	16	25	4
5	25	36	9

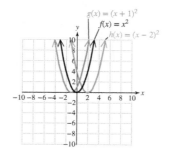

Figure 11-8

Skill Practice Refer to the graph of $f(x) = (x - h)^2$ to determine the value of h.

3.

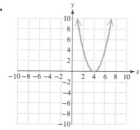

Example 3 illustrates the following properties of quadratic functions of the form $f(x) = (x - h)^2$.

Answer

3. $h = 4$

Graphs of $f(x) = (x - h)^2$

A function of the type $f(x) = (x - h)^2$ represents a horizontal shift of the graph of $f(x) = x^2$.

If $h > 0$, then the graph of $f(x) = (x - h)^2$ is the same as the graph of $f(x) = x^2$ shifted h units to the *right*.

If $h < 0$, then the graph of $f(x) = (x - h)^2$ is the same as the graph of $f(x) = x^2$ shifted $|h|$ units to the *left*.

From Example 3 we have

$$h(x) = (x - 2)^2 \qquad \text{and} \qquad g(x) = (x + 1)^2$$

$$g(x) = [x - (-1)]^2$$

$y = x^2$ shifted 2 units to the right

$y = x^2$ shifted $|-1|$ unit to the left

Example 4   **Graphing Functions of the Form $f(x) = (x - h)^2$**

Sketch the functions p and q.

   a. $p(x) = (x - 7)^2$ **b.** $q(x) = (x + 1.6)^2$

Solution:

   a. $p(x) = (x - 7)^2$

      Because $h = 7 > 0$, shift the graph of $f(x) = x^2$ to the *right* 7 units (Figure 11-9).

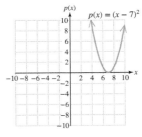

Figure 11-9

   b. $q(x) = (x + 1.6)^2$

      $q(x) = [x - (-1.6)]^2$

      Because $h = -1.6 < 0$, shift the graph of $f(x) = x^2$ to the *left* 1.6 units (Figure 11-10).

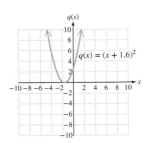

Figure 11-10

Answer

4.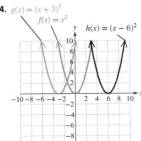

Skill Practice

   4. Graph the functions f, g, and h on the same coordinate system.

$$f(x) = x^2$$
$$g(x) = (x + 3)^2$$
$$h(x) = (x - 6)^2$$

3. Quadratic Functions of the Form $f(x) = ax^2$

Examples 5 and 6 investigate functions of the form $f(x) = ax^2$ $(a \neq 0)$.

Example 5   **Graphing Functions of the Form** $f(x) = ax^2$

Graph the functions f, g, and h on the same coordinate system.

$$f(x) = x^2 \qquad g(x) = 2x^2 \qquad h(x) = \frac{1}{2}x^2$$

Solution:

Several function values for f, g, and h are shown in Table 11-3 for selected values of x.
The corresponding graphs are pictured in Figure 11-11.

Table 11-3

x	$f(x) = x^2$	$g(x) = 2x^2$	$h(x) = \frac{1}{2}x^2$
-3	9	18	$\frac{9}{2}$
-2	4	8	2
-1	1	2	$\frac{1}{2}$
0	0	0	0
1	1	2	$\frac{1}{2}$
2	4	8	2
3	9	18	$\frac{9}{2}$

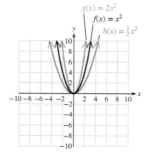

Figure 11-11

Skill Practice

5. Graph the functions f, g, and h on the same coordinate system.

   $f(x) = x^2$

   $g(x) = 3x^2$

   $h(x) = \frac{1}{3}x^2$

In Example 5, the function values defined by $g(x) = 2x^2$ are twice those of $f(x) = x^2$. The graph of $g(x) = 2x^2$ is the same as the graph of $f(x) = x^2$ *stretched vertically* by a factor of 2 (the graph appears narrower than $f(x) = x^2$).

In Example 5, the function values defined by $h(x) = \frac{1}{2}x^2$ are one-half those of $f(x) = x^2$. The graph of $h(x) = \frac{1}{2}x^2$ is the same as the graph of $f(x) = x^2$ *shrunk vertically* by a factor of $\frac{1}{2}$ (the graph appears wider than $f(x) = x^2$).

Example 6   **Graphing Functions of the Form** $f(x) = ax^2$

Graph the functions f, g, and h on the same coordinate system.

$$f(x) = -x^2 \qquad g(x) = -3x^2 \qquad h(x) = -\frac{1}{3}x^2$$

Answers

5.

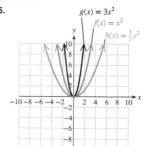

Solution:

Several function values for f, g, and h are shown in Table 11-4 for selected values of x. The corresponding graphs are pictured in Figure 11-12.

Table 11-4

x	$f(x) = -x^2$	$g(x) = -3x^2$	$h(x) = -\frac{1}{3}x^2$
-3	-9	-27	-3
-2	-4	-12	$-\frac{4}{3}$
-1	-1	-3	$-\frac{1}{3}$
0	0	0	0
1	-1	-3	$-\frac{1}{3}$
2	-4	-12	$-\frac{4}{3}$
3	-9	-27	-3

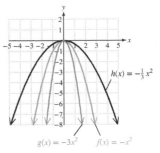

Figure 11-12

Skill Practice

6. Graph the functions f, g, and h on the same coordinate system.

$$f(x) = -x^2 \qquad g(x) = -2x^2 \qquad h(x) = -\frac{1}{2}x^2$$

Example 6 illustrates that if the coefficient of the squared term is negative, the parabola opens downward. The graph of $g(x) = -3x^2$ is the same as the graph of $f(x) = -x^2$ with a *vertical stretch* by a factor of $|-3|$. The graph of $h(x) = -\frac{1}{3}x^2$ is the same as the graph of $f(x) = -x^2$ with a *vertical shrink* by a factor of $|-\frac{1}{3}|$.

Graphs of $f(x) = ax^2$

1. If $a > 0$, the parabola opens upward. Furthermore,
   - If $0 < a < 1$, then the graph of $f(x) = ax^2$ is the same as the graph of $f(x) = x^2$ with a *vertical shrink* by a factor of a.
   - If $a > 1$, then the graph of $f(x) = ax^2$ is the same as the graph of $f(x) = x^2$ with a *vertical stretch* by a factor of a.
2. If $a < 0$, the parabola opens downward. Furthermore,
   - If $0 < |a| < 1$, then the graph of $f(x) = ax^2$ is the same as the graph of $f(x) = -x^2$ with a *vertical shrink* by a factor of $|a|$.
   - If $|a| > 1$, then the graph of $f(x) = ax^2$ is the same as the graph of $f(x) = -x^2$ with a *vertical stretch* by a factor of $|a|$.

Answer

6.

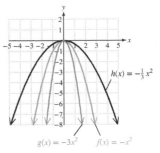

$f(x) = -x^2$ $h(x) = -\frac{1}{2}x^2$
$g(x) = -2x^2$

4. Quadratic Functions of the Form $f(x) = a(x - h)^2 + k$

We can summarize our findings from Examples 1–6 by graphing functions of the form $f(x) = a(x - h)^2 + k$ $(a \neq 0)$.

The graph of $f(x) = x^2$ has its vertex at the origin $(0, 0)$. The graph of $f(x) = a(x - h)^2 + k$ is the same as the graph of $f(x) = x^2$ shifted to the right or left h units and shifted up or down k units. Therefore, the vertex is shifted from $(0, 0)$ to (h, k). The axis of symmetry is the vertical line through the vertex. Therefore, the axis of symmetry must be the line $x = h$.

Graphs of $f(x) = a(x - h)^2 + k$

1. The vertex is (h, k).
2. The axis of symmetry is the line $x = h$.
3. If $a > 0$, the parabola opens upward, and k is the **minimum value** of the function.
4. If $a < 0$, the parabola opens downward, and k is the **maximum value** of the function.

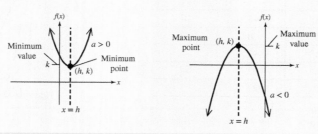

Example 7   **Graphing a Function of the Form $f(x) = a(x - h)^2 + k$**

Given the function defined by $f(x) = 2(x - 3)^2 + 4$

a. Identify the vertex.
b. Sketch the function.
c. Identify the axis of symmetry.
d. Identify the maximum or minimum value of the function.
e. Use the graph to determine the domain and range of f in interval notation.

Solution:

a. The function is in the form $f(x) = a(x - h)^2 + k$, where $a = 2$, $h = 3$, and $k = 4$. Therefore, the vertex is $(3, 4)$.

b. The graph of f is the same as the graph of $f(x) = x^2$ shifted to the right 3 units, shifted up 4 units, and stretched vertically by a factor of 2 (Figure 11-13).

c. The axis of symmetry is the line $x = 3$.

d. Because $a > 0$, the function opens upward. Therefore, the minimum function value is 4. Notice that the minimum value is the minimum y-value on the graph.

e. The domain is all real numbers:$(-\infty, \infty)$. The vertex is the lowest point on the parabola, and its y-coordinate is 4. Therefore, the range is $[4, \infty)$.

TIP: We can find additional points to the right or left of the vertex and use the symmetry of the parabola to refine the sketch of the curve.

x	f(x)
4	6
5	12

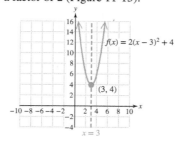

Figure 11-13

Skill Practice

7. Given the function defined by $g(x) = 3(x + 1)^2 - 3$
   a. Identify the vertex.
   b. Sketch the graph.
   c. Identify the axis of symmetry.
   d. Identify the maximum or minimum value of the function.
   e. Determine the domain and range in interval notation.

Answers

7. **a.** Vertex: $(-1, -3)$
   b.

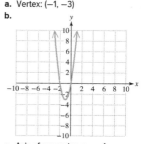

   c. Axis of symmetry: $x = -1$
   d. Minimum value: -3
   e. Domain: $(-\infty, \infty)$; range: $[-3, \infty)$

818   **Chapter 11**   Quadratic Equations and Functions

Topic: Using the Maximum and Minimum Features

Some graphing calculators have *Minimum* and *Maximum* features that enable the user to approximate the minimum and maximum values of a function.

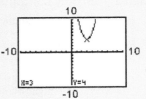

Example 8   **Graphing a Function of the Form**
$f(x) = a(x - h)^2 + k$

Given the function defined by $g(x) = -(x + 2)^2 - \dfrac{7}{4}$

a. Identify the vertex.

b. Sketch the function.

c. Identify the axis of symmetry.

d. Identify the maximum or minimum value of the function.

e. Use the graph to determine the domain and range of f in interval notation.

Solution:

a. $g(x) = -(x + 2)^2 - \dfrac{7}{4}$

$$= -1[x - (-2)]^2 + \left(-\dfrac{7}{4}\right)$$

The function is in the form $g(x) = a(x - h)^2 + k$, where $a = -1$, $h = -2$, and $k = -\frac{7}{4}$. Therefore, the vertex is $\left(-2, -\frac{7}{4}\right)$.

b. The graph of g is the same as the graph of $f(x) = x^2$ shifted to the left 2 units, shifted down $\frac{7}{4}$ units, and opening downward (Figure 11-14).

c. The axis of symmetry is the line $x = -2$.

d. The parabola opens downward, so the maximum function value is $-\frac{7}{4}$.

e. The domain is all real numbers: $(-\infty, \infty)$.

The vertex is the highest point on the parabola, and its y-coordinate is $-\frac{7}{4}$. Therefore, the range is $\left(-\infty, -\frac{7}{4}\right]$.

Figure 11-14

Answers

8. a. Vertex: (4, 2)

   b.

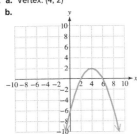

Skill Practice

8. Given the function defined by $h(x) = -\dfrac{1}{2}(x - 4)^2 + 2$

   a. Identify the vertex.

   b. Sketch the graph.

   c. Identify the axis of symmetry.

   d. Identify the maximum or minimum value of the function.

   e. Determine the domain and range in interval notation.

c. Axis of symmetry: $x = 4$

d. Maximum value: 2

e. Domain: $(-\infty, \infty)$; range: $(-\infty, 2]$

Vocabulary and Key Concepts

1. **a.** The graph of a quadratic function, $f(x) = ax^2 + bx + c$, is a _____.

   b. The parabola defined by $f(x) = ax^2 + bx + c$ $(a \neq 0)$ will open upward if a _____ 0 and will open downward if a _____ 0.

   c. If a parabola opens upward, the vertex is the (highest/lowest) point on the graph. If a parabola opens downward, the vertex is the (highest/lowest) point on the graph.

   d. Given $f(x) = a(x - h)^2 + k$ $(a \neq 0)$, the vertex of the parabola is given by the ordered pair _____. If the parabola opens _____, the value of k is the minimum value of the function. If the parabola opens _____, the value of k is the maximum value of the function.

   e. Given $f(x) = a(x - h)^2 + k$ $(a \neq 0)$, the axis of symmetry of the parabola is the vertical line that passes through the _____. An equation of the axis of symmetry is _____.

Review Exercises

For Exercises 2–8, solve the equations.

2. $x^2 + x - 5 = 0$

3. $(y - 3)^2 = -4$

4. $\sqrt{2a + 2} = a + 1$

5. $5t(t - 2) = -3$

6. $2z^2 - 3z - 9 = 0$

7. $x^{2/3} + 5x^{1/3} + 6 = 0$

8. $m^2(m^2 + 6) = 27$

Concept 1: Quadratic Functions of the Form $f(x) = x^2 + k$

9. Describe how the value of k affects the graph of a function defined by $f(x) = x^2 + k$.

For Exercises 10–17, graph the functions. **(See Examples 1–2.)**

10. $g(x) = x^2 + 1$

11. $f(x) = x^2 + 2$

12. $p(x) = x^2 - 3$

13. $q(x) = x^2 - 4$

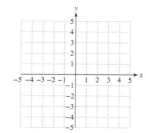 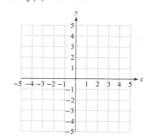 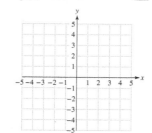 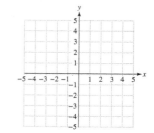

14. $T(x) = x^2 + \dfrac{3}{4}$

15. $S(x) = x^2 + \dfrac{3}{2}$

16. $M(x) = x^2 - \dfrac{5}{4}$

17. $n(x) = x^2 - \dfrac{1}{3}$

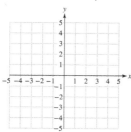 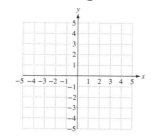 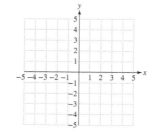 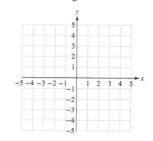

820 Chapter 11 Quadratic Equations and Functions

Concept 2: Quadratic Functions of the Form $f(x) = (x - h)^2$

18. Describe how the value of h affects the graph of a function defined by $f(x) = (x - h)^2$.

For Exercises 19–26, graph the functions. **(See Examples 3–4.)**

19. $r(x) = (x + 1)^2$

20. $h(x) = (x + 2)^2$

21. $k(x) = (x - 3)^2$

22. $L(x) = (x - 4)^2$

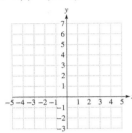 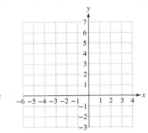 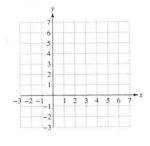 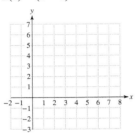

23. $A(x) = \left(x + \dfrac{3}{4}\right)^2$

24. $r(x) = \left(x + \dfrac{3}{2}\right)^2$

25. $W(x) = (x - 1.25)^2$

26. $V(x) = (x - 2.5)^2$

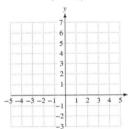 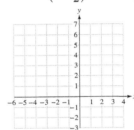 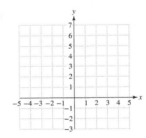 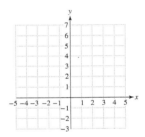

Concept 3: Quadratic Functions of the Form $f(x) = ax^2$

27. Describe how the value of a affects the graph of a function defined by $f(x) = ax^2$, where $a \neq 0$.

28. How do you determine whether the graph of a function defined by $h(x) = ax^2 + bx + c$ ($a \neq 0$) opens upward or downward?

For Exercises 29–36, graph the functions. **(See Examples 5–6.)**

29. $f(x) = 4x^2$

30. $g(x) = 3x^2$

31. $h(x) = \dfrac{1}{4}x^2$

32. $f(x) = \dfrac{1}{5}x^2$

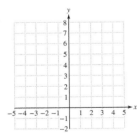 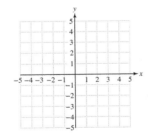 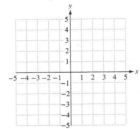 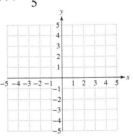

33. $c(x) = -x^2$

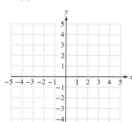

34. $g(x) = -4x^2$

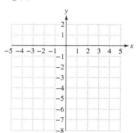

35. $v(x) = -\dfrac{1}{5}x^2$

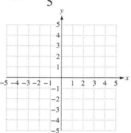

36. $f(x) = -\dfrac{1}{4}x^2$

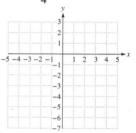

Concept 4: Quadratic Functions of the Form $f(x) = a(x - h)^2 + k$

For Exercises 37–44, match the function with its graph.

37. $f(x) = -\dfrac{1}{4}x^2$

38. $g(x) = (x + 3)^2$

39. $k(x) = (x - 3)^2$

40. $h(x) = \dfrac{1}{4}x^2$

41. $t(x) = x^2 + 2$

42. $m(x) = x^2 - 4$

43. $p(x) = (x + 1)^2 - 3$

44. $n(x) = -(x - 2)^2 + 3$

a.

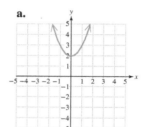

b.

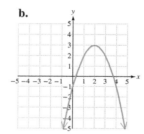

c.

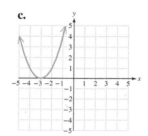

d.

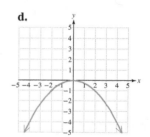

e.

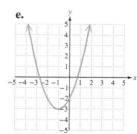

f.

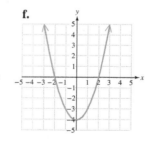

g.

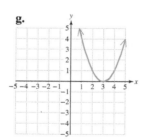

h.

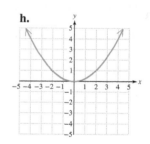

For Exercises 45–64, graph the parabola and the axis of symmetry. Label the coordinates of the vertex, and write the equation of the axis of symmetry. Use the graph to write the domain and range in interval notation. **(See Examples 7–8.)**

45. $f(x) = (x - 3)^2 + 2$

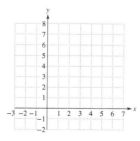

46. $f(x) = (x - 2)^2 + 3$

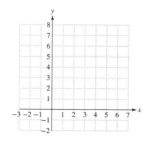

47. $f(x) = (x + 1)^2 - 3$

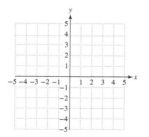

48. $f(x) = (x + 3)^2 - 1$

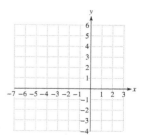

822   **Chapter 11**   Quadratic Equations and Functions

49. $f(x) = -(x-4)^2 - 2$ **50.** $f(x) = -(x-2)^2 - 4$ **51.** $f(x) = -(x+3)^2 + 3$ **52.** $f(x) = -(x+2)^2 + 2$

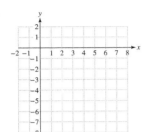   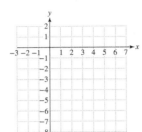   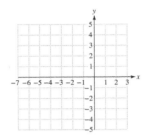   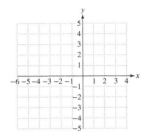

53. $f(x) = (x+1)^2 + 1$ **54.** $f(x) = (x-4)^2 - 4$ **55.** $f(x) = 3(x-1)^2$ **56.** $f(x) = -3(x-1)^2$

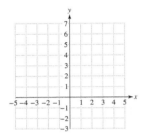   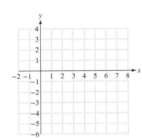   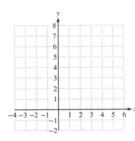   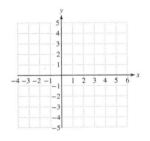

57. $f(x) = -4x^2 + 3$ **58.** $f(x) = 4x^2 + 3$ **59.** $f(x) = 2(x+3)^2 - 1$ **60.** $f(x) = -2(x+3)^2 - 1$

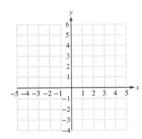   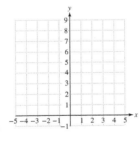   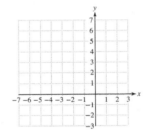   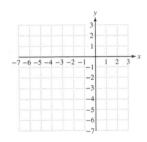

61. $f(x) = -\dfrac{1}{4}(x-1)^2 + 2$ **62.** $f(x) = \dfrac{1}{4}(x-1)^2 + 2$ **63.** $f(x) = \dfrac{1}{3}(x-2)^2 + 1$ **64.** $f(x) = -\dfrac{1}{3}(x-2)^2 + 1$

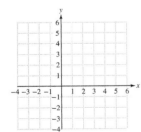   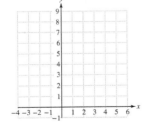   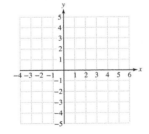   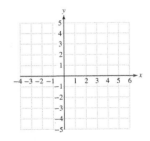

65. Compare the graphs of the following equations to the graph of $y = x^2$.

    a. $y = x^2 + 3$

    b. $y = (x+3)^2$

    c. $y = 3x^2$

66. Compare the graphs of the following equations to the graph of $y = x^2$.

    a. $y = (x-2)^2$

    b. $y = 2x^2$

    c. $y = x^2 - 2$

For Exercises 67–78, write the coordinates of the vertex and determine if the vertex is a maximum point or a minimum point. Then write the maximum or minimum value.

67. $f(x) = 4(x - 6)^2 - 9$

68. $g(x) = 3(x - 4)^2 - 7$

69. $p(x) = -\frac{2}{5}(x - 2)^2 + 5$

70. $h(x) = -\frac{3}{7}(x - 5)^2 + 10$

71. $k(x) = \frac{1}{2}(x + 8)^2$

72. $m(x) = \frac{2}{9}(x + 11)^2$

73. $n(x) = -6x^2 + \frac{21}{4}$

74. $q(x) = -4x^2 + \frac{1}{6}$

75. $A(x) = 2(x - 7)^2 - \frac{3}{2}$

76. $B(x) = 5(x - 3)^2 - \frac{1}{4}$

77. $F(x) = 7x^2$

78. $G(x) = -7x^2$

79. True or false: The function defined by $g(x) = -5x^2$ has a maximum value but no minimum value.

80. True or false: The function defined by $f(x) = 2(x - 5)^2$ has a maximum value but no minimum value.

81. True or false: If the vertex $(-2, 8)$ represents a minimum point, then the minimum value is -2.

82. True or false: If the vertex $(-2, 8)$ represents a maximum point, then the maximum value is 8.

Expanding Your Skills

83. A suspension bridge is 120 ft long. Its supporting cable hangs in a shape that resembles a parabola. The function defined by $H(x) = \frac{1}{90}(x - 60)^2 + 30$ (where $0 \le x \le 120$) approximates the height $H(x)$ (in feet) of the supporting cable a distance of x ft from the end of the bridge (see figure).

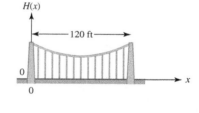

   a. What is the location of the vertex of the parabolic cable?

   b. What is the minimum height of the cable?

   c. How high are the towers at either end of the supporting cable?

84. A 50-m bridge over a crevasse is supported by a parabolic arch. The function defined by $f(x) = -0.16(x - 25)^2 + 100$ (where $0 \le x \le 50$) approximates the height $f(x)$ (in feet) of the supporting arch x meters from the end of the bridge (see figure).

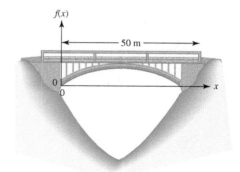

   a. What is the location of the vertex of the arch?

   b. What is the maximum height of the arch (relative to the origin)?

85. The staging platform for a fireworks display is 6 ft above ground, and the mortars leave the platform at 96 ft/sec. The height of the mortars $h(t)$ (in feet) can be modeled by $h(t) = -16(t - 3)^2 + 150$, where t is the time in seconds after launch.

   a. If the fuses are set for 3 sec after launch, at what height will the fireworks explode?

   b. Will the fireworks explode at their maximum height? Explain.

824   **Chapter 11**   Quadratic Equations and Functions

Section 11.5 Vertex of a Parabola: Applications and Modeling

Concepts

1. Writing a Quadratic Function in the Form $f(x) = a(x - h)^2 + k$
2. Vertex Formula
3. Determining the Vertex and Intercepts of a Quadratic Function
4. Applications and Modeling of Quadratic Functions

1. Writing a Quadratic Function in the Form $f(x) = a(x - h)^2 + k$

The graph of a quadratic function is a parabola, and if the function is written in the form $f(x) = a(x - h)^2 + k$ $(a \neq 0)$, then the vertex is (h, k). A quadratic function can be written in the form $f(x) = a(x - h)^2 + k$ $(a \neq 0)$ by completing the square. The process is similar to the steps to solve a quadratic equation by completing the square. However, in this context working with a function, we will perform all algebraic manipulations on the right side of the equation.

Example 1   **Writing a Quadratic Function in the Form**
$f(x) = a(x - h)^2 + k$ $(a \neq 0)$

Given $f(x) = x^2 + 8x + 13$

a. Write the function in the form $f(x) = a(x - h)^2 + k$.

b. Identify the vertex, axis of symmetry, and minimum function value.

Solution:

a. $f(x) = x^2 + 8x + 13$

       Rather than dividing by the leading coefficient on both sides, we will factor out the leading coefficient from the variable terms on the right-hand side.

$= 1(x^2 + 8x) + 13$

$= 1(x^2 + 8x \quad) + 13$

       Next, complete the square on the expression within the parentheses: $\left[\frac{1}{2}(8)\right]^2 = 16$.

$= 1(x^2 + 8x + 16 - 16) + 13$

       Rather than add 16 to both sides of the function, we *add and subtract* 16 within the parentheses on the right-hand side. This has the effect of adding 0 to the right-hand side.

$= 1(x^2 + 8x + 16) - 16 + 13$

       Use the associative property of addition to regroup terms and isolate the perfect square trinomial within the parentheses.

$= (x + 4)^2 - 3$

       Factor and simplify.

b. $f(x) = (x + 4)^2 - 3$

The vertex is $(-4, -3)$.

The axis of symmetry is $x = -4$.

Because $a > 0$, the parabola opens upward.

The minimum value is -3 (Figure 11-15).

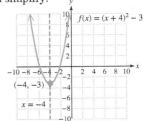

Figure 11-15

Avoiding Mistakes

Do not factor out the leading coefficient from the constant term.

Answers

1. a. $f(x) = (x + 4)^2 - 17$
  b. Vertex: $(-4, -17)$; axis of symmetry: $x = -4$; minimum value: -17

Skill Practice

1. Given: $f(x) = x^2 + 8x - 1$

  a. Write the function in the form $f(x) = a(x - h)^2 + k$.

  b. Identify the vertex, axis of symmetry, and minimum value of the function.

| Example 2 | **Analyzing a Quadratic Function** |

Given $f(x) = -2x^2 + 12x - 16$

a. Write the function in the form $f(x) = a(x - h)^2 + k$.

b. Find the vertex, axis of symmetry, and maximum function value.

c. Find the x- and y-intercepts.

d. Sketch the graph of the function.

Solution:

a. $f(x) = -2x^2 + 12x - 16$

To find the vertex, write the function in the form $f(x) = a(x - h)^2 + k$.

$= -2(x^2 - 6x \quad) - 16$

If the leading coefficient is not 1, factor the coefficient from the variable terms.

$= -2(x^2 - 6x + 9 - 9) - 16$

Add and subtract the quantity $\left[\frac{1}{2}(-6)\right]^2 = 9$ within the parentheses.

$= -2(x^2 - 6x + 9) + (-2)(-9) - 16$

To remove the term -9 from the parentheses, we must first apply the distributive property. When -9 is removed from the parentheses, it carries with it a factor of -2.

$= -2(x - 3)^2 + 18 - 16$

Factor and simplify.

$= -2(x - 3)^2 + 2$

b. $f(x) = -2(x - 3)^2 + 2$

The vertex is (3, 2). The axis of symmetry is $x = 3$. Because $a < 0$, the parabola opens downward and the maximum value is 2.

c. The y-intercept is given by $f(0) = -2(0)^2 + 12(0) - 16 = -16$.

The y-intercept is (0, −16).

To find the x-intercept(s), find the real solutions to the equation $f(x) = 0$.

$f(x) = -2x^2 + 12x - 16$

$0 = -2x^2 + 12x - 16$ Substitute $f(x) = 0$.

$0 = -2(x^2 - 6x + 8)$ Factor.

$0 = -2(x - 4)(x - 2)$

$x = 4$ or $x = 2$

The x-intercepts are (4, 0) and (2, 0).

TIP: In Example 2(c), we could have used the form of the equation found in part (a) to find the intercepts.

d. Using the information from parts (a)–(c), sketch the graph (Figure 11-16).

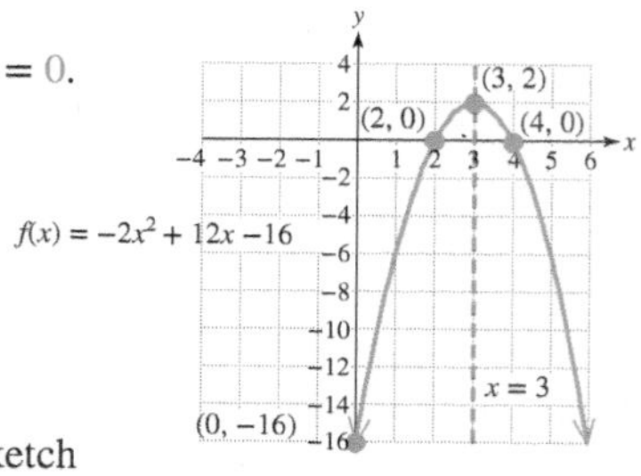

Figure 11-16

826   Chapter 11   Quadratic Equations and Functions

> **Skill Practice**
>
> **2.** Given $g(x) = -x^2 + 6x - 5$
>   **a.** Write the function in the form $g(x) = a(x - h)^2 + k$.
>   **b.** Identify the vertex, axis of symmetry, and maximum value of the function.
>   **c.** Determine the x- and y-intercepts.
>   **d.** Graph the function.

2. Vertex Formula

Completing the square and writing a quadratic function in the form $f(x) = a(x - h)^2 + k$ ($a \neq 0$) is one method to find the vertex of a parabola. Another method is to use the vertex formula. The **vertex formula** can be derived by completing the square on $f(x) = ax^2 + bx + c$ ($a \neq 0$).

$f(x) = ax^2 + bx + c \ (a \neq 0)$

$$= a\left(x^2 + \frac{b}{a}x \qquad \right) + c \qquad \text{Factor } a \text{ from the variable terms.}$$

$$= a\left(x^2 + \frac{b}{a}x + \frac{b^2}{4a^2} - \frac{b^2}{4a^2}\right) + c \qquad \text{Add and subtract } \left[\tfrac{1}{2}(b/a)\right]^2 = b^2/(4a^2) \text{ within the parentheses.}$$

$$= a\left(x^2 + \frac{b}{a}x + \frac{b^2}{4a^2}\right) + (a)\left(-\frac{b^2}{4a^2}\right) + c \qquad \begin{array}{l}\text{Apply the distributive property} \\ \text{and remove the term } -b^2/(4a^2) \\ \text{from the parentheses.}\end{array}$$

$$= a\left(x + \frac{b}{2a}\right)^2 - \frac{b^2}{4a} + c \qquad \text{Factor the trinomial and simplify.}$$

$$= a\left(x + \frac{b}{2a}\right)^2 + c - \frac{b^2}{4a} \qquad \begin{array}{l}\text{Apply the commutative property} \\ \text{of addition to reverse the last} \\ \text{two terms.}\end{array}$$

$$= a\left(x + \frac{b}{2a}\right)^2 + \frac{4ac}{4a} - \frac{b^2}{4a} \qquad \text{Obtain a common denominator.}$$

$$= a\left(x + \frac{b}{2a}\right)^2 + \frac{4ac - b^2}{4a}$$

$$= a\left[x - \left(-\frac{b}{2a}\right)\right]^2 + \frac{4ac - b^2}{4a}$$

$$f(x) = a(x \quad - \quad h)^2 \quad + \quad k$$

The function is in the form $f(x) = a(x - h)^2 + k$, where

$$h = \frac{-b}{2a} \qquad \text{and} \qquad k = \frac{4ac - b^2}{4a}$$

Therefore, the vertex is $\left(\dfrac{-b}{2a}, \dfrac{4ac - b^2}{4a}\right)$.

Although the y-coordinate of the vertex is given by $\dfrac{4ac - b^2}{4a}$, it is usually easier to determine the x-coordinate of the vertex first and then find y by evaluating the function at $x = -b/(2a)$.

Answers

2. a. $g(x) = -(x - 3)^2 + 4$
  b. Vertex: $(3, 4)$; axis of symmetry: $x = 3$; maximum value: 4
  c. x-intercepts: $(5, 0)$ and $(1, 0)$; y-intercept: $(0, -5)$
  d.

The Vertex Formula

For $f(x) = ax^2 + bx + c$ $(a \neq 0)$, the vertex is given by

$$\left(\frac{-b}{2a}, \frac{4ac - b^2}{4a} \right) \quad \text{or} \quad \left(\frac{-b}{2a}, f\left(\frac{-b}{2a} \right) \right)$$

3. Determining the Vertex and Intercepts of a Quadratic Function

Example 3   **Determining the Vertex and Intercepts of a Quadratic Function**

Given: $h(x) = x^2 - 2x + 5$

a. Use the vertex formula to find the vertex.

b. Find the x- and y-intercepts.

c. Sketch the function.

Solution:

a. $h(x) = x^2 - 2x + 5$

$a = 1 \qquad b = -2 \qquad c = 5 \qquad$ Identify a, b, and c.

The x-coordinate of the vertex is $\dfrac{-b}{2a} = \dfrac{-(-2)}{2(1)} = 1$.

The y-coordinate of the vertex is $h(1) = (1)^2 - 2(1) + 5 = 4$.

The vertex is $(1, 4)$.

b. The y-intercept is given by $h(0) = (0)^2 - 2(0) + 5 = 5$.

The y-intercept is $(0, 5)$.

To find the x-intercept(s), find the real solutions to the equation $h(x) = 0$.

$h(x) = x^2 - 2x + 5$

$0 = x^2 - 2x + 5 \qquad$ This quadratic equation is not factorable. Apply the quadratic formula: $a = 1, b = -2, c = 5$

$x = \dfrac{-(-2) \pm \sqrt{(-2)^2 - 4(1)(5)}}{2(1)}$

$= \dfrac{2 \pm \sqrt{4 - 20}}{2(1)}$

$= \dfrac{2 \pm \sqrt{-16}}{2}$

$= \dfrac{2 \pm 4i}{2}$

$= 1 \pm 2i$

The solutions to the equation $h(x) = 0$ are not real numbers. Therefore, there are no x-intercepts.

c.

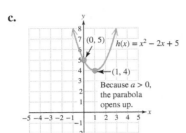

$(0, 5)$ $h(x) = x^2 - 2x + 5$

$(1, 4)$

Because $a > 0$, the parabola opens up.

> **TIP:** The location of the vertex and the direction that the parabola opens can be used to determine whether the function has any x-intercepts.
> Given $h(x) = x^2 - 2x + 5$, the vertex $(1, 4)$ is above the x-axis. Furthermore, because $a > 0$, the parabola opens upward. Therefore, it is not possible for the graph to cross the x-axis (Figure 11-17).

Figure 11-17

Skill Practice

3. Given: $f(x) = x^2 + 4x + 6$
   a. Use the vertex formula to find the vertex of the parabola.
   b. Determine the x- and y-intercepts.
   c. Sketch the graph.

4. Applications and Modeling of Quadratic Functions

| Example 4 | **Applying a Quadratic Function** |

The crew from Extravaganza Entertainment launches fireworks at an angle of 60° from the horizontal. The height of one particular type of display can be approximated by

$$h(t) = -16t^2 + 128\sqrt{3}\,t$$

where $h(t)$ is measured in feet and t is measured in seconds.

a. How long will it take the fireworks to reach their maximum height? Round to the nearest second.

b. Find the maximum height. Round to the nearest foot.

© Royalty Free/Corbis RF

Answers

3. **a.** Vertex: $(-2, 2)$
   b. x-intercepts: none; y-intercept: $(0, 6)$
   c.

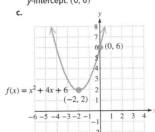

$f(x) = x^2 + 4x + 6$ $(-2, 2)$ $(0, 6)$

Solution:

$$h(t) = -16t^2 + 128\sqrt{3}\,t$$

This parabola opens downward; therefore, the maximum height of the fireworks will occur at the vertex of the parabola.

$$a = -16 \qquad b = 128\sqrt{3} \qquad c = 0$$

Identify a, b, and c, and apply the vertex formula.

The x-coordinate of the vertex is

$$\frac{-b}{2a} = \frac{-128\sqrt{3}}{2(-16)} = \frac{-128\sqrt{3}}{-32} \approx 6.9$$

The y-coordinate of the vertex is approximately

$$h(6.9) = -16(6.9)^2 + 128\sqrt{3}(6.9) \approx 768$$

The vertex is (6.9, 768).

a. The fireworks will reach their maximum height in 6.9 sec.

b. The maximum height is 768 ft.

Skill Practice

4. An object is launched into the air with an initial velocity of 48 ft/sec from the top of a building 288 ft high. The height $h(t)$ of the object after t seconds is given by

$$h(t) = -16t^2 + 48t + 288$$

a. Find the time it takes for the object to reach its maximum height.

b. Find the maximum height.

In Example 5 we will learn how to write a quadratic model of a parabola given three points by using a system of equations and the standard form of a parabola: $y = ax^2 + bx + c$.

This process involves substituting the x- and y-coordinates of the three given points into the quadratic model. Then we solve the resulting system of three equations.

Example 5   **Writing a Quadratic Model** ————————

Write an equation of a parabola that passes through the points $(1, -1)$, $(-1, -5)$, and $(2, 4)$.

Solution:

Substitute $(1, -1)$ into the equation

$y = ax^2 + bx + c$ ——————————⟶ $(-1) = a(1)^2 + b(1) + c$

$\qquad\qquad\qquad\qquad\qquad\qquad -1 = a + b + c$

$\qquad\qquad\qquad\qquad\qquad\qquad a + b + c = -1$

Substitute $(-1, -5)$ into the equation

$y = ax^2 + bx + c$ ——————————⟶ $(-5) = a(-1)^2 + b(-1) + c$

$\qquad\qquad\qquad\qquad\qquad\qquad -5 = a - b + c$

$\qquad\qquad\qquad\qquad\qquad\qquad a - b + c = -5$

Substitute $(2, 4)$ into the equation

$y = ax^2 + bx + c$ ——————————⟶ $(4) = a(2)^2 + b(2) + c$

$\qquad\qquad\qquad\qquad\qquad\qquad 4 = 4a + 2b + c$

$\qquad\qquad\qquad\qquad\qquad\qquad 4a + 2b + c = 4$

Solve the system: $\boxed{A}$ $a + \ b + c = -1$

$\qquad\qquad\qquad\qquad\quad \boxed{B}$ $a - \ b + c = -5$

$\qquad\qquad\qquad\qquad\quad \boxed{C}$ $4a + 2b + c = \ \ 4$

Answers

4. a. 1.5 sec   **b.** 324 ft

830   Chapter 11   Quadratic Equations and Functions

Notice that the c variables all have a coefficient of 1. Therefore, we choose to eliminate the c variable.

$$\boxed{A}\quad a+b+c=-1 \longrightarrow \qquad a+b+c=-1$$
$$\boxed{B}\quad a-b+c=-5 \underset{\text{Multiply by } -1.}{\longrightarrow} \quad \underline{-a+b-c=5}$$
$$\qquad\qquad\qquad\qquad\qquad\qquad 2b\quad=\quad 4$$
$$\qquad\qquad\qquad\qquad\qquad\qquad\; b=\quad 2\quad\boxed{D}$$

$$\boxed{B}\quad a-b+c=-5 \longrightarrow \qquad a-b+c=-5$$
$$\boxed{C}\quad 4a+2b+c=4 \underset{\text{Multiply by } -1.}{\longrightarrow} \quad \underline{-4a-2b-c=-4}$$
$$\qquad\qquad\qquad\qquad\qquad\qquad -3a-3b\quad=-9\quad\boxed{E}$$

Substitute b with 2 in equation $\boxed{E}$: $-3a-3(2)=-9$
$$-3a-6=-9$$
$$-3a=-3$$
$$a=1$$

Substitute a and b in equation $\boxed{A}$ to solve for c: $(1)+(2)+c=-1$
$$3+c=-1$$
$$c=-4$$

Substitute $a=1$, $b=2$, and $c=-4$ in the standard form of the parabola for the final answer.

$$y=ax^2+bx+c$$
$$y=(1)x^2+(2)x+(-4) \longrightarrow y=x^2+2x-4$$

A graph of $y=x^2+2x-4$ is shown in Figure 11-18. Notice that the graph of the function passes through the points $(1,-1)$, $(-1,-5)$, and $(2,4)$.

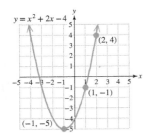

Figure 11-18

Answer

5. $a=-1$, $b=-1$, $c=3$;

$\quad y=-x^2-x+3$

Skill Practice

5. Write an equation of the parabola that passes through the points $(1,1)$, $(-2,1)$, and $(3,-9)$.

Section 11.5   **Practice Exercises**

Vocabulary and Key Concepts

1. **a.** Given $f(x)=ax^2+bx+c$ $(a\neq 0)$, the vertex formula gives the x-coordinate of the vertex as _____. The y-coordinate can be found by evaluating the function at $x=$ _____.

   b. Answer true or false. A parabola may have no x-intercepts.

   c. Answer true or false. A parabola may have one x-intercept.

   d. Answer true or false. A parabola may have two x-intercepts.

   e. Answer true or false. A parabola may have three x-intercepts.

Review Exercises

2. How does the graph of $f(x)=-2x^2$ compare with the graph of $y=x^2$?

3. How does the graph of $p(x)=\frac{1}{4}x^2$ compare with the graph of $y=x^2$?

4. How does the graph of $Q(x)=x^2-\frac{8}{3}$ compare with the graph of $y=x^2$?

5. How does the graph of $r(x) = x^2 + 7$ compare with the graph of $y = x^2$?

6. How does the graph of $s(x) = (x - 4)^2$ compare with the graph of $y = x^2$?

7. How does the graph of $t(x) = (x + 10)^2$ compare with the graph of $y = x^2$?

8. Find the coordinates of the vertex of the parabola defined by $g(x) = 2(x + 3)^2 - 4$.

For Exercises 9–16, find the value of n to complete the square. Factor the resulting trinomial.

9. $x^2 - 8x + n$ **10.** $x^2 + 4x + n$ **11.** $y^2 + 7y + n$ **12.** $a^2 - a + n$

13. $b^2 + \dfrac{2}{9}b + n$ **14.** $m^2 - \dfrac{2}{7}m + n$ **15.** $t^2 - \dfrac{1}{3}t + n$ **16.** $p^2 + \dfrac{1}{4}p + n$

Concept 1: Writing a Quadratic Function in the Form $f(x) = a(x - h)^2 + k$

For Exercises 17–28, write the function in the form $f(x) = a(x - h)^2 + k$ by completing the square. Then identify the vertex.
(See Examples 1–2.)

17. $g(x) = x^2 - 8x + 5$ **18.** $h(x) = x^2 + 4x + 5$ **19.** $n(x) = 2x^2 + 12x + 13$

20. $f(x) = 4x^2 + 16x + 19$ **21.** $p(x) = -3x^2 + 6x - 5$ **22.** $q(x) = -2x^2 + 12x - 11$

23. $k(x) = x^2 + 7x - 10$ **24.** $m(x) = x^2 - x - 8$ **25.** $F(x) = 5x^2 + 10x + 1$

26. $G(x) = 4x^2 + 4x - 7$ **27.** $P(x) = -2x^2 + x$ **28.** $Q(x) = -3x^2 + 12x$

Concept 2: Vertex Formula

For Exercises 29–40, find the vertex by using the vertex formula. **(See Example 3.)**

29. $Q(x) = x^2 - 4x + 7$ **30.** $T(x) = x^2 - 8x + 17$ **31.** $r(x) = -3x^2 - 6x - 5$

32. $s(x) = -2x^2 - 12x - 19$ **33.** $N(x) = x^2 + 8x + 1$ **34.** $M(x) = x^2 + 6x - 5$

35. $m(x) = \dfrac{1}{2}x^2 + x + \dfrac{5}{2}$ **36.** $n(x) = \dfrac{1}{2}x^2 + 2x + 3$ **37.** $k(x) = -x^2 + 2x + 2$

38. $h(x) = -x^2 + 4x - 3$ **39.** $A(x) = -\dfrac{1}{3}x^2 + x$ **40.** $B(x) = -\dfrac{2}{3}x^2 - 2x$

For Exercises 41–44, find the vertex two ways:

    a. by completing the square and writing in the form $f(x) = a(x - h)^2 + k$.

    b. by using the vertex formula.

41. $p(x) = x^2 + 8x + 1$ **42.** $F(x) = x^2 + 4x - 2$ **43.** $f(x) = 2x^2 + 4x + 6$ **44.** $g(x) = 3x^2 + 12x + 9$

832   **Chapter 11** Quadratic Equations and Functions

Concept 3: Determining the Vertex and Intercepts of a Quadratic Function

For Exercises 45–52

    a. Find the vertex.

    b. Find the y-intercept.

    c. Find the x-intercept(s), if they exist.

    d. Use this information to graph the function. **(See Examples 2–3.)**

45. $f(x) = x^2 + 2x - 3$ **46.** $f(x) = x^2 + 4x + 3$ **47.** $f(x) = 2x^2 - 2x + 4$ **48.** $f(x) = 2x^2 - 12x + 19$

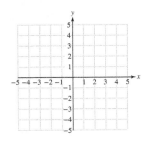 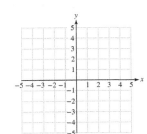 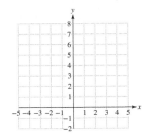 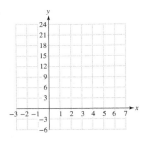

49. $f(x) = -x^2 + 3x - \dfrac{9}{4}$ **50.** $f(x) = -x^2 - \dfrac{3}{2}x - \dfrac{9}{16}$ **51.** $f(x) = -x^2 - 2x + 3$ 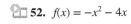**52.** $f(x) = -x^2 - 4x$

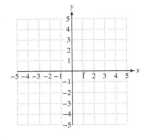 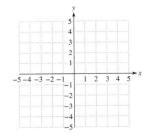 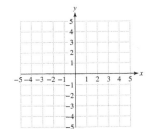 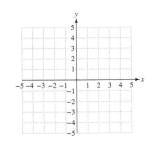

Concept 4: Applications and Modeling of Quadratic Functions

 53. A set of fireworks mortar shells is launched from the staging platform at 100 ft/sec from an initial height of 8 ft above the ground. The height of the fireworks, $h(t)$, can be modeled by

$$h(t) = -16t^2 + 100t + 8, \text{ where } t \text{ is the time in seconds after launch. } \textbf{(See Example 4.)}$$

    a. What is the maximum height that the shells can reach before exploding?

    b. For how many seconds after launch would the fuses need to be set so that the mortar shells would in fact explode at the maximum height?

54. A baseball player throws a ball, and the height of the ball (in feet) can be approximated by

$$y(x) = -0.011x^2 + 0.577x + 5$$

where x is the horizontal position of the ball measured in feet from the origin.

    a. For what value of x will the ball reach its highest point? Round to the nearest foot.

    b. What is the maximum height of the ball? Round to the nearest tenth of a foot.

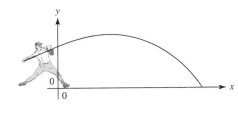

55. Gas mileage depends in part on the speed of the car. The gas mileage of a subcompact car is given by $m(x) = -0.04x^2 + 3.6x - 49$, where $20 \leq x \leq 70$ represents the speed in miles per hour and $m(x)$ is given in miles per gallon.

    a. At what speed will the car get the maximum gas mileage?

    b. What is the maximum gas mileage?

56. Gas mileage depends in part on the speed of the car. The gas mileage of a luxury car is given by $L(x) = -0.015x^2 + 1.44x - 21$, where $25 \leq x \leq 70$ represents the speed in miles per hour and $L(x)$ is given in miles per gallon.

    a. At what speed will the car get the maximum gas mileage?

    b. What is the maximum gas mileage? Round to the nearest whole unit.

57. The *Clostridium tetani* bacterium is cultured to produce tetanus toxin used in an inactive form for the tetanus vaccine. The amount of toxin produced per batch increases with time and then becomes unstable. The amount of toxin $b(t)$ (in grams) as a function of time t (in hours) can be approximated by:

$$b(t) = -\frac{1}{1152}t^2 + \frac{1}{12}t$$

    a. How many hours will it take to produce the maximum yield?

    b. What is the maximum yield?

58. The bacterium *Pseudomonas aeruginosa* is cultured with an initial population of 10^4 active organisms. The population of active bacteria increases up to a point, and then due to a limited food supply and an increase of waste products, the population of living organisms decreases. Over the first 48 hr, the population $P(t)$ can be approximated by:

$$P(t) = -1718.75t^2 + 82{,}500t + 10{,}000$$

$$\text{where } 0 \leq t \leq 48$$

    a. Find the time required for the population to reach its maximum value.

    b. What is the maximum population?

For Exercises 59–64, use the standard form of a parabola given by $y = ax^2 + bx + c$ to write an equation of a parabola that passes through the given points. **(See Example 5.)**

59. $(0, 4), (1, 0)$ and $(-1, -10)$

60. $(0, 3), (3, 0), (-1, 8)$

61. $(2, 1), (-2, 5),$ and $(1, -4)$

62. $(1, 2), (-1, -6),$ and $(2, -3)$

63. $(2, -4), (1, 1),$ and $(-1, -7)$

64. $(1, 4), (-1, 6),$ and $(2, 18)$

Expanding Your Skills

65. A farmer wants to fence a rectangular corral adjacent to the side of a barn; however, she has only 200 ft of fencing and wants to enclose the largest possible area. See the figure.

    a. If x represents the length of the corral and y represents the width, explain why the dimensions of the corral are subject to the constraint $2x + y = 200$.

    b. The area of the corral is given by $A = xy$. Use the constraint equation from part (a) to express A as a function of x, where $0 < x < 100$.

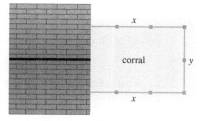

    c. Use the function from part (b) to find the dimensions of the corral that will yield the maximum area. [*Hint:* Find the vertex of the function from part (b).]

834   **Chapter 11** Quadratic Equations and Functions

66. A veterinarian wants to construct two equal-sized pens of maximum area out of 240 ft of fencing. See the figure.

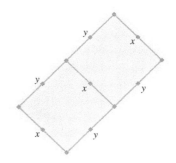

  a. If x represents the length of each pen and y represents the width of each pen, explain why the dimensions of the pens are subject to the constraint $3x + 4y = 240$.

  b. The area of each individual pen is given by $A = xy$. Use the constraint equation from part (a) to express A as a function of x, where $0 < x < 80$.

  c. Use the function from part (b) to find the dimensions of an individual pen that will yield the maximum area. [*Hint:* Find the vertex of the function from part (b).]

Graphing Calculator Exercises

For Exercises 67–72, graph the functions in Exercises 45–50 on a graphing calculator. Use the *Max* or *Min* feature to approximate the vertex.

67. $Y_1 = x^2 + 2x - 3$ (Exercise 45)

68. $Y_1 = x^2 + 4x + 3$ (Exercise 46)

69. $Y_1 = 2x^2 - 2x + 4$ (Exercise 47)

70. $Y_1 = 2x^2 - 12x + 19$ (Exercise 48)

71. $Y_1 = -x^2 + 3x - \dfrac{9}{4}$ (Exercise 49)

72. $Y_1 = -x^2 - \dfrac{3}{2}x - \dfrac{9}{16}$ (Exercise 50)

Group Activity

Creating a Quadratic Model of the Form $y = a(x - h)^2 + k$

Estimated time: 20 minutes

Group Size: 3

In an earlier group activity, we modeled the path of a softball that was thrown from right field to third base. The data points are given in the table. The values of t represent the time in seconds after the ball was released, and y represents the height of the ball in feet.

Time (sec) t	0	0.2	0.4	0.6	0.8	1.0	1.2	1.4	1.6	1.8	2.0
Height (ft) y	5	11	16	19	21	22	21	19	16	12	6

1. Graph the points defined by (t, y) in the table.

2. Select a point that you think best represents the vertex of the parabola. Label this point (h, k).

$(h, k) =$ _____

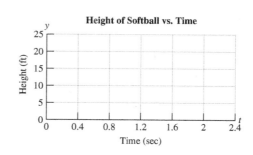

Height of Softball vs. Time

3. Substitute the values of h and k into the formula $y = a(t - h)^2 + k$, and write the equation here.

$$y = a(t - \underline{\hspace{1cm}})^2 + \underline{\hspace{1cm}}$$

4. Choose a different point (t, y) from the graph. Substitute these values into the equation in step 3 and then solve for a.

5. Substitute the values of h, k, and a that you found in steps 2 and 4 into the equation $y = a(t - h)^2 + k$.

6. Use the function found in step 5 to approximate the height of the ball after 0.7 sec.

7. Use the function found in step 5 to approximate the height of the ball after 1.8 sec. How well does this value match the observed value of 12 ft?

Chapter 11   Summary

Section 11.1   Square Root Property and Completing the Square

Key Concepts

The **square root property** states that

If $x^2 = k$ then $x = \pm\sqrt{k}$

Follow these steps to solve a quadratic equation in the form $ax^2 + bx + c = 0$ $(a \neq 0)$ by completing the square and applying the square root property:

1. Divide both sides by a to make the leading coefficient 1.
2. Isolate the variable terms on one side of the equation.
3. Complete the square: Add the square of one-half the linear term coefficient to both sides of the equation. Then factor the resulting perfect square trinomial.
4. Apply the square root property and solve for x.

Examples

Example 1

$$(x - 5)^2 = -13$$
$$x - 5 = \pm\sqrt{-13} \quad \text{(square root property)}$$
$$x = 5 \pm i\sqrt{13}$$

The solution set is $\{5 \pm i\sqrt{13}\}$.

Example 2

$$2x^2 - 12x - 16 = 0$$
$$\frac{2x^2}{2} - \frac{12x}{2} - \frac{16}{2} = \frac{0}{2}$$
$$x^2 - 6x - 8 = 0$$
$$x^2 - 6x = 8$$
$$x^2 - 6x + 9 = 8 + 9 \qquad \textit{Note: } [\tfrac{1}{2}(-6)]^2 = 9$$
$$(x - 3)^2 = 17$$
$$x - 3 = \pm\sqrt{17}$$
$$x = 3 \pm \sqrt{17}$$

The solution set is $\{3 \pm \sqrt{17}\}$.

Section 11.2   Quadratic Formula

Key Concepts

The solutions to a quadratic equation
$ax^2 + bx + c = 0$ $(a \neq 0)$ are given by the **quadratic formula**

$$x = \frac{-b \pm \sqrt{b^2 - 4ac}}{2a}$$

The **discriminant** of a quadratic equation $ax^2 + bx + c = 0$ is $b^2 - 4ac$. If a, b, and c are rational numbers, then

1. If $b^2 - 4ac > 0$, then there will be two real solutions. Moreover,
   a. If $b^2 - 4ac$ is a perfect square, the solutions will be rational numbers.
   b. If $b^2 - 4ac$ is not a perfect square, the solutions will be irrational numbers.
2. If $b^2 - 4ac < 0$, then there will be two imaginary solutions.
3. If $b^2 - 4ac = 0$, then there will be one rational solution.

   Three methods to solve a quadratic equation are

1. Factoring and applying the zero product rule.
2. Completing the square and applying the square root property.
3. Using the quadratic formula.

Example

Example 1

$$3x^2 - 2x + 4 = 0$$

$$a = 3 \qquad b = -2 \qquad c = 4$$

$$x = \frac{-(-2) \pm \sqrt{(-2)^2 - 4(3)(4)}}{2(3)}$$

$$= \frac{2 \pm \sqrt{4 - 48}}{6}$$

$$= \frac{2 \pm \sqrt{-44}}{6} \qquad \text{The discriminant is } -44. \text{ Therefore, there will be two imaginary solutions.}$$

$$= \frac{2 \pm 2i\sqrt{11}}{6}$$

$$= \frac{\overset{1}{2}(1 \pm i\sqrt{11})}{\underset{3}{6}}$$

$$= \frac{1 \pm i\sqrt{11}}{3}$$

$$= \frac{1}{3} \pm \frac{\sqrt{11}}{3}i$$

The solution set is $\left\{ \dfrac{1}{3} \pm \dfrac{\sqrt{11}}{3}i \right\}$.

Section 11.3   Equations in Quadratic Form

Key Concepts

Substitution can be used to solve equations that are in quadratic form.

Example

Example 1

$$x^{2/3} - x^{1/3} - 12 = 0 \qquad \text{Let } u = x^{1/3}.$$

$$u^2 - u - 12 = 0$$

$$(u - 4)(u + 3) = 0$$

$$u = 4 \qquad \text{or} \qquad u = -3$$

$$x^{1/3} = 4 \qquad \text{or} \qquad x^{1/3} = -3$$

$$x = 64 \qquad \text{or} \qquad x = -27 \qquad \text{Cube both sides.}$$

The solution set is $\{64, -27\}$.

Section 11.4   Graphs of Quadratic Functions

Key Concepts

A quadratic function of the form $f(x) = x^2 + k$ shifts the graph of $f(x) = x^2$ up k units if $k > 0$ and down $|k|$ units if $k < 0$.

A quadratic function of the form $f(x) = (x - h)^2$ shifts the graph of $f(x) = x^2$ to the right h units if $h > 0$ and to the left $|h|$ units if $h < 0$.

The graph of a quadratic function of the form $f(x) = ax^2$ is a parabola that opens upward when $a > 0$ and opens downward when $a < 0$. If $|a| > 1$, the graph of $f(x) = x^2$ is stretched vertically by a factor of $|a|$. If $0 < |a| < 1$, the graph of $f(x) = x^2$ is shrunk vertically by a factor of $|a|$.

A quadratic function of the form $f(x) = a(x - h)^2 + k$ has vertex (h, k). If $a > 0$, the vertex represents the minimum point. If $a < 0$, the vertex represents the maximum point.

Examples

Example 1

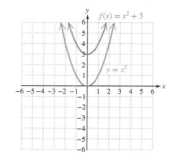

Example 2

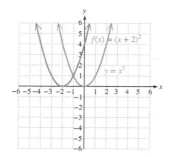

Example 3

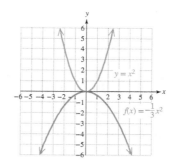

Example 4

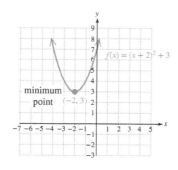

Section 11.5 Vertex of a Parabola: Applications and Modeling

Key Concepts

Completing the square is a technique used to write a quadratic function $f(x) = ax^2 + bx + c$ $(a \neq 0)$ in the form $f(x) = a(x - h)^2 + k$ for the purpose of identifying the vertex (h, k).

The **vertex formula** finds the vertex of a quadratic function $f(x) = ax^2 + bx + c$ $(a \neq 0)$.

The vertex is

$$\left(\frac{-b}{2a}, \frac{4ac - b^2}{4a} \right) \quad \text{or} \quad \left(\frac{-b}{2a}, f\left(\frac{-b}{2a} \right) \right)$$

Examples

Example 1

$$f(x) = 3x^2 + 6x + 11$$
$$= 3(x^2 + 2x \qquad) + 11$$
$$= 3(x^2 + 2x + 1 - 1) + 11$$
$$= 3(x^2 + 2x + 1) - 3 + 11$$
$$= 3(x + 1)^2 + 8$$
$$= 3[x - (-1)]^2 + 8$$

The vertex is $(-1, 8)$. Because $a = 3 > 0$, the parabola opens upward and the vertex $(-1, 8)$ is a minimum point.

Example 2

$$f(x) = 3x^2 + 6x + 11$$
$$a = 3 \qquad b = 6 \qquad c = 11$$
$$x = \frac{-6}{2(3)} = -1$$
$$f(-1) = 3(-1)^2 + 6(-1) + 11 = 8$$

The vertex is $(-1, 8)$.

Chapter 11 Review Exercises

Section 11.1

For Exercises 1–8, solve the equations by using the square root property.

1. $x^2 = 5$

2. $2y^2 = -8$

3. $a^2 = 81$

4. $3b^2 = -19$

5. $(x - 2)^2 = 72$

6. $(2x - 5)^2 = -9$

7. $(3y - 1)^2 = 3$

8. $3(m - 4)^2 = 15$

 9. The length of each side of an equilateral triangle is 10 in. Find the exact height of the triangle. Then round to the nearest tenth of an inch.

10. Use the square root property to find the length of the sides of a square whose area is 81 in^2.

 11. Use the square root property to find the exact length of the sides of a square whose area is 150 in^2. Then round to the nearest tenth of an inch.

For Exercises 12–15, find the value of n so that the expression is a perfect square trinomial. Then factor the trinomial.

12. $x^2 + 16x + n$

13. $x^2 - 9x + n$

14. $y^2 + \frac{1}{2}y + n$

15. $z^2 - \frac{2}{5}z + n$

For Exercises 16–21, solve the equation by completing the square and applying the square root property.

16. $w^2 + 4w + 13 = 0$

17. $4y^2 - 8y - 20 = 0$

18. $2x^2 = 12x + 6$

19. $-t^2 + 8t - 25 = 0$

20. $3x^2 + 2x = 1$

21. $b^2 + \frac{7}{2}b = 2$

22. Solve for r. $V = \pi r^2 h$ $(r > 0)$

23. Solve for s. $A = 6s^2$ $(s > 0)$

Section 11.2

24. Describe the type and number of solutions to a quadratic equation whose discriminant is less than zero.

For Exercises 25–30, determine the type (rational, irrational, or imaginary) and number of solutions for the equations by using the discriminant.

25. $x^2 - 5x = -6$

26. $2y^2 = -3y$

27. $z^2 + 23 = 17z$

28. $a^2 + a + 1 = 0$

29. $10b + 1 = -25b^2$

30. $3x^2 + 15 = 0$

For Exercises 31–38, solve the equations by using the quadratic formula.

31. $y^2 - 4y + 1 = 0$

32. $m^2 - 5m + 25 = 0$

33. $6a(a - 1) = 10 + a$

34. $3x(x - 3) = x - 8$

35. $b^2 - \frac{4}{25} = \frac{3}{5}b$

36. $k^2 + 0.4k = 0.05$

37. $-32 + 4x - x^2 = 0$

38. $8y - y^2 = 10$

For Exercises 39–42, solve using any method.

39. $3x^2 - 4x = 6$

40. $\frac{w}{8} - \frac{2}{w} = \frac{3}{4}$

41. $y^2 + 14y = -46$

42. $(a + 1)^2 = 11$

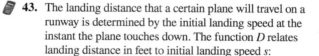 **43.** The landing distance that a certain plane will travel on a runway is determined by the initial landing speed at the instant the plane touches down. The function D relates landing distance in feet to initial landing speed s:

$$D(s) = \frac{1}{10}s^2 - 3s + 22 \text{ for } s \geq 50$$

where s is in feet per second.

a. Find the landing distance for a plane traveling 150 ft/sec at touchdown.

b. If the landing speed is too fast, the pilot may run out of runway. If the speed is too slow, the plane may stall. Find the maximum initial landing speed of a plane for a runway that is 1000 ft long. Round to one decimal place.

44. The recent population of Kenya (in thousands) can be approximated by $P(t) = 4.62t^2 + 564.6t + 13{,}128$ where t is the number of years since 1974.

    a. If this trend continues, predict the number of people in Kenya for the year 2025.

    b. In what year after 1974 will the population of Kenya reach 50 million? (*Hint:* 50 million equals 50,000 thousand.)

45. A custom-built kitchen island is in the shape of a rectangle. The length is 1 ft more than twice the width. If the area is 22.32 ft^2, determine the dimensions of the island. Round the length and width to the nearest tenth of a foot.

© Photodisc/Getty Images RF

46. Lincoln, Nebraska, Kansas City, Missouri, and Omaha, Nebraska, form the vertices of a right triangle. The distance between Lincoln and Kansas City is 10 mi more than 3 times the distance between Lincoln and Omaha. If the distance from Omaha and Kansas City is 167 mi, find the distance between Lincoln and Omaha. Round to the nearest mile.

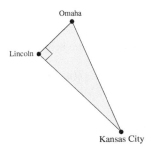

Section 11.3

For Exercises 47–56, solve the equations.

47. $x - 4\sqrt{x} - 21 = 0$

48. $n - 6\sqrt{n} + 8 = 0$

49. $y^4 - 11y^2 + 18 = 0$

50. $2m^4 - m^2 - 3 = 0$

51. $t^{2/5} + t^{1/5} - 6 = 0$

52. $p^{2/5} - 3p^{1/5} + 2 = 0$

53. $\dfrac{2t}{t+1} + \dfrac{-3}{t-2} = 1$

54. $\dfrac{1}{m-2} - \dfrac{m}{m+3} = 2$

55. $(x^2 + 5)^2 + 2(x^2 + 5) - 8 = 0$

56. $(x^2 - 3)^2 - 5(x^2 - 3) + 4 = 0$

Section 11.4

For Exercises 57–64, graph the function and write the domain and range in interval notation.

57. $g(x) = x^2 - 5$ **58.** $f(x) = x^2 + 3$

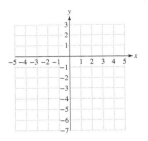 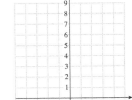

59. $h(x) = (x - 5)^2$ **60.** $k(x) = (x + 3)^2$

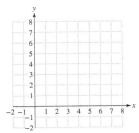 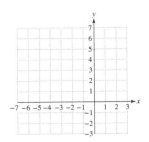

61. $m(x) = -2x^2$

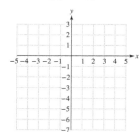

62. $n(x) = -4x^2$

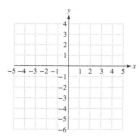

63. $p(x) = -2(x - 5)^2 - 5$

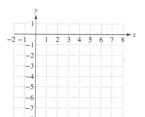

64. $q(x) = -4(x + 3)^2 + 3$

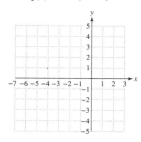

For Exercises 65–66, write the coordinates of the vertex of the parabola and determine if the vertex is a maximum point or a minimum point. Then write the maximum or the minimum value.

65. $t(x) = \dfrac{1}{3}(x - 4)^2 + \dfrac{5}{3}$

66. $s(x) = -\dfrac{5}{7}(x - 1)^2 - \dfrac{1}{7}$

For Exercises 67–68, write the equation of the axis of symmetry of the parabola.

67. $a(x) = -\dfrac{3}{2}\left(x + \dfrac{2}{11}\right)^2 - \dfrac{4}{13}$

68. $w(x) = -\dfrac{4}{3}\left(x - \dfrac{3}{16}\right)^2 + \dfrac{2}{9}$

Section 11.5

For Exercises 69–72, write the function in the form $f(x) = a(x - h)^2 + k$ by completing the square. Then write the coordinates of the vertex.

69. $z(x) = x^2 - 6x + 7$

70. $b(x) = x^2 - 4x - 44$

71. $p(x) = -5x^2 - 10x - 13$

72. $q(x) = -3x^2 - 24x - 54$

For Exercises 73–76, find the coordinates of the vertex of each parabola by using the vertex formula.

73. $f(x) = -2x^2 + 4x - 17$

74. $g(x) = -4x^2 - 8x + 3$

75. $m(x) = 3x^2 - 3x + 11$

76. $n(x) = 3x^2 + 2x - 7$

77. For the quadratic equation $y = \dfrac{3}{4}x^2 - 3x$,

   a. Write the coordinates of the vertex.

   b. Find the x- and y-intercepts.

   c. Use this information to sketch a graph of the parabola.

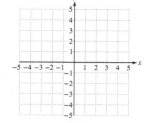

78. For the quadratic equation $y = -(x + 2)^2 + 4$,

   a. Write the coordinates of the vertex.

   b. Find the x- and y-intercepts.

   c. Use this information to sketch a graph of the parabola.

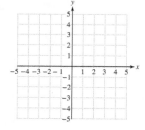

79. The height $h(t)$ (in feet) of a projectile fired vertically into the air from the ground is given by the equation $h(t) = -16t^2 + 96t$, where t represents the number of seconds after launch.

   a. How long will it take the projectile to reach its maximum height?

   b. What is the maximum height?

80. The weekly profit, $P(x)$ (in dollars), for a catering service is given by $P(x) = -0.053x^2 + 15.9x + 7.5$. In this context, x is the number of meals prepared.

   a. Find the number of meals that should be prepared to obtain the maximum profit.

   b. What is the maximum profit?

81. Write an equation of a parabola that passes through the points $(-3, -4)$, $(-2, -5)$, and $(1, 4)$.

82. Write an equation of a parabola that passes through the points $(4, 18)$, $(-2, 12)$, and $(-1, 8)$.

Chapter 11   Test

For Exercises 1–3, solve the equation by using the square root property.

1. $(x + 3)^2 = 25$

2. $(p - 2)^2 = 12$

3. $(m + 1)^2 = -1$

4. Find the value of n so that the expression is a perfect square trinomial. Then factor the trinomial $d^2 + 11d + n$.

For Exercises 5–6, solve the equation by completing the square and applying the square root property.

5. $2x^2 + 12x - 36 = 0$

6. $2x^2 = 3x - 7$

For Exercises 7–8,

   a. Write the equation in standard form $ax^2 + bx + c = 0$.

   b. Identify a, b, and c.

   c. Find the discriminant.

   d. Determine the number and type (rational, irrational, or imaginary) of solutions.

7. $x^2 - 3x = -12$

8. $y(y - 2) = -1$

For Exercises 9–10, solve the equation by using the quadratic formula.

9. $3x^2 - 4x + 1 = 0$

10. $x(x + 6) = -11 - x$

11. The base of a triangle is 3 ft less than twice the height. The area of the triangle is 14 ft^2. Find the base and the height. Round the answers to the nearest tenth of a foot.

12. A circular garden has an area of approximately 450 ft^2. Find the radius. Round the answer to the nearest tenth of a foot.

For Exercises 13–21, solve the equation.

13. $x - \sqrt{x} - 6 = 0$

14. $y^{2/3} + 2y^{1/3} = 8$

15. $(3y - 8)^2 - 13(3y - 8) + 30 = 0$

16. $p^4 - 15p^2 = -54$

17. $3 = \dfrac{y}{2} - \dfrac{1}{y + 1}$

18. $2x^2 - 9x = 5$

19. $x^2 - 8x + 1 = 0$

20. $(x + 7)^2 = -24$

21. $x(x - 12) = -13$

22. Find the vertex of $y = x^2 - 6x - 8$ two ways,

   a. By completing the square.

   b. By using the vertex formula.

For Exercises 23–25, graph the function. Use the graph to write the domain and range in interval notation.

23. $h(x) = x^2 - 4$

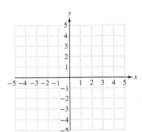

24. $f(x) = -(x - 4)^2$

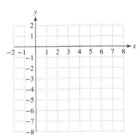

25. $g(x) = \dfrac{1}{2}(x + 2)^2 - 3$

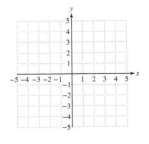

26. A child launches a toy rocket from the ground. The height of the rocket can be determined by its horizontal distance from the launch pad x by

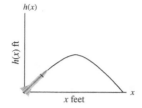

$$h(x) = -\frac{x^2}{256} + x$$

where x and $h(x)$ are in feet. How many feet from the launch pad will the rocket hit the ground?

27. The recent population of India (in millions) can be approximated by $P(t) = 0.135t^2 + 12.6t + 600$, where $t = 0$ corresponds to the year 1974.

   a. Use the function to estimate the number of people in India in the year 2014.

   b. Approximate the year in which the population of India reached 1 billion (1000 million). (Round to the nearest year.)

28. Explain the relationship between the graphs of $y = x^2$ and $y = x^2 - 2$.

29. Explain the relationship between the graphs of $y = x^2$ and $y = (x + 3)^2$.

30. Explain the relationship between the graphs of $y = 4x^2$ and $y = -4x^2$.

31. Given the function defined by

$$f(x) = -(x - 4)^2 + 2$$

   a. Identify the vertex of the parabola.

   b. Does this parabola open upward or downward?

   c. Does the vertex represent the maximum or minimum point of the function?

   d. What is the maximum or minimum value of the function f?

   e. Write an equation for the axis of symmetry.

32. For the function defined by $g(x) = 2x^2 - 20x + 51$, find the vertex by using two methods.

   a. Complete the square to write $g(x)$ in the form $g(x) = a(x - h)^2 + k$. Identify the vertex.

   b. Use the vertex formula to find the vertex.

33. Given $f(x) = x^2 + 4x - 12$

   a. Write the equation for the function in the form $f(x) = a(x - h)^2 + k$.

   b. Determine the vertex.

   c. Find the x- and y-intercepts.

   d. Determine the maximum or minimum value.

   e. Write an equation for the axis of symmetry.

34. A farmer has 400 ft of fencing with which to enclose a rectangular field. The field is situated such that one of its sides is adjacent to a river and requires no fencing. The area of the field (in square feet) can be modeled by

$$A(x) = -\frac{x^2}{2} + 200x$$

where x is the length of the side parallel to the river (measured in feet).

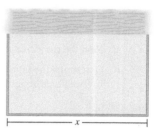

   a. Determine the value of x that maximizes the area of the field.

   b. Determine the maximum area that can be enclosed.

Chapters 1–11   Cumulative Review Exercises

1. Given $A = \{2, 4, 6, 8, 10\}$ and $B = \{2, 8, 12, 16\}$

   a. Find $A \cup B$.   **b.** Find $A \cap B$.

2. Perform the indicated operations and simplify.

$$(2x^2 - 5) - (x + 3)(5x - 2)$$

3. Simplify completely. $4^0 - \left(\frac{1}{2}\right)^{-3} - 81^{1/2}$

4. Perform the indicated operation. Write the answer in scientific notation.

$$(3 \times 10^{12})(6 \times 10^{-3})$$

5. a. Factor completely. $x^3 + 2x^2 - 9x - 18$

    b. Divide by using long division. Identify the quotient and remainder.

$$(x^3 + 2x^2 - 9x - 18) \div (x - 3)$$

6. Multiply. $(\sqrt{x} - \sqrt{2})(\sqrt{x} + \sqrt{2})$

7. Simplify. $\dfrac{4}{\sqrt{2x}}$

8. Jacques invests a total of $10,000 in two mutual funds. After 1 yr, one fund produced 12% growth, and the other lost 3%. Find the amount invested in each fund if the total investment grew by $900.

9. Solve the system of equations.

$$\frac{1}{9}x - \frac{1}{3}y = -\frac{13}{9}$$

$$x - \frac{1}{2}y = \frac{9}{2}$$

10. An object is fired straight up into the air from an initial height of 384 ft with an initial velocity of 160 ft/sec. The height in feet is given by

$$h(t) = -16t^2 + 160t + 384$$

where t is the time in seconds after launch.

    a. Find the height of the object after 3 sec.

    b. Find the height of the object after 7 sec.

    c. Find the time required for the object to hit the ground.

11. Solve. $(x - 3)^2 + 16 = 0$

12. Solve. $2x^2 + 5x - 1 = 0$

13. Find the value of n so that the expression is a perfect square trinomial. Then factor the trinomial $x^2 + 10x + n$.

14. Factor completely. $2x^3 + 250$

15. Graph the equation. $3x - 5y = 10$

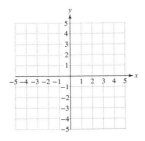

16. a. Find the x-intercepts of the function defined by $g(x) = 2x^2 - 9x + 10$.

    b. What is the y-intercept?

17. Explain why this relation is *not* a function.

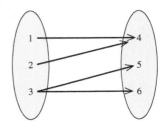

18. Graph the function defined by $f(x) = \dfrac{1}{x}$.

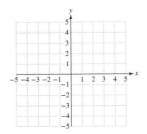

19. The quantity y varies directly as x and inversely as z. If $y = 15$ when $x = 50$ and $z = 10$, find y when $x = 65$ and $z = 5$.

20. The yearly number of flights (including passenger flights and cargo flights) at a large airport can be approximated by $F(x) = 300{,}000 + 0.008x$, where x is the number of passengers.

    a. Is this function linear, quadratic, constant, or other?

    b. Find the y-intercept and interpret its meaning in the context of this problem.

    c. What is the slope of the function and what does the slope mean in the context of this problem?

21. Let $m(x) = \sqrt{x + 4}$ and $n(x) = x^2 + 2$. Find

    a. The domain of m **b.** The domain of n

22. Consider the graph of $y = f(x)$. Find

   a. The domain   **b.** The range

   c. $f(1)$ **d.** $f(0)$

   e. For what value(s) of x is $f(x) = 0$?

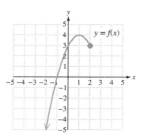

23. Solve. $\sqrt{8x + 5} = \sqrt{2x} + 2$

24. Solve for f. $\dfrac{1}{p} + \dfrac{1}{q} = \dfrac{1}{f}$

25. Solve. $\dfrac{15}{t^2 - 2t - 8} = \dfrac{1}{t - 4} + \dfrac{2}{t + 2}$

26. Simplify. $\dfrac{y - \dfrac{4}{y - 3}}{y - 4}$

27. Given the function defined by $f(x) = 2(x - 3)^2 + 1$

   a. Write the coordinates of the vertex.

   b. Does the graph of the function open upward or downward?

   c. Write the coordinates of the y-intercept.

   d. Find the x-intercepts, if possible.

   e. Sketch the function.

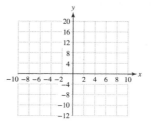

28. Find the vertex of the parabola.

$$f(x) = x^2 - 16x + 2$$

Conic Sections

13

CHAPTER OUTLINE

Mathematics in Engineering

In this chapter, we will revisit our study of parabolas as well as two new curves called *ellipses* and *hyperbolas*. These curves are called **conic sections**. Conic sections and their three-dimensional counterparts have numerous applications in engineering. For example, the mirror in a reflecting telescope has cross sections in the shape of a parabola. This is important because the curved surface of the mirror focuses light to a common point called the **focus**. This targeted focusing of light enables astronomers to view an image from a distant star with better clarity.

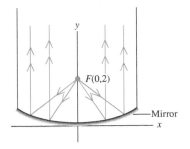

© Aaron Roeth Photography

The cooling towers for nuclear power plants have cross sections in the shape of a hyperbola. One advantage of a hyperbolic cooling tower is that air accelerates as it rises inside, toward the narrow portion of the tower. This provides for an efficient, nonturbulent flow. Then, above the narrow part, the tower flares out for efficient dispersal of warm air.

The ellipse is an oval-shaped curve that also has numerous applications such as in architectural design and for describing the orbits of planets. For example, the Roman Coliseum is an elliptical stone and concrete amphitheater in the center of Rome, built between 70 A.D. and 80 A.D. The Coliseum seated approximately 50,000 spectators and was used for gladiatorial contests among other things.

© Michael Evans/Life File/Getty Images RF

Section 13.1   Distance Formula, Midpoint Formula, and Circles

Concepts

1. Distance Formula
2. Circles
3. Writing an Equation of a Circle
4. The Midpoint Formula

> **TIP:** Squaring any real-valued quantity results in a nonnegative real number. Therefore, the absolute value bars can be dropped.

1. Distance Formula

Suppose we are given two points (x_1, y_1) and (x_2, y_2) in a rectangular coordinate system. The distance between the two points can be found by using the Pythagorean theorem (Figure 13-1).

First draw a right triangle with the distance d as the hypotenuse. The length of the horizontal leg a is $|x_2 - x_1|$, and the length of the vertical leg b is $|y_2 - y_1|$. From the Pythagorean theorem we have

$$d^2 = a^2 + b^2$$

$$= |x_2 - x_1|^2 + |y_2 - y_1|^2$$

$$= (x_2 - x_1)^2 + (y_2 - y_1)^2$$

$$d = \pm\sqrt{(x_2 - x_1)^2 + (y_2 - y_1)^2}$$

$$= \sqrt{(x_2 - x_1)^2 + (y_2 - y_1)^2}$$

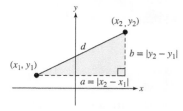

Figure 13-1

Because distance is positive, reject the negative value.

The Distance Formula

The distance d between the points (x_1, y_1) and (x_2, y_2) is

$$d = \sqrt{(x_2 - x_1)^2 + (y_2 - y_1)^2}$$

Example 1   Finding the Distance Between Two Points

Find the distance between the points $(-2, 3)$ and $(4, -1)$ (Figure 13-2).

Solution:

$$\underset{(x_1, y_1)}{(-2, 3)} \quad \text{and} \quad \underset{(x_2, y_2)}{(4, -1)}$$

Label the points.

$$d = \sqrt{(x_2 - x_1)^2 + (y_2 - y_1)^2}$$

$$= \sqrt{[(4) - (-2)]^2 + [(-1) - (3)]^2}$$

Apply the distance formula.

$$= \sqrt{(6)^2 + (-4)^2}$$

$$= \sqrt{36 + 16}$$

$$= \sqrt{52}$$

$$= \sqrt{4 \cdot 13}$$

$$= 2\sqrt{13}$$

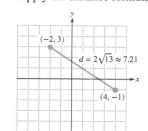

Figure 13-2

Skill Practice

1. Find the distance between the points $(-4, -2)$ and $(2, -5)$.

Answer

1. $3\sqrt{5}$

TIP: The order in which the points are labeled does not affect the result of the distance formula. For example, if the points in Example 1 had been labeled in reverse, the distance formula would still yield the same result:

$$\begin{array}{lll} (-2, 3) & \text{and} & (4, -1) \end{array}$$
$$(x_2, y_2) \qquad\qquad (x_1, y_1)$$

$$d = \sqrt{(x_2 - x_1)^2 + (y_2 - y_1)^2}$$
$$= \sqrt{[(-2) - (4)]^2 + [3 - (-1)]^2}$$
$$= \sqrt{(-6)^2 + (4)^2}$$
$$= \sqrt{36 + 16}$$
$$= \sqrt{52}$$
$$= 2\sqrt{13}$$

2. Circles

A **circle** is defined as the set of all points in a plane that are equidistant from a fixed point called the **center**. The fixed distance from the center is called the **radius** and is denoted by r, where $r > 0$.

Suppose a circle is centered at the point (h, k) and has radius, r (Figure 13-3). The distance formula can be used to derive an equation of the circle.

Let (x, y) be any arbitrary point on the circle. Then, by definition, the distance between (h, k) and (x, y) must be r.

$$\sqrt{(x - h)^2 + (y - k)^2} = r$$
$$(x - h)^2 + (y - k)^2 = r^2 \qquad \text{Square both sides.}$$

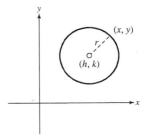

Figure 13-3

Standard Equation of a Circle

The **standard equation of a circle**, centered at (h, k) with radius r, is given by

$$(x - h)^2 + (y - k)^2 = r^2 \qquad \text{where } r > 0.$$

Note: If a circle is centered at the origin $(0, 0)$, then $h = 0$ and $k = 0$, and the equation simplifies to $x^2 + y^2 = r^2$.

Example 2   **Graphing a Circle**

Find the center and radius of the circle. Then graph the circle.

$$(x - 3)^2 + (y + 4)^2 = 36$$

Solution:

$$(x - 3)^2 + (y + 4)^2 = 36$$
$$(x - 3)^2 + [y - (-4)]^2 = (6)^2$$
$$h = 3, k = -4, \text{ and } r = 6$$

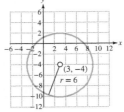

Figure 13-4

The equation is in standard form $(x - h)^2 + (y - k)^2 = r^2$. The center is $(3, -4)$, and the radius is $r = 6$. To graph the circle, first locate the center. From the center, mark points 6 units to the right, left, above, and below the center. Then sketch the circle through these four points (Figure 13-4).

Note that the center of the circle is not actually part of the circle. It is drawn as an open dot for reference.

Answer

2. Center: $(-1, 2)$; radius: 3

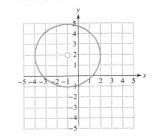

Skill Practice Find the center and radius of the circle. Then graph the circle.

   2. $(x + 1)^2 + (y - 2)^2 = 9$

Calculator Connections

Topic: Graphing a Circle

Graphing calculators are designed to graph *functions*, in which y is written in terms of x. A circle is not a function. However, it can be graphed as the union of two functions—one representing the top semicircle and the other representing the bottom semicircle.

Solving for y in Example 2, we have

$$(x - 3)^2 + (y + 4)^2 = 36$$

Graph these functions as Y_1 and Y_2, using a square viewing window.

$$(y + 4)^2 = 36 - (x - 3)^2$$

$$y + 4 = \pm\sqrt{36 - (x - 3)^2}$$

$$y = -4 \pm \sqrt{36 - (x - 3)^2}$$

$$Y_1 = -4 + \sqrt{36 - (x - 3)^2}$$

$$Y_2 = -4 - \sqrt{36 - (x - 3)^2}$$

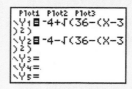
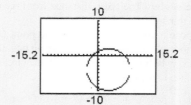

Notice that the image from the calculator does not show the upper and lower semicircles connecting at their endpoints, when in fact the semicircles should "hook up." This is due to the calculator's limited resolution.

Example 3　Graphing a Circle

Find the center and radius of each circle. Then graph the circle.

a. $x^2 + \left(y - \dfrac{10}{3}\right)^2 = \dfrac{25}{9}$　　　**b.** $x^2 + y^2 = 10$

Solution:

a. $x^2 + \left(y - \dfrac{10}{3}\right)^2 = \dfrac{25}{9}$

$(x - 0)^2 + \left(y - \dfrac{10}{3}\right)^2 = \left(\dfrac{5}{3}\right)^2$

The equation is now in standard form
$(x - h)^2 + (y - k)^2 = r^2$.

The center is $\left(0, \dfrac{10}{3}\right)$ and the radius is $\dfrac{5}{3}$
(Figure 13-5).

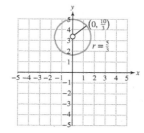

Figure 13-5

b. $x^2 + y^2 = 10$

$(x - 0)^2 + (y - 0)^2 = (\sqrt{10})^2$

$(x - h)^2 + (y - k)^2 = r^2$

The center is $(0, 0)$ and the radius is $\sqrt{10} \approx 3.16$ (Figure 13-6).

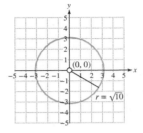

Figure 13-6

Skill Practice Find the center and radius of the circle. Then graph the circle.

3. $\left(x + \dfrac{7}{2}\right)^2 + y^2 = \dfrac{9}{4}$

Sometimes it is necessary to complete the square to write an equation of a circle in standard form.

Example 4 **Writing an Equation of a Circle in the Form** $(x - h)^2 + (y - k)^2 = r^2$

Identify the center and radius of the circle given by the equation.

$$x^2 + y^2 + 2x - 16y + 61 = 0$$

Solution:

$x^2 + y^2 + 2x - 16y + 61 = 0$	To identify the center and radius, write the equation in the form $(x - h)^2 + (y - k)^2 = r^2$.
$(x^2 + 2x \quad) + (y^2 - 16y \quad) = -61$	Group the x terms and group the y terms. Move the constant to the right-hand side.
$(x^2 + 2x + 1) + (y^2 - 16y + 64) = -61 + 1 + 64$	• Complete the square on x. Add $\left[\frac{1}{2}(2)\right]^2 = 1$ to both sides of the equation. • Complete the square on y. Add $\left[\frac{1}{2}(-16)\right]^2 = 64$ to both sides of the equation.
$(x + 1)^2 + (y - 8)^2 = 4$ $[x - (-1)]^2 + (y - 8)^2 = 2^2$	Factor and simplify. Standard form: $(x - h)^2 + (y - k)^2 = r^2$

The center is $(-1, 8)$ and the radius is 2.

Skill Practice Identify the center and radius of the circle given by the equation.

4. $x^2 + y^2 - 10x + 4y - 7 = 0$

Answers

3. Center: $\left(-\dfrac{7}{2}, 0\right)$; radius: $\dfrac{3}{2}$

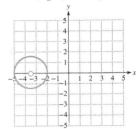

4. Center: $(5, -2)$; radius: 6

3. Writing an Equation of a Circle

Example 5   Writing an Equation of a Circle

Write an equation of the circle shown in Figure 13-7.

Solution:

The center is $(-3, 2)$; therefore, $h = -3$ and $k = 2$.
From the graph, $r = 2$.

$$(x - h)^2 + (y - k)^2 = r^2$$

$$[x - (-3)]^2 + (y - 2)^2 = (2)^2$$

$$(x + 3)^2 + (y - 2)^2 = 4$$

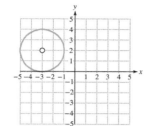

Figure 13-7

Avoiding Mistakes

Be sure that you *subtract* both coordinates of the center, when substituting the coordinates into the standard form of a circle.

Skill Practice

5. Write an equation for a circle whose center is $(6, -1)$ and whose radius is 8.

4. The Midpoint Formula

Consider two points in the coordinate plane and the line segment determined by the points. It is sometimes necessary to determine the point that is halfway between the endpoints of the segment. This point is called the *midpoint*.

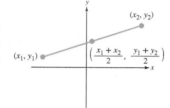

TIP: The midpoint of a line segment is found by taking the *average* of the *x*-coordinates and the *average* of the *y*-coordinates of the endpoints.

Midpoint Formula

Given two points (x_1, y_1) and (x_2, y_2), the midpoint of the line segment between the two points is given by

$$\text{Midpoint:} \quad \left(\frac{x_1 + x_2}{2}, \frac{y_1 + y_2}{2} \right)$$

Example 6   Finding the Midpoint of a Segment

Find the midpoint of the line segment with the given endpoints.

    a. $(-4, 6)$ and $(8, 1)$ **b.** $(-1.2, -3.1)$ and $(-6.6, 1.2)$

Solution:

    a. $(-4, 6)$ and $(8, 1)$

        (x_1, y_1) (x_2, y_2)

$$\left(\frac{-4 + 8}{2}, \frac{6 + 1}{2} \right) \qquad \text{Apply the midpoint formula: } \left(\frac{x_1 + x_2}{2}, \frac{y_1 + y_2}{2} \right)$$

$$\left(2, \frac{7}{2} \right) \qquad \text{Simplify.}$$

The midpoint of the segment is $\left(2, \frac{7}{2}\right)$.

Avoiding Mistakes

Always remember that the midpoint of a line segment is a *point*. The answer should be an ordered pair, (x, y).

Answer

5. $(x - 6)^2 + (y + 1)^2 = 64$

b. $(-1.2, -3.1)$ and $(-6.6, 1.2)$

$\quad\underset{(x_1, y_1)}{}\qquad\qquad\underset{(x_2, y_2)}{}$

$\left(\dfrac{-1.2 + (-6.6)}{2}, \dfrac{-3.1 + 1.2}{2}\right)$ Apply the midpoint formula.

$(-3.9, -0.95)$ Simplify.

Skill Practice Find the midpoint of the line segment with the given endpoints.

6. $(5, 6)$ and $(-10, 4)$ **7.** $(-2.6, -6.3)$ and $(1.2, 4.1)$

| **Example 7** | **Applying the Midpoint Formula** |

Suppose that $(-2, 3)$ and $(4, 1)$ are endpoints of a diameter of a circle.

a. Find the center of the circle.   **b.** Write an equation of the circle.

Solution:

a. Because the midpoint of a diameter of a circle is the center of the circle, apply the midpoint formula. See Figure 13-8.

$(-2, 3)$ and $(4, 1)$
$\underset{(x_1, y_1)}{}\qquad\quad\underset{(x_2, y_2)}{}$

$\left(\dfrac{x_1 + x_2}{2}, \dfrac{y_1 + y_2}{2}\right)$

$\left(\dfrac{-2 + 4}{2}, \dfrac{3 + 1}{2}\right)$ Apply the midpoint formula.

$(1, 2)$ Simplify.

Figure 13-8

The center of the circle is $(1, 2)$.

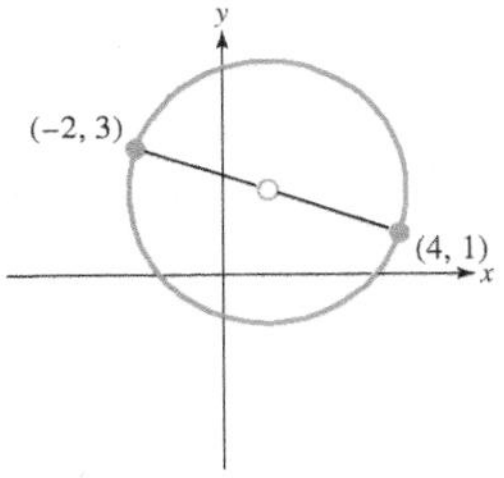

b. The radius can be determined by finding the distance between the center and either endpoint of the diameter.

$(1, 2)$ and $(4, 1)$
$\underset{(x_1, y_1)}{}\qquad\quad\underset{(x_2, y_2)}{}$

$d = \sqrt{(x_2 - x_1)^2 + (y_2 - y_1)^2}$ Apply the distance formula.

$d = \sqrt{(4 - 1)^2 + (1 - 2)^2}$ Substitute $(1, 2)$ and $(4, 1)$ for (x_1, y_1) and (x_2, y_2).

$= \sqrt{(3)^2 + (-1)^2}$ Simplify.

$= \sqrt{10}$

The circle is represented by $(x - 1)^2 + (y - 2)^2 = (\sqrt{10})^2$

$\qquad\qquad$ or $(x - 1)^2 + (y - 2)^2 = 10$.

Skill Practice

8. Suppose that $(3, 2)$ and $(7, 10)$ are endpoints of a diameter of a circle.
   a. Find the center of the circle.
   b. Write an equation of the circle.

Answers

6. $\left(-\dfrac{5}{2}, 5\right)$ **7.** $(-0.7, -1.1)$

8. a. $(5, 6)$
   b. $(x - 5)^2 + (y - 6)^2 = 20$

Section 13.1   Practice Exercises

Vocabulary and Key Concepts

1. **a.** The distance between two distinct points (x_1, y_1) and (x_2, y_2) is given by $d =$ _____.

    b. A _____ is the set of all points equidistant from a fixed point called the _____.

    c. The distance from the center of a circle to any point on the circle is called the _____ and is often denoted by r.

    d. The standard equation of a circle with center (h, k) and radius r is given by _____.

    e. The midpoint of the line segment with endpoints (x_1, y_1) and (x_2, y_2) is given by _____.

Concept 1: Distance Formula

For Exercises 2–16, use the distance formula to find the distance between the two points. **(See Example 1.)**

2. $(-2, 7)$ and $(4, -5)$

3. $(1, 10)$ and $(-2, 4)$

4. $(0, 5)$ and $(-3, 8)$

5. $(6, 7)$ and $(3, 2)$

6. $\left(\dfrac{2}{3}, \dfrac{1}{5}\right)$ and $\left(-\dfrac{5}{6}, \dfrac{3}{10}\right)$

7. $\left(-\dfrac{1}{2}, \dfrac{5}{8}\right)$ and $\left(-\dfrac{3}{2}, \dfrac{1}{4}\right)$

8. $(4, 13)$ and $(4, -6)$

9. $(-2, 5)$ and $(-2, 9)$

10. $(8, -6)$ and $(-2, -6)$

11. $(7, 2)$ and $(15, 2)$

12. $(-6, -2)$ and $(-3, -5)$

13. $(-1, -5)$ and $(-5, -9)$

14. $(3\sqrt{5}, 2\sqrt{7})$ and $(-\sqrt{5}, -3\sqrt{7})$

15. $(4\sqrt{6}, -2\sqrt{2})$ and $(2\sqrt{6}, \sqrt{2})$

16. $(6, 0)$ and $(0, -1)$

17. Explain how to find the distance between 5 and -7 on the y-axis.

18. Explain how to find the distance between 15 and -37 on the x-axis.

19. Find the values of y such that the distance between the points $(4, 7)$ and $(-4, y)$ is 10 units.

20. Find the values of x such that the distance between the points $(-4, -2)$ and $(x, 3)$ is 13 units.

21. Find the values of x such that the distance between the points $(x, 2)$ and $(4, -1)$ is 5 units.

22. Find the values of y such that the distance between the points $(-5, 2)$ and $(3, y)$ is 10 units.

For Exercises 23–26, determine if the three points define the vertices of a right triangle.

23. $(-3, 2), (-2, -4),$ and $(3, 3)$

24. $(1, -2), (-2, 4),$ and $(7, 1)$

25. $(-3, -2), (4, -3),$ and $(1, 5)$

26. $(1, 4), (5, 3),$ and $(2, 0)$

Concept 2: Circles

For Exercises 27–47, identify the center and radius of the circle and then graph the circle. Complete the square, if necessary. **(See Examples 2–4.)**

27. $(x - 4)^2 + (y + 2)^2 = 9$

28. $(x - 3)^2 + (y + 1)^2 = 16$

29. $(x + 1)^2 + (y + 1)^2 = 1$

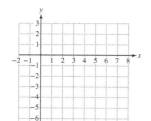

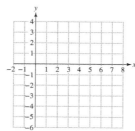

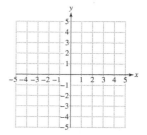

30. $(x-4)^2 + (y-4)^2 = 4$

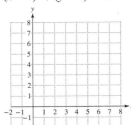

31. $x^2 + (y-2)^2 = 4$

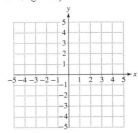

32. $(x+1)^2 + y^2 = 1$

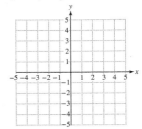

33. $(x-3)^2 + y^2 = 8$

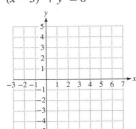

34. $x^2 + (y+2)^2 = 20$

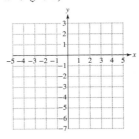

35. $x^2 + y^2 = 6$

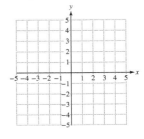

36. $x^2 + y^2 = 15$

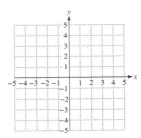

37. $\left(x + \dfrac{4}{5}\right)^2 + y^2 = \dfrac{64}{25}$

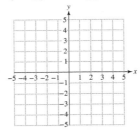

38. $x^2 + \left(y - \dfrac{5}{2}\right)^2 = \dfrac{9}{4}$

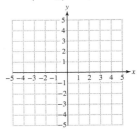

39. $x^2 + y^2 - 2x - 6y - 26 = 0$

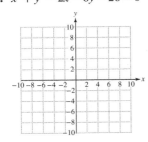

40. $x^2 + y^2 + 4x - 8y + 16 = 0$

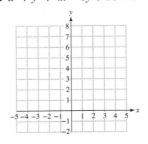

41. $x^2 + y^2 - 6y + 5 = 0$

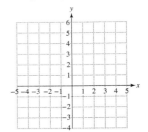

938   **Chapter 13**   Conic Sections

42. $x^2 + 2x + y^2 - 15 = 0$

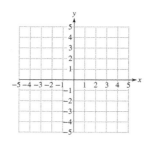

43. $x^2 + y^2 + 6y + \dfrac{65}{9} = 0$

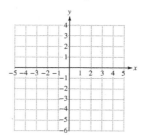

44. $x^2 + y^2 - 12x + 12y + 71 = 0$

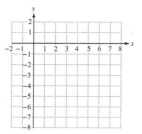

45. $x^2 + y^2 + 2x + 4y - 4 = 0$

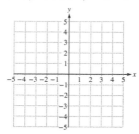

46. $2x^2 + 2y^2 = 32$

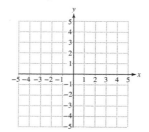

47. $3x^2 + 3y^2 = 3$

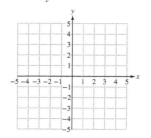

Concept 3: Writing an Equation of a Circle

48. If the diameter of a circle is 10 ft, what is the radius?

For Exercises 49–54, write an equation that represents the graph of the circle. **(See Example 5.)**

49.

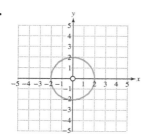

50.

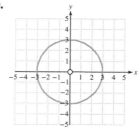

51.

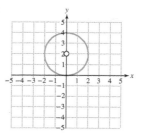

52.

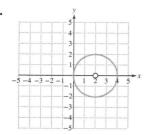

53.

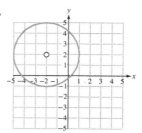

54.

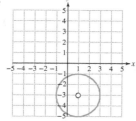

55. Write an equation of a circle centered at the origin with a radius of 7.

56. Write an equation of a circle centered at the origin with a radius of 12.

57. Write an equation of a circle centered at $(-3, -4)$ with a diameter of 12.

58. Write an equation of a circle centered at $(5, -1)$ with a diameter of 8.

59. A cell tower is a site where antennas, transmitters, and receivers are placed to create a cellular network. Suppose that a cell tower is located at a point $A(5, 3)$ on a map and its range is 1.5 mi. Write an equation that represents the boundary of the area that can receive a signal from the tower. Assume that all distances are in miles.

60. A radar transmitter on a ship has a range of 20 nautical miles. If the ship is located at a point $(-28, 32)$ on a map, write an equation for the boundary of the area within the range of the ship's radar. Assume that all distances on the map are represented in nautical miles.

Concept 4: The Midpoint Formula

For Exercises 61–64, find the midpoint of the line segment. Check your answers by plotting the midpoint on the graph.

61.

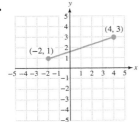

62.

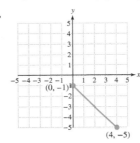

63.

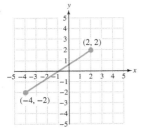

64.

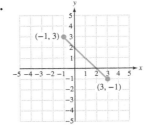

For Exercises 65–72, find the midpoint of the line segment between the two given points. **(See Example 6.)**

65. $(4, 0)$ and $(-6, 12)$

66. $(-7, 2)$ and $(-3, -2)$

67. $(-3, 8)$ and $(3, -2)$

68. $(0, 5)$ and $(4, -5)$

69. $(5, 2)$ and $(-6, 1)$

70. $(-9, 3)$ and $(0, -4)$

71. $(-2.4, -3.1)$ and $(1.6, 1.1)$

72. $(0.8, 5.3)$ and $(-4.2, 7.1)$

73. Two courier trucks leave the warehouse to make deliveries. One travels 20 mi north and 30 mi east. The other truck travels 5 mi south and 50 mi east. If the two drivers want to meet for lunch at a restaurant at a point halfway between them, where should they meet relative to the warehouse? (*Hint:* Label the warehouse as the origin, and find the coordinates of the restaurant. See the figure.)

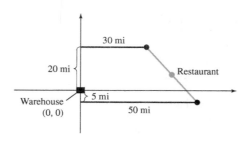

74. A map of a hiking area is drawn so that the Visitor Center is at the origin of a rectangular grid. Two hikers are located at positions $(-1, 1)$ and $(-3, -2)$ with respect to the Visitor Center where all units are in miles. A campground is located exactly halfway between the hikers. What are the coordinates of the campground?

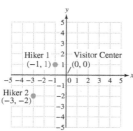

For Exercises 75–78, the two given points are endpoints of a diameter of a circle.

   a. Find the center of the circle.

   b. Write an equation of the circle. **(See Example 7.)**

75. $(-1, 2)$ and $(3, 4)$ **76.** $(-3, 3)$ and $(7, -1)$ **77.** $(-2, 3)$ and $(2, 3)$ **78.** $(-1, 3)$ and $(-1, -3)$

Expanding Your Skills

79. Write an equation of a circle whose center is $(4, 4)$ and is tangent to the x- and y-axes. (*Hint:* Sketch the circle first.)

80. Write an equation of a circle whose center is $(-3, 3)$ and is tangent to the x- and y-axes. (*Hint:* Sketch the circle first.)

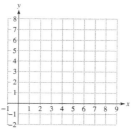

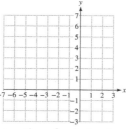

81. Write an equation of a circle whose center is $(1, 1)$ and that passes through the point $(-4, 3)$.

82. Write an equation of a circle whose center is $(-3, -1)$ and that passes through the point $(5, -2)$.

Graphing Calculator Exercises

For Exercises 83–88, graph the circle from the indicated exercise on a square viewing window, and approximate the center and the radius from the graph.

83. $(x - 4)^2 + (y + 2)^2 = 9$ (Exercise 27)   **84.** $(x - 3)^2 + (y + 1)^2 = 16$ (Exercise 28)

85. $x^2 + (y - 2)^2 = 4$ (Exercise 31)   **86.** $(x + 1)^2 + y^2 = 1$ (Exercise 32)

87. $x^2 + y^2 = 6$ (Exercise 35)   **88.** $x^2 + y^2 = 15$ (Exercise 36)

Create. Transformations, Piecewise-Defined Functions, and Probability

Transformations, Piecewise-Defined Functions, and Probability

15

Mathematics in Animation

Have you ever watched a low-quality animated cartoon in which a character is racing across the screen? Instead of moving the character across the screen, the illusion of movement is accomplished by moving the background elements such as the trees and the clouds in the *opposite* direction. That is, if the character is portrayed to move from left to right, then the background trees and clouds move from right to left. Animators accomplish this by using **transformations** of the curves representing the clouds and trees. Transformations include shifting a curve to the left, right, up, or down, along with shrinking or stretching the curve in the horizontal or vertical direction. In this chapter, we will study the transformations of basic functions.

The concept of a piecewise-defined function is also presented in this chapter. A piecewise-defined function is made up of a series of functions, each defined on an indicated domain. The concept of restricting the domain of a function on an interval is also used in computer gaming to draw figures mathematically. For example, the ice cream cone shown here was rendered from the equations

$$y = \sqrt{25 - x^2},\, y = 2.5x - 10 \text{ for } 0 \le x \le 4, \text{ and } y = -2.5x - 10 \text{ for } -4 \le x \le 0.$$

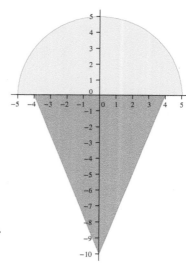

2   **Chapter 15**   Transformations, Piecewise-Defined Functions, and Probability

Section 15.1 **Transformations of Graphs and Piecewise-Defined Functions**

Concepts

1. Transformations of Graphs
2. Piecewise-Defined Functions

1. Transformations of Graphs

The graph of a quadratic function of the form $y = a(x - h)^2 + k$ has the shape of a parabola. The values of a, h, and k have the following effects on the graph of the parent function $y = x^2$.

- The value of h shifts the graph of $y = x^2$ to the left or right.
- The value of k shifts the graph of $y = x^2$ upward or downward.
- The value of a will stretch the graph vertically if $|a| > 1$ and shrink the graph vertically if $0 < |a| < 1$.
- Finally, if $a < 0$, the graph is reflected across the x-axis.

Shifting, stretching, shrinking, and reflecting the graph of a function is sometimes called *transforming graphs*. Such transformations can be extended to the graphs of any function. Given a function defined by $y = f(x)$, the graph of $y = a \cdot f(x - h) + k$ can be graphed according to the following guidelines.

Shifting and Reflecting the Graph of a Function

Given a function defined by $y = a \cdot f(x - h) + k$, then

If $k > 0$, shift the graph of $y = f(x)$ upward by k units.
If $k < 0$, shift the graph of $y = f(x)$ downward by $|k|$ units.

If $h > 0$, shift the graph of $y = f(x)$ to the right by h units.
If $h < 0$, shift the graph of $y = f(x)$ to the left by $|h|$ units.

If $a < 0$, reflect the graph of $y = f(x)$ across the x-axis.
If $|a| > 1$, stretch the graph of $y = f(x)$ vertically.
If $0 < |a| < 1$, shrink the graph of $y = f(x)$ vertically.

Example 1   **Shifting the Graph of a Function**

Graph the functions, and determine the domain and range of each.

a. $f(x) = \sqrt{x - 2}$ **b.** $g(x) = |x + 1| - 4$

Solution:

a. The graph of $y = \sqrt{x}$ is shown in black (Figure 15-1). The graph of $f(x) = \sqrt{x - 2}$ is in the form $y = f(x - h)$, where $h = 2$. Since $h > 0$, shift the graph to the right (shown in blue).

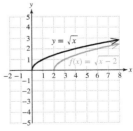

Figure 15-1

The domain of f is: $[2, \infty)$
The range of f is: $[0, \infty)$

b. The graph of $y = |x|$ is shown in black (Figure 15-2). The graph of $g(x) = |x + 1| - 4$ is in the form $y = g(x - h) + k$, where $h = -1$ and $k = -4$. Since $h < 0$, shift the graph to the left. Since $k < 0$, shift the graph downward (shown in red).

The domain of g is: $(-\infty, \infty)$
The range of g is: $[-4, \infty)$

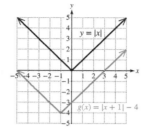

Figure 15-2

Skill Practice Graph the functions and determine the domain and range.

1. $g(x) = |x + 3|$ **2.** $f(x) = \sqrt{x - 3} - 1$

Example 2   **Reflecting the Graph of a Function**

Graph the function and determine the domain and range. $g(x) = -x^3$

Solution:

The graph of $y = x^3$ is shown in Figure 15-3. The graph of $g(x) = -x^3$ is the graph of $y = x^3$ reflected across the x-axis (Figure 15-4).

The domain of g is $(-\infty, \infty)$.
The range of g is $(-\infty, \infty)$.

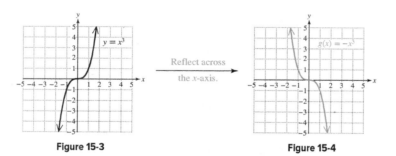

Figure 15-3   **Figure 15-4**

Skill Practice Graph the function and give the domain and range.

3. $h(x) = -|x|$

In Examples 3 and 4, we analyze graphs involving a vertical shrink or stretch from the parent function.

Answers

1. Domain: $(-\infty, \infty)$; range: $[0, \infty)$

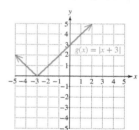

2. Domain: $[3, \infty)$; range: $[-1, \infty)$

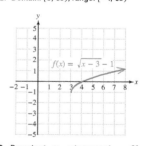

3. Domain: $(-\infty, \infty)$; range: $(-\infty, 0]$

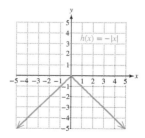

4   Chapter 15   Transformations, Piecewise-Defined Functions, and Probability

| **Example 3** | **Stretching and Shrinking the Graph of a Function** |

Graph the function and determine the domain and range. $f(x) = 3\sqrt{x}$

Solution:

The graph of $y = \sqrt{x}$ is the basic square root graph (Figure 15-5).

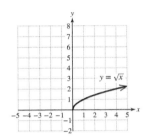

Figure 15-5

The graph of $f(x) = 3\sqrt{x}$ is the graph of $y = a\sqrt{x}$, where $a = 3$. Since $a > 1$, graph of f is the graph of $y = \sqrt{x}$ with a vertical stretch by a factor of 3 (Figure 15-6).

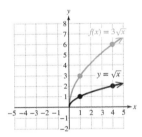

Figure 15-6

Notice that for each point on the graph of $y = \sqrt{x}$, the y-coordinate is multiplied by 3. For example, the point (1, 1) on the graph of $y = \sqrt{x}$ corresponds to the point (1, 3) on the graph of f. The point (4, 2) on the graph of $y = \sqrt{x}$ corresponds to the point (4, 6) on the graph of f.

The domain of f is $[0, \infty)$.
The range of f is $[0, \infty)$.

Skill Practice   Graph the function and determine the domain and range.

   4. $f(x) = 4|x|$

Answer

4. Domain: $(-\infty, \infty)$
    Range: $[0, \infty)$

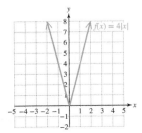

In Example 4, we apply multiple transformations to the graph of $y = f(x)$. In such a case, we apply a horizontal shift to the right or left first. Then we apply any vertical shrink, stretch, or reflection, followed by a vertical shift upward or downward.

Example 4	**Applying Multiple Transformations to a Graph**

Graph the function and determine the domain and range. $f(x) = -\dfrac{1}{2}|x - 1|$

Solution:

The graph of $y = |x|$ is the parent function (Figure 15-7).

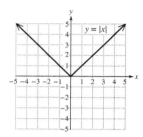

Figure 15-7

Next, the expression $x - 1$ within the absolute value bars indicates a shift to the right 1 unit (Figure 15-8).

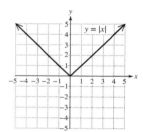

Figure 15-8

Next, the factor of $-\frac{1}{2}$ shrinks the graph vertically and reflects the graph over the x-axis. That is, the y-coordinates of the graph of $y = |x - 1|$ are multiplied by $-\frac{1}{2}$. For example, the point $(3, 2)$ on the graph of $y = |x - 1|$ (shown in green in Figure 15-9) corresponds to the point $(3, -1)$ on the graph of $f(x) = -\frac{1}{2}|x - 1|$ (shown in blue).

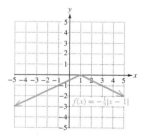

Figure 15-9

The domain of f is $(-\infty, \infty)$.
The range of f is $(-\infty, 0]$.

Skill Practice   Graph the function and determine the domain and range.

5. $g(x) = -2(x + 3)^2$

Answer

5. Domain: $(-\infty, \infty)$
    Range: $[0, \infty)$

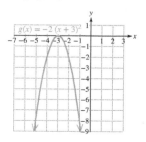

2. Piecewise-Defined Functions

Sometimes a function may be defined by more than one rule on different intervals within the domain. Such a function is called a **piecewise-defined function**. The function $y = k(x)$ pictured in Figure 15-10 is defined piecewise.

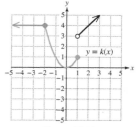

$$k(x) = \begin{cases} 4 & \text{if } x \leq -2 \\ x^2 & \text{if } -2 < x \leq 1 \\ x+2 & \text{if } x > 1 \end{cases}$$

Figure 15-10

- For x values less than or equal to -2, the function is constant and follows the first rule, $k(x) = 4$ (pictured in red).
- For x values greater than -2 and less than or equal to 1, the function follows the second rule, $k(x) = x^2$ (pictured in blue).
- For x values greater than 1, the function follows the third rule, $k(x) = x + 2$ (pictured in black).

TIP: The open dot indicates that the point (1, 3) is *not* included in the graph.

Example 5   **Evaluating a Piecewise-Defined Function**

Evaluate the function for the given values of x.

a. $k(0)$

b. $k(-3)$

c. $k(5)$ $k(x) = \begin{cases} 4 & \text{if } x \leq -2 \\ x^2 & \text{if } -2 < x \leq 1 \\ x+2 & \text{if } x > 1 \end{cases}$

d. $k(1)$

e. $k(-2)$

Solution:

To evaluate a piecewise-defined function, the value of x determines which rule to use.

a. To evaluate $k(0)$, note that $x = 0$ is on the interval $-2 < x \leq 1$. Use the *second* rule.

$$k(x) = x^2 \quad \text{for } -2 < x \leq 1$$

$$k(0) = (0)^2$$

$$= 0$$

b. To evaluate $k(-3)$, note that $x = -3$ is on the interval $x \leq -2$. Use the *first* rule.

$$k(x) = 4 \quad \text{for } x \leq -2$$

$$k(-3) = 4$$

c. To evaluate $k(5)$, note that $x = 5$ is on the interval $x > 1$. Use the *third* rule.

$$k(x) = x + 2 \quad \text{for } x > 1$$

$$k(5) = (5) + 2$$

$$= 7$$

d. To evaluate $k(1)$, note that $x = 1$ is the right endpoint of the interval $-2 < x \le 1$. Use the *second* rule.

$$k(x) = x^2 \quad \text{for } -2 < x \le 1$$
$$k(1) = (1)^2$$
$$= 1$$

e. To evaluate $k(-2)$, we see that $x = -2$ is on the interval $x \le -2$. Use the *first* rule. Note that $x = -2$ is *not* in the interval $-2 < x \le 1$.

$$k(x) = 4 \quad \text{for } x \le -2$$
$$k(-2) = 4$$

> **TIP:** The function values in Example 5 can be confirmed with the graph of $y = k(x)$ given in Figure 15-10.

Skill Practice Evaluate the function for the given values of x.

$$g(x) = \begin{cases} x - 4 & \text{if } x < -1 \\ |x| & \text{if } -1 \le x < 3 \\ 5 & \text{if } x \ge 3 \end{cases}$$

6. $g(-2)$ **7.** $g(4)$ **8.** $g(-0.5)$ **9.** $g(-1)$ **10.** $g(3)$

To graph a piecewise-defined function, graph each component function, showing only the portion of that function over the indicated domain.

Example 6   **Graphing a Piecewise-Defined Function**

Graph the function defined by $f(x) = \begin{cases} x + 3 & \text{for } x < -1 \\ |x| & \text{for } x \ge -1 \end{cases}$

Solution:

The first rule $f(x) = x + 3$ defines a line with slope of 1 and y-intercept $(0, 3)$. This line should be graphed only on the interval $x < -1$ (that is, to the left of $x = -1$). The point $(-1, 2)$ is an open dot, because the point is not part of the graph of the function. See Figure 15-11 (red portion of graph).

The second rule, $f(x) = |x|$ is the absolute value function. Its graph is a "V" shape with vertex at the origin. We sketch this function only for x values of -1 and greater. The point $(-1, 1)$ is a closed dot to show that it is part of the graph of the function. See Figure 15-11 (blue portion of the graph).

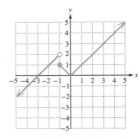

Figure 15-11

From the graph, we see that the domain of f is $(-\infty, \infty)$. The range is $(-\infty, \infty)$.

Answers

6. -6 **7.** 5   **8.** 0.5
9. 1   **10.** 5
11.

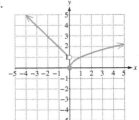

Skill Practice

11. Graph the function defined by $f(x) = \begin{cases} -x + 1 & \text{for } x < 0 \\ \sqrt{x} & \text{for } x \ge 0 \end{cases}$

8   **Chapter 15** Transformations, Piecewise-Defined Functions, and Probability

Vocabulary and Key Concepts

1. Explain how the graph of $g(x) = (x + 2)^2 - 8$ is related to the graph of $y = x^2$.

2. Explain how the graph of $h(x) = -(x - 3)^2 + 5$ is related to the graph of $y = x^2$.

Concept 1: Transformations of Graphs

For Exercises 3–8, match the function with its graph.

3. $f(x) = x$ **4.** $f(x) = x^2$ **5.** $f(x) = x^3$

6. $f(x) = |x|$ **7.** $f(x) = \sqrt{x}$ **8.** $f(x) = \dfrac{1}{x}$

a.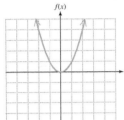

b.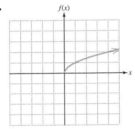

c.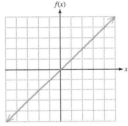

d.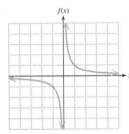

e.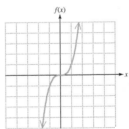

f.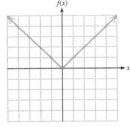

For Exercises 9–29, graph the function. Also determine the domain and range. **(See Examples 1–4)**

9. $f(x) = |x| - 4$ **10.** $g(x) = \sqrt{x} + 3$ **11.** $p(x) = \sqrt{x - 3}$

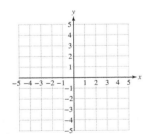   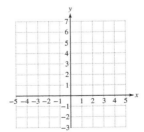   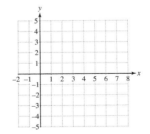

12. $q(x) = |x - 4|$

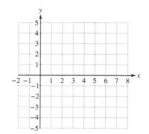

13. $h(x) = (x - 1)^3$

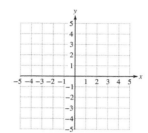

14. $k(x) = (x + 4)^2$

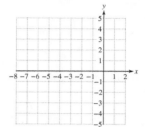

15. $t(x) = x^3 - 1$

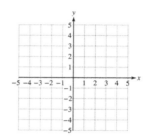

16. $w(x) = x^2 + 4$

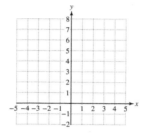

17. $n(x) = 2|x|$

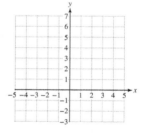

18. $v(x) = 3x^2$

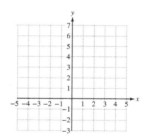

19. $f(x) = \sqrt{x + 1} - 4$

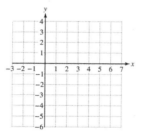

20. $g(x) = |x - 2| + 5$

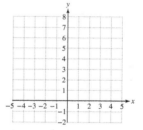

21. $c(x) = |x + 3| + 2$

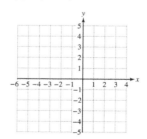

22. $d(x) = \sqrt{x - 4} + 2$

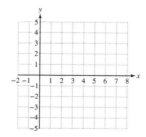

23. $h(x) = -\sqrt{x}$

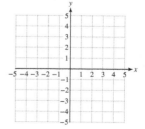

10   **Chapter 15** Transformations, Piecewise-Defined Functions, and Probability

24. $k(x) = -\dfrac{1}{x}$

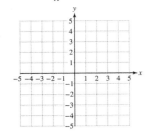

25. $v(x) = -(x-1)^2 - 3$

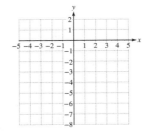

26. $f(x) = -(x+2)^2 + 4$

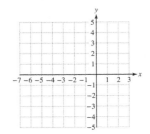

27. $r(x) = -2|x+3| - 2$

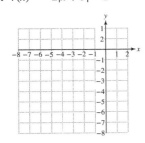

28. $t(x) = -3\sqrt{x+4} - 1$

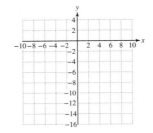

29. $t(x) = \dfrac{1}{2}(x-2)^2 + 1$

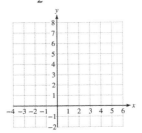

Concept 2: Piecewise-Defined Functions

For Exercises 30–32, match the function with its graph.

30. $f(x) = -x + 2;\ x < -1$

a.

31. $f(x) = -x + 2;\ x \le -1$

b.

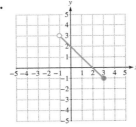

32. $f(x) = -x + 2;\ -1 < x \le 3$

c.

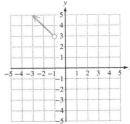

For Exercises 33–36, evaluate the function for the given values of x. **(See Example 5)**

33. $f(x) = \begin{cases} x^2 - 3 & \text{for } x \le 1 \\ 2x + 1 & \text{for } x > 1 \end{cases}$

    a. $f(3)$

    b. $f(0)$

    c. $f(1)$

    d. $f(\tfrac{3}{2})$

34. $g(x) = \begin{cases} -|x| + 4 & \text{for } x \le 2 \\ x - 5 & \text{for } x > 2 \end{cases}$

    a. $g(4)$

    b. $g(-1)$

    c. $g(2)$

    d. $g(-3)$

35. $h(x) = \begin{cases} 7 & \text{for } x < -2 \\ |x-3| & \text{for } -2 \le x \le 1 \\ \sqrt{x} & \text{for } x > 1 \end{cases}$

   a. $h(4)$

   b. $h(-3)$

   c. $h(-1)$

   d. $h(-2)$

   e. $h(1)$

36. $k(x) = \begin{cases} x+2 & \text{for } x < -3 \\ 1 & \text{for } -3 \le x \le 3 \\ x^3 & \text{for } x > 3 \end{cases}$

   a. $k(4)$

   b. $k(-4)$

   c. $k(-2)$

   d. $k(-3)$

   e. $k(3)$

37. **a.** Graph $f(x) = x$ for $x < 0$.

   b. Graph $g(x) = \sqrt{x}$ for $x \ge 0$.

   c. Sketch both $y = f(x)$ and $y = g(x)$ on the same graph to represent the piecewise defined function, h.
   (See Example 6)

$$h(x) = \begin{cases} x & \text{for } x < 0 \\ \sqrt{x} & \text{for } x \ge 0 \end{cases}$$

a.
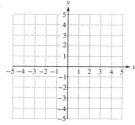

b.
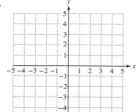

c.
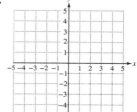

38. **a.** Graph $f(x) = |x|$ for $x \le 1$.

   b. Graph $g(x) = 2$ for $x > 1$.

   c. Sketch both $y = f(x)$ and $y = g(x)$ on the same graph to represent the piecewise-defined function, h.

$$h(x) = \begin{cases} |x| & \text{for } x \le 1 \\ 2 & \text{for } x > 1 \end{cases}$$

a.
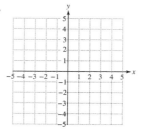

b.
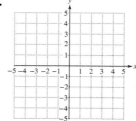

c.
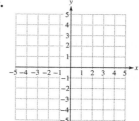

12   **Chapter 15**   Transformations, Piecewise-Defined Functions, and Probability

For Exercises 39–45, graph the function. Also determine the domain and range. **(See Example 6)**

39. $f(x) = \begin{cases} 3 & \text{for } x \le -1 \\ x^3 & \text{for } x > -1 \end{cases}$

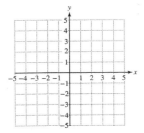

40. $g(x) = \begin{cases} \dfrac{1}{x} & \text{for } x < 0 \\ x + 1 & \text{for } x \ge 0 \end{cases}$

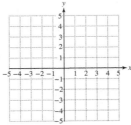

41. $h(x) = \begin{cases} x + 1 & \text{for } x < 2 \\ -x - 1 & \text{for } x \ge 2 \end{cases}$

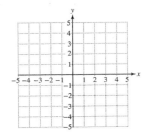

42. $k(x) = \begin{cases} 2x & \text{for } x < 1 \\ -2x & \text{for } x \ge 1 \end{cases}$

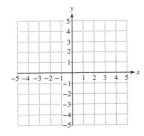

43. $p(x) = \begin{cases} x^2 - 4 & \text{for } x \le 0 \\ 2x - 4 & \text{for } x > 0 \end{cases}$

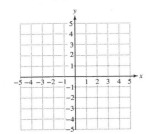

44. $q(x) = \begin{cases} -x - 1 & \text{for } x < -1 \\ \sqrt{x + 1} & \text{for } x \ge -1 \end{cases}$

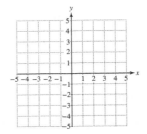

45. $f(x) = \begin{cases} -x & \text{for } x < 0 \\ x & \text{for } x \ge 0 \end{cases}$

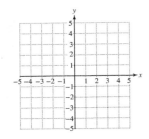

46. What basic function resembles the graph of $y = f(x)$ from Exercise 45?

47. A bicyclist rides at a steady speed of 16 mph for 35 min. Then she encounters a hill and her average speed immediately slows to 10 mph for the next 25 min. Then, after reaching the summit, she rides down the hill and her speed increases at a rate of 2 mph per minute until she reaches the finish line 7 min later.

The bicyclist's speed can be approximated by the piecewise-defined function, where t is time measured in minutes and $s(t)$ is speed in mph.

$$s(t) = \begin{cases} 16 & \text{for } 0 \le t \le 35 \\ 10 & \text{for } 35 < t \le 60 \\ 2t - 110 & \text{for } 60 < t \le 67 \end{cases}$$

a. Evaluate $s(30)$ and interpret the meaning in the context of this problem.

b. Evaluate $s(40)$ and interpret the meaning.

c. Evaluate $s(65)$ and interpret the meaning.

d. Find the bicyclist's speed at the end of the ride.

e. Sketch $y = s(t)$.

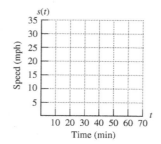

48. A sled accelerates (gains speed) down a hill and then slows down after it reaches a flat portion of ground. The speed of the sled can be approximated by the piecewise-defined function.

$$S(t) = \begin{cases} 1.5t & \text{for } 0 \le t \le 16 \\ \dfrac{24}{t - 15} & \text{for } t > 16 \end{cases}$$

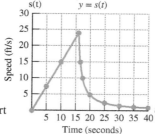

where t is in seconds and $S(t)$ is in feet per second.

a. Evaluate $S(0)$, $S(10)$, $S(16)$, $S(20)$, and $S(25)$.

b. Locate the points defined by the function values in part (a) on the graph of $y = S(t)$.

For Exercises 49–52, produce a rule for the function whose graph is shown.

49.

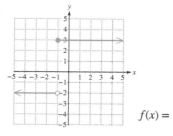

$$f(x) = \begin{cases} \end{cases}$$

50.

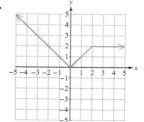

$$f(x) = \begin{cases} \end{cases}$$

14   **Chapter 15**   Transformations, Piecewise-Defined Functions, and Probability

51.

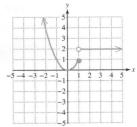

$$f(x) = \left\{ \rule{0pt}{20pt} \right.$$

52.

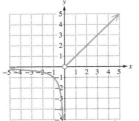

$$f(x) = \left\{ \rule{0pt}{20pt} \right.$$

53. A shopping cart rolls across a parking lot at a *constant* speed and then crashes into a tree and *stops*. Which graph of speed as a function of time represents this scenario? Explain your answer.

a.   **b.**

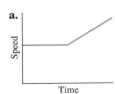

c.   **d.**

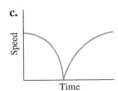

54. A student makes $8 per hour for the first 40 hr worked in a week. Then she makes time and a half ($12/hr) for the work exceeding 40 hr. Which graph best depicts her total salary as a function of time? Explain your reasoning.

a.   **b.**

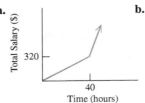

c.   **d.**

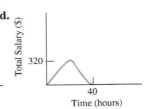

Expanding Your Skills

For Exercises 55–56, graph the function.

55. $f(x) = \begin{cases} -x - 3 & \text{for } x \leq -1 \\ x^2 & \text{for } -1 < x < 2 \\ 4 & \text{for } x \geq 2 \end{cases}$

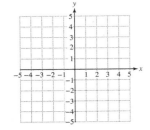

56. $g(x) = \begin{cases} 3 & \text{for } x < -2 \\ |x| & \text{for } -2 \leq x < 1 \\ -x + 2 & \text{for } x \geq 1 \end{cases}$

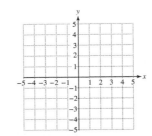

Fundamentals of Counting   **Section 15.2**

1. Fundamental Principle of Counting

Concepts

1. Fundamental Principle of Counting
2. Permutations
3. Combinations
4. Comparing Permutations and Combinations

A child makes an ice cream sundae with one scoop of ice cream plus a syrup. Suppose there are three choices of ice cream (vanilla, chocolate, and strawberry) and two choices of syrup (fudge and caramel). For each of the three ice cream choices there are two possible syrups, yielding $3 \cdot 2 = 6$ possible sundae combinations (Figure 15-12).

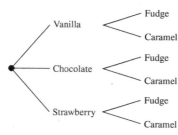

Figure 15-12

This example illustrates the **fundamental principle of counting**.

> **Fundamental Principle of Counting**
>
> If one event can occur in m different ways and a second event can occur in n different ways, then the sequence of both events can occur in $m \cdot n$ different ways.

The fundamental principle of counting can be extended to more than two events as demonstrated in Example 1.

Example 1   **Applying the Fundamental Principle of Counting**

Suppose Denisha visits Jimmy G's, a Cajun restaurant in Houston, Texas. She opts for a combo-meal in which she may choose from 12 different entrées, 4 different soups, and 3 different desserts. How many different dinners can she choose if she selects one item from each category?

Solution:

Applying the fundamental principle of counting, we have 144 different dinners.

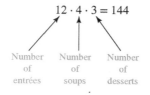

Skill Practice

1. Ten-year-old Max chooses his outfit for school each morning. He has 5 pairs of pants, 8 shirts, and 3 caps. Each day he chooses one pair of pants, one shirt, and one cap. How many different outfits can he choose?

Sometimes the events in a sequence depend on a preceding event as shown in Example 2.

Answer
1. $5 \cdot 8 \cdot 3 = 120$

16   Chapter 15   Transformations, Piecewise-Defined Functions, and Probability

---

> **Example 2**   Applying the Fundamental Principle of Counting

Maximus has five different photos that he wants to arrange on a shelf. In how many different ways can he arrange the five photos?

Solution:

Think of the photo arrangement as five different slots on the shelf (Figure 15-13).

Figure 15-13

(cat nap): © Flickr Open/Getty Images RF
(kitten): © Lilun_Li/Getty Images RF
(family): © Martin Barraud/Caia Image/Glow Images RF
(dog): © Ammit Jack/Shutterstock
(puppies): © DAJ/amana images RF/Getty Images RF

The first slot can have any of the five pictures. However, once the first picture is in place, there are only four available for the second slot. Similarly, once the first two pictures are in place, there are only three remaining, and so on. The total number of photo arrangements is

$$\underline{\ 5\ } \cdot \underline{\ 4\ } \cdot \underline{\ 3\ } \cdot \underline{\ 2\ } \cdot \underline{\ 1\ } = 120.$$

Skill Practice

2. Chuck has seven award-winning photos to arrange in a row on the wall of his gallery. In how many ways can he arrange his photos on the wall?

The solution to Example 2 could have been written using factorial notation.

$$5 \cdot 4 \cdot 3 \cdot 2 \cdot 1 = 5!$$

Let n be a positive integer. Recall that $n!$ (read as "n factorial") is defined as the product of integers from 1 to n. That is,

$$n! = n(n-1)(n-2) \cdots (1) \text{ and by definition, } 0! = 1.$$

> **Example 3**   Applying the Fundamental Principle of Counting

Suppose eight horses run in a race. How many first-, second-, and third-place arrangements are possible assuming no ties?

Solution:

Any of the eight horses can come in first place. That leaves seven possibilities for second place, and six possibilities for third. Therefore, there are $8 \cdot 7 \cdot 6 = 336$ possible first-, second-, and third-place arrangements.

Skill Practice

3. Ten performers are finalists in a talent competition that awards first- and second-place prizes. How many first- and second-place arrangements are possible?

Answers

2. $7! = 5040$ **3.** $10 \cdot 9 = 90$

2. Permutations

The scenario presented in Example 3 has three different horses selected in a specified order from a group of eight horses. Each of the 336 arrangements is called a permutation of eight horses taken three at a time. In general, an ordered arrangement of r different items selected from n different items is called a **permutation** of n items taken r at a time. The number of all such arrangements is given by the following formula.

> **Permutation Rule**
>
> If $_nP_r$ represents the number of permutations of n items taken r at a time, then
>
> $$_nP_r = \frac{n!}{(n-r)!}$$

Other commonly used notations for the number of permutations of n items taken r at a time are P_r^n and $P(n, r)$.

From Example 3, we found the number of ways three different horses could be selected from eight horses in a race in a specified order. This value is equivalent to $_8P_3$.

$$_8P_3 = \frac{8!}{(8-3)!} = \frac{8!}{5!} = \frac{8 \cdot 7 \cdot 6 \cdot 5 \cdot 4 \cdot 3 \cdot 2 \cdot 1}{5 \cdot 4 \cdot 3 \cdot 2 \cdot 1} = 8 \cdot 7 \cdot 6 = 336$$

This is consistent with the result of Example 3.

Example 4 **Computing Permutations**

Compute. **a.** $_{12}P_4$ **b.** $_7P_7$

Solution:

a. $_{12}P_4 = \dfrac{12!}{(12-4)!} = \dfrac{12!}{8!} = \dfrac{12 \cdot 11 \cdot 10 \cdot 9 \cdot 8 \cdot 7 \cdot 6 \cdot 5 \cdot 4 \cdot 3 \cdot 2 \cdot 1}{8 \cdot 7 \cdot 6 \cdot 5 \cdot 4 \cdot 3 \cdot 2 \cdot 1}$

$$= 12 \cdot 11 \cdot 10 \cdot 9$$
$$= 11{,}880$$

This result implies that there are 11,880 ways to select 4 items from a group of 12 items, where the 4 items are selected in a specified order.

b. $_7P_7 = \dfrac{7!}{(7-7)!} = \dfrac{7!}{0!} = \dfrac{7!}{1} = 7! = 5040$

This result implies that there are 5040 ways to select seven out of seven items in a specific order.

Avoiding Mistakes

Remember that by definition, $0! = 1$.

Skill Practice Compute.

4. a. $_6P_3$ **b.** $_9P_1$

Answer

4. a. 120 **b.** 9

18   **Chapter 15**   Transformations, Piecewise-Defined Functions, and Probability

Example 5 will apply the permutation formula to solve a counting problem.

Example 5   **Applying Permutations to a Counting Problem**

From a group of nine students, four are to be selected to receive cash prizes of $100, $50, $25, and $10, respectively. In how many ways can the four students be selected?

Solution:

Because four different students are to be selected from a group of nine in a specified order, we have $_9P_4$.

$$_9P_4 = \frac{9!}{(9-4)!} = \frac{9!}{5!} = \frac{9 \cdot 8 \cdot 7 \cdot 6 \cdot 5 \cdot 4 \cdot 3 \cdot 2 \cdot 1}{5 \cdot 4 \cdot 3 \cdot 2 \cdot 1} = 9 \cdot 8 \cdot 7 \cdot 6 = 3024$$

There are 3024 ways to pick four different students from a group of nine in a specific order.

Skill Practice

5. From a group of 10 employees, Ali must choose 3 to receive bonuses of $1000, $500, and $300. In how many ways can three employees be chosen to receive these bonuses?

TIP: The order of selection is important in Example 5, because the four prizes are different. For example, suppose person A is awarded the $100 prize and B is awarded the $50 prize. It would be a different outcome if B got the $100 prize and A received the $50 prize.

3. Combinations

In Example 5, we saw that a permutation defines a selection of four distinct items in a specified order from nine items. Now we will compare an event in which the order is important to one in which the order is not important.

Suppose that from a group of four members of student government we want to select two to serve as president and vice-president. If we label the students as A, B, C, and D, we can list all possible selections. The first student listed is designated as president and the second student listed is designated as vice-president. There are 12 possible outcomes shown here.

$$\left.\begin{matrix} \text{AB} & \text{AC} & \text{AD} & \text{BC} & \text{BD} & \text{CD} \\ \text{BA} & \text{CA} & \text{DA} & \text{CB} & \text{DB} & \text{DC} \end{matrix}\right\} \quad \text{12 permutations}$$

These outcomes represent the set of all permutations of four students taken two at a time. Therefore, the number of president/vice-president selections can also be found by computing

$$_4P_2 = \frac{4!}{(4-2)!} = \frac{4!}{2!} = \frac{4 \cdot 3 \cdot 2 \cdot 1}{2 \cdot 1} = 12$$

Now suppose that we want to choose two students from the group of four to form a safety committee. In this case, there is no specific label assigned to the two students selected (in other words, we are not assigning roles to the students such as president or vice-president). In some sense, the two people selected are "equals." They are not holding distinguishable positions. In such a case, we can see that the order of selection is not important. Hence, selecting A first followed by B forms the same committee as selecting B first followed by A. We do not want to count the outcomes AB and BA twice. Therefore, there are only six possible groups as shown here.

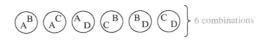

Answer

5. $_{10}P_3 = 720$

In this situation, the order of selection is not important. In general, an *unordered* selection of r different items taken from n different items is called a **combination** of n items taken r at a time. The number of all such groupings is given by the following formula.

Combination Rule

If $_nC_r$ represents the number of combinations of n items taken r at a time, then

$$_nC_r = \frac{n!}{(n-r)! \cdot r!}$$

To count the number of ways two students can be selected from a group of four without regard to order, we compute $_4C_2$.

$$_4C_2 = \frac{4!}{(4-2)! \cdot 2!} = \frac{4!}{2! \cdot 2!} = \frac{4 \cdot 3 \cdot 2 \cdot 1}{(2 \cdot 1) \cdot (2 \cdot 1)} = 6$$

Notice that the combination formula differs from the permutation formula by a factor of $r!$ in the denominator. In this example, there is an additional factor of 2! in the denominator. This factor divides out the repeated arrangements within the groups of two that result from order. In other words, the factor of 2! divides the total list of permutations by 2 to divide out the repeated arrangements such as AB and BA, AC and CA, and so on.

Example 6   **Computing Combinations**

Compute.   **a.** $_{10}C_2$ **b.** $_{12}C_{12}$

Solution:

a. $_{10}C_2 = \dfrac{10!}{(10-2)! \cdot 2!} = \dfrac{10!}{8! \cdot 2!} = \dfrac{10 \cdot 9 \cdot 8!}{8! \cdot 2 \cdot 1} = 45$

This result implies that there are 45 ways to select 2 items from a group of 10 when the order of selection is not considered.

b. $_{12}C_{12} = \dfrac{12!}{(12-12)! \cdot 12!} = \dfrac{12!}{0! \cdot 12!} = \dfrac{12!}{1 \cdot 12!} = 1$

This result implies that there is one way to select 12 items from a group of 12 without regard to order.

Skill Practice Compute.

6. a. $_8C_2$ **b.** $_{10}C_1$

TIP: The number of combinations of n items taken r at a time can also be found by computing the number of permutations and dividing the result by $r!$. The factor of $r!$ divides out repeated combinations that result from order within the permutations. Therefore, the combination formula

$$_nC_r = \frac{n!}{(n-r)! \cdot r!}$$ can also

be written as $_nC_r = \frac{_nP_r}{r!}$.

TIP: You might have noticed that the formula to compute $_nC_r$ follows the same format as the formula used to compute the coefficients of a binomial expansion.

Calculator Connections

Most scientific and graphing calculators have a permutation function and a combination function.

```
4 nPr 2
                    12
4 nCr 2
                     6
12 nCr 12
                     1
```

20   **Chapter 15** Transformations, Piecewise-Defined Functions, and Probability

| Example 7 | **Applying Combinations to a Counting Problem** |

Sara picked out 15 different CDs that she likes equally well. However, she only has enough money to purchase 4 CDs. In how many ways can she select 4 CDs from the group of 15?

Solution:

In this example, there is no implied order. Therefore, the number of ways she can select 4 CDs from 15 CDs is given by $_{15}C_4$.

$$_{15}C_4 = \frac{15!}{(15-4)! \cdot 4!} = \frac{15!}{11! \cdot 4!} = \frac{15 \cdot 14 \cdot 13 \cdot 12 \cdot \cancel{11!}}{\cancel{11!} \cdot 4 \cdot 3 \cdot 2 \cdot 1} = 1365$$

Skill Practice

7. Coach Petersen has 8 girls on her tennis team, but is only able to take 5 of them to tennis camp for the summer. In how many ways can she select 5 girls from the group of 8?

4. Comparing Permutations and Combinations

In this section, three different rules for counting have been presented: the fundamental principle of counting, the permutation rule, and the combination rule. Perhaps the most difficult part of solving a counting problem is to select the most appropriate rule to apply.

- The fundamental principle of counting can always be applied, but it is not always the most convenient method.
- The permutation rule can be applied when r different items are selected from a group of n different items in a specified order.
- The combination rule can be applied when r different items are selected from a group of n different items in no specific order.

Answer

7. $_8C_5 = 56$

| Section 15.2 | Practice Exercises |

Concept 1: Fundamental Principle of Counting

For Exercises 1–6, evaluate the factorial expression.

1. $5!$

2. $6!$

3. $8!$

4. $4!$

5. $0!$

6. $1!$

For Exercises 7–12, apply the fundamental principle of counting. **(See Examples 1–3)**

7. At a certain hospital the dinner menu consists of 4 choices of entrées, 3 choices of salads, 8 choices of beverages, and 6 choices of desserts. How many different meals can be formed if a patient chooses one item from each category?

8. Mr. Dehili must dress for an important business meeting. He can choose his outfit from 3 different suits, 6 different shirts, and 12 different ties. Assuming that Mr. Dehili has no regard for color combination, how many different outfits can he form, given that he picks one item from each category?

9. In how many different ways can 6 people be seated in a row?

10. In how many different ways can 10 children line up to leave the classroom?

11. In a garden show, the best four flower arrangements receive the honors of first place, second place, third place, and honorable mention. How many ways can the awards be given if there are 16 arrangements to choose from?

12. At the All-State Music Festival, a group of 3 soloists will be awarded a blue ribbon, a red ribbon, and a silver ribbon. How many arrangements of the ribbons are possible if there are 12 soloists at the festival?

Concept 2: Permutations

13. Evaluate $_{10}P_3$ and interpret its meaning.

14. Evaluate $_7P_2$ and interpret its meaning.

For Exercises 15–22, compute the permutation. **(See Example 4)**

15. $_{12}P_5$

16. $_6P_4$

17. $_7P_1$

18. $_5P_1$

19. $_8P_8$

20. $_4P_4$

21. $_7P_6$

22. $_3P_2$

23. In how many ways can a chairperson and an assistant chairperson be selected for the English department if there are eight faculty members qualified for the positions? **(See Example 5)**

24. How many five-letter passwords can be formed from the letters in the name *Fermat?*

25. How many six-letter permutations can be made from the word *Euclid.*

26. In how many ways can five different cereal boxes be displayed on a shelf?

Concept 3: Combinations

27. Evaluate $_{10}C_3$ and interpret its meaning.

28. Evaluate $_7C_2$ and interpret its meaning.

For Exercises 29–36, compute the combination. **(See Example 6)**

29. $_{12}C_9$

30. $_6C_4$

31. $_7C_1$

32. $_5C_1$

33. $_8C_8$

34. $_4C_4$

35. $_7C_6$

36. $_3C_2$

37. How many tests can be made if an instructor selects 12 questions from a bank of 15 questions? **(See Example 7)**

38. A Shakespeare Festival offers five plays during one season. If Olivia can purchase tickets for three plays, how many combinations of plays will she have to choose from?

39. Nora and Stu decide to order two different desserts and plan to share them. How many different ways can they choose two desserts from five different desserts listed on the menu?

40. A team of 4 officers is selected to investigate a case. How many ways can the team be selected from 16 officers?

22   **Chapter 15** Transformations, Piecewise-Defined Functions, and Probability

Concept 4: Comparing Permutations and Combinations

41. Given the set of elements {W, X, Y, Z},

    a. List all permutations of two elements

    b. List all combinations of two elements.

42. Given the set of elements {A, B, C},

    a. List all permutations of two elements.

    b. List all combinations of two elements.

For Exercises 43–50, use the permutation or combination rule.

43. How many first-, second-, and third-place finishes are possible in a dog race containing 10 dogs?

44. In how many ways can a judge award blue, red, and yellow ribbons to 3 films at a film festival if there are 12 films entered in the contest?

45. Heather wants to invite 11 girls from her fifth-grade class to a slumber party. However, her mother will only allow her to invite six people. In how many ways can she invite 6 girls out of the 11 to her party?

46. How many different five-member committees can be formed from 100 U.S. senators?

47. A book club offers 5 books for $9.99 as an introductory offer. If you can choose from a list of 10 books, in how many ways can you make your selection of 5?

48. A basketball coach must pick 5 players from a roster of 12 to start a game. In how many ways can he choose his staring 5 players assuming that all players have equal ability?

49. Suppose there are eight employees who work at a chain coffee shop in Chicago. The manager wants to select two employees to work at two new shops (shop A and shop B) to help train new employees. If one of the selected employees is to work in shop A and the other is to work in shop B, how many possible selections can the manager make?

50. A disc jockey has five songs that he must play in a half-hour period. How many different ways can he arrange the five songs?

Mixed Exercises

For Exercises 51–66, use an appropriate rule of counting.

51. Most radio stations that were licensed after 1927 have four call letters starting with K or W such as WROD. Assuming no repetitions of letters, how many four-letter sets are possible?

52. A lock on a school locker consists of three different numbers taken from 1 to 39 in a specific order. How many three-number codes are possible?

53. In how many ways can a book buyer select 4 books from a list of 10 different books?

54. How many samples of size 6 can be selected from a population of 30 members?

55. Three men and three women have reserved six seats in a row at a concert. In how many ways can they arrange themselves if the men and women are to alternate seats and a man must sit in the first seat?

56. Three men and three women have reserved six seats in a row at a concert. In how many ways can they arrange themselves if the men must all sit together and the women must all sit together?

57. A musician plans to perform nine selections. In how many ways can she arrange the musical selections?

58. From a pool of 12 candidates, the offices of president, vice-president, treasurer, and secretary must be filled. In how many different ways can the offices be filled?

59. From a jury pool of 40 people, 12 are to be selected. In how many different ways can a jury of 12 be selected?

60. To play the Georgia lottery, a person must choose 6 numbers (in any order) from a list of 49 numbers. How many different choices of 6 numbers are possible?

61. A committee is to be formed from a collection of 10 men and 8 women. How many committees can be made consisting of exactly 3 men and 1 woman?

62. A committee is to be formed from a collection of 10 men and 8 women. How many committees can be made consisting of 2 men and 2 women?

63. If a fair coin is flipped three times, how many different sequences of heads and tails can be formed?

64. If a couple plans to have four children, how many different gender sequences can be formed?

65. In how many ways can a 10-question true or false test be answered assuming that a student answers all questions?

66. At a pizza place, a customer can order a pizza with or without any of the following options: pepperoni, sausage, mushrooms, peppers, onions, olives, or anchovies. How many different pizzas can be formed?

Expanding Your Skills

67. In how many ways can the batting order be determined for a co-ed softball team with six women and three men if

    a. There are no restrictions?

    b. The first and the last batters must be women?

    c. The men must all be after the women?

68. In how many ways can a group of six men and five women be lined up for a photograph if

    a. There are no restrictions?

    b. The men and women must alternate?

    c. There must be a man on each end?

69. Given the set of numbers $\{2, 3, 4, 5, 6, 7, 8\}$,

    a. How many different three-digit numbers can be formed?

    b. How many different three-digit numbers can be formed if the number cannot have repeated digits?

    c. How many different three-digit numbers can be formed if the number is to be even and repetition of digits is allowed?

70. Given the set of numbers $\{1, 2, 3, 4, 5, 6, 7\}$,

    a. How many different four-digit numbers can be formed?

    b. How many different four-digit numbers can be formed if the number cannot have repeated digits?

    c. How many different four-digit numbers can be formed if the number is to be divisible by 5 and repetition of digits is allowed?

For Exercises 71–74, use the following description of a standard deck of 52 cards. A standard deck of cards has four suits (clubs, diamonds, hearts, and spades). Each suit has 13 cards. The hearts and diamonds are red cards, and the clubs and spades are black cards. Assume that five cards are selected from a standard deck. In how many ways can the following occur?

71. All five cards are black.

72. All five cards are hearts.

73. There are three diamonds and two clubs.

74. There are three red cards and two black cards.

24   **Chapter 15**   Transformations, Piecewise-Defined Functions, and Probability

Section 15.3   Introduction to Probability

1. Basic Definitions

The study of probability provides a mathematical means to measure the likelihood of an event occurring. It is of particular interest because of its application to everyday events.

- The National Cancer Institute estimates that a woman has a 1 in 8 chance of developing breast cancer in her lifetime.
- The probability of winning the California Fantasy Five lottery grand prize is

$$\frac{1}{575,757}$$

- Genetic DNA analysis can be used to determine the risk that a child will be born with cystic fibrosis. If both parents test positive, the probability is 25% that a child will be born with the disease.

To begin our discussion, we must first understand some basic definitions.

An activity with observable outcomes is called an **experiment**. Each repetition of an experiment is called a **trial**. The result of a trial is called an **outcome** of the experiment. The set of all possible outcomes of an experiment is called the **sample space**, *S*, of the experiment.

For example, if a single die is rolled, the sample space is $\{1, 2, 3, 4, 5, 6\}$. If a coin is tossed, the outcomes are heads (H) or tails (T). The sample space is $\{H, T\}$.

Any subset of a sample space is called an **event**. For example, if we define event, E_1, as the event that a number greater than 4 is rolled on a die, then, $E_1 = \{5, 6\}$. If event E_2 is the event that a coin lands as a head, then $E_2 = \{H\}$.

> **TIP:** The word *die* is the singular of the word *dice*. Therefore, we may roll a pair of dice, but we roll a single die.

2. Probability of an Event

The number of elements in a sample space is denoted by $n(S)$. The number of elements in the sample space that are also in event E is denoted by $n(E)$. The notation $P(E)$ denotes the probability of event E, defined as follows.

> **Probability of Event, *E***
>
> In a sample space S of equally likely outcomes, the **probability of *E*** is given by
>
> $$P(E) = \frac{\text{number of elements in the event}}{\text{number of elements in the sample space}} = \frac{n(E)}{n(S)}$$

For the event, E_1, of rolling a number greater than 4 on a die, we have $E_1 = \{5, 6\}$ and $S = \{1, 2, 3, 4, 5, 6\}$. Then

$$P(E_1) = \frac{n(E_1)}{n(S)} = \frac{2}{6} = \frac{1}{3}$$

For the event, E_2, that a coin will land as a head, we have $E_2 = \{H\}$ and $S = \{H, T\}$. Then

$$P(E_2) = \frac{n(E_2)}{n(S)} = \frac{1}{2}$$

The value of a probability can be written as a fraction, as a decimal, or as a percent. Therefore, $P(E_2) = \frac{1}{2}$, or 0.5 or 50%. In words, this means that theoretically we expect half (50%) of the outcomes to land as a head. This does not necessarily mean that exactly one out of every two coin tosses will land as a head. Instead, it is a ratio that we expect experimental observations to approach after a large number of trials. For example, if we flip a coin 1000 times, we might get 493 heads for a ratio of $\frac{493}{1000}$, or 0.493. This value is close to the theoretical value of 0.500.

Example 1   **Computing Probabilities**

A box contains two red, four white, and one blue marble. Suppose one marble is selected at random. Find the probability of selecting

a. A red marble.

b. A white marble.

c. A green marble.

Solution:

Denote the sample space as $S = \{R_1, R_2, W_1, W_2, W_3, W_4, B_1\}$.

a. Let R represent the event of selecting a red marble. Because there are two red marbles, then $R = \{R_1, R_2\}$. Then

$$P(R) = \frac{n(R)}{n(S)} = \frac{2}{7}$$

b. Let W represent the event of selecting a white marble. Because there are four white marbles, then $W = \{W_1, W_2, W_3, W_4,\}$. Then $P(W) = \frac{4}{7}$.

c. Let G represent the event of selecting a green marble. Because there are no green marbles in the box, then G equals the empty set. $G = \{\ \}$. Then $P(G) = \frac{0}{7} = 0$.

Skill Practice

1. A bag of M&M's contains 7 red, 10 brown, 8 yellow, and 4 blue candies. Find the probability of choosing:

a. A red M&M.

b. A brown M&M.

c. A blue M&M.

From Example 1(c), the event of selecting a green marble is impossible. The probability of an **impossible event** is 0. An event that is certain to happen is called a **certain event**. Its probability is 1. For example, if a die is tossed, the probability that the die will land as a number between 0 and 7 is certain to happen. Any of the six outcomes 1, 2, 3, 4, 5, 6 will satisfy the event. Therefore, the probability of rolling a number between 0 and 7 is $\frac{6}{6} = 1$. In general, for any event E,

$$0 \leq P(E) \leq 1$$

The counting rules we have already learned can be helpful in determining the number of elements in an event and in a sample space. This is illustrated in Example 2.

Answer

1. a. $\frac{7}{29}$ b. $\frac{10}{29}$ c. $\frac{4}{29}$

Example 2   Applying the Counting Rules to Probability

Suppose a group of politicians consists of nine men and five women. If three people are selected at random to form a committee, what is the probability that all are women?

Solution:

Let W represent the event that a committee of three women is selected.

Let S represent the sample space consisting of all possible committees of three with no restrictions.

There are 14 people available to form a committee of 3. If no restrictions are imposed, the number of possible committees of three is given by $_{14}C_3 = 364$. The number of possible committees of three selected from the group of women is given by $_5C_3 = 10$. Therefore, the probability of selecting a committee that consists of all women is given by

$$P(W) = \frac{n(W)}{n(S)} = \frac{_5C_3}{_{14}C_3} = \frac{10}{364} = \frac{5}{182}$$

Skill Practice

2. A cooler of drinks contains eight bottles of water and four sodas. If two drinks are chosen at random what is the probability that both are water?

3. Estimating Probabilities from Observed Data

We were able to compute the probabilities in Examples 1 and 2 because the sample space was known. Sometimes we need to collect information from a series of repeated trials to help us estimate probabilities.

Example 3   Estimating Probabilities from Observed Data

In a carnival game, Erin will win a prize if she can toss a ring around the neck of a bowling pin. After observing 200 players that had gone before her, she learns that 15 players won a prize. Based on this observation, what is the probability of winning a prize?

Solution:

In this situation, we may think of the outcomes of the 200 trials as the sample space. In this case, 15 trials came out as wins. Therefore, if W represents the event of a win, then

$$P(W) = \frac{15}{200} = \frac{3}{40}, \text{ or } 7.5\%$$

Skill Practice

3. In a class of 88 students, it was observed that 11 were left-handed. Based on this observation, what is the probability of being left-handed?

Answers

2. $\dfrac{_8C_2}{_{12}C_2} = \dfrac{28}{66} = \dfrac{14}{33}$

3. $\dfrac{11}{88} = \dfrac{1}{8}$ or 0.125

| Example 4 | **Determining Probabilities from a Graph** |

The data in the pie chart (Figure 15-14) categorize the number of accidental deaths in the United States for a recent year.

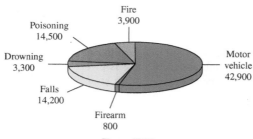

Number of Accidental Deaths by
Principal Type, U.S.

Fire
3,900

Poisoning
14,500

Drowning
3,300

Motor
vehicle
42,900

Falls
14,200

Firearm
800

Figure 15-14

a. Based on the chart, what is the probability that an accidental death is caused by fire?

b. What is the probability that an accidental death is caused by a motor vehicle?

Solution:

First note that the total number of accidental deaths depicted in the graph is 79,600.

a. Let F represent the event that the death is caused by fire.

$$\text{Then } P(F) = \frac{3900}{79,600} = \frac{39}{796} \text{ or about 4.9\%.}$$

b. Let M represent the event that the death was caused by a motor vehicle.

$$\text{Then } P(M) = \frac{42,900}{79,600} = \frac{429}{796} \text{ or about 53.9\%.}$$

Skill Practice

4. Based on Figure 15-14 in Example 4, what is the probability that an accidental death is caused by drowning?

4. Events Expressed as Alternatives

A compound event in probability involves two or more events. If two events are expressed as alternatives, they can be considered as a compound event often joined by the word *or*.

Answer

4. $\dfrac{3300}{79,600} = \dfrac{33}{796} \approx 4.1\%$

Example 5	**Finding the Probability of Two or More Events**

The safety and security department at a certain college asked a sample of 265 students to respond to the following question.

"Do you think that the College has adequate lighting on campus at night?"

The table shows the results of the survey by gender and response.

	Yes	**No**	**No Opinion**	**Total**
Male	92	7	4	103
Female	36	102	24	162
Total	128	109	28	265

If one student is selected at random from the group, find the probability that

a. The student answered yes or had no opinion.

b. The student answered no or was female.

Solution:

a. Let Y be the event that a student answered yes, and let Z represent the event that the student had no opinion. There are 128 people who answered "yes" and 28 who had "no opinion." The total number of unique elements in the event Y or Z is 156. Therefore,

$$P(Y \text{ or } Z) = \frac{156}{265} \text{ or about } 58.9\%$$

b. Let N be the event that a student answered no, and let F be the event that a student is female. The events N and F "overlap." That is, some people who answered "no" are also "female." We must be careful not to count any element in the sample space twice. There are 109 people who answered "no" (some of whom are female). Counting 109 "no" answers and the remaining females, we have a total of $109 + 36 + 24 = 169$ unduplicated individuals who answered "no" or who are "female." Therefore,

$$P(N \text{ or } F) = \frac{169}{265} \text{ or about } 63.8\%$$

Skill Practice

5. Fifty college students were asked if they owned a PC or MAC computer. The chart shows the results of the survey. If one student is selected at random from this group, what is the probability that:

a. The student has a MAC or no computer?

b. The student is a male or owns a PC?

	PC	**MAC**	**No Computer**	**Total**
Male	18	8	5	31
Female	12	3	4	19
Total	30	11	9	50

Answer

5. a. $\frac{2}{5}$ **b.** $\frac{43}{50}$

Section 15.3   Practice Exercises

Review Exercises

1. In how many ways can 4 songs be selected from 10 different songs without regard to order?

2. Samira wants her father to buy her six toys, but he only has enough money to buy two. In how many ways can Samira's father choose two toys from six?

3. In how many different orders can the five musical notes A, B, C, D, and E be played?

4. In how many ways can Mr. Zahnan rank three movies from a group of seven?

Concept 1: Basic Definitions

5. Which of the values can represent the probability of an event?

    a. 57%   **b.** $\dfrac{3}{2}$ **c.** $\dfrac{1}{4}$

    d. 0.8   **e.** 120%   **f.** -0.41

6. Which of the values can represent the probability of an event?

    a. 0.5   **b.** $\dfrac{2}{3}$ **c.** $-\dfrac{7}{5}$

    d. 1.00   **e.** 150%   **f.** 3.7

7. Which of the values can represent the probability of an event?

    a. 1.62   **b.** $-\dfrac{2}{7}$ **c.** 0.00

    d. 200%   **e.** 1.00   **f.** 0.87

8. Which of the values can represent the probability of an event?

    a. 4.5   **b.** 4.5%   **c.** $\dfrac{5}{4}$

    d. -0.6 **e.** 0.00   **f.** 0.02%

Concept 2: Probability of an Event

9. If a single die is rolled, what is the probability that it will come up as an odd number?

10. If a single die is rolled, what is the probability that it will come up as a number divisible by 3?

11. If a single die is rolled, what is the probability that it will come up as a number less than 5?

12. If a single die is rolled, what is the probability that it will come up as a number greater than 5?

13. A jar contains 7 yellow marbles, 3 red marbles, and 6 green marbles. What is the probability of selecting a red marble? **(See Example 1)**

14. A jar contains 4 yellow marbles, 10 red marbles, and 6 green marbles. What is the probability of selecting a yellow marble?

15. In a group of eight students three are female and five are male. If a committee of two is to be selected at random, what is the probability that

    a. Both members are female? **(See Example 2)**

    b. Both members are male?

16. In a group of 10 students at a community college, 6 are freshmen and 4 are sophomores. If a committee of two is selected at random, what is the probability that

    a. Both members are sophomores?

    b. Both members are freshmen?

30   **Chapter 15**   Transformations, Piecewise-Defined Functions, and Probability

17. In the California Fantasy Five lottery a player wins the grand prize if the player picks the winning 5 numbers (in any order) out of 39 numbers.

   a. What is the probability that a player will win the grand prize?

   b. What is the probability that a player will not win the grand prize?

   c. Joanne thinks that the probability of winning the grand prize in the lottery is 0.50, because according to her "There's a 50-50 chance of winning, because you either win or lose." What is wrong with Joanne's logic?

18. In the Florida lottery, a player wins a grand prize if the player picks the winning 6 numbers (in any order) out of 53 numbers.

   a. What is the probability that a player will win the grand prize?

   b. What is the probability that a player will not win the grand prize?

Concept 3: Estimating Probabilities from Observed Data

19. The final exam in a course in contemporary science resulted in the following distribution.

Grade	A	B	C	D	F
Number of Students	8	15	21	10	5

   a. What is the probability that a student selected at random received an "A" in the course?
   (See Example 3)

   b. What is the probability that a student did not pass the course if a passing grade is a "C" or better?

20. A sample of students is taken from a physical education class at a 4-year college. The distribution is given in the table. If one student is selected at random, find the probability that

   a. The student is a sophomore.

   b. The student is not a senior.

Class	Number of Students
Freshman	15
Sophomore	11
Junior	6
Senior	3

21. The tardy record for a group of second-graders for one school year is given in the table. If one student is picked at random, find the probability that the student was late:

   a. Exactly 3 days.

   b. Between 1 and 5 days, inclusive.

   c. At least 4 days.

   d. More than 5 days or fewer than 2 days.

Number of Days Late	Number of Students
0	4
1	2
2	14
3	10
4	16
5	18
6	10
7	6

22. The table displays the length of stay for vacationers at a small motel.

   a. What is the probability that a vacationer will stay for 4 days?

   b. What is the probability that a vacationer will stay for less than 4 days?

Length of Stay in Days	Frequency
2	14
3	13
4	18
5	28
6	11
7	30
8	6

23. The data in the pie chart categorize the method by which workers in a college town commute to work. If one working member of the community is selected at random, find the probability that the individual

  a. Commutes by bicycle?
  (See Example 4)

  b. Does not use public transportation.

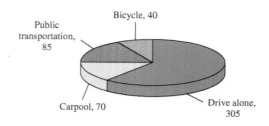

Method of Commuting to and from Work

Bicycle, 40
Public transportation, 85
Carpool, 70
Drive alone, 305

24. The data in the pie chart categorize the blood types in a sample of students. If one student is selected at random, find the probability that the individual

  a. Has blood type B.

  b. Does not have blood type O.

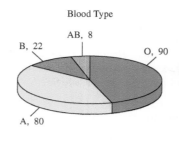

Blood Type

AB, 8
B, 22
O, 90
A, 80

Concept 4: Events Expressed as Alternatives

For Exercises 25–30, use the following table categorizing a sample of smokers and nonsmokers according to their blood pressure levels. (See Example 5)

	Normal Blood Pressure	Elevated blood Pressure	Total
Smokers	32	18	50
Nonsmokers	71	9	80
Total	103	27	130

If one person from the sample is selected at random, find the probability that

25. The person has elevated blood pressure.

26. The person is a nonsmoker.

27. The person has normal blood pressure.

28. The person is a smoker or has normal blood pressure.

29. The person is a nonsmoker or has normal blood pressure.

30. The person is a nonsmoker or has elevated blood pressure.

For Exercises 31–36, use the following table categorizing a sample of alcoholics and nonalcoholics according to their cholesterol level.

	Elevated Cholesterol	Normal Cholesterol	Total
Alcoholic	120	30	150
Nonalcoholic	60	240	300
Total	180	270	450

If one person from the sample is selected at random, find the probability that

31. The person is nonalcoholic.

32. The person has elevated cholesterol.

32   **Chapter 15**   Transformations, Piecewise-Defined Functions, and Probability

33. The person does not have elevated cholesterol.

34. The person is an alcoholic or has elevated cholesterol.

35. The person is a nonalcoholic or has normal cholesterol.

36. The person is an nonalcoholic or has elevated cholesterol.

A standard deck of cards has 52 cards divided into four suits: clubs, diamonds, hearts, and spades. Each suit has 13 cards consisting of an ace, a king, a queen, a jack, and cards numbered from 2 to 10. Assume that one card is selected from a standard deck. For Exercises 37–48, find the probability of selecting the indicated card.

37. A heart

38. A face card (face cards are jacks, queens, and kings)

39. A red card (hearts and diamonds are red)

40. A red card or a jack

41. A heart or a 6

42. A spade or a heart

43. A club

44. A 5 or a 10

45. A black card (clubs and spades are black)

46. A black card or an ace

47. A diamond or a 2

48. A club or a diamond

Expanding Your Skills

49. The firefighters in one county in the United States consist of 600 members: 120 women and 480 men. Over a 5-year period, 160 firefighters were promoted. The table shows the breakdown of promotions for male and female firefighters.

	Promoted	Not Promoted	Total
Male	140	340	480
Female	20	100	120
Total	160	440	600

If one firefighter is selected at random, what is the probability that

a. The firefighter is a female?

b. The firefighter was promoted?

c. The firefighter is male or was not promoted?

d. The firefighter was promoted, given that he is male?

e. The firefighter was promoted, given that she is female?

f. Write the probabilities in parts (d) and (e) in decimal form (round to 3 decimal places). What does the difference in probabilities mean in the context of this problem?

50. The following table depicts the grade distribution for a college algebra class based on age and grades.

	A	B	C	F	Total
17–26 years	150	220	370	180	920
27–36 years	140	200	220	90	650
37–46 years	150	120	60	40	370
Total	440	540	650	310	1940

If one student is selected at random from the group, find the probability that

a. The student received an "A" in the course.

b. The student was in the 27–36 age group.

c. The student was in the 37–46 age group or received a "B" in the course.

d. The student received an "A" in the course, given that the student is in the 37–46 age group.

e. The student received an "A" in the course given that the student is in the 17–26 age group.

f. Write the probabilities in parts (d) and (e) in decimal form (round to 3 decimal places). What does the difference in probabilities mean in the context of this problem?

Chapter 15   Summary

Transformation of Graphs and Piecewise-Defined Functions

Key Concepts

The graph of $y = a \cdot f(x - h) + k$ is the graph of $y = f(x)$ with the following transformations.

- Horizontal shift h units
- Vertical shift k units
- Vertical shrink if $0 < |a| < 1$
- Vertical stretch if $|a| > 1$
- Reflection across the x-axis if $a < 0$

Examples

Example 1

Graph $y = -\sqrt{x - 1} - 2$ by shifting the graph of $y = \sqrt{x}$ 1 unit to the right, reflecting $y = \sqrt{x}$ over the x-axis, and shifting the graph 2 units downward.

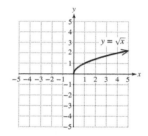

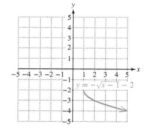

A **piecewise-defined function** is defined by more than one rule on different intervals within the domain.

Example 2

Graph the piecewise-defined function.

$$f(x) = \begin{cases} |x| & \text{for } x < 1 \\ x^2 & \text{for } x \geq 1 \end{cases}$$

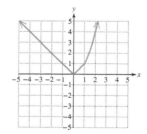

34   **Chapter 15** Transformations, Piecewise-Defined Functions, and Probability

Section 15.2   Fundamentals of Counting

Key Concepts

The **fundamental principle of counting** states that if one event can occur in m different ways and a second event can occur in n different way, then the sequence of both events can occur in $m \cdot n$ different ways.

A **permutation** is an ordered arrangement of items. The number of permutations of n items taken r at a time is given by $_nP_r = \dfrac{n!}{(n-r)!}$.

A **combination** is an unordered arrangement of items. The number of combinations of n items taken r at a time is given by $_nC_r = \dfrac{n!}{(n-r)! \cdot r!}$.

Examples

Example 1

The number of ways six people can stand in line for a picture is $6 \cdot 5 \cdot 4 \cdot 3 \cdot 2 \cdot 1 = 720$.

Example 2

The number of ways that a president and vice president can be selected from a board of five directors is

$$_5P_2 = \frac{5!}{(5-2)!} = \frac{5!}{3!} = \frac{5 \cdot 4 \cdot 3!}{3!} = 20$$

Example 3

The number of ways that a two-person subcommittee can be selected from a five-person committee is

$$_5C_2 = \frac{5!}{(5-2)! \cdot 2!} = \frac{5!}{3! \cdot 2!} = \frac{5 \cdot 4 \cdot 3!}{3! \cdot (2 \cdot 1)} = 10$$

Section 15.3   Introduction to Probability

Key Concepts

The **sample space** S of an experiment is the set of all possible outcomes. An **event** E is a subset of the sample space.

The **probability of an event** E is given by

$$P(E) = \frac{\text{number of elements in the event}}{\text{number of elements in the sample space}}$$

$$= \frac{n(E)}{n(S)}$$

The probability of an event E is a value between 0 and 1, inclusive. That is, $0 \le P(E) \le 1$. The probability of an **impossible event** is 0. The probability of a **certain event** is 1.

Examples

Example 1

A person is holding five cards consisting of two kings, one queen, and two jacks.

a. What is the probability of selecting a jack from this hand?

$$P(\text{jack}) = \frac{n(\text{jacks})}{n(\text{total cards})} = \frac{2}{5}$$

b. What is the probability of selecting a face card?

$$P(\text{face card}) = \frac{n(\text{face cards})}{n(\text{total cards})} = \frac{5}{5} = 1$$

c. What is the probability of selecting an ace?

$$P(\text{ace}) = \frac{n(\text{aces})}{n(\text{total cards})} = \frac{0}{5} = 0$$

Chapter 15   Review Exercises

Section 15.1

For Exercises 1–4, graph the function.

1. $f(x) = x^2 - 2$

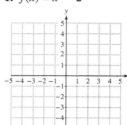

2. $g(x) = 2|x - 2|$

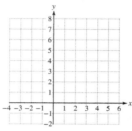

3. $f(x) = \sqrt{x - 2} + 1$

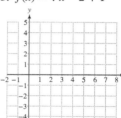

4. $h(x) = -x^3 - 1$

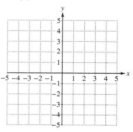

For Exercises 5–8, evaluate the function for the given values of x.

5. $h(x) = \begin{cases} x^2 & \text{if } x < -2 \\ x + 4 & \text{if } -2 \le x < 1 \\ \sqrt{x} & \text{if } x \ge 1 \end{cases}$

    a. $h(-2)$ **b.** $h(0)$ **c.** $h(1)$ **d.** $h(4)$

6. $g(x) = \begin{cases} \dfrac{1}{x} & \text{if } x \le -1 \\ x^3 & \text{if } x > -1 \end{cases}$

    a. $g(-2)$ **b.** $g(-1)$ **c.** $g(0)$ **d.** $g(2)$

7. $f(x) = \begin{cases} 2x - 1 & \text{if } x < 4 \\ \sqrt{x - 1} & \text{if } x \ge 4 \end{cases}$

    a. $f(-2)$ **b.** $f(0)$ **c.** $f(4)$ **d.** $f(10)$

8. $h(x) = \begin{cases} 4x + 1 & \text{if } x < 0 \\ (x - 5)^2 & \text{if } x \ge 0 \end{cases}$

    a. $h(0)$ **b.** $h(2)$ **c.** $h(-1)$ **d.** $h(-2)$

For Exercises 9–12, graph the function.

9. $g(x) = \begin{cases} x^2 & \text{if } x \le 2 \\ 4 & \text{if } x > 2 \end{cases}$

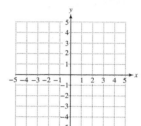

10. $f(x) = \begin{cases} |x| & \text{if } x < 1 \\ x^3 & \text{if } x \ge 1 \end{cases}$

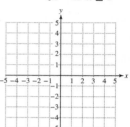

11. $g(x) = \begin{cases} -x - 1 & \text{if } x < -1 \\ x + 2 & \text{if } x \ge -1 \end{cases}$

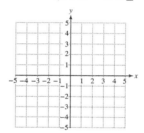

12. $h(x) = \begin{cases} |x| & \text{if } x \le -3 \\ 2 & \text{if } x > -3 \end{cases}$

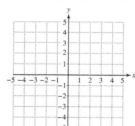

Section 15.2

For Exercises 13–18, evaluate the expression.

13. $_5P_2$

14. $_6P_1$

15. $_5C_2$

16. $_6C_1$

17. $_3P_3$

18. $_3C_3$

19. In taking a survey, 5 different people need to be selected at random from group of 30. In how many ways can this be done?

20. In how many ways can four different vases be arranged on a shelf?

36   **Chapter 15** Transformations, Piecewise-Defined Functions, and Probability

21. A combination lock has a 4-digit code. How many different codes can be made from 10 digits (0, 1, 2, 3 . . . 9) with no repetition of any digit?

22. A restaurant offers a complete dinner including one appetizer, one entrée, and one dessert. If the restaurant has three appetizers, four entrées, and three desserts, how many different meals can be selected?

Section 15.3

23. Which of the values can represent the probability of an event?

    a. $\dfrac{1}{6}$ **b.** $0.\overline{3}$ **c.** 0 **d.** 75% **e.** 125% **f.** 0.75%

24. Which of the values can represent the probability of an event?

    a. $\dfrac{1}{2}$ **b.** 150% **c.** 0.185 **d.** 1.00

    e. 2.5% **f.** 2.5

25. In a lottery, a player can win a grand prize if the player chooses the correct 6 numbers from 46 numbers. What is the probability that the player wins the grand prize?

26. What is the probability of choosing 3 red cards from a deck of cards that contains 26 red cards and 26 black cards?

27. At a state fair there is a game where a player throws a ball to knock down some pins. If enough pins are knocked down, then the player wins a prize. Richard observes that in 150 games, 12 people won. Based on this observation, what is the probability of winning a prize?

28. Ben realizes that he mixed up four new batteries with two old batteries in a box. If he selects one battery at random, what is the probability that he will get a new battery?

29. A sample was taken of the viewers of a popular cable news network. The distribution of ages is given in the table. Suppose that one person is selected at random from the sample.

Age (yr)	Number of Viewers
<18	12
18 to 34	37
35 to 54	84
55 to 74	60
75 to 94	52

What is the probability that

    a. The person is younger than 18?

    b. The person is between 18 and 34, inclusive?

    c. The person is 55 or older?

A standard deck of cards has 52 cards divided into four suits: clubs, diamonds, hearts, and spades. Each suit has 13 cards consisting of an ace, a king, a queen, a jack, and cards numbered from 2 to 10. Assume that one card is selected from a standard deck. For Exercises 30–33, find the probability of selecting the indicated card.

30. The ace of hearts

31. A 5

32. An 8, 9, or 10

33. A diamond or a jack

Chapter 15   Test

For Exercises 1–4, graph the function. Also write the domain and range in interval notation.

1. a. $h(x) = |x|$ **b.** $f(x) = |x - 3|$

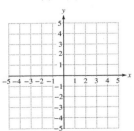
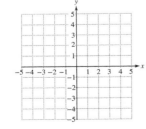

2. a. $f(x) = x^2$ **b.** $g(x) = -x^2 + 2$

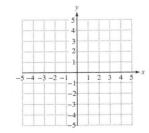
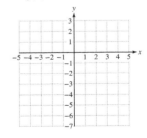

3. a. $h(x) = \sqrt{x}$

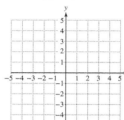

b. $g(x) = \sqrt{x+2} - 3$

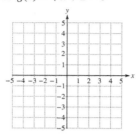

8. $g(x) = \begin{cases} |x| & \text{if } x < 4 \\ \sqrt{x} & \text{if } x \geq 4 \end{cases}$

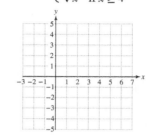

4. a. $f(x) = x^3$

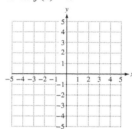

b. $g(x) = (x-2)^3 + 1$

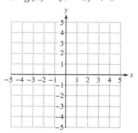

9. $f(x) = \begin{cases} 2x & \text{if } x \leq 1 \\ \dfrac{1}{x} & \text{if } x > 1 \end{cases}$

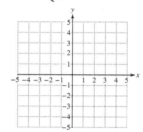

For Exercises 5–6, evaluate the function for the given values of x.

5. $f(x) = \begin{cases} x + 4 & \text{if } x < 1 \\ -x^2 & \text{if } x \geq 1 \end{cases}$

    a. $f(-2)$ **b.** $f(0)$ **c.** $f(1)$ **d.** $f(3)$

6. $g(x) = \begin{cases} \dfrac{1}{x} & \text{if } x < -1 \\ 0 & \text{if } -1 \leq x \leq 2 \\ \sqrt{x} & \text{if } x > 2 \end{cases}$

    a. $g(9)$ **b.** $g(1)$ **c.** $g(0)$ **d.** $g(-3)$

10. $h(x) = \begin{cases} x^2 - 2 & \text{if } x \leq 1 \\ 2x & \text{if } x > 1 \end{cases}$

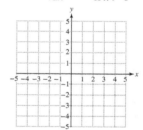

For Exercises 7–10, graph the function. Also determine the domain and range.

7. $h(x) = \begin{cases} x^2 + 3 & \text{if } x < 0 \\ x + 3 & \text{if } x \geq 0 \end{cases}$

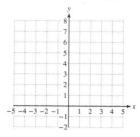

For Exercises 11–15, evaluate the permutation or combination.

11. $_4P_2$ **12.** $_4C_2$

13. $_7P_5$ **14.** $_8P_8$

15. $_8C_8$

16. A shelf can hold two different plants, three different vases, and two different pictures. In how many ways can these items be arranged?

17. There are 18 little league teams in one conference. Among the teams there will be a first-place winner, a second-place winner, and a third-place winner. How many arrangements of these places are possible?

18. How many four-letter passwords can be formed from the letters in the name *Euclid?*

19. A baseball team is selected from a pool of 20 possible players. In how many ways can 9 players be selected? Assume that each player can play any position.

20. There are five parking spaces and 12 cars that have access. How many ways can 5 cars be chosen to park in the spaces?

21. Nick has won an award for basketball, for football, for bowling, and for soccer. He only has room for three awards to be displayed on a shelf. In how many ways can he display his awards?

22. A spinner has six sections of equal size colored red, green, blue, purple, yellow, and pink. What is the probability of the spinner landing on a pink or a red section?

23. Five people at a restaurant ordered drinks. Three ordered soda and two ordered coffee. The server forgot who ordered which drinks. If the server comes to the table with one soda, what is the probability that he will deliver it to a person who ordered it?

24. The grade distribution for a history class is given in the table. A person is selected at random from the class.

Grade	Number of Students
A	12
B	8
C	14
D	5
F	3

What is the probability that

a. The person earned an "A"?

b. The person passed the class with a "C" or better?

25. A psychology student performs a study to compare the attitudes of men and women concerning the violence on television. The table shows the results from a random sample of 200 people who were asked the question, "Is there too much violence on television?"

	Yes	No	Maybe
Male	14	62	22
Female	47	35	20

Suppose that a person is selected at random from the sample. What is the probability that

a. The person is a female?

b. The person thinks that there is too much violence on television?

c. The person answered "no" or "maybe"?

d. The person is a male or the person thinks there is too much violence on television?

Additional Topics Appendix

Additional Factoring

1. Factoring by Using Substitution

The trinomial $u^2 + 4u - 21$ has a leading coefficient 1 and factors as $(u + 7)(u - 3)$. Now compare the following polynomials to $u^2 + 4u - 21$. In each case, the variable expressions in the first and second terms are the same. Furthermore, the coefficients are 1, 4, and -21. By letting the single variable u represent the variable expression in parentheses, the polynomial is a quadratic trinomial in u.

Concepts

1. Factoring by Using Substitution
2. Factoring 1 Term with 3 Terms
3. Additional Factoring Strategies

Polynomial	**Substitution**	**New form**
$u^2 + 4u - 21$		
$(a + b)^2 + 4(a + b) - 21$	Let $u = a + b$	$u^2 + 4u - 21$
$(y - 3)^2 + 4(y - 3) - 21$	Let $u = y - 3$	$u^2 + 4u - 21$

With an appropriate substitution, the polynomials are easier to factor.

Example 1 **Factoring by Using Substitution**

Factor completely. $(a + b)^2 + 4(a + b) - 21$

Solution:

$(a + b)^2 + 4(a + b) - 21$ The polynomial is a quadratic trinomial with variable $(a + b)$.

$= u^2 + 4u - 21$ Let $u = a + b$.

$= (u + 7)(u - 3)$ Factor the trinomial.

$= [(a + b) + 7][(a + b) - 3]$ Back substitute.

$= (a + b + 7)(a + b - 3)$ Simplify.

Skill Practice Factor completely.

 1. $(w - 6)^2 - 3(w - 6) - 10$

In Examples 2 and 3, we use substitution to factor a difference of squares and a sum of cubes.

Answer

1. $(w - 11)(w - 4)$

| Example 2 | **Factoring by Using Substitution** |

Factor completely. $9(4x - 1)^2 - 25$

Solution:

$9(4x - 1)^2 - 25$	The polynomial is a difference of squares.
$= 9u^2 - 25$	Let $u = 4x - 1$.
$= (3u - 5)(3u + 5)$	Factor as $a^2 - b^2 = (a - b)(a + b)$.
$= [3(4x - 1) - 5][3(4x - 1) + 5]$	Back substitute.
$= (12x - 3 - 5)(12x - 3 + 5)$	Apply the distributive property and simplify.
$= (12x - 8)(12x + 2)$	The remaining factors each have a common factor.
$= 4(3x - 2)2(6x + 1)$	Factor out 4 from the first binomial and 2 from the second binomial.
$= 8(3x - 2)(6x + 1)$	Simplify.

Skill Practice Factor completely.

2. $(2x + 1)^2 - 9$

| Example 3 | **Factoring by Using Substitution** |

Factor completely. $(x + 1)^3 + 8$

Solution:

$(x + 1)^3 + 8$	The polynomial is a sum of cubes.
$= u^3 + 8$	Let $u = x + 1$.
$= (u + 2)(u^2 - 2u + 4)$	Factor as $a^3 + b^3 = (a + b)(a^2 - ab + b^2)$.
$= [(x + 1) + 2][(x + 1)^2 - 2(x + 1) + 4]$	Back substitute.
$= (x + 3)[(x^2 + 2x + 1) - 2x - 2 + 4]$	Apply the distributive property.
$= (x + 3)(x^2 + 3)$	Simplify.

Skill Practice Factor completely.

3. $(y + 3)^3 + 64$

---

2. Factoring 1 Term with 3 Terms

When confronted with a 4-term polynomial, sometimes the standard method of grouping does not apply. For example, consider the polynomial $x^2 - y^2 - 6y - 9$. Notice that grouping 2 terms with 2 terms does not result in common binomial factors.

$$x^2 - y^2 \mid -6y - 9$$

$$= 1(x^2 - y^2) - 3(2x - 3)$$

Binomial factors do not match.

Answers

2. $4(x - 1)(x + 2)$

3. $(y + 7)(y^2 + 2y + 13)$

However, if a factor of -1 is removed from the last three terms, the last three terms result in a perfect square trinomial. This is called grouping 1 term with 3 terms.

Example 4   **Factoring by Grouping 1 Term with 3 Terms**

Factor completely. $x^2 - y^2 - 6y - 9$

Solution:

This polynomial has 4 terms. However, the standard grouping method does not work even if we try rearranging terms.

$x^2 - y^2 - 6y - 9$	We might try grouping one term with three terms. The reason is that after factoring out -1 from the last three terms we have a perfect square trinomial.
$= x^2 - 1(y^2 + 6y + 9)$	
$= x^2 - (y + 3)^2$ $\longleftarrow$ difference of squares	The resulting expression is a difference of squares.
$= x^2 - u^2$	The difference of squares can be factored by using substitution. Let $u = y + 3$.
$= (x + u)(x - u)$	Factor.
$= [x + (y + 3)][x - (y + 3)]$	Back substitute.
$= (x + y + 3)(x - y - 3)$	Simplify.

Skill Practice   Factor completely.

  4. $n^2 - m^2 - 8m - 16$

The difference of squares $(x)^2 - (y + 3)^2$ can also be factored without using a substitution.

$$(x)^2 - (y + 3)^2$$
$$= [x + (y + 3)][x - (y + 3)]$$
$$= (x + y + 3)(x - y - 3)$$

3. Additional Factoring Strategies

Thus far, we have learned how to factor polynomials that fit the following patterns.

- Difference of squares
- Difference of cubes
- Sum of cubes
- Perfect square trinomials
- Nonperfect square trinomials
- Grouping 2 terms by 2 terms
- Grouping 3 terms by 1 term

Answer

4. $(n + m + 4)(n - m - 4)$

A-4   Additional Topics Appendix

Many polynomials do not fit any of these patterns, and many polynomials do not factor using these techniques. However, sometimes a combination of patterns exists and we can find the factored form. In Example 5, the polynomial has 6 terms. We might try grouping 3 terms with 3 terms or 4 terms with 2 terms, or even 2 terms, 2 terms and 2 terms. In any case, we should expect to try a variety of approaches before a workable strategy is identified.

Example 5   Factoring a Polynomial

Factor completely. $2ac + 2a - bc - b - c - 1$

Solution:

$2ac + 2a - bc - b - c - 1$ The polynomial has 6 terms. After considerable trial and error, we might try grouping the first 2 terms, the second 2 terms, and the last 2 terms.

$= 2ac + 2a \mid -bc - b \mid -c - 1$

$= 2a(c + 1) - b(c + 1) - 1(c + 1)$ Factor out the GCF from each pair of terms.

$= (c + 1)(2a - b - 1)$ Factor out the common factor of $c + 1$.

Skill Practice   Factor completely.

5. $xy + 2y + 3xz + 6z - x - 2$

Answer

5. $(x + 2)(y + 3z - 1)$

Section A.1   Practice Exercises

Vocabulary and Key Concepts

1. Given the expression $(3x - 2)^2 - (3x - 2) - 12$, what substitution could be used for u to make this a simpler quadratic trinomial in terms of u?

2. Given the expression $49(p - 3)^2 - 36$, what substitution could be used for u to make this a simpler difference of squares in terms of u?

3. What would be the first step to factor $x^2 - 4x + 4 - y^2$ by grouping 3 terms with 1 term?

4. What would be the first two steps to factor $9a^2 - 4b^2 - 20b - 25$ by grouping 1 term with 3 terms?

Concept 1: Factoring by Using Substitution

For Exercises 5–20, factor completely. **(See Examples 1–3.)**

5. $(4t - 1)^2 + 3(4t - 1) - 4$

6. $(2p + 5)^2 - 4(2p + 5) - 12$

7. $2(w - 2)^2 - 5(w - 2) - 3$

8. $3(y + 4)^2 + 11(y + 4) - 4$

9. $25(x + 4)^2 - y^2$

10. $36(y - 5)^2 - z^2$

11. $9(5a - 3)^2 - 4$

12. $25(3b + 7)^2 - 16$

13. $(t - 2)^2 - (2t + 1)^2$

14. $(w + 3)^2 - (3w - 5)^2$

15. $(a + b)^3 + c^3$

16. $(x + 4)^3 - y^3$

17. $27c^3 - (d + 2)^3$

18. $125v^3 + (w - 1)^3$

19. $4x^2 + 28x(2y + 1) + 49(2y + 1)^2$

20. $9a^2 - 12a(b + 1) + 4(b + 1)^2$

Concept 2: Factoring 1 Term with 3 Terms

For Exercises 21–28, factor completely. **(See Example 4.)**

21. $x^2 - 10x + 25 - y^2$

22. $m^2 - 22m + 121 - n^2$

23. $a^2 - x^2 - 18xy - 81y^2$

24. $c^2 - a^2 + 16ab - 64b^2$

25. $25a^2 + 20ab + 4b^2 - 100c^2$

26. $36x^2 + 60xy + 25y^2 - 121z^2$

27. $64w^2 - 9t^2 + 24tp - 16p^2$

28. $49k^2 - 25m^2 + 30mn - 9n^2$

Concept 3: Additional Strategies and Mixed Exercises

For Exercises 29–68, factor completely. **(See Examples 1–5.)**

29. $x^2 - 4y^2 - x - 2y$

30. $9v^2 - w^2 - 3v + w$

31. $w^7 + 8w^4 - w^3 - 8$

32. $t^5 - 125t^2 - 4t^3 + 500$

33. $xy - 4x + 2yz - 8z - 2y + 8$

34. $ax + 4a + 2bx + 8b - cx - 4c$

35. $x^2 + xy - 2y^2 + x - y$

36. $a^2 + 2ab - 3b^2 - b + a$

37. $n^6 - 63n^3 - 64$

38. $m^6 + 7m^3 - 8$

39. $(a + b)^2 - 6(a + b)(c - d) + 9(c - d)^2$

40. $(x + 1)^2 - 4(x + 1)(x - 2) + 4(x - 2)^2$

41. $4x^4 - 10x^3 - 36x^2 + 90x$

42. $15x^4 - 5x^3 - 60x^2 + 20x$

43. $a^2 + 2ab + b^2 - a - b$

44. $v^2 + 6vw + 9w^2 - v - 3w$

45. $x^2(x + y) - y^2(x + y)$

46. $u^2(u - v) - v^2(u - v)$

47. $(a + 3)^4 + 6(a + 3)^3$

48. $(4 - b)^4 - 2(4 - b)^3$

49. $24(3x + 5)^3 - 30(3x + 5)^2$

50. $10(2y + 3)^2 + 15(2y + 3)$

51. $\dfrac{1}{100}x^2 + \dfrac{1}{35}x + \dfrac{1}{49}$

52. $\dfrac{1}{25}a^2 + \dfrac{1}{15}a + \dfrac{1}{36}$

53. $(5x^2 - 1)^2 - 4(5x^2 - 1) - 5$

54. $(x^3 + 4)^2 - 10(x^3 + 4) + 24$

55. $16p^4 - q^4$

56. $s^4t^4 - 81$

57. $y^3 + \dfrac{1}{64}$

58. $z^3 + \dfrac{1}{125}$

59. $6a^3 + a^2b - 6ab^2 - b^3$

60. $4p^3 + 12p^2q - pq^2 - 3q^3$

61. $\dfrac{1}{9}t^2 + \dfrac{1}{6}t + \dfrac{1}{16}$

62. $\dfrac{1}{25}y^2 + \dfrac{1}{5}y + \dfrac{1}{4}$

A-6   Additional Topics Appendix

63. $6ax + 2bx - by - 3ay$

64. $5pq - 4q - 12 + 15p$

65. $x^8 - 1$

66. $y^8 - 256$

67. $25c^2 - 9d^2 + 5c - 3d$

68. $5wx^3 + 5wy^3 - 2zx^3 - 2zy^3$

Section A.2   Mean, Median, and Mode

Concepts

1. Mean
2. Median
3. Mode
4. Weighted Mean

1. Mean

When given a list of numerical data, it is often desirable to obtain a single number that represents the central value of the data. In this section, we discuss three such values called the mean, median, and mode.

> **Definition of a Mean**
>
> The **mean** (or average) of a set of numbers is the sum of the values divided by the number of values. We can write this as a formula.
>
> $$\text{Mean} = \frac{\text{sum of the values}}{\text{number of values}}$$

> **Example 1   Finding the Mean of a Data Set**
>
> A small business employs five workers. Their yearly salaries are
>
> $42,000 $36,000 $45,000 $35,000 $38,000
>
> **a.** Find the mean yearly salary for the five employees.
>
> **b.** Suppose the owner of the business makes $218,000 per year. Find the mean salary for all six individuals (that is, include the owner's salary).

Solution:

a. Mean salary of five employees

$$= \frac{42{,}000 + 36{,}000 + 45{,}000 + 35{,}000 + 38{,}000}{5}$$

Avoiding Mistakes

When computing a mean remember to add the data first before dividing.

$$= \frac{196{,}000}{5} \qquad \text{Add the data values.}$$

$$= 39{,}200 \qquad \text{Divide.}$$

The mean salary for employees is $39,200.

b. Mean of all six individuals

$$= \frac{42{,}000 + 36{,}000 + 45{,}000 + 35{,}000 + 38{,}000 + 218{,}000}{6}$$

$$= \frac{414{,}000}{6}$$

$$= 69{,}000$$

The mean salary with the owner's salary included is $69,000.

Skill Practice Housing prices for five homes in one neighborhood are given.

   $108,000 $149,000 $164,000 $118,000 $144,000

1. Find the mean of these five prices.
2. Suppose a new home is built in the neighborhood for $1.3 million ($1,300,000). Find the mean price of all six homes.

2. Median

In Example 1, you may have noticed that the mean salary was greatly affected by the unusually high value of $218,000. For this reason, you may want to use a different measure of "center" called the median. The median is the "middle" number in an ordered list of numbers.

Finding the Median

To compute the **median** of a list of numbers, first arrange the numbers in order from least to greatest.

- If the number of data values in the list is *odd*, then the median is the middle number in the list.
- If the number of data values is *even*, there is no single middle number. Therefore, the median is the mean (average) of the two middle numbers in the list.

Example 2   **Finding the Median of a Data Set**

Consider the salaries of the five workers from Example 1.

   $42,000 $36,000 $45,000 $35,000 $38,000

a. Find the median salary for the five workers.

b. Find the median salary including the owner's salary of $218,000.

Solution:

a. 35,000   36,000   38,000   42,000   45,000   Arrange the data in order.

Because there are five data values (an *odd* number), the median is the middle number.

The median is $38,000.

b. Now consider the scores of all six individuals (including the owner). Arrange the data in order.

   35,000   36,000   38,000   42,000   45,000   218,000

$$\frac{38,000 + 42,000}{2}$$

There are six data values (an *even* number). The median is the average of the two middle numbers.

$$= \frac{80,000}{2}$$ Add the two middle numbers.

$$= 40,000$$ Divide.

The median of all six salaries is $40,000.

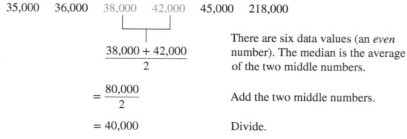

> **Skill Practice** Housing prices for five homes in one neighborhood are given.
>
> $108,000 $149,000 $164,000 $118,000 $144,000
>
> **3.** Find the median price of these five houses.
>
> **4.** Suppose a new home is built in the neighborhood for $1,300,000. Find the median price of all six homes. Compare this price with the mean in Skill Practice Exercise 2.

In Examples 1 and 2, the mean of all six salaries is $69,000, whereas the median is $40,000. These examples show that the median is a better representation for a central value when the data list has an unusually high (or low) value.

Example 3   **Determining the Median of a Data Set**

The average monthly temperatures (in °C) for the South Pole are given in the table. Find the median temperature. (*Source:* NOAA)

Jan.	Feb.	March	April	May	June	July	Aug.	Sept.	Oct.	Nov.	Dec.
−2.9	−9.5	−19.2	−20.7	−21.7	−23.0	−25.7	−26.1	−24.6	−18.9	−9.7	−3.4

Solution:

First arrange the numbers in order from least to greatest.

−26.1 −25.7 −24.6 −23.0 −21.7 −20.7 −19.2 −18.9 −9.7 −9.5 −3.4 −2.9

$$\text{Median} = \frac{-20.7 + (-19.2)}{2} = -19.95$$

There are 12 data values (an *even* number). Therefore, the median is the average of the two middle numbers. The median temperature at the South Pole is −19.95°C.

> **TIP:** Note that the median may not be one of the original data values.

> **Skill Practice** The gain or loss for a stock is given for an 8-day period. Find the median gain or loss.
>
> **5.** −2.4   −2.0   1.25   0.6   −1.8   −0.4   0.6   −0.9

3. Mode

A third representative value for a list of data is called the mode.

> **Definition of a Mode**
>
> The **mode** of a set of data is the value or values that occur most often.
> - If two values occur most often we say the data are bimodal.
> - If more than two values occur most often, we say there is no mode.

Answers

3. $144,000   **4.** $146,500
5. −0.65

| Example 4 | **Finding the Mode of a Data Set** |

The student-to-teacher ratio is given for elementary schools for ten selected states. For example, California has a student-to-teacher ratio of 20.6. This means that there are approximately 20.6 students per teacher in California elementary schools. (*Source: National Center for Education Statistics*)

ME	ND	WI	NH	RI	IL	IN	MS	CA	UT
12.5	13.4	14.1	14.5	14.8	16.1	16.1	16.1	20.6	21.9

Find the mode of the student-to-teacher ratio for these states.

Solution:

The data value 16.1 appears most often. Therefore, the mode is 16.1 students per teacher.

Skill Practice The monthly rainfall amounts (in inches) for Houston, Texas, are given. Find the mode. (*Source:* NOAA)

6. 4.5   3.0   3.2   3.5   5.1   6.8
       4.3   4.5   5.6   5.3   4.5   3.8

| Example 5 | **Finding the Mode of a Data Set** |

Find the mode of the list of average monthly temperatures for Albany, New York. Values are in °F.

Jan.	Feb.	March	April	May	June	July	Aug.	Sept.	Oct.	Nov.	Dec.
22	25	35	47	58	66	71	69	61	49	39	26

Solution:

No data value occurs most often. There is no mode for this set of data.

Skill Practice

7. Find the mode of the weights in pounds of babies born one day at Brackenridge Hospital in Austin, Texas.

   7.2   8.1   6.9   9.3   8.3   7.7   7.9   6.4   7.5

| Example 6 | **Finding the Mode of a Data Set** |

The grades for a quiz in college algebra are as follows. The scores are out of a possible 10 points.

9	4	6	9	9	8	2	1	4	9
5	10	10	5	7	7	9	8	7	3
9	7	10	7	10	1	7	4	5	6

Answers

6. 4.5 in.   **7.** There is no mode.

Solution:

Sometimes arranging the data in order makes it easier to find the repeated values.

1	1	2	3	4	4	4	5	5	5
6	6	7	7	7	7	7	7	8	8
9	9	9	9	9	9	10	10	10	10

The score of 7 occurs 6 times. The score of 9 occurs 6 times. There are two modes, 7 and 9, because these scores both occur more than any other score. We say that these data are *bimodal*.

Skill Practice

8. The ages of children participating in an after-school sports program are given. Find the mode(s).

13	15	17	15	14	15	16	16
15	16	12	13	15	14	16	15
15	16	16	13	16	13	14	18

TIP: To remember the difference between median and mode, think of the *median* of a highway that goes down the *middle*. Think of the word *mode* as sounding similar to the word *most*.

4. Weighted Mean

Sometimes data values in a list appear multiple times. In such a case, we can compute a weighted mean. In Example 7, we demonstrate how to use a weighted mean to compute a grade point average (GPA). To compute GPA, each grade is assigned a numerical value. For example, an "A" is worth 4 points, a "B" is worth 3 points, and so on. Then each grade for a course is "weighted" by the number of credit-hours that the course is worth.

Example 7   **Using a Weighted Mean to Compute GPA**

At a certain college, the grades A–F are assigned numerical values as follows.

$$A = 4.0 \qquad B+ = 3.5 \qquad B = 3.0 \qquad C+ = 2.5$$
$$C = 2.0 \qquad D+ = 1.5 \qquad D = 1.0 \qquad F = 0.0$$

Elmer takes the following classes with the grades as shown. Determine Elmer's GPA.

Course	Grade	Number of Credit-Hours
Prealgebra	A = 4 pts	3
Study Skills	C = 2 pts	1
First Aid	B+ = 3.5 pts	2
English I	D = 1.0 pt	4

Solution:

The data in the table can be visualized as follows.

4 pts	4 pts	4 pts	2 pts	3.5 pts	3.5 pts	1 pt	1 pt	1 pt	1 pt
A	A	A	C	B+	B+	D	D	D	D

3 of these   1 of these   2 of these   4 of these

Answer

8. There are two modes, 15 and 16.

The number of grade points earned for each course is the product of the grade for the course and the number of credit-hours for the course. For example:

Grade points for Prealgebra: (4 pts)(3 credit-hours) = 12 points

Course	Grade	Number of Credit-Hours (Weights)	Product Number of Grade Points	
Prealgebra	A = 4 pts	3	(4 pts)(3 credit-hours)	= 12 pts
Study Skills	C = 2 pts	1	(2 pts)(1 credit-hour)	= 2 pts
First Aid	B+ = 3.5 pts	2	(3.5 pts)(2 credit-hours)	= 7 pts
English I	D = 1.0 pt	4	(1 pt)(4 credit-hours)	= 4 pts
		Total hours: 10	Total grade points:	25 pts

To determine GPA, we will add the number of grade points earned for each course and then divide by the total number of credit-hours taken.

$$\text{Mean} = \frac{25}{10} = 2.5 \qquad \text{Elmer's GPA for this term is 2.5.}$$

Skill Practice

9. Clyde received the following grades for the semester. Use the numerical values assigned to grades from Example 7 to find Clyde's GPA.

Course	Grade	Credit-Hours
Math	B+	4
Science	C	3
Speech	A	3

In Example 7, notice that the value of each grade is "weighted" by the number of credit-hours. The grade of "A" for Prealgebra is weighted three times. The grade of "C" for the study skills course is weighted one time. The grade that hurt Elmer's GPA was the "D" in English. Not only did he receive a low grade, but the course was weighted heavily (4 credit-hours). In Exercise 47, we recompute Elmer's GPA with a "B" in English to see how this grade affects his GPA.

Answer

9. 3.2

Section A.2 Practice Exercises

Concept 1: Mean

For Exercises 1–7, find the mean of each set of numbers. **(See Example 1.)**

1. 93, 96, 88, 72, 91

2. 4, 6, 5, 10, 4, 5, 8

3. 3, 8, 5, 7, 4, 2, 7, 4

4. 0, 5, 7, 4, 7, 2, 4, 3

5. 7, 6, 5, 10, 8, 4, 8, 6, 0

6. −10, −13, −18, −20, −15

7. −22, −14, −12, −16, −15

8. Compute the mean of your test scores for this class up to this point.

9. The flight times in hours for six flights between New York and Los Angeles are given. Find the mean flight time. Round to the nearest tenth of an hour.

5.5, 6.0, 5.8, 5.8, 6.0, 5.6

10. A nurse takes the temperature of a patient every 10 min and records the temperatures as follows: 98°F, 98.4°F, 98.9°F, 100.1°F, and 99.2°F. Find the patient's mean temperature.

11. The number of Calories for six different chicken sandwiches and chicken salads is given in the table.

    a. What is the mean number of Calories for a chicken sandwich? Round to the nearest whole unit.

    b. What is the mean number of Calories for a salad with chicken? Round to the nearest whole unit.

    c. What is the difference in the means?

Chicken Sandwiches	Salads with Chicken
360	310
370	325
380	350
400	390
400	440
470	500

12. The heights of the players from two NBA teams are given in the table. All heights are in inches.

    a. Find the mean height for the players on the Philadelphia 76ers.

    b. Find the mean height for the players on the Milwaukee Bucks.

    c. What is the difference in the mean heights?

13. Zach received the following scores for his first four tests: 98%, 80%, 78%, 90%.

    a. Find Zach's mean test score.

    b. Zach got a 59% on his fifth test. Find the mean of all five tests.

    c. How did the low score of 59% affect the overall mean of five tests?

Philadelphia 76ers' Height (in.)	Milwaukee Bucks' Height (in.)
83	70
83	83
72	82
79	72
77	82
84	85
75	75
76	75
82	78
79	77

14. The prices of four steam irons are $50, $30, $25, and $45.

    a. Find the mean of these prices.

    b. An iron that costs $140 is added to the list. What is the mean of all five irons?

    c. How does the expensive iron affect the mean?

Concept 2: Median

For Exercises 15–20, find the median for each set of numbers. **(See Examples 2–3.)**

15. 16, 14, 22, 13, 20, 19, 17

16. 32, 35, 22, 36, 30, 31, 38

17. 109, 118, 111, 110, 123, 100

18. 134, 132, 120, 135, 140, 118

19. −58, −55, −50, −40, −40, −55

20. −82, −90, −99, −82, −88, −87

21. The infant mortality rates for five countries are given in the table. Find the median.

Country	Infant Mortality Rate (Deaths per 1000)
Sweden	3.93
Japan	4.10
Finland	3.82
Andorra	4.09
Singapore	3.87

22. The snowfall amounts for 5 winter months in Burlington, Vermont, are given in the table. Find the median.

Month	Snowfall (in.)
November	6.6
December	18.1
January	18.8
February	16.8
March	12.4

23. Jonas Slackman played 8 golf tournaments, each with 72-holes of golf. His scores for the tournaments are given. Find the median score.

$-3, -5, 1, 4, -8, 2, 8, -1$

24. Andrew Strauss recorded the daily low temperature (in °C) at his home in Virginia for 8 days in January. Find the median temperature.

$5, 6, -5, 1, -4, -11, -8, -5$

25. The number of passengers (in millions) on 9 leading airlines for a recent year is listed. Find the median number of passengers. (*Source:* International Airline Transport Association)

48.3, 42.4, 91.6, 86.8, 46.5, 71.2, 45.4, 56.4, 51.7

26. For a recent year the number of albums sold (in millions) is listed for the 10 best sellers. Find the median number of albums sold.

2.7, 3.0, 4.8, 7.4, 3.4, 2.6, 3.0, 3.0, 3.9, 3.2

Concept 3: Mode

For Exercises 27–32, find the mode(s) for each set of numbers. **(See Examples 4–5.)**

27. 4, 5, 3, 8, 4, 9, 4, 2, 1, 4

28. 12, 14, 13, 17, 19, 18, 19, 17, 17

29. $-28, -21, -24, -23, -24, -30, -21$

30. $-45, -42, -40, -41, -49, -49, -42$

31. 90, 89, 91, 77, 88

32. 132, 253, 553, 255, 552, 234

33. The table gives the monthly precipitation for Portland, Oregon for selected months. Find the mode.

Month	Rainfall (in.)
January	4.88
February	3.66
March	3.66
April	2.72
May	2.48
June	1.69

34. The table gives the number of hazardous waste sites for selected states. Find the mode.

State	Number of Sites
Florida	51
New Jersey	112
Michigan	67
Wisconsin	39
California	96
Pennsylvania	94
Illinois	39
New York	90

35. The unemployment rates for nine countries are given. Find the mode. **(See Example 6.)**

6.3%, 7.0%, 5.8%, 9.1%, 5.2%, 8.8%, 8.4%, 5.8%, 5.2%

36. The list gives the number of children who were absent from class for an 11-day period. Find the mode.

4, 1, 6, 2, 4, 4, 4, 2, 2, 3, 2

Mixed Exercises

37. Six test scores for Jonathan's history class are listed. Find the mean and median. Round to the nearest tenth if necessary. Does the mean or median give a better overall score for Jonathan's performance?

92%, 98%, 43%, 98%, 97%, 85%

38. Nora's math test results are listed. Find the mean and median. Round to the nearest tenth if necessary. Does the mean or median give a better overall score for Nora's performance?

52%, 85%, 89%, 90%, 83%, 89%

39. Listed below are monthly costs for seven health insurance companies for a self-employed person, 55 years of age, and in good health. Find the mean, median, and mode (if one exists). Round to the nearest dollar. (*Source:* eHealth Insurance Company, 2007)

$312, $225, $221, $256, $308, $280, $147

40. The salaries for seven Associate Professors at a large university are listed. Find the mean, median, and mode (if one exists). Round to the nearest dollar.

$104,000, $107,000, $67,750, $82,500, $73,500, $88,300, $104,000

41. The prices of 10 single-family, three-bedroom homes for sale in Santa Rosa, California, are listed for a recent year. Find the mean, median, and mode (if one exists).

$850,000, $835,000, $839,000, $829,000,

$850,000, $850,000, $850,000, $847,000,

$1,850,000, $825,000

42. The prices of 10 single-family, three-bedroom homes for sale in Boston, Massachusetts, are listed for a recent year. Find the mean, median, and mode (if one exists).

$300,000, $2,495,000, $2,120,000, $220,000,

$194,000, $391,000, $315,000, $330,000,

$435,000, $250,000

Concept 4: Weighted Mean

For Exercises 43–46, use the following numerical values assigned to grades to compute GPA. Round each GPA to the hundredths place. **(See Example 7.)**

A = 4.0	B+ = 3.5	B = 3.0	C+ = 2.5
C = 2.0	D+ = 1.5	D = 1.0	F = 0.0

43. Compute the GPA for the following grades. Round to the nearest hundredth.

Course	Grade	Number of Credit-Hours (Weights)
Intermediate Algebra	B	4
Theater	C	1
Music Appreciation	A	3
World History	D	5

44. Compute the GPA for the following grades. Round to the nearest hundredth.

Course	Grade	Number of Credit-Hours (Weights)
General Psychology	B+	3
Beginning Algebra	A	4
Student Success	A	1
Freshman English	B	3

45. Compute the GPA for the following grades. Round to the nearest hundredth.

Course	Grade	Number of Credit-Hours (Weights)
Business Calculus	B+	3
Biology	C	4
Library Research	F	1
American Literature	A	3

46. Compute the GPA for the following grades. Round to the nearest hundredth.

Course	Grade	Number of Credit-Hours (Weights)
University Physics	C+	5
Calculus I	A	4
Computer Programming	D	3
Swimming	A	1

47. Refer to the table given in Example 7. Replace the grade of "D" in English I with a grade of "B" and compute the GPA. How did Elmer's GPA differ with a better grade in the 4-hour English class?

Expanding Your Skills

48. There are 20 students enrolled in a 12th-grade math class. The graph displays the number of students by age. First complete the table, and then find the mean.

Number of Students by Age Group

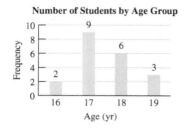

Age (yr)	Number of Students	Product
16		
17		
18		
19		
Total:		

49. A survey was made in a neighborhood of 37 houses. The graph represents the number of residents who live in each house. Complete the table and determine the mean number of residents per house.

Number of Houses for Each Number of Residents

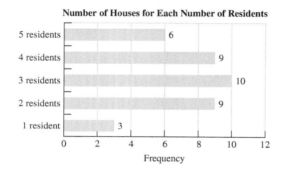

Number of Residents in Each House	Number of Houses	Product
1		
2		
3		
4		
5		
Total:		

Introduction to Geometry

Section A.3

1. Perimeter

In this section, we present several facts and formulas that may be used throughout the text in applications of geometry. One of the most important uses of geometry involves the measurement of objects of various shapes. We begin with an introduction to perimeter, area, and volume for several common shapes and objects.

Concepts

1. Perimeter
2. Area
3. Volume
4. Angles
5. Triangles

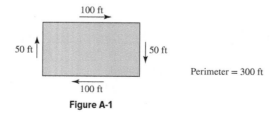

Perimeter = 300 ft

Figure A-1

Perimeter is defined as the distance around a figure. If we were to put up a fence around a field, the perimeter would determine the amount of fencing. For example, in Figure A-1 the distance around the field is 300 ft. For a polygon (a closed figure constructed from line

A-16   Additional Topics Appendix

segments), the perimeter is the sum of the lengths of the sides. For a circle, the distance around the outside is called the circumference.

Rectangle	Square	Triangle	Circle
$P = 2\ell + 2w$	$P = 4s$	$P = a + b + c$	Circumference: $C = 2\pi r$

$d = 2r$

For a circle, r represents the length of a radius—the distance from the center to any point on the circle. The length of a diameter, d, of a circle is twice that of a radius. Thus, $d = 2r$. The number π is a constant equal to the circumference of a circle divided by the length of a diameter. That is, $\pi = \frac{C}{d}$. The value of π is often approximated by 3.14 or $\frac{22}{7}$.

Example 1   **Finding Perimeter and Circumference**

Find the perimeter or circumference as indicated. Use 3.14 for π.

a. Perimeter of the rectangle

3.1 ft

5.5 ft

b. Circumference of the circle

6 cm

Solution:

a. $P = 2\ell + 2w$

$= 2(5.5 \text{ ft}) + 2(3.1 \text{ ft})$ Substitute $\ell = 5.5$ ft and $w = 3.1$ ft.

$= 11 \text{ ft} + 6.2 \text{ ft}$

$= 17.2 \text{ ft}$ The perimeter is 17.2 ft.

b. $C = 2\pi r$

$\approx 2(3.14)(6 \text{ cm})$ Substitute 3.14 for π and $r = 6$ cm.

$= 6.28(6 \text{ cm})$

$= 37.68 \text{ cm}$ The circumference is 37.68 cm.

TIP: If a calculator is used to find the circumference of a circle, use the π key to get a more accurate answer.

Skill Practice

1. Find the perimeter of the square.

7.25 in.

2. Find the circumference. Use 3.14 for π.

2 in.

Answers

1. 29 in.   **2.** 12.56 in.

2. Area

The area of a geometric figure is the number of square units that can be enclosed within the figure. In applications, we would find the area of a region if we were laying carpet or putting down sod for a lawn. For example, the rectangle shown in Figure A-2 encloses 6 square inches (6 in.^{2}).

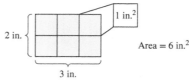

Figure A-2

The formulas used to compute the area for several common geometric shapes are given here:

Rectangle	Square	Parallelogram	Triangle	Trapezoid	Circle
$A = \ell w$	$A = s^2$	$A = bh$	$A = \frac{1}{2}bh$	$A = \frac{1}{2}(b_1 + b_2)h$	$A = \pi r^2$

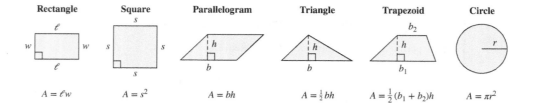

| **Example 2** | **Finding Area** |

Find the area.

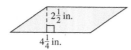

Solution:

$A = bh$ — The figure is a parallelogram.

$= (4\frac{1}{4} \text{ in.})(2\frac{1}{2} \text{ in.})$ — Substitute $b = 4\frac{1}{4}$ in. and $h = 2\frac{1}{2}$ in.

$= \left(\frac{17}{4} \text{ in.}\right)\left(\frac{5}{2} \text{ in.}\right)$

$= \frac{85}{8} \text{ in.}^2 \text{ or } 10\frac{5}{8} \text{ in.}^2$

TIP: The units of area are given in square units such as square inches (in.^{2}), square feet (ft^2), square yards (yd^2), square centimeters (cm^2), and so on.

Skill Practice Find the area.

3.

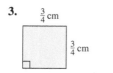

Answer

3. $\frac{9}{16}$ cm^2

A-18   Additional Topics Appendix

Example 3	**Finding Area**

Find the area.

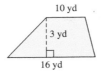

Solution:

$$A = \frac{1}{2}(b_1 + b_2)h$$ The figure is a trapezoid.

$$= \frac{1}{2}(16 \text{ yd} + 10 \text{ yd})(3 \text{ yd})$$ Substitute $b_1 = 16$ yd, $b_2 = 10$ yd, and $h = 3$ yd.

$$= \frac{1}{2}(26 \text{ yd})(3 \text{ yd})$$

$$= (13 \text{ yd})(3 \text{ yd})$$

$$= 39 \text{ yd}^2$$ The area is 39 yd^2.

Skill Practice Find the area.

4.

Example 4	**Finding the Area of a Circle**

Find the area of a circular fountain if the diameter is 50 ft. Use 3.14 for π.

Solution:

$$A = \pi r^2$$ We need the radius, which is $\frac{1}{2}$ the diameter. $r = \frac{1}{2}(50) = 25$ ft

$$\approx (3.14)(25 \text{ ft})^2$$ Substitute 3.14 for π and $r = 25$ ft.

$$= (3.14)(625 \text{ ft}^2)$$

$$= 1962.5 \text{ ft}^2$$ The area of the fountain is 1962.5 ft^2.

Skill Practice Find the area of the circular region. Use 3.14 for π.

5.

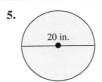

Answers

4. 30 m^2 **5.** 314 in.^{2}

3. Volume

The volume of a solid is the number of cubic units that can be enclosed within a solid. The solid shown in Figure A-3 contains 18 cubic inches (18 in.^{3}). In applications, volume might refer to the amount of water in a swimming pool.

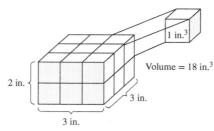

Figure A-3

The formulas used to compute the volume of several common solids are given here:

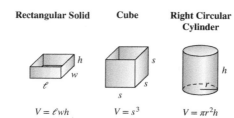

Rectangular Solid	Cube	Right Circular Cylinder
$V = \ell w h$	$V = s^3$	$V = \pi r^2 h$

> **TIP:** Notice that the volume formulas for the three figures just shown are given by the product of the area of the base and the height of the figure:
>
> $V = \ell w h$ $V = s \cdot s \cdot s$ $V = \pi r^2 h$
>   ↑   ↑   ↑
> Area of   Area of   Area of
> Rectangular Base   Square Base   Circular Base

Two additional geometric solids often used in geometry are the right circular cone and the sphere.

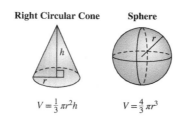

Right Circular Cone	Sphere
$V = \frac{1}{3} \pi r^2 h$	$V = \frac{4}{3} \pi r^3$

Example 5	**Finding Volume**

Find the volume.

$1\frac{1}{2}$ ft
$1\frac{1}{2}$ ft
$1\frac{1}{2}$ ft

Animation

A-20   Additional Topics Appendix

Solution:

$$V = s^3$$ The object is a cube.

$$= \left(1\tfrac{1}{2} \text{ ft}\right)^3$$ Substitute $s = 1\tfrac{1}{2}$ ft.

$$= \left(\frac{3}{2} \text{ ft}\right)^3$$

$$= \left(\frac{3}{2} \text{ ft}\right)\left(\frac{3}{2} \text{ ft}\right)\left(\frac{3}{2} \text{ ft}\right)$$

$$= \frac{27}{8} \text{ ft}^3, \text{ or } 3\tfrac{3}{8} \text{ ft}^3$$

> **TIP:** The units of volume are cubic units such as cubic inches (in.³), cubic feet (ft³), cubic yards (yd³), cubic centimeters (cm³), and so on.

Skill Practice Find the volume.

6.

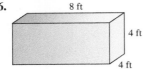

8 ft
4 ft
4 ft

| **Example 6** | **Finding Volume** |

Find the volume. Round to the nearest whole unit.

$h = 12$ cm
$r = 4$ cm

Solution:

$$V = \frac{1}{3}\pi r^2 h$$ The object is a right circular cone.

$$\approx \frac{1}{3}(3.14)(4 \text{ cm})^2(12 \text{ cm})$$ Substitute 3.14 for π, $r = 4$ cm, and $h = 12$ cm.

$$= \frac{1}{3}(3.14)(16 \text{ cm}^2)(12 \text{ cm})$$

$$= 200.96 \text{ cm}^3$$

$$\approx 201 \text{ cm}^3$$ Round to the nearest whole unit.

Skill Practice Find the volume. Use 3.14 for π. Round to the nearest whole unit.

7.

$r = 2$ in.

Answers

6. 128 ft³   **7.** 33 in.³

Example 7	**Finding Volume in an Application**

An underground gas tank is in the shape of a right circular cylinder. Find the volume of the tank. Use 3.14 for π.

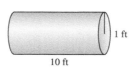
1 ft

10 ft

Solution:

$V = \pi r^2 h$

$\approx (3.14)(1 \text{ ft})^2(10 \text{ ft})$ Substitute 3.14 for π, $r = 1$ ft, and $h = 10$ ft.

$= (3.14)(1 \text{ ft}^2)(10 \text{ ft})$

$= 31.4 \text{ ft}^3$ The tank holds 31.4 ft^3 of gasoline.

Skill Practice

8. Find the volume of soda in the can. Use 3.14 for π. Round to the nearest whole unit.

12 cm

⊢ 6 cm ⊣

4. Angles

Applications involving angles and their measure come up often in the study of algebra, trigonometry, calculus, and applied sciences. The most common unit to measure an angle is the degree (°). Several angles and their corresponding degree measure are shown in Figure A-4.

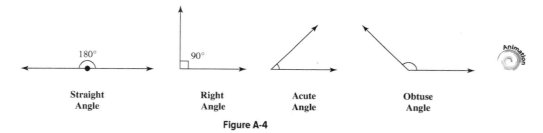

180°	90°		
Straight Angle	**Right Angle**	**Acute Angle**	**Obtuse Angle**

Figure A-4

- An angle that measures 90° is a **right angle** (right angles are often marked with a square or corner symbol, ☐).
- An angle that measures 180° is called a **straight angle**.
- An angle that measures between 0° and 90° is called an **acute angle**.
- An angle that measures between 90° and 180° is called an **obtuse angle**.
- Two angles with the same measure are **congruent angles**.

The measure of an angle will be denoted by the symbol m written in front of the angle. Therefore, the measure of $\angle A$ is denoted $m(\angle A)$.

Answer

8. 339 cm^3

A-22   Additional Topics Appendix

- Two angles are **complementary** if the sum of their measures is 90°.

- Two angles are **supplementary** if the sum of their measures is 180°.

$$m(\angle x) + m(\angle y) = 90°$$

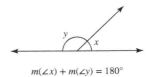

$$m(\angle x) + m(\angle y) = 180°$$

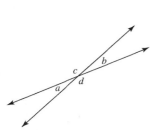

Figure A-5

When two lines intersect, four angles are formed (Figure A-5). In Figure A-5, $\angle a$ and $\angle b$ are a pair of vertical angles. Another set of vertical angles is the pair $\angle c$ and $\angle d$. An important property of vertical angles is that the measures of two vertical angles are *equal*. In the figure, $m(\angle a) = m(\angle b)$ and $m(\angle c) = m(\angle d)$.

Parallel lines are lines that lie in the same plane and do not intersect. In Figure A-6, the lines L_1 and L_2 are parallel lines. If a line intersects two parallel lines, the line forms eight angles with the parallel lines.

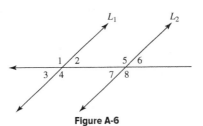

Figure A-6

The measures of angles 1–8 in Figure A-6 have the following special properties.

L_1 and L_2 are Parallel	Name of Angles	Property
	The following pairs of angles are called alternate interior angles:	Alternate interior angles are equal in measure.
	$\angle 2$ and $\angle 7$	$m(\angle 2) = m(\angle 7)$
	$\angle 4$ and $\angle 5$	$m(\angle 4) = m(\angle 5)$
	The following pairs of angles are called alternate exterior angles:	Alternate exterior angles are equal in measure.
	$\angle 1$ and $\angle 8$	$m(\angle 1) = m(\angle 8)$
	$\angle 3$ and $\angle 6$	$m(\angle 3) = m(\angle 6)$
	The following pairs of angles are called corresponding angles:	Corresponding angles are equal in measure.
	$\angle 1$ and $\angle 5$	$m(\angle 1) = m(\angle 5)$
	$\angle 2$ and $\angle 6$	$m(\angle 2) = m(\angle 6)$
	$\angle 3$ and $\angle 7$	$m(\angle 3) = m(\angle 7)$
	$\angle 4$ and $\angle 8$	$m(\angle 4) = m(\angle 8)$

> **Example 8**   **Finding the Measures of Angles in a Diagram**
>
> Find the measure of each angle and explain how the angle is related to the given angle of 70°.
>
>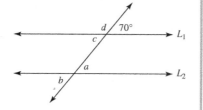
>
>   **a.** $\angle a$ **b.** $\angle b$
>
>   **c.** $\angle c$ **d.** $\angle d$
>
> **Solution:**
>
>   **a.** $m(\angle a) = 70°$ $\angle a$ is a corresponding angle to the given angle of 70°.
>
>   **b.** $m(\angle b) = 70°$ $\angle b$ and the given angle of 70° are alternate exterior angles.
>
>   **c.** $m(\angle c) = 70°$ $\angle c$ and the given angle of 70° are vertical angles.
>
>   **d.** $m(\angle d) = 110°$ $\angle d$ is the supplement of the given angle of 70°.
>
> ---
>
> **Skill Practice** Refer to the figure. Assume that lines L_1 and L_2 are parallel.
>
> **9.** Given that $m(\angle 3) = 23°$, find $m(\angle 2)$, $m(\angle 4)$, $m(\angle 7)$, and $m(\angle 8)$.
>
>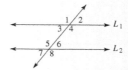

5. Triangles

Triangles are categorized by the measures of the angles (Figure A-7) and by the number of equal sides or angles (Figure A-8).

- An **acute triangle** is a triangle in which all three angles are acute.
- A **right triangle** is a triangle in which one angle is a right angle.
- An **obtuse triangle** is a triangle in which one angle is obtuse.

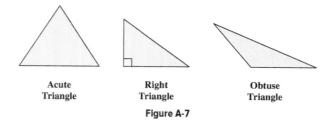

Figure A-7

- An **equilateral triangle** is a triangle in which all three sides (and all three angles) are equal in measure.
- An **isosceles triangle** is a triangle in which two sides are equal in measure (the angles opposite the equal sides are also equal in measure).
- A **scalene triangle** is a triangle in which no sides (or angles) are equal in measure.

Answer

9. $m(\angle 2) = 23°$; $m(\angle 4) = 157°$;
     $m(\angle 7) = 23°$; $m(\angle 8) = 157°$

A-24　　Additional Topics Appendix

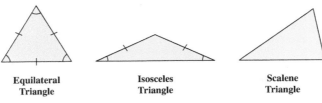

Equilateral
Triangle

Isosceles
Triangle

Scalene
Triangle

Figure A-8

The following important property is true for all triangles.

Sum of the Angles in a Triangle

The sum of the measures of the angles of a triangle is 180°.

Example 9　　### Finding the Measures of Angles in a Diagram

Find the measure of each angle in the figure.

a. ∠a

b. ∠b

c. ∠c

d. ∠d

e. ∠e

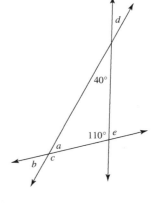

Solution:

a. $m(\angle a) = 30°$　　The sum of the angles in a triangle is 180°.

b. $m(\angle b) = 30°$　　∠a and ∠b are vertical angles and have equal measures.

c. $m(\angle c) = 150°$　　∠c and ∠a are supplementary angles (∠c and ∠b are also supplementary).

d. $m(\angle d) = 40°$　　∠d and the given angle of 40° are vertical angles.

e. $m(\angle e) = 70°$　　∠e and the given angle of 110° are supplementary angles.

Skill Practice For Exercises 10–14, refer to the figure. Find the measure of the indicated angle.

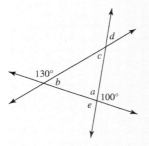

10. ∠a　　　**11.** ∠b　　　**12.** ∠c　　　**13.** ∠d　　　**14.** ∠e

Section A.3   Practice Exercises

Concept 1: Perimeter

1. Would you measure area or perimeter to determine the amount of decorative fence needed to enclose a garden?

2. Identify which of the following units could be measures of perimeter.

    a. Square inches (in.^{2})   **b.** Meters (m)   **c.** Cubic feet (ft^3)

    d. Cubic meters (m^3)   **e.** Miles (mi)   **f.** Square centimeters (cm^2)

    g. Square yards (yd^2)   **h.** Cubic inches (in.^{3})   **i.** Kilometers (km)

For Exercises 3–10, find the perimeter or circumference of each figure. Use 3.14 for π. **(See Example 1.)**

3.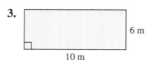
6 m
10 m

4.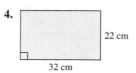
22 cm
32 cm

5.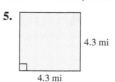
4.3 mi
4.3 mi

6.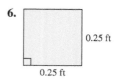
0.25 ft
0.25 ft

7.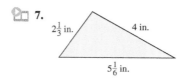
$2\frac{1}{3}$ in.   4 in.
$5\frac{1}{6}$ in.

8.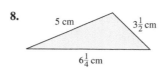
5 cm $3\frac{1}{2}$ cm
$6\frac{1}{4}$ cm

9.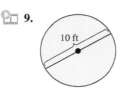
10 ft

10.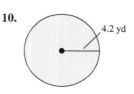
4.2 yd

Concept 2: Area

11. Identify which of the following units could be measures of area.

    a. Square inches (in.^{2})   **b.** Meters (m)   **c.** Cubic feet (ft^3)

    d. Cubic meters (m^3)   **e.** Miles (mi)   **f.** Square centimeters (cm^2)

    g. Square yards (yd^2)   **h.** Cubic inches (in.^{3})   **i.** Kilometers (km)

12. Would you measure area or perimeter to determine the amount of carpeting needed for a room?

For Exercises 13–26, find the area. Use 3.14 for π. **(See Examples 2–4.)**

13.
11 cm
3 cm

14.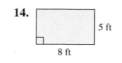
5 ft
8 ft

15.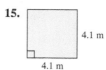
4.1 m
4.1 m

16.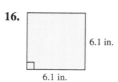
6.1 in.
6.1 in.

17.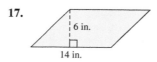
6 in.
14 in.

18.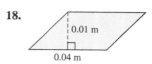
0.01 m
0.04 m

A-26   Additional Topics Appendix

19.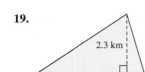

20.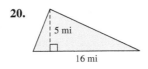

21.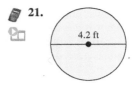

22.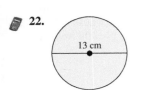

23.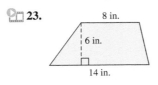

24.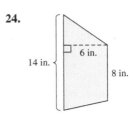

25.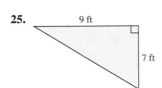

26.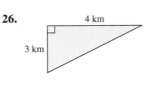

Concept 3: Volume

27. Identify which of the following units could be measures of volume.

    a. Square inches (in.^{2})   **b.** Meters (m)   **c.** Cubic feet (ft^3)

    d. Cubic meters (m^3)   **e.** Miles (mi)   **f.** Square centimeters (cm^2)

    g. Square yards (yd^2)   **h.** Cubic inches (in.^{3})   **i.** Kilometers (km)

28. Would you measure perimeter, area, or volume to determine the amount of water needed to fill a swimming pool?

For Exercises 29–36, find the volume of each figure. Use 3.14 for π. **(See Examples 5–7.)**

29.

30.

31.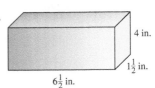

32.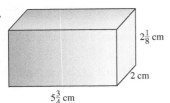

33.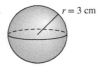

34.

35.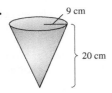

36.

37. A florist sells balloons and needs to know how much helium to order. Each balloon is approximately spherical with a radius of 9 in. How much helium is needed to fill one balloon? Use 3.14 for π.

38. Find the volume of a spherical ball whose radius is 2 in. Use 3.14 for π. Round to the nearest whole unit.

39. Find the volume of a snow cone in the shape of a right circular cone whose radius is 3 cm and whose height is 12 cm. Use 3.14 for π.

40. A landscaping supply company has a pile of gravel in the shape of a right circular cone whose radius is 10 yd and whose height is 18 yd. Find the volume of the gravel. Use 3.14 for π.

Mixed Exercises: Perimeter, Area, and Volume

41. A wall measuring 20 ft by 8 ft can be painted for $40.

   a. What is the price per square foot?

   b. At this rate, how much would it cost to paint the remaining three walls that measure 20 ft by 8 ft, 16 ft by 8 ft, and 16 ft by 8 ft?

42. Suppose it costs $336 to carpet a 16 ft by 12 ft room.

   a. What is the price per square foot?

   b. At this rate, how much would it cost to carpet a room that is 20 ft by 32 ft?

43. If you were to purchase wood to frame a photograph, would you measure the perimeter or area of the photograph?

44. If you were to purchase sod (grass) for your front yard, would you measure the perimeter or area of the yard?

45. How much fencing is needed to enclose a triangularly shaped garden whose sides measure 12 ft, 22 ft, and 20 ft?

46. A regulation soccer field is 100 yd long by 60 yd wide. Find the perimeter of the field.

47. **a.** An American football field is 360 ft long by 160 ft wide. What is the area of the field?

   b. How many pieces of sod, each 1 ft wide and 3 ft long, are needed to sod an entire field? (*Hint:* First find the area of a piece of sod.)

48. The Transamerica Pyramid in San Francisco is a tower with triangular sides (excluding the "wings"). Each side measures 145 ft wide with a height of 853 ft. What is the area of each side?

© R. Morley/PhotoLink/ Getty Images RF

49. **a.** Find the area of a circular pizza that is 8 in. in diameter (the radius is 4 in.). Use 3.14 for π.

   b. Find the area of a circular pizza that is 12 in. in diameter (the radius is 6 in.).

   c. Assume that the 8-in. diameter and 12-in. diameter pizzas are both the same thickness. Which would provide more pizza, two 8-in. pizzas or one 12-in. pizza?

50. **a.** Find the area of a rectangular pizza that is 12 in. by 8 in.

   b. Find the area of a circular pizza that has a 16-in. diameter. Use 3.14 for π.

   c. Assume that the two pizzas have the same thickness. Which would provide more pizza? Two rectangular pizzas or one circular pizza?

51. Find the volume of a soup can in the shape of a right circular cylinder if its radius is 3.2 cm and its height is 9 cm. Use 3.14 for π.

52. Find the volume of a coffee mug whose radius is 2.5 in. and whose height is 6 in. Use 3.14 for π.

A-28   Additional Topics Appendix

Concept 4: Angles

For Exercises 53–58, answer true or false. If an answer is false, explain why.

53. The sum of the measures of two right angles equals the measure of a straight angle.

54. Two right angles are complementary.

55. Two right angles are supplementary.

56. Two acute angles cannot be supplementary.

57. Two obtuse angles cannot be supplementary.

58. An obtuse angle and an acute angle can be supplementary.

59. If possible, find two acute angles that are supplementary.

60. If possible, find two acute angles that are complementary. Answers may vary.

61. If possible, find an obtuse angle and an acute angle that are supplementary. Answers may vary.

62. If possible, find two obtuse angles that are supplementary.

63. What angle is its own complement?

64. What angle is its own supplement?

 65. Refer to the figure.

    a. State all the pairs of vertical angles.

    b. State all the pairs of supplementary angles.

    c. If the measure of ∠4 is 80°, find the measures of ∠1, ∠2, and ∠3.

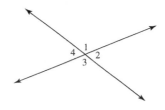

66. Refer to the figure.

    a. State all the pairs of vertical angles.

    b. State all the pairs of supplementary angles.

    c. If the measure of ∠a is 25°, find the measures of ∠b, ∠c, and ∠d.

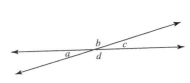

For Exercises 67–70, the measure of an angle is given. Find the measure of its complement.

67. 33°   **68.** 87°   **69.** 12°   **70.** 45°

For Exercises 71–74, the measure of an angle is given. Find the measure of its supplement.

71. 33°   **72.** 87°   **73.** 122°   **74.** 90°

For Exercises 75–82, refer to the figure. Assume that L_1 and L_2 are parallel lines. **(See Example 8.)**

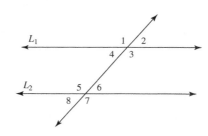

75. $m(\angle 5) = m(\angle \text{_____})$ Reason: Vertical angles have equal measures.

76. $m(\angle 5) = m(\angle \text{_____})$ Reason: Alternate interior angles have equal measures.

77. $m(\angle 5) = m(\angle \text{_____})$ Reason: Corresponding angles have equal measures.

78. $m(\angle 7) = m(\angle \text{_____})$ Reason: Corresponding angles have equal measures.

79. $m(\angle 7) = m(\angle \text{_____})$ Reason: Alternate exterior angles have equal measures.

80. $m(\angle 7) = m(\angle \text{_____})$ Reason: Vertical angles have equal measures.

81. $m(\angle 3) = m(\angle \text{_____})$ Reason: Alternate interior angles have equal measures.

82. $m(\angle 3) = m(\angle \text{_____})$ Reason: Vertical angles have equal measures.

83. Find the measures of angles a–g in the figure. Assume that L_1 and L_2 are parallel.

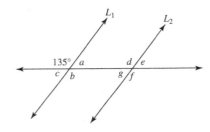

84. Find the measures of angles a–g in the figure. Assume that L_1 and L_2 are parallel.

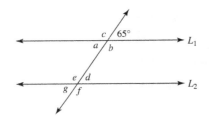

Concept 5: Triangles

For Exercises 85–88, identify the triangle as equilateral, isosceles, or scalene.

85.

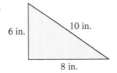

86.

87.

88.

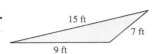

89. True or False? If a triangle is equilateral, then it is not scalene.

90. True or False? If a triangle is isosceles, then it is also scalene.

91. Can a triangle be both a right triangle and an obtuse triangle? Explain.

92. Can a triangle be both a right triangle and an isosceles triangle? Explain.

A-30   Additional Topics Appendix

For Exercises 93–96, find the measure of each missing angle.

93.

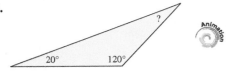

94.

95.

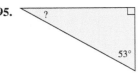

96.

97. Refer to the figure. Find the measures of angles $a-j$. **(See Example 9.)**

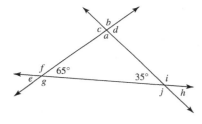

98. Refer to the figure. Find the measures of angles $a-j$.

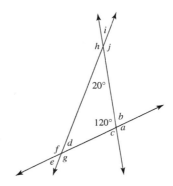

99. Refer to the figure. Find the measures of angles $a-k$. Assume that L_1 and L_2 are parallel.

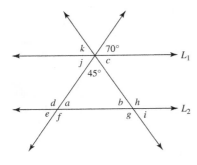

100. Refer to the figure. Find the measures of angles $a-k$. Assume that L_1 and L_2 are parallel.

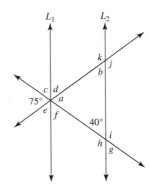

Expanding Your Skills

For Exercises 101–102, find the perimeter.

101.

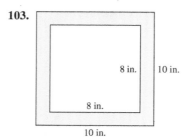

5 ft

16 ft

20 ft

102.

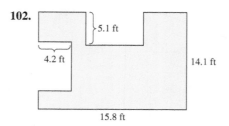

5.1 ft

4.2 ft

14.1 ft

15.8 ft

For Exercises 103–106, find the area of the shaded region. Use 3.14 for π.

103.

8 in.

10 in.

8 in.

10 in.

104.

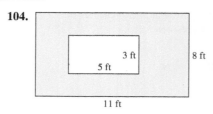

3 ft

5 ft

8 ft

11 ft

105.

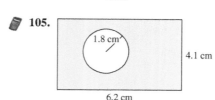

1.8 cm

4.1 cm

6.2 cm

106.

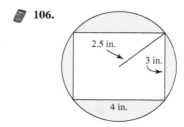

2.5 in.

3 in.

4 in.

Solving Systems of Linear Equations by Using Matrices

Section A.4

1. Introduction to Matrices

We have already learned how to solve systems of linear equations by using the substitution method and the addition method. We now present a third method called the Gauss-Jordan method that uses matrices to solve a linear system.

A **matrix** is a rectangular array of numbers (the plural of *matrix* is *matrices*). The rows of a matrix are read horizontally, and the columns of a matrix are read vertically. Every number or entry within a matrix is called an element of the matrix.

The **order of a matrix** is determined by the number of rows and number of columns. A matrix with m rows and n columns is an $m \times n$ (read as "m by n") matrix. Notice that with the order of a matrix, the number of rows is given first, followed by the number of columns.

Concepts

1. Introduction to Matrices
2. Solving Systems of Linear Equations by Using the Gauss-Jordan Method

> **Example 1**   **Determining the Order of a Matrix**

Determine the order of each matrix.

a. $\begin{bmatrix} 2 & -4 & 1 \\ 5 & \pi & \sqrt{7} \end{bmatrix}$ **b.** $\begin{bmatrix} 1.9 \\ 0 \\ 7.2 \\ -6.1 \end{bmatrix}$ **c.** $\begin{bmatrix} 1 & 0 & 0 \\ 0 & 1 & 0 \\ 0 & 0 & 1 \end{bmatrix}$ **d.** $[a \quad b \quad c]$

Solution:

  a. This matrix has two rows and three columns. Therefore, it is a 2×3 matrix.

  b. This matrix has four rows and one column. Therefore, it is a 4×1 matrix.
  A matrix with one column is called a **column matrix**.

  c. This matrix has three rows and three columns. Therefore, it is a 3×3 matrix.
  A matrix with the same number of rows and columns is called a **square matrix**.

  d. This matrix has one row and three columns. Therefore, it is a 1×3 matrix.
  A matrix with one row is called a **row matrix**.

Skill Practice Determine the order of the matrix.

1. $\begin{bmatrix} -5 & 2 \\ 1 & 3 \\ 8 & 9 \end{bmatrix}$ **2.** $[4 - 8]$ **3.** $\begin{bmatrix} 5 \\ 10 \\ 15 \end{bmatrix}$ **4.** $\begin{bmatrix} 2 & -0.5 \\ -1 & 6 \end{bmatrix}$

A matrix can be used to represent a system of linear equations written in standard form. To do so, we extract the coefficients of the variable terms and the constants within the equation. For example, consider the system

$$2x - y = 5$$
$$x + 2y = -5$$

The matrix **A** is called the **coefficient matrix**.

$$\mathbf{A} = \begin{bmatrix} 2 & -1 \\ 1 & 2 \end{bmatrix}$$

If we extract both the coefficients and the constants from the equations, we can construct the **augmented matrix** of the system:

$$\left[\begin{array}{cc|c} 2 & -1 & 5 \\ 1 & 2 & -5 \end{array}\right]$$

A vertical bar is inserted into an augmented matrix to designate the position of the equal signs.

> **Example 2**   **Writing an Augmented Matrix for a System
> of Linear Equations**

Write the augmented matrix for each linear system.

a. $-3x - 4y = 3$
       $2x + 4y = 2$

b. $2x \qquad - 3z = 14$
            $2y + z = 2$
       $x + y \qquad = 4$

Answers
1. 3×2 **2.** 1×2
3. 3×1 **4.** 2×2

Solution:

a. $\begin{bmatrix} -3 & -4 & | & 3 \\ 2 & 4 & | & 2 \end{bmatrix}$

b. $\begin{bmatrix} 2 & 0 & -3 & | & 14 \\ 0 & 2 & 1 & | & 2 \\ 1 & 1 & 0 & | & 4 \end{bmatrix}$

> **TIP:** Notice that zeros are inserted to denote the coefficient of each missing term.

Skill Practice Write the augmented matrix for each system.

5. $-x + y = 4$
$2x - y = 1$

6. $2x - y + z = 14$
$-3x + 4y = 8$
$x - y + 5z = 0$

Example 3 **Writing a Linear System from an Augmented Matrix**

Write a system of linear equations represented by each augmented matrix. Use x, y, and z as the variables.

a. $\begin{bmatrix} 2 & -5 & | & -8 \\ 4 & 1 & | & 6 \end{bmatrix}$

b. $\begin{bmatrix} 2 & -1 & 3 & | & 14 \\ 1 & 1 & -2 & | & -5 \\ 3 & 1 & -1 & | & 2 \end{bmatrix}$

c. $\begin{bmatrix} 1 & 0 & 0 & | & 4 \\ 0 & 1 & 0 & | & -1 \\ 0 & 0 & 1 & | & 0 \end{bmatrix}$

Solution:

a. $2x - 5y = -8$
$4x + y = 6$

b. $2x - y + 3z = 14$
$x + y - 2z = -5$
$3x + y - z = 2$

c. $x + 0y + 0z = 4$ $x = 4$
$0x + y + 0z = -1$ or $y = -1$
$0x + 0y + z = 0$ $z = 0$

Skill Practice Write a system of linear equations represented by each augmented matrix. Use x, y, and z as the variables.

7. $\begin{bmatrix} 2 & 3 & | & 5 \\ -1 & 8 & | & 1 \end{bmatrix}$

8. $\begin{bmatrix} -3 & 2 & 1 & | & 4 \\ 14 & 1 & 0 & | & 20 \\ -8 & 3 & 5 & | & 6 \end{bmatrix}$

9. $\begin{bmatrix} 1 & 0 & 0 & | & -8 \\ 0 & 1 & 0 & | & 2 \\ 0 & 0 & 1 & | & 15 \end{bmatrix}$

2. Solving Systems of Linear Equations by Using the Gauss-Jordan Method

We know that interchanging two equations results in an equivalent system of linear equations. Interchanging two rows in an augmented matrix results in an equivalent augmented matrix. Similarly, because each row in an augmented matrix represents a linear equation, we can perform the following elementary row operations that result in an equivalent augmented matrix.

Elementary Row Operations

The following *elementary row operations* performed on an augmented matrix produce an equivalent augmented matrix:

- Interchange two rows.
- Multiply every element in a row by a nonzero real number.
- Add a multiple of one row to another row.

Answers

5. $\begin{bmatrix} -1 & 1 & | & 4 \\ 2 & -1 & | & 1 \end{bmatrix}$

6. $\begin{bmatrix} 2 & -1 & 1 & | & 14 \\ -3 & 4 & 0 & | & 8 \\ 1 & -1 & 5 & | & 0 \end{bmatrix}$

7. $2x + 3y = 5$
$-x + 8y = 1$

8. $-3x + 2y + z = 4$
$14x + y = 20$
$-8x + 3y + 5z = 6$

9. $x = -8, y = 2, z = 15$

When we are solving a system of linear equations by any method, the goal is to write a series of simpler but equivalent systems of equations until the solution is obvious. The *Gauss-Jordan method* uses a series of elementary row operations performed on the augmented matrix to produce a simpler augmented matrix. In particular, we want to produce an augmented matrix that has 1's along the diagonal of the matrix of coefficients and 0's for the remaining entries in the matrix of coefficients. A matrix written in this way is said to be written in **reduced row echelon form**. For example, the augmented matrix from Example 3(c) is written in reduced row echelon form.

$$\begin{bmatrix} 1 & 0 & 0 & | & 4 \\ 0 & 1 & 0 & | & -1 \\ 0 & 0 & 1 & | & 0 \end{bmatrix}$$

The solution to the corresponding system of equations is easily recognized as $x = 4$, $y = -1$, and $z = 0$.

Similarly, matrix **B** represents a solution of $x = a$ and $y = b$ to a system of two linear equations.

$$\mathbf{B} = \begin{bmatrix} 1 & 0 & | & a \\ 0 & 1 & | & b \end{bmatrix}$$

Example 4	**Solving a System by Using the Gauss-Jordan Method**

Solve by using the Gauss-Jordan method.

$$2x - y = 5$$
$$x + 2y = -5$$

Solution:

$$\begin{bmatrix} 2 & -1 & | & 5 \\ 1 & 2 & | & -5 \end{bmatrix}$$ Set up the augmented matrix.

$\xrightarrow{R_1 \Leftrightarrow R_2}$ $\begin{bmatrix} 1 & 2 & | & -5 \\ 2 & -1 & | & 5 \end{bmatrix}$ Switch row 1 and row 2 to get a 1 in the upper left position.

$\xrightarrow{-2R_1 + R_2 \Rightarrow R_2}$ $\begin{bmatrix} 1 & 2 & | & -5 \\ 0 & -5 & | & 15 \end{bmatrix}$ Multiply row 1 by -2 and add the result to row 2. This produces an entry of 0 below the upper left position.

$\xrightarrow{-\frac{1}{5}R_2 \Rightarrow R_2}$ $\begin{bmatrix} 1 & 2 & | & -5 \\ 0 & 1 & | & -3 \end{bmatrix}$ Multiply row 2 by $-\frac{1}{5}$ to produce a 1 along the diagonal in the second row.

$\xrightarrow{-2R_2 + R_1 \Rightarrow R_1}$ $\begin{bmatrix} 1 & 0 & | & 1 \\ 0 & 1 & | & -3 \end{bmatrix}$ Multiply row 2 by -2 and add the result to row 1. This produces a 0 in the first row, second column.

$$\mathbf{C} = \begin{bmatrix} 1 & 0 & | & 1 \\ 0 & 1 & | & -3 \end{bmatrix}$$

The matrix **C** is in reduced row echelon form. From the augmented matrix, we have $x = 1$ and $y = -3$. The solution set is $\{(1, -3)\}$.

Skill Practice

10. Solve by using the Gauss-Jordan method.

$$x - 2y = -21$$
$$2x + y = -2$$

The order in which we manipulate the elements of an augmented matrix to produce reduced row echelon form was demonstrated in Example 4. In general, the order is as follows.

*   First produce a 1 in the first row, first column. Then use the first row to obtain 0's in the first column below this element.
*   Next, if possible, produce a 1 in the second row, second column. Use the second row to obtain 0's above and below this element.
*   Next, if possible, produce a 1 in the third row, third column. Use the third row to obtain 0's above and below this element.
*   The process continues until reduced row echelon form is obtained.

Example 5   **Solving a System by Using the Gauss-Jordan Method**

Solve by using the Gauss-Jordan method.

$$x \qquad\qquad = -y + 5$$
$$-2x \qquad + 2z = y - 10$$
$$3x + 6y + 7z = 14$$

Solution:

First write each equation in the system in standard form.

$$x \qquad\qquad = -y + 5 \longrightarrow \quad x + y \qquad\quad = 5$$
$$-2x + \qquad 2z = y - 10 \longrightarrow -2x - y + 2z = -10$$
$$3x + 6y + 7z = 14 \qquad \longrightarrow \quad 3x + 6y + 7z = 14$$

$$\begin{bmatrix} 1 & 1 & 0 & | & 5 \\ -2 & -1 & 2 & | & -10 \\ 3 & 6 & 7 & | & 14 \end{bmatrix}$$ Set up the augmented matrix.

$$\begin{array}{l} 2R_1 + R_2 \Rightarrow R_2 \longrightarrow \\ -3R_1 + R_3 \Rightarrow R_3 \longrightarrow \end{array} \begin{bmatrix} 1 & 1 & 0 & | & 5 \\ 0 & 1 & 2 & | & 0 \\ 0 & 3 & 7 & | & -1 \end{bmatrix}$$ Multiply row 1 by 2 and add the result to row 2.
Multiply row 1 by −3 and add the result to row 3.

$$\begin{array}{l} -1R_2 + R_1 \Rightarrow R_1 \longrightarrow \\ -3R_2 + R_3 \Rightarrow R_3 \longrightarrow \end{array} \begin{bmatrix} 1 & 0 & -2 & | & 5 \\ 0 & 1 & 2 & | & 0 \\ 0 & 0 & 1 & | & -1 \end{bmatrix}$$ Multiply row 2 by −1 and add the result to row 1.
Multiply row 2 by −3 and add the result to row 3.

Answer
10. $\{(-5, 8)\}$

$$2R_3 + R_1 \Rightarrow R_1 \longrightarrow \begin{bmatrix} 1 & 0 & 0 & | & 3 \\ 0 & 1 & 0 & | & 2 \\ 0 & 0 & 1 & | & -1 \end{bmatrix}$$
$$-2R_3 + R_2 \Rightarrow R_2 \longrightarrow$$

Multiply row 3 by 2 and add the result to row 1.
Multiply row 3 by -2 and add the result to row 2.

From the reduced row echelon form of the matrix, we have $x = 3$, $y = 2$, and $z = -1$. The solution set is $\{(3, 2, -1)\}$.

Skill Practice Solve by using the Gauss-Jordan method.

11. $x + \;\; y + \;\; z = 2$
$\quad\;\; x - \;\; y + \;\; z = 4$
$\quad\;\; x + 4y + 2z = 1$

It is particularly easy to recognize a system of dependent equations or an inconsistent system of equations from the reduced row echelon form of an augmented matrix. This is demonstrated in Examples 6 and 7.

Example 6	**Solving a System of Dependent Equations by Using the Gauss-Jordan Method**

Solve by using the Gauss-Jordan method.

$$x - 3y = 4$$
$$\frac{1}{2}x - \frac{3}{2}y = 2$$

Solution:

$$\begin{bmatrix} 1 & -3 & | & 4 \\ \frac{1}{2} & -\frac{3}{2} & | & 2 \end{bmatrix}$$ Set up the augmented matrix.

$$-\tfrac{1}{2}R_1 + R_2 \Rightarrow R_2 \longrightarrow \begin{bmatrix} 1 & -3 & | & 4 \\ 0 & 0 & | & 0 \end{bmatrix}$$ Multiply row 1 by $-\frac{1}{2}$ and add the result to row 2.

The second row of the augmented matrix represents the equation $0 = 0$. The equations are dependent. The solution set is $\{(x, y)\,|\,x - 3y = 4\}$.

Skill Practice Solve by using the Gauss-Jordan method.
12. $4x - 6y = 16$
$\quad\;\; 6x - 9y = 24$

Answers
11. $\{(1, -1, 2)\}$
12. Infinitely many solutions;
$\quad \{(x, y)\,|\,4x - 6y = 16\}$;
$\quad$ dependent equations

| **Example 7** | **Solving an Inconsistent System by Using the Gauss-Jordan Method** |

Solve by using the Gauss-Jordan method.

$$x + 3y = 2$$
$$-3x - 9y = 1$$

Solution:

$$\begin{bmatrix} 1 & 3 & | & 2 \\ -3 & -9 & | & 1 \end{bmatrix} \qquad \text{Set up the augmented matrix.}$$

$$\xrightarrow{3R_1 + R_2 \Rightarrow R_2} \begin{bmatrix} 1 & 3 & | & 2 \\ 0 & 0 & | & 7 \end{bmatrix} \qquad \begin{array}{l} \text{Multiply row 1 by 3 and add the} \\ \text{result to row 2.} \end{array}$$

The second row of the augmented matrix represents the contradiction $0 = 7$. The system is inconsistent. There is no solution, { }.

Skill Practice Solve by using the Gauss-Jordan method.

13. $6x + 10y = 1$
$15x + 25y = 3$

| **Calculator Connections** |

Topic: Entering a Matrix into a Calculator

Many graphing calculators have a matrix editor in which the user defines the order of the matrix and then enters the elements of the matrix. For example, consider the system of equations and the related 2×3 augmented matrix.

$$\begin{array}{l} 2x - 3y = -13 \\ 3x + y = 8 \end{array} \qquad \mathbf{A} = \begin{bmatrix} 2 & -3 & | & -13 \\ 3 & 1 & | & 8 \end{bmatrix}$$

Matrix **A** is entered as shown.

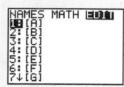

Once an augmented matrix has been entered into a graphing calculator, a *rref* function can be used to transform the matrix into reduced row echelon form.

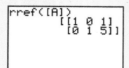 The solution set to the system is $\{(1, 5)\}$.

Answer

13. No solution; { }; inconsistent system

A-38   Additional Topics Appendix

Section A.4   Practice Exercises

Vocabulary and Key Concepts

1. **a.** A _____ is a rectangular array of numbers. The order of a matrix is $m \times n$ where m is the number of _____ and n is the number of _____.

    b. A matrix that has exactly one column is called a _____ matrix. A matrix that has exactly _____ row is called a row matrix, and a matrix with the same number of rows and columns is called a _____ matrix.

    c. Given the system of equations shown, matrix **A** is called the _____ matrix. The matrix **B** is called the _____ matrix.

$$\begin{array}{c} 3x - 2y = 6 \\ 4x + 5y = 9 \end{array} \qquad A = \begin{bmatrix} 3 & -2 \\ 4 & 5 \end{bmatrix} \qquad B = \left[\begin{array}{cc|c} 3 & -2 & 6 \\ 4 & 5 & 9 \end{array}\right]$$

    d. The matrix **A** is said to be written in reduced _____ form.

$$A = \left[\begin{array}{cc|c} 1 & 0 & 8 \\ 0 & 1 & 2 \end{array}\right]$$

Review Exercises

2. How much 50% acid solution should be mixed with pure acid to obtain 20 L of a mixture that is 70% acid?

For Exercises 3–5, solve the system by using any method.

3. $\begin{aligned} x - 6y &= 9 \\ x + 2y &= 13 \end{aligned}$

4. $\begin{aligned} x + y - z &= 8 \\ x - 2y + z &= 3 \\ x + 3y + 2z &= 7 \end{aligned}$

5. $\begin{aligned} 2x - y + z &= -4 \\ -x + y + 3z &= -7 \\ x + 3y - 4z &= 22 \end{aligned}$

Concept 1: Introduction to Matrices

For Exercises 6–14, (**a**) determine the order of each matrix and (**b**) determine if the matrix is a row matrix, a column matrix, a square matrix, or none of these. **(See Example 1.)**

6. $\begin{bmatrix} 4 \\ 5 \\ -3 \\ 0 \end{bmatrix}$

7. $\begin{bmatrix} 5 \\ -1 \\ 2 \end{bmatrix}$

8. $\begin{bmatrix} -9 & 4 & 3 \\ -1 & -8 & 4 \\ 5 & 8 & 7 \end{bmatrix}$

9. $\begin{bmatrix} 3 & -9 \\ -1 & -3 \end{bmatrix}$

10. $[4 \quad -7]$

11. $[0 \quad -8 \quad 11 \quad 5]$

12. $\begin{bmatrix} 5 & -8.1 & 4.2 & 0 \\ 4.3 & -9 & 18 & 3 \end{bmatrix}$

13. $\begin{bmatrix} \frac{1}{3} & \frac{3}{4} & 6 \\ -2 & 1 & -\frac{7}{8} \end{bmatrix}$

14. $\begin{bmatrix} 5 & 1 \\ -1 & 2 \\ 0 & 7 \end{bmatrix}$

For Exercises 15–18, set up the augmented matrix. **(See Example 2.)**

15. $\begin{aligned} x - 2y &= -1 \\ 2x + y &= -7 \end{aligned}$

16. $\begin{aligned} x - 3y &= 3 \\ 2x - 5y &= 4 \end{aligned}$

17. $\begin{aligned} x - 2y &= 5 - z \\ 2x + 6y + 3z &= -2 \\ 3x - y - 2z &= 1 \end{aligned}$

18. $\begin{aligned} 5x - 17 &= -2z \\ 8x + 6z &= 26 + y \\ 8x + 3y - 12z &= 24 \end{aligned}$

For Exercises 19–22, write a system of linear equations represented by the augmented matrix. Use x, y, and z as the variables. **(See Example 3.)**

19. $\begin{bmatrix} 4 & 3 & | & 6 \\ 12 & 5 & | & -6 \end{bmatrix}$

20. $\begin{bmatrix} -2 & 5 & | & -15 \\ -7 & 15 & | & -45 \end{bmatrix}$

21. $\begin{bmatrix} 1 & 0 & 0 & | & 4 \\ 0 & 1 & 0 & | & -1 \\ 0 & 0 & 1 & | & 7 \end{bmatrix}$

22. $\begin{bmatrix} 1 & 0 & 0 & | & 0.5 \\ 0 & 1 & 0 & | & 6.1 \\ 0 & 0 & 1 & | & 3.9 \end{bmatrix}$

Concept 2: Solving Systems of Linear Equations by Using the Gauss-Jordan Method

23. Given the matrix **E**

$$\mathbf{E} = \begin{bmatrix} 3 & -2 & | & 8 \\ 9 & -1 & | & 7 \end{bmatrix}$$

   a. What is the element in the second row and third column?

   b. What is the element in the first row and second column?

24. Given the matrix **F**

$$\mathbf{F} = \begin{bmatrix} 1 & 8 & | & 0 \\ 12 & -13 & | & -2 \end{bmatrix}$$

   a. What is the element in the second row and second column?

   b. What is the element in the first row and third column?

25. Given the matrix **Z**

$$\mathbf{Z} = \begin{bmatrix} 2 & 1 & | & 11 \\ 2 & -1 & | & 1 \end{bmatrix}$$

write the matrix obtained by multiplying the elements in the first row by $\frac{1}{2}$.

26. Given the matrix **J**

$$\mathbf{J} = \begin{bmatrix} 1 & 1 & | & 7 \\ 0 & 3 & | & -6 \end{bmatrix}$$

write the matrix obtained by multiplying the elements in the second row by $\frac{1}{3}$.

27. Given the matrix **K**

$$\mathbf{K} = \begin{bmatrix} 5 & 2 & | & 1 \\ 1 & -4 & | & 3 \end{bmatrix}$$

write the matrix obtained by interchanging rows 1 and 2.

28. Given the matrix **L**

$$\mathbf{L} = \begin{bmatrix} 9 & 6 & | & 13 \\ -7 & 2 & | & 19 \end{bmatrix}$$

write the matrix obtained by interchanging rows 1 and 2.

29. Given the matrix **M**

$$\mathbf{M} = \begin{bmatrix} 1 & 5 & | & 2 \\ -3 & -4 & | & -1 \end{bmatrix}$$

write the matrix obtained by multiplying the first row by 3 and adding the result to row 2.

30. Given the matrix **N**

$$\mathbf{N} = \begin{bmatrix} 1 & 3 & | & -5 \\ -2 & 2 & | & 12 \end{bmatrix}$$

write the matrix obtained by multiplying the first row by 2 and adding the result to row 2.

31. Given the matrix **R**

$$\mathbf{R} = \begin{bmatrix} 1 & 3 & 0 & | & -1 \\ 4 & 1 & -5 & | & 6 \\ -2 & 0 & -3 & | & 10 \end{bmatrix}$$

   a. Write the matrix obtained by multiplying the first row by -4 and adding the result to row 2.

   b. Using the matrix obtained from part (a), write the matrix obtained by multiplying the first row by 2 and adding the result to row 3.

32. Given the matrix **S**

$$\mathbf{S} = \begin{bmatrix} 1 & 2 & 0 & | & 10 \\ 5 & 1 & -4 & | & 3 \\ -3 & 4 & 5 & | & 2 \end{bmatrix}$$

   a. Write the matrix obtained by multiplying the first row by -5 and adding the result to row 2.

   b. Using the matrix obtained from part (a), write the matrix obtained by multiplying the first row by 3 and adding the result to row 3.

A-40   Additional Topics Appendix

For Exercises 33–36, use the augmented matrices **A**, **B**, **C**, and **D** to answer true or false.

$$\mathbf{A} = \begin{bmatrix} 6 & -4 & | & 2 \\ 5 & -2 & | & 7 \end{bmatrix} \qquad \mathbf{B} = \begin{bmatrix} 5 & -2 & | & 7 \\ 6 & -4 & | & 2 \end{bmatrix} \qquad \mathbf{C} = \begin{bmatrix} 1 & -\frac{2}{3} & | & \frac{1}{3} \\ 5 & -2 & | & 7 \end{bmatrix} \qquad \mathbf{D} = \begin{bmatrix} 5 & -2 & | & 7 \\ -12 & 8 & | & -4 \end{bmatrix}$$

33. The matrix **A** is a 2×3 matrix.

34. Matrix **B** is equivalent to matrix **A**.

35. Matrix **A** is equivalent to matrix **C**.

36. Matrix **B** is equivalent to matrix **D**.

37. What does the notation $R_2 \Leftrightarrow R_1$ mean when one is performing the Gauss-Jordan method?

38. What does the notation $2R_3 \Rightarrow R_3$ mean when one is performing the Gauss-Jordan method?

39. What does the notation $-3R_1 + R_2 \Rightarrow R_2$ mean when one is performing the Gauss-Jordan method?

40. What does the notation $4R_2 + R_3 \Rightarrow R_3$ mean when one is performing the Gauss-Jordan method?

For Exercises 41–56, solve the system by using the Gauss-Jordan method. For systems that do not have one unique solution, also state the number of solutions and whether the system is inconsistent or the equations are dependent. **(See Example 4–7.)**

41. $\begin{aligned} x - 2y &= -1 \\ 2x + y &= -7 \end{aligned}$

42. $\begin{aligned} x - 3y &= 3 \\ 2x - 5y &= 4 \end{aligned}$

43. $\begin{aligned} x + 3y &= 6 \\ -4x - 9y &= 3 \end{aligned}$

44. $\begin{aligned} 2x - 3y &= -2 \\ x + 2y &= 13 \end{aligned}$

45. $\begin{aligned} x + 3y &= 3 \\ 4x + 12y &= 12 \end{aligned}$

46. $\begin{aligned} 2x + 5y &= 1 \\ -4x - 10y &= -2 \end{aligned}$

47. $\begin{aligned} x - y &= 4 \\ 2x + y &= 5 \end{aligned}$

48. $\begin{aligned} 2x - y &= 0 \\ x + y &= 3 \end{aligned}$

49. $\begin{aligned} x + 3y &= -1 \\ -3x - 6y &= 12 \end{aligned}$

50. $\begin{aligned} x + y &= 4 \\ 2x - 4y &= -4 \end{aligned}$

51. $\begin{aligned} 3x + y &= -4 \\ -6x - 2y &= 3 \end{aligned}$

52. $\begin{aligned} 2x + y &= 4 \\ 6x + 3y &= -1 \end{aligned}$

53. $\begin{aligned} x + y + z &= 6 \\ x - y + z &= 2 \\ x + y - z &= 0 \end{aligned}$

54. $\begin{aligned} 2x - 3y - 2z &= 11 \\ x + 3y + 8z &= 1 \\ 3x - y + 14z &= -2 \end{aligned}$

55. $\begin{aligned} x - 2y &= 5 - z \\ 2x + 6y + 3z &= -10 \\ 3x - y - 2z &= 5 \end{aligned}$

56. $\begin{aligned} 5x &= 10z + 15 \\ x - y + 6z &= 23 \\ x + 3y - 12z &= 13 \end{aligned}$

Graphing Calculator Exercises

For Exercises 57–62, use the matrix features on a graphing calculator to express each augmented matrix in reduced row echelon form. Compare your results to the solution you obtained in the indicated exercise.

57. $\begin{bmatrix} 1 & -2 & | & -1 \\ 2 & 1 & | & -7 \end{bmatrix}$

Compare with Exercise 41.

58. $\begin{bmatrix} 1 & -3 & | & 3 \\ 2 & -5 & | & 4 \end{bmatrix}$

Compare with Exercise 42.

59. $\begin{bmatrix} 1 & 3 & | & 6 \\ -4 & -9 & | & 3 \end{bmatrix}$

Compare with Exercise 43.

60. $\begin{bmatrix} 2 & -3 & | & -2 \\ 1 & 2 & | & 13 \end{bmatrix}$

Compare with Exercise 44.

61. $\begin{bmatrix} 1 & 1 & 1 & | & 6 \\ 1 & -1 & 1 & | & 2 \\ 1 & 1 & -1 & | & 0 \end{bmatrix}$

Compare with Exercise 53.

62. $\begin{bmatrix} 2 & -3 & -2 & | & 11 \\ 1 & 3 & 8 & | & 1 \\ 3 & -1 & 14 & | & -2 \end{bmatrix}$

Compare with Exercise 54.

Determinants and Cramer's Rule

1. Introduction to Determinants

Associated with every square matrix is a real number called the **determinant** of the matrix. The determinant of a square matrix **A**, denoted det **A**, is written by enclosing the elements of the matrix within two vertical bars. For example,

$$\text{If} \quad \mathbf{A} = \begin{bmatrix} 2 & -1 \\ 6 & 0 \end{bmatrix} \quad \text{then} \quad \det \mathbf{A} = \begin{vmatrix} 2 & -1 \\ 6 & 0 \end{vmatrix}$$

$$\text{If} \quad \mathbf{B} = \begin{bmatrix} 0 & -5 & 1 \\ 4 & 0 & \frac{1}{2} \\ -2 & 10 & 1 \end{bmatrix} \quad \text{then} \quad \det \mathbf{B} = \begin{vmatrix} 0 & -5 & 1 \\ 4 & 0 & \frac{1}{2} \\ -2 & 10 & 1 \end{vmatrix}$$

Determinants have many applications in mathematics, including solving systems of linear equations, finding the area of a triangle, determining whether three points are collinear, and finding an equation of a line between two points.

The determinant of a 2×2 matrix is defined as follows.

Definition of a Determinant of a 2 × 2 Matrix

The determinant of the matrix $\begin{bmatrix} a & b \\ c & d \end{bmatrix}$ is the real number $ad - bc$. It is written as

$$\begin{vmatrix} a & b \\ c & d \end{vmatrix} = ad - bc$$

Example 1   **Evaluating a 2 × 2 Determinant**

Evaluate the determinants.

a. $\begin{vmatrix} 6 & -2 \\ 5 & \frac{1}{3} \end{vmatrix}$ **b.** $\begin{vmatrix} 2 & -11 \\ 0 & 0 \end{vmatrix}$

Solution:

a. $\begin{vmatrix} 6 & -2 \\ 5 & \frac{1}{3} \end{vmatrix}$ For this determinant, $a = 6$, $b = -2$, $c = 5$, and $d = \frac{1}{3}$.

$$ad - bc = (6)\left(\frac{1}{3}\right) - (-2)(5)$$
$$= 2 + 10$$
$$= 12$$

b. $\begin{vmatrix} 2 & -11 \\ 0 & 0 \end{vmatrix}$ For this determinant, $a = 2$, $b = -11$, $c = 0$, $d = 0$.

$$ad - bc = (2)(0) - (-11)(0)$$
$$= 0 - 0$$
$$= 0$$

TIP: Example 1(b) illustrates that the value of a determinant having a row of all zeros is 0. The same is true for a determinant having a column of all zeros.

Skill Practice   Evaluate the determinants.

1. $\begin{vmatrix} 2 & 8 \\ -1 & 5 \end{vmatrix}$ **2.** $\begin{vmatrix} -6 & 0 \\ 4 & 0 \end{vmatrix}$

Answers

1. 18   **2.** 0

2. Determinant of a 3 × 3 Matrix

To find the determinant of a 3 × 3 matrix, we first need to define the **minor** of an element of the matrix. For any element of a 3 × 3 matrix, the minor of that element is the determinant of the 2 × 2 matrix obtained by deleting the row and column in which the element resides. For example, consider the matrix

$$\begin{bmatrix} 5 & -1 & 6 \\ 0 & -7 & 1 \\ 4 & 2 & 6 \end{bmatrix}$$

The minor of the element 5 is found by deleting the first row and first column and then evaluating the determinant of the remaining 2 × 2 matrix:

$$\begin{bmatrix} 5 & -1 & 6 \\ 0 & -7 & 1 \\ 4 & 2 & 6 \end{bmatrix}$$ Now evaluate the determinant: $\begin{vmatrix} -7 & 1 \\ 2 & 6 \end{vmatrix} = (-7)(6) - (1)(2)$

$$= -44$$

For this matrix, the minor for the element 5 is −44.

To find the minor of the element −7, delete the second row and second column, and then evaluate the determinant of the remaining 2 × 2 matrix.

$$\begin{bmatrix} 5 & -1 & 6 \\ 0 & -7 & 1 \\ 4 & 2 & 6 \end{bmatrix}$$ Now evaluate the determinant: $\begin{vmatrix} 5 & 6 \\ 4 & 6 \end{vmatrix} = (5)(6) - (6)(4) = 6$

For this matrix, the minor for the element −7 is 6.

Example 2   **Determining the Minor for Elements in a 3 × 3 Matrix**

Find the minor for each element in the first column of the matrix.

$$\begin{bmatrix} 3 & 4 & -1 \\ 2 & -4 & 5 \\ 0 & 1 & -6 \end{bmatrix}$$

Solution:

For 3: $\begin{bmatrix} 3 & 4 & -1 \\ 2 & -4 & 5 \\ 0 & 1 & -6 \end{bmatrix}$ The minor is: $\begin{vmatrix} -4 & 5 \\ 1 & -6 \end{vmatrix} = (-4)(-6) - (5)(1) = 19$

For 2: $\begin{bmatrix} 3 & 4 & -1 \\ 2 & -4 & 5 \\ 0 & 1 & -6 \end{bmatrix}$ The minor is: $\begin{vmatrix} 4 & -1 \\ 1 & -6 \end{vmatrix} = (4)(-6) - (-1)(1) = -23$

For 0: $\begin{bmatrix} 3 & 4 & -1 \\ 2 & -4 & 5 \\ 0 & 1 & -6 \end{bmatrix}$ The minor is: $\begin{vmatrix} 4 & -1 \\ -4 & 5 \end{vmatrix} = (4)(5) - (-1)(-4) = 16$

Skill Practice   Find the minor for the element 3.

3. $\begin{bmatrix} -1 & 8 & -6 \\ \frac{1}{2} & 3 & 2 \\ 5 & 7 & 4 \end{bmatrix}$

Answer

3. $\begin{vmatrix} -1 & -6 \\ 5 & 4 \end{vmatrix} = 26$

The determinant of a 3×3 matrix is defined as follows.

> ## Definition of a Determinant of a 3×3 Matrix
>
> $$\begin{vmatrix} a_1 & b_1 & c_1 \\ a_2 & b_2 & c_2 \\ a_3 & b_3 & c_3 \end{vmatrix} = a_1 \cdot \begin{vmatrix} b_2 & c_2 \\ b_3 & c_3 \end{vmatrix} - a_2 \cdot \begin{vmatrix} b_1 & c_1 \\ b_3 & c_3 \end{vmatrix} + a_3 \cdot \begin{vmatrix} b_1 & c_1 \\ b_2 & c_2 \end{vmatrix}$$

From this definition, we see that the determinant of a 3×3 matrix can be written as

$$a_1 \cdot (\text{minor of } a_1) - a_2 \cdot (\text{minor of } a_2) + a_3 \cdot (\text{minor of } a_3)$$

Evaluating determinants in this way is called *expanding minors*.

Example 3   **Evaluating a 3×3 Determinant**

Evaluate the determinant. $\begin{vmatrix} 2 & 4 & 2 \\ 1 & -3 & 0 \\ -5 & 5 & -1 \end{vmatrix}$

Solution:

$$\begin{vmatrix} 2 & 4 & 2 \\ 1 & -3 & 0 \\ -5 & 5 & -1 \end{vmatrix} = 2 \cdot \begin{vmatrix} -3 & 0 \\ 5 & -1 \end{vmatrix} - (1) \cdot \begin{vmatrix} 4 & 2 \\ 5 & -1 \end{vmatrix} + (-5) \cdot \begin{vmatrix} 4 & 2 \\ -3 & 0 \end{vmatrix}$$

$$= 2[(-3)(-1) - (0)(5)] - 1[(4)(-1) - (2)(5)] - 5[(4)(0) - (2)(-3)]$$

$$= 2(3) - 1(-14) - 5(6)$$

$$= 6 + 14 - 30$$

$$= -10$$

Skill Practice   Evaluate the determinant.

4. $\begin{vmatrix} -2 & 4 & 9 \\ 5 & -1 & 2 \\ 1 & 1 & 6 \end{vmatrix}$

Although we defined the determinant of a matrix by expanding the minors of the elements in the first column, *any row or column can be used*. However, we must choose the correct ·sign to apply to each term in the expansion. The following array of signs is helpful.

$$\begin{array}{ccc} + & - & + \\ - & + & - \\ + & - & + \end{array}$$

The signs alternate for each row and column, beginning with $+$ in the first row, first column.

TIP: There is another method to determine the signs for each term of the expansion. For the a_{ij} element, multiply the term by $(-1)^{i+j}$.

Answer

4. -42

A-44   Additional Topics Appendix

| Example 4 | **Evaluating a 3 × 3 Determinant** |

Evaluate the determinant by expanding minors about the elements in the second row.

$$\begin{vmatrix} 2 & 4 & 2 \\ 1 & -3 & 0 \\ -5 & 5 & -1 \end{vmatrix}$$

Solution:

Signs obtained from the array of signs

$$\begin{vmatrix} 2 & 4 & 2 \\ 1 & -3 & 0 \\ -5 & 5 & -1 \end{vmatrix} = -(1) \cdot \begin{vmatrix} 4 & 2 \\ 5 & -1 \end{vmatrix} + (-3) \cdot \begin{vmatrix} 2 & 2 \\ -5 & -1 \end{vmatrix} - (0) \cdot \begin{vmatrix} 2 & 4 \\ -5 & 5 \end{vmatrix}$$

$$= -1[(4)(-1) - (2)(5)] - 3[(2)(-1) - (2)(-5)] - 0$$

$$= -1(-14) - 3(8)$$

$$= 14 - 24$$

$$= -10$$

Notice that the value of the determinant is the same as the result obtained in Example 3.

Skill Practice Evaluate the determinant.

5. $$\begin{vmatrix} 4 & -1 & 2 \\ 3 & 6 & -8 \\ 0 & \frac{1}{2} & 5 \end{vmatrix}$$

Calculator Connections

Topic: Evaluating a Determinant

The determinant of a matrix can be evaluated on a graphing calculator. First use the matrix editor to enter the elements of the matrix. Then use a *det* function to evaluate the determinant. The determinant from Examples 3 and 4 is evaluated below.

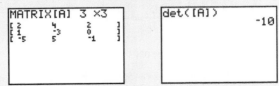

In Example 4, the third term in the expansion of minors was zero because the element 0 when multiplied by its minor is zero. To simplify the arithmetic in evaluating a determinant of a 3 × 3 matrix, expand about the row or column that has the most 0 elements.

Answer

5. 154

3. Cramer's Rule

In this section, we will learn another method to solve a system of linear equations. This method is called **Cramer's rule**.

Cramer's Rule for a 2 × 2 System of Linear Equations

The solution to the system $a_1x + b_1y = c_1$

$$a_2x + b_2y = c_2$$

is given by $x = \dfrac{\mathbf{D}_x}{\mathbf{D}}$ and $y = \dfrac{\mathbf{D}_y}{\mathbf{D}}$

where $\mathbf{D} = \begin{vmatrix} a_1 & b_1 \\ a_2 & b_2 \end{vmatrix}$ (and $\mathbf{D} \neq 0$) $\mathbf{D}_x = \begin{vmatrix} c_1 & b_1 \\ c_2 & b_2 \end{vmatrix}$ $\mathbf{D}_y = \begin{vmatrix} a_1 & c_1 \\ a_2 & c_2 \end{vmatrix}$

Example 5   **Using Cramer's Rule to Solve a 2 × 2 System of Linear Equations**

Solve the system by using Cramer's rule. $3x - 5y = 11$

$$-x + 3y = -5$$

Solution:

For this system: $a_1 = 3$ $b_1 = -5$ $c_1 = 11$

$$a_2 = -1 \quad b_2 = 3 \quad c_2 = -5$$

$$\mathbf{D} = \begin{vmatrix} 3 & -5 \\ -1 & 3 \end{vmatrix} = (3)(3) - (-5)(-1) = 9 - 5 = 4$$

$$\mathbf{D}_x = \begin{vmatrix} 11 & -5 \\ -5 & 3 \end{vmatrix} = (11)(3) - (-5)(-5) = 33 - 25 = 8$$

$$\mathbf{D}_y = \begin{vmatrix} 3 & 11 \\ -1 & -5 \end{vmatrix} = (3)(-5) - (11)(-1) = -15 + 11 = -4$$

Therefore, $x = \dfrac{\mathbf{D}_x}{\mathbf{D}} = \dfrac{8}{4} = 2$ $y = \dfrac{\mathbf{D}_y}{\mathbf{D}} = \dfrac{-4}{4} = -1$

Check the ordered pair $(2, -1)$ in both original equations.

Check: $3x - 5y = 11 \longrightarrow 3(2) - 5(-1) \overset{?}{=} 11$ ✓

$-x + 3y = -5 \longrightarrow -(2) + 3(-1) \overset{?}{=} -5$ ✓

The solution set is $\{(2, -1)\}$.

Skill Practice Solve using Cramer's rule.

6. $2x + \ y = 5$
    $-x - 3y = 5$

Answer

6. $\{(4, -3)\}$

TIP: Here are some memory tips to help you remember Cramer's rule to solve:

$$a_1x + b_1y = c_1$$
$$a_2x + b_2y = c_2$$

Coefficients of
x-terms   y-terms

1. The determinant **D** is the determinant of the coefficients of x and y.

$$D = \begin{vmatrix} a_1 & b_1 \\ a_2 & b_2 \end{vmatrix}$$

x-coefficients
replaced by c_1 and c_2

2. The determinant D_x has the column of x-term coefficients replaced by c_1 and c_2.

$$D_x = \begin{vmatrix} c_1 & b_1 \\ c_2 & b_2 \end{vmatrix}$$

y-coefficients
replaced by c_1 and c_2

3. The determinant D_y has the column of y-term coefficients replaced by c_1 and c_2.

$$D_y = \begin{vmatrix} a_1 & c_1 \\ a_2 & c_2 \end{vmatrix}$$

It is important to note that the linear equations must be written in standard form to apply Cramer's rule.

Example 6   **Using Cramer's Rule to Solve a 2 × 2 System of Linear Equations**

Solve the system by using Cramer's rule.

$$-16y = -40x - 7$$
$$40y = 24x + 27$$

Solution:

$$-16y = -40x - 7 \longrightarrow 40x - 16y = -7$$
$$40y = 24x + 27 \longrightarrow -24x + 40y = 27$$

Rewrite each equation in standard form.

For this system:
$$a_1 = 40 \qquad b_1 = -16 \qquad c_1 = -7$$
$$a_2 = -24 \qquad b_2 = 40 \qquad c_2 = 27$$

$$D = \begin{vmatrix} 40 & -16 \\ -24 & 40 \end{vmatrix} = (40)(40) - (-16)(-24) = 1216$$

$$D_x = \begin{vmatrix} -7 & -16 \\ 27 & 40 \end{vmatrix} = (-7)(40) - (-16)(27) = 152$$

$$D_y = \begin{vmatrix} 40 & -7 \\ -24 & 27 \end{vmatrix} = (40)(27) - (-7)(-24) = 912$$

Therefore,
$$x = \frac{D_x}{D} = \frac{152}{1216} = \frac{1}{8} \qquad y = \frac{D_y}{D} = \frac{912}{1216} = \frac{3}{4}$$

The ordered pair $\left(\dfrac{1}{8}, \dfrac{3}{4}\right)$ checks in both original equations.

The solution set is $\left\{ \left(\dfrac{1}{8}, \dfrac{3}{4}\right) \right\}$.

Skill Practice Solve by using Cramer's rule.

7. $9x = 12y - 8$
    $30y = -18x - 7$

Answer

7. $\left\{ \left(-\dfrac{2}{3}, \dfrac{1}{6}\right) \right\}$

Cramer's rule can be used to solve a 3×3 system of linear equations by using a similar pattern of determinants.

Cramer's Rule for a 3×3 System of Linear Equations

The solution to the system

$$a_1 x + b_1 y + c_1 z = d_1$$
$$a_2 x + b_2 y + c_2 z = d_2$$
$$a_3 x + b_3 y + c_3 z = d_3$$

is given by $\qquad x = \dfrac{\mathbf{D}_x}{\mathbf{D}} \qquad y = \dfrac{\mathbf{D}_y}{\mathbf{D}} \qquad$ and $\qquad z = \dfrac{\mathbf{D}_z}{\mathbf{D}}$

Where $\mathbf{D} = \begin{vmatrix} a_1 & b_1 & c_1 \\ a_2 & b_2 & c_2 \\ a_3 & b_3 & c_3 \end{vmatrix}$ (and $\mathbf{D} \neq 0$) $\quad \mathbf{D}_x = \begin{vmatrix} d_1 & b_1 & c_1 \\ d_2 & b_2 & c_2 \\ d_3 & b_3 & c_3 \end{vmatrix}$

$$\mathbf{D}_y = \begin{vmatrix} a_1 & d_1 & c_1 \\ a_2 & d_2 & c_2 \\ a_3 & d_3 & c_3 \end{vmatrix} \qquad \mathbf{D}_z = \begin{vmatrix} a_1 & b_1 & d_1 \\ a_2 & b_2 & d_2 \\ a_3 & b_3 & d_3 \end{vmatrix}$$

Example 7 **Using Cramer's Rule to Solve a 3×3 System of Linear Equations**

Solve the system by using Cramer's rule.

$$2x - 3y + 5z = 11$$
$$-5x + 7y - 2z = -6$$
$$9x - 2y + 3z = 4$$

Solution:

$$\mathbf{D} = \begin{vmatrix} 2 & -3 & 5 \\ -5 & 7 & -2 \\ 9 & -2 & 3 \end{vmatrix} = 2 \cdot \begin{vmatrix} 7 & -2 \\ -2 & 3 \end{vmatrix} - (-5) \cdot \begin{vmatrix} -3 & 5 \\ -2 & 3 \end{vmatrix} + 9 \cdot \begin{vmatrix} -3 & 5 \\ 7 & -2 \end{vmatrix}$$

$$= 2(17) + 5(1) + 9(-29)$$
$$= -222$$

TIP: In Example 7, we expanded the determinants about the first column.

$$\mathbf{D}_x = \begin{vmatrix} 11 & -3 & 5 \\ -6 & 7 & -2 \\ 4 & -2 & 3 \end{vmatrix} = 11 \cdot \begin{vmatrix} 7 & -2 \\ -2 & 3 \end{vmatrix} - (-6) \cdot \begin{vmatrix} -3 & 5 \\ -2 & 3 \end{vmatrix} + 4 \cdot \begin{vmatrix} -3 & 5 \\ 7 & -2 \end{vmatrix}$$

$$= 11(17) + 6(1) + 4(-29)$$
$$= 77$$

$$\mathbf{D}_y = \begin{vmatrix} 2 & 11 & 5 \\ -5 & -6 & -2 \\ 9 & 4 & 3 \end{vmatrix} = 2 \cdot \begin{vmatrix} -6 & -2 \\ 4 & 3 \end{vmatrix} - (-5) \cdot \begin{vmatrix} 11 & 5 \\ 4 & 3 \end{vmatrix} + 9 \cdot \begin{vmatrix} 11 & 5 \\ -6 & -2 \end{vmatrix}$$

$$= 2(-10) + 5(13) + 9(8)$$
$$= 117$$

$$\mathbf{D}_z = \begin{vmatrix} 2 & -3 & 11 \\ -5 & 7 & -6 \\ 9 & -2 & 4 \end{vmatrix} = 2 \cdot \begin{vmatrix} 7 & -6 \\ -2 & 4 \end{vmatrix} - (-5) \cdot \begin{vmatrix} -3 & 11 \\ -2 & 4 \end{vmatrix} + 9 \cdot \begin{vmatrix} -3 & 11 \\ 7 & -6 \end{vmatrix}$$

$$= 2(16) + 5(10) + 9(-59)$$

$$= -449$$

$$x = \frac{\mathbf{D}_x}{\mathbf{D}} = \frac{77}{-222} = -\frac{77}{222}$$

$$y = \frac{\mathbf{D}_y}{\mathbf{D}} = \frac{117}{-222} = -\frac{39}{74}$$

$$z = \frac{\mathbf{D}_z}{\mathbf{D}} = \frac{-449}{-222} = \frac{449}{222}$$

The solution $\left(-\frac{77}{222}, -\frac{39}{74}, \frac{449}{222} \right)$ checks in each of the original equations.

The solution set is $\left\{ \left(-\frac{77}{222}, -\frac{39}{74}, \frac{449}{222} \right) \right\}$.

Skill Practice Solve by using Cramer's rule.

8. $x + 3y - 3z = -14$
$x - 4y + z = 2$
$x + y + 2z = 6$

Cramer's rule may seem cumbersome for solving a 3×3 system of linear equations. However, it provides convenient formulas that can be programmed into a computer or calculator to solve for x, y, and z. Cramer's rule can also be extended to solve a 4×4 system of linear equations, a 5×5 system of linear equations, and in general an $n \times n$ system of linear equations.

It is important to remember that Cramer's rule does not apply if $\mathbf{D} = 0$. In such a case, either the equations are dependent or the system is inconsistent, and another method may be needed to analyze the system.

Example 8 **Analyzing a Dependent System of Equations**

Solve the system. Use Cramer's rule if possible. $2x - 3y = 6$
$-6x + 9y = -18$

Solution:

> **TIP:** When Cramer's rule does not apply, that is, when $\mathbf{D} = 0$, you may also use the substitution method or the Gauss-Jordan method to get a solution.

$$\mathbf{D} = \begin{vmatrix} 2 & -3 \\ -6 & 9 \end{vmatrix} = (2)(9) - (-3)(-6) = 18 - 18 = 0$$

Because $\mathbf{D} = 0$, Cramer's rule does not apply. Using the addition method to solve the system, we have

$$2x - 3y = 6 \quad \xrightarrow{\text{Multiply by 3.}} \quad 6x - 9y = 18$$
$$-6x + 9y = -18 \quad \longrightarrow \quad \underline{-6x + 9y = -18}$$
$$0 = 0 \quad \text{The equations are dependent.}$$

The solution set is $\{(x, y) \mid 2x - 3y = 6\}$.

Answer

8. $\{(-2, 0, 4)\}$

Skill Practice Solve. Use Cramer's rule if possible.

9. $x - 6y = 2$
$2x - 12y = -2$

TIP: In a 2×2 system of equations, if **D** = 0, then the equations are dependent or the system is inconsistent.

- If **D** = 0 and both **D**$_x$ = 0 and **D**$_y$ = 0, then the equations are dependent and the system has infinitely many solutions.
- If **D** = 0 and either **D**$_x \neq$ 0 or **D**$_y \neq$ 0, then the system is inconsistent and has no solution.

Answer

9. { }; inconsistent system

Section A.5   Practice Exercises

Vocabulary and Key Concepts

1. a. Given the matrix $\mathbf{A} = \begin{bmatrix} a & b \\ c & d \end{bmatrix}$, the _____ of **A** is denoted det **A** and is written as $\begin{vmatrix} a & b \\ c & d \end{vmatrix}$. The value of det **A** is the real number equal to _____.

b. Given a 3×3 matrix, the _____ of an element in the matrix is the determinant of the 2×2 matrix formed by deleting the row and column in which the element resides.

c. Complete the expression on the right to represent the value of the 3×3 determinant shown here.

$$\begin{vmatrix} a_1 & b_1 & c_1 \\ a_2 & b_2 & c_2 \\ a_3 & b_3 & c_3 \end{vmatrix} = a_1 \begin{vmatrix} b_2 & c_2 \\ b_3 & c_3 \end{vmatrix} - \square \begin{vmatrix} b_1 & c_1 \\ b_3 & c_3 \end{vmatrix} + a_3 \begin{vmatrix} \square & \square \\ \square & \square \end{vmatrix}$$

Concept 1: Introduction to Determinants

For Exercises 2–7, evaluate the determinant of the 2×2 matrix. **(See Example 1.)**

2. $\begin{vmatrix} -3 & 1 \\ 5 & 2 \end{vmatrix}$

3. $\begin{vmatrix} 5 & 6 \\ 4 & 8 \end{vmatrix}$

4. $\begin{vmatrix} -2 & 2 \\ -3 & -5 \end{vmatrix}$

5. $\begin{vmatrix} 5 & -1 \\ 1 & 0 \end{vmatrix}$

6. $\begin{vmatrix} \frac{1}{2} & 3 \\ -2 & 4 \end{vmatrix}$

7. $\begin{vmatrix} -3 & \frac{1}{4} \\ 8 & -2 \end{vmatrix}$

Concept 2: Determinant of a 3×3 Matrix

For Exercises 8–11, evaluate the minor corresponding to the given element from matrix **A**. **(See Example 2.)**

$$\mathbf{A} = \begin{bmatrix} 4 & -1 & 8 \\ 2 & 6 & 0 \\ -7 & 5 & 3 \end{bmatrix}$$

8. 4

9. −1

10. 2

11. 3

For Exercises 12–15, evaluate the minor corresponding to the given element from matrix **B**.

$$\mathbf{B} = \begin{bmatrix} -2 & 6 & 0 \\ 4 & -2 & 1 \\ 5 & 9 & -1 \end{bmatrix}$$

12. 6 **13.** 5 **14.** 1 **15.** 0

16. Construct the sign array for a 3×3 matrix.

17. Evaluate the determinant of matrix **B**, using expansion by minors. **(See Exercises 3–4.)**

$$\mathbf{B} = \begin{bmatrix} 0 & 1 & 2 \\ 3 & -1 & 2 \\ 3 & 2 & -2 \end{bmatrix}$$

  a. About the first column

  b. About the second row

18. Evaluate the determinant of matrix **C**, using expansion by minors.

$$\mathbf{C} = \begin{bmatrix} 4 & 1 & 3 \\ 2 & -2 & 1 \\ 3 & 1 & 2 \end{bmatrix}$$

  a. About the first row

  b. About the second column

19. When evaluating the determinant of a 3×3 matrix, explain the advantage of being able to choose any row or column about which to expand minors.

For Exercises 20–25, evaluate the determinant. **(See Examples 3–4.)**

20. $\begin{vmatrix} 8 & 2 & -4 \\ 4 & 0 & 2 \\ 3 & 0 & -1 \end{vmatrix}$

21. $\begin{vmatrix} 5 & 2 & 1 \\ 3 & -6 & 0 \\ -2 & 8 & 0 \end{vmatrix}$

22. $\begin{vmatrix} -2 & 1 & 3 \\ 1 & 4 & 4 \\ 1 & 0 & 2 \end{vmatrix}$

23. $\begin{vmatrix} 3 & 2 & 1 \\ 1 & -1 & 2 \\ 1 & 0 & 4 \end{vmatrix}$

24. $\begin{vmatrix} -5 & 4 & 2 \\ 0 & 0 & 0 \\ 3 & -1 & 5 \end{vmatrix}$

25. $\begin{vmatrix} 0 & 5 & -8 \\ 0 & -4 & 1 \\ 0 & 3 & 6 \end{vmatrix}$

For Exercises 26–31, evaluate the determinant.

26. $\begin{vmatrix} x & 3 \\ y & -2 \end{vmatrix}$

27. $\begin{vmatrix} a & 2 \\ b & 8 \end{vmatrix}$

28. $\begin{vmatrix} a & 5 & -1 \\ b & -3 & 0 \\ c & 3 & 4 \end{vmatrix}$

29. $\begin{vmatrix} x & 0 & 3 \\ y & -2 & 6 \\ z & -1 & 1 \end{vmatrix}$

30. $\begin{vmatrix} p & 0 & q \\ r & 0 & s \\ t & 0 & u \end{vmatrix}$

31. $\begin{vmatrix} f & e & 0 \\ d & c & 0 \\ b & a & 0 \end{vmatrix}$

Concept 3: Cramer's Rule

For Exercises 32–34, evaluate the determinants represented by $\mathbf{D}$, $\mathbf{D}_x$, and $\mathbf{D}_y$.

32. $x - 4y = 2$
$3x + 2y = 1$

33. $4x + 6y = 9$
$-2x + y = 12$

34. $-3x + 8y = -10$
$5x + 5y = -13$

For Exercises 35–40, solve the system by using Cramer's rule. **(See Examples 5–6.)**

35. $2x + y = 3$
$x - 4y = 6$

36. $2x - y = -1$
$3x + y = 6$

37. $4y = x - 8$
$3x = -7y + 5$

38. $7x - 4 = -3y$
$5x = 4y + 9$

39. $4x - 3y = 5$
$2x + 5y = 7$

40. $2x + 3y = 4$
$6x - 12y = -5$

For Exercises 41–46, solve for the indicated variable by using Cramer's rule. **(See Example 7.)**

41. $2x - y + 3z = 9$
$x + 4y + 4z = 5$ for x
$3x + 2y + 2z = 5$

42. $x + 2y + 3z = 8$
$2x - 3y + z = 5$ for y
$3x - 4y + 2z = 9$

43. $3x - 2y + 2z = 5$
$6x + 3y - 4z = -1$ for z
$3x - y + 2z = 4$

44. $4x + 4y - 3z = 3$
$8x + 2y + 3y = 0$ for x
$4x - 4y + 6z = -3$

45. $5x + 6z = 5$
$-2x + y = -6$ for y
$3y - z = 3$

46. $8x + y = 1$
$7y + z = 0$ for y
$x - 3z = -2$

47. When does Cramer's rule not apply in solving a system of equations?

48. How can a system be solved if Cramer's rule does not apply?

For Exercises 49–58, solve the system by using Cramer's rule, if possible. Otherwise, use another method. If a system does not have a unique solution, determine the number of solutions and whether the system is inconsistent or the equations are dependent. **(See Example 8.)**

49. $4x - 2y = 3$
$-2x + y = 1$

50. $6x - 6y = 5$
$x - y = 8$

51. $4x + y = 0$
$x - 7y = 0$

52. $-3x - 2y = 0$
$-x + 5y = 0$

53. $x + 5y = 3$
$2x + 10y = 6$

54. $-2x - 10y = -4$
$x + 5y = 2$

55. $x = 3$
$-x + 3y = 3$
$y + 2z = 4$

56. $4x + z = 7$
$y = 2$
$x + z = 4$

57. $x + y + 8z = 3$
$2x + y + 11z = 4$
$x + 3z = 0$

58. $-8x + y + z = 6$
$2x - y + z = 3$
$3x - z = 0$

Expanding Your Skills

For Exercises 59–62, solve the equation.

59. $\begin{vmatrix} 6 & x \\ 2 & -4 \end{vmatrix} = 14$

60. $\begin{vmatrix} y & -2 \\ 8 & 7 \end{vmatrix} = 30$

61. $\begin{vmatrix} 3 & 1 & 0 \\ 0 & 4 & -2 \\ 1 & 0 & w \end{vmatrix} = 10$

62. $\begin{vmatrix} -1 & 0 & 2 \\ 4 & t & 0 \\ 0 & -5 & 3 \end{vmatrix} = -4$

For Exercises 63–64, evaluate the determinant by using expansion by minors about the first column.

63. $\begin{vmatrix} 1 & 0 & 3 & 0 \\ 0 & 1 & 2 & 4 \\ -2 & 0 & 0 & 1 \\ 4 & -1 & -2 & 0 \end{vmatrix}$

64. $\begin{vmatrix} 5 & 2 & 0 & 0 \\ 0 & 4 & -1 & 1 \\ -1 & 0 & 3 & 0 \\ 0 & -2 & 1 & 0 \end{vmatrix}$

A-52   Additional Topics Appendix

For Exercises 65–66, refer to the following system of four variables.

$$x + y + z + w = 0$$
$$2x \quad\;\; - z + w = 5$$
$$2x + y \quad\;\; - w = 0$$
$$y + z \quad\quad = -1$$

65. a. Evaluate the determinant $\mathbf{D}$.

    b. Evaluate the determinant $\mathbf{D}_x$.

    c. Solve for x by computing $\dfrac{\mathbf{D}_x}{\mathbf{D}}$.

66. a. Evaluate the determinant $\mathbf{D}_y$.

    b. Solve for y by computing $\dfrac{\mathbf{D}_y}{\mathbf{D}}$.

67. Two angles are complementary. The measure of one angle is $\frac{5}{7}$ the measure of the other. Find the measures of the two angles.

68. Two angles are supplementary. The measure of the larger angle is $61°$ more than $\frac{3}{4}$ the measure of the smaller angle. Find the measures of the angles.

69. A theater charges $80 per ticket for seats in section A, $50 per ticket for seats in section B, and $30 per ticket for seats in section C. For one performance, 3000 tickets were sold for a total of $165,000 in revenue. If the total number of tickets in sections A and C is equal to the number of tickets sold in section B, how many tickets in each section were sold?

70. The measure of the largest angle in a triangle is $80°$ larger than the sum of the measures of the other two angles. The measure of the smallest angle is $22°$ less than the measure of the middle angle. Find the measure of each angle.

71. Suppose 1000 people were surveyed in southern California, and 445 said that they worked-out at least three times a week. If $\frac{1}{2}$ of the women and $\frac{3}{8}$ of the men said that they worked-out at least three times a week, how many men and how many women were in the survey?

72. During a 1-hr television program, there were 22 commercials. Some commercials were 15 sec long and some were 30 sec long. Find the number of 15-sec commercials and the number of 30-sec commercials if the total playing time for commercials was 9.5 min.

Review of the Set of Real Numbers

1. Sets of Real Numbers

The numbers we are familiar with in everyday life comprise the **set of real numbers**. Every real number corresponds to a unique point on a number line.

For example:

Several subsets of the real numbers are given in Table B-1. We use the symbols { } to enclose the elements of a set.

Concepts

1. Sets of Real Numbers
2. Symbols and Mathematical Language
3. Operations on Real Numbers
4. Exponents and Square Roots
5. Order of Operations
6. Properties of Real Numbers
7. Simplifying Expressions

Table B-1

Set	Definition
Natural numbers	$\{1, 2, 3, \ldots\}$
Whole numbers	$\{0, 1, 2, 3, \ldots\}$
Integers	$\{\ldots, -3, -2, -1, 0, 1, 2, 3, \ldots\}$
Rational numbers	the set of numbers of the form $\frac{p}{q}$ where p and q are integers and $q \neq 0$.
Irrational numbers	the set of real numbers that are not rational

Rational numbers can be written as a ratio of two integers such as $\frac{1}{3}$ or $\frac{3}{4}$. When expressed in decimal form a rational number is either a repeating decimal or a terminating decimal such as $0.\overline{3}$ or 0.75. The decimal form of an irrational number is non-repeating and non-terminating. Examples of irrational numbers are π and $\sqrt{2}$.

2. Symbols and Mathematical Language

In mathematics, the symbol < (meaning "is less than") and the symbol > (meaning "is greater than") are used to express inequalities. These and other inequality symbols are summarized in Table B-2.

Table B-2

Inequality	In Words	Example
$a < b$	a is less than b	$5 < 7$
$a > b$	a is greater than b	$8 > 3$
$a \leq b$	a is less than or equal to b	$8 \leq 9$
$a \geq b$	a is greater than or equal to b	$3 \geq 3$
$a < x < b$	x is between a and b	$3 < 4 < 5$
$a \neq b$	a is not equal to b	$4 \neq 6$

The operations of addition, subtraction, multiplication, and division can be denoted several ways. These along with other common operations on real numbers are summarized in (Table B-3).

Table B-3

Operation	Symbols	Translation/Example
Addition	$a + b$	"the **sum** of a and b" "the sum of 8 and -4" $\Rightarrow 8 + (-4)$
Subtraction	$a - b$	"the **difference** of a and b" "the difference of -8 and 2" $\Rightarrow -8 - 2$
Multiplication	$a \times b, a \cdot b, a(b),$ $(a)b, (a)(b), ab$	"the **product** of a and b" "the product of 3 and -2" $\Rightarrow 3(-2)$
Division	$a \div b, \dfrac{a}{b}, a/b, b\overline{)a}$	"the **quotient** of a and b" "the quotient of 10 and 5" $\Rightarrow \dfrac{10}{5}$
Absolute value	$|a|$	"the **absolute value** of a" "the absolute value of -3" $\Rightarrow |-3|$
Opposite	$-a$	"the **opposite** of a" "the opposite of 7" $\Rightarrow -(7)$
Reciprocal	$\dfrac{1}{a} (a \neq 0)$	"the **reciprocal** of a" "the reciprocal of 5" $\Rightarrow \dfrac{1}{5}$
Square root	$\sqrt{a}$	"the **square root** of a" "the square root of 64" $\Rightarrow \sqrt{64}$

3. Operations on Real Numbers

The **absolute value** of a real number a, denoted $|a|$, is its distance from 0 on the number line. Two numbers that are the same distance from 0 but on opposite sides of the number line are called **opposites**. The opposite of a is denoted $-a$.

Example 1   Finding Opposites and Absolute Value

a. Find the opposite of 5.

b. Find the opposite of $-\dfrac{1}{2}$.

c. Evaluate $|-6|$.

d. Evaluate $|2.7|$.

e. Evaluate $-|-8|$.

Solution:

a. The opposite of 5 is -5.

b. The opposite of $-\dfrac{1}{2}$ is $\dfrac{1}{2}$.

c. $|-6| = 6$

d. $|2.7| = 2.7$

e. $-|-8| = -8$ Take the opposite of the absolute value of -8.

The rules for adding, subtracting, multiplying, and dividing real numbers are given as follows.

Addition of Two Real Numbers

- To add two numbers with the *same sign:* Add the absolute values of the numbers and apply the common sign to the sum.

  example:

  $-3 + (-7) = -(3 + 7) = -10$

- To add two numbers with *unlike signs:* Subtract the smaller absolute value from the larger absolute value. Then apply the sign of the number having the larger absolute value.

  examples:

  $10 + (-4) = 10 - 4 = 6$

  $-8 + 5 = -(8 - 5) = -3$

Subtraction of Two Real Numbers

Add the opposite of the second number to the first number. In symbols:

$a - b = a + (-b)$

examples:

$8 - (-4) = 8 + (4) = 12$

$-3 - 6 = -3 + (-6) = -9$

Multiplication and Division of Two Real Numbers

- The product or quotient of two real numbers with the *same* sign is positive.

  example:

  $-20 \cdot (-4) = 80$

- The product or quotient of two real numbers with *unlike* signs is negative.

  example:

  $\dfrac{30}{-2} = -15$

Notes:

- The product of any real number and 0 is 0.

  example: $5 \cdot 0 = 0$

- The quotient of 0 and any nonzero real number is 0.

  example: $0 \div 6 = 0$

- The quotient of a real number and 0 is undefined.

  example: $6 \div 0$ is undefined

4. Exponents and Square Roots

We can use **exponents** to represent repeated multiplication. For example, the product

$$3 \cdot 3 \cdot 3 \cdot 3 \cdot 3 \qquad \text{can be written as} \qquad 3^5.$$

with labels: exponent pointing to the 5, base pointing to the 3.

The expression 3^5 is written in exponential form. The exponent (or **power**) is 5 and represents the number of times the **base** 3 is used as a factor. The expression 3^5 is read as "three to the fifth power." In general,

$$x^n = \underbrace{x \cdot x \cdot x \cdots \cdot x}_{\text{the factor } x \text{ occurs } n \text{ times}}$$

The number b is a **square root** of a if $b^2 = a$. A **radical sign**, $\sqrt{\ }$, is used to denote the principle (or positive) square root of a nonnegative real number.

Example 2	**Evaluating Expressions Containing Exponents and Square Roots**

Evaluate.   **a.** 2^4 **b.** $\sqrt{36}$

Solution:

a. $2^4 = 2 \cdot 2 \cdot 2 \cdot 2 = 16$

b. $\sqrt{36} = 6$ because $6^2 = 36$.

5. Order of Operations

Algebraic expressions often have more than one operation. In such a case, it is important to follow the order of operations.

Order of Operations

Step 1 Simplify expressions within parentheses and other grouping symbols first. These include absolute value bars, fraction bars, and radicals. If imbedded parentheses are present, start with the innermost parentheses.

Step 2 Evaluate expressions involving exponents, radicals, and absolute value.

Step 3 Perform multiplication or division in the order that they occur from left to right.

Step 4 Perform addition or subtraction in the order that they occur from left to right.

Example 3	**Applying the Order of Operations**

Simplify. $50 \div [15 - 2(4 + 6) + 15] \cdot 2^3$

Solution:

$50 \div [15 - 2(4 + 6) + 15] \cdot 2^3$

$= 50 \div [15 - 2(10) + 15] \cdot 2^3$	Simplify inside the inner parentheses.
$= 50 \div [15 - 20 + 15] \cdot 2^3$	Simplify inside [ ]. Within [ ], we perform multiplication before addition or subtraction.
$= 50 \div [-5 + 15] \cdot 2^3$	Within [ ], subtract and add from left to right.
$= 50 \div [10] \cdot 2^3$	Simplify within [ ].
$= 50 \div [10] \cdot 8$	Evaluate the exponential expressions.
$= 5 \cdot 8$	Divide and multiply from left to right.
$= 40$	Multiply.

Example 4	**Applying the Order of Operations within a Formula**

Given $x = -3$, evaluate the expressions.   **a.** x^2 **b.** $-x^2$

Solution:

a. x^2

$= (\ \ )^2$	Use parentheses in place of the variable.
$= (-3)^2$	Substitute -3 for x.
$= 9$	Evaluate expressions with exponents.

b. $-x^2$

$= -(\ \ )^2$	Use parentheses in place of the variable.
$= -(-3)^2$	Substitute -3 for x.
$= -(9)$	Simplify $(-3)^2$ first. Note that $(-3)^2 = 9$.
$= -9$	Now take the opposite of 9.

TIP: The expression $-(-3)^2$ is equivalent to $-1(-3)^2$. The order of operations indicates that we should square -3 first, and then multiply the result by -1.

6. Properties of Real Numbers

Several properties of real numbers are reviewed in Table B-4.

Table B-4

Property Name	Algebraic Representation	Example	Description/Notes
Commutative property of addition	$a + b = b + a$	$5 + 3 = 3 + 5$	The order in which two real numbers are added or multiplied does not affect the result.
Commutative property of multiplication	$a \cdot b = b \cdot a$	$(5)(3) = (3)(5)$	
Associative property of addition	$(a + b) + c = a + (b + c)$	$(2 + 3) + 7 = 2 + (3 + 7)$	The manner in which two real numbers are grouped under addition or multiplication does not affect the result.
Associative property of multiplication	$(a \cdot b)c = a(b \cdot c)$	$(2 \cdot 3)7 = 2(3 \cdot 7)$	
Distributive property of multiplication over addition	$a(b + c) = ab + ac$	$3(5 + 2) = 3 \cdot 5 + 3 \cdot 2$	A factor outside the parentheses is multiplied by each term inside the parentheses.
Identity property of addition	0 is the identity element for addition because $a + 0 = 0 + a = a$	$5 + 0 = 0 + 5 = 5$	Any number added to the identity element, 0, will remain unchanged.
Identity property of multiplication	1 is the identity element for multiplication because $a \cdot 1 = 1 \cdot a = a$	$5 \cdot 1 = 1 \cdot 5 = 5$	Any number multiplied by the identity element, 1, will remain unchanged.
Inverse property of addition	a and $(-a)$ are additive inverses because $a + (-a) = 0$ and $(-a) + a = 0$	$3 + (-3) = 0$	The sum of a number and its additive inverse (**opposite**) is the identity element, 0.
Inverse property of multiplication	a and $\frac{1}{a}$ are multiplicative inverses because $a \cdot \dfrac{1}{a} = 1$ and $\dfrac{1}{a} \cdot a = 1$ (provided $a \neq 0$)	$5 \cdot \frac{1}{5} = 1$	The product of a number and its multiplicative inverse (**reciprocal**) is the identity element, 1.

7. Simplifying Expressions

We can simplify expressions containing variables by adding or subtracting *like* terms. Recall that *like* terms have the same variables and the corresponding variables are raised to the same powers. To combine *like* terms, we use the distributive property. The same result may also be obtained by adding or subtracting the coefficients of each term and leaving the variable factors unchanged.

$$5x + 2x - 3x = 4x$$

Example 5	**Simplifying Expressions**

Simplify. $4x - 3(2x - 8) - 1 + 5x$

Solution:

$4x - 3(2x - 8) - 1 + 5x$

$= 4x - 6x + 24 - 1 + 5x$ Apply the distributive property.

$= 4x - 6x + 5x + 24 - 1$ Arrange *like* terms together.

$= 3x + 23$ Combine *like* terms.

Section B.1   Practice Exercises

For Exercises 1–8, refer to sets

$A = \{-6, -\sqrt{5}, -\frac{7}{8}, -0.\overline{3}, 0, \frac{4}{9}, \pi, 7, 10.4\}$ and $B = \{-2, -\pi, -\frac{1}{2}, 0, 1, \sqrt{3}, \frac{5}{4}, 8\}$

1. List all rational numbers in set A.

2. List all irrational numbers in set A.

3. List all integers in set A.

4. List all whole numbers in set A.

5. List all natural numbers in set B.

6. List all integers in set B.

7. List all irrational numbers in set B.

8. List all rational numbers in set B.

9. Find the opposite of -9.

10. Find the opposite of -13.

11. Find the opposite of $\frac{2}{3}$.

12. Find the opposite of $\frac{1}{4}$.

For Exercises 13–20, evaluate the expression.

13. $|-4|$

14. $|-12.6|$

15. $|8.5|$

16. $|3|$

17. $-|22|$

18. $-|8|$

19. $-|-13|$

20. $-|-7|$

For Exercises 21–28, write the expression in words.

21. $5 > -2$

22. $8 \leq 9$

23. $-3 \geq -4$

24. $\frac{1}{2} > -\frac{1}{2}$

25. $6 < 10 < 12$

26. $-1 < 0 < 1$

27. $2 \neq -5$

28. $\frac{2}{3} \neq -\frac{2}{3}$

For Exercises 29–38, write the English phrase as an algebraic expression.

29. The product of 6 and 3

30. The difference of 7 and 4

B-8   Appendix B

31. The quotient of 20 and 5

32. The sum of 2 and 12

33. The absolute value of -5

34. The absolute value of -13

35. The sum of 2 and the absolute value of -8.

36. The difference of 10 and the absolute value of -1

37. The product of 4 and the reciprocal of 3

38. The quotient of 8 and the square root of 16

For Exercises 39–58, add or subtract as indicated.

39. $8 + (-10)$ **40.** $23 + (-9)$ **41.** $51 - 32$ **42.** $12 - 15$

43. $0 + 16$ **44.** $26 + 0$ **45.** $-13 - 20$ **46.** $-5 - 30$

47. $-2.1 + (-2.2)$ **48.** $-4.0 + (-0.5)$ **49.** $-19 - (-3)$ **50.** $-7 - (-28)$

51. $0 - 19$ **52.** $0 - 41$ **53.** $5.2 - (-0.4)$ **54.** $0.03 - (-1.2)$

55. $-\dfrac{3}{4} - \dfrac{3}{8}$ **56.** $-\dfrac{5}{2} - \dfrac{1}{6}$ **57.** $-\dfrac{7}{3} - \left(-\dfrac{1}{9}\right)$ **58.** $-\dfrac{7}{10} - \left(-\dfrac{4}{5}\right)$

For Exercises 59–78, multiply or divide as indicated.

59. $3(-9)$ **60.** $(-8)(2)$ **61.** $(-5)(-7)$ **62.** $(-11)(-3)$

63. $0 \cdot 32$ **64.** $0 \cdot (-12)$ **65.** $(2.05)(-4.2)$ **66.** $(-10.7)(3.4)$

67. $\left(-\dfrac{5}{9}\right) \cdot \left(-\dfrac{3}{2}\right)$ **68.** $\left(-\dfrac{1}{6}\right) \cdot \left(-\dfrac{12}{7}\right)$ **69.** $-56 \div (-8)$ **70.** $-51 \div (-3)$

71. $-78 \div 13$ **72.** $112 \div (-16)$ **73.** $0 \div (-5)$ **74.** $0 \div 12$

75. $3.1 \div 0$ **76.** $-1.4 \div 0$ **77.** $\left(-\dfrac{7}{8}\right) \div \left(-\dfrac{7}{4}\right)$ **78.** $\left(-\dfrac{3}{11}\right) \div \left(\dfrac{21}{22}\right)$

For Exercises 79–92, simplify using the order of operations.

79. $|-14| - |-5|$ **80.** $\sqrt{81} - |-4|$ **81.** $10 \div 5 \cdot 4$ **82.** $12 \div 2 - 3$

83. $6 + 42 \div 7 - 10$ **84.** $21 - 3 \cdot 5 + 6$ **85.** $(8 - 5)^2 - (2 + 3)^2$ **86.** $16 - (10 - 3)^2 + 2 \cdot 7$

87. $3^3 - 2 + 5(3 - 7)$ **88.** $6 - 4^2 + (8 \div 4 + 5)$ **89.** $12 - \sqrt{25} + 4^2 \div 2$ **90.** $\sqrt{81} - \sqrt{16} \div 4 + 18$

91. $\dfrac{6 + 8 - (-2)}{-40 \div 8 - 1}$ **92.** $\dfrac{\sqrt{32 \div 2} + 7}{-52 + (7 \cdot 4 + 2)}$

For Exercises 93–96, evaluate the expressions given $a = 3$, $b = -5$, $c = 9$, and $d = -2$.

93. $a^2 - b^2$ **94.** $c \div a - b$ **95.** $b + \sqrt{c} \cdot d$ **96.** $-a^2 + c$

97. The area of a trapezoid is given by the formula $A = \frac{1}{2}(b_1 + b_2)h$. Find the area of the given trapezoid.

$b_1 = 28$ in.

$h = 20$ in.

$b_2 = 18$ in.

98. The surface area of a rectangular solid with a square base is given by $S = 4ab + 2a^2$. Find the surface area of the given rectangular solid.

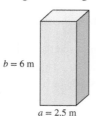

$b = 6$ m

$a = 2.5$ m

For Exercises 99–104, identify the property that is shown. Choose from the commutative property of addition, commutative property of multiplication, associative property of addition, associative property of multiplication, or distributive property of multiplication over addition.

99. $4(8 \cdot 14) = (4 \cdot 8)(14)$

100. $(7 + 4) + 6 = 7 + (4 + 6)$

101. $-6(3 + 9) = -6(3) + -6(9)$

102. $9 \cdot 2 = 2 \cdot 9$

103. $5 + 15 = 15 + 5$

104. $9(11 + 4) = 9(11) + 9(4)$

105. What is the identity element for multiplication? Use it in an example.

106. What is the identity element for addition? Use it in an example.

107. **a.** What is another name for multiplicative inverse?

   b. Write the multiplicative inverse of 4.

108. **a.** What is another name for the additive inverse?

   b. Write the additive inverse of 6.

For Exercises 109–116, simplify the expression by applying the distributive property.

109. $5(a + 9)$

110. $3(x + 12)$

111. $-7(y - z)$

112. $-2(a - b)$

113. $\frac{1}{3}(6b + 9c - 15)$

114. $\frac{1}{5}(10h - 20k - 5)$

115. $-(2x - 3y + 8)$

116. $-(-3p - q + 9)$

For Exercises 117–124, simplify the expression by clearing parentheses and combining like terms.

117. $5a + 2(a + 7)$

118. $6b - 3(b + 4)$

119. $8y - 3(y + 2) - 19$

120. $9k - 3(k - 4) + 8$

121. $4w + 9u - (5w - 3u)$

122. $-5m + 2(m + 4n) - 7n$

123. $2g - 4[2 - 3(g - 4h) - 2]$

124. $3p + 8[q - (p - 4) - 3p]$

Section B.2 — Review of Linear Equations and Linear Inequalities

Concepts

1. Solving Linear Equations in One Variable
2. Problem Solving
3. Linear Inequalities

1. Solving Linear Equations in One Variable

An equation that can be written in the form $ax + b = c$, where $a \neq 0$, is called a **linear equation in one variable**. The steps for solving a linear equation in one variable are given next.

Solving a Linear Equation in One Variable

Step 1 Simplify both sides of the equation.
- Clear parentheses
- Consider clearing fractions or decimals (if any are present) by multiplying both sides of the equation by a common denominator of all terms.
- Combine *like* terms

Step 2 Use the addition or subtraction property of equality to collect the variable terms on one side of the equation.

Step 3 Use the addition or subtraction property of equality to collect the constant terms on the other side of the equation.

Step 4 Use the multiplication or division property of equality to make the coefficient of the variable term equal to 1.

Step 5 Check your answer.

Example 1   Solving Linear Equations in One Variable

Solve. $\dfrac{1}{3}x + \dfrac{1}{4}x = x + 5$

Solution:

$$\frac{1}{3}x + \frac{1}{4}x = x + 5 \qquad \text{The LCD (least common denominator) is 12.}$$

$$12\left(\frac{1}{3}x + \frac{1}{4}x\right) = 12(x + 5) \qquad \text{Multiply both sides by 12.}$$

$$\frac{12}{1}\left(\frac{1}{3}x\right) + \frac{12}{1}\left(\frac{1}{4}x\right) = \frac{12}{1}(x) + \frac{12}{1}(5) \qquad \text{Apply the distributive property.}$$

$$4x + 3x = 12x + 60$$

$$7x = 12x + 60 \qquad \text{Combine } like \text{ terms.}$$

$$-5x = 60 \qquad \text{Subtract } 12x \text{ from both sides.}$$

$$x = -12 \qquad \text{Divide both sides by } -5.$$

The answer can be checked by substituting $x = -12$ back into the original equation and verifying that the left-hand side equals the right-hand side.

The solution set is $\{-12\}$.

2. Problem Solving

Solving word problems in mathematics takes practice and often a little patience. We also offer the following guidelines for problem solving.

Problem-Solving Guidelines

Step 1   Read the problem carefully.

Step 2   Assign labels to unknown quantities.

Step 3   Write a verbal model.

Step 4   Write a mathematical equation.

Step 5   Solve the equation.

Step 6   Interpret the results and write the answer in words.

Example 2   **Solving an Application Involving Principal and Interest**

Kadriana took out two student loans for a total of $8500. One loan was for 5% simple interest and the other was for 8% simple interest. If the total interest after one year was $530, find the amount borrowed at each rate.

Solution:

We have two unknown values. We arbitrarily let x represent the amount borrowed at 5%. Then the remaining principal, $8500 - x$, is the amount borrowed at 8%.

Step 1:   Read the problem.

	5% Loan	8% Loan	Total
Principal	x	$8500 - x$	
Interest	$0.05x$	$0.08(8500 - x)$	530

Step 2:   Label the variables. A chart may help to organize the information given in the problem.

$$\binom{\text{Interest from}}{5\% \text{ loan}} + \binom{\text{Interest from}}{8\% \text{ loan}} = \binom{\text{Total}}{\text{interest}}$$

Step 3:   Verbal model

$$0.05x + 0.08(8500 - x) = 530$$

Step 4:   Mathematical equation

$$0.05x + 680 - 0.08x = 530$$

Step 5:   Solve the equation. Combine *like* terms.

$$-0.03x + 680 = 530$$

$$-0.03x = -150$$

Subtract 680 from both sides.

$$\frac{-0.03x}{-0.03} = \frac{-150}{-0.03}$$

Divide both sides by −0.03.

$$x = 5000$$

Step 6:   Write the answer in words.

The amount borrowed at 5% is $5000. The amount borrowed at 8% is given by $8500 - x = 8500 - 5000 = 3500$. Thus, $3500 was borrowed at 8%.

Example 3	Solving an Application Involving Distance, Rate, and Time

Two cars leave a rest area at 12:00 P.M. One car travels north on Interstate 25 through Colorado and the other travels south. The southbound car travels 10 mph slower than the northbound car. After 2 hours, the cars are 260 miles apart. How fast is the northbound car traveling?

Solution: Step 1: Read the problem.

Let x represent the speed of the northbound car.   Step 2: Label the variables.

	Distance	**Rate**	**Time**
Northbound Car	$2(x)$	x	2
Southbound Car	$2(x-10)$	$x-10$	2

$$d = rt \quad \text{distance} = (\text{rate})(\text{time})$$

$$\begin{pmatrix} \text{Distance by} \\ \text{northbound car} \end{pmatrix} + \begin{pmatrix} \text{distance by} \\ \text{southbound car} \end{pmatrix} = \begin{pmatrix} \text{total} \\ \text{distance} \end{pmatrix}$$ Step 3: Verbal model

$$2x \quad + \quad 2(x-10) \quad = 260$$ Step 4: Mathematical equation

$$2x + 2x - 20 = 260$$ Step 5: Solve the equation.

$$4x - 20 = 260$$

$$4x = 280$$

$$x = 70$$

The northbound car travels 70 mph.   Step 6: Interpret the answer.

3. Linear Inequalities

A linear inequality is a mathematical sentence written with one of the symbols, $<, >,$ $\leq,$ or $\geq$. The solution to an inequality can be visualized graphically on a number line or can be written in interval notation. For any real numbers a and b, Table B-5 summarizes the solution sets for five general inequalities.

Table B-5

Inequality	**Graph**	**Interval Notation**
$x > a$		(a, ∞)
$x \geq a$		$[a, \infty)$
$x < a$		$(-\infty, a)$
$x \leq a$		$(-\infty, a]$
$a < x < b$		(a, b)

The use of a parenthesis (or) indicates that an endpoint is not included in the solution. The use of a square bracket [or] indicates that an endpoint *is* included in the solution. Note that a parenthesis is always used for infinity.

The steps to solve a linear inequality mirror those to solve a linear equation. **However, if an inequality is multiplied or divided by a negative number, then the direction of the inequality sign must be reversed.** This is demonstrated in Example 4.

Example 4   **Solving a Linear Inequality** ———————

Solve the inequality. Graph the solution set and write the solution set in interval notation.

$$-4(x - 3) + 1 \leq x + 23$$

Solution:

$$-4(x - 3) + 1 \leq x + 23$$

$$-4x + 12 + 1 \leq x + 23 \qquad \text{Apply the distributive property.}$$

$$-4x + 13 \leq x + 23 \qquad \text{Combine } like \text{ terms.}$$

$$-4x - x + 13 \leq x - x + 23 \qquad \text{Subtract } x \text{ from both sides.}$$

$$-5x + 13 \leq 23$$

$$-5x + 13 - 13 \leq 23 - 13 \qquad \text{Subtract 13 from both sides.}$$

$$-5x \leq 10$$

$$\frac{-5x}{-5} \geq \frac{10}{-5} \qquad \text{Divide both sides by } -5. \text{ Reverse the direction of the inequality sign.}$$

$$x \geq -2$$

Graph:

$$\begin{array}{ccccccccccc} \leftarrow & \!\!\!\!+ & \!\!\!\!+ & \!\!\!\!+ & \!\!\!\![& \!\!\!\!+ & \!\!\!\!+ & \!\!\!\!+ & \!\!\!\!+ & \!\!\!\!+ & \!\!\!\!\rightarrow \\ -5 & -4 & -3 & -2 & -1 & 0 & 1 & 2 & 3 & 4 & 5 \end{array}$$

Interval notation: $[-2, \infty)$

Section B.2   Practice Exercises

For Exercises 1–30, solve the equation.

1. $4x = -84$

2. $-3y = 72$

3. $\dfrac{t}{5} = 12$

4. $\dfrac{r}{3} = 13$

5. $6 + p = -14$

6. $-5 + q = -23$

7. $7x + 12 = 33$

8. $-3x - 4 = -1$

9. $4(x + 5) = 14$

10. $5(y - 2) = -22$

11. $3b + 25 = 5b - 21$

12. $4c - 9 = 6c + 17$

13. $3w + 2(w - 7) = 7(w - 1)$

14. $x + 5(x - 4) = 3(x - 8) - 5$

15. $\frac{1}{5}y - \frac{3}{10}y = y - \frac{2}{5}y + 1$

16. $\frac{2}{3}q + 2 - \frac{1}{9}q = \frac{5}{9}q + \frac{4}{3}q$

17. $\frac{5}{6}(x + 2) = \frac{1}{3}x - \frac{3}{2}$

18. $\frac{1}{4}(6 - p) = \frac{3}{8}(2 + 3p)$

19. $0.2a + 6 = 1.8a - 2.8$

20. $0.3(v - 3) = 1.4v - 3.1$

21. $0.72t - 1.18 = 0.28(4 - t)$

22. $0.08(100 - 73x) = 1.2(1 - 5x)$

23. $-4(x + 1) - 2x = -2(3x + 2) - x$

24. $5(z + 3) - 2z + 6(1 - z) = 4 - 2(1 + z)$

25. $11 - 5(y + 3) = -2[2y - 3(1 - y)]$

26. $-4p + 2[p - 4(2 - p)] = 4(p - 5)$

27. $-8m - 2[4 - 3(m + 1)] = 4(3 - m) + 4$

28. $10x - 5[1 + 3(1 - 2x)] = [4(x - 3) + 27] + x$

29. $4 - 6[2y - 2(y + 3)] = 7 - y$

30. $-3(x + 4) + 2x + 12 = -6(x - 5)$

For Exercises 31–40, solve.

31. Five times the product of 8 and a number is 20. What is the number?

32. One half of the total of 6 times a number and 20 is 4. What is the number?

33. The sum of three consecutive integers is −57. Find the integers.

34. The sum of three consecutive odd integers is 111. Find the integers.

35. If Casey invested $2500 in an account and earned $112.50 in interest the first year, what was the simple interest rate?

36. Roberto deposited $4050 in an account that made $202.50 simple interest the first year. Find the simple interest rate.

37. Ketul made a total investment of $3500 into two accounts earning 4.2% simple interest and 3.8% simple interest. If his total interest after 1 year was $141.40, how much was invested in each account?

38. Kaitlin borrowed $1800, part from her parents and part from a bank. The bank charged 8% interest but her parents only charged 2%. If she paid off the loan in 1 year and paid a total of $102 interest, how much did she borrow from her parents?

39. A car and a truck leave home at the same time traveling in opposite directions. The truck travels 4 mph slower than the car. If the distance between the two vehicles is 372 mi after 3 hr, find the speed of each vehicle.

40. Juan and Peter both leave a shopping center at the same time going in opposite directions. Juan is on his bike and travels 3 mph faster than Peter who is on his skateboard. After 1.5 hr they are 19.5 mi apart. How fast does Peter travel.

For Exercises 41–56, solve the inequality. Graph the solution set and write the set in interval notation.

41. $3 - x > 5$

$\begin{array}{ccccccc} + & + & + & + & + & + & + \\ -7 & -6 & -5 & -4 & -3 & -2 & -1 \end{array}$

42. $4 - 2d < 6$

$\begin{array}{cccccccc} + & + & + & + & + & + & + & + \\ -2 & -1 & 0 & 1 & 2 & 3 & 4 & 5 \end{array}$

43. $4y + 6 \geq -18$

$\begin{array}{ccccccccc} + & + & + & + & + & + & + & + & + \\ -7 & -6 & -5 & -4 & -3 & -2 & -1 & 0 & 1 \end{array}$

44. $3r - 13 \leq 27$

$\begin{array}{cccccc} + & + & + & + & + & ++ \\ 8 & 9 & 10 & 11 & 12 & 14 \end{array}$

45. $8m - 15 < 9m - 13$

$\begin{array}{cccccccc} + & + & + & + & + & + & + & + \\ -3 & -2 & -1 & 0 & 1 & 2 & 3 & 4 \end{array}$

46. $6n + 23 > -3n - 13$

$\begin{array}{cccccccc} + & + & + & + & + & + & + & + \\ -5 & -4 & -3 & -2 & -1 & 0 & 1 & 2 \end{array}$

47. $1 - 5(2t - 7) < 38t$

$\begin{array}{ccccccc} + & + & + & + & + & + & + \\ 0 & 1 & 2 & 3 & 4 & 5 & 6 \end{array}$

48. $9r + 3(r - 14) \geq 6$

$\begin{array}{cccccccc} + & + & + & + & + & + & + & + \\ 3 & 4 & 5 & 6 & 7 & 8 & 9 & 10 \end{array}$

49. $-5 < 4p + 2 \leq 6$

$\begin{array}{cccccc} + & + & + & + & + & + \\ -3 & -2 & -1 & 0 & 1 & 2 \end{array}$

50. $-8 \leq 7 + 5k \leq 17$

$\begin{array}{cccccccc} + & + & + & + & + & + & + & + \\ -4 & -3 & -2 & -1 & 0 & 1 & 2 & 3 \end{array}$

51. $2 > -y + 1 > -6$

$\begin{array}{ccccccccccc} + & + & + & + & + & + & + & + & + & + & + \\ -2 & -1 & 0 & 1 & 2 & 3 & 4 & 5 & 6 & 7 & 8 \end{array}$

52. $0 \geq -3x \geq -10$

$\begin{array}{cccccc} + & + & + & + & ++ \\ -1 & 0 & 1 & 2 & 3 & 4 \end{array}$

53. $\dfrac{1}{7}h + 2 > \dfrac{5}{14}h - \dfrac{1}{2}$

$\begin{array}{ccccccccc} + & + & + & + & + & + & + & + & + \\ 5 & 6 & 7 & 8 & 9 & 10 & 11 & 12 & 13 \end{array}$

54. $\dfrac{2}{3}b - \dfrac{1}{6} \leq 3b + \dfrac{5}{6}$

$\begin{array}{cccccccc} + & + & + & + & + & + & + & + \\ -1 & 0 & 1 & 2 & 3 & 4 & 5 & 6 \end{array}$

55. $0.4w + 3.1(w - 1) \leq -3.8$

$\begin{array}{ccccccc} + & + & + & + & + & + & + \\ -5 & -4 & -3 & -2 & -1 & 0 & 1 \end{array}$

56. $2.1x - 2(x + 5.1) > -8.2$

$\begin{array}{cccccccc} + & + & + & + & + & + & + & + \\ 19 & 20 & 21 & 22 & 23 & 24 & 25 & 26 \end{array}$

Review of Graphing

1. Plotting Ordered Pairs

In Figure B-1, we review some important features of a rectangular coordinate system. The x- and y-axes are perpendicular lines that cross at a common point called the **origin**. The arrows indicate the positive direction for the x- and y-axes. The four regions in the graph are called **quadrants**. Each point in a rectangular coordinate system is represented by an **ordered pair**. Figure B-2 shows the location of the following ordered pairs: $(4, 1)$, $(-2, 5)$, $(5, -2)$, $(-2, 1)$, $(0, 4)$, and $\left(-\frac{7}{2}, -2\right)$. For example, to plot the point represented by $(-2, 5)$ move -2 units in the x direction (left) and 5 units in the y direction (up) and draw a dot.

Concepts

1. Plotting Ordered Pairs
2. Graphing Linear Equations in Two Variables
3. x- and y-Intercepts
4. Horizontal and Vertical Lines
5. Slope of a Line
6. Slope-Intercept Form
7. Point-Slope Formula

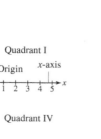

Figure B-1

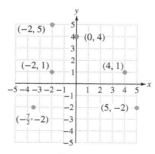

Figure B-2

2. Graphing Linear Equations in Two Variables

An equation that can be written in the form $Ax + By = C$ (where A and B are not both 0) is called a linear equation in two variables. The equation $3x + y = 5$ is a linear equation in two variables. A solution to such an equation is an ordered pair (x, y) that when substituted into the equation makes the equation a true statement. For example, the ordered pair $(-1, 8)$ is a solution to the equation $3x + y = 5$ because $3(-1) + 8 = 5$. A linear equation in two variables has infinitely many solutions that when plotted form a line in a rectangular coordinate system. To find a solution to a linear equation in two variables, we substitute any real number for one of the variables in the equation and then solve for the other variable.

| **Example 1** | **Graphing a Linear Equation in Two Variables** |

Complete the ordered pairs to form solutions to the equation $3x + y = 5$. Then graph the equation.

$$(1, \ ) \qquad (\ , -4) \qquad (0, \ ) \qquad (\ , 0)$$

Solution:

The ordered pairs can also be represented in tabular form as follows.

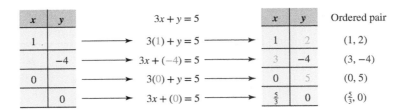

x	y
1	
	-4
0	
	0

$3x + y = 5$

$3(1) + y = 5$
$3x + (-4) = 5$
$3(0) + y = 5$
$3x + (0) = 5$

x	y	Ordered pair
1	2	$(1, 2)$
3	-4	$(3, -4)$
0	5	$(0, 5)$
$\frac{5}{3}$	0	$(\frac{5}{3}, 0)$

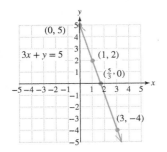

Figure B-3

The ordered pairs are graphed in Figure B-3. Notice that the points all "line up." The line drawn through the points represents all solutions to the equation. Therefore, we say the line represents the graph of the equation.

3. x- and y-Intercepts

In Example 1, the points $(\frac{5}{3}, 0)$ and $(0, 5)$ lie on the x-axis and y-axis, respectively. The point $(\frac{5}{3}, 0)$ is called an x-intercept and the point $(0, 5)$ is called a y-intercept. In general, the x- and y-intercepts of a graph are points where the graph intersects the x- and y-axes, respectively. Notice that the x-intercept $(\frac{5}{3}, 0)$ has a y-coordinate of 0. The y-intercept $(0, 5)$ has an x-coordinate of 0.

Finding x- and y-Intercepts

Step 1   Find the x-intercept(s) by substituting $y = 0$ into the equation and solving for x.

Step 2   Find the y-intercept(s) by substituting $x = 0$ into the equation and solving for y.

Example 2 Finding *x*- and *y*-Intercepts

Given $7x - 3y = 6$, find the *x*- and *y*-intercepts of the graph of the equation.

Solution:

To find the *x*-intercept, substitute zero for *y*:

$$7x - 3(0) = 6$$

$$7x = 6$$

$$x = \frac{6}{7}$$

To find the *y*-intercept, substitute zero for *x*:

$$7(0) - 3y = 6$$

$$-3y = 6$$

$$y = -2$$

The *x*-intercept is $(\frac{6}{7}, 0)$ and the *y*-intercept is $(0, -2)$.

4. Horizontal and Vertical Lines

An equation of the form $x = k$ is a vertical line in a rectangular coordinate system. An equation of the form $y = k$ is a horizontal line.

Example 3 Graphing Horizontal and Vertical Lines

Graph the lines. **a.** $x = 4$ **b.** $-2y = 5$

Solution:

a. The equation $x = 4$ is in the form $x = k$. Therefore, the graph of the equation is a vertical line that passes through the *x*-axis at 4.

The solutions to the equation $x = 4$ are ordered pairs whose *x*-coordinate is 4 and whose *y*-coordinate has no restriction. Several such solutions are $(4, 0)$, $(4, 1)$, $(4, 2)$, $(4, 3)$, and so on.

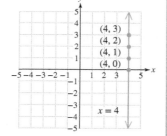

b. The equation $-2y = 5$ is equivalent to $y = -\frac{5}{2}$. The equation is in the form $y = k$. Therefore, the graph of the equation is a horizontal line passing through the *y*-axis at $-\frac{5}{2}$.

The solutions to the equation $y = -\frac{5}{2}$ are ordered pairs whose *y*-coordinate is $-\frac{5}{2}$ and whose *x*-coordinate has no restriction. Several such solutions are $(0, -\frac{5}{2})$, $(1, -\frac{5}{2})$, $(2, -\frac{5}{2})$, and so on.

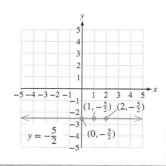

B-18   Appendix B

5. Slope of a Line

The slope of a line (often denoted by m) is a measure of the line's "steepness." It measures the ratio of an incremental change in y to an incremental change in x between two points on the line.

The slope is $\frac{3}{2}$.

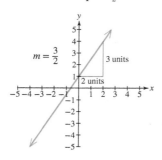

The slope is 4.

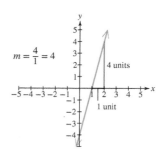

The slope of a line may be positive, negative, zero, or undefined.

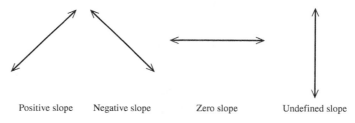

Positive slope   Negative slope   Zero slope   Undefined slope

To find the slope of a line containing the points (x_1, y_1) and (x_2, y_2), we use the slope formula.

> ### Slope Formula
>
> The slope of a line passing through the distinct points (x_1, y_1) and (x_2, y_2) is
>
> $$m = \frac{y_2 - y_1}{x_2 - x_1} \text{ provided } x_2 - x_1 \neq 0.$$

Example 4   **Finding the Slope Given Two Points on a Line**

Find the slope of the line between $(-3, -4)$ and $(7, -1)$.

Solution:

$$\overset{(x_1, y_1)}{(-3, -4)} \quad \overset{(x_2, y_2)}{(7, -1)} \qquad \text{Label the points.}$$

$$m = \frac{y_2 - y_1}{x_2 - x_1} = \frac{-1 - (-4)}{7 - (-3)} = \frac{3}{10} \qquad \text{The slope is } \frac{3}{10}.$$

The slopes, m_1 and m_2, of two lines can be used to determine whether the lines are parallel or perpendicular.

- Two lines that are parallel have the same slope. That is, $m_1 = m_2$.
- The slopes of perpendicular lines are related such that one slope is the opposite of the reciprocal of the other.

  That is, $m_1 = -\frac{1}{m_2}$.

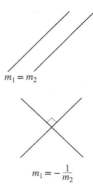

$m_1 = m_2$

$m_1 = -\frac{1}{m_2}$

6. Slope-Intercept Form

A linear equation in two variables written in the form $y = mx + b$ is said to be in slope-intercept form. In such a case, m is the slope, and $(0, b)$ is the y-intercept. To write a linear equation in slope-intercept form, solve the equation for y.

Example 5   **Writing an Equation in Slope-Intercept Form**

Given $2x + 5y = 20$,

a. Write the equation in slope-intercept form.

b. Identify the slope and y-intercept.

c. Graph the line using the slope and y-intercept.

Solution:

a. $2x + 5y = 20$ To write in the form $y = mx + b$, solve for y.

$5y = -2x + 20$ Subtract $2x$ from both sides.

$\dfrac{5y}{5} = \dfrac{-2x}{5} + \dfrac{20}{5}$ Divide by 5.

$y = -\dfrac{2}{5}x + 4$ The equation is in slope-intercept form.

b. The slope is $-\frac{2}{5}$ and the y-intercept is $(0, 4)$.

c. To graph the line using the slope and y-intercept, first plot the y-intercept. Then we can use the slope to find a second point on the line.

The slope can be interpreted as $\frac{-2}{5}$, which indicates that we move two units in the negative y-direction (down) and 5 units in the positive x-direction (right). See Figure B-4.

The slope can also be interpreted as $\frac{2}{-5}$ which indicates that we move two units in the positive y direction (up) and 5 units in the negative x-direction (left). See Figure B-4.

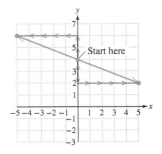

Figure B-4

Example 6   **Determining Whether Lines are Parallel, Perpendicular, or Neither**

Determine whether the lines l_1 and l_2 are parallel, perpendicular, or neither.

l_1: $2x - 3y = 12$ l_2: $6x + 4y = 4$

Solution:

Write each line in slope-intercept form and compare the slopes.

$l_1: 2x - 3y = 12$

$$-3y = -2x + 12$$

$$\frac{-3y}{-3} = \frac{-2x}{-3} + \frac{12}{-3}$$

$$y = \frac{2}{3}x - 4$$

The slope of l_1 is $\frac{2}{3}$.

$l_2: 6x + 4y = 4$

$$4y = -6x + 4$$

$$\frac{4y}{4} = \frac{-6x}{4} + \frac{4}{4}$$

$$y = -\frac{3}{2}x + 1$$

The slope of l_2 is $-\frac{3}{2}$.

The slope of l_1 is the opposite of the reciprocal of the slope of l_2. Therefore, the lines are perpendicular.

7. Point-Slope Formula

The point-slope formula is a useful tool to find an equation of a line given a point on the line and the slope of the line.

Point-Slope Formula

The **point-slope formula** is given by

$$y - y_1 = m(x - x_1)$$

where m is the slope of the line and (x_1, y_1) is a known point on the line.

Example 7   **Writing an Equation of a Line Given Two Points**

Write an equation of the line passing through the points $(-2, -1)$ and $(-4, 5)$. Write the final answer in slope-intercept form and in standard form.

Solution:

We can find the slope of the line by using the slope formula. Once the slope is known, we can apply the point-slope formula using the slope and either given point.

$(-2, -1)$ and $(-4, 5)$
$\ \ (x_1, y_1) \qquad (x_2, y_2)$ Label the points.

$m = \dfrac{y_2 - y_1}{x_2 - x_1} = \dfrac{5 - (-1)}{-4 - (-2)} = \dfrac{6}{-2} = -3$ Apply the slope formula.

$y - y_1 = m(x - x_1)$

$y - (-1) = -3[x - (-2)]$ Apply the point-slope formula.

$y + 1 = -3(x + 2)$

$y + 1 = -3x - 6$

$y = -3x - 7$ (slope-intercept form)   Solve for y.

or

$3x + y = -7$ (standard form)   Write in the form $Ax + By = C$.

Section B.3   Practice Exercises

For Exercises 1–8, plot the points on a rectangular coordinate system.

1. $(2, 4)$

2. $(4, 2)$

3. $(4, -3)$

4. $(0, 2)$

5. $(-3, 0)$

6. $(0, 0)$

7. $\left(-\frac{3}{2}, -2\right)$

8. $(-1, 3)$

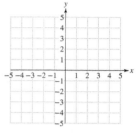

For Exercises 9–16, identify the quadrant in which each point is located.

9. $(20, -6)$

10. $(-3, -3)$

11. $\left(-13, -\frac{7}{8}\right)$

12. $\left(\frac{12}{7}, 5\right)$

13. $(\pi, 14)$

14. $(7.8, -42)$

15. $(-3.8, 6.2)$

16. $(-7.8, 42)$

For Exercises 17–22, complete the table and graph the line.

17. $x + y = 4$

x	y
3	
	-1
0	

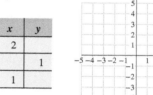

18. $3x - y = 6$

x	y
2	
	1
1	

19. $y = 5x$

x	y
0	
$\frac{2}{5}$	
-1	

20. $y = -2x + 3$

x	y
1	
$\frac{1}{2}$	
-1	

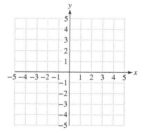

21. $y = \frac{2}{3}x + 1$

x	y
3	
-3	
0	

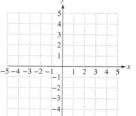

22. $y = -\frac{4}{3}x + 2$

x	y
3	
0	
-1	

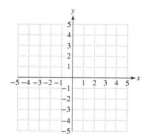

B-22   Appendix B

For Exercises 23–34, find the x- and y-intercepts.

23. $3x - 2y = 18$

24. $x - 4y = 16$

25. $5x + y = -15$

26. $-6x - y = 6$

27. $\frac{1}{2}x + y = 2$

28. $x - \frac{1}{3}y = -4$

29. $-3x + 4y = 0$

30. $6x - 5y = 0$

31. $y = -\frac{2}{3}x - 3$

32. $y = \frac{3}{5}x + 1$

33. $y = 6x - 5$

34. $y = -2x - 3$

For Exercises 35–40, write the equation in the form $x = k$ or $y = k$ and identify the line as horizontal or vertical.

35. $2x = 6$

36. $5y = 10$

37. $-3y + 1 = 2$

38. $7x - 1 = 3$

39. $5x = 0$

40. $\frac{2}{3}y = 0$

For Exercises 41–46, determine the slope of the line passing through the given points.

41. $(3, -4)$ and $(5, 0)$

42. $(-7, 4)$ and $(-14, -3)$

43. $(-2, -2)$ and $(-5, -10)$

44. $(6, 1)$ and $(0, -2)$

45. $(5, -12)$ and $(2, 1)$

46. $(0, 4)$ and $(9, 0)$

For Exercises 47–56, write the equation in slope-intercept form or the form $x = k$ or $y = k$. Then identify the slope and the y-intercept (if they exist).

47. $4x - 5y = 6$

48. $2x - 5y = 11$

49. $-6x + 2y = 3$

50. $-x + 3y = 4$

51. $5x - 1 = 4$

52. $2y - 3 = 0$

53. $x + 4y = 0$

54. $8x + 2y = 0$

55. $y + 4 = 8$

56. $x - 3 = 5$

For Exercises 57–62, graph the line given the slope and y-intercept.

57. Slope is $\frac{1}{2}$, y-intercept is $(0, -2)$

58. Slope is -3, y-intercept is $(0, 1)$

59. Slope is $-\frac{3}{2}$, y-intercept is $(0, 3)$

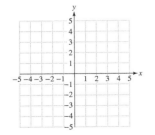

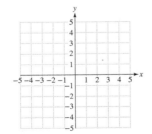

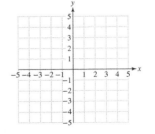

60. Slope is $\frac{5}{3}$, y-intercept is $(0, -1)$

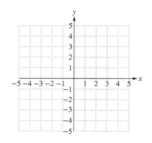

61. Slope is 4, y-intercept is $(0, -2)$

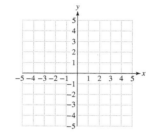

62. Slope is 2, y-intercept is $(0, -3)$

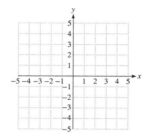

For Exercises 63–74, graph the line.

63. $2x - 3y = 12$

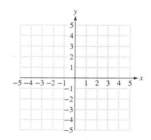

64. $2x + 4y = -8$

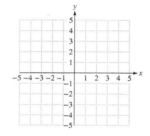

65. $x - 2y = -4$

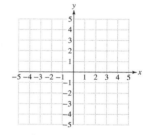

66. $6x - y = 4$

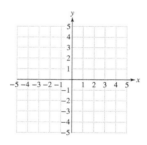

67. $4x + y = 0$

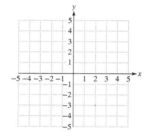

68. $-x - 3y = 0$

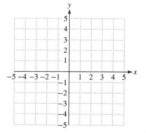

69. $y = -\frac{2}{3}x + 1$

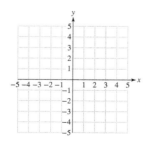

70. $y = \frac{1}{4}x - 1$

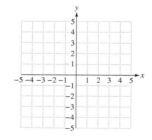

71. $-2x + 1 = 5$

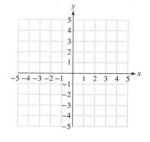

B-24   Appendix B

72. $4y - 2 = 6$

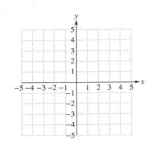

73. $y = 3x - 3$

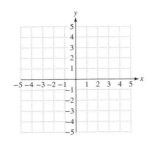

74. $y = -4x - 4$

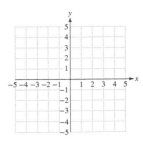

For Exercises 75–82, determine if the lines are parallel, perpendicular, or neither.

75. l_1: $-2x + y = 1$
     l_2: $2x - y = 3$

76. l_1: $y = 3x + 6$
     l_2: $-x + 3y = -3$

77. l_1: $-2x + 5y = 5$
     l_2: $5x - 2y = -2$

78. l_1: $-7x + y = 1$
     l_2: $-7x = 0$

79. l_1: $x + y = 7$
     l_2: $x - y = -2$

80. l_1: $y = -\dfrac{1}{4}x + 2$
     l_2: $2x + 8y = 24$

81. l_1: $y = 6$
     l_2: $y = -2$

82. l_1: $x = 3$
     l_2: $y = 0$

For Exercises 83–92, find an equation of the line given the following information. Write the final answer in slope-intercept form and in standard form.

83. The slope is -3 and the line passes through $(-5, -2)$.

84. The slope is $\frac{1}{2}$ and the line passes through $(5, 0)$.

85. The line passes through $(-3, -4)$ and $(-1, 4)$.

86. The line passes through $(-1, 7)$ and $(4, -3)$.

87. The line passes through $(4, 2)$ and is parallel to the line $3y = 6x - 1$.

88. The line passes through $(-5, 6)$ and is parallel to the line $4x = y - 3$.

89. The line passes through $(1, -2)$ and is perpendicular to the line $-2x + 4y = 5$.

90. The line passes through $(3, 0)$ and is perpendicular to the line $3x + 9y = 1$.

91. The line passes through $(4, -9)$ and is parallel to the line $x = 3$.

92. The line passes through $(-7, 2)$ and is perpendicular to the line $2y = 8$.

Review of Systems of Linear Equations in Two Variables

1. Solving Systems of Equations by the Graphing Method

Two or more linear equations can form a system of linear equations. For example, the following is a system of linear equations.

$$2x + y = 5$$
$$-x + y = 2$$

A solution to a system of equations is an ordered pair that satisfies both equations. Graphically, a solution to a system of linear equations is a point of intersection of the two lines.

Example 1   **Solving a System of Linear Equations by Graphing**

Solve by graphing. $2x + y = 5$

$$-x + y = 2$$

Solution:

First, graph the line defined by each equation. To graph the lines, we will use the slope-intercept form of each equation.

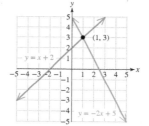

$$2x + y = 5 \xrightarrow{\text{slope-intercept form}} y = -2x + 5$$

$$-x + y = 2 \longrightarrow y = x + 2$$

From the graph, we estimate the point of intersection to be $(1, 3)$. The solution must be checked in each original equation.

$$2x + y = 5 \longrightarrow 2(1) + (3) \stackrel{?}{=} 5 \longrightarrow 5 = 5 \checkmark \text{ True}$$

$$-x + y = 2 \longrightarrow -(1) + (3) \stackrel{?}{=} 2 \longrightarrow 2 = 2 \checkmark \text{ True}$$

The solution set is $\{(1, 3)\}$.

---

2. Solving Systems of Equations by the Substitution Method

The graphing method to solve a system of linear equations can be cumbersome because of the limited accuracy of the graph. We will review two algebraic methods to solve systems of linear equations. The first is called the substitution method.

| Example 2 | **Solving a System of Linear Equations by Using the Substitution Method** |

Solve by using the substitution method: $3x - y = 6$

$2x + 5y = 4$

Solution:

The first step in the substitution method is to isolate one of the variables in one of the equations. It is generally easiest to solve for a variable whose coefficient is 1 or -1. Therefore, we will isolate y in the first equation.

First equation: $3x - y = 6$

$$-y = -3x + 6$$

$$y = \underline{3x - 6}$$

Second equation: $2x + 5y = 4$ Now substitute $3x - 6$ for y in the other equation.

$$2x + 5(3x - 6) = 4$$

$$2x + 15x - 30 = 4$$

$$17x - 30 = 4$$

$$17x = 34$$

$$x = 2$$

We can find the value of y by substituting $x = 2$ into either of the two equations. However, we will use the equation $y = 3x - 6$ because y is already isolated.

$y = 3x - 6$ First equation

$y = 3(2) - 6$ Substitute $x = 2$.

$y = 0$

The solution set is $\{(2, 0)\}$.   The check is left to the reader.

3. Solving Systems of Equations by the Addition Method

A second method to solve a system of linear equations is called the addition method (also called the elimination method). The basis of this method is to eliminate one of the variables by adding two equations that have opposite coefficients for that variable.

| Example 3 | **Solving a System of Linear Equations by Using the Addition Method** |

Solve by using the addition method. $2x = 5y - 4$

$3(x + y) = y + 13$

Solution:

To use the addition method, first write each equation in standard form $Ax + By = C$.

$2x = 5y - 4 \xrightarrow{\text{subtract } 5y} 2x - 5y = -4 \xrightarrow{\hspace{2cm}} 2x - 5y = -4$

$3(x + y) = y + 13 \xrightarrow[\text{clear parentheses}]{} 3x + 3y = y + 13 \xrightarrow[\text{subtract } y]{} 3x + 2y = 13$

We will now eliminate one of the variables by multiplying one or both equations by appropriate constants to create opposite coefficients on that variable. Suppose we want to eliminate the x variable. To do so, we want the coefficients on x to be 6 and -6 (the number 6 is the LCM of the original coefficients 2 and 3).

$2x - 5y = -4$ —— To create an x-coefficient of 6, multiply both sides by 3. ——▸ $6x - 15y = -12$

$3x + 2y = 13$ ————————————————————▸ $-6x - 4y = -26$
To create an x-coefficient of -6, multiply both sides by -2.
————————————
$-19y = -38$

Add the equations.
With the x variable
eliminated, solve for y.

$y = 2$

Substitute $y = 2$ back into either original equation. We will use the first.

$2x = 5y - 4$

$2x = 5(2) - 4$ Substitute $y = 2$ into the first equation.

$2x = 10 - 4$ Solve for x.

$2x = 6$

$x = 3$

The solution set is $\{(3, 2)\}$.   The check is left for the reader.

Two linear equations in a system may represent parallel lines. In such a case, the system has no solution because there is no point of intersection. A system of equations that has no solution is called an **inconsistent system**.

Example 4   **Identifying an Inconsistent System**

Solve the system of linear equations. $2x + y = 4$

$4x + 2y = 0$

Solution:

Using the addition method we have

$2x + y = 4$ —— multiply by -2 ——▸ $-4x - 2y = -8$

$4x + 2y = 0$ ————————▸ $4x + 2y = 0$
————————————
$0 = -8$ (contradiction)

This system has no solution $\{\ \}$. The system is inconsistent.

Graphing the linear equations in Example 4, we see that the lines are indeed parallel and that there is no point of intersection (Figure B-5). In general if a system of equations results in a contradiction (such as $0 = -8$), then there is no solution.

Two linear equations may represent the same line. In such a case, all points on the common line are solutions to the system. That is, there are infinitely many solutions, and the equations are **dependent**.

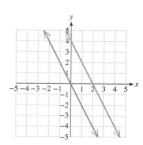

Figure B-5

| Example 5 | **Solving a System of Dependent Equations** |

Solve the system. $6x - 9y = 18$

$$\frac{1}{2}x - \frac{3}{4}y = \frac{3}{2}$$

Solution:

First note that we can clear fractions in the second equation by multiplying by the LCD of all fractions in the equation.

$6x - 9y = 18 \longrightarrow 6x - 9y = 18 \longrightarrow 6x - 9y = 18$

$\frac{1}{2}x - \frac{3}{4}y = \frac{3}{2} \xrightarrow[\text{multiply by } 4]{} 2x - 3y = 6 \xrightarrow[\text{multiply by } -3]{} -6x + 9y = -18$

$$0 = 0$$

The system reduces to the identity, $0 = 0$. This tells us that the equations have the same (identical) solution set, and that the equations are dependent.

Both equations can be written in slope-intercept form as $y = \frac{2}{3}x - 2$. All points on this line are solutions to the system. Therefore, we can write the solution set as $\{(x, y) \mid y = \frac{2}{3}x - 2\}$.

4. Applications of Systems of Equations

A system of equations is often useful to solve application problems where there are two unknown quantities.

| Example 6 | **Solving an Application Using a System of Linear Equations** |

Ashlee invested a total of $6000 in two accounts. One account pays 3.5% simple interest, and the other pays 5% simple interest. At the end of one year, she earned $276 in interest. Find the amount invested in each account.

Solution:

Let x represent the amount invested at 3.5%.
Let y represent the amount invested at 5%.

We have two variables, and therefore, we need two independent equations relating the variables. One equation relates the amount invested (principal), the second equation relates the amount of interest earned.

$$\begin{pmatrix} \text{Principal} \\ \text{invested at 3.5\%} \end{pmatrix} + \begin{pmatrix} \text{Principal} \\ \text{invested at 5\%} \end{pmatrix} = \begin{pmatrix} \text{Total} \\ \text{invested} \end{pmatrix} \qquad x + y = 6000$$

$$\begin{pmatrix} \text{Interest} \\ \text{earned at 3.5\%} \end{pmatrix} + \begin{pmatrix} \text{Interest} \\ \text{earned at 5\%} \end{pmatrix} = \begin{pmatrix} \text{Total} \\ \text{interest} \end{pmatrix} \qquad 0.035x + 0.05y = 276$$

$$x + y = 6000 \xrightarrow{\text{multiply by } -35} -35x - 35y = -210{,}000$$

$$0.035x + 0.05y = 276 \xrightarrow{\text{multiply by } 1000} \underline{\quad 35x + 50y = 276{,}000 \quad}$$

$$15y = 66{,}000$$

$$y = 4400$$

$$x + y = 6000$$

$$x + 4400 = 6000 \quad \text{Substitute } y = 4400 \text{ back into the first equation.}$$

$$x = 1600$$

Interpret the results: $x = 1600$ means that \$1600 was invested at 3.5%.
$y = 4400$ means that \$4400 was invested at 5%.

Section B.4   Practice Exercises

For Exercises 1–4, solve the system by graphing.

1. $3x + y = 1$
$-2x + 2y = -6$

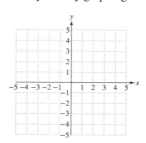

2. $3x - 2y = -6$
$4x + y = 3$

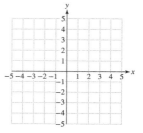

3. $2x = 8$
$-3x + 5y = -2$

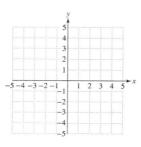

4. $y + 3 = 1$
$x - 2y = 3$

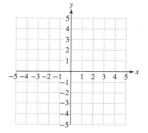

For Exercises 5–8, solve the systems by using the substitution method.

5. $y = 3x - 4$
$-2x + 5y = -7$

6. $x = 4y + 1$
$-2x + 5y = -20$

7. $9x - 4y = 9$
$x + 6y = 1$

8. $-4x - 2y = -14$
$3x + y = 9$

For Exercises 9–12, solve the systems by using the addition method.

9. $2x + y = -5$
$-3x + 4y = -31$

10. $-6x + 5y = 1$
$x - 3y = -11$

11. $5x - 6y = 16$
$3x - 4y = 10$

12. $7x + 2y = 19$
$5x + 3y = 12$

B-30   Appendix B

Mixed Exercises

For Exercises 13–24, solve the systems using any method. For systems that do not have one unique solution, also state the number of solutions and whether the system is inconsistent or the equations are dependent.

13. $5x + 2y = 10$
$-10x - 4y = 20$

14. $-3x + y = 6$
$9x - 3y = 0$

15. $3x + y - 7 = x - 4$
$3x + 4y + 4 = -6y + 5$

16. $7y - 8y - 3 = -3x + 4$
$5(2x - y) - 12 = 13$

17. $-2x = -y - 14$
$4x - 2y = 28$

18. $y = 0.4x - 0.3$
$\dfrac{2}{5}x - y = \dfrac{3}{10}$

19. $x + y = 3200$
$0.06x + 0.04y = 172$

20. $x + y = 4500$
$0.07x + 0.05y = 291$

21. $\dfrac{1}{3}x + \dfrac{1}{2}y = \dfrac{2}{3}$
$y = \dfrac{2}{3}x - \dfrac{4}{3}$

22. $-y = \dfrac{1}{8}x - \dfrac{1}{8}$
$-\dfrac{1}{4}x + \dfrac{1}{2}y = \dfrac{13}{8}$

23. $u - v = 3$
$6u - 4v = 13$

24. $5v + 6w = -11$
$3v + w = -4$

25. Gordan has $10,000 to invest. In one account he earns 6% simple interest and in the other he earns 4.5% simple interest. How much did he invest in each account if he makes $570 in interest after 1 year?

26. Greg has $8500 to invest. In one account he earns 5.5% simple interest. In another account he earns 4% simple interest. How much did he invest in each account if he made $415 in interest in one year?

27. Two angles are complementary (the sum of their measures is 90°). The difference in the measures of the larger angle and the smaller angle is 14°. Find the measure of each angle.

28. Two angles are supplementary (the sum of their measures is 180°). The measure of one angle is 11 times the measure of the other angle. Find the measure of each angle.

29. The sum of Denisha's age and her sister's age is 48. If Denisha is 4 years older than her sister, find each of their ages.

30. In a right triangle, one acute angle measures 10° less than 4 times the measure of the other acute angle. Find the measure of each acute angle.

Review of Polynomials and Properties of Exponents   **Section B.5**

1. Properties of Exponents

Concepts

1. Properties of Exponents
2. Scientific Notation
3. Addition and Subtraction of Polynomials
4. Multiplication of Polynomials
5. Division of Polynomials

Recall that expressions with exponents can be simplified using the following definitions and properties.

Properties and Definitions Involving Exponents

Assume that a and b are real numbers such that $a \neq 0$, $b \neq 0$ and m and n are integers.

Property/Definition		Example
Multiplication of like bases:	$b^m b^n = b^{m+n}$	$x^3 x^5 = x^{3+5} = x^8$
Division of like bases:	$\dfrac{b^m}{b^n} = b^{m-n}$	$\dfrac{y^7}{y^3} = y^{7-3} = y^4$
The power rule:	$(b^m)^n = b^{m \cdot n}$	$(5^4)^2 = 5^{4 \cdot 2} = 5^8$
Power of a product:	$(ab)^m = a^m b^m$	$(5x)^2 = 5^2 x^2 = 25x^2$
Power of a quotient:	$\left(\dfrac{a}{b}\right)^m = \dfrac{a^m}{b^m}$	$\left(\dfrac{x}{4}\right)^3 = \dfrac{x^3}{4^3} = \dfrac{x^3}{64}$
Definition of b^0:	$b^0 = 1$	$5^0 = 1$
Definition of b^{-n}:	$b^{-n} = \left(\dfrac{1}{b}\right)^n = \dfrac{1}{b^n}$	$x^{-6} = \left(\dfrac{1}{x}\right)^6 = \dfrac{1}{x^6}$

These properties and definitions may be combined to simplify exponential expressions.

Example 1   **Simplifying Exponential Expressions**

Simplify.   **a.** $\dfrac{x^4 x^6}{x^3}$ **b.** $(2y^3)^4$ **c.** $\left(\dfrac{pw^2}{2z^5}\right)^3$

d. $\dfrac{4x^6 z^{-3}}{y^{-2}}$ **e.** $\left(\dfrac{1}{2}\right)^{-3} + \left(\dfrac{1}{4}\right)^0$

Solution:

a. $\dfrac{x^4 x^6}{x^3} = \dfrac{x^{4+6}}{x^3} = \dfrac{x^{10}}{x^3} = x^{10-3} = x^7$

b. $(2y^3)^4 = 2^4 (y^3)^4 = 2^4 y^{3 \cdot 4} = 16y^{12}$

c. $\left(\dfrac{pw^2}{2z^5}\right)^3 = \dfrac{p^3 w^6}{2^3 z^{15}} = \dfrac{p^3 w^6}{8z^{15}}$

d. $\dfrac{4x^6 z^{-3}}{y^{-2}} = \dfrac{4x^6 y^2}{z^3}$

e. $\left(\dfrac{1}{2}\right)^{-3} + \left(\dfrac{1}{4}\right)^0 = \left(\dfrac{2}{1}\right)^3 + 1 = 8 + 1 = 9$

2. Scientific Notation

Recall that scientific notation is a convenient method to write very large or very small numbers. A positive number is in scientific notation if it is written in the form $a \times 10^n$, where $1 \leq a < 10$ and n is an integer. See Table B-6.

Table B-6

Number	Equivalent Form	Scientific Notation
4200	4.2×1000	4.2×10^3
0.008	$8 \times 0.001 = 8 \times \dfrac{1}{1000} = 8 \times \dfrac{1}{10^3}$	8×10^{-3}

Writing a number in scientific notation can be done easily by moving the decimal point to the left or right and then multiplying the resulting number by the appropriate power of 10.

$$730,000 = 7.3 \times 10^5 \qquad\qquad 0.000046 = 4.6 \times 10^{-5}$$

Example 2	**Multiplying and Dividing Numbers in Scientific Notation**

Perform the indicated operations and write the answer in scientific notation.

$$\frac{(6 \times 10^3)(9 \times 10^5)}{2 \times 10^{-2}}$$

Solution:

$$\frac{(6 \times 10^3)(9 \times 10^5)}{2 \times 10^{-2}} = \frac{(6)(9) \times 10^3 10^5}{2 \times 10^{-2}} \qquad \text{Multiply the numerators.}$$

$$= \frac{54 \times 10^8}{2 \times 10^{-2}} \qquad \text{Simplify.}$$

$$= \left(\frac{54}{2}\right) \times \frac{10^8}{10^{-2}} \qquad \text{Divide.}$$

$$= 27 \times 10^{8-(-2)} \qquad \text{Simplify.}$$

$$= 27 \times 10^{10} \qquad \text{This number is not in proper scientific notation.}$$

$$= (2.7 \times 10^1) \times 10^{10} \qquad \text{Write 27.0 as } = 2.7 \times 10^1.$$

$$= 2.7 \times 10^{11}$$

3. Addition and Subtraction of Polynomials

To add or subtract polynomials, we add or subtract *like* terms.

> **Example 3**   **Adding and Subtracting Polynomials**
>
> Perform the indicated operations.
>
> $$\left(2x^4 - 5x^2 - \frac{3}{4}x\right) + (7x^2 + 13) - \left(8x^4 + x^3 + \frac{1}{4}x\right)$$
>
> **Solution:**
>
> $$\left(2x^4 - 5x^2 - \frac{3}{4}x\right) + (7x^2 + 13) - \left(8x^4 + x^3 + \frac{1}{4}x\right)$$
>
> $= 2x^4 - 5x^2 - \dfrac{3}{4}x + 7x^2 + 13 - 8x^4 - x^3 - \dfrac{1}{4}x$ Apply the distributive property.
>
> $= 2x^4 - 8x^4 - x^3 - 5x^2 + 7x^2 - \dfrac{3}{4}x - \dfrac{1}{4}x + 13$ Collect *like* terms.
>
> $= -6x^4 - x^3 + 2x^2 - \dfrac{4}{4}x + 13$ Add *like* terms.
>
> $= -6x^4 - x^3 + 2x^2 - x + 13$ Simplify.

4. Multiplication of Polynomials

To multiply polynomials, multiply each term in the first polynomial by each term in the second polynomial by using the distributive property. Then combine *like* terms.

> **Example 4**   **Multiplying Polynomials**
>
> Multiply.   **a.** $(2y + 5)(6y^2 - 4y + 3)$ **b.** $(2x - 3y)(5x + 7y)$
>
> **Solution:**
>
> **a.** $(2y + 5)(6y^2 - 4y + 3)$
>
> $= 2y(6y^2) + 2y(-4y) + 2y(3) + 5(6y^2) + 5(-4y) + 5(3)$ Multiply.
>
> $= 12y^3 - 8y^2 + 6y + 30y^2 - 20y + 15$ Simplify.
>
> $= 12y^3 + 22y^2 - 14y + 15$ Combine *like* terms.
>
> **b.** $(2x - 3y)(5x + 7y)$
>
> $= 2x(5x) + 2x(7y) + (-3y)(5x) + (-3y)(7y)$ Multiply.
>
> $= 10x^2 + 14xy - 15xy - 21y^2$ Simplify.
>
> $= 10x^2 - xy - 21y^2$ Combine *like* terms.

When squaring a binomial such as $(a + b)^2$, we can write the expression as $(a + b)(a + b)$. Proceeding as in Example 4, we have $(a + b)(a + b) = a^2 + ab + ab + b^2 = a^2 + 2ab + b^2$. The resulting trinomial is a **perfect square trinomial.**

To multiply the product of conjugates such as $(a + b)(a - b)$, we have $a^2 - ab + ab - b^2 = a^2 - b^2$. This result is called a **difference of squares.**

These general results are summarized in Table B-7.

Table B-7

Product	Example
The square of a binomial results in a perfect square trinomial.	
1.　$(a + b)^2 = a^2 + 2ab + b^2$	1.　$(2x + 5y)^2 = (2x)^2 + 2(2x)(5y) + (5y)^2$ $= 4x^2 + 20xy + 25y^2$
2.　$(a - b)^2 = a^2 - 2ab + b^2$	2.　$(4m - 3n)^2 = (4m)^2 - 2(4m)(3n) + (3n)^2$ $= 16m^2 - 24mn + 9n^2$
The product of conjugate factors results in a difference of squares.	
3.　$(a + b)(a - b) = a^2 - b^2$	3.　$(7w + 3)(7w - 3) = (7w)^2 - (3)^2$ $= 49w^2 - 9$

5. Division of Polynomials

Division of polynomials is presented in two separate cases.

1. To divide a polynomial by a monomial divisor (that is, when the divisor has only one term), we use the properties:

$$\frac{a + b}{c} = \frac{a}{c} + \frac{b}{c} \quad \text{and} \quad \frac{a - b}{c} = \frac{a}{c} - \frac{b}{c}.$$

2. If the divisor has more than one term, we use long division.

Example 5　**Dividing a Polynomial by a Monomial**

Divide.　$(15xy^2 - 5x^2y^3 + 10x^3y^6) \div (5x^2y^2)$

Solution:

We can write the expression as $\dfrac{15xy^2 - 5x^2y^3 + 10x^3y^6}{5x^2y^2}$

$= \dfrac{15xy^2}{5x^2y^2} - \dfrac{5x^2y^3}{5x^2y^2} + \dfrac{10x^3y^6}{5x^2y^2}$　　Divide each term in the numerator by $5x^2y^2$.

$= \dfrac{3}{x} - y + 2xy^4$　　Simplify each term.

| **Example 6** | **Using Long Division to Divide Polynomials** |

Divide. $(8x^3 + 14x^2 - 7) \div (x + 3)$

Solution:

Write the polynomials in long division format. The term $0x$ is inserted in the dividend as a place holder for the missing power of x.

$$\begin{array}{r} 8x^2 \\ x+3 \enclose{longdiv}{8x^3 + 14x^2 + 0x - 7} \end{array}$$

Divide the leading term of the dividend by the leading term of the divisor ($8x^3/x$). The result, $8x^2$, is the first term in the quotient.

$$\begin{array}{r} 8x^2 \\ x+3 \enclose{longdiv}{8x^3 + 14x^2 + 0x - 7} \\ -(8x^3 + 24x^2) \end{array}$$

Multiply $8x^2$ by the divisor and subtract the result.

$$\begin{array}{r} 8x^2 \\ x+3 \enclose{longdiv}{8x^3 + 14x^2 + 0x - 7} \\ \underline{-8x^3 - 24x^2} \\ -10x^2 + 0x \end{array}$$

Subtract the quantity $8x^3 + 24x^2$. To do this we can add the opposite.
Bring down the next column and repeat the process.

$$\begin{array}{r} 8x^2 - 10x \\ x+3 \enclose{longdiv}{8x^3 + 14x^2 + 0x - 7} \\ \underline{-8x^3 - 24x^2} \\ -10x^2 + 0x \\ -(-10x - 30x) \end{array}$$

$$\begin{array}{r} 8x^2 - 10x + 30 \\ x+3 \enclose{longdiv}{8x^3 + 14x^2 + 0x - 7} \\ \underline{-8x^3 - 24x^2} \\ -10x^2 + 0x \\ \underline{10x + 30x} \\ 30x - 7 \\ -(30x + 90) \end{array}$$

$$\begin{array}{r} 8x^2 - 10x + 30 \\ x+3 \enclose{longdiv}{8x^3 + 14x^2 + 0x - 7} \\ \underline{-8x^3 - 24x^2} \\ -10x^2 + 0x \\ \underline{10x + 30x} \\ 30x - 7 \\ \underline{-30x - 90} \\ -97 \end{array}$$

Therefore, $(8x^3 + 14x^2 - 7) \div (x + 3) = 8x^2 - 10x + 30 + \dfrac{-97}{x + 3}$.

Section B.5 Practice Exercises

For this exercise set, assume that all variables represent nonzero real numbers.

For Exercises 1–8, simplify and state the property used. Choose from multiplication of like bases, division of like bases, power rule, power of a product, or power of a quotient.

1. $6^2 \cdot 6^5$

2. $(x^3)^4$

3. $\dfrac{y^{10}}{y^7}$

4. $(10p)^5$

5. $\left(\dfrac{w}{4}\right)^4$

6. $x^{10} \cdot x^3 \cdot x$

7. $(q^5)^6$

8. $\dfrac{z^4}{z^4}$

For Exercises 9–28, simplify. Write the answers with positive exponents.

9. 3^0

10. 5^{-1}

11. $\left(\dfrac{1}{2}\right)^{-1}$

12. $(-6)^0$

13. $(-5)^{-2}$

14. $\left(\dfrac{2}{3}\right)^{-2}$

15. $6^{-1} + (-4)^0$

16. $(-2)^{-2} + 8^{-1}$

17. $\dfrac{r^2 \cdot r^6}{r^{10}}$

18. $\dfrac{t^3 \cdot t^7}{t^{13}}$

19. $\dfrac{b^3}{b^4 \cdot b^{-3}}$

20. $\dfrac{c^{-2}}{c^{-5} \cdot c^2}$

21. $(3x^2)^3$

22. $(-7y^4)^2$

23. $\dfrac{6w^2z}{2z^{-1}}$

24. $\dfrac{-8m^4n^{-2}}{4n^3}$

25. $\left(\dfrac{a^2b^{-1}}{c^3d^{-4}}\right)^{-2}$

26. $\left(\dfrac{p^{-3}q}{r^2s^{-1}}\right)^{-3}$

27. $(5^0w^2z) \cdot (w^{-3}z^{-4})$

28. $(4p^{-3}q) \cdot (p^{-2}q^4)$

For Exercises 29–36, write the number in scientific notation.

29. 3,050,000

30. 82,500,000

31. 0.0000251

32. 0.0038

33. For a recent year there were 89,600,000 people who watched the Super Bowl.

34. Mont Blanc, a mountain in the Alps, is about 15,800 ft high.

35. A single blood cell is approximately 0.00039 in. long.

36. The shortest flash of light recorded was 0.000 000 000 000 000 69 seconds.

For Exercises 37–44, perform the operation. Write the answer in scientific notation.

37. $(2.4 \times 10^1)(1.5 \times 10^3)$

38. $(8 \times 10^{-5})(1.2 \times 10^9)$

39. $\dfrac{6.3 \times 10^{14}}{3 \times 10^{-2}}$

40. $\dfrac{9.6 \times 10^{-12}}{4 \times 10^3}$

41. $(3 \times 10^{-5})(7.3 \times 10^2)$

42. $(2.1 \times 10^{13})(5 \times 10^{-2})$

43. $\dfrac{(4 \times 10^3)(1.2 \times 10^{-4})}{(6 \times 10^{10})}$

44. $\dfrac{(2.8 \times 10^2)(4 \times 10^4)}{(7 \times 10^{-6})}$

For Exercises 45–50, add or subtract as indicated.

45. $(5p^3 + 2p - 3) + (8p^3 - 4p^2 + 14)$

46. $(2m^2 - 3m + 9) - (-3m^2 + 2m - 8)$

47. $\left(10n^2 - \dfrac{3}{8}n + 2\right) - \left(11n^2 + \dfrac{5}{8}n - 6\right)$

48. $(a^2 - 5a + 10) + \left(-3a^3 + \dfrac{1}{2}a^2 - 13\right)$

49. $(-u^2v + 6u^2 - 2uv^2) + (11u^2 + 7uv^2) - (9u^2v + u^2 + 3uv^2)$

50. $(8a^2b - 5ab + 12ab^2) - (4a^2b - 6ab - ab^2) + (10a^2b + 3ab^2)$

For Exercises 51–66, multiply the polynomials.

51. $4p(p^3 - 5p^2 + 2p + 8)$

52. $5mn(-3m^2 + 6mn + n^2)$

53. $(3x + y)(-2x - 5y)$

54. $(4u - 7v)(3u - v)$

55. $(8b + 4)(2b - 3)$

56. $(-5a + 2)(5a - 3)$

57. $(x - 3y)(x^2 - 3xy + 5y^2)$

58. $(3p - 5q)(p - 2pq + q)$

59. $(3h - 8)(3h + 8)$

60. $(k - 5)(k + 5)$

61. $(4x - 5)^2$

62. $(3y + 8)^2$

63. $\left(\dfrac{1}{3}t^2 - 9\right)\left(\dfrac{1}{3}t^2 + 9\right)$

64. $\left(ab - \dfrac{3}{4}\right)\left(ab + \dfrac{3}{4}\right)$

65. $(0.2x^2 - 3)^2$

66. $(1.2y^2 + 4)^2$

For Exercises 67–76, divide the polynomials.

67. $(6a^3b^2 - 18a^2b^2 + 3ab^2 - 9ab) \div (3ab)$

68. $(8x^4y^4 + 4x^3y^2 - 12x^2y^4 + 4x^2y^2) \div (4x^2y^2)$

69. $(x^3 - 2x^2 - 4x + 33) \div (x + 3)$

70. $(2y^3 - 7y^2 + y + 10) \div (y - 2)$

71. $(2p^3 - 17p^2 + 39p - 10) \div (p - 5)$

72. $(t^3 - t^2 - 10t + 4) \div (t + 3)$

73. $(10m^5 - 16m^4 + 8m^3 + 8m^2 - 2m) \div (-2m)$

74. $(-25b^5 + 10b^4 - 5b^3 - 35b^2) \div (-5b^2)$

75. $(8a^3 - 9) \div (2a - 3)$

76. $(32k^3 + 5) \div (2k - 1)$

Section B.6   Review of Factoring Polynomials and Solving Quadratic Equations

Concepts

1. Factoring Polynomials
2. Solving Quadratic Equations Using the Zero Product Rule

1. Factoring Polynomials

Factoring Strategy

Step 1 Factor out the GCF.

Step 2 Identify whether the polynomial has two terms, three terms, or more than three terms.

Step 3 If the polynomial has more than three terms, try factoring by grouping.

Step 4 If the polynomial has three terms, check first for a perfect square trinomial. Otherwise, factor the trinomial with the trial-and-error method or the ac-method.

Step 5 If the polynomial has two terms, determine if it fits the pattern for
- A difference of squares: $a^2 - b^2 = (a - b)(a + b)$
- A sum of squares: $a^2 + b^2$ prime
- A difference of cubes: $a^3 - b^3 = (a - b)(a^2 + ab + b^2)$
- A sum of cubes: $a^3 + b^3 = (a + b)(a^2 - ab + b^2)$

Step 6 Be sure to factor the polynomial completely.

Step 7 Check by multiplying.

Example 1   **Factoring Binomials**

Factor completely.   **a.** $81w^4 - 1$ **b.** $2y^3 + 128$

Solution:

When factoring a binomial, determine if it fits any of the following patterns.

$$a^2 - b^2 = (a + b)(a - b)$$ Difference of squares

$$a^3 - b^3 = (a - b)(a^2 + ab + b^2)$$ Difference of cubes

$$a^3 + b^3 = (a + b)(a^2 - ab + b^2)$$ Sum of cubes

a. $81w^4 - 1$ The GCF is 1.

$= (9x^2)^2 - (1)^2$ This is a difference of squares, $a^2 - b^2$, where $a = 9x^2$ and $b = 1$.

$= (9x^2 + 1)(9x^2 - 1)$ Apply the formula $a^2 - b^2 = (a + b)(a - b)$.

$= (9x^2 + 1)(3x + 1)(3x - 1)$ The factor $9x^2 - 1$ factors further as a difference of squares. $9x^2 - 1 = (3x + 1)(3x - 1)$.

b. $2y^3 + 128$ The GCF is 2.

$= 2(y^3 + 64)$ Factor out 2.

$= 2[(y)^3 + (4)^3]$ The resulting binomial is a sum of cubes, $a^3 + b^3$, where $a = y$ and $b = 4$.

$= 2(y + 4)(y^2 - 4y + 16)$ Apply the formula $a^3 + b^3 = (a + b)(a^2 - ab + b^2)$

Avoiding Mistakes

The binomial $9x^2 - 1$ is a difference of squares and is factored as $(3x + 1)(3x - 1)$. However, the binomial $9x^2 + 1$ is a sum of squares and cannot be factored over the real numbers.

> **TIP:** Recall that a factoring problem may be checked by multiplication.
>
> $2(y + 4)(y^2 - 4y + 16) = (2y + 8)(y^2 - 4y + 16)$
> $$= 2y(y^2) + 2y(-4y) + 2y(16) + 8(y^2) + 8(-4y) + 8(16)$$
> $$= 2y^3 - 8y^2 + 32y + 8y^2 - 32y + 128$$
> $$= 2y^3 + 128$$

In Examples 2 and 3, we review factoring quadratic trinomials. Example 2 demonstrates the ac-method.

Example 2   **Factoring a Trinomial by Using the ac-Method**

Factor completely. $-10x + 60x^2 - 120$

Solution:

$-10x + 60x^2 - 120$

$= 60x^2 - 10x - 120$	Write the trinomial in descending order.
$= 10(6x^2 - x - 12)$	Factor out the greatest common factor, 10. The trinomial is in the form $ax^2 + bx + c$ where $a = 6$, $b = -1$, and $c = -12$.
	Find the product $ac = 6(-12) = -72$. Find two numbers whose product is -72 and whose sum is -1. The numbers are -9 and 8.
$= 10(6x^2 - 9x + 8x - 12)$	Write the middle term of the trinomial as the sum of two terms whose coefficients are -9 and 8.
$= 10[3x(2x - 3) + 4(2x - 3)]$	Factor the four-term polynomial by grouping.
$= 10[(2x - 3)(3x + 4)]$	Factor out the common binomial $(2x - 3)$ from each term.
$= 10(2x - 3)(3x + 4)$	

In Example 3, we revisit the trial-and-error technique to factor a trinomial, and the patterns associated with perfect square trinomials.

Example 3   **Factoring Trinomials**

Factor completely.   **a.** $49w^2 - 28w + 4$ **b.** $5x^4y - 8x^3y + 3x^2y$

Solution:

Check first to see if the trinomial is a perfect square trinomial, in which case factor as the square of a binomial.

$$\text{Perfect square trinomials} \quad \begin{cases} a^2 + 2ab + b^2 = (a + b)^2 \\ a^2 - 2ab + b^2 = (a - b)^2 \end{cases}$$

Otherwise factor the trinomial using the trial-and-error method or the ac-method.

a. $49w^2 - 28w + 4$ The GCF is 1.

$= (7w)^2 - 2(7w)(2) + (2)^2$ The polynomial is a perfect square trinomial, $a^2 - 2ab + b^2$ where $a = 7w$ and $b = 2$.

$= (7w - 2)^2$ Apply the formula $a^2 - 2ab + b^2 = (a - b)^2$.

b. $5x^4y - 8x^3y + 3x^2y$ The GCF is x^2y.

$= x^2y(5x^2 - 8x + 3)$ Factor out x^2y. The factored form of $5x^2 - 8x + 3$ must be a product of binomials of the form:

$$\overbrace{(\Box x - \Box)(\Box x - \Box)}$$

factors of 5 (top), factors of 3 (bottom)

The signs within parentheses must both be negative for a product of 3 and a sum of $-8x$.

Trying all possible combinations we have:

$$(5x - 1)(x - 3) = 5x^2 - 15x - x + 3$$
$$= 5x^2 - 16x + 3 \qquad \text{Wrong middle term.}$$
$$(5x - 3)(x - 1) = 5x^2 - 5x - 3x + 3$$
$$= 5x^2 - 8x + 3 \qquad \text{Correct!}$$

Therefore, $5x^4y - 8x^3y + 3x^2y = x^2y(5x - 3)(x - 1)$

Example 4   **Factoring a Four-Term Polynomial**

Factor completely. $6ab + 8ax + 15bx + 20x^2$

Solution:

This polynomial has 4 terms. Therefore, try factoring by grouping.

$6ab + 8ax + 15bx + 20x^2$ The GCF is 1.

$= 6ab + 8ax \mid + 15bx + 20x^2$ Group the first pair of terms and the second pair of terms.

$= 2a(3b + 4x) + 5x(3b + 4x)$ Factor out the GCF from each pair. Note that the two resulting terms share a common binomial factor.

$= (3b + 4x)(2a + 5x)$ Factor out the common binomial factor.

---

2. Solving Quadratic Equations Using the Zero Product Rule

A quadratic equation is an equation of the form $ax^2 + bx + c = 0$, where $a \neq 0$. To solve a quadratic equation in this form, we factor the expression $ax^2 + bx + c$ and set each factor equal to zero.

Example 5   ## Solving Quadratic Equations

Solve.   **a.** $(2x - 1)(x - 3) = 0$ **b.** $10x^2 + 50x = 140$

Solution:

a. $(2x - 1)(x - 3) = 0$ The equation is already in factored form and set equal to zero.

$2x - 1 = 0$ or $x - 3 = 0$ Set each factor equal to zero.

$2x = 1$ or $x = 3$ Solve each equation.

$x = \dfrac{1}{2}$ or $x = 3$

The solution set is $\left\{ \dfrac{1}{2}, 3 \right\}$.

b. $10x^2 + 50x = 140$

$10x^2 + 50x - 140 = 0$ Write the equation in the form $ax^2 + bx + c = 0$.

$10(x^2 + 5x - 14) = 0$ Factor out the GCF.

$10(x - 2)(x + 7) = 0$ Factor the trinomial.

$\cancel{10 = 0}$ or $x - 2 = 0$ or $x + 7 = 0$ Set each factor equal to zero.

$x = 2$ or $x = -7$

The solution set is $\{2, -7\}$.

Section B.6   Practice Exercises

1. Write the formula to factor the difference of squares, $a^2 - b^2$.

2. Write the formula to factor the difference of cubes, $a^3 - b^3$.

3. Write the formula to factor the sum of cubes, $a^3 + b^3$.

4. Is it possible to factor the sum of squares $a^2 + b^2$ over the real numbers?

For Exercises 5–50,

    a. Factor out the GCF and identify the category in which the polynomial best fits. Choose from

- difference of squares
- sum of squares
- difference of cubes
- sum of cubes
- trinomial (perfect square trinomial)
- trinomial (nonperfect square trinomial)
- four terms—grouping
- none of these

    b. Factor the polynomial completely.

5. $t^2 - 100$

6. $4m^2 - 49n^2$

7. $y^3 + 27$

8. $x^3 + 1$

9. $d^2 + 3d - 28$

10. $c^2 + 5c - 24$

11. $x^2 - 12x + 36$

12. $p^2 + 16p + 64$

13. $2ax^2 - 5ax + 2bx - 5b$

14. $8x^2 - 4bx + 2ax - ab$

15. $10y^2 + 3y - 4$

16. $12z^2 + 11z + 2$

17. $10p^2 - 640$

18. $50a^2 - 72$

19. $z^4 - 64z$

20. $t^4 - 8t$

21. $b^3 - 4b^2 - 45b$

22. $y^3 - 14y^2 + 40y$

23. $9w^2 + 24wx + 16x^2$

24. $4k^2 - 20kp + 25p^2$

25. $60x^2 - 20x + 30ax - 10a$

26. $50x^2 - 200x + 10cx - 40c$

27. $x^3 + 4x^2 - 9x - 36$

28. $m^3 + 5m^2 - 4m - 20$

29. $w^4 - 16$

30. $k^4 - 81$

31. $t^6 - 8$

32. $p^6 + 27$

33. $8p^2 - 22p + 5$

34. $9m^2 - 3m - 20$

35. $36y^2 - 12y + 1$

36. $9a^2 + 42a + 49$

37. $x^2 + 4x - xy - 4y$

38. $m^2 - 6m + mn - 6n$

39. $2x^2 + 50$

40. $4y^2 + 64$

41. $12r^2s^2 + 7rs^2 - 10s^2$

42. $7z^2w^2 - 10zw^2 - 8w^2$

43. $x^2 + 8xy - 33y^2$

44. $s^2 - 9st - 36t^2$

45. $m^6 + n^3$

46. $a^3 - b^6$

47. $x^2(a + b) - x(a + b) - 12(a + b)$

48. $y^2(y + 2) + 10y(y + 2) + 9(y + 2)$

49. $x^2 - 4x$

50. $y^2 - 9y$

For Exercises 51–64, solve the equation.

51. $(2x + 5)(x - 3) = 0$

52. $(4x - 1)(x + 6) = 0$

53. $x(x - 5) = 0$

54. $y(y + 7) = 0$

55. $5(w + 3) = 0$

56. $-2(t - 10) = 0$

57. $z^2 - 2z - 8 = 0$

58. $p^2 - 15p - 16 = 0$

59. $6x^2 - 7x = 5$

60. $4x^2 = x + 14$

61. $2x(x - 10) = -9x - 12$

62. $x(x - 12) + 5 = -30$

63. $w^3 - w^2 - w + 1 = 0$

64. $z^3 - 4z^2 - 16z + 64 = 0$

Review of Rational Expressions

1. Definition of a Rational Expression

A rational expression is an expression of the form $\frac{p}{q}$, where p and q are polynomials. The following are rational expressions.

$$\frac{x^2 + x - 4}{x - 2}, \quad \frac{1}{x^3}, \quad \frac{2x}{5}$$

A rational expression is defined for all real numbers except those that make the denominator equal to zero. For example,

$\dfrac{x^2 + x - 4}{x - 2}$ The expression is defined for all real numbers except 2. We say that 2 is a restricted value in the expression.

$\dfrac{1}{x^3}$ The expression is defined for all real numbers except 0. We say that 0 is a restricted value in the expression.

$\dfrac{2x}{5}$ The expression is defined for all real numbers with no restrictions

2. Simplifying Rational Expressions

The expressions $\frac{6}{12}$, $\frac{2}{4}$, and $\frac{1}{2}$ are all equivalent. However, the value $\frac{1}{2}$ is in lowest terms. To simplify a rational expression to lowest terms, first factor the numerator and denominator. Then reduce the common factors that form a ratio of 1.

Example 1   **Simplifying a Rational Expression to Lowest Terms**

Simplify to lowest terms. $\dfrac{x^2 + 10x + 9}{x^2 - 1}$

Solution:

$\dfrac{x^2 + 10x + 9}{x^2 - 1} = \dfrac{(x + 1)(x + 9)}{(x + 1)(x - 1)}$ Factor numerator and denominator.

$\quad = \dfrac{(x + 1)(x + 9)}{(x + 1)(x - 1)}$ Simplify $\dfrac{(x + 1)}{(x + 1)}$ to 1.

$\quad = \dfrac{x + 9}{x - 1}$ (where $x \neq 1$ and $x \neq -1$)

In Example 1, it is important to realize that the original restrictions on the variable $x \neq 1$ and $x \neq -1$, are still in effect even after the expression is simplified. That is,

$$\frac{x^2 + 10x + 9}{x^2 - 1} = \frac{x + 9}{x - 1} \quad \text{for } x \neq 1 \text{ and } x \neq -1.$$

3. Multiplying and Dividing Rational Expressions

To multiply two rational expressions, factor the numerator and denominator of each expression. Then simplify common factors that form a ratio of 1.

| Example 2 | **Multiplying Rational Expressions** |

Multiply and simplify the result. $\dfrac{2x-4}{4x+4} \cdot \dfrac{2x^2-7x-4}{x^2-6x+8}$

Solution:

$$\dfrac{2x-4}{4x+4} \cdot \dfrac{2x^2-7x-4}{x^2-6x+8} = \dfrac{2(x-2)}{4(x+1)} \cdot \dfrac{(2x+1)(x-4)}{(x-4)(x-2)} \qquad \text{Factor.}$$

$$= \dfrac{2\overset{1}{\cancel{(x-2)}}}{2 \cdot 2(x+1)} \cdot \dfrac{(2x+1)\overset{1}{\cancel{(x-4)}}}{\cancel{(x-4)}\cancel{(x-2)}} \qquad \text{Simplify ratios of 1.}$$

$$= \dfrac{2x+1}{2(x+1)}$$

TIP: In the expression $\dfrac{2x+1}{2(x+1)}$, do not try to "cancel" the 2's. The 2 in the numerator is not a factor of the numerator.

To divide two rational expressions, multiply the first expression by the reciprocal of the second expression.

| Example 3 | **Dividing Rational Expressions** |

Divide and simplify. $\dfrac{-x^2+x}{-x^2} \div \dfrac{3x^2+2x-5}{5x}$

Solution:

$$\dfrac{-x^2+x}{-x^2} \div \dfrac{3x^2+2x-5}{5x} = \dfrac{-x^2+x}{-x^2} \cdot \dfrac{5x}{3x^2+2x-5} \qquad \begin{array}{l}\text{Multiply the first expression}\\ \text{by the reciprocal of the}\\ \text{second.}\end{array}$$

$$= \dfrac{-x(x-1)}{-x \cdot x} \cdot \dfrac{5x}{(3x+5)(x-1)} \qquad \text{Factor.}$$

$$= \dfrac{\overset{1}{\cancel{(-x)}}\overset{1}{\cancel{(x-1)}}}{\cancel{(-x)} \cdot x} \cdot \dfrac{5\overset{1}{\cancel{x}}}{(3x+5)\cancel{(x-1)}} \qquad \text{Simplify ratios of 1.}$$

$$= \dfrac{5}{3x+5}$$

4. Adding and Subtracting Rational Expressions

To add or subtract a rational expression it is necessary that the expressions have a common denominator. To add or subtract expressions with a common denominator add or subtract the terms in the numerators and write the result over the common denominator. Then simplify the expression to lowest terms if possible.

Example 4	**Subtracting Rational Expressions with a Common Denominator**

Subtract. $\dfrac{x^2 - 2x}{x - 5} - \dfrac{8x - 25}{x - 5}$

Solution:

$\dfrac{x^2 - 2x}{x - 5} - \dfrac{8x - 25}{x - 5} = \dfrac{x^2 - 2x - (8x - 25)}{x - 5}$ Subtract terms in the numerator. Use parentheses to help you remember to subtract both terms in the numerator of the second expression.

$= \dfrac{x^2 - 2x - 8x + 25}{x - 5}$ Apply the distributive property.

$= \dfrac{x^2 - 10x + 25}{x - 5}$ Combine *like* terms.

$= \dfrac{(x - 5)(x - 5)}{x - 5}$ Factor and simplify.

$= x - 5$

To add or subtract two rational expressions that do not have a common denominator, it is necessary to convert each expression to an equivalent rational expression with a common denominator. The steps below outline the process to find the least common denominator of two or more rational expressions.

Finding the LCD of Two or More Rational Expressions

Step 1   Factor all denominators completely.

Step 2   The LCD is the product of unique factors from the denominators, where each factor is raised to the highest power to which it appears in any denominator.

For example, the LCD of the expressions $\dfrac{2}{5x^2y^4}$ and $\dfrac{1}{7x^3y}$ is given by the product:

$5^1 \cdot 7^1 \cdot x^3 \cdot y^4 = 35x^3y^4$.

To convert a rational expression to an equivalent expression with a common denominator, we multiply the numerator and denominator by the factors in the LCD that are missing from the denominator of the original expression. This is mathematically feasible because we are multiplying the original expression by 1. For example, we convert $\dfrac{2}{5x^2y^4}$ and $\dfrac{1}{7x^3y}$ to equivalent expressions with a denominator of $35x^3y^4$ as follows.

$\dfrac{2}{5x^2y^4} = \dfrac{2 \cdot 7x}{5x^2y^4 \cdot 7x} = \dfrac{14x}{35x^3y^4}$ Note that $\dfrac{7x}{7x} = 1$.

$\dfrac{1}{7x^3y} = \dfrac{1 \cdot 5y^3}{7x^3y \cdot 5y^3} = \dfrac{5y^3}{35x^3y^4}$ Note that $\dfrac{5y^3}{5y^3} = 1$.

Example 5	**Subtracting Two Rational Expressions with Different Denominators**

Subtract the rational expressions. $\dfrac{3x}{x^2 + 7x + 10} - \dfrac{2x}{x^2 + 6x + 8}$

Solution:

$$\dfrac{3x}{x^2 + 7x + 10} - \dfrac{2x}{x^2 + 6x + 8}$$

$= \dfrac{3x}{(x+2)(x+5)} - \dfrac{2x}{(x+4)(x+2)}$
Factor the denominators.
The LCD is $(x+2)(x+5)(x+4)$.

$= \dfrac{3x(x+4)}{(x+2)(x+5)(x+4)} - \dfrac{2x(x+5)}{(x+4)(x+2)(x+5)}$
Convert each expression to an equivalent expression with the LCD.

$= \dfrac{3x(x+4) - 2x(x+5)}{(x+2)(x+5)(x+4)}$
Subtract the numerators.

$= \dfrac{3x^2 + 12x - 2x^2 - 10x}{(x+2)(x+5)(x+4)}$
Apply the distributive property.

$= \dfrac{x^2 + 2x}{(x+2)(x+5)(x+4)}$
Combine *like* terms.

$= \dfrac{x(x+2)}{(x+2)(x+5)(x+4)}$
Factor and simplify.

$= \dfrac{x}{(x+5)(x+4)}$

5. Simplifying Complex Fractions

A complex fraction is a fraction whose numerator or denominator contains one or more rational expressions. For example:

$$\dfrac{1 - \dfrac{4}{3y}}{y - \dfrac{16}{9y}}$$

One method to simplify such an expression is to multiply the numerator and denominator of the complex fraction by the LCD of all four individual fractions. This is demonstrated in Example 6.

| Example 6 | **Simplifying a Complex Fraction** |

Simplify. $\dfrac{1 - \dfrac{4}{3y}}{y - \dfrac{16}{9y}}$

Solution:

$\dfrac{1 - \dfrac{4}{3y}}{y - \dfrac{16}{9y}}$ The LCD of the expressions $\dfrac{1}{1}, \dfrac{4}{3y}, \dfrac{y}{1},$ and $\dfrac{16}{9y}$ is $9y$.

$\dfrac{1 - \dfrac{4}{3y}}{y - \dfrac{16}{9y}} = \dfrac{9y\left(1 - \dfrac{4}{3y}\right)}{9y\left(y - \dfrac{16}{9y}\right)} = \dfrac{(9y)\cdot 1 - (9y)\cdot \dfrac{4}{3y}}{(9y)\cdot y - (9y)\cdot \dfrac{16}{9y}}$ Apply the distributive property.

$\qquad = \dfrac{9y - 12}{9y^2 - 16}$ Simplify.

$\qquad = \dfrac{3(3y \overset{1}{-} 4)}{(3y - 4)(3y + 4)}$ Factor and simplify to lowest terms.

$\qquad = \dfrac{3}{3y + 4}$

The expression in Example 6 could also have been simplified by using the order of operations to combine the expressions in the numerator and denominator separately and then dividing the resulting expressions.

6. Solving Rational Equations

An equation with one or more rational expressions is called a rational equation. To solve a rational equation, we offer the following steps.

Solving a Rational Equation

Step 1 Factor the denominators of all rational expressions. Identify the restricted values.

Step 2 Identify the LCD of all expressions in the equation.

Step 3 Multiply both sides of the equation by the LCD.

Step 4 Solve the resulting equation.

Step 5 Check potential solutions in the original equation.

> **Example 7**   **Solving a Rational Equation**

Solve. $\dfrac{4}{y-4} + \dfrac{y}{2} = \dfrac{y}{y-4}$

Solution:

$\dfrac{4}{y-4} + \dfrac{y}{2} = \dfrac{y}{y-4}$	**Step 1:** The denominators are already factored. Note that $y \neq 4$.
$2(y-4)\left(\dfrac{4}{y-4} + \dfrac{y}{2}\right) = 2(y-4)\left(\dfrac{y}{y-4}\right)$	**Step 2:** The LCD is $2(y-4)$.
	Step 3: Multiply by the LCD.
$\dfrac{2(y-4)}{1} \cdot \left(\dfrac{4}{y-4}\right) + \dfrac{2(y-4)}{1} \cdot \dfrac{y}{2} = \dfrac{2(y-4)}{1} \cdot \left(\dfrac{y}{y-4}\right)$	Apply the distributive property.
$2 \cdot 4 + (y-4)y = 2y$	**Step 4:** Solve the resulting equation.
$8 + y^2 - 4y = 2y$	Apply the distributive property to clear parentheses.
$y^2 - 4y - 2y + 8 = 0$	The equation is quadratic. Set the equation equal to zero.
$y^2 - 6y + 8 = 0$	
$(y-4)(y-2) = 0$	Factor.
$y - 4 = 0 \quad \text{or} \quad y - 2 = 0$	Set each factor equal to zero.
$y = 4 \quad \text{or} \quad y = 2$	

TIP: Before solving a rational equation note any values of the variable for which the equation is undefined. In Example 7, the equation $\dfrac{4}{y-4} + \dfrac{y}{2} = \dfrac{y}{y-4}$ is not defined for $y = 4$ because this value makes the denominator zero in the first and third rational expressions. If one of your potential solutions matches a restricted value, then you automatically know that this value cannot be a solution to the original equation.

Step 5: Check each potential solution.

Check $y = 4$:

$\dfrac{4}{(4)-4} + \dfrac{(4)}{2} \overset{?}{=} \dfrac{(4)}{(4)-4}$

$\dfrac{4}{0} + \dfrac{4}{2} \overset{?}{=} \dfrac{4}{0}$ (Undefined)

Check $y = 2$:

$\dfrac{4}{(2)-4} + \dfrac{(2)}{2} \overset{?}{=} \dfrac{(2)}{(2)-4}$

$\dfrac{4}{-2} + 1 \overset{?}{=} \dfrac{2}{-2}$

$-2 + 1 = -1 \checkmark$

The solution set is $\{2\}$. The value $y = 4$ does not check because it makes the denominator zero in one or more of the rational expressions.

Section B.7   Practice Exercises

For Exercises 1–6, determine the restricted values of the expression.

1. $\dfrac{x+2}{x+4}$

2. $\dfrac{x-5}{x-1}$

3. $\dfrac{2x}{25x^2 - 9}$

4. $\dfrac{5y}{4y^2 - 49}$

5. $\dfrac{t-7}{8}$

6. $\dfrac{x+2}{5}$

For Exercises 7–12, simplify the expression to lowest terms.

7. $\dfrac{3x^4y^7}{12xy^8}$

8. $\dfrac{21ab^5}{7a^3b^4}$

9. $\dfrac{t^2-4}{2t-4}$

10. $\dfrac{m^2-9}{3m-9}$

11. $\dfrac{2y^2+5y-12}{2y^2+y-6}$

12. $\dfrac{2x^2+20x+48}{4x^2-144}$

For Exercises 13–22, multiply or divide as indicated and simplify.

13. $\dfrac{2x}{15y^2}\cdot\dfrac{3y^5}{4x^2}$

14. $\dfrac{4s^2t}{8t^3}\cdot\dfrac{2t^5}{6s^4}$

15. $\dfrac{5y-15}{10y+40}\cdot\dfrac{2y^2+y-28}{2y^2-13y+21}$

16. $\dfrac{x^2-36}{x^2-4x-12}\cdot\dfrac{4x+8}{4x-24}$

17. $\dfrac{a^2b^3}{5c^2}\div\dfrac{ab}{15c^3}$

18. $\dfrac{m^3}{14n^5}\div\dfrac{m^7}{21n}$

19. $\dfrac{p^2-36}{2p-4}\div\dfrac{2p+12}{p^2-2p}$

20. $\dfrac{y^2+y}{y^2-y-12}\div\dfrac{5y+5}{y^2-5y+4}$

21. $\dfrac{t^2+7t}{3-t}\div\dfrac{t^2-49}{t^2-3t}$

22. $\dfrac{x^2-2x}{2-x}\div\dfrac{x^2+5x}{x^2-25}$

For Exercises 23–26, find the LCD for each pair of expressions.

23. $\dfrac{1}{4x^3y^7},\dfrac{1}{8xy^{10}}$

24. $\dfrac{1}{16ab^4},\dfrac{1}{24a^2b^2}$

25. $\dfrac{1}{x^2-x-12},\dfrac{1}{x^2-9}$

26. $\dfrac{1}{x^2+10x+9},\dfrac{1}{x^2-81}$

For Exercises 27–40, add or subtract as indicated.

27. $\dfrac{1}{2x}-\dfrac{5}{6x}$

28. $\dfrac{7}{15t}-\dfrac{4}{5t}$

29. $\dfrac{1}{2x^3y}+\dfrac{5}{4xy^2}$

30. $\dfrac{1}{3a^2b^4}+\dfrac{7}{9a^2b}$

31. $\dfrac{x^2}{x-7}-\dfrac{14x-49}{x-7}$

32. $\dfrac{z^2}{z-10}-\dfrac{20z-100}{z-10}$

33. $\dfrac{7x}{4x-2}+\dfrac{5x}{2x-1}$

34. $\dfrac{-8}{5x+4}+\dfrac{7}{10x+8}$

35. $\dfrac{x}{x^2+x-12}-\dfrac{2}{x^2+3x-4}$

36. $\dfrac{4y}{y^2-4y+4}+\dfrac{3}{y^2-7y+10}$

37. $\dfrac{-3}{y-2}+\dfrac{2y+11}{y^2+y-6}-\dfrac{2}{y+3}$

38. $\dfrac{-2}{x+2}+\dfrac{x}{x-1}+\dfrac{3x-6}{x^2+x-2}$

39. $\dfrac{5}{x-3}-\dfrac{x+2}{x-3}$

40. $\dfrac{3x}{x+2}-\dfrac{4x+2}{x+2}$

For Exercises 41–48, simplify the complex fractions.

41. $\dfrac{\dfrac{3}{a}+\dfrac{4}{b}}{\dfrac{7}{a}-\dfrac{1}{b}}$

42. $\dfrac{\dfrac{2}{p}-\dfrac{4}{q}}{\dfrac{2}{p}+\dfrac{1}{q}}$

43. $\dfrac{8x-\dfrac{1}{2x}}{1-\dfrac{1}{4x}}$

44. $\dfrac{\dfrac{1}{2}-\dfrac{1}{2t}}{1-\dfrac{1}{t^2}}$

45. $\dfrac{\dfrac{u^2-v^2}{uv}}{\dfrac{u+v}{uv}}$

46. $\dfrac{\dfrac{a^2-b^2}{ab}}{\dfrac{2a-2b}{ab}}$

47. $\dfrac{\dfrac{1}{y-5}}{\dfrac{2}{y+5}+\dfrac{1}{y^2-25}}$

48. $\dfrac{\dfrac{3}{x+1}}{\dfrac{2}{x^2-1}+\dfrac{1}{x-1}}$

For Exercises 49–56, solve the equation.

49. $\dfrac{1}{8}-\dfrac{3}{4x}=\dfrac{1}{2x}$

50. $\dfrac{3}{10}-\dfrac{4}{5x}=\dfrac{1}{x}$

51. $\dfrac{5}{x-3}=\dfrac{2}{x-3}$

52. $\dfrac{6}{x+2}=\dfrac{4}{x+2}$

53. $1+\dfrac{6}{x}=-\dfrac{8}{x^2}$

54. $1=\dfrac{8}{x}-\dfrac{15}{x^2}$

55. $\dfrac{4x+11}{x^2-4}-\dfrac{5}{x+2}=\dfrac{2x}{x^2-4}$

56. $\dfrac{3x}{x+1}-2=\dfrac{12}{x^2-1}$

Student Answer Appendix

Chapter 1

Chapter Opener Puzzle

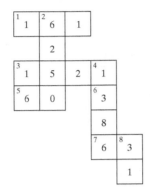

Section 1.1 Practice Exercises, pp. 6–8

1. a. periods   **b.** hundreds   **c.** thousands
3. 7: ones; 5: tens; 4: hundreds; 3: thousands;
1: ten-thousands; 2: hundred-thousands; 8: millions
5. Tens   **7.** Ones   **9.** Hundreds   **11.** Thousands
13. Hundred-thousands   **15.** Billions
17. Ten-thousands   **19.** Millions   **21.** Ten-millions
23. Billions   **25.** 5 tens + 8 ones; $5 \times 10 + 8 \times 1$
27. 5 hundreds + 3 tens + 9 ones;
$5 \times 100 + 3 \times 10 + 9 \times 1$
29. 5 hundreds + 3 ones; $5 \times 100 + 3 \times 1$
31. 1 ten-thousand + 2 hundreds + 4 tens + 1 one;
$1 \times 10,000 + 2 \times 100 + 4 \times 10 + 1 \times 1$
33. 524   **35.** 150   **37.** 1,906   **39.** 85,007
41. Ones, thousands, millions, billions
43. Two hundred forty-one
45. Six hundred three
47. Thirty-one thousand, five hundred thirty
49. One hundred thousand, two hundred thirty-four
51. Nine thousand, five hundred thirty-five
53. Twenty thousand, three hundred twenty
55. One thousand, three hundred seventy-seven
57. 6,005   **59.** 672,000   **61.** 1,484,250
63.

65. 10   **67.** 4   **69.** 8 is greater than 2, or 2 is less than 8
71. 3 is less than 7, or 7 is greater than 3   **73.** <
75. >   **77.** <   **79.** >   **81.** <   **83.** <
85. False   **87.** 99   **89.** There is no greatest whole
number.   **91.** 7   **93.** 964

Section 1.2 Practice Exercises, pp. 16–20

1. a. addends   **b.** sum   **c.** commutative   **d.** 4; 4
e. associative   **f.** polygon   **g.** perimeter
3. 3 hundreds + 5 tens + 1 one; $3 \times 100 + 5 \times 10 + 1 \times 1$

5. 1 hundred + 7 ones; $1 \times 100 + 7 \times 1$ **7.** 4012
9.

+	0	1	2	3	4	5	6	7	8	9
0	0	1	2	3	4	5	6	7	8	9
1	1	2	3	4	5	6	7	8	9	10
2	2	3	4	5	6	7	8	9	10	11
3	3	4	5	6	7	8	9	10	11	12
4	4	5	6	7	8	9	10	11	12	13
5	5	6	7	8	9	10	11	12	13	14
6	6	7	8	9	10	11	12	13	14	15
7	7	8	9	10	11	12	13	14	15	16
8	8	9	10	11	12	13	14	15	16	17
9	9	10	11	12	13	14	15	16	17	18

11. Addends: 2, 8; sum: 10
13. Addends: 11, 10; sum: 21
15. Addends: 5, 8, 2; sum: 15
17. 74   **19.** 58   **21.** 48   **23.** 19   **25.** 588
27. 798   **29.** 237   **31.** 198   **33.** 84   **35.** 115
37. 937   **39.** 850   **41.** 41   **43.** 29   **45.** 1003
47. 836   **49.** 24,004   **51.** 132,658   **53.** 21 + 30
55. 13 + 8   **57.** 23 + (9 + 10)   **59.** (41 + 3) + 22
61. The sum of any number and 0 is that number.
a. 423   **b.** 25   **c.** 67   **63.** 100 + 42; 142
65. 23 + 81; 104   **67.** 76 + 2; 78   **69.** 1320 + 448; 1768
71. For example: The sum of 54 and 24
73. For example: 88 added to 12
75. For example: The total of 4, 23, and 77
77. For example: 10 increased by 8   **79.** 276 people
81. 58,493,000 viewers   **83.** $45,500   **85.** $245
87. 13,538 participants   **89.** 821,024 nonteachers
91. 104 cm   **93.** 110 m   **95.** 42 yd   **97.** 288 ft

Section 1.2 Calculator Connections, p. 21

99. 9,536,940   **100.** 908,788   **101.** 8,163,940
102. 192,780   **103.** 21,491,394   **104.** 5,257,179
105. $148,500,000   **106.** 128,107,616 votes

Section 1.3 Practice Exercises, pp. 28–31

1. minuend; subtrahend; difference
3. 1151   **5.** 899   **7.** 0 < 10
9. Minuend: 12; subtrahend: 8; difference: 4
11. Minuend: 21; subtrahend: 12; difference: 9
13. Minuend: 9; subtrahend: 6; difference: 3
15. 18 + 9 = 27   **17.** 27 + 75 = 102   **19.** 5
21. 3   **23.** 6   **25.** 45   **27.** 61   **29.** 1126
31. 321   **33.** 10,004   **35.** 1103   **37.** 17   **39.** 49
41. 104   **43.** 521   **45.** 23   **47.** 4764   **49.** 1403
51. 2217   **53.** 378   **55.** 713   **57.** 30,941
59. 5,662,119   **61.** 78 − 23; 55   **63.** 78 − 6; 72
65. 422 − 100; 322   **67.** 1090 − 72; 1018
69. 50 − 13; 37   **71.** 103 − 35; 68

SA-2   **Student Answer Appendix**

73. For example: 93 minus 27
75. For example: Subtract 85 from 165.
77. The expression $7 - 4$ means 7 minus 4, yielding a difference of 3. The expression $4 - 7$ means 4 minus 7 which results in a difference of -3. (This is a mathematical skill we have not yet learned.)   **79.** $33   **81.** 55 more hits
83. 8 plants   **85.** 2479 times   **87.** 13 m   **89.** 10 yd
91. 30 thousand marriages   **93.** 119 thousand marriages

Section 1.3 Calculator Connections, p. 31
95. 4,447,302   **96.** 897,058,513   **97.** 2,906,455
98. 49,408 mi^2 **99.** 17,139 mi^2 **100.** The difference in land area between Colorado and Rhode Island is 102,673 mi^2.
101. 13,093 mi^2

Section 1.4 Practice Exercises, pp. 36–38
1. rounding   **3.** 26   **5.** 5007   **7.** Ten-thousands
9. If the digit in the tens place is 0, 1, 2, 3, or 4, then change the tens and ones digits to 0. If the digit in the tens place is 5, 6, 7, 8, or 9, increase the digit in the hundreds place by 1 and change the tens and ones digits to 0.
11. 340   **13.** 730   **15.** 9400   **17.** 8500   **19.** 35,000
21. 3000   **23.** 10,000   **25.** 109,000   **27.** 490,000
29. $77,000,000   **31.** 239,000 mi   **33.** 160   **35.** 180
37. 500   **39.** 2100   **41.** $151,000,000
43. $11,000,000 more   **45.** $10,000,000
47. a. year 4; $3,500,000   **b.** year 6; $2,000,000
49. Massachusetts; 79,000 students   **51.** 71,000 students
53. Answers may vary.   **55.** 10,000 mm   **57.** 440 in.

Section 1.5 Practice Exercises, pp. 47–50
1. a. factors; product   **b.** commutative   **c.** associative
d. 0; 0   **e.** 7; 7   **f.** distributive   **g.** area   **h.** $l \times w$
3. 1,010,000   **5.** 5400   **7.** 6×5; 30
9. 3×9; 27   **11.** Factors: 13, 42; product: 546
13. Factors: 3, 5, 2; product: 30
15. For example: 5×12; $5 \cdot 12$; $5(12)$
17. d   **19.** e   **21.** c   **23.** 8×14
25. $(6 \times 2) \times 10$ **27.** $(5 \times 7) + (5 \times 4)$
29. 144   **31.** 52   **33.** 655   **35.** 1376
37. 11,280   **39.** 23,184   **41.** 378,126   **43.** 448
45. 1632   **47.** 864   **49.** 2431   **51.** 6631
53. 19,177   **55.** 186,702   **57.** 21,241,448
59. 4,047,804   **61.** 24,000   **63.** 2,100,000
65. 72,000,000   **67.** 36,000,000   **69.** 60,000,000
71. 2,400,000,000   **73.** $1000   **75.** $2,720,000
77. 4000 minutes   **79.** $1665   **81.** 287,500 sheets
83. 372 mi   **85.** 276 ft^2 **87.** 5329 cm^2
89. 105,300 mi^2 **91. a.** 2400 in.^{2} **b.** 42 windows
c. 100,800 in.^{2} **93.** 128 ft^2

Section 1.6 Practice Exercises, pp. 58–61
1. a. dividend; divisor, quotient   **b.** 1   **c.** 5   **d.** 0
e. undefined   **f.** remainder
3. 4944   **5.** 1253   **7.** 664,210   **9.** 902
11. Dividend: 72; divisor: 8; quotient: 9
13. Dividend: 64; divisor: 8; quotient: 8
15. Dividend: 45; divisor: 9; quotient: 5
17. You cannot divide a number by zero (the quotient is undefined). If you divide zero by a number (other than zero), the quotient is always zero.

19. 15   **21.** 0   **23.** Undefined   **25.** 1
27. Undefined   **29.** 0   **31.** $2 \times 3 = 6$, $2 \times 6 \neq 3$
33. Multiply the quotient and the divisor to get the dividend.
35. 13   **37.** 41   **39.** 486   **41.** 409   **43.** 203
45. 822   **47.** Correct   **49.** Incorrect; 253 R2
51. Correct   **53.** Incorrect; 25 R3   **55.** 7 R5
57. 10 R2   **59.** 27 R1   **61.** 197 R2   **63.** 42 R4
65. 1557 R1   **67.** 751 R6   **69.** 835 R2   **71.** 479 R9
73. 43 R19   **75.** 308   **77.** 1259 R26   **79.** 229 R96
81. 302   **83.** 497 ÷ 71; 7   **85.** 877 ÷ 14; 62 R9
87. 42 ÷ 6; 7   **89.** 14 classrooms
91. 5 cases; 8 cans left over   **93.** 52 mph   **95.** 22 lb
97. 1200 ÷ 20 = 60; approximately 60 words per minute
99. Yes, they can all attend if they sit in the second balcony.
101. a. 12 loads   **b.** 2 oz

Section 1.6 Calculator Connections, p. 61
103. 7,665,000,000 bbl   **104.** 13,000 min
105. $888 billion   **106.** Each crate weighs 255 lb.

Chapter 1 Problem Recognition Exercises, p. 62
1. a. 65   **b.** 676   **c.** 39   **d.** 4   **2. a.** 6   **b.** 85   **c.** 1734
d. 119   **3. a.** 293, 712   **b.** 5122   **c.** 87 R18   **d.** 5006
4. a. 1112   **b.** 10 R86   **c.** 1340   **d.** 139, 764
5. a. 197   **b.** 156   **6. a.** 6225   **b.** 6004
7. 4180   **8.** 41,800   **9.** 418,000   **10.** 4,180,000
11. 35,000   **12.** 3500   **13.** 350   **14.** 35
15. 246,000   **16.** 2,820,000   **17.** 20,000   **18.** 540,000

Section 1.7 Practice Exercises, pp. 67–70
1. a. base; 4   **b.** powers   **c.** square root; 81
d. order; operations   **e.** variable; constants   **f.** mean
3. True   **5.** False   **7.** True   **9.** 9^4 **11.** 2^7
13. 3^6 **15.** $4^4 \cdot 2^3$ **17.** $8 \cdot 8 \cdot 8 \cdot 8$
19. $4 \cdot 4 \cdot 4 \cdot 4 \cdot 4 \cdot 4 \cdot 4$ **21.** 8   **23.** 9   **25.** 27
27. 125   **29.** 32   **31.** 81   **33.** 1   **35.** 1
37. The number 1 raised to any power equals 1.   **39.** 1000
41. 100,000   **43.** 2   **45.** 6   **47.** 10   **49.** 0
51. No, addition and subtraction should be performed in the order in which they appear from left to right.   **53.** 26
55. 1   **57.** 49   **59.** 3   **61.** 2   **63.** 53   **65.** 8
67. 45   **69.** 24   **71.** 4   **73.** 40   **75.** 90   **77.** 25
79. 4   **81.** 81   **83.** 18   **85.** 0   **87.** 5   **89.** 6
91. 3   **93.** 201   **95.** 109   **97.** 18
99. The average mileage rating was 34 mpg.
101. 121 mm per month   **103.** 24   **105.** 70

Section 1.7 Calculator Connections, p. 70
107. 24,336   **108.** 174,724   **109.** 248,832
110. 1,500,625   **111.** 79,507   **112.** 357,911
113. 8028   **114.** 293,834   **115.** 66,049   **116.** 1728
117. 35   **118.** 43

Section 1.8 Practice Exercises, pp. 76–80
1. 4 ÷ 0   **3.** 71 + 14; 85   **5.** 2 · 14; 28
7. 102 − 32; 70   **9.** 10 · 13; 130
11. 24 ÷ 6; 4   **13.** 5 + 13 + 25; 43

15. For example: sum, added to, increased by, more than, plus, total of **17.** For example: difference, minus, decreased by, less, subtract **19.** Denali is 6074 ft higher than White Mountain Peak. **21.** 18,960,000 barrels per day
23. The whole screen has 12,096 pixels.
25. There will be 120 classes of Prealgebra.
27. There will be 9 gal used.
29. Jeannette will pay $42,236 for 1 year.
31. The Prius can go 1100 mi.
33. The maximum capacity is 3150 seats.
35. Jackson's monthly payment was $390.
37. Each trip will take 2 hr. **39.** Perimeter
41. The cost will be $86. **43.** The cost is $1020.
45. There will be $36 left in Gina's account.
47. The total bill was $154,032.
49. a. Latayne will receive $48. **b.** She can buy 6 CDs.
51. Michael Jordan scored 33,454 points with the Bulls.
53. a. One bottle will last for 30 days. **b.** The owner should order a refill no later than September 28.
55. a. The distance is 360 mi. **b.** 14 in. represents 840 mi.
57. 104 boxes will be filled completely with 2 books left over.
59. a. Marc needs five $20 bills. **b.** He will receive $16 in change. **61.** He earned $520.

Chapter 1 Review Exercises, pp. 88–92

1. Ten-thousands **2.** Hundred-thousands **3.** 92,046
4. 503,160 **5.** 3 millions + 4 hundred-thousands + 8 hundreds + 2 tens; $3 \times 1,000,000 + 4 \times 100,000 + 8 \times 100 + 2 \times 10$ **6.** 3 ten-thousands + 5 hundreds + 5 tens + 4 ones; $3 \times 10,000 + 5 \times 100 + 5 \times 10 + 4 \times 1$
7. Two hundred forty-five
8. Thirty thousand, eight hundred sixty-one **9.** 3602
10. 800,039
11.
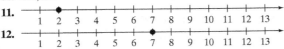
12.
13. True **14.** False **15.** Addends: 105, 119; sum: 224
16. Addends: 53, 21; sum: 74 **17.** 71 **18.** 54
19. 17,410 **20.** 70,642 **21. a.** Commutative property **b.** Associative property **c.** Commutative property
22. $403 + 79; 482$ **23.** $44 + 92; 136$ **24.** $36 + 7; 43$
25. $23 + 6; 29$ **26. a.** 96 cars **b.** 66 Fords
27. 45,797 thousand seniors **28.** 177 m
29. Minuend: 14; subtrahend: 8; difference: 6
30. Minuend: 102; subtrahend: 78; difference: 24
31. 26 **32.** 20 **33.** 121 **34.** 1090 **35.** 31,019
36. 34,188 **37.** $38 - 31; 7$ **38.** $111 - 15; 96$
39. $251 - 42; 209$ **40.** $90 - 52; 38$ **41.** 71,892,438 tons
42. $7,200,000 **43.** 2336 thousand visitors
44. 5,000,000 **45.** 9,330,000 **46.** 800,000
47. 1500 **48.** 13,000,000 people **49.** 163,000 m³
50. Factors: 32, 12; product: 384
51. Factors: 33, 40; product: 1320 **52. a.** Yes **b.** Yes
c. No **53.** c **54.** e **55.** d **56.** a
57. b **58.** 6106 **59.** 52,224 **60.** 3,000,000
61. $429 **62.** 7714 lb
63. 7; divisor: 6, dividend: 42, quotient: 7
64. 13; divisor: 4, dividend: 52, quotient: 13 **65.** 3
66. 1 **67.** Undefined **68.** 0
69. Multiply the quotient and the divisor to get the dividend.

70. Multiply the whole number part of the quotient and the divisor, and then add the remainder to get the dividend.
71. 58 **72.** 41 R7 **73.** 52 R3 **74.** $\frac{72}{4}$; 18
75. $9)\overline{108}$; 12 **76.** 26 photos with 1 left over
77. a. 4 T-shirts **b.** 5 hats **78.** 8^5 **79.** $2^4 \cdot 5^3$
80. 125 **81.** 256 **82.** 1 **83.** 1,000,000 **84.** 8
85. 12 **86.** 7 **87.** 75 **88.** 90 **89.** 15 **90.** 28
91. 55 **92.** 8 **93.** $89 **94.** 8 houses per month
95. a. The Cincinnati Zoo has 13,000 more animals than the San Diego Zoo. **b.** The San Diego Zoo has 50 more species than the Cincinnati Zoo. **96. a.** 21 mi **b.** 840 mi
97. He will receive $19,600,000 per year.
98. a. She should purchase 48 plants. **b.** The plants will cost $144. **c.** The fence will cost $80. **d.** Aletha's total cost will be $224.

Chapter 1 Test, pp. 92–93

1. a. Hundreds **b.** Thousands **c.** Millions
d. Ten-thousands **2. a.** 4,065,000 **b.** Twenty-one million, three hundred twenty-five thousand **c.** Twelve million, two hundred eighty-seven thousand **d.** 729,000 **e.** Eleven million, four hundred ten thousand
3. a. $14 > 6$ **b.** $72 < 81$ **4.** 129 **5.** 328
6. 113 **7.** 227 **8.** 2842 **9.** 447 **10.** 21 R9
11. 546 **12.** 8103 **13.** 20 **14.** 1,500,000,000
15. 336 **16.** 0 **17.** Undefined
18. a. The associative property of multiplication; the expression shows a change in grouping.
b. The commutative property of multiplication; the expression shows a change in the order of the factors.
19. a. 4900 **b.** 12,000 **c.** 8,000,000
20. There were approximately 1,430,000 people.
21. 4 **22.** 24 **23.** 48 **24.** 33
25. Jennifer has a higher average of 29. Brittany has an average of 28.
26. a. 442 thousand users **b.** The largest increase was between year 3 and year 4. The increase was 15,430 thousand.
27. The North Side Fire Department is the busiest with an average of five calls per week.
28. 156 mm **29.** Perimeter: 350 ft; area: 6016 ft²
30. 4,560,000 m²

Chapter 2
Chapter Opener Puzzle

3	5	6	ᴬ1	2	4
ᴮ1	2	3	ᶜ4	ᴰ6	ᴱ5
6	4	2	5	3	1
2	1	ᶠ4	6	5	3
ᴳ5	3	1	ᴴ2	4	ᴵ6
4	6	5	3	ᴶ1	2

SA-4   **Student Answer Appendix**

Section 2.1 Practice Exercises, pp. 102–106

1. a. fractions   **b.** numerator; denominator   **c.** proper
d. improper   **e.** mixed
3. Numerator: 2; denominator: 3
5. Numerator: 12; denominator: 11
7. $6 \div 1; 6$ **9.** $2 \div 2; 1$ **11.** $0 \div 3; 0$
13. $2 \div 0$; undefined   **15.** $\frac{3}{4}$ **17.** $\frac{5}{9}$ **19.** $\frac{1}{6}$ **21.** $\frac{3}{8}$
23. $\frac{3}{4}$ **25.** $\frac{1}{8}$ **27.** $\frac{41}{103}$ **29.** $\frac{10}{21}$ **31.** Proper
33. Improper   **35.** Improper   **37.** Proper
39. $\frac{5}{2}$ **41.** $\frac{12}{4}$ **43.** $\frac{9}{8}$ **45.** $\frac{7}{4}; 1\frac{3}{4}$ **47.** $\frac{13}{8}; 1\frac{5}{8}$
49. $\frac{7}{4}$ **51.** $\frac{38}{9}$ **53.** $\frac{24}{7}$ **55.** $\frac{29}{4}$ **57.** $\frac{137}{12}$
59. $\frac{171}{8}$ **61.** 19   **63.** 7   **65.** $4\frac{5}{8}$ **67.** $7\frac{4}{5}$
69. $2\frac{7}{10}$ **71.** $5\frac{7}{9}$ **73.** $12\frac{1}{11}$ **75.** $3\frac{5}{6}$ **77.** $44\frac{1}{7}$
79. $1056\frac{1}{5}$ **81.** $810\frac{3}{11}$ **83.** $12\frac{7}{15}$

85.
$$\frac{3}{4}$$
(number line from 0 to 1, point at $\frac{3}{4}$)

87.
$$\frac{1}{3}$$
(number line from 0 to 1, point at $\frac{1}{3}$)

89.
$$\frac{2}{3}$$
(number line from 0 to 1, point at $\frac{2}{3}$)

91.
$$1\frac{1}{6}$$
(number line from 0 to 2, point at $1\frac{1}{6}$)

93.
$$1\frac{2}{3}$$
(number line from 0 to 2, point at $1\frac{2}{3}$)

95. False   **97.** True

Section 2.2 Practice Exercises, pp. 111–113

1. a. factor   **b.** prime   **c.** composite   **d.** prime
3. $\frac{8}{12}; \frac{4}{12}$ **5.** $\frac{5}{4}; \frac{3}{4}$ **7.** $\frac{7}{12}$; proper   **9.** $4\frac{3}{5}$
11. For example: $2 \cdot 4$ and $1 \cdot 8$
13. For example: $4 \cdot 6$ and $2 \cdot 2 \cdot 2 \cdot 3$
15.

Product	36	42	30	15	81
Factor	12	7	30	15	27
Factor	3	6	1	1	3
Sum	15	13	31	16	30

17. A whole number is divisible by 2 if it is an even number.
19. A whole number is divisible by 3 if the sum of its digits
is divisible by 3.   **21. a.** No   **b.** Yes   **c.** Yes   **d.** No
23. a. No   **b.** No   **c.** No   **d.** No
25. a. Yes   **b.** Yes   **c.** No   **d.** No
27. a. Yes   **b.** No   **c.** Yes   **d.** Yes
29. Yes   **31.** Prime   **33.** Composite   **35.** Composite
37. Prime   **39.** Neither   **41.** Composite
43. Prime   **45.** Composite
47. There are two whole numbers that are neither prime
nor composite, 0 and 1.   **49.** False

51. 2, 3, 5, 7, 11, 13, 17, 19, 23, 29, 31, 37, 41, 43, 47
53. No, 9 is not a prime number.   **55.** Yes
57. $2 \cdot 5 \cdot 7$ **59.** $2 \cdot 2 \cdot 5 \cdot 13$ or $2^2 \cdot 5 \cdot 13$
61. $3 \cdot 7 \cdot 7$ or $3 \cdot 7^2$ **63.** $2 \cdot 3 \cdot 23$
65. $2 \cdot 2 \cdot 2 \cdot 7 \cdot 11$ or $2^3 \cdot 7 \cdot 11$ **67.** Prime
69. 1, 2, 3, 4, 6, 12   **71.** 1, 2, 4, 8, 16, 32
73. 1, 3, 9, 27, 81   **75.** 1, 2, 3, 4, 6, 8, 12, 16, 24, 48
77. No   **79.** Yes   **81.** Yes   **83.** No   **85.** Yes
87. No   **89.** Yes   **91.** No

Section 2.3 Practice Exercises, pp. 118–121

1. lowest   **3.** $5 \cdot 29$ **5.** $2 \cdot 2 \cdot 23$ or $2^2 \cdot 23$
7. $5 \cdot 17$ **9.** $3 \cdot 5 \cdot 13$
11. (circle diagram)   **13.** (rectangle diagram)
15. False   **17.** $\neq$ **19.** $=$ **21.** $=$
23. $\neq$ **25.** $\frac{1}{2}$ **27.** $\frac{1}{3}$ **29.** $\frac{9}{5}$ **31.** $\frac{5}{4}$ **33.** $\frac{4}{5}$
35. 1   **37.** 2   **39.** 1   **41.** $\frac{3}{4}$ **43.** 3   **45.** $\frac{7}{10}$
47. $\frac{13}{15}$ **49.** $\frac{77}{39}$ **51.** $\frac{2}{5}$ **53.** $\frac{2}{7}$ **55.** 0
57. Undefined   **59.** $\frac{3}{5}$ **61.** $\frac{3}{4}$ **63.** $\frac{5}{3}$ **65.** $\frac{21}{11}$
67. $\frac{17}{100}$ **69.** Heads: $\frac{5}{12}$; tails: $\frac{7}{12}$ **71. a.** $\frac{3}{13}$ **b.** $\frac{10}{13}$
73. a. Jonathan: $\frac{5}{7}$; Jared: $\frac{6}{7}$ **b.** Jared sold the greater
fractional part.   **75. a.** Raymond: $\frac{10}{11}$; Travis: $\frac{9}{11}$
b. Raymond read the greater fractional part.
77. a. 300,000,000   **b.** 36,000,000   **c.** $\frac{3}{25}$
79. For example: $\frac{6}{8}, \frac{9}{12}, \frac{12}{16}$ **81.** For example: $\frac{6}{9}, \frac{4}{6}, \frac{2}{3}$

Section 2.3 Calculator Connections, p. 121

83. $\frac{8}{9}$ **84.** $\frac{13}{14}$ **85.** $\frac{41}{51}$ **86.** $\frac{21}{10}$ **87.** $\frac{29}{30}$
88. $\frac{13}{7}$ **89.** $\frac{3}{2}$ **90.** $\frac{31}{19}$

Section 2.4 Practice Exercises, pp. 128–132

1. a. one-tenth   **b.** $\frac{1}{2}bh$
3. Numerator: 10; denominator: 14; $\frac{5}{7}$
5. Numerator: 25; denominator: 15; $\frac{5}{3}$ **7.**
9. (grid diagram)   **11.** $\frac{1}{8}$ **13.** 6   **15.** $\frac{3}{16}$ **17.** $\frac{14}{81}$
19. $\frac{24}{35}$ **21.** $\frac{8}{11}$ **23.** $\frac{24}{5}$ **25.** $\frac{65}{36}$ **27.** $\frac{2}{15}$ **29.** $\frac{5}{8}$

31. $\frac{35}{4}$　**33.** $\frac{8}{3}$　**35.** $\frac{4}{5}$　**37.** 8　**39.** 12　**41.** $\frac{30}{7}$

43. 10　**45.** $\frac{5}{3}$　**47.** $\frac{3}{8}$　**49.** 24　**51.** $\frac{1}{1000}$

53. $\frac{1}{1,000,000}$　**55.** $\frac{1}{81}$　**57.** $\frac{27}{8}$　**59.** 27　**61.** $\frac{1}{225}$

63. 2　**65.** $\frac{2}{9}$　**67.** 　**69.**

71. 44 cm^2　**73.** 32 m^2　**75.** 4 yd^2　**77.** $\frac{1}{4}$ cm^2

79. $\frac{195}{256}$ in.^{2}　**81.** 48 yd^2　**83.** 9 cm^2

85. The amount left is 10 gal.

87. Trey ate $\frac{1}{8}$ of the pizza for breakfast.

89. Corrine will prepare $4\frac{1}{8}$ lb.　**91.** 6,550,000

93. First place: $800; second place: $300; third place: $100

95. a. $\frac{1}{36}$　**b.** $\frac{1}{6}$　**97.** $\frac{1}{5}$　**99.** $\frac{8}{9}$　**101.** $\frac{1}{32}$

103. They are the same.

Section 2.5 Practice Exercises, pp. 138–141

1. reciprocals　**3.** $\frac{18}{5}$　**5.** 2　**7.** $\frac{5}{3}$　**9.** 1　**11.** 1

13. $\frac{8}{7}$　**15.** $\frac{9}{10}$　**17.** $\frac{1}{4}$　**19.** No reciprocal exists.

21. $\frac{1}{3}$　**23.** multiplying　**25.** $\frac{8}{25}$　**27.** $\frac{35}{26}$　**29.** $\frac{35}{9}$

31. 5　**33.** 1　**35.** $\frac{21}{2}$　**37.** $\frac{3}{5}$　**39.** $\frac{1}{4}$　**41.** 20

43. 16　**45.** $\frac{90}{13}$　**47.** 20　**49** $\frac{7}{2}$　**51.** $\frac{5}{36}$

53. 8　**55.** $\frac{2}{5}$　**57.** $\frac{40}{3}$　**59.** 2　**61.** $\frac{55}{56}$　**63.** $\frac{3}{2}$

65. $\frac{2}{3} \cdot 6$ multiplies $\frac{2}{3}$ by $\frac{6}{1}$, and $\frac{2}{3} \div 6$ multiplies $\frac{2}{3}$ by $\frac{1}{6}$.
So $\frac{2}{3} \cdot 6 = 4$ and $\frac{2}{3} \div 6 = \frac{1}{9}$.　**67.** $\frac{3}{7}$　**69.** $\frac{7}{6}$　**71.** $\frac{7}{32}$

73. $\frac{9}{400}$　**75.** 49　**77.** $\frac{7}{16}$　**79.** 18

81. Li wrapped 54 packages.　**83.** 24 cups of juice

85. The stack will be 12 in. high.

87. a. 27 commercials in 1 hr　**b.** 648 commercials in 1 day

89. a. Ricardo's mother will pay $16,000.
b. Ricardo will have to pay $8000.　**c.** He will have to finance $216,000.　**91. a.** She plans to sell $\frac{3}{4}$ acre.
b. She will keep $\frac{3}{2}$ or $1\frac{1}{2}$ acres.

93. She can prepare 14 samples.

95. 12 ft, because $30 \div \frac{5}{2} = 12$.　**97.** Less　**99.** More

Chapter 2 Problem Recognition Exercises, p. 142

1. a. $\frac{16}{5}$　**b.** $\frac{16}{5}$　**c.** $\frac{20}{9}$　**d.** $\frac{9}{20}$

2. a. $\frac{40}{7}$　**b.** $\frac{40}{7}$　**c.** $\frac{35}{18}$　**d.** $\frac{18}{35}$

3. a. $\frac{27}{2}$　**b.** $\frac{27}{2}$　**c.** $\frac{32}{3}$　**d.** $\frac{3}{32}$

4. a. 9　**b.** 9　**c.** 25　**d.** $\frac{1}{25}$

5. a. $\frac{25}{36}$　**b.** 1　**c.** 1　**d.** $\frac{25}{36}$

6. a. 0　**b.** 0　**c.** Undefined　**d.** 0

7. a. $\frac{8}{189}$　**b.** $\frac{7}{96}$　**c.** $\frac{2}{21}$　**d.** $\frac{21}{128}$

8. a. $\frac{7}{27}$　**b.** $\frac{7}{12}$　**c.** $\frac{3}{7}$　**d.** $\frac{27}{28}$

9. a. $\frac{27}{20}$　**b.** $\frac{108}{5}$　**c.** $\frac{3}{80}$　**d.** $\frac{3}{5}$

10. a. $\frac{2}{5}$　**b.** $\frac{1}{250}$　**c.** 160　**d.** $\frac{8}{5}$

11. a. $\frac{2}{3}$　**b.** $\frac{2}{3}$　**c.** $\frac{2}{3}$　**d.** $\frac{3}{2}$

12. a. $\frac{3}{5}$　**b.** $\frac{5}{3}$　**c.** 60　**d.** 60

13. a. 32　**b.** 2　**c.** 2　**d.** 32

14. a. $\frac{1}{14}$　**b.** $\frac{2}{7}$　**c.** $\frac{1}{14}$　**d.** $\frac{2}{7}$

15. a. $\frac{8}{3}$　**b.** 96　**c.** $\frac{1}{9}$　**d.** 144

16. a. $\frac{1}{6}$　**b.** $\frac{3}{8}$　**c.** $\frac{2}{9}$　**d.** $\frac{9}{8}$

Section 2.6 Practice Exercises, pp. 147–149

1. improper　**3.** $\frac{26}{9}$　**5.** $\frac{12}{11}$　**7.** $\frac{2}{9}$　**9.** $\frac{17}{5}$

11. $\frac{11}{7}$　**13.** $12\frac{5}{6}$　**15.** $9\frac{3}{4}$　**17.** $7\frac{2}{5}$　**19.** $1\frac{2}{3}$

21. 38　**23.** $27\frac{2}{3}$　**25.** $72\frac{1}{2}$　**27.** 0　**29.** $7\frac{1}{2}$

31. $2\frac{4}{25}$　**33.** $\frac{34}{55}$　**35.** $4\frac{5}{12}$　**37.** $2\frac{6}{17}$　**39.** 2

41. 0　**43.** 17　**45.** $4\frac{2}{3}$　**47.** $1\frac{3}{4}$

49. Tabitha earned $38.　**51.** $642\frac{1}{2}$ lb

53. a. 7 weeks old　**b.** $8\frac{1}{2}$ weeks old

55. a. Lucy earned $72 more than Ricky.　**b.** Together they earned $922.

57. 2　**59.** $5\frac{1}{3}$　**61.** $1\frac{4}{5}$　**63.** 0

65. $1\frac{1}{6}$　**67.** 0　**69.** $1\frac{1}{2}$　**71.** Undefined　**73.** $2\frac{5}{8}$

75. $2\frac{3}{8}$　**77.** The total cost is $168.

Section 2.6 Calculator Connections, p. 149

79. $318\frac{1}{4}$ **80.** $3\frac{1}{15}$ **81.** $17\frac{18}{19}$ **82.** $466\frac{1}{5}$

83. $2\frac{99}{146}$ **84.** $2\frac{404}{753}$ **85.** $480\frac{1}{8}$ **86.** $280\frac{5}{27}$

Chapter 2 Review Exercises, pp. 156–159

1. $\frac{1}{2}$ **2.** $\frac{4}{7}$ **3. a.** $\frac{5}{3}$ **b.** Improper

4. a. $\frac{1}{6}$ **b.** Proper   **5.** $\frac{7}{15}$ **6.** $\frac{23}{8}$ or $2\frac{7}{8}$ **7.** $\frac{7}{6}$ or $1\frac{1}{6}$

8. $\frac{43}{7}$ **9.** $\frac{57}{5}$ **10.** 17   **11.** $5\frac{2}{9}$ **12.** $1\frac{2}{21}$

13.–15.

16. $134\frac{3}{7}$ **17.** $60\frac{11}{13}$ **18.** 21, 51, 1200

19. 55, 140, 260, 1200   **20.** 58, 124, 140, 260, 1200
21. Prime   **22.** Composite   **23.** Neither
24. Neither   **25.** $2 \cdot 2 \cdot 2 \cdot 2 \cdot 2 \cdot 2$ or 2^6
26. $2 \cdot 3 \cdot 5 \cdot 11$ **27.** $2 \cdot 2 \cdot 3 \cdot 3 \cdot 5 \cdot 5$ or $2^2 \cdot 3^2 \cdot 5^2$
28. 1, 2, 3, 4, 6, 8, 12, 16, 24, 48
29. 1, 2, 4, 5, 8, 10, 16, 20, 40, 80   **30.** $\neq$ **31.** $=$

32. $\frac{1}{4}$ **33.** $\frac{2}{7}$ **34.** $\frac{3}{2}$ **35.** $\frac{7}{3}$ **36.** 1   **37.** 2

38. $\frac{4}{5}$ **39.** $\frac{7}{10}$ **40.** $\frac{14}{15}, \frac{1}{15}$ **41. a.** $\frac{3}{5}$ **b.** $\frac{2}{5}$

42. $\frac{6}{35}$ **43.** $\frac{32}{9}$ **44.** 63   **45.** 15   **46.** $\frac{1}{5}$ **47.** $\frac{12}{7}$

48. $\frac{1}{10,000}$ **49.** $\frac{1}{625}$ **50.** $\frac{1}{1000}$ **51.** $\frac{1}{17}$

52. $A = \frac{1}{2}bh$ **53.** $A = lw$ **54.** 51 ft^2

55. $\frac{10}{3}$ or $3\frac{1}{3}$ m^2 **56.** 40 yd^2

57. Maximus requires $\frac{7}{2}$ or $3\frac{1}{2}$ yd of lumber.
58. There are 900 African American students.
59. There are 300 Asian American students.
60. There are 300 Hispanic female students.
61. There are 750 Caucasian male students.

62. 1   **63.** 1   **64.** $\frac{2}{7}$ **65.** $\frac{1}{7}$

66. Reciprocal does not exist.   **67.** 6   **68.** $\frac{1}{5}$

69. multiplying   **70.** $\frac{16}{9}$ **71.** $\frac{7}{5}$ **72.** $\frac{1}{21}$ **73.** $\frac{1}{6}$

74. $\frac{8}{3}$ **75.** 14   **76.** $\frac{1}{64}$ **77.** $\frac{4}{5}$ **78.** $\frac{18}{5}$

79. $\frac{1}{52}$ **80.** $\frac{4}{5} \times 20$; 16   **81.** $18 \div \frac{2}{3}$; 27

82. 36 bags of candy   **83.** Amelia earned \$576.

84. The area is $\frac{640}{3}$ or $213\frac{1}{3}$ ft^2.

85. Yes. $9 \div \frac{3}{8} = 24$ so he will have 24 pieces, which is more than enough for his class.

86. $23\frac{7}{15}$ **87.** $23\frac{2}{3}$ **88.** 8   **89.** $22\frac{1}{2}$ **90.** 0

91. $1\frac{1}{2}$ **92.** $\frac{10}{11}$ **93.** $4\frac{1}{2}$ **94.** $2\frac{3}{11}$ **95.** $\frac{3}{5}$

96. 0   **97.** It will take $3\frac{1}{8}$ gal.

98. There will be 10 pieces.

Chapter 2 Test, pp. 159–160

1. a. $\frac{5}{8}$ **b.** Proper   **2. a.** $\frac{7}{3}$ **b.** Improper

3. $\frac{11}{2}$; $5\frac{1}{2}$

4. $\frac{7}{7}$ is an improper fraction because the numerator is greater than or equal to the denominator.

5. a. $3\frac{2}{3}$ **b.** $\frac{34}{9}$ **6.**

7.

8.

9.

10. a. Composite   **b.** Neither   **c.** Prime
d. Neither   **e.** Prime   **f.** Composite
11. a. 1, 3, 5, 9, 15, 45   **b.** $3 \cdot 3 \cdot 5$ or $3^2 \cdot 5$
12. a. Add the digits of the number. If the sum is divisible by 3, then the original number is divisible by 3.
b. Yes.   **13. a.** No   **b.** Yes   **c.** Yes   **d.** No   **14.** $=$

15. $\neq$ **16.** $\frac{10}{7}$ or $1\frac{3}{7}$ **17.** $\frac{6}{7}$

18. a. Christine: $\frac{3}{5}$; Brad: $\frac{4}{5}$

b. Brad has the greater fractional part completed.

19. $\frac{19}{69}$ **20.** $\frac{25}{2}$ or $12\frac{1}{2}$ **21.** $\frac{4}{9}$ **22.** $\frac{1}{2}$ **23.** $\frac{4}{15}$

24. $\frac{3}{4}$ **25.** $\frac{4}{35}$ **26.** $9\frac{3}{5}$ **27.** $\frac{13}{12}$

28. $\frac{44}{3}$ or $14\frac{2}{3}$ cm^2 **29.** $20 \div \frac{1}{4}$

30. 48 quarter-pounders
31. 5 dogs are female pure breeds.

32. They can build on a maximum of $\frac{2}{5}$ acre.

Chapters 1–2 Cumulative Review Exercises, pp. 160–161

1.

Mountain	Height (ft)	
	Standard Form	Words
Mt. Foraker (Alaska)	17,400	Seventeen thousand, four hundred
Mt. Kilimanjaro (Tanzania)	19,340	Nineteen thousand, three hundred forty
El Libertador (Argentina)	22,047	Twenty-two thousand, forty-seven
Mont Blanc (France-Italy)	15,771	Fifteen thousand, seven hundred seventy-one

2. 1430   **3.** 139   **4.** 214,344   **5.** 24   **6.** 1863
7. 18 R2   **8.** 120,000,000,000   **9.** 184   **10.** 6
11. 22   **12.** 16   **13.** 4   **14.** d   **15.** c   **16.** b
17. e   **18.** a   **19. a.** $\frac{4}{7}$ **b.** $\frac{7}{3}$ or $2\frac{1}{3}$
20. a. Proper   **b.** Improper   **c.** Improper
21. a. 1, 2, 3, 5, 6, 10, 15, 30   **b.** $2 \cdot 3 \cdot 5$
22. a. $\frac{12}{7}$ **b.** $\frac{2}{5}$ **23.** $\frac{119}{171}$ **24.** $\frac{5}{6}$
25. Yes. $\frac{8}{13} \cdot \frac{5}{16} = \frac{5}{26}$ and $\frac{5}{16} \cdot \frac{8}{13} = \frac{5}{26}$
26. Yes. $\left(\frac{1}{2} \cdot \frac{2}{9}\right) \cdot \frac{5}{3} = \frac{1}{9} \cdot \frac{5}{3} = \frac{5}{27}$ and
$\frac{1}{2} \cdot \left(\frac{2}{9} \cdot \frac{5}{3}\right) = \frac{1}{2} \cdot \frac{10}{27} = \frac{5}{27}$
27. $\frac{6}{25}$ **28.** $\frac{11}{9}$ or $1\frac{2}{9}$ m^2 **29.** 50 ft^2
30. $\frac{3}{40}$ of the students are males from out of state.

Chapter 3

Chapter Opener Puzzles

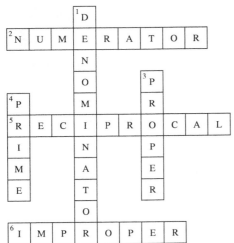

Section 3.1 Practice Exercises, pp. 167–170

1. like   **3.** 8 ft   **5.** 20 m   **7.** 7 fourths
9.   **11.** $\frac{13}{11}$ **13.** $\frac{9}{5}$ **15.** 1

17. $\frac{2}{3}$ **19.** $\frac{13}{10}$ **21.** $\frac{5}{2}$

23. Bethany has $\frac{5}{2}$ or $2\frac{1}{2}$ cups of bleach and water mixture.

25. 11 baskets   **27.** 6 fifths

29.

31. $\frac{3}{8}$ **33.** $\frac{3}{2}$ **35.** 2   **37.** $\frac{2}{3}$ **39.** $\frac{2}{5}$ **41.** $\frac{1}{4}$
43. $\frac{1}{4}$ g is left.   **45.** $\frac{3}{2}$ **47.** $\frac{12}{5}$ **49.** 1   **51.** $\frac{4}{5}$
53. $\frac{5}{2}$ **55.** $\frac{7}{4}$ **57.** $\frac{81}{100}$ **59.** $\frac{5}{3}$ **61.** $\frac{9}{5}$ **63.** $\frac{16}{7}$
65. $\frac{13}{3}$ **67.** $\frac{1}{3}$ **69.** $\frac{12}{7}$ or $1\frac{5}{7}$ m   **71.** $\frac{7}{2}$ or $3\frac{1}{2}$ in.
73. There was $\frac{1}{2}$ gal left over.   **75.** He used $\frac{3}{8}$ L.
77. a. Thilan walked $5\frac{1}{2}$ mi total.   **b.** He walked an average of $\frac{11}{12}$ mi per day.
79. Perimeter: 2 ft; area: $\frac{15}{64}$ ft^2
81. Perimeter: $\frac{70}{3}$ or $23\frac{1}{3}$ yd; area: $\frac{286}{9}$ or $31\frac{7}{9}$ yd^2
83. $\frac{3}{5} + \frac{2}{5}$; 1   **85.** $\frac{11}{15} - \frac{8}{15}$; $\frac{1}{5}$

Section 3.2 Practice Exercises, pp. 176–179

1. a. multiple   **b.** least common multiple
c. least common denominator
3. $\frac{1}{2}$ **5.** $\frac{5}{3}$ **7.** 6
9. a. 48, 72, 240   **b.** 4, 8, 12
11. a. 72, 360, 108   **b.** 6, 12, 9
13. 50   **15.** 48   **17.** 120   **19.** 72   **21.** 60
23. 75   **25.** 120   **27.** 210   **29.** 540   **31.** 60
33. 240   **35.** 180   **37.** 180
39. The shortest length of floor space is 60 in. (5 ft).
41. It will take 120 hr (5 days) for the satellites to be lined up again.

SA-8   Student Answer Appendix

43. $\frac{14}{21}$ **45.** $\frac{10}{16}$ **47.** $\frac{12}{16}$ **49.** $\frac{12}{15}$ **51.** $\frac{49}{42}$

53. $\frac{121}{99}$ **55.** $\frac{15}{39}$ **57.** $\frac{11,000}{4000}$ **59.** $\frac{15}{70}$ **61.** >

63. <   **65.** =   **67.** <   **69.** $\frac{7}{8}$ **71.** $\frac{2}{3}, \frac{3}{4}, \frac{7}{8}$

73. $\frac{1}{4}, \frac{5}{16}, \frac{3}{8}$ **75.** $\frac{13}{12}, \frac{17}{15}, \frac{4}{3}$

77. The longest cut is above the left eye. The shortest cut is on the right hand.

79. The greatest amount is $\frac{2}{3}$ lb of turkey. The least amount is $\frac{3}{5}$ lb of ham.

81. a and b

Section 3.3 Practice Exercises, pp. 186–188

1. a. is   **b.** is not   **3.** $\frac{12}{14}$ **5.** $\frac{14}{21}$ **7.** $\frac{25}{5}$ **9.** $\frac{8}{4}$

11. $\frac{80}{100}$ **13.** $\frac{5}{40}$ **15.** $\frac{19}{24}$ **17.** $\frac{1}{6}$ **19.** $\frac{1}{4}$ **21.** $\frac{83}{42}$

23. $\frac{27}{40}$ **25.** $\frac{1}{3}$ **27.** $\frac{25}{36}$ **29.** $\frac{5}{8}$ **31.** $\frac{25}{8}$ **33.** $\frac{8}{3}$

35. $\frac{17}{3}$ **37.** $\frac{2}{7}$ **39.** $\frac{89}{100}$ **41.** $\frac{1}{100}$ **43.** $\frac{391}{1000}$

45. $\frac{9}{8}$ **47.** $\frac{23}{60}$ **49.** $\frac{9}{16}$ **51.** $\frac{1}{36}$ **53.** $\frac{7}{12}$ **55.** $\frac{7}{3}$

57. $\frac{4}{3}$ **59.** $\frac{38}{35}$ **61.** $\frac{13}{125}$ **63.** $\frac{23}{24}$

65. Inez added $1\frac{1}{8}$ cups.

67. The storm delivered $\frac{5}{32}$ in. of rain.

69. The trough now holds the original amount of 5 gal.

71. a. $\frac{13}{36}$ **b.** $\frac{23}{36}$ **73.** $2\frac{3}{5}$ m

75. $a = \frac{3}{8}$ ft, $b = \frac{3}{8}$ ft; perimeter: 3 ft   **77.** b

Section 3.4 Practice Exercises, pp. 194–198

1. $\frac{19}{15}$ **3.** $\frac{13}{6}$ **5.** $\frac{24}{5}$ **7.** $\frac{1}{2}$ **9.** $7\frac{4}{11}$ **11.** $15\frac{3}{7}$

13. $15\frac{9}{16}$ **15.** $10\frac{13}{15}$ **17.** 5   **19.** 2   **21.** $3\frac{1}{5}$

23. $8\frac{2}{3}$ **25.** $14\frac{1}{2}$ **27.** $23\frac{1}{8}$ **29.** $19\frac{17}{48}$ **31.** $9\frac{7}{8}$

33. $42\frac{2}{7}$ **35.** $11\frac{3}{5}$ **37.** $2\frac{2}{15}$ **39.** $12\frac{1}{6}$ **41.** $2\frac{5}{14}$

43. $\frac{3}{3}$ **45.** $\frac{12}{12}$ **47.** $11\frac{1}{2}$ **49.** $1\frac{3}{4}$ **51.** $7\frac{13}{14}$

53. $3\frac{1}{6}$ **55.** $2\frac{7}{9}$ **57.** $2\frac{3}{17}$ **59.** $6\frac{5}{14}$ **61.** $7\frac{7}{24}$

63. $6\frac{2}{15}$ **65.** $\frac{11}{16}$ **67.** $9\frac{7}{36}$ **69.** $\frac{29}{32}$ **71.** $10\frac{20}{21}$

73. $\frac{32}{35}$ **75.** $7\frac{13}{72}$ **77.** $7\frac{3}{4}$ in.   **79.** The index finger is longer.   **81.** The total is $16\frac{11}{12}$ hr.   **83.** $3\frac{5}{12}$ ft

85. $\frac{1}{32}$ in.   **87.** The printing area width is 6 in.

89. There is $2\frac{5}{6}$ hr remaining.   **91.** The blinds will hang $\frac{1}{3}$ ft below the window.   **93. a.** $3\frac{3}{8}$ L   **b.** $\frac{5}{8}$ L

95. 4   **97.** $4\frac{1}{4}$

Section 3.4 Calculator Connections, p. 199

98. $\frac{211}{168}$ or $1\frac{43}{168}$ **99.** $\frac{11}{30}$ **100.** $\frac{37}{132}$ **101.** $\frac{137}{391}$

102. $\frac{2509}{54}$ or $46\frac{25}{54}$ **103.** $\frac{2171}{84}$ or $25\frac{71}{84}$ **104.** $\frac{402}{77}$ or $5\frac{17}{77}$

105. $\frac{213}{68}$ or $3\frac{9}{68}$

Chapter 3 Problem Recognition Exercises, pp. 199–200

1. a. $\frac{9}{5}$ or $1\frac{4}{5}$ **b.** $\frac{14}{25}$ **c.** $\frac{7}{2}$ or $3\frac{1}{2}$ **d.** 1

2. a. $\frac{10}{9}$ or $1\frac{1}{9}$ **b.** $\frac{8}{5}$ or $1\frac{3}{5}$ **c.** $\frac{13}{6}$ or $2\frac{1}{6}$ **d.** $\frac{1}{2}$

3. a. $\frac{17}{4}$ or $4\frac{1}{4}$ **b.** $\frac{5}{4}$ or $1\frac{1}{4}$ **c.** $\frac{11}{6}$ or $1\frac{5}{6}$ **d.** $\frac{33}{8}$ or $4\frac{1}{8}$

4. a. $\frac{221}{18}$ or $12\frac{5}{18}$ **b.** $\frac{26}{17}$ or $1\frac{9}{17}$ **c.** $\frac{3}{2}$ or $1\frac{1}{2}$ **d.** $\frac{43}{6}$ or $7\frac{1}{6}$

5. a. $\frac{29}{8}$ or $3\frac{5}{8}$ **b.** $\frac{3}{2}$ or $1\frac{1}{2}$ **c.** $\frac{32}{3}$ or $10\frac{2}{3}$ **d.** $\frac{35}{8}$ or $4\frac{3}{8}$

6. a. $\frac{11}{6}$ or $1\frac{5}{6}$ **b.** $\frac{5}{3}$ or $1\frac{2}{3}$ **c.** $\frac{17}{3}$ or $5\frac{2}{3}$ **d.** $\frac{22}{3}$ or $7\frac{1}{3}$

7. a. $\frac{53}{15}$ or $3\frac{8}{15}$ **b.** $\frac{73}{13}$ or $4\frac{13}{15}$ **c.** $\frac{14}{5}$ or $2\frac{4}{5}$ **d.** $\frac{63}{10}$ or $6\frac{3}{10}$

8. a. $\frac{25}{18}$ or $1\frac{7}{18}$ **b.** $\frac{50}{9}$ or $5\frac{5}{9}$ **c.** $\frac{7}{9}$ **d.** $\frac{43}{9}$ or $4\frac{7}{9}$

9. a. 1   **b.** $\frac{106}{45}$ or $2\frac{16}{45}$ **c.** $\frac{81}{25}$ or $3\frac{6}{25}$ **d.** $\frac{56}{45}$ or $1\frac{11}{45}$

10. a. 1   **b.** $\frac{58}{21}$ or $2\frac{16}{21}$ **c.** $\frac{40}{21}$ or $1\frac{19}{21}$ **d.** $\frac{49}{9}$ or $5\frac{4}{9}$

Section 3.5 Practice Exercises, pp. 205–208

1. $2\frac{6}{7}$ **3.** $12\frac{2}{9}$ **5.** $2\frac{2}{3}$ **7.** $3\frac{13}{36}$ **9.** $\frac{67}{13}$ **11.** $\frac{39}{10}$

13. $5\frac{4}{5}$ **15.** $1\frac{11}{19}$ **17.** $2\frac{1}{4}$ **19.** $3\frac{2}{3}$ **21.** $7\frac{1}{2}$ **23.** $4\frac{2}{7}$

25. 13   **27.** $\frac{13}{25}$ **29.** $1\frac{10}{27}$ **31.** 1   **33.** $1\frac{3}{7}$

35. a. The difference is $\frac{3}{10}$ sec.   **b.** The average is $3\frac{3}{5}$ sec.

37. a. The total weight loss is 51 lb.   **b.** The average is $8\frac{1}{2}$ lb.

c. The difference is $6\frac{1}{2}$ lb.   **39.** The stock dropped $3\frac{7}{8}$.

41. George will receive $26,750.

43. Each piece is $3\frac{13}{16}$ ft.   **45.** $2\frac{1}{4}$ lb of cheese was eaten.

47. 20 loaves can be made.   **49.** The new rate is $7\frac{1}{4}$ points.

51. Stephanie will need $11\frac{1}{4}$ yd for the dresses.

53. Wilma has $1\frac{1}{12}$ lb left.   **55.** Joan saves $152\frac{1}{2}$ gal.

57. She needs $15\frac{1}{3}$ ft more.   **59.** The perimeter is 100 in.

61. Matt needs $76\frac{1}{3}$ ft of gutter.

63. The area of the whole roof is $1022\frac{7}{16}$ ft².

65. a. The area is $247\frac{1}{2}$ m².   **b.** They will need 65 m.

67. $152\frac{3}{4}$ m²

Chapter 3 Review Exercises, pp. 213–215

1. 8 books   **2.** 18 cm   **3.** 12 mi   **4.** 11 CDs
5. Fractions with the same denominators are considered like fractions.
6. For example: like fractions: $\frac{4}{7}, \frac{2}{7}$; unlike fractions: $\frac{1}{9}, \frac{3}{16}$.

7. $\frac{3}{2}$ **8.** $\frac{2}{3}$ **9.** $\frac{1}{2}$ **10.** 1   **11.** $\frac{9}{7}$ **12.** 3

13. $\frac{3}{4}$ **14.** $\frac{20}{9}$ **15.** $\frac{11}{13}$ **16.** $\frac{1}{7}$ **17.** 12 in. or 1 ft

18. a. $\frac{28}{5}$ in.   **b.** $\frac{12}{5}$ in.
19. a. 7, 14, 21, 28   **b.** 13, 26, 39, 52   **c.** 22, 44, 66, 88
20. 6 and 8 have many common multiples including 24, 48, and 72. Of all the common multiples, 24 is the least.
21. a. 1, 2, 4, 5, 10, 20, 25, 50, 100   **b.** 1, 5, 13, 65
c. 1, 2, 5, 7, 10, 14, 35, 70   **22. a.** $2 \cdot 2 \cdot 5 \cdot 5$ **b.** $5 \cdot 13$
c. $2 \cdot 5 \cdot 7$ **23.** 150   **24.** 1584   **25.** 420
26. 96   **27.** They will meet on the 12th day.

28. $\frac{15}{48}$ **29.** $\frac{63}{35}$ **30.** $\frac{35}{60}$ **31.** $\frac{170}{150}$ **32.** $<$

33. $>$ **34.** $=$ **35.** $\frac{8}{15}, \frac{72}{105}, \frac{7}{10}, \frac{27}{35}$ **36.** $\frac{17}{24}$

37. $\frac{29}{100}$ **38.** $\frac{1}{25}$ **39.** $\frac{1}{2}$ **40.** $\frac{47}{11}$ **41.** $\frac{43}{20}$

42. $\frac{4}{15}$ **43.** $\frac{1}{34}$ **44.** $\frac{37}{1000}$ **45.** $\frac{17}{40}$ **46.** $\frac{12}{7}$

47. $\frac{1}{15}$ **48.** $\frac{3}{5}$ **49. a.** $\frac{35}{4}$ or $8\frac{3}{4}$ m   **b.** $\frac{315}{128}$ or $2\frac{59}{128}$ m²

50. a. $\frac{23}{3}$ or $7\frac{2}{3}$ yd   **b.** $\frac{7}{2}$ or $3\frac{1}{2}$ yd²   **51.** $11\frac{11}{63}$

52. $14\frac{7}{16}$ **53.** $2\frac{5}{8}$ **54.** $1\frac{11}{12}$ **55.** $3\frac{1}{24}$ **56.** $2\frac{8}{15}$

57. $12\frac{5}{14}$ **58.** $6\frac{3}{16}$ **59.** $3\frac{2}{5}$ **60.** $3\frac{3}{14}$ **61.** $63\frac{15}{16}$

62. $50\frac{1}{2}$ **63.** 8; $8\frac{5}{18}$ **64.** 11; $10\frac{14}{15}$ **65.** 50; $50\frac{9}{40}$

66. 23; $22\frac{71}{75}$ **67.** Corry drove a total of $8\frac{1}{6}$ hr.

68. Denise will have $\frac{7}{8}$ acre left.   **69.** $12\frac{2}{5}$ **70.** $1\frac{1}{4}$

71. $\frac{4}{27}$ **72.** 18   **73.** 12   **74.** $9\frac{1}{3}$
75. The appraised value is $144,000.
76. There are $1\frac{1}{4}$ lb of nuts in each bag.

Chapter 3 Test, p. 216

1. $\frac{7}{5}$ **2.** $\frac{1}{2}$ **3.** When subtracting like fractions, keep the same denominator and subtract the numerators. When multiplying fractions, multiply the denominators as well as the numerators.
4. a. 24, 48, 72, 96   **b.** 1, 2, 3, 4, 6, 8, 12, 24
c. $2 \cdot 2 \cdot 2 \cdot 3$ or $2^3 \cdot 3$

5. 240   **6.** $\frac{35}{63}$ **7.** $\frac{33}{63}$ **8.** $\frac{36}{63}$ **9.** $\frac{11}{21}, \frac{5}{9}, \frac{4}{7}$

10. $\frac{9}{16}$ **11.** $\frac{1}{3}$ **12.** $\frac{1}{3}$ **13.** $\frac{2}{3}$ **14.** $17\frac{3}{8}$

15. $2\frac{1}{11}$ **16.** $60\frac{5}{12}$ **17.** $1\frac{1}{2}$ **18.** $\frac{25}{6}$ or $4\frac{1}{6}$

19. 7   **20.** $\frac{12}{295}$ **21.** $\frac{10}{3}$ or $3\frac{1}{3}$ **22.** 1 lb is needed.
23. The Ford Expedition can tow 8950 lb.
24. Area: $25\frac{2}{25}$ m²; perimeter: $20\frac{1}{5}$ m
25. Justin has $10,500 for cabinets.
26. The difference is $4\frac{2}{3}$ ft.

Chapters 1–3 Cumulative Review Exercises, p. 217

1. Twenty-three million, four hundred thousand, eight hundred six
2. 96   **3.** 48   **4.** 1728   **5.** 3   **6.** 1,500,000,000
7. $4^2 \cdot 5^4 \cdot 8^2$ **8.** 36   **9.** 17, 19, 23, 29, 31
10. $2 \cdot 5 \cdot 7$ **11.** Numerator: 21; denominator: 17
12. $\frac{4}{16}$ or $\frac{1}{4}$ **13.** $\frac{17}{22}$ had pepperoni and $\frac{5}{22}$ did not have pepperoni.   **14. a.** Improper   **b.** Proper   **c.** Improper
15. b   **16. a.** Composite   **b.** Composite   **c.** Prime
17. $2 \cdot 2 \cdot 2 \cdot 3 \cdot 3 \cdot 5$ or $2^3 \cdot 3^2 \cdot 5$ **18.** $\frac{1}{5}$ **19.** $\frac{3}{8}$

20. $\frac{4}{7}$ **21.** $\frac{3}{4}$ **22.** $\frac{33}{16}$ **23.** $\frac{2}{5}$ **24.** $\frac{305}{22}$ or $13\frac{19}{22}$

25. $\frac{26}{17}$ or $1\frac{9}{17}$ **26.** $\frac{10}{3}$ or $3\frac{1}{3}$
27. The distance around is approximately 88 cm.
28. $4\frac{1}{3}$ yd   **29.** $7\frac{7}{8}$ m²   **30. a.** $2\frac{3}{10}$ **b.** $6\frac{4}{5}$

Chapter 4

Chapter Opener Puzzle

Mathematicians shop at the $\dfrac{d}{1}\dfrac{e}{2}\dfrac{c}{3}\dfrac{i}{4}\dfrac{m}{5}\dfrac{a}{6}\dfrac{l}{7}\dfrac{l}{8}$

Section 4.1 Practice Exercises, pp. 226–229

1. a. decimal

 b. tenths; hundredths; thousandths

3. 100   **5.** 10,000   **7.** $\dfrac{1}{100}$ **9.** $\dfrac{1}{10,000}$
11. Tenths   **13.** Hundredths   **15.** Tens
17. Ten-thousandths   **19.** Thousandths   **21.** Ones
23. Nine-tenths   **25.** Twenty-three hundredths
27. Thirty-three thousandths
29. Four hundred seven ten-thousandths
31. Three and twenty-four hundredths
33. Five and nine-tenths   **35.** Fifty-two and three-tenths
37. Six and two hundred nineteen thousandths
39. 8472.014   **41.** 700.07   **43.** 2,469,000.506
45. $3\dfrac{7}{10}$ **47.** $2\dfrac{4}{5}$ **49.** $\dfrac{1}{4}$ **51.** $\dfrac{11}{20}$ **53.** $20\dfrac{203}{250}$
55. $15\dfrac{1}{2000}$ **57.** $\dfrac{42}{5}$ **59.** $\dfrac{157}{50}$ **61.** $\dfrac{47}{2}$ **63.** $\dfrac{1191}{100}$
65. 34.2, 34.25, 34.29, 34.3   **67.** 0.042, 0.043, $\frac{4}{10}$, 0.42, 0.43
69. <   **71.** >   **73.** >   **75.** <   **77.** a, b
79. 0.3444, 0.3493, 0.3558, 0.3585, 0.3664
81. These numbers are equivalent, but they represent different levels of accuracy.
83. 7.1   **85.** 49.9   **87.** 33.42   **89.** 9.096
91. 21.0   **93.** 7.000   **95.** 0.0079   **97.** 0.0036 mph

	Number	Hundreds	Tens	Tenths	Hun-dredths	Thou-sandths
99.	971.0948	1000	970	971.1	971.09	971.095
101.	21.9754	0	20	22.0	21.98	21.975

103. 0.972

Section 4.2 Practice Exercises, pp. 235–239

1. b, c   **3.** b, c   **5.** 23.5   **7.** 8.603   **9.** 2.8300
11. 63.2   **13.** 8.951   **15.** 15.991   **17.** 79.8005
19. 31.0148   **21.** 62.6032   **23.** 100.414   **25.** 128.44
27. 82.063   **29.** 14.24   **31.** 3.68   **33.** 12.32
35. 5.677   **37.** 1.877   **39.** 57.368   **41.** 21.6646
43. 14.765   **45.** 159.558   **47.** 15.347   **49.** 6.581
51. 19.912   **53.** 10.3327   **55.** 5.9156   **57.** 9.001
59. a. 321.724 days   **b.** 156.73 days
61. a. The water is rising 1.7 in./hr.   **b.** At 1:00 P.M. the level will be 11 in.   **c.** At 3:00 P.M. the level will be 14.4 in.

63.

Check No.	Description	Payment	Deposit	Balance
				$ 245.62
2409	Electric bill	$ 52.48		193.14
2410	Groceries	72.44		120.70
2411	Department store	108.34		12.36
	Paycheck		$1084.90	1097.26
2412	Restaurant	23.87		1073.39
	Transfer from savings		200	1273.39

65. 1.35 million cells per microliter
67. The pile containing the two nickels and two pennies is higher.
69. $x = 8.9$ in.; $y = 15.4$ in.; the perimeter is 98.8 in.
71. $x = 2.075$ ft; $y = 2.59$ ft; the perimeter is 22.17 ft.
73. 27.2 mi   **75.** 7 mm

Section 4.2 Calculator Connections, p. 239

77. IBM decreased by $1.99 per share.
78. FedEx increased by $6.56 per share.
79. Between March and April, FedEx increased the most, by $6.36 per share.
80. Between February and March, IBM increased the most, by $3.04 per share.
81. Between January and February, FedEx decreased the most, by $2.78 per share.
82. Between January and February, IBM decreased the most, by $6.92 per share.

Section 4.3 Practice Exercises, pp. 245–247

1. front   **3.** 1000   **5.** 0.01   **7.** 0.4   **9.** 3.6   **11.** 8
13. 0.18   **15.** 17.904   **17.** 0.028   **19.** 100   **21.** 30
23. 0.07   **25.** 0.2   **27.** 37.35   **29.** 4.176
31. 4.736   **33.** 2.891   **35.** 114.88   **37.** 2.248
39. 0.00144   **41.** $(0.3)^2 = 0.09$, which is not equal to 0.9.
43. 0.0036   **45.** 6.25   **47.** 0.16   **49.** 1.69
51. 0.001   **53.** 0.0016   **55.** The decimal point will move to the right two places.
57. a. 51   **b.** 510   **c.** 5100   **d.** 51,000
59. The decimal point will move to the left one place.
61. 3490   **63.** 96,590   **65.** 0.933   **67.** 0.05403
69. 20.01   **71.** 0.00005   **73.** 324¢   **75.** 37¢
77. $3.47   **79.** $20.41   **81. a.** $1   **b.** $1.50
83. 2,600,000   **85.** 400,000   **87.** $20,549,000,000
89. a. 201.6 lb of gasoline   **b.** 640 lb of CO_2
91. The bill was $423.61.   **93.** $48.81 can be saved.
95. 0.00115 km^2 **97.** The area is 333 yd^2.
99. a. 0.09   **b.** 0.3   **101.** 0.1   **103.** 0.6

Section 4.4 Practice Exercises, pp. 255–258

1. a. repeating   **b.** terminating
3. 5280   **5.** 3.776   **7.** 2.02   **9.** 0.9   **11.** 0.18
13. 0.53   **15.** 21.1   **17.** 1.96   **19.** 0.035
21. 16.84   **23.** 0.12   **25.** 0.16   **27.** $5.\overline{3}$ **29.** $3.1\overline{6}$

31. $2.\overline{15}$　**33.** 503　**35.** 9.92　**37.** 56　**39.** 2.975
41. $208.\overline{3}$　**43.** 48.5　**45.** 1100　**47.** 42,060
49. The decimal point will move to the left two places.
51. 0.03923　**53.** 9.802　**55.** 0.00027
57. 0.00102　**59. a.** 2.4　**b.** 2.44　**c.** 2.444
61. a. 1.9　**b.** 1.89　**c.** 1.889
63. a. 3.6　**b.** 3.63　**c.** 3.626　**65.** 0.26　**67.** 14.8
69. 20.667　**71.** 35.67　**73.** 111.3
75. Unreasonable; $960　**77.** Unreasonable; $140,000
79. The monthly payment is $42.50.
81. a. 13 bulbs would be needed (rounded up to the nearest whole unit).　**b.** $9.75　**c.** The energy efficient fluorescent bulb would be more cost effective.
83. Babe Ruth's batting average was 0.342.
85. 2.2 mph　**87.** 47.265　**89.** b, d

Section 4.4 Calculator Connections, p. 258

91. 1149686.166　**92.** 3411.4045　**93.** 1914.0625
94. 69,568.83693　**95.** 95.6627907　**96.** 293.5070423
97. Answers will vary.　**98.** Answers will vary.
99. a. 0.37　**b.** Yes the claim is accurate. The decimal, 0.37 is greater than $0.\overline{3}$, which is equal to $\frac{1}{3}$.
100. 272 people per square mile
101. a. 1,600,000 mi per day　**b.** $66,666.\overline{6}$ mph
102. When we say that 1 year is 365 days, we are ignoring the 0.256 day each year. In 4 years, that amount is $4 \times 0.256 = 1.024$, which is another whole day. This is why we add one more day to the calendar every 4 years.

Chapter 4 Problem Recognition Exercises, p. 259

1. a. 223.04　**b.** 12,304　**c.** 23.04　**d.** 1.2304　**e.** 123.05
f. 1.2304　**g.** 12,304　**h.** 123.03
2. a. 6078.3　**b.** 5,078,300　**c.** 4078.3　**d.** 5.0783
e. 5078.301　**f.** 5.0783　**g.** 5,078,300　**h.** 5078.299
3. a. 7.191　**b.** 7.191　**4. a.** 730.4634　**b.** 730.4634
5. a. 52.64　**b.** 52.64　**6. a.** 59.384　**b.** 59.384
7. a. 86.4　**b.** 5.4　**8. a.** 185　**b.** 46.25
9. a. 80　**b.** 448　**10. a.** 54　**b.** 496.8
11. 1　**12.** 1　**13.** 4000　**14.** 6,400,000
15. 200,000　**16.** 2700　**17.** 1,350,000,000
18. 1,700,000　**19.** 4.4001　**20.** 76.7001

Section 4.5 Practice Exercises, pp. 265–268

1. 0.9　**3.** 0.141　**5.** $\frac{3}{5}$　**7.** $\frac{7}{20}$
9. 4.25　**11.** $\frac{4}{10}$; 0.4
13. $\frac{98}{100}$; 0.98　**15.** 0.28　**17.** 0.632　**19.** 0.875
21. 3.2　**23.** 5.25　**25.** 1.2　**27.** 0.75
29. 3.3125　**31.** 7.45　**33.** 0.88　**35.** $3.\overline{8}$
37. $0.4\overline{6}$　**39.** $0.52\overline{7}$　**41.** $0.\overline{54}$　**43.** $0.\overline{126}$
45. $1.1\overline{36}$　**47.** 0.143　**49.** 0.08　**51.** 0.9　**53.** 0.71
55. 1.2　**57. a.** $0.\overline{1}$　**b.** $0.\overline{2}$　**c.** $0.\overline{4}$　**d.** $0.\overline{5}$
If we memorize that $\frac{1}{9} = 0.\overline{1}$, then $\frac{2}{9} = 2 \cdot \frac{1}{9} = 2 \cdot 0.\overline{1} = 0.\overline{2}$, and so on.

59.

	Decimal Form	Fraction Form
a.	0.45	$\frac{9}{20}$
b.	1.625	$\frac{13}{8}$ or $1\frac{5}{8}$
c.	$0.\overline{7}$	$\frac{7}{9}$
d.	$0.\overline{45}$	$\frac{5}{11}$

61.

	Decimal Form	Fraction Form
a.	$0.\overline{3}$	$\frac{1}{3}$
b.	2.125	$\frac{17}{8}$ or $2\frac{1}{8}$
c.	$0.8\overline{63}$	$\frac{19}{22}$
d.	1.68	$\frac{42}{25}$

63.

Stock	Closing Price ($) (Decimal)	Closing Price ($) (Fraction)
McGraw-Hill	69.25	$69\frac{1}{4}$
Walgreens	44.95	$44\frac{19}{20}$
Home Depot	38.50	$38\frac{1}{2}$
General Electric	37.44	$37\frac{11}{25}$

65. =　**67.** <　**69.** >　**71.** <　**73.** =　**75.** <
77. $\frac{1}{10}, 0.\overline{1}, \frac{1}{5}$

79. $1.75, 1.\overline{7}, 1.8$

81. $\frac{9}{9} = 1$　**83.** 7

Section 4.6 Practice Exercises, pp. 274–277

1. a. $\frac{17}{20}$　**b.** 4.6　**3.** 313.72　**5.** $\frac{107}{27}$　**7.** $\frac{5}{4}$　**9.** 6.96
11. 6.25　**13.** 10　**15.** 8.77　**17.** 25.75　**19.** 2
21. 12.98　**23.** 4　**25.** 12.1　**27.** 67.35　**29.** 25.05
31. 23.4　**33.** 1.28　**35.** 10.83　**37.** 2.84
39. $0.93\overline{5}$　**41.** $4.4\overline{3}$

SA-12 **Student Answer Appendix**

43. a. 471 mi **b.** 62.8 mph
45. Jorge will be charged $98.75.
47. She has 24.3 g left for dinner.
49. Caren should get $4.77 in change.
51. Duncan's average is 78.75.
53. The average snowfall per month is 14.54 in.
55. Answers will vary.
57. a. 29.8 **b.** Overweight **59.** 3.475 **61.** 0.52

Section 4.6 Calculator Connections, p. 278

63. a. 237 shares **b.** $13.90 will be left over.
64. a. Approximately 921,800 homes could be powered.
b. Approximately 342,678 additional homes could be powered.
65. a. Marty will have to finance $120,000. **b.** There are 360 months in 30 yr. **c.** He will pay $287,409.60 **d.** He will pay $167,409.60 in interest.
66. a. Gwen needs to finance $94,000. **b.** There are 180 months in 15 yr. **c.** Gwen will pay $152,820.00. **d.** She will pay $58,820.00 in interest.
67. Each person will get approximately $13,410.10.
68. The average price is $110.28.

Chapter 4 Review Exercises, pp. 285–288

1. The 3 is in the tens place, 2 is in the ones place, 1 is in the tenths place, and 6 is in the hundredths place.
2. The 2 is in the ones place, 0 is in the tenths place, 7 is in the hundredths place, and 9 is in the thousandths place.
3. Five and seven-tenths **4.** Ten and twenty-one hundredths **5.** Fifty-one and eight thousandths
6. One hundred nine and one-hundredth **7.** 33,015.047
8. 100.01 **9.** $4\frac{4}{5}$ **10.** $\frac{1}{40}$ **11.** $\frac{13}{10}$ **12.** $\frac{27}{4}$
13. > **14.** < **15.** 4.3875, 4.3953, 4.4839, 4.5000, 4.5142
16. 89.92 **17.** 34.890
18. a. The amount in the box is less than the advertised amount. **b.** The amount rounds to 12.5 oz.
19. a, b **20.** b, c **21.** 49.743 **22.** 273.22 **23.** 5.45
24. 1.902 **25.** 197.96 **26.** 38.993 **27.** 7.809 **28.** 82.265
29. $x = 4.5$ in., $y = 5.07$ in.; the perimeter is 201 in.
30. a. Between days 1 and 2, the increase was $0.194.
b. Between days 3 and 4, the decrease was $0.209.
31. 3.74 in. **32.** 8.19 **33.** 74.113 **34.** 264.44
35. 346.5 **36.** 85,490 **37.** 100.34 **38.** 0.9201
39. 1.0422 **40.** 28,100,000 **41.** 432,000
42. a. Eight batteries cost $15.96 on sale. **b.** A customer can save $2.03. **43.** The call will cost $5.75.
44. Area = 940 ft²; perimeter = 127 ft
45. a. 7280 people **b.** 18,580 people **46.** 17.1
47. 42.8 **48.** $4.1\overline{3}$ **49.** $8.7\overline{6}$ **50.** 27 **51.** 0.03
52. 4.9393 **53.** 9.0234 **54.** 553,800 **55.** 260
56.

	$8.\overline{6}$	**$52.\overline{52}$**	**$0.\overline{409}$**
Tenths	8.7	52.5	0.4
Hundredths	8.67	52.53	0.41
Thousandths	8.667	52.525	0.409
Ten-thousandths	8.6667	52.5253	0.4094

57. 11.62 **58.** 11.97 **59. a.** $0.50 per roll **b.** $0.57 per roll **c.** The 12-pack is better.

60. $\frac{6}{10}$; 0.6 **61.** $\frac{35}{100}$; 0.35 **62.** $\frac{54}{1000}$; 0.054 **63.** 2.4
64. 3.52 **65.** 0.192 **66.** 0.4375 **67.** $0.58\overline{3}$ **68.** $1.52\overline{7}$
69. $4.3\overline{18}$ **70.** $0.\overline{153846}$ **71.** 0.29 **72.** 0.87 **73.** 3.67
74. 2.83 **75.** $\frac{2}{9}$ **76.** $1\frac{2}{3}$ **77.** $3\frac{1}{3}$ **78.** $5\frac{7}{9}$
79.

Stock	Closing Price ($) (Decimal)	Closing Price ($) (Fraction)
Ford	13.02	$13\frac{1}{50}$
Microsoft	30.50	$30\frac{1}{2}$
Citibank	4.37	$4\frac{37}{100}$

80. > **81.** = **82.** < **83.** 0.28 **84.** 0.713
85. 5 **86.** 125.6 **87.** 78.5 **88.** 25.12
89. $89.90 will be saved by buying the combo package.
90. Marvin must drive 34 mi more.

Chapter 4 Test, pp. 289–290

1. a. Tens place **b.** Hundredths place
2. Five hundred nine and twenty-four thousandths
3. $1\frac{13}{50}$; $\frac{63}{50}$ **4.** 0.4419, 0.4484, 0.4489, 0.4495
5. b is correct. **6.** 52.832 **7.** 21.29 **8.** 126.45
9. 5.08 **10.** 1.22 **11.** 12.2243 **12.** $120.\overline{6}$
13. 439.81 **14.** 4.592 **15.** 57,923 **16.** 8012
17. 0.002931 **18. a.** 61.4°F **b.** 1.4°F
19. a. 50,500,000 votes **b.** 51,000,000 votes **c.** The difference is approximately 500,000 in favor of Al Gore.
20. a. 67.5 in.² **b.** 75.5 in.² **c.** 157.3 in.²
21. He made $3094.75. **22.** She will pay approximately $37.50 per month. **23.** He will use 10 gal of gas.
24.

Year	Time in Seconds (Decimal)	Time in Seconds (Fraction)
1998	38.24	$38\frac{6}{25}$
2002	38.23	$38\frac{23}{100}$
2006	37.30	$37\frac{3}{10}$
2010	38.21	$38\frac{21}{100}$

25. $3.2, 3\frac{1}{2}, 3.\overline{5}$

26. 9.57 **27.** 47.25 **28. a.** 38.8 mi **b.** 5.5 mi/day

Chapters 1–4 Cumulative Review Exercises, pp. 290–291

1. 14　**2.** 4039　**3.** 4840　**4.** 3872　**5.** 2,415,000
6. Dividend: 4530; divisor: 225; whole-number part of the quotient: 20; remainder: 30　**7.** To check a division problem, multiply the whole-number part of the quotient and the divisor. Then add the remainder to get the dividend. That is, $20 \times 225 + 30 = 4530$.　**8.** The difference between sales for Wal-Mart and Sears is $181,956 million.

9. $\frac{6}{55}$　**10.** $\frac{4}{7}$　**11.** $\frac{49}{100}$　**12.** 2　**13.** $\frac{2}{3}$　**14.** 0

15. There is $9000 left.　**16.** $\frac{2}{5}$　**17.** $\frac{97}{100}$　**18.** $\frac{38}{11}$

19. $\frac{33}{7}$　**20.** $\frac{3}{2}$　**21.** Area: $\frac{15}{64}$ ft²; perimeter: 2 ft

22. The average is $1\frac{3}{16}$ km.　**23.** 174.13
24. 668.79　**25.** 75.275　**26.** 16　**27.** 339.12
28. 46.48　**29. a.** 3.75248　**b.** 3.75248　**c.** Commutative property of multiplication
30.

Bone	Length (in.) (Decimal)	Length (in.) (Mixed Number)
Femur	19.875	$19\frac{7}{8}$
Fibula	15.9375	$15\frac{15}{16}$
Humerus	14.375	$14\frac{3}{8}$
Innominate bone (hip)	7.5	$7\frac{1}{2}$

Chapter 5

Chapter Opener Puzzles

4	1	2	5	3
2	3	4	1	5
1	ᵃ2	5	3	ᶜ4
3	5	1	4	2
ᵈ5	4	ᵇ3	2	1

a. 20.25　**b.** 202.5　**c.** 0.2025　**d.** 2.025

Section 5.1 Practice Exercises, pp. 298–300

1. ratio　**3.** 5 : 6 and $\frac{5}{6}$　**5.** 11 to 4 and $\frac{11}{4}$

7. 1 : 2 and 1 to 2　**9. a.** $\frac{3}{2}$　**b.** $\frac{2}{3}$　**c.** $\frac{3}{5}$

11. a. $\frac{21}{52}$　**b.** $\frac{21}{31}$　**13.** $\frac{2}{3}$　**15.** $\frac{1}{5}$　**17.** $\frac{4}{1}$　**19.** $\frac{11}{5}$

21. $\frac{6}{5}$　**23.** $\frac{1}{2}$　**25.** $\frac{3}{2}$　**27.** $\frac{6}{7}$　**29.** $\frac{8}{9}$　**31.** $\frac{7}{1}$

33. $\frac{1}{8}$　**35.** $\frac{5}{4}$　**37.** $\frac{4}{11}$　**39. a.** $\frac{6}{16} = \frac{3}{8}$　**b.** $\frac{\frac{1}{2}}{1\frac{1}{3}} = \frac{3}{8}$

41. $\frac{1}{11}$　**43.** $\frac{10}{1}$　**45.** $\frac{15}{32}$　**47.** $\frac{20}{61}$　**49.** $\frac{2}{3}$

51. $\frac{1}{4}$　**53.** 13 units　**55. a.** 1.5　**b.** $1.\overline{6}$　**c.** 1.6

d. 1.625; yes　**57.** Answers will vary.

Section 5.2 Practice Exercises, pp. 304–307

1. a. rate　**b.** unit　**3.** 3 : 5 and $\frac{3}{5}$　**5.** $\frac{4}{3}$　**7.** $\frac{9}{17}$　**9.** $\frac{\$32}{5 \text{ ft}^2}$

11. $\frac{117 \text{ mi}}{2 \text{ hr}}$　**13.** $\frac{\$29}{4 \text{ hr}}$　**15.** $\frac{1 \text{ page}}{2 \text{ sec}}$　**17.** $\frac{65 \text{ calories}}{4 \text{ crackers}}$

19. $\frac{\$15}{2 \text{ trays}}$　**21.** a, c, d　**23.** 113 mi/day
25. 96 km/hr　**27.** $55 per payment　**29.** $0.69/lb
31. $256,000 per person　**33.** 14.3 m/sec
35. $0.219 per oz　**37.** $0.995 per liter
39. $52.50 per tire　**41.** $5.417 per bodysuit
43. a. $0.334/oz　**b.** $0.334/oz　**c.** Both sizes cost the same amount per ounce.
45. The larger can is $0.123 per ounce. The smaller can is $0.164 per ounce. The larger can is the better buy.
47. Coca-Cola: 3.25 g/fl oz; Mello Yello: 3.92 g/fl oz; Ginger Ale: 3 g/fl oz; Mello Yello has the greatest amount per fluid oz.
49. 130,000 platelets per microliter; Since the patient's platelet count is above 20,000 per microliter, the patient does *not* have a life-threatening condition.
51. 43,000 prisoners per year　**53. a.** $0.76 per month
b. $1.90 per month　**c.** IBM

Section 5.2 Calculator Connections, pp. 307–308

55. a. 9.9 wins/year　**b.** 8.6 wins/year　**c.** Shula
56. a. 2.1 wins/loss　**b.** 1.5 wins/loss　**c.** Shula
57. a. $0.38 per ounce　**b.** $0.18 per ounce
c. $0.19 per ounce; The best buy is Dial.
58. The unit prices are $0.181 per ounce, $0.280 per ounce, and $0.255 per ounce. The best buy is the 48-oz jar.
59. a. $0.401/oz　**b.** $0.167/oz
c. $0.322/oz; The best buy is the 12-oz can.
60. a. $0.062/oz　**b.** $0.023/oz; The case of twelve 12-fl-oz cans for $3.33 is the better buy.

Section 5.3 Practice Exercises, pp. 313–315

1. a. equation　**b.** proportion　**3.** $\frac{1}{15}$　**5.** $\frac{3 \text{ apples}}{1 \text{ pie}}$

7. $\frac{22 \text{ mi}}{3 \text{ gal}}$　**9.** $\frac{4}{16} = \frac{5}{20}$　**11.** $\frac{25}{15} = \frac{10}{6}$　**13.** $\frac{2}{3} = \frac{4}{6}$

15. $\frac{30}{25} = \frac{12}{10}$　**17.** $\frac{\$6.25}{1 \text{ hr}} = \frac{\$187.50}{30 \text{ hr}}$　**19.** $\frac{1 \text{ in.}}{7 \text{ mi}} = \frac{5 \text{ in.}}{35 \text{ mi}}$

21. No　**23.** Yes　**25.** Yes　**27.** Yes　**29.** Yes
31. Yes　**33.** No　**35.** Divide by 2　**37.** Divide by 5
39. Divide by 8　**41.** Divide by 0.6　**43.** Yes
45. No　**47.** $x = 4$　**49.** $x = 3$　**51.** $p = 75$
53. $n = 12$　**55.** $t = 12$　**57.** $y = 36$　**59.** $x = 3$
61. $m = \frac{15}{2}$ or $7\frac{1}{2}$ or 7.5　**63.** $k = 30$　**65.** $h = 2.5$
67. $x = 4$　**69.** $z = \frac{1}{80}$

Chapter 5 Problem Recognition Exercises, p. 315

1. a. Proportion; $\frac{15}{2}$ **b.** Product of fractions; $\frac{15}{32}$

2. a. Product of fractions; $\frac{3}{25}$ **b.** Proportion; 4

3. a. Product of fractions; $\frac{3}{49}$ **b.** Proportion; 4

4. a. Proportion; 2   **b.** Product of fractions; $\frac{6}{25}$

5. a. Proportion; 9   **b.** Product of fractions; 32

6. a. Product of fractions; 8   **b.** Proportion; $\frac{98}{5}$

7. a. 14   **b.** $\frac{5}{2}$ **c.** $\frac{3}{5}$ **d.** $\frac{18}{245}$

8. a. $\frac{3}{25}$ **b.** $\frac{3}{5}$ **c.** $\frac{16}{3}$ **d.** $\frac{112}{15}$

9. a. 4   **b.** $\frac{98}{5}$ **c.** $\frac{48}{35}$ **d.** $\frac{49}{25}$

10. a. 18   **b.** $\frac{29}{3}$ **c.** $\frac{11}{18}$ **d.** 22

Section 5.4 Practice Exercises, pp. 321–325

1. a. similar   **b.** proportional   **3.** =   **5.** ≠

7. $n = \frac{20}{3}$ or $6\frac{2}{3}$ or $6.\overline{6}$ **9.** $k = 6$ **11.** $y = 4.9$

13. Pam can drive 610 mi on 10 gal of gas.
15. 78 kg of crushed rock will be required.
17. The actual distance is about 80 mi.
19. There are 3800 male students.
21. Heads would come up about 315 times.
23. There would be approximately 3 earned runs for a 9-inning game.   **25.** Pierre can buy 684€.
27. 45 visits would be a result of falls.

29. $\frac{2}{3}$ cup of water   **31. a.** 195 e-mails   **b.** 585 min or 9.75 hr

33. 0.98 megabyte or 980 kilobytes   **35.** 29.08 in.
37. 252 mL of acid
39. There are approximately 357 bass in the lake.
41. There are approximately 4000 bison in the park.
43. $x = 24$ cm, $y = 36$ cm   **45.** $x = 1$ yd, $y = 10.5$ yd
47. $x = 15$ cm, $y = 4$ in.   **49.** The flagpole is 12 ft high.
51. The platform is 2.4 m high.   **53.** $x = 17.5$ in.
55. $x = 6$ ft, $y = 8$ ft   **57.** $x = 21$ ft; $y = 21$ ft; $z = 53.2$ ft

Section 5.4 Calculator Connections, p. 325

59. There were approximately 166,005 crimes committed.
60. The Washington Monument is approximately 555 ft tall.
61. Approximately 15,400 women would be expected to have breast cancer.
62. Approximately 295,000 men would be expected to have prostate disease.

Chapter 5 Review Exercises, pp. 330–332

1. 5 to 4 and $\frac{5}{4}$ **2.** 3 : 1 and $\frac{3}{1}$ **3.** 8 : 7 and 8 to 7

4. a. $\frac{2}{3}$ **b.** $\frac{3}{2}$ **c.** $\frac{3}{5}$ **5. a.** $\frac{4}{5}$ **b.** $\frac{5}{4}$ **c.** $\frac{5}{9}$

6. a. $\frac{12}{52}$ **b.** $\frac{12}{40}$ **7.** $\frac{4}{1}$ **8.** $\frac{7}{5}$ **9.** $\frac{2}{5}$ **10.** $\frac{1}{4}$

11. $\frac{9}{2}$ **12** $\frac{4}{13}$ **13.** $\frac{4}{3}$ **14.** $\frac{170}{13}$

15. a. This year's enrollment is 1520 students.   **b.** $\frac{4}{19}$

16. $\frac{19}{12}$ **17.** $\frac{1}{5}$ **18.** $\frac{24}{49}$ **19.** $\frac{4 \text{ hot dogs}}{9 \text{ min}}$

20. $\frac{2 \text{ mi}}{17 \text{ min}}$ **21.** $\frac{650 \text{ tons}}{9 \text{ ft}}$ **22.** $\frac{473 \text{ crimes}}{5000 \text{ people}}$

23. All unit rates have a denominator of 1, and reduced rates may not.   **24.** 33 mph   **25.** 4° per hour
26. 90 times/sec   **27.** 11 min/lawn   **28.** $0.599 per ounce
29. $6.667 per towel   **30. a.** $0.262/oz   **b.** $0.280/oz; The 32-oz bottle is the better buy.   **31. a.** $0.175/oz
b. $0.159/oz; The 44-oz jar is the better buy.
32. $0.499 per ounce   **33.** The difference is about 25¢ per roll or $0.25 per roll.   **34.** 0.6275 in./hr
35. a. There was an increase of 120,000 hybrid vehicles.
b. There will be 10,000 additional hybrid vehicles per month.
36. a. There was an increase of 63 lb.   **b.** Americans increased the amount of vegetables in their diet by 3.5 lb per year.

37. $\frac{16}{14} = \frac{12}{10\frac{1}{2}}$ **38.** $\frac{8}{20} = \frac{6}{15}$ **39.** $\frac{5}{3} = \frac{10}{6}$

40. $\frac{4}{3} = \frac{20}{15}$ **41.** $\frac{\$11}{1 \text{ hr}} = \frac{\$88}{8 \text{ hr}}$ **42.** $\frac{2 \text{ in.}}{5 \text{ mi}} = \frac{6 \text{ in.}}{15 \text{ mi}}$

43. No   **44.** Yes   **45.** Yes   **46.** No   **47.** Yes
48. No   **49.** No   **50** Yes   **51.** $x = 4$ **52.** $y = 27$
53. $b = 3$ **54.** $p = 2$ **55.** $h = 13.6$ **56.** $k = 0.9$
57. The human equivalent is 84 years.
58. Lavu can buy 42,750 yen.
59. Alabama had approximately 4,600,000 people.
60. The tax would be $6.96.   **61.** $x = 10$ in., $y = 62.1$ in.
62. The building is 8 m high.   **63.** $x = 1.6$ yd, $y = 1.8$ yd
64. $x = 10.8$ cm, $y = 30$ cm

Chapter 5 Test, pp. 332–333

1. 25 to 521, 25 : 521, $\frac{25}{521}$ **2. a.** $\frac{17}{23}$ **b.** $\frac{17}{6}$ **3.** $\frac{2}{15}$

4. $\frac{11}{6}$ **5.** $\frac{5}{8}$ **6. a.** $\frac{21}{125}$ **b.** $\frac{9}{125}$ **c.** The poverty ratio

was greater in New Mexico.   **7. a.** $\frac{\frac{1}{2}}{1\frac{1}{2}} = \frac{1}{3}$ **b.** $\frac{30}{90} = \frac{1}{3}$

8. $\frac{85 \text{ mi}}{2 \text{ hr}}$ **9.** $\frac{10 \text{ lb}}{3 \text{ weeks}}$ **10.** $\frac{1 \text{ g}}{2 \text{ cookies}}$

11. 21.45 g/cm^3 **12.** 2.29 oz/lb   **13.** $0.22 per ounce
14. $0.50 per ring   **15.** Generic: $0.044 per caplet; Advil: $0.179 capsule. The generic pain reliever is the better buy.
16. They form equal ratios or rates.

17. $\frac{42}{15} = \frac{28}{10}$ **18.** $\frac{20 \text{ pages}}{12 \text{ min}} = \frac{30 \text{ pages}}{18 \text{ min}}$

19. $\dfrac{\$15}{1\ \text{hr}} = \dfrac{\$75}{5\ \text{hr}}$ **20.** No   **21.** $p = 35$ **22.** $x = 12.5$
23. $n = 5$ **24.** $y = 6$ **25.** It will take 7.5 min.
26. Cherise spends 30 hr each week on homework outside of class.   **27.** There are approximately 27 goldfish in her pond.
28. $x = 1\frac{1}{2}\ \text{mi},\ y = 8\ \text{mi}$ **29.** 16 cm

Chapters 1–5 Cumulative Review Exercises, pp. 334–335

1. Five hundred three thousand, forty-two
2. Approximately 1400   **3.** 22,600,000   **4.** 22 R 3
5. 22.1875   **6.** 6   **7.**

8. $\dfrac{7}{5}$ **9.** $\dfrac{39}{14}$ **10.** $\dfrac{9}{25}$
11. Bruce has $4\frac{1}{2}$ in. of sandwich left.   **12.** 2   **13.** $\dfrac{35}{9}$
14. $\dfrac{9}{13}$ **15.** Emil needs $13\frac{1}{12}$ ft of wallpaper border.
16. It sold $61\frac{11}{16}$ acres, and $20\frac{9}{16}$ acres were left.
17. There are 59 ninths.   **18.** One thousand four and seven hundred one thousandths   **19.** 28.057
20. $\dfrac{109}{25}$ **21.** 4392.3   **22.** 2.379   **23.** 130.9 cm
24. $\dfrac{61}{44}$ or 61 : 44   **25.** $\dfrac{13}{1}$ **26.** $\dfrac{7}{50}$; Approximately 7 out of 50 deaths are due to cancer.   **27.** 125 people/mi^2
28. a. Yes **b.** No   **29.** $x = 4.5$
30. Jim can drive 100 mi on 4 gal.

Chapter 6
Chapter Opener Puzzle

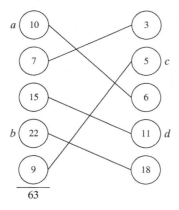

Section 6.1 Practice Exercises, pp. 343–345
1. percent   **3.** 48%   **5.** 50%   **7.** 25%   **9.** 2%
11. 70%   **13.** Replace the symbol % by $\times \dfrac{1}{100}$ (or $\div$ 100).
Then reduce the fraction to lowest terms.

15. $\dfrac{3}{100}$ **17.** $\dfrac{21}{25}$ **19.** $\dfrac{1}{4}$ **21.** $\dfrac{17}{500}$ **23.** $\dfrac{23}{20}$ or $1\frac{3}{20}$
25. $\dfrac{7}{4}$ or $1\frac{3}{4}$ **27.** $\dfrac{1}{200}$ **29.** $\dfrac{1}{400}$ **31.** $\dfrac{2}{3}$ **33.** $\dfrac{49}{200}$
35. Replace the % symbol by $\times$ 0.01 (or $\div$ 100).
37. 0.72   **39.** 0.66   **41.** 0.129   **43.** 0.4105
45. 2.01   **47.** 0.0075   **49.** 0.1625   **51.** 0.622
53. 25%   **55.** 100%   **57.** 150%   **59.** d   **61.** b
63. a   **65.** d   **67.** b   **69.** c   **71.** 0.076; $\dfrac{19}{250}$
73. 0.043; $\dfrac{43}{1000}$ **75.** 0.02; $\dfrac{1}{50}$ **77.** 0.35; $\dfrac{7}{20}$
79. 40% = 0.4 or $\dfrac{2}{5}$; 42% = 0.42 or $\dfrac{21}{50}$; 59% = 0.59 or $\dfrac{59}{100}$; 73% = 0.73 or $\dfrac{73}{100}$

Section 6.2 Practice Exercises, pp. 350–353
1. a. False **b.** True **c.** True   **3.** $\dfrac{13}{10}$ or $1\frac{3}{10}$
5. $\dfrac{1}{200}$ **7.** $0.06\overline{3}$ **9.** 0.003   **11.** 162%   **13.** 26%
15. 125%   **17.** 77%   **19.** 27%   **21.** 19%
23. 175%   **25.** 12.4%   **27.** 0.6%   **29.** 101.4%
31. 71%   **33.** 95%   **35.** 87.5% or $87\frac{1}{2}$%
37. 81.25% or $81\frac{1}{4}$%   **39.** $83.\overline{3}$% or $83\frac{1}{3}$%
41. $44.\overline{4}$% or $44\frac{4}{9}$%   **43.** 25%   **45.** 10%
47. $66.\overline{6}$% or $66\frac{2}{3}$%   **49.** 175%   **51.** 135%
53. $122.\overline{2}$% or $122\frac{2}{9}$%   **55.** $166.\overline{6}$% or $166\frac{2}{3}$%
57. 42.9%   **59.** 7.7%   **61.** 45.5%   **63.** 86.7%
65. The fraction $\frac{1}{2}$ = 0.5 and $\frac{1}{2}$% = 0.5% = 0.005.
67. 25% = 0.25 and 0.25% = 0.0025
69. a, c   **71.** a, c
73.

	Fraction	Decimal	Percent
a.	$\frac{1}{4}$	0.25	25%
b.	$\frac{23}{25}$	0.92	92%
c.	$\frac{3}{20}$	0.15	15%
d.	$\frac{8}{5}$ or $1\frac{3}{5}$	1.6	160%
e.	$\frac{1}{100}$	0.01	1%
f.	$\frac{1}{200}$	0.005	0.5%

75.

	Fraction	Decimal	Percent
a.	$\frac{7}{50}$	0.14	14%
b.	$\frac{87}{100}$	0.87	87%
c.	1	1	100%
d.	$\frac{1}{3}$	$0.\overline{3}$	$33.\overline{3}$% or $33\frac{1}{3}$%
e.	$\frac{1}{500}$	0.002	0.2%
f.	$\frac{19}{20}$	0.95	95%

77. 1.4 > 100%   **79.** 0.052 < 50%

Section 6.3 Practice Exercises, pp. 359–363

1. a. percent **b.** cross **3.** 130%

5. 37.5% or $37\frac{1}{2}$% **7.** 1% **9.** $\frac{1}{50}$ **11.** 0.82

13. 1 **15.** Yes **17.** No **19.** Yes

21. 45

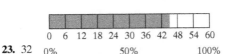

23. 32

25. Amount: 12; base: 20; $p = 60$ **27.** Amount: 99; base: 200; $p = 49.5$ **29.** Amount: 50; base: 40; $p = 125$

31. $\frac{10}{100} = \frac{12}{120}$ **33.** $\frac{80}{100} = \frac{72}{90}$ **35.** $\frac{104}{100} = \frac{21,684}{20,850}$

37. 108 employees **39.** 0.2 **41.** 560

43. Pedro pays $20,160 in taxes.

45. Approximately 219 of the 304 teens were not wearing seat belts. **47.** 36 **49.** 230 lb **51.** 1350

53. Albert makes $1600 per month. **55.** Amiee has a total of 35 e-mails. **57.** 35% **59.** 120% **61.** 87.5%

63. She answered 72.5% correctly. **65.** 20%

67. 26.7% **69.** 70 mm of rain fell in August.

71. Approximately 1900 freshmen were admitted.

73. Terry made approximately 36.5% of his three-point shots. **75. a.** 106 five-person households own dogs. **b.** 23 three-person households own dogs.

77. 73 were Chevys. **79.** There were 180 total vehicles.

81. $331.20 **83.** $11.60 **85.** $6.30

Section 6.4 Practice Exercises, pp. 368–371

1. Divide both sides of the equation by 26 to get $x = 2.5$.

3. $x = 9$ **5.** $x = 300$ **7.** $x = 825$ **9.** $x = 420$

11. $x = (0.35)(700); x = 245$

13. $(0.0055)(900) = x; x = 4.95$

15. $x = (1.33)(600); x = 798$

17. 50% equals one-half of the number. So multiply the number by $\frac{1}{2}$.

19. $2 \times 14 = 28$ **21.** $\frac{1}{2} \times 40 = 20$

23. There is 3.84 oz of sodium hypochlorite.

25. Marino completed approximately 5015 passes.

27. $18 = 0.4x; x = 45$ **29.** $0.92x = 41.4; x = 45$

31. $3.09 = 1.03x; x = 3$

33. There were 1175 subjects tested.

35. At that time, the population was about 280 million.

37. 13% **39.** 108% **41.** 0.5% **43.** 17%

45. $x \cdot 480 = 120; x = 25\%$

47. $666 = x \cdot 740; x = 90\%$

49. $x \cdot 300 = 400; x = 133.3\%$

51. 70% of the hot dogs were sold.

53. a. There are 80 total employees. **b.** 12.5% missed 3 days of work. **c.** 75% missed 1 to 5 days of work.

55. There were 35 million total hospital stays that year.

57. Approximately 12.6% of Florida's panthers live in Everglades National Park. **59.** 416 parents would be expected to have started saving for their children's education. **61.** The total cost is $2400. **63.** 15.6 min of commercials would be expected. **65.** 6,350,000 people ages 25–34 made over $10/hr. **67.** There is a total of 16,000,000 workers in the 16–24 age group.

69. a. 200 beats per minute. **b.** Between 120 and 170 beats per minute.

Chapter 6 Problem Recognition Exercises, p. 372

1. 8.2 **2.** 4.1 **3.** 16.4 **4.** 41 **5.** 164 **6.** 12.3

7. Greater than **8.** Less than **9.** Greater than

10. Greater than **11.** 3000 **12.** 24% **13.** 4.8

14. 15% **15.** 70 **16.** 36 **17.** 6.3 **18.** 250

19. 300% **20.** 0.7 **21.** 75,000 **22.** 37.5%

23. 25 **24.** 135 **25.** 100 **26.** 6000 **27.** 0.8%

28. 125% **29.** 2.6 **30.** 20 **31.** 75% **32.** 6.05

33. $133\frac{1}{3}$% **34.** 400%

Section 6.5 Practice Exercises, pp. 379–382

1. a. $\begin{pmatrix} \text{Sales} \\ \text{tax} \end{pmatrix} = \begin{pmatrix} \text{sales tax} \\ \text{rate} \end{pmatrix} \cdot \begin{pmatrix} \text{cost of} \\ \text{merchandise} \end{pmatrix}$

b. $(\text{Commission}) = \begin{pmatrix} \text{commission} \\ \text{rate} \end{pmatrix} \cdot \begin{pmatrix} \text{total} \\ \text{sales} \end{pmatrix}$

c. $(\text{Discount}) = \begin{pmatrix} \text{discount} \\ \text{rate} \end{pmatrix} \cdot \begin{pmatrix} \text{original} \\ \text{price} \end{pmatrix}$

d. $(\text{Markup}) = \begin{pmatrix} \text{markup} \\ \text{rate} \end{pmatrix} \cdot \begin{pmatrix} \text{original} \\ \text{price} \end{pmatrix}$

3. 12 **5.** 28 **7.** 26,000 **9.** 24% **11.** 8.8

	Cost of Merchandise	Sales Tax Rate	Amount of Tax	Total Cost
13.	$ 20.00	5%	$1.00	$ 21.00
15.	$ 12.50	4%	$0.50	$ 13.00
17.	$110.00	2.5%	$2.75	$112.75
19.	$ 55.00	6%	$3.30	$ 58.30

21. The total bill is $71.66. **23.** The tax rate is 7%.

25. The price is $44.50.

	Total Sales	Commission Rate	Amount of Commission
27.	$ 20,000.00	5%	$ 1000.00
29.	$125,000.00	8%	$10,000.00
31.	$ 5400.00	10%	$ 540.00

33. Zach made $3360 in commission. **35.** Rodney's commission rate is 15%. **37.** Her sales were $1,400,000.

39. Kabir's commission totaled $5810.00.

	Original Price	Discount Rate	Amount of Discount	Sale Price
41.	$175.00	15%	$ 26.25	$148.75
43.	$900.00	30%	$270.00	$630.00
45.	$110.00	30%	$ 33.00	$ 77.00
47.	$ 58.40	40%	$ 23.36	$ 35.04

49. a. The discount is $55.   **b.** The discounted yearly membership will cost $495.   **51.** The discount rate is 20%.
53. The set of dishes is not free. After the first discount, the price was 50% or one-half of $112, which is $56. Then the second discount is 50% or one-half of $56, which is $28.
55. The discount is $47.00, and the discount rate is 20%.

	Original Price	Markup Rate	Amount of Markup	Retail Price
57.	$ 92.00	5%	$ 4.60	$ 96.60
59.	$110.00	8%	$ 8.80	$118.80
61.	$325.00	30%	$ 97.50	$422.50
63.	$ 45.00	20%	$ 9.00	$ 54.00

65. a. The markup is $27.00.   **b.** The retail price is $177.00.
c. The total price is $189.39.   **67.** The markup rate is 25%.
69. The markup rate is 54%.

Section 6.6 Practice Exercises, pp. 385–387

1. a. $\left(\dfrac{\text{Percent}}{\text{increase}}\right) = \left(\dfrac{\text{amount of increase}}{\text{original value}}\right) \times 100\%$

b. $\left(\dfrac{\text{Percent}}{\text{decrease}}\right) = \left(\dfrac{\text{amount of decrease}}{\text{original value}}\right) \times 100\%$

3. a. The total price will be $68.25.   **b.** The total price with the 20% discount would be $54.60.   **c.** Damien will save $13.65.   **5.** Pablo's commission is $31.50.
7. Multiply the decimal by 100% by moving the decimal point 2 places to the right and attaching the % sign.
9. 5%   **11.** 12%   **13. a.** Increase   **b.** 11
15. a. Decrease   **b.** 10   **17 a.** Decrease   **b.** 9
19. a. Increase   **b.** 12   **21.** c   **23.** 75%
25. 100%   **27.** 10%   **29.** 3%   **31.** a   **33.** 5%
35. 68%   **37.** 25.3%   **39.** 15%

Section 6.6 Calculator Connections, p. 388

	Country	Population in 2005 (Millions)	Population in 2010 (Millions)	Change (Millions)	Percent Increase or Decrease
41.	Mexico	110.8	112.3	1.5	1.4% increase
42.	France	61.4	62.6	1.2	2.0% increase
43.	Bulgaria	8.11	7.78	0.33	4.1% decrease
44.	Trinidad	1.075	1.047	0.028	2.6% decrease

45. a. An increase of 6.35 million people   **b.** Between 2008 and 2009, there was a 71.2% increase in unemployment.
c. A decrease of 0.43 million people   **d.** Between 2009 and 2010, there was a 2.8% decrease in unemployment.
46. 8.7%

Section 6.7 Practice Exercises, pp. 394–396

1. a. Simple; principal   **b.** $I = Prt$ **c.** Compound
d. $A = P \cdot \left(1 + \dfrac{r}{n}\right)^{n \cdot t}$

	U.S. National Parks	Visitors in 2000 (Thousands)	Visitors in 2004 (Thousands)	Change	Percent Increase or Decrease
3.	Bryce Canyon, UT	1099	987	112	10% decrease
5.	Denali, AK	364	404	40	11% increase

7. $900, $6900   **9.** $1212, $6262   **11.** $2160, $14,160
13. $1890.00, $12,390.00   **15. a.** $350   **b.** $2850
17. a. $48   **b.** $448   **19.** $12,360   **21.** $5625
23. There are 6 total compounding periods.
25. There are 24 total compounding periods.
27. a. $560   **b.**

Year	Interest Earned	Total Amount in Account
1	$20.00	$520.00
2	20.80	540.80
3	21.63	**562.43**

29. a. $8960   **b.** $8998.91

Year	Interest Earned	Total Amount in Account
1	$320.00	$8320.00
2	332.80	8652.80
3	346.11	**8998.91**

c. $38.91
31. A = total amount in the account;
P = principal; r = annual interest rate;
n = number of compounding periods per year;
t = time in years

Section 6.7 Calculator Connections, p. 397

33. $6230.91   **34.** $14,725.49   **35.** $6622.88
36. $4373.77   **37.** $10,934.43   **38.** $9941.60
39. $16,019.47   **40.** $10,555.99

Chapter 6 Review Exercises, pp. 404–407

1. 75%   **2.** 33%   **3.** 125%   **4.** 50%   **5.** b, c
6. c, d   **7.** f   **8.** d   **9.** a   **10.** b
11. c   **12.** e   **13.** e   **14.** c   **15.** f   **16.** a
17. d   **18.** b   **19.** $\dfrac{21}{50}$; 0.42   **20.** $\dfrac{1}{5}$; 0.20
21. 0.0615   **22.** 0.0529   **23.** $\dfrac{183}{2000}$ **24.** $\dfrac{101}{2000}$
25. 17%   **26.** 44%   **27.** 80%   **28.** 175%
29. 12%   **30.** 110%   **31.** 0.5%   **32.** 40%
33. 87.5%   **34.** 76%   **35.** 60%   **36.** 10%

	Fraction	Decimal	Percent
37.	$\dfrac{9}{20}$	0.45	45%
38.	1	1	100%
39.	$\dfrac{3}{50}$	0.06	6%
40.	$\dfrac{6}{5}$	1.2	120%
41.	$\dfrac{9}{1000}$	0.009	0.9%
42.	$\dfrac{3}{4}$	0.75	75%

43. Amount: 67.50; base: 150; $p = 45$
44. Amount: 360; base: 3000; $p = 12$
45. Amount: 30.24; base: 144; $p = 21$
46. Amount: 31.8; base: 30; $p = 106$
47. $\dfrac{6}{8} = \dfrac{75}{100}$ **48.** $\dfrac{27}{180} = \dfrac{15}{100}$ **49.** $\dfrac{840}{420} = \dfrac{200}{100}$
50. $\dfrac{6}{2000} = \dfrac{0.3}{100}$ **51.** 6   **52.** 3.68   **53.** 12.5%
54. 0.32%   **55.** 39   **56.** 20
57. Approximately 11 people would be no-shows.
58. 850 people were surveyed.
59. Victoria spends 40% on rent.
60. There are 65 cars.   **61.** $0.18 \cdot 900 = x$; $x = 162$
62. $x = 0.29 \cdot 404$; $x = 117.16$
63. $18.90 = x \cdot 63$; $x = 30\%$
64. $x \cdot 250 = 86$; $x = 34.4\%$
65. $30 = 0.25 \cdot x$; $x = 120$
66. $26 = 1.30 \cdot x$; $x = 20$
67. The original price is $68.00.
68. Veronica read 55% of the novel.
69. Elaine can consume 720 fat calories.
70. a. 39,000,000   **b.** 80,800,000
71. The sales tax is $76.74.
72. The sales tax rate is 7%.
73. a. The tax is $7.22.   **b.** The tax rate is 8%.
74. The total amount for 4 nights will be $1053.00.
75. The commission rate was approximately 10.6%.
76. Andre earned $163 in commission.
77. Sela will earn $131 that day.
78. The commission rate is 3.5%.
79. The discount is $8.69. The sale price is $20.26.
80. The discount is $174.70. The final price is $1522.30.
81. The markup rate is 30%.
82. The baskets will sell for $59 each.
83. a. Increase   **b.** 25%   **84. a.** Decrease   **b.** 80%
85. 118.3%   **86.** 43.75%   **87.** 123%   **88.** 5233%
89. $1224, $11,424   **90.** $1400; $8400
91. Jean-Luc will have to pay $2687.50.
92. Kyle's brother will owe him $840.
93.

Year	Interest	Total
1	$240.00	$6240.00
2	249.60	6489.60
3	259.58	**6749.18**

94.

Compound Periods	Interest	Total
Period 1 (end of first 6 months)	$150.00	$10,150.00
Period 2 (end of year 1)	152.25	10,302.25
Period 3 (end of 18 months)	154.53	10,456.78
Period 4 (end of year 2)	156.85	10,613.63

95. $995.91   **96.** $2624.17   **97.** $16,976.32
98. $9813.88

Chapter 6 Test, pp. 408–409

1. 22%   **2.**

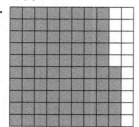

3. a. $0.054; \dfrac{27}{500}$ **b.** $0.0015; \dfrac{3}{2000}$ **c.** $1.70; \dfrac{17}{10}$
4. a. $\dfrac{1}{100}$ **b.** $\dfrac{1}{4}$ **c.** $\dfrac{1}{3}$ **d.** $\dfrac{1}{2}$ **e.** $\dfrac{2}{3}$ **f.** $\dfrac{3}{4}$ **g.** 1   **h.** $\dfrac{3}{2}$
5. $0.028; \dfrac{7}{250}$ **6.** $0.099; \dfrac{99}{1000}$
7. Multiply the fraction by 100%.   **8.** 60%
9. 0.4%   **10.** 175%   **11.** 71.4%
12. Multiply the decimal by 100%.   **13.** 32%
14. 5.2%   **15.** 130%   **16.** 0.6%   **17.** 36
18. 19.2   **19.** 350   **20.** 200   **21.** 90%   **22.** 50%
23. a. 730 mg   **b.** 98.6%   **24.** 390 m³   **25.** 420 m³
26. a. The amount of sales tax is $2.10.   **b.** The sales tax rate is 7%.
27. Charles will earn $610.
28. The discount rate of this product is 60%.
29. 29.6%   **30. a.** $1200   **b.** $6200   **31.** $31,268.76

Chapters 1–6 Cumulative Review Exercises, pp. 409–411

1. Millions place
2.

Country	Area (mi²)	
	Standard Form	Words
a. United States	3,539,245	Three million, five hundred thirty-nine thousand, two hundred forty-five
b. Saudi Arabia	830,000	Eight hundred thirty thousand
c. Falkland Islands	4,700	Four thousand, seven hundred
d. Colombia	401,044	Four hundred one thousand, forty-four

3. 3,488,200   **4.** 87   **5.** 3185   **6.** 11
7. a. Improper   **b.** Improper   **c.** Proper   **d.** Proper
8. $\dfrac{4}{3}$ or $1\dfrac{1}{3}$ **9.** 24   **10.** $\dfrac{3}{2}$ or $1\dfrac{1}{2}$ **11.** $\dfrac{2}{3}$
12. $\dfrac{15}{32}$ yd²   **13.** 9 km   **14.** $\dfrac{473}{1000}$ **15.** $15\dfrac{1}{10}$
16. $\dfrac{459}{2}$ or $229\dfrac{1}{2}$ in.²
17. a. 18, 36, 54, 72   **b.** 1, 2, 3, 6, 9, 18   **c.** $2 \cdot 3^2$
18. a. $\dfrac{5}{2}$ **b.** $\dfrac{5}{6}$ **19.** 0.375   **20.** $1.\overline{3}$ **21.** $0.\overline{7}$
22. 0.75   **23.** 65.3%   **24.** 42.1%   **25.** 0.085

26. 8500   **27.** 8.5   **28.** 850,000   **29.** $p = 20$
30. $p = 3.75$ **31.** $p = 6\frac{1}{2}$ **32.** $p = 27$

33. It will take $2\frac{1}{2}$ hr.

34. The unit price is $0.25 per ounce.
35. It will take about 7.2 min.
36. The DC-10 flew 514 mph.   **37.** 13%
38. a. 5 million   **b.** Approximately 0.045 million people per year or 45,000 people per year
39. Kevin will have $15,080.
40. There is $91,473.02 paid in interest.

Chapter 7

Chapter Opener Puzzle

Section 7.1 Practice Exercises, pp. 419–423

1. a. measure   **b.** conversion   **3.** 1 mi   **5.** 3 ft
7. $\frac{1}{3}$ yd   **9.** b   **11.** a   **13.** c   **15.** 6 ft   **17.** 72 in.
19. 10,560 ft   **21.** 8 yd   **23.** $\frac{3}{4}$ ft   **25.** $\frac{1}{3}$ mi   **27.** b
29. a   **31.** 3 yd   **33.** 42 in.   **35.** $2\frac{1}{4}$ mi   **37.** 18 ft
39. $4\frac{2}{3}$ yd   **41.** 563,200 yd   **43.** $4\frac{3}{4}$ yd   **45.** 72 in.
47. 50,688 in.   **49.** 0.2 mi   **51.** 101,376 in.
53. a. 128 in.   **b.** $10\frac{2}{3}$ ft   **55. a.** 3.5 ft   **b.** 42 in.
57. 10′8″   **59.** 12 ft   **61.** 8′6″   **63.** 1 ft 9 in.
65. 8 ft 10 in.   **67.** 28 ft   **69.** 3′2″   **71.** 6 ft 1 in.
73. $5\frac{1}{2}$ ft   **75.** 18 pieces of border are needed.
77. 50 ft 8 in. is needed.   **79.** The plumber used 7′2″ of pipe.   **81.** 7 ft is left over.   **83.** Each piece is 2 ft 3 in. long.   **85.** The total length is 46′.   **87.** 4 rolls
89. 6 yd^2 **91.** 3 ft^2 **93.** 720 in.^{2} **95.** 27 ft^2

Section 7.2 Practice Exercises, pp. 427–429

1. c

	Object	in.	ft	yd	mi
3.	Length of a hallway	144 in.	12 ft	4 yd	
5.	Height of a tree	216 in.	18 ft	6 yd	
7.	Perimeter of a backyard	1,800 in.	150 ft	50 yd	

9. 2 pt   **11.** 16 oz   **13.** 365 days   **15.** 4 qt   **17.** d
19. b   **21.** 730 days   **23.** $1\frac{1}{2}$ hr   **25.** 3 min   **27.** 3 days
29. 1 hr   **31.** 1512 hr   **33.** 80.5 min   **35.** 175.25 min
37. Gil ran for 5 hr 35 min.   **39.** The total time was 1 hr 34 min.   **41.** 2 lb   **43.** 4000 lb   **45.** 64 oz
47. $1\frac{1}{2}$ tons or 1.5 tons   **49.** 10 lb 8 oz   **51.** 8 lb 2 oz
53. 6 lb 8 oz   **55.** The total weight is 312 lb 8 oz.
57. The truck will have to make 2 trips.   **59.** 2 c
61. 24 qt   **63.** 16 c   **65.** $\frac{1}{2}$ gal   **67.** 16 fl oz   **69.** 6 tsp
71. Yes, 3 c is 24 fl oz, so the 48-fl-oz jar will suffice.
73. The unit price for the 24-fl-oz jar is about $0.112 per ounce, and the unit price for the 1-qt jar is about $0.103 per ounce; therefore the 1-qt jar is the better buy.

Section 7.2 Calculator Connections, p. 429

	Object	fl oz	c	pt	qt	gal
75.	Bottle of canola oil	32 fl oz	4 c	2 pt	1 qt	0.25 gal
76.	Can of soda	12 fl oz	1.5 c	0.75 pt	0.375 qt	0.09375 gal
77.	Laundry detergent	128 fl oz	16 c	8 pt	4 qt	1 gal
78.	Container of gasoline	640 fl oz	80 c	40 pt	20 qt	5 gal
79.	Bottle of Gatorade	16 fl oz	2 c	1 pt	0.5 qt	0.125 gal
80.	Container of orange juice	24 fl oz	3 c	1.5 pt	0.75 qt	0.1875 gal
81.	Bottle of spring water	8 fl oz	1 c	0.5 pt	0.25 qt	0.0625 gal
82.	Milkshake	16 fl oz	2 c	1 pt	0.5 qt	0.125 gal
83.	Jug of maple syrup	64 fl oz	8 c	4 pt	2 qt	0.5 gal

Section 7.3 Practice Exercises, pp. 434–438

1. a. metric   **b.** prefix   **c.** meter; m   **3.** 1.25 mi
5. 3 lb   **7.** 1440 min   **9.** 56 oz   **11.** b, f, g
13. 3.2 cm or 32 mm   **15.** 2.1 cm or 21 mm
17. a. 5 cm   **b.** 2 cm   **c.** 14 cm   **d.** 10 cm^2
19. a   **21.** d   **23.** d   **25.** $\frac{1 \text{ km}}{1000 \text{ m}}$ **27.** $\frac{1 \text{ m}}{100 \text{ cm}}$
29. $\frac{1 \text{ m}}{10 \text{ dm}}$ **31.** 2.43 km   **33.** 10.3 m   **35.** 50,000 mm
37. 4000 m   **39.** 43.1 mm   **41.** 0.3328 km

SA-20 **Student Answer Appendix**

43. 0.345 m **45.** 250 m **47.** 400.3 dm **49.** 0.007 cm
51. 2091 cm **53.** 2.538 km **55.** 0.27 km
57. No, she needs 1.04 m of framing. **59.** It will take
13 tiles. **61.** There can be 24 parking spaces.
63. 300 cm² **65.** 41,000 cm²

Section 7.4 Practice Exercises, pp. 443–447

1. a. gram; g **b.** liter; L **c.** cubic **d.** microgram

	Object	mm	cm	m	km
3.	Distance between Orlando and Miami	670,000,000	67,000,000	670,000	670
5.	Length of a screw	25	2.5	0.025	0.000025
7.	Thickness of a dime	1.35	0.135	0.00135	0.00000135

9. 0.539 kg **11.** 2500 g **13.** 33.4 mg **15.** 9 kg
17. 4.5 g

	Object	mg	cg	g	kg
19.	Bag of cat food	1,580,000	158,000	1580	1.58
21.	Can of tuna	170,000	17,000	170	0.17
23.	Box of raisins	425,000	42,500	425	0.425
25.	Dose of acetaminophen	325	32.5	0.325	0.000325

27. < **29.** = **31.** < **33.** Cubic centimeter
35. 3.2 L **37.** 700 cL **39.** 0.42 dL **41.** 64 mL
43. 40 cc

	Object	mL	cL	L	kL
45.	1 Tablespoon	15	1.5	0.015	0.000015
47.	Bottle of vinegar	355	35.5	0.355	0.000355
49.	Bottle of soda pop	2,000	200	2	0.002
51.	Capacity of a cooler	37,700	3,770	37.7	0.0377

53. c **55.** b **57.** c, d **59.** 11.2014 dm **61.** 0.6 g
63. 0.019 kL **65.** Stacy gets 9.45 g per week.
67. The price is $1.65 per liter. **69.** A 6-pack contains
4.26 L. **71.** 520 mg of sodium per 1-qt bottle
73. 5.25 g of the drug would be given in 1 wk. **75.** 2 mL
77. 500 people **79.** 9.6 mg **81. a.** 400 mg
b. 8000 mg or 8 g **83.** 10 mcg **85.** 200 mcg
87. 1 mg **89.** 3 mL **91.** 3.6 g **93.** 3.3 metric tons
95. 10,900 kg

Chapter 7 Problem Recognition Exercises, p. 447

1. 9 qt **2.** 2.2 m **3.** 12 oz **4.** 300 mL **5.** 4 yd

6. 6030 g **7.** $\frac{3}{4}$ ft **8.** 2640 ft **9.** 3 tons

10. 4 qt **11.** $\frac{1}{2}$ T **12.** 0.021 km **13.** 36 cc

14. 4 lb **15.** 4.322 kg **16.** 5000 mm **17.** 2.5 c
18. 8.5 min **19.** 0.5 gal **20.** 3.25 c **21.** 5460 g

22. 902 cL **23.** 16,016 yd **24.** 3 lb **25.** 3240 lb
26. 4600 m **27.** 2.5 days **28.** 8 mL

Section 7.5 Practice Exercises, pp. 453–456

1. a. Fahrenheit; 32; 212 **b.** Celsius; 0; 100
3. d, f **5.** b, e **7.** c, f **9.** b, g **11.** b
13. a **15.** 5.1 cm **17.** 8.8 yd **19.** 122 m
21. 1.1 m **23.** 15.2 cm **25.** 2.7 kg **27.** 0.4 oz
29. 1.2 lb **31.** 1980 kg **33.** 5.7 L **35.** 4 fl oz
37. 32 fl oz **39.** The box of sugar costs $0.100 per ounce,
and the packets cost $0.118 per ounce. The 2-lb box is the
better buy. **41.** 18 mi is about 28.98 km. Therefore the
30-km race is longer than 18 mi.
43. 97 lb is approximately 43.65 kg. **45.** The price is
approximately $7.22 per gallon. **47.** A hockey puck is
1 in. thick. **49.** Tony weighs about 222 lb.
51. 45 cc is 1.5 fl oz. **53.** 40.8 ft **55.** 77°F
57. 20°C **59.** 86°F **61.** 7232°F **63.** It is a hot day.
The temperature is 95°F.
65. In Italy, the Celsius scale is used. Converting 25°C to
Fahrenheit gives 77°F which would be a warm day.

67. $F = \frac{9}{5}C + 32 = \frac{9}{5} \cdot 100 + 32 = 9(20) + 32$
$= 180 + 32 = 212$ **69.** The Navigator weighs
approximately 2.565 metric tons. **71.** The average weight
of the blue whale is approximately 240,000 lb.

Chapter 7 Review Exercises, pp. 462–463

1. 4 ft **2.** 39 in. **3.** 3520 yd **4.** $1\frac{1}{4}$ mi

5. $1\frac{1}{3}$ mi **6.** 2640 ft **7.** 72 in. **8.** 0.1 mi

9. 9 ft 3 in. **10.** 6'4" **11.** 2'10" **12.** 3 ft 9 in.
13. 21' **14.** 9 ft 4 in. **15.** 2 ft 1 in. **16.** 3 yd 1 ft

17. $7\frac{1}{2}$ ft **18.** There is 102 ft or 34 yd of wire left.

19. 3 days **20.** 360 sec **21.** 80 oz **22.** 168 hr

23. $1\frac{1}{2}$ c **24.** 500 lb **25.** $1\frac{3}{4}$ tons **26.** 2.5 hr

27. 0.5 hr **28.** 16 pt **29.** $\frac{3}{4}$ lb **30.** 4 gal

31. 144.5 min **32.** The total weight was 11 lb 13 oz.

33. 375 lb will go to each location. **34.** There are $2\frac{1}{4}$ gal
of soda. **35.** b **36.** a **37.** c **38.** d
39. 520 mm **40.** 9.1 cm **41.** 2338 m **42.** 0.093 km
43. 3.4 m **44.** 0.21 dam **45.** 0.04 m **46.** 300 cm
47. 1200 mm **48.** 402.3 km **49.** The difference is
3688 m. **50.** 22.6 cm **51.** 610 cg **52.** 0.42 kg
53. 3.212 g **54.** 70 g **55.** 50 mg **56.** 100 cg
57. 0.3 L **58.** 240 L **59.** 8.3 L **60.** 124 cc
61. 22.5 cL **62.** 490 L **63.** Perimeter: 6.5 m; area:
2.5 m² **64.** 5 glasses can be filled. **65.** The difference
is 64.8 kg. **66.** No, the board is 25 cm too short.
67. a. 3.2 mg **b.** 44.8 mg **68.** 450 mcg
69. There is 1.2 cc or 1.2 mL of fluid left. **70.** Clayton
took 5 g. **71.** 15.75 cm **72.** 2.5 fl oz **73.** 5 oz
74. 5.26 cm **75.** 1.04 m **76.** 45 kg **77.** 74.53 mi
78. 5.7 L **79.** 45 cc **80.** 11,250 kg
81. The difference in height is 38.2 cm.
82. There are approximately 6.72 servings.

83. The total amount of cough syrup is approximately 0.42 L.
84. The marathon is approximately 26.2 mi.

85. $C = \dfrac{5}{9}(F - 32)$　　**86.** 82.2°C to 85°C

87. $F = \dfrac{9}{5}C + 32$　　**88.** 46.4°F

Chapter 7 Test, pp. 464–465

1. c, d, g, j　　**2.** f, h, i　　**3.** a, b, e　　**4.** $8\dfrac{1}{3}$ yd

5. 5.5 tons　　**6.** 10 mi　　**7.** 10 fl oz of liquid
8. 20 min　　**9.** 9′　　**10.** 4′2″　　**11.** He lost 7 oz.
12. 19 ft 7 in.　　**13.** 75.25 min　　**14.** 2.4 cm or 24 mm
15. c　　**16.** 1.158 km　　**17.** 15 mL　　**18. a.** Cubic
centimeters　**b.** 235 cc　**c.** 1000 cc　　**19.** 41,100 cg
20. 7 servings　　**21.** 2.1 qt　　**22.** 109 yd　　**23.** 2.8 mi
24. 2929 m　　**25.** 50.8 cm tall and 96.52-cm wingspan
26. 11 lb　　**27.** 190.6°C　　**28.** 35.6°F　　**29.** 28 mg
30. 1750 mcg per week

Chapter 7 Cumulative Review Exercises, pp. 465–466

1. a. 2000　**b.** 42,100　　**2.** 56 cm　　**3.** 180 cm²
4. 4　　**5. a.** Ford Motor Company spends the most. That
amount is $7400 million or $7,400,000,000.　**b.** The difference
between IBM and Motorola is $302 million or $302,000,000.
c. The total amount spent is $26,917 million or $26,917,000,000.

6. $\dfrac{6}{39}$　　**7.** The number 32,542 is not divisible by 3

because the sum of the digits (16) is not divisible by 3.
8. $2 \cdot 2 \cdot 3 \cdot 3 \cdot 3$　　**9.** 540 in.²
10. $\frac{1}{4}$ of the recipe would call for $\frac{3}{4}$ c of oatmeal. This is less
than 1 c so Keesha does have enough.　　**11.** 10

12. $\dfrac{7}{5}$　　**13.** $9\dfrac{1}{2}$　　**14.** $18\dfrac{8}{9}$　　**15.** $2\dfrac{6}{17}$　　**16.** $3\dfrac{5}{6}$

	Fraction	Decimal
17.	$\dfrac{1}{3}$	$0.\overline{3}$
18.	$\dfrac{9}{20}$	0.45
19.	$\dfrac{5}{4}$	1.25
20.	$\dfrac{7}{2}$	3.5
21.	$\dfrac{3}{8}$	0.375
22.	$\dfrac{1}{25}$	0.04

23. a. $\dfrac{6}{5}$　**b.** $\dfrac{6}{11}$　　**24.** 40 bottles　　**25.** 90 cars

26. 6.7 beds per nurse　　**27.** No　　**28.** 80%

29. $x = \dfrac{16}{3}$ yd　　**30.** 2290 trees　　**31.** 27 people

32. 6%　　**33.** $15,000 in sales　　**34.** $1020 in interest
35. 5.8 kg　　**36.** 12.9 lb　　**37.** 182.9 cm　　**38.** 6 ft
39. 7 pt　　**40.** 3.3 L

Chapter 8

Chapter Opener Puzzles

1. e　　**2.** d　　**3.** c　　**4.** a　　**5.** f　　**6.** b

Section 8.1 Practice Exercises, pp. 473–477

1. a. point　**b.** line　**c.** segment　**d.** $P; Q$　**e.** angle;
vertex　**f.** right; 180　**g.** protractor　**h.** acute; obtuse
i. complementary; supplementary　**j.** parallel
k. perpendicular
3. A line extends forever in both directions. A line
segment is a portion of a line between and including two
endpoints.　**5.** Ray　**7.** Point　**9.** Line
11. For example:

$$X \quad Y \qquad Y \quad X$$
$$\bullet\!-\!\!-\!\!-\!\bullet\ \text{or}\ \bullet\!-\!\!-\!\!-\!\bullet$$

13. For example:　　　　　　　　　　**15.**

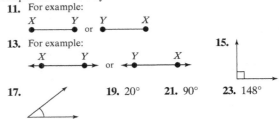

17.　　　　**19.** 20°　　**21.** 90°　　**23.** 148°

25. Right　　**27.** Obtuse　　**29.** Acute　　**31.** Straight
33. 10°　　**35.** 63°　　**37.** 60.5°　　**39.** 1°　　**41.** 100°
43. 53°　　**45.** 142.6°　　**47.** 1°
49. No, because the sum of two angles that are both greater
than 90° will be more than 180°.
51. Yes. For two angles to add to 90°, the angles themselves
must both be less than 90°.　　**53.** A 90° angle
55.　　　　　　　　　　　**57.**

59. $m(\angle a) = 41°; m(\angle b) = 139°; m(\angle c) = 139°$
61. $m(\angle a) = 26°; m(\angle b) = 112°;$
$m(\angle c) = 26°; m(\angle d) = 42°$
63. The two lines are perpendicular.　　**65.** Vertical angles
67. a, c or b, h or e, g or f, d　　**69.** a, e or f, b
71. $m(\angle a) = 55°; m(\angle b) = 125°;$
$\quad m(\angle c) = 55°; m(\angle d) = 55°;$
$\quad m(\angle e) = 125°; m(\angle f) = 55°;$
$\quad m(\angle g) = 125°$
73. $m(\angle a) = 120°; m(\angle b) = 60°; m(\angle c) = 120°;$
$\quad m(\angle d) = 120°; m(\angle e) = 60°; m(\angle f) = 120°;$
$\quad m(\angle g) = 60°$
75. True　　**77.** True　　**79.** False　　**81.** True
83. True　　**85.** 70°　　**87.** 90°　　**89. a.** 48°　**b.** 48°
c. 132°　　**91.** 180°　　**93.** 120°

Section 8.2 Practice Exercises, pp. 482–485

1. a. 180　**b.** acute; right; obtuse　**c.** equilateral
d. isosceles　**e.** scalene　**f.** hypotenuse; legs
g. Pythagorean; c^2
3. Yes　　**5.** No　　**7.** No　　**9.** $m(\angle a) = 54°$
11. $m(\angle b) = 78°$　　**13.** $m(\angle a) = 60°, m(\angle b) = 80°$
15. $m(\angle a) = 40°, m(\angle b) = 72°$　　**17.** c, f　　**19.** b, d
21. b, c, e　　**23.** 7　　**25.** 49　　**27.** 16　　**29.** 4
31. 6　　**33.** 36　　**35.** 81　　**37.** 9　　**39.** $c = 5$ m
41. $b = 12$ yd　　**43.** Leg = 10 ft

45. Hypotenuse = 40 in.   **47.** The brace is 20 in. long.
49. The height is 9 km.
51. The car is 25 mi from the starting point.
53. 24 m   **55.** 30 km
57. $c = 5$ in.; perimeter = 28 in.   **59.** Perimeter = 72 ft

Section 8.2 Calculator Connections, pp. 486–487

	Square Root	Estimate	Calculator Approximation (Round to 3 Decimal Places)
	$\sqrt{50}$	is between 7 and 8	7.071
61.	$\sqrt{10}$	is between 3 and 4	3.162
62.	$\sqrt{90}$	is between 9 and 10	9.487
63.	$\sqrt{116}$	is between 10 and 11	10.770
64.	$\sqrt{65}$	is between 8 and 9	8.062
65.	$\sqrt{5}$	is between 2 and 3	2.236
66.	$\sqrt{48}$	is between 6 and 7	6.928

67. 20.682   **68.** 56.434   **69.** 1116.244   **70.** 7100.423
71. 0.7   **72.** 0.5   **73.** 0.748   **74.** 0.906
75. $b = 21$ ft   **76.** $a = 16$ cm
77. Hypotenuse = 11.180 mi
78. Hypotenuse = 8.246 m   **79.** Leg = 18.439 in.
80. Leg = 9.950 ft   **81.** The diagonal length is 1.41 ft.
82. The length of the diagonal is 134.16 ft.
83. The length of the diagonal is 35.36 ft.

Section 8.3 Practice Exercises, pp. 494–498

1. a. perimeter   **b.** area
3. a. acute triangle   **b.** scalene triangle
5. a. right triangle   **b.** isosceles triangle
7. a. obtuse triangle   **b.** isosceles triangle
9. a, b, c, d, e, h   **11.** a, b, e   **13.** a, b, e, h
15. 80 cm   **17.** 260 mm   **19.** 10.7 m
21. 10 ft 6 in.   **23.** 5 ft or 60 in.
25. $x = 550$ mm; $y = 3$ dm; perimeter = 26 dm or 2600 mm
27. 280 ft of rain gutters is needed.   **29.** 576 yd^2
31. 54 m^2 **33.** 656 in.^{2} **35.** 18.4 ft^2 **37.** 12.375 ft^2
39. 148.5 yd^2 **41.** 280 mm^2 **43.** 60 in.^{2}
45. The area to be carpeted is 382.5 ft^2. The area to be tiled is 13.5 ft^2.   **47.** The area of the sign is 16.5 yd^2.
49. a. The area is 483 ft^2.   **b.** They will need 2 paint kits.
51. The area is increased by 9 times.
53. False   **55.** True

Section 8.4 Practice Exercises, pp. 503–506

1. a. radius   **b.** diameter   **c.** circumference
d. diameter   **e.** 3.14; $\frac{22}{7}$ **f.** Either formula can be used.
3. 1260 cm^2 **5.** 630 cm^2
7. Yes. Since a rectangle is a special type of parallelogram (one that contains four right angles), the area formula for a parallelogram applies to a rectangle.
9. 12 in.   **11.** 3 m   **13.** 4 in.   **15.** 8.3 m   **17.** c
19. π is the circumference divided by the diameter. That is, $\pi = \frac{C}{d}$.   **21. a.** 4π m   **b.** 12.56 m

23. a. 20π cm   **b.** 62.8 cm   **25. a.** 4.2π cm   **b.** 13.188 cm
27. a. 5π km   **b.** 15.7 km   **29.** 18.84 cm   **31.** 14.13 in.
33. 6.908 cm   **35. a.** 49π m^2 **b.** 154 m^2
37. a. 441π in.^{2} **b.** 1386 in.^{2}
39. a. 156.25π mm^2 **b.** 491 mm^2
41. a. 38.44π ft^2 **b.** 121 ft^2 **43.** 2.72 ft^2
45. 55.04 in.^{2} **47.** 18.28 in.^{2} **49.** 113.04 mm^2
51. 222.39 in.^{2} **53.** 16.642 mi   **55.** 2826 ft^2
57. a. ≈ 804 mi^2 **b.** ≈ 79 mi^2
59. a. 81.64 in.   **b.** 147 times   **61. a.** 21 in.   **b.** 43.8 ft

Section 8.4 Calculator Connections, p. 507

62. Area ≈ 517.1341 cm^2; circumference ≈ 80.6133 cm
63. Area ≈ 81.7128 ft^2; circumference ≈ 32.0442 ft
64. Area ≈ 70.8822 in.^{2}; circumference ≈ 29.8451 in.
65. Area ≈ 8371.1644 mm^2; circumference ≈ 324.3380 mm
66.

Diameter	Cost	Area	Cost per in.^{2}
8 in.	$ 6.50	50.27 in.^{2}	$ 0.129
12 in.	12.40	113.10 in.^{2}	0.110

The 12-in. is the better buy.

Chapter 8 Problem Recognition Exercises, p. 508

1. Area = 25 ft^2; perimeter = 20 ft
2. Area = 144 m^2; perimeter = 48 m
3. Area = 12 m^2 or 120,000 cm^2; perimeter 14 m or 1400 cm   **4.** Area = 1ft^2 or 144 in.^{2}; perimeter = 5 ft or 60 in.   **5.** Area = $\frac{1}{3}$ yd^2 or 3 ft^2; perimeter = 3 yd or 9 ft
6. Area = 0.473 km^2 or 473,000 m^2; perimeter = 3.24 km or 3240 m   **7.** Area = 6 yd^2; perimeter = 12 yd
8. Area = 30 cm^2; perimeter = 30 cm
9. Area = 44 m^2; perimeter = 32 m
10. Area = 88 in.^{2}; perimeter = 40 in.
11. Area ≈ 28.26 yd^2; circumference ≈ 18.84 yd
12. Area ≈ 1256 cm^2; circumference ≈ 125.6 cm
13. Area ≈ 154 cm^2; circumference ≈ 44 cm
14. Area ≈ 616 ft^2; circumference ≈ 88 ft
15. Area ≈ 38.28 ft^2; perimeter ≈ 26.28 ft

Section 8.5 Practice Exercises, pp. 513–517

1. a. s^3 **b.** lwh **c.** $\pi r^2 h$ **d.** cone; sphere
3. $C \approx 25.12$ in; $A \approx 50.24$ in.^{2} **5.** 187.52 cm^2
7. b, d   **9.** Area = 1 ft^2; volume = 1 ft^3
11. Area = 1 km^2; volume = 1 km^3 **13.** 2.744 cm^3
15. 48 ft^3 **17.** 12.56 mm^3 **19.** 3052.08 yd^3
21. 235.5 cm^3 **23.** 452.16 ft^3 **25.** 289 in.^{3}
27. 314 ft^3 **29.** 10 ft^3 **31. a.** 2575 ft^3 **b.** 19,260 gal
33. 502 mm^3 **35.** 32 ft^3 **37.** 56 in.^{3}
39. $\frac{11}{36}$ ft^3 or 0.306 ft^3 or 528 in.^{3} **41.** 109.3 in.^{3}
43. 450 ft^3 **45.** 84.78 in.^{3} **47.** 50,240 cm^3

Chapter 8 Review Exercises, pp. 523–526

1. d   **2.** a   **3.** c   **4.** b
5. The measure of an acute angle is between 0° and 90°.
6. The measure of an obtuse angle is between 90° and 180°.

7. The measure of a straight angle is 180°.
8. The measure of a right angle is 90°.
9. a. 57° **b.** 147° **10. a.** 70° **b.** 160° **11.** 60°
12. 90° **13.** 175° **14.** 180° **15.** b **16.** b, c
17. a, c **18.** 62° **19.** 118° **20.** 118° **21.** 62°
22. 62° **23.** 118° **24.** 118° **25.** $m(\angle x) = 40°$
26. $m(\angle x) = 80°; m(\angle y) = 32°$
27. An obtuse triangle has one obtuse angle.
28. An equilateral triangle has three sides of equal length and three angles of equal measure.
29. A right triangle has a right (90°) angle.
30. An acute triangle has three acute angles.
31. An isosceles triangle has two sides of equal length and two angles of equal measure.
32. A scalene triangle has no sides or angles of equal measure.
33. 5 **34.** 7 **35.** 10 **36.** 8
37. The sum of the squares of the legs of a right triangle equals the square of the hypotenuse. **38.** $b = 7$ cm
39. $c = 20$ ft **40.** 13 m of string is extended.
41. They both have sides of equal length, but a square also has four right angles.
42. A parallelogram must have both pairs of opposite sides parallel.
43. A square is a rectangle with four sides of equal length.
44. A rectangle is a parallelogram with four right angles.
45. 90 cm **46.** 17.3 m **47.** 56 mi **48.** 400 yd
49. 42 ft **50.** 15.5 ft **51.** 20 in.^{2} **52.** 51 ft^2
53. 7056 ft^2 **54.** The area is 36 m^2. The perimeter is 36 m.
55. 90 mm **56.** 6.4 ft **57.** 22.5 mm **58.** 1.6 ft
59. $C = 50.24$ m; $A = 200.96$ m^2
60. $C = 13.2$ yd; $A = 13.86$ yd^2
61. $C = 440$ in.; $A = 15,400$ in.^{2}
62. $C = 125.6$ ft; $A = 1256$ ft^2
63. 134.88 in.^{2} **64. a.** 28.26 cm^2 **b.** 7.065 cm^2 **c.** No
65. 5.57 yd^2 **66.** 25,000 cm^3 **67.** 226.08 ft^3
68. 14,130 in.^{3} **69.** 37.68 km^3 **70.** 995 in.^{3}
71. 113 in.^{3} **72.** 335 in.^{3} **73.** 28,500 in.^{3} **74.** $2\frac{1}{3}$ ft^3

Chapter 8 Test, pp. 527–528

1. d **2.** c **3.** 74° **4.** 33° **5.** 103°
6. $\frac{5}{2}$ ft or $2\frac{1}{2}$ ft **7.** $\frac{55}{7}$ ft or $7\frac{6}{7}$ ft **8.** 70,650 ft^2
9. 48 ft^2 **10. a.** 2 **b.** 16 **11.** Obtuse
12. Acute **13.** Right **14.** Straight
15. $m(\angle x) = 125°, m(\angle y) = 55°$ **16.** They are each 45°.
17. 49° **18.** 180° **19.** $m(\angle A) = 80°$ **20.** 12 ft
21. 100 m **22.** d **23.** c **24.** f **25.** b **26.** a
27. e **28.** 96 in. **29.** 3 rolls are needed.
30. The area is 72 in.^{2} **31.** The area of the rectangular pizza is 96 in.^{2} The area of the round pizza is approximately 113.04 in.^{2} The round pizza is larger by about 17 in.^{2}
32. The volume is about 151 ft^3. **33.** The volume is 1260 in.^{3} **34.** The volume is 2002 cm^3.

Chapters 1–8 Cumulative Review Exercises, pp. 529–530

1. 3835 **2.** 0 **3.** Undefined **4.** 666,000
5. 2,511,000 **6.** $\frac{3}{5}, \frac{2}{3}, \frac{5}{6}$ **7.** There is $10\frac{1}{2}$ fl oz left.

8. 18 **9.** $\frac{1}{18}$ **10.** $\frac{6}{5}$ **11.** 60 **12.** $\frac{67}{60}$ **13.** $\frac{67}{60}$
14. $16\frac{1}{2}$ **15.** $\frac{46}{9}$ **16.** Four glasses cost $47.96.
17. Geraldo will save the cost of one shirt which is $13.49.

	Fraction	Decimal
18.	$\frac{3}{8}$	0.375
19.	$\frac{2}{9}$	$0.\overline{2}$
20.	$\frac{1}{50}$	0.02

21. $\frac{2}{3}$ **22.** $n = 37.35$ **23.** 17 pizzas **24.** 34 mpg
25. $3436 per hour **26.** 52.8 **27.** 72 **28.** 130%
29. 20% markup **30.** 16% discount **31.** 10 ft
32. Yes, $4\frac{1}{2}$ ft is 54 in. **33.** There is a total of $1\frac{1}{4}$ c or 10 fl oz of liquid. **34.** 100 kph ≈ 62 mph **35.** 41°F
36. 13.3 m **37.** 11 ft **38.** 1256 cm^2
39. 3 yd^2 or 27 ft^2 **40.** 452 in.^{3}

Chapter 9

Chapter Opener Puzzle

a. 6-month **b.** 0.46% **c.** 1.02% **d.** 0.60% **e.** 1-year

Section 9.1 Practice Exercises, pp. 538–543

1. a. Statistics **b.** table; cells **c.** pictograph
3. Mt. Kosciusko; Australia **5.** 2514 ft **7.** 3.6 yr
9. 2.8 yr **11.** Men
13.

	Dog	Cat	Neither
Boy	4	1	3
Girl	3	4	5

15. a. The 18- to 29-year age group has the greatest percentage of Internet users.
b.

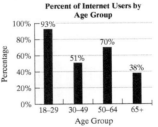

17.

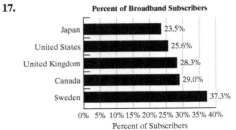

19. a. One icon represents 100 servings sold. **b.** About 450 servings **c.** Sunday **21. a.** Barnes & Noble/B. Dalton has approximately $4.5 billion in book sales.
b. There is approximately $11.5 billion in book sales.
23. 48.4% **25.** The trend for women over 65 in the labor force shows a slight increase. **27.** For example: 18%
29. The most cars were sold in 2008. 22,400 cars were sold.
31. 4800 cars
33. The greatest increase was between 2007 and 2008.
35. a.

Average Height for Girls, Ages 2–9

b. Approximately 56 in.
37. There are 14 servings per container, which means that there is 8 g × 14 = 112 g of fat in one container.
39. The daily value of fat is approximately 61.5 g.

Section 9.2 Practice Exercises pp. 545–549

1. a. frequency **b.** histogram
3. There are 72 data. **5.** 9–12
7.

Class Intervals (Age in Years)	Tally	Frequency (Number of Professors)
56–58	II	2
59–61	I	1
62–64	I	1
65–67	HH II	7
68–70	HH	5
71–73	IIII	4

a. The class of 65–67 has the most values.
b. There are 20 values represented in the table.
c. Of the professors, 25% retire when they are 68 to 70 years old.
9.

Class Intervals (Amount in Gal)	Tally	Frequency (Number of Customers)
8.0–9.9	IIII	4
10.0–11.9	I	1
12.0–13.9	HH	5
14.0–15.9	IIII	4
16.0–17.9		0
18.0–19.9	II	2

a. The 12.0–13.9 class has the highest frequency.
b. There are 16 data values represented in the table.
c. Of the customers, 12.5% purchased 18 to 19.9 gal of gas.
11. The class widths are not the same. **13.** There are too few classes. **15.** The class intervals overlap. For example, it is unclear whether the data value 12 should be placed in the first class or the second class.

17.

Class Interval (Height, in.)	Frequency (Number of Students)
62–63	2
64–65	3
66–67	4
68–69	4
70–71	4
72–73	3

19.

Heights of Valencia College Students

21.

Number of Calories in 100 g of Selected Fruits

Section 9.3 Practice Exercises, pp. 553–555

1. circle; sectors
3. 64,000 **5.** 640 **7.** 25% **9.** 2.5 times
11. There were 15.6 million viewers represented.
13. *The Young and the Restless* has 2 times as many viewers. **15.** Of the viewers, approximately 17% watch *General Hospital*. **17.** There are 960 Latina CDs.
19. There are 640 CDs that are classical or jazz.
21. 13.5 million Wii systems were sold.
23. 5.5 million Play Station 3 systems were sold.
25. **27.** **29.**

31. **33.**

35.

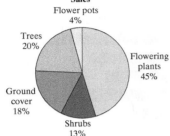

Sunshine Nursery Distribution of Sales
- Flower pots 4%
- Trees 20%
- Flowering plants 45%
- Ground cover 18%
- Shrubs 13%

37. a.

	Expenses	Percent	Number of Degrees
Tuition	$9000	75%	270°
Books	600	5%	18°
Housing	2400	20%	72°

b.

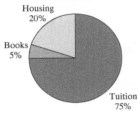

College Expenses for a Semester
- Housing 20%
- Books 5%
- Tuition 75%

Section 9.4 Practice Exercises, pp. 561–565

1. a. mean **b.** median **c.** mean **d.** mode **e.** weighted
3. 6   **5.** 4   **7.** 15.2   **9.** 8.76 in.   **11.** 5.8 hr
13. a. 397 Cal **b.** 386 Cal **c.** There is only an 11-Cal difference in the means.   **15. a.** 86.5% **b.** 81%
c. The low score of 59% decreased Zach's average by 5.5%.
17. 17   **19.** 110.5   **21.** 52.5   **23.** 3.93 deaths per 1000
25. 58 years old   **27.** 51.7 million passengers   **29.** 4
31. No mode   **33.** 21, 24   **35.** $300   **37.** 5.2%
39. These data are bimodal: $2.49 and $2.51.
41. Mean: 85.5%; median: 94.5%; The median gave Jonathan a better overall score.   **43.** Mean: $250; median: $256; mode: There is no mode.   **45.** Mean: $942,500; median: $848,500; mode: $850,000

47.

Age (yr)	Number of Students	Product
16	7	112
17	9	153
18	6	108
19	3	57
Total:	25	430

The mean age is 17.2 years.

49. The mean number of students per class is approximately 28.   **51.** 3.59   **53.** 2.73

Section 9.5 Practice Exercises, pp. 569–572

1. a. experiment **b.** sample **c.** probability
d. complement **e.** 1
3. Mean: 17.2; median: 16; no mode   **5.** Mean: 8.875; median: 8.5; mode: 8   **7.** Mean: 16.5; median: 18.5; mode: 20
9. {1, 2, 3, 4, 5, 6, 7, 8, 9, 10}   **11.** {2, 3, 4, 5, 6, 7, 8, 9, 10, 11, 12}
13. 3 ways   **15.** c, d, g, h   **17.** $\frac{2}{6} = \frac{1}{3}$
19. $\frac{3}{6} = \frac{1}{2}$ **21.** $\frac{5}{8}$ **23.** $\frac{1}{8}$ **25.** 1
27. An impossible event is one in which the probability is 0.
29. $\frac{12}{52} = \frac{3}{13}$ **31.** $\frac{12}{16} = \frac{3}{4}$
33. a. $\frac{18}{120} = \frac{3}{20}$ **b.** $\frac{27}{120} = \frac{9}{40}$ **c.** 30%
35. a. $\frac{21}{60} = \frac{7}{20}$ **b.** 50% **37. a.** $\frac{7}{29}$ **b.** $\frac{11}{29}$ **c.** 62%
39. $1 - \frac{2}{11} = \frac{9}{11}$ **41.** $100\% - 1.2\% = 98.8\%$

Chapter 9 Review Exercises, pp. 577–580

1. Godiva   **2.** Breyers   **3.** Blue Bell has 2 times more sodium than Edy's Grand.   **4.** There is a 10-g difference.   **5.** 374 acres   **6.** The difference is 260 acres.
7. The difference is 4 acres.   **8.** The greatest increase was between 1950 and 1960.   **9.** 1 icon represents 50 tornadoes.   **10.** 300   **11.** June   **12.** 75   **13.** 2010
14. 4900   **15.** Increasing   **16.** ≈7000
17.

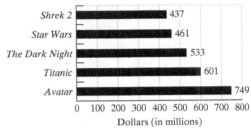

High Grossing Movies in the United States
- Shrek 2: 437
- Star Wars: 461
- The Dark Night: 533
- Titanic: 601
- Avatar: 749

Dollars (in millions)

18.

Class Intervals (Age)	Frequency
18–21	4
22–25	5
26–29	4
30–33	3
34–37	1
38–41	1
42–45	2

19.

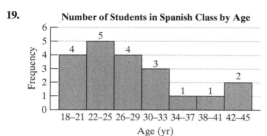

Number of Students in Spanish Class by Age

20. There are 24 types of subs.

21. $\frac{2}{3}$ of the subs contain beef.

22. $\frac{1}{3}$ of the subs do not contain beef.

23. a.

Education Level	Number of People	Percent	Number of Degrees
Grade school	10	5%	18°
High school	50	25%	90°
Some college	60	30%	108°
Four-year degree	40	20%	72°
Postgraduate	40	20%	72°

b.

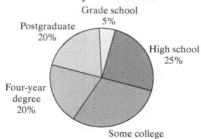

Percent by Education Level

Grade school 5%
Postgraduate 20%
High school 25%
Four-year degree 20%
Some college 30%

24. Mean: 17.5; median: 18; mode: 20

25. The mean daily calcium intake is approximately 1060 mg.

26. The median is 20,562 seats.   **27.** 4

28. The mean age is 10.95 years.

Age (yr)	Number of Children	Product
10	8	80
11	6	66
12	5	60
13	1	13

29. {blue, green, brown, black, gray, white}

30. $\frac{1}{6}$ **31.** a, c, d, e, g   **32. a.** $\frac{1}{2}$ **b.** $\frac{1}{2}$ **c.** 0

Chapter 9 Test, pp. 581–583

1.

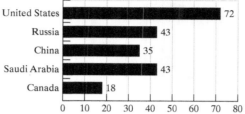

World's Major Producers of Primary Energy (Quadrillions of Btu)

United States 72
Russia 43
China 35
Saudi Arabia 43
Canada 18

2. The year 1820 had the greatest percent of workers employed in farm occupations. This was 72%.

3.

Percent of U.S. Workers in Farm Occupations

72%, 59%, 38%, 17%, 3%

4. Approximately 10% of U.S. workers were employed in farm occupations in the year 1960.

5. $1000   **6.** $4500   **7.** February   **8.** Seattle

9. 1.73 in.   **10.** May

11.

Number of Minutes Used Monthly	Tally	Frequency
51–100	ⅢⅠ	6
101–150	‖	2
151–200	‖‖	3
201–250	‖	2
251–300	‖‖‖	4
301–350	‖‖	3

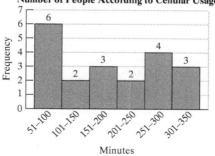

Number of People According to Cellular Usage

6, 2, 3, 2, 4, 3

12. 66 people would have carpet.   **13.** 40 people would have tile.   **14.** 270 people would have something other than linoleum.   **15.** 19,173 ft   **16.** 19,340 ft
17. There is no mode.   **18.** Mean: $14.60; median: $15; mode $16

19. a. $\{1, 2, 3, 4, 5, 6, 7, 8\}$ **b.** $\frac{1}{8}$ **c.** $\frac{1}{2}$ **d.** $\frac{1}{4}$

20. a. $\frac{2}{7}$ **b.** $\frac{5}{7}$ **21.** 3.09   **22.** c

Chapters 1–9 Cumulative Review Exercises, pp. 583–585

1. a. Millions **b.** Ten-thousands **c.** Hundreds
2. 12,645   **3.** $700 \times 1200 = 840,000$ **4.** Divisor: 23; dividend: 651; quotient: 28; remainder: 7

5. $\frac{3}{8}$ **6.** $\frac{2}{3}$ **7.** $\frac{5}{2}$ **8.** $\frac{3}{2}$ **9.** $\frac{1}{3}$ **10.** $\frac{37}{100}$

11. 2   **12.** $\frac{1}{6}$

13.

Stock	Yesterday's Closing Price ($)	Increase/ Decrease	Today's Closing Price ($)
RylGold	13.28	0.27	13.55
NetSolve	9.51	−0.17	9.34
Metals USA	14.35	0.10	14.45
PAM Transpt	18.09	0.09	18.18
Steel Tch	21.63	−0.37	21.26

14. 6841.2   **15.** 6.8412   **16.** 68,412   **17. a.** 0.75 million km² or equivalently, 750,000 km² **b.** 20.3%
18. Quick Cut Lawn Company's rate is 0.55 hr per customer. Speedy Lawn Company's rate is 0.5 hr per customer. Speedy Lawn Company is faster.
19. 125 min or 2 hr 5 min   **20.** $x = 5$ m, $y = 22.4$ m
21. 122 people   **22.** 17.02 million   **23.** 65%
24. $1404   **25.** 29 in.   **26.** 18 qt   **27.** 9 yd 1 ft
28. 9.64 km or 9640 m   **29.** 4 lb 3 oz   **30.** Obtuse
31. Right   **32.** Acute   **33.** Area: 8 ft²   **34.** 66 m³
35.

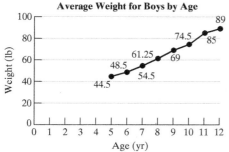

Average Weight for Boys by Age

36. Mean: 105; median: 123   **37.** 3
38. {yellow, blue, red, green}
39. $\frac{1}{4}$ **40.** $\frac{3}{4}$

Chapter 10

Chapter Opener Puzzle

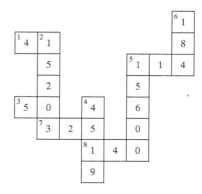

Section 10.1 Practice Exercises, pp. 594–596

1. a. positive; negative **b.** integers **c.** rational; irrational **d.** absolute **e.** opposites   **3.** −86 m
5. $3800   **7.** −$500   **9.** −14 lb   **11.** 140,000
13. [number line with point at 4]
15. [number line with points at −3 and 2]
17. [number line with points at −3 and 4]
19. [number line with point at −1]
21. [number line with points at −1 and 3]
23. [number line with points at −3 and 1]

25. Rational   **27.** Rational   **29.** Rational
31. Irrational   **33.** Irrational   **35.** Rational
37. >   **39.** >   **41.** <   **43.** <   **45.** >
47. >   **49.** <   **51.** <   **53.** 2   **55.** 4.5
57. $\frac{5}{2}$ **59.** 0   **61.** 3.2   **63.** 21

65. a. −8 **b.** $|-12|$ **67. a.** 7.8 **b.** $|7.8|$ **69.** $\left|-\frac{4}{5}\right|$
71. Neither, they are equal.   **73.** −5   **75.** 12
77. $\frac{1}{6}$ **79.** $-\frac{2}{11}$ **81.** −8.1   **83.** 1.14
85. −6   **87.** $-(-2)$ **89.** $|7|$ **91.** $|-3|$
93. $-|14|$ **95.** $-|-30|$ **97.** −2   **99.** −5.3
101. 15   **103.** 4.7   **105.** $-\frac{12}{17}$ **107.** $\frac{3}{8}$

Section 10.2 Practice Exercises, pp. 602–604

1. a. 0 **b.** negative; positive **c.** Subtract the smaller absolute value from the larger absolute value. The sum takes on the sign of the addend with the greater absolute value.
3. >   **5.** =   **7.** <   **9.** −2   **11.** 2   **13.** −8
15. 6   **17.** −7   **19.** −4
21. To add two numbers with the same sign, add their absolute values and apply the common sign.

SA-28 Student Answer Appendix

23. 15 **25.** −73 **27.** −124 **29.** 89 **31.** 52
33. −22 **35.** −24 **37.** 45 **39.** 0 **41.** 0
43. 9 **45.** −26 **47.** −41 **49.** −150 **51.** −17
53. −41 **55.** 2 **57.** −30 **59.** 10 **61.** −8
63. 0 **65.** −12 **67.** 26 **69.** −38.3 **71.** −2
73. $-3\frac{1}{2}$ **75.** −10.2 **77.** 1.4 **79.** $\frac{3}{16}$ **81.** $-\frac{7}{12}$
83. $-1\frac{1}{2}$ **85.** Sum, added to, increased by, more than, plus, total
87. 89 + (−11); 78 **89.** −2 + (−4) + 14 + 20; 28
91. −12 + (−4.5); −16.5 **93.** $-\frac{1}{3} + 2; \frac{5}{3}$
95. $-\frac{1}{5} + 1; \frac{4}{5}$ **97.** −6°F **99.** −$16.11
101. $320.32 **103.** For example: −6 + (−8)
105. For example: 5 + (−5)

Section 10.2 Calculator Connections, p. 604
106. −120 **107.** −566 **108.** −68.221 **109.** −332.5
110. 711 **111.** 339

Section 10.3 Practice Exercises, pp. 609–611

1. a. (−b) **b.** −5 + 4 **3.** −47 **5.** $\frac{1}{36}$ **7.** $-\frac{41}{36}$
9. −4 **11.** 2 + (−9); −7 **13.** 4 + 3; 7
15. −3 + (−15); −18 **17.** −11 + 13; 2
19. 52 **21.** −33 **23.** −12 **25.** 8 **27.** 0
29. 161 **31.** −34 **33.** −22 **35.** −26 **37.** −1
39. 32 **41.** −15
43. Minus, difference, decreased, less than, subtract from
45. 14 − 23; −9 **47.** 5 − 12; −7 **49.** 105 − 110; −5
51. 320 − (−20); 340 **53.** −35 − 24; −59
55. −34 − 21; −55 **57.** −8.3 **59.** −4.2 **61.** 5.5
63. 8.3 **65.** $\frac{5}{6}$ **67.** $\frac{2}{5}$ **69.** $-1\frac{1}{2}$ **71.** $-\frac{7}{4}$
73. 0 **75.** −1 **77.** 16 **79.** 1 **81.** 52 **83.** 5.2
85. 6423°F **87.** The balance was $18,085.51.
89. The difference is 0.18 point.
91. His new balance is −$375. **93.** 64,827 ft
95. The range is 3° − (−8°) = 11°.
97. For example, 4 − 10 **99.** −11, −15, −19
101. $-1, -\frac{4}{3}, -\frac{5}{3}$ **103.** Positive **105.** Positive
107. Negative **109.** Negative

Section 10.3 Calculator Connections, p. 612
111. −413 **112.** −433 **113.** 66.77 **114.** 20.06
115. 112.8 **116.** 129.7

Chapter 10 Problem Recognition Exercises, p. 612
1. −12 **2.** −2 **3.** −12 **4.** −2 **5.** 55 **6.** −35
7. −35 **8.** 55 **9.** 21.4 **10.** −83.8 **11.** −83.8
12. 21.4 **13.** 2 **14.** −41 **15.** −41 **16.** 2
17. 4 **18.** 4 **19.** 20 **20.** 20 **21.** $-\frac{9}{8}$ or $-1\frac{1}{8}$

22. $-\frac{11}{8}$ or $-1\frac{3}{8}$ **23.** $-\frac{9}{8}$ or $-1\frac{1}{8}$ **24.** $\frac{9}{8}$ or $1\frac{1}{8}$
25. $-\frac{17}{18}$ **26.** $-\frac{11}{18}$ **27.** $-\frac{11}{18}$ **28.** $\frac{11}{18}$
29. $-\frac{13}{4}$ or $-3\frac{1}{4}$ **30.** $\frac{7}{2}$ or $3\frac{1}{2}$ **31.** $-\frac{9}{2}$ or $-4\frac{1}{2}$
32. 4 **33.** $\frac{9}{4}$ or $2\frac{1}{4}$ **34.** $-\frac{9}{5}$ or $-1\frac{4}{5}$
35. −1.999 **36.** −1.987 **37.** 0 **38.** 0
39. −112 **40.** 28

Section 10.4 Practice Exercises, pp. 619–622
1. a. positive; negative **b.** positive; negative
c. reciprocals **3.** 19 **5.** −44 **7.** 17 **9.** −15
11. −48 **13.** 45 **15.** −72 **17.** 3.84 **19.** −2.4
21. −7.7 **23.** 0 **25.** $\frac{4}{7}$ **27.** $-\frac{1}{7}$ **29.** $-\frac{5}{2}$ or $-2\frac{1}{2}$
31. $\frac{13}{3}$ or $4\frac{1}{3}$ **33.** 0 **35.** 4.9 **37.** −3(−1); 3
39. −5 · 3; −15 **41.** 1.3(−3); −3.9 **43.** 3(−12);
−36 customers **45.** 4(−8); −32 yd **47.** 400
49. −88 **51.** 0 **53.** 1 **55.** −1 **57.** −100
59. 100 **61.** −27 **63.** −27 **65.** −0.008
67. $-\frac{8}{27}$ **69.** 36 **71.** −36 **73.** −3 **75.** −7
77. $\frac{5}{3}$ **79.** $\frac{2}{3}$ **81.** Undefined **83.** 0 **85.** 4
87. 1.3 **89.** $-\frac{10}{7}$ **91.** Undefined **93.** $\frac{5}{8}$
95. $-\frac{3}{4}$ **97.** −100 ÷ 20; −5 **99.** −32 ÷ (−64); $\frac{1}{2}$
101. −52 ÷ 13; −4 **103.** 2 **105.** −48 **107.** 3
109. 3 **111.** 20 **113.** −15 **115.** $-\frac{2}{5}$ **117.** $\frac{7}{6}$
119. $(-2)^{50}$ **121.** $(5)^{41}$ **123.** Negative
125. Positive

Section 10.4 Calculator Connections, p. 622
127. −359,723 **128.** 594,125 **129.** 5290.18
130. 54 **131.** −629 **132.** −33

Chapter 10 Problem Recognition Exercises, p. 622
1. 20 **2.** −75 **3.** 10 **4.** −3 **5.** 72
6. −34 **7.** 18 **8.** −38 **9.** −80 **10.** 80
11. −80 **12.** 80 **13.** −16 **14.** −72 **15.** −5
16. 25 **17.** 24 **18.** 24 **19.** −24 **20.** −24
21. $-\frac{27}{50}$ **22.** $-\frac{2}{3}$ **23.** $-\frac{23}{45}$ **24.** $\frac{77}{45}$ **25.** $-\frac{13}{9}$
26. $\frac{6}{7}$ **27.** $-\frac{13}{4}$ or $-3\frac{1}{4}$ **28.** $-\frac{29}{36}$ **29.** 55.1
30. −9.44 **31.** −93.91 **32.** −0.02 **33.** $\frac{12}{11}$
34. $-\frac{1}{6}$ **35.** 0 **36.** Undefined **37.** −21,000
38. 40,000 **39.** 0 **40.** 1

Section 10.5 Practice Exercises, pp. 625–626

1. 44 **3.** $-\dfrac{3}{4}$ **5.** 3.08 **7.** −120 **9.** 1 **11.** −44

13. 29 **15.** −150 **17.** −3.3 **19.** 64 **21.** 16
23. −20 **25.** −16 **27.** 11 **29.** 2 **31.** −5

33. −8 **35.** 8 **37.** −96 **39.** −2 **41.** $-\dfrac{3}{2}$

43. $\dfrac{1}{3}$ **45.** $5\dfrac{1}{2}$ **47.** 14 **49.** −5 **51.** 38

53. −2 **55.** $\dfrac{1}{5}$ **57.** −1 **59.** $\dfrac{3}{7}$ **61.** $-\dfrac{1}{3}$

63. −2° **65.** −3 **67.** −129.28°F **69.** 3 **71.** −1

Chapter 10 Review Exercises, pp. 631–633

1. −10,227 **2.** −$5 billion **3.** 15° **4.** $10
5. – 8.

9. 4, 4 **10.** $\dfrac{1}{2}, \dfrac{1}{2}$ **11.** −3.5, 3.5 **12.** −6, 6

13. a. 9 **b.** −9 **14. a.** −1.5 **b.** −1.5 **15.** >
16. < **17.** > **18.** < **19.** < **20.** >
21. 4 **22.** 3 **23.** −5 **24.** −3
25. To add two numbers with the same sign, add their
absolute values and apply the common sign.
26. To add two numbers with different signs, subtract the
smaller absolute value from the larger absolute value. Then
apply the sign of the number having the larger absolute value.
27. 13 **28.** −15 **29.** −70 **30.** −0.88 **31.** −10.66

32. $\dfrac{3}{4}$ **33.** $-\dfrac{9}{10}$ **34.** $-\dfrac{1}{3}$ **35.** 23 + (−35); −12

36. 57 + (−10); 47 **37.** −5 + (−13) + 20; 2
38. −42 + 12; −30 **39.** −12 + 3; −9
40. −89 + (−22); −111 **41.** 3 **42.** −15
43. 1. Leave the first number (the minuend) unchanged.
2. Change the subtraction sign to an addition sign.
3. Add the opposite of the second number (the subtrahend).
44. 27 **45.** −25 **46.** 22 **47.** −419 **48.** −7.4

49. −0.7 **50.** $-\dfrac{5}{4}$ **51.** $\dfrac{20}{21}$

52. For example: The difference of 4 and 6
53. For example: 23 minus negative 6
54. For example: 14 subtracted from −2
55. For example: Subtract −7 from −25.
56. The temperature rose 5°F.
57. Sam's balance is now $92.
58. The average is 1 above par.
59. −18 **60.** −3 **61.** 15 **62.** 56 **63.** −70

64. −156.5 **65.** $\dfrac{7}{4}$ **66.** $-\dfrac{17}{10}$ or $-1\dfrac{7}{10}$

67. Undefined **68.** 0 **69.** −32 **70.** $\dfrac{9}{5}$ or $1\dfrac{4}{5}$

71. 36 **72.** −36 **73.** $-\dfrac{27}{64}$ **74.** $-\dfrac{27}{64}$ **75.** 1

76. −1 **77.** Negative **78.** Positive
79. −45 ÷ (−15); 3 **80.** −4 · 19; −76

81. 30(−5); −150 **82.** −136 ÷ (−8); 17 **83.** −11
84. −2 **85.** −7 **86.** 4 **87.** 0 **88.** −1

89. $\dfrac{17}{64}$ **90.** −5 **91.** $\dfrac{1}{8}$ **92.** −1°

Chapter 10 Test, pp. 633–634

1. a. −$220 **b.** 26 **2.** −3, 0, 4, −1

3. −3, $-\dfrac{3}{5}$, 0, 4, −1, $\dfrac{4}{7}$ **4.** $\sqrt{7}$, −π **5.** <

6. > **7.** > **8.** > **9.** < **10.** <
11. −5 **12.** −28 **13.** 9 **14.** −41 **15.** 0.6

16. −2.3 **17.** $-\dfrac{26}{21}$ or $-1\dfrac{5}{21}$ **18.** $\dfrac{3}{8}$

19. −72 **20.** 88 **21.** 2 **22.** −18 **23.** Undefined

24. 0 **25.** $-\dfrac{3}{8}$ **26.** $\dfrac{13}{6}$ **27. a.** Positive **b.** Negative

28. a. 64 **b.** −64 **c.** −64 **d.** −64 **29.** −3(−7); 21
30. −13 + 8; −5 **31.** 18 − (−4); 22

32. $6 \div \left(-\dfrac{2}{3}\right)$; −9 **33.** −8.1 + 5; −3.1

34. −3 + 15 + (−6) + (−1); 5 **35.** 3 **36.** −60

37. −19 **38.** −55 **39.** $-\dfrac{22}{15}$ **40.** $\dfrac{2}{13}$

41. 0 **42.** $\dfrac{3}{4}$ **43.** 1°

Chapters 1–10 Cumulative Review Exercises, pp. 634–635

1. 3613 **2.** 2569 **3.** 177 **4.** 18,960

5. 2 · 2 · 2 · 2 · 3 · 3 · 5 or $2^4 \cdot 3^2 \cdot 5$ **6.** $\dfrac{5}{8}$

7. Harold got $\dfrac{11}{14}$ of the quiz correct.

8. Amy will have 8 packages. **9.** 80 **10.** $\dfrac{5}{16}$

11. $6\dfrac{7}{15}$ **12.** $3\dfrac{4}{7}$ **13. a.** 34.230 **b.** 9.0

14. $2.09 **15.** 490.92 **16.** 115 **17.** $\dfrac{2}{5}$

18. The aircraft used 2491 gal/hr. **19.** 21 mi
20. x = 2.7 cm; y = 7 cm **21.** 192 **22.** 112%
23. 250 **24.** The sale price is $68.80. **25.** 28 in.

26. 5 gal **27.** 0.06 L **28.** $1\dfrac{7}{8}$ lb

29. The distance is 10 mi. **30.** 16.5 yd² **31.** $5\dfrac{1}{16}$ m²

32. A = 7.065 km²; C = 9.42 km
33.

Number of Miles	Tally	Frequency (Number of Walkers)
3	II	2
4	IIII	5
5	I	1
6	II	2

34.

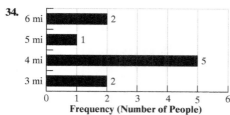

35. 4.3 mi   **36.** $216   **37.** 55   **38.** −12

39. −20   **40.** $\frac{1}{6}$

Chapter 11

Chapter Opener Puzzle

1	4	2	^A6	5	3
5	6	^B3	4	2	1
^C6	1	5	3	4	2
3	2	^D4	1	6	5
4	5	1	2	3	6
^E2	3	6	5	1	^F4

Section 11.1 Practice Exercises, pp. 642–645

1. a. variable **b.** commutative; $x + 6$ **c.** $b \cdot a$; $6x$
d. associative; $(-5 + 7) + x$ **e.** $a \cdot (b \cdot c)$; $(-5 \cdot 7)x$
f. $a \cdot b + a \cdot c$; $4x + 20$ **3.** $8p$ **5.** $t + 4$ **7.** $v - 6$
9. $\frac{4}{n}$ **11.** $2g$ **13. a.** −12 **b.** 30 **15. a.** 5 **b.** −15
17. a. −49 **b.** −49 **19. a.** −16 **b.** −64   **21.** −4
23. 24   **25.** $\frac{1}{2}$ **27.** 5   **29.** $P = 16.6$ in.   **31.** $A = \frac{77}{2}$ m²
33. $w + 5$ **35.** $b + (-\frac{1}{3})$ or $b - \frac{1}{3}$ **37.** $2r$ **39.** $-st$
41. yx **43.** $-p + 7$ **45.** $(-2 \cdot 6)b$; $-12b$
47. $(3 + 8) + t$; $11 + t$ **49.** $(-4.2 + 2.5) + r$; $-1.7 + r$
51. $(3 \cdot 6)x$; $18x$ **53.** $\left(-\frac{4}{7} \cdot -\frac{7}{4}\right)d$; d
55. $(-9 + (-12)) + h$; $-21 + h$ **57.** $4x + 32$
59. $-2p - 8$ **61.** $-10t + 30$ **63.** $10 - 5x$
65. $4a + 16b - 4c$ **67.** $\frac{8}{3} + 4g$ **69.** $-3 + n$
71. $a + 8$ **73.** $-3x - 9 + 5y$ **75.** $5q + 2s + 3t$
77. $12x$ **79.** $12 + 6x$ **81.** $6 + 6k$ **83.** $-7 - k$
85. $-4 - p$ **87.** $-32 + 8p$ **89.** $4a$ **91.** $4 + 8a$
93. $5 + \frac{5}{9}y$ **95.** $5y$

Section 11.2 Practice Exercises, pp. 648–650

1. a. term **b.** variable; constant **c.** coefficient **d.** like
3. $6p + 18$ **5.** $-24q$ **7.** $9 - h$ **9.** variable term
11. constant term   **13.** variable term

15. variable term   **17.** 6, −4   **19.** −14, 12
21. 1, −1   **23.** 5, −8, −3   **25.** *Like* terms
27. Unlike terms   **29.** *Like* terms
31. Unlike terms   **33.** Unlike terms   **35.** *Like* terms
37. $14rs$ **39.** $8h$ **41.** $3x^2 + 9$ **43.** $6x - 15y$
45. $-3k$ **47.** $4uv + 6u$ **49.** $-16m - 9$
51. $-9a + 5b + 20$ **53.** $-6p^2 - 2p + 7$
55. $2y - \frac{5}{6}$ **57.** $\frac{5}{8}a + 9$ **59.** $-3x^2 - 1.9x$
61. $-0.9a + 7.6$ **63.** $5t - 28$ **65.** $-6x - 16$
67. $6y - 14$ **69.** $7q$ **71.** $-2n - 4$ **73.** $-6a - b$
75. $4x + 23$ **77.** $2z - 11$ **79.** $-w - 4y + 9$
81. $8a - 9b$ **83.** $-5m + 6n - 10$ **85.** $12z + 7$
87. $-7x - 7$ **89.** $-21y + 28$ **91.** $-2q + 20$
93. $-107a - 213b$

Section 11.3 Practice Exercises, pp. 654–656

1. a. linear **b.** solution **c.** equivalent **d.** addition
e. subtraction   **3.** $-13a + 16b$ **5.** $8h - 2k + 13$
7. $-3z + 4$ **9.** −1 is a solution.   **11.** 26 is a solution.
13. 12 is not a solution.   **15.** $-\frac{1}{2}$ is a solution.
17. 0 is a solution.   **19.** 4 is not a solution.   **21.** 0
23. 7   **25.** −3.2   **27.** 37   **29.** 16   **31.** −15
33. $\frac{7}{6}$ **35.** 3.1   **37.** 34   **39.** 52   **41.** 0   **43.** 100
45. −28   **47.** 3   **49.** −46   **51.** −13.6   **53.** $-\frac{13}{10}$
55. 7   **57.** −1   **59.** −6   **61.** $\frac{13}{12}$ **63.** −1.4
65. 12   **67.** −5   **69.** 13   **71.** −0.79   **73.** $\frac{13}{8}$
75. 49   **77.** −15   **79.** 26   **81.** −3   **83.** −5

Section 11.4 Practice Exercises, pp. 661–662

1. a. multiplication **b.** division
3. 45   **5.** 21   **7.** −13   **9.** $-\frac{7}{6}$ **11.** $\frac{1}{3}$
13. $-\frac{7}{4}$ **15.** −7   **17.** 5.1   **19.** −3   **21.** −7
23. 13   **25.** 21   **27.** −21   **29.** 4   **31.** 30
33. $-\frac{1}{3}$ **35.** 4.1   **37.** $-\frac{2}{5}$ **39.** 0   **41.** $\frac{4}{15}$
43. 20   **45.** −31   **47.** $\frac{5}{6}$ **49.** 0   **51.** −16
53. −3   **55.** −8   **57.** −48   **59.** $\frac{1}{3}$ **61.** $\frac{4}{3}$
63. 30   **65.** −15   **67.** $\frac{5}{12}$ **69.** $-\frac{21}{10}$ **71.** 27.9
73. −1.8   **75.** −22   **77.** 15   **79.** $-\frac{2}{5}$ **81.** 12
83. −5   **85.** 3   **87.** −1

Section 11.5 Practice Exercises, pp. 667–669

1. Add 6 to both sides first.
3. −12   **5.** $-\frac{5}{8}$ **7.** 0   **9.** 4   **11.** −6
13. 5   **15.** $\frac{4}{3}$ **17.** −2.4   **19.** −1.12   **21.** 9

23. -12 **25.** $\dfrac{1}{4}$ **27.** -27 **29.** -3 **31.** $\dfrac{9}{8}$

33. 1 **35.** $\dfrac{7}{3}$ **37.** 2 **39.** -2 **41.** -3

43. -4 **45.** $\dfrac{4}{5}$ **47.** -12 **49.** 15 **51.** 3

53. 6 **55.** $-\dfrac{1}{2}$ **57.** $\dfrac{15}{11}$ **59.** 5

Chapter 11 Problem Recognition Exercises, p. 669

1. Equation   **2.** Expression   **3.** Expression
4. Equation   **5.** Equation   **6.** Expression
7. equation; 4 **8.** equation; $\dfrac{19}{3}$ **9.** expression; $4x - 8$
10. expression; $-k + 18$ **11.** equation; 15
12. equation; -2 **13.** equation; 7 **14.** equation; 32
15. expression; $2x - 1$ **16.** expression; $-6t - 16$
17. equation; $\dfrac{23}{5}$ **18.** equation; 6 **19.** equation; -12
20. equation; 9 **21.** expression; $-8x - 6$
22. expression; $y + 3$ **23.** equation; 2
24. equation; 30 **25.** equation; -1
26. equation; $-\dfrac{1}{2}$ **27.** equation; $-\dfrac{1}{7}$ **28.** equation; 3
29. expression; $5p + 14$ **30.** expression; $3y - 15$

Section 11.6 Practice Exercises, pp. 675–677

1. No   **3.** -45 **5.** $\dfrac{14}{5}$ **7.** -0.75

9. a. $\dfrac{x}{3} = -8$ **b.** The number is -24.
11. a. $-30 - x = 42$ **b.** The number is -72.
13. a. $30 + x = 13$ **b.** The number is -17.
15. a. $\dfrac{x}{4} - 5 = -12$ **b.** The number is -28.
17. a. $\dfrac{1}{2} + x = 4$ **b.** The number is $\dfrac{7}{2}$ or $3\dfrac{1}{2}$.
19. a. $-12x = x + 26$ **b.** The number is -2.
21. a. $10(x + 5.1) = 56$ **b.** The number is 0.5.
23. a. $3x = 2x - 10$ **b.** The number is -10.
25. The pieces should be 3 m and 9 m.
27. Metallica had 10 hits while Boyz II Men had 16 hits.
29. The soccer field is 100 yd by 130 yd.
31. Jim used 50 min over the 500 min.
33. The pieces are $1\dfrac{1}{3}$ ft and $2\dfrac{2}{3}$ ft long.
35. Tampa Bay had 48 points and Oakland had 21 points.
37. Charlene's rent is $650 a month with a security deposit of $300.   **39.** Stefan worked 6 hr of overtime.
41. Raul took 12 hr in the fall and 16 hr in the spring.
43. Ann-Marie must sell $1250 of merchandise each week.

Chapter 11 Review Exercises, pp. 685–686

1. a. $a + 8$ **b.** 43 years old   **2. a.** $-\dfrac{16}{9}$ **b.** -1

c. -4 **d.** -4 **3.** -18 **4.** $\dfrac{99}{7}$m^3 **5. a.** $-5 + t$

b. $3h$ **6. a.** $(-4 \cdot 2)p$; $-8p$ **b.** $m + (10 - 12)$; $m - 2$
7. $6b + 15$ **8.** $4k - 8m + 12$ **9.** $3, -5, 12$
10. $-6, -1, 2, 1$ **11.** Unlike terms   **12.** *Like* terms
13. *Like* terms   **14.** Unlike terms
15. $6x + 4y + 10$ **16.** $7a + 9b + 9$ **17.** $-u - 11v$
18. $p - 16$ **19.** -3 is a solution.   **20.** -3 is not a solution.   **21.** If a constant is being added to the variable term, use the subtraction property. If a constant is being subtracted from the variable term, use the addition property.
22. -35 **23.** -12 **24.** 14 **25.** 24 **26.** 1.1 **27.** 5
28. $\dfrac{3}{2}$ **29.** $-\dfrac{11}{10}$ **30.** $\dfrac{5}{4}$ **31.** -7 **32.** 4
33. -26 **34.** 35 **35.** 20 **36.** -21 **37.** -2
38. -4 **39.** $\dfrac{9}{7}$ **40.** $-\dfrac{8}{3}$ **41.** 6 **42.** -17
43. -1 **44.** 2 **45.** 8 **46.** -12 **47.** 10 **48.** 24
49. -28 **50.** -7 **51.** $\dfrac{4}{3}$ **52.** $\dfrac{9}{5}$ **53.** -3
54. -6 **55. a.** $-6x = x + 2$ **b.** $-\dfrac{2}{7}$

56. a. $-9 + 3 + 2x = -2$ **b.** 2 **57. a.** $\dfrac{1}{3} - x = 2$
b. $-\dfrac{5}{3}$ **58. a.** $\dfrac{x}{8} - 2 = \dfrac{1}{4}$ **b.** 18
59. Johnny Depp had 50 appearances and Tom Hanks had 66 appearances.   **60.** Marty made 25 text messages over the allotted 400.   **61.** The width is 40 in. and the length is 72 in.

Chapter 11 Test, pp. 686–687

1. $\$19.95m$ **2.** -15 **3.** $A = 34.25$ ft^2
4. Associative property of multiplication
5. Commutative property of addition
6. Associative property of addition
7. Distributive property of multiplication over addition
8. Commutative property of multiplication
9. $4a + 24$ **10.** $-13b + 8$ **11.** $16y + 3$
12. $7 - 7w$ **13.** $-x + 4$ **14.** $y + 22$ **15.** An expression is a collection of terms. An equation has an equal sign that indicates that two expressions are equal.
16. a. Expression   **b.** Equation   **c.** Expression
d. Equation   **e.** Expression   **f.** Expression
17. -2 **18.** 18 **19.** -72 **20.** $-\dfrac{1}{2}$ **21.** -1
22. 0.2 **23.** $-\dfrac{13}{16}$ **24.** $\dfrac{1}{2}$ **25.** 3 **26.** -84
27. 0 **28.** 2 **29.** The number is -5.
30. The budget for *New Moon* was $50 million.
31. The lengths are 60 cm and 240 cm.
32. Sela used 770 kWh.

Chapters 1–11 Cumulative Review Exercises, pp. 687–689

1. a. Hundreds   **b.** Ten-thousands   **c.** Hundred-thousands   **2.** $46,000$ **3.** $1,290,000$ **4.** $25,400$
5. Dividend is 39,190; divisor is 46; quotient is 851; remainder is 44.
6. a. Prime   **b.** Composite   **c.** Composite
7. $\dfrac{23}{8}$ **8.** $\dfrac{6}{5}$ **9.** $\dfrac{28}{125}$ **10.** $\dfrac{13}{100}$ **11.** $\dfrac{79}{150}$

SA-32 Student Answer Appendix

12. 7 ft^2 **13.** $\frac{31}{8}$ **14.** $5\frac{3}{5}$ **15.** $8\frac{2}{3}$ **16.** 13.95

17. 0.5 **18.** 31.221 **19.** 43.752 **20.** 3.56

21. Sarah makes \$20 per room. **22.** 8.1

23. $\frac{4}{5}$ **24.** 56

25. Kitty Treats costs \$0.92 per ounce. Cat Goodies costs \$0.90 per ounce. Cat Goodies is the better buy.

	Decimal	Fraction	Percent
26.	0.15	$\frac{3}{20}$	15%
27.	0.125	$\frac{1}{8}$	12.5%
28.	1.1	$\frac{11}{10}$	110%
29.	$0.\overline{2}$	$\frac{2}{9}$	$22.\overline{2}\%$
30.	0.002	$\frac{1}{500}$	0.2

31. 21 glasses can be filled. **32.** 101.75 min **33.** 0.68 L

34. 3200 m **35.** 4500 cg **36.** 1256 in.²

37. The area is 67.5 in.² **38.** 995 in.² **39.** 18.84 yd

40. 24 mm **41.** 10 **42.** 9.5 **43.** 12

44.

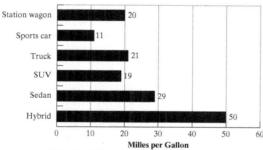

Miles per Gallon Comparison

45. a. Approximately 166 students **b.** 130 students

46. 3 **47.** −12 **48.** −25 **49.** −9

50. $-5x - 13$ **51.** $-2y - 18$ **52.** −4 **53.** −8

54. 2 **55.** $-\frac{8}{3}$

Additional Topics Appendix

Section A.1 Practice Exercises pp. A-3–A-5

1. Energy **3.** 15,000 ft·lb **5.** 225 ft·lb

7. 12,000 ft·lb **9.** 2,334,000 ft·lb **11.** 6,224,000 ft·lb

13. 68 Btu **15.** 5,800,000 Btu **17.** 798,228 ft·lb

19. $\frac{3}{4}$ hr or 0.75 hr **21.** $\frac{5}{2}$ hr or 2.5 hr

23. $\frac{11}{10}$ hr or 1.1 hr **25.** 443 Cal **27.** 1250 Cal

29. 933 Cal **31.** $60 \frac{\text{ft·lb}}{\text{sec}}$ **33.** $135 \frac{\text{ft·lb}}{\text{sec}}$

35. $200 \frac{\text{ft·lb}}{\text{sec}}$ **37.** 2 hp **39.** 11 hp

41. $173,250 \frac{\text{ft·lb}}{\text{sec}}$ **43.** $118,250 \frac{\text{ft·lb}}{\text{sec}}$

45. a. 630,000 Wh **b.** 630 kWh **c.** \$51.66

Section A.2 Practice Exercises pp. A-8–A-9

1. scientific notation **3.** 10^5 **5.** 10^6 **7.** 10^{-2}

9. 10^{-1} **11.** No **13.** Yes **15.** Yes **17.** No

19. 2.5×10^{13} mi **21.** 6.25×10^{-2} in. **23.** 5×10^3

25. 6.2×10^4 **27.** 9×10^{-4} **29.** 5.8×10^{-1}

31. 2.55×10^7 **33.** 1.16×10^{-4} **35.** 1.5×10^{-1}

37. 1.34×10^4 **39.** 30,000 **41.** 0.00002 **43.** 0.0021

45. 5500 **47.** 61,300,000 **49.** 0.000404

51. 0.0000502 **53.** 7,070,000

	Planet	Mass	Scientific Notation
55.	Venus	4.87×10^{24}	Already in scientific notation
57.	Mars	0.64×10^{24}	6.4×10^{23}
59.	Saturn	586.5×10^{24}	5.865×10^{26}
61.	Neptune	102.4×10^{24}	1.024×10^{26}

Section A.3 Practice Exercises pp. A-14–A-17

1. a. x; y-axis **b.** ordered **c.** origin; $(0, 0)$ **d.** quadrants **e.** negative **f.** III

3., 5., 7.

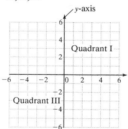

9., 11., 13.

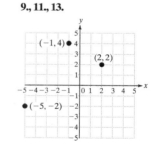

15. First move to the left 1.8 units from the origin. Then go up 3.1 units. Place a dot at the final location. The point is in Quadrant II.

17., 19., 21.

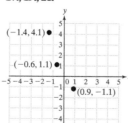

23., 25., 27.

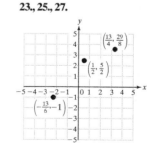

29., 31., 33.

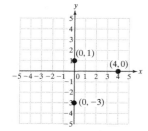

35. Quadrant IV   **37.** Quadrant III   **39.** x-axis
41. y-axis   **43.** Quadrant II   **45.** Quadrant I
47. $(0, 3)$ **49.** $(2, 3)$ **51.** $(-5, -2)$ **53.** $(4, -2)$
55. $(-2, -5)$
57.

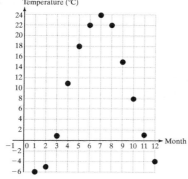

$(1, -6), (2, -5), (3, 1), (4, 11), (5, 18),$
$(6, 22), (7, 24), (8, 22), (9, 15), (10, 8),$
$(11, 1), (12, -4)$

59.

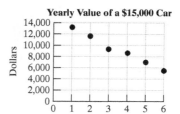

$(1, 13200), (2, 11352), (3, 9649), (4, 8201), (5, 6971),$
$(6, 5925)$

61.

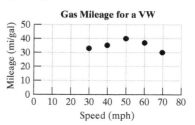

$(30, 33), (40, 35), (50, 40), (60, 37), (70, 30)$

Student Answer Appendix

Chapter 1

Section 1.1 Practice Exercises, pp. 17–21

1. a. product **b.** factors **c.** numerator; b **d.** lowest
e. 1; 4 **f.** reciprocals **g.** multiple **h.** least
3. Numerator: 2; denominator: 3; proper
5. Numerator: 5; denominator: 2; improper
7. Numerator: 4; denominator: 4; improper
9. Numerator: 5; denominator: 1; improper
11. $\frac{3}{4}$ **13.** $\frac{4}{3}$ **15.** $\frac{1}{6}$ **17.** $\frac{2}{3}$ **19.** $\frac{5}{2}$ or $2\frac{1}{2}$ **21.** $\frac{6}{2}$ or 3
23. The set of whole numbers includes the number 0 and the set of natural numbers does not.
25. For example: $\frac{2}{4}$ **27.** Prime **29.** Composite
31. Composite **33.** Prime **35.** $2 \times 2 \times 3 \times 3$
37. $2 \times 3 \times 7$ **39.** $2 \times 5 \times 11$ **41.** $3 \times 3 \times 3 \times 5$
43. $\frac{1}{5}$ **45.** $\frac{8}{3}$ or $2\frac{2}{3}$ **47.** $\frac{7}{8}$ **49.** $\frac{3}{4}$ **51.** $\frac{5}{8}$ **53.** $\frac{4}{3}$ or $1\frac{1}{3}$
55. False: When adding or subtracting fractions, it is necessary to have a common denominator.
57. $\frac{4}{3}$ or $1\frac{1}{3}$ **59.** $\frac{2}{3}$ **61.** $\frac{9}{2}$ or $4\frac{1}{2}$ **63.** $\frac{3}{5}$ **65.** $\frac{5}{3}$ or $1\frac{2}{3}$
67. $\frac{90}{13}$ or $6\frac{12}{13}$ **69.** \$704 **71.** 35 students **73.** 8 pieces
75. 8 jars **77.** $\frac{3}{7}$ **79.** $\frac{1}{2}$ **81.** 30 **83.** 40 **85.** $\frac{7}{8}$
87. $\frac{43}{40}$ or $1\frac{3}{40}$ **89.** $\frac{3}{26}$ **91.** $\frac{29}{36}$ **93.** $\frac{6}{5}$ or $1\frac{1}{5}$ **95.** $\frac{35}{48}$
97. $\frac{7}{24}$ **99.** $\frac{51}{28}$ or $1\frac{23}{28}$ **101.** $\frac{11}{12}$ cup sugar **103.** $\frac{7}{50}$ in.
105. $\frac{46}{5}$ or $9\frac{1}{5}$ **107.** $\frac{1}{6}$ **109.** $\frac{11}{54}$ **111.** $\frac{7}{2}$ or $3\frac{1}{2}$
113. $\frac{13}{8}$ or $1\frac{5}{8}$ **115.** $\frac{59}{12}$ or $4\frac{11}{12}$ **117.** $\frac{1}{8}$ **119.** $8\frac{19}{24}$ in.
121. $1\frac{7}{12}$ hr **123.** $2\frac{1}{4}$ lb **125.** 25 in.

Section 1.2 Calculator Connections, pp. 30–31

1. ≈ 3.464101615 **2.** ≈ 9.949874371
3. ≈ 12.56637061 **4.** ≈ 1.772453851

Section 1.2 Practice Exercises, pp. 31–34

1. a. variable **b.** constants **c.** set **d.** inequalities **e.** a is less than b **f.** c is greater than or equal to d **g.** 5 is not equal to 6
h. opposites **i.** $|a|$; 0 **3.** $8\frac{1}{4}$ or $\frac{33}{4}$ **5.** 15 **7.** 3
9. 4 **11.** 5.3 **13.** $\frac{1}{80}$ **15. a.** \$3.87 **b.** \$10.32
c. \$12.90 **17. a.** 375 calories **b.** 630 calories **c.** 270 calories
19.

$$-6\ -5\ -4\ -3\ -2\ -1\ \ 0\ \ 1\ \ 2\ \ 3\ \ 4\ \ 5\ \ 6$$

21. a; rational **23.** b; rational **25.** a; rational
27. c; irrational **29.** a; rational **31.** a; rational
33. b; rational **35.** c; irrational **37.** For example: $\pi, -\sqrt{2}, \sqrt{3}$
39. For example: $-4, -1, 0$ **41.** For example: $-\frac{3}{4}, \frac{1}{2}, 0.206$

43. $-\frac{3}{2}, -4, 0.\overline{6}, 0, 1$ **45.** 1 **47.** $-4, 0, 1$ **49. a.** >
b. > **c.** < **d.** > **51.** -18 **53.** 6.1 **55.** $\frac{5}{8}$ **57.** $-\frac{7}{3}$
59. 3 **61.** $-\frac{7}{3}$ **63.** 8 **65.** -72.1 **67.** 2 **69.** 1.5
71. -1.5 **73.** $\frac{3}{2}$ **75.** -10 **77.** $-\frac{1}{2}$
79. False, $|n|$ is never negative. **81.** True **83.** False
85. True **87.** False **89.** False **91.** False
93. True **95.** True **97.** False **99.** True
101. True **103.** True **105.** For all $a < 0$

Section 1.3 Calculator Connections, pp. 41–42

1. 2 **2.** 91 **3.** 84 **4.** 12 **5.** 49 **6.** 18
1–3.

```
(4+6)/(8-3)
              2
110-5*(2+1)-4
             91
100-2*(5-3)^3
             84
```

4–6.

```
3+(4-1)2
            12
(12-6+1)2
            49
3*8-√(32+2²)
            18
```

7. 4 **8.** 27 **9.** 0.5

7–9.

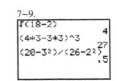

Section 1.3 Practice Exercises, pp. 42–45

1. a. quotient; product; sum; difference **b.** base; exponent; power **c.** 8^2 **d.** p^4 **e.** radical; square **f.** order of operations
3. 56 **5.** -19 **7.** $\left(\frac{1}{6}\right)^4$ **9.** a^3b^2 **11.** $(5c)^5$
13. a. x **b.** Yes, 1 **15.** $x \cdot x \cdot x$ **17.** $2b \cdot 2b \cdot 2b$
19. $10 \cdot y \cdot y \cdot y \cdot y$ **21.** $2 \cdot w \cdot z \cdot z$ **23.** 36 **25.** $\frac{1}{49}$
27. 0.008 **29.** 64 **31.** 9 **33.** 2 **35.** 12 **37.** 4
39. $\frac{1}{3}$ **41.** $\frac{5}{9}$ **43.** 20 **45.** 60 **47.** 8 **49.** 78 **51.** 0
53. $\frac{7}{6}$ **55.** 45 **57.** 16 **59.** 15 **61.** 19 **63.** 75 **65.** 3
67. 39 **69.** 26 **71.** $\frac{5}{12}$ **73.** $\frac{5}{2}$ **75. a.** 0.12
b. Yes. $0.12 < 0.20$ **77.** 57,600 ft² **79.** 21 ft² **81.** $3x$
83. $\frac{x}{7}$ or $x \div 7$ **85.** $2 - a$ **87.** $2y + x$ **89.** $4(x + 12)$
91. $3 - Q$ **93.** $2y^3$; 16 **95.** $|z - 8|$; 2 **97.** $5\sqrt{x}$; 10
99. $yz - x$; 16 **101.** 1 **103.** $\frac{1}{4}$
105. a. $36 \div 4 \cdot 3$ Division must be performed before
$\qquad = 9 \cdot 3$ multiplication.
$\qquad = 27$
b. $36 - 4 + 3$ Subtraction must be performed before
$\qquad = 32 + 3$ addition.
$\qquad = 35$

107. This is acceptable, provided division and multiplication are performed in order from left to right, and subtraction and addition are performed in order from left to right.

Section 1.4 Practice Exercises, pp. 51–53

1. a. negative **b.** b **3.** >   **5.** >   **7.** >   **9.** −6
11. 3   **13.** 3   **15.** −3   **17.** −17   **19.** 7   **21.** −19
23. −23   **25.** −5   **27.** −3   **29.** 0   **31.** 0   **33.** −5
35. −3   **37.** 0   **39.** −23   **41.** −6   **43.** −3   **45.** 21.3
47. $-\dfrac{3}{14}$ **49.** $-\dfrac{1}{6}$ **51.** $-\dfrac{15}{16}$ **53.** $\dfrac{1}{20}$ **55.** −2.4 or $-\dfrac{12}{5}$
57. $\dfrac{1}{4}$ or 0.25   **59.** 0   **61.** $-\dfrac{7}{8}$ **63.** −1   **65.** $\dfrac{11}{9}$
67. −23.08   **69.** −0.002117   **71.** To add two numbers with different signs, subtract the smaller absolute value from the larger absolute value and apply the sign of the number with the larger absolute value.   **73.** −1   **75.** 10   **77.** 5   **79.** 1
81. −6 + (−10); −16   **83.** −3 + 8; 5   **85.** −21 + 17; −4
87. 3(−14 + 20); 18   **89.** [−7 + (−2)] + 5; −4
91. −5 + 13 + (−11); −3°F
93. −8 + 1 + 2 + (−5) = −10; Amara lost 10 lb.
95. a. 52.23 + (−52.95) **b.** Yes   **97.** −6; She was 6 below par.

Section 1.5 Calculator Connections, p. 59

1. −13   **2.** −2   **3.** 711
1–3.

```
-8+(-5)
             -13
4+(-5)+(-1)
              -2
627-(-84)
             711
```

4. −0.18   **5.** −17.7   **6.** −990   **7.** −17   **8.** 38
4–6.

```
-0.06-0.12
             -.18
-3.2+(-14.5)
            -17.7
-472+(-518)
             -990
```

7–8.

```
-12-9+4
              -17
209-108+(-63)
               38
```

Section 1.5 Practice Exercises, pp. 59–62

1. a. $-b$ **b.** positive   **3.** x^2 **5.** $-b + 2$ **7.** 9   **9.** −3
11. −12   **13.** 4   **15.** −2   **17.** 8   **19.** −8   **21.** 2
23. 6   **25.** 40   **27.** −40   **29.** 0   **31.** −20   **33.** −24
35. 25   **37.** −5   **39.** $-\dfrac{3}{2}$ **41.** $\dfrac{41}{24}$ **43.** $\dfrac{2}{5}$ **45.** $-\dfrac{2}{3}$
47. 9.2   **49.** −5.72   **51.** −10   **53.** −14   **55.** −20
57. −173.188   **59.** 3.243   **61.** 6 − (−7); 13
63. 3 − 18; −15   **65.** −5 − (−11); 6   **67.** −1 − (−13); 12
69. −32 − 20; −52   **71.** 200 + 400 + 600 + 800 − 1000; $1000
73. 152°F   **75.** 19,881 m   **77.** 13   **79.** −9   **81.** 5
83. −25   **85.** −2   **87.** $-\dfrac{11}{30}$ **89.** $-\dfrac{29}{9}$ **91.** −2
93. −11   **95.** 2   **97.** −7   **99.** 5   **101.** 5   **103.** 3

Chapter 1 Problem Recognition Exercises, p. 62

1. Add their absolute values and apply a negative sign.
2. Subtract the smaller absolute value from the larger absolute value. Apply the sign of the number with the larger absolute value.
3. a. 6 **b.** −6 **c.** −22 **d.** 22 **e.** −22   **4. a.** −2 **b.** −8
c. −8 **d.** −2 **e.** 8   **5. a.** 0 **b.** 0 **c.** 50 **d.** 0 **e.** −50
6. a. $-\dfrac{1}{6}$ **b.** $\dfrac{1}{6}$ **c.** $-\dfrac{7}{6}$ **d.** $\dfrac{7}{6}$ **e.** $-\dfrac{7}{6}$ **7. a.** −3.6 **b.** 10.6
c. 3.6 **d.** 3.6 **e.** −10.6   **8. a.** 4 **b.** −4 **c.** 6 **d.** 6
9. a. −270 **b.** −110 **c.** −90 **d.** −270   **10. a.** 402
b. −108 **c.** 484 **d.** 24

Section 1.6 Calculator Connections, pp. 69–70

1. −30   **2.** −2   **3.** 625   **4.** 625   **5.** −625   **6.** −5.76
1–3.

```
-6(5)
             -30
-5.2/2.6
              -2
(-5)(-5)(-5)(-5)
             625
```

4–6.

```
(-5)^4
             625
-5^4
            -625
-2.4²
           -5.76
```

7. 5.76   **8.** −1   **9.** 4   **10.** −36
7–8.

```
(-2.4)²
            5.76
(-1)(-1)(-1)
              -1
```

9–10.

```
-8.4/-2.1
               4
90/(-5)(2)
             -36
```

Section 1.6 Practice Exercises, pp. 70–74

1. a. $\dfrac{1}{a}$ **b.** 0 **c.** 0 **d.** undefined **e.** positive **f.** negative
g. 1; $-\dfrac{3}{2}$ **h.** All of these   **3.** True   **5.** False   **7.** −56
9. 143   **11.** −12.76   **13.** $\dfrac{3}{4}$ **15.** 36   **17.** −36
19. $-\dfrac{27}{125}$ **21.** 0.0016   **23.** −6   **25.** $\dfrac{15}{17}$ **27.** 1
29. $-\dfrac{1}{5}$ **31.** (−2)(−7) = 14   **33.** −5 · 0 = 0
35. No number multiplied by zero equals 6.   **37.** (−6)(4) = −24
39. 6   **41.** −6   **43.** −8   **45.** 8   **47.** 0   **49.** Undefined
51. 0   **53.** 0   **55.** $-\dfrac{3}{2}$ **57.** $\dfrac{3}{10}$ **59.** −2   **61.** −7.912
63. 0.092   **65.** −6   **67.** 2.1   **69.** 9   **71.** −9   **73.** $-\dfrac{64}{27}$
75. 340   **77.** $\dfrac{14}{9}$ **79.** −30   **81.** 96   **83.** 2   **85.** −1
87. $-\dfrac{4}{33}$ **89.** $-\dfrac{4}{7}$ **91.** −24   **93.** $-\dfrac{1}{20}$ **95.** −23
97. 12   **99.** $\dfrac{9}{7}$ **101.** Undefined   **103.** −48   **105.** −6
107. −1   **109.** 7   **111.** −4   **113.** −40   **115.** $\dfrac{7}{2}$
117. No. The first expression is equivalent to 10 ÷ (5x). The second is 10 ÷ 5 · x.   **119.** −3.75(0.3); −1.125
121. $\dfrac{16}{5} \div \left(-\dfrac{8}{9}\right)$; $-\dfrac{18}{5}$ **123.** −0.4 + 6(−0.42); −2.92
125. $-\dfrac{1}{4} - 6\left(-\dfrac{1}{3}\right)$; $\dfrac{7}{4}$ **127.** 3(−2) + 3 = −3; loss of $3
129. 2(5) + 3(−3) = 1; Lorne was one sale above quota for the week.
131. $\dfrac{12 + (-15) + 4 + (-9) + 3}{5} = -1$; The average loss was 1 oz.
133. a. −10 **b.** 24 **c.** In part (a), we subtract; in part (b), we multiply.

Chapter 1 Problem Recognition Exercises, p. 74

1. a. −4 **b.** 32 **c.** −12 **d.** 2   **2. a.** 10 **b.** 14 **c.** −24
d. −6   **3. a.** −27 **b.** −324 **c.** −4 **d.** −45   **4. a.** 30
b. 24 **c.** −81 **d.** −9   **5. a.** 50 **b.** −15 **c.** $\dfrac{1}{2}$ **d.** 5
6. a. −5 **b.** −24 **c.** −16 **d.** −80   **7. a.** 64 **b.** 12 **c.** $\dfrac{1}{4}$
d. −20   **8. a.** −7 **b.** −24 **c.** −63 **d.** −18   **9. a.** −400
b. 85 **c.** −16 **d.** 75   **10. a.** 7 **b.** 294 **c.** $\dfrac{2}{3}$ **d.** −35
11. a. 8 **b.** 4 **c.** 4 **d.** 8   **12. a.** −16 **b.** 2 **c.** −2 **d.** 16

Section 1.7 Practice Exercises, pp. 84–87

1. a. constant **b.** coefficient **c.** 1; 1 **d.** like **3.** 7 **5.** 18

7. $-\dfrac{27}{5}$ or -5.4 **9.** 0 **11.** $\dfrac{1}{3}$ **13.** $\dfrac{11}{15}$ **15.** $-8 + 5$

17. $x + 8$ **19.** 4(5) **21.** $-12x$ **23.** $x + (-3); -3 + x$

25. $4p + (-9); -9 + 4p$ **27.** $x + (4 + 9); x + 13$

29. $(-5 \cdot 3)x; -15x$ **31.** $\left(\dfrac{6}{11} \cdot \dfrac{11}{6}\right)x; x$ **33.** $\left(-4 \cdot -\dfrac{1}{4}\right)t; t$

35. $(-8 + 2) + y; -6 + y$ **37.** $(-5 \cdot 2)x; -10x$

39. Reciprocal **41.** 0 **43.** $30x + 6$ **45.** $-2a - 16$

47. $15c - 3d$ **49.** $-7y + 14$ **51.** $-\dfrac{2}{3}x + 4$ **53.** $\dfrac{1}{3}m - 1$

55. $-2p - 10$ **57.** $6w + 10z - 16$ **59.** $4x + 8y - 4z$

61. $6w - x + 3y$ **63.** $6 + 2x$ **65.** $24z$ **67.** $-14x$

69. $-4 - 4x$ **71.** b **73.** i **75.** g **77.** d **79.** h

81.

Term	Coefficient
$2x$	2
$-y$	-1
$18xy$	18
5	5

83.

Term	Coefficient
$-x$	-1
$8y$	8
$-9x^2y$	-9
-3	-3

85. The variable factors are different. **87.** The variables are the same and raised to the same power. **89.** For example: $5y, -2x, 6$

91. $-6p$ **93.** $-6y^2$ **95.** $7x^3y - 4$ **97.** $3t - \dfrac{7}{5}$

99. $-6x + 22$ **101.** $4w$ **103.** $-3x + 17$ **105.** $10t - 44w$

107. $-18u$ **109.** $-2t + 7$ **111.** $51a - 27$ **113.** -6

115. $4q - \dfrac{1}{3}$ **117.** $6n$ **119.** $2x + 18$ **121.** $2.2c - 0.32$

123. $-2x - 34$ **125.** $9z - 35$ **127.** Equivalent

129. Not equivalent. The terms are not *like* terms and cannot be combined. **131.** Not equivalent; subtraction is not commutative.
133. Equivalent **135. a.** 55 **b.** 210

Chapter 1 Review Exercises, pp. 94–96

1. Improper **2.** Proper **3.** Improper **4.** Improper

5. $2 \times 2 \times 2 \times 2 \times 7$ **6.** $\dfrac{6}{5}$ **7.** $\dfrac{35}{36}$ **8.** $\dfrac{13}{16}$ **9.** $\dfrac{2}{7}$

10. $\dfrac{6}{5}$ or $1\dfrac{1}{5}$ **11.** 3 **12.** $\dfrac{17}{10}$ or $1\dfrac{7}{10}$ **13.** 357 million km²

14. a. 7, 1 **b.** 7, -4, 0, 1 **c.** 7, 0, 1 **d.** 7, $\frac{1}{3}$, -4, 0, $-0.\overline{2}$, 1
e. $-\sqrt{3}, \pi$ **f.** 7, $\frac{1}{3}$, -4, 0, $-\sqrt{3}$, $-0.\overline{2}$, π, 1 **15.** $\dfrac{1}{2}$ **16.** 6

17. $\sqrt{7}$ **18.** 0 **19.** False **20.** False **21.** True
22. True **23.** True **24.** True **25.** False **26.** True

27. True **28.** 0 **29.** 60 **30.** 3 **31.** 4 **32.** $x \cdot \dfrac{2}{3}$ or $\dfrac{2}{3}x$

33. $\dfrac{7}{y}$ or $7 \div y$ **34.** $2 + 3b$ **35.** $a - 5$ **36.** $5k + 2$

37. $13z - 7$ **38.** 216 **39.** 225 **40.** 6 **41.** $\dfrac{1}{10}$

42. $\dfrac{1}{16}$ **43.** $\dfrac{27}{8}$ **44.** 13 **45.** 11 **46.** 7 **47.** 10

48. 2 **49.** 4 **50.** 15 **51.** -17 **52.** $\dfrac{11}{63}$ **53.** $-\dfrac{5}{22}$

54. $-\dfrac{14}{15}$ **55.** $-\dfrac{27}{10}$ **56.** -2.15 **57.** -4.28 **58.** 3

59. 8 **60.** 4 **61.** When a and b are both negative or when a and b have different signs and the number with the larger absolute value is negative. **62.** No. He is still overdrawn by \$8. **63.** -12 **64.** 33 **65.** -1 **66.** -17

67. $-\dfrac{29}{18}$ **68.** $-\dfrac{19}{24}$ **69.** -1.2 **70.** -4.25 **71.** -10.2

72. 12.09 **73.** $\dfrac{10}{3}$ **74.** $-\dfrac{17}{20}$ **75.** -1 **76.** If $a < b$

77. $-7 - (-18)$; 11 **78.** $-6 - 41$; -47 **79.** $7 - 13$; -6
80. $[20 - (-7)] - 5$; 22 **81.** $[6 + (-12)] - 21$; -27
82. 175°F **83.** -170 **84.** -91 **85.** -2 **86.** 3

87. $-\dfrac{1}{6}$ **88.** $-\dfrac{8}{11}$ **89.** 0 **90.** Undefined **91.** 0

92. 2.25 **93.** $-\dfrac{3}{2}$ **94.** $\dfrac{1}{4}$ **95.** -30 **96.** 450 **97.** $\dfrac{1}{4}$

98. $-\dfrac{1}{7}$ **99.** -2 **100.** $\dfrac{18}{7}$ **101.** 17 **102.** 6

103. $-\dfrac{7}{120}$ **104.** 4.4 **105.** $-\dfrac{1}{3}$ **106.** -1 **107.** -2

108. 11 **109.** 36 **110.** -6 **111.** 70.6 **112.** True
113. False, any nonzero real number raised to an even power is positive. **114.** True **115.** True **116.** False, the product of two negative numbers is positive. **117.** True **118.** True
119. For example: $2 + 3 = 3 + 2$ **120.** For example: $(2 + 3) + 4 = 2 + (3 + 4)$ **121.** For example: $5 + (-5) = 0$
122. For example: $7 + 0 = 7$ **123.** For example: $5 \cdot 2 = 2 \cdot 5$
124. For example: $(8 \cdot 2)10 = 8(2 \cdot 10)$
125. For example: $3 \cdot \dfrac{1}{3} = 1$ **126.** For example: $8 \cdot 1 = 8$
127. $5x - 2y = 5x + (-2y)$, then use the commutative property of addition.
128. $3a - 9y = 3a + (-9y)$, then use the commutative property of addition. **129.** $3y, 10x, -12, xy$ **130.** 3, 10, -12, 1
131. $8a - b - 10$ **132.** $-7p - 11q + 16$ **133.** $-8z - 18$
134. $20w - 40y + 5$ **135.** $p - 2w$ **136.** $-h + 14m$
137. $-14q - 1$ **138.** $-5.7b + 2.4$ **139.** $4x + 24$
140. $50y + 105$

Chapter 1 Test, pp. 96–97

1. $\dfrac{15}{4}$ **2.** $\dfrac{3}{2}$ **3.** $3\dfrac{1}{16}$ **4.** $2\dfrac{3}{8}$

5. Rational, all repeating decimals are rational numbers.
6. a. $(4x)(4x)(4x)$ **b.** $4 \cdot x \cdot x \cdot x$
7.

8. a. False **b.** True **c.** True **d.** True **9. a.** Commutative property of multiplication **b.** Identity property of addition
c. Associative property of addition **d.** Inverse property of multiplication **e.** Associative property of multiplication
10. a. Twice the difference of a and b **b.** b subtracted from twice a

11. $\dfrac{\sqrt{c}}{d^2}$ or $\sqrt{c} \div d^2$ **12.** $12 - (-4)$; 16 **13.** $6 - 8$; -2

14. $\dfrac{10}{-12}$; $-\dfrac{5}{6}$ **15.** $-\dfrac{7}{8}$ **16.** -12 **17.** 28 **18.** -12

19. -32 **20.** 96 **21.** 0 **22.** Undefined **23.** 6 **24.** 4.66

25. -28 **26.** $\dfrac{2}{3}$ **27.** $\dfrac{1}{3}$ **28.** 9 **29.** -8 **30.** The difference is 9.5°C. **31. a.** $5 + 2 + (-10) + 4$ **b.** He gained 1 yd.
32. $-6k - 8$ **33.** $-12x + 2y - 4$ **34.** $-4p - 23$
35. $-12m - 24p + 21$ **36.** $4p - \dfrac{4}{3}$ **37.** 5 **38.** 18
39. -6 **40.** -32

SA-4   Student Answer Appendix

Chapter 2

Section 2.1 Practice Exercises, pp. 109–111

1. a. equation **b.** solution **c.** linear **d.** solution set
3. Expression **5.** Equation **7.** Substitute the value into the equation and determine if the right-hand side is equal to the left-hand side. **9.** No **11.** Yes **13.** Yes **15.** $\{-1\}$
17. $\{20\}$ **19.** $\{-17\}$ **21.** $\{-16\}$ **23.** $\{0\}$ **25.** $\{1.3\}$
27. $\left\{\frac{11}{2}\right\}$ or $\left\{5\frac{1}{2}\right\}$ **29.** $\{-2\}$ **31.** $\{-2.13\}$ **33.** $\{-3.2675\}$
35. $\{9\}$ **37.** $\{-4\}$ **39.** $\{0\}$ **41.** $\{-15\}$ **43.** $\left\{-\frac{4}{5}\right\}$
45. $\{-10\}$ **47.** $\{4\}$ **49.** $\{41\}$ **51.** $\{-127\}$
53. $\{-2.6\}$ **55.** $-8 + x = 42$; The number is 50.
57. $x - (-6) = 18$; The number is 12.
59. $x \cdot 7 = -63$ or $7x = -63$; The number is -9.
61. $x - 3.2 = 2.1$; The number is 5.3.
63. $\frac{x}{12} = \frac{1}{3}$; The number is 4.
65. $x + \frac{5}{8} = \frac{13}{8}$; The number is 1. **67. a.** $\{10\}$ **b.** $\left\{-\frac{1}{9}\right\}$
69. a. $\{-12\}$ **b.** $\left\{\frac{22}{3}\right\}$ **71.** $\{-36\}$ **73.** $\{16\}$ **75.** $\{2\}$
77. $\left\{-\frac{7}{4}\right\}$ **79.** $\{11\}$ **81.** $\{-36\}$ **83.** $\left\{\frac{7}{2}\right\}$ **85.** $\{4\}$
87. $\{3.6\}$ **89.** $\{0.4084\}$ **91.** Yes **93.** No **95.** Yes
97. Yes **99.** For example: $y + 9 = 15$ **101.** For example:
$2p = -8$ **103.** For example: $5a + 5 = 5$ **105.** $\{-1\}$ **107.** $\{7\}$

Section 2.2 Practice Exercises, pp. 118–120

1. a. conditional **b.** contradiction **c.** empty or null
d. identity **3.** $4w + 8$ **5.** $6y - 22$ **7.** $\{19\}$ **9.** $\{-3\}$
11. $\{-5\}$ **13.** $\{2\}$ **15.** $\{6\}$ **17.** $\left\{\frac{5}{2}\right\}$ **19.** $\{-42\}$
21. $\left\{-\frac{3}{4}\right\}$ **23.** $\{5\}$ **25.** $\{-4\}$ **27.** $\{-26\}$ **29.** $\{10\}$
31. $\{-8\}$ **33.** $\left\{-\frac{7}{3}\right\}$ **35.** $\{0\}$ **37.** $\{-3\}$ **39.** $\{-2\}$
41. $\left\{\frac{9}{2}\right\}$ **43.** $\left\{-\frac{1}{3}\right\}$ **45.** $\{10\}$ **47.** $\{-6\}$ **49.** $\{0\}$
51. $\{-2\}$ **53.** $\left\{-\frac{25}{4}\right\}$ **55.** $\left\{\frac{10}{3}\right\}$ **57.** $\{-0.25\}$
59. $\{ \}$; contradiction **61.** $\{-15\}$; conditional equation
63. The set of real numbers; identity **65.** One solution
67. Infinitely many solutions **69.** $\{7\}$ **71.** $\left\{\frac{1}{2}\right\}$ **73.** $\{0\}$
75. The set of real numbers **77.** $\{-46\}$ **79.** $\{2\}$
81. $\left\{\frac{13}{2}\right\}$ **83.** $\{-5\}$ **85.** $\{ \}$ **87.** $\{2.205\}$ **89.** $\{10\}$
91. $\{-1\}$ **93.** $a = 15$ **95.** $a = 4$
97. For example: $5x + 2 = 2 + 5x$

Section 2.3 Practice Exercises, pp. 126–127

1. a. clearing fractions **b.** clearing decimals **3.** $\{-2\}$
5. $\{-5\}$ **7.** $\{ \}$ **9.** $18, 36$ **11.** $100; 1000; 10,000$
13. $30, 60$ **15.** $\{4\}$ **17.** $\{-12\}$ **19.** $\left\{-\frac{15}{4}\right\}$
21. $\{8\}$ **23.** $\{3\}$ **25.** $\{15\}$ **27.** $\{ \}$
29. The set of real numbers **31.** $\{5\}$ **33.** $\{2\}$ **35.** $\{-15\}$
37. $\{6\}$ **39.** $\{107\}$ **41.** The set of real numbers **43.** $\{67\}$
45. $\{90\}$ **47.** $\{4\}$ **49.** $\{4\}$ **51.** $\{ \}$ **53.** $\{-0.25\}$
55. $\{-6\}$ **57.** $\left\{\frac{8}{3}\right\}$ or $\left\{2\frac{2}{3}\right\}$ **59.** $\{-11\}$ **61.** $\left\{\frac{1}{10}\right\}$
63. $\{-2\}$ **65.** $\{-1\}$ **67.** $\{2\}$

Chapter 2 Problem Recognition Exercises, p. 128

1. Expression; $-4b + 18$ **2.** Expression; $20p - 30$
3. Equation; $\{-8\}$ **4.** Equation; $\{-14\}$

5. Equation; $\left\{\frac{1}{3}\right\}$ **6.** Equation; $\left\{-\frac{4}{3}\right\}$
7. Expression; $6z - 23$ **8.** Expression; $-x - 9$
9. Equation; $\left\{\frac{7}{9}\right\}$ **10.** Equation; $\left\{-\frac{13}{10}\right\}$
11. Equation; $\{20\}$ **12.** Equation; $\{-3\}$
13. Equation; $\left\{\frac{1}{2}\right\}$ **14.** Equation; $\{-6\}$
15. Expression; $\frac{5}{8}x + \frac{7}{4}$ **16.** Expression; $-26t + 18$
17. Equation; $\{ \}$ **18.** Equation; $\{ \}$
19. Equation; $\left\{\frac{23}{12}\right\}$ **20.** Equation; $\left\{\frac{5}{8}\right\}$
21. Equation; The set of real numbers
22. Equation; The set of real numbers
23. Equation; $\left\{\frac{1}{2}\right\}$ **24.** Equation; $\{0\}$
25. Expression; 0 **26.** Expression; -1
27. Expression; $2a + 13$ **28.** Expression; $8q + 3$
29. Equation; $\{10\}$ **30.** Equation; $\left\{-\frac{1}{20}\right\}$
31. Expression; $-\frac{1}{6}y + \frac{1}{3}$ **32.** Expression; $\frac{7}{10}x + \frac{2}{5}$

Section 2.4 Practice Exercises, pp. 135–138

1. a. consecutive **b.** even **c.** odd **d.** 1 **e.** 2 **f.** 2
3. $x - 5,682,080$ **5.** $10x$ **7.** $3x - 20$ **9.** The number is -4.
11. The number is -3. **13.** The number is 5. **15.** The number is -5. **17.** The number is 3. **19. a.** $x + 1, x + 2$
b. $x - 1, x - 2$ **21.** The integers are -34 and -33.
23. The integers are 13 and 15. **25.** The sides are 14 in., 15 in., 16 in., 17 in., and 18 in. **27.** The integers are -54, -52, and -50.
29. The integers are 13, 15, and 17. **31.** The lengths of the pieces are 33 cm and 53 cm. **33.** Karen's music library has 23 playlists and Claran's library has 35 playlists. **35.** There were 201 Republicans and 232 Democrats. **37.** There were 190 passenger cars and 230 SUVs sold. **39.** The Congo River is 4370 km long, and the Nile River is 6825 km. **41.** The area of Africa is 30,065,000 km². The area of Asia is 44,579,000 km².
43. They walked 12.3 mi on the first day and 8.2 mi on the second.
45. The pieces are 9 in., 17 in., and 22 in. **47.** The integers are 42, 43, and 44. **49.** The winner earned $14 million and the runner-up earned $5 million. **51.** The number is 11. **53.** The page numbers are 470 and 471. **55.** The number is 10. **57.** The deepest point in the Arctic Ocean is 5122 m.
59. The number is $\frac{7}{16}$. **61.** The number is 2.5.

Section 2.5 Practice Exercises, pp. 143–146

1. a. simple **b.** 100 **3.** The numbers are 21 and 22.
5. 12.5% **7.** 85% **9.** 0.75 **11.** 1050.8
13. 885 **15.** 2200 **17.** Molly will have to pay $106.99.
19. Approximately 231,000 cases **21.** 2% **23.** Javon's taxable income was $84,000. **25.** Aidan would earn $9 more in the CD.
27. Bob borrowed $1200. **29.** The rate is 6%.
31. Perry needs to invest $3302. **33. a.** $7.44 **b.** $54.56
35. The original price was $470.59. **37.** The discount rate is 12%.
39. The original dosage was 15 cc. **41.** The tax rate is 5%.
43. The original cost was $11.58 per pack.
45. The original price was $210,000. **47.** Alina made $4600 that month. **49.** Diane sold $645 over $200 worth of merchandise.

Section 2.6 Calculator Connections, p. 152

1. 140.056 **2.** 31.831 **3.** 1.273 **4.** 0.455
1–2. 3–4.

```
880/(2π)
          140.0563499
1600/(π*(4)²)
          31.83098862
```

```
20/(5π)
          1.273239545
10/(7π)
          .4547284088
```

Section 2.6 Practice Exercises, pp. 152–156

1. $\{-5\}$ **3.** $\{0\}$ **5.** $\{-2\}$ **7.** $\{\}$ **9.** $a = P - b - c$

11. $y = x + z$ **13.** $q = p - 250$ **15.** $b = \dfrac{A}{h}$

17. $t = \dfrac{PV}{nr}$ **19.** $x = 5 + y$ **21.** $y = -3x - 19$

23. $y = \dfrac{-2x + 6}{3}$ or $y = -\dfrac{2}{3}x + 2$

25. $x = \dfrac{y + 9}{-2}$ or $x = -\dfrac{1}{2}y - \dfrac{9}{2}$

27. $y = \dfrac{-4x + 12}{-3}$ or $y = \dfrac{4}{3}x - 4$

29. $y = \dfrac{-ax + c}{b}$ or $y = -\dfrac{a}{b}x + \dfrac{c}{b}$

31. $t = \dfrac{A - P}{Pr}$ or $t = \dfrac{A}{Pr} - \dfrac{1}{r}$

33. $c = \dfrac{a - 2b}{2}$ or $c = \dfrac{a}{2} - b$ **35.** $y = 2Q - x$

37. $a = MS$ **39.** $R = \dfrac{P}{I^2}$

41. The length is 7 ft and the width is 5 ft.
43. The length is 120 yd and the width is 30 yd.
45. The length is 195 m and the width is 100 m.
47. The sides are 22 m, 22 m, and 27 m.
49. "Adjacent supplementary angles form a straight angle." The words *Supplementary* and *Straight* both begin with the same letter.
51. The angles are 23.5° and 66.5°.
53. The angles are 34.8° and 145.2°.
55. $x = 20$; the vertical angles measure 37°.
57. The measures of the angles are 30°, 60°, and 90°.
59. The measures of the angles are 42°, 54°, and 84°.
61. $x = 17$; the measures of the angles are 34° and 56°.

63. a. $A = lw$ **b.** $w = \dfrac{A}{l}$ **c.** The width is 29.5 ft.

65. a. $P = 2l + 2w$ **b.** $l = \dfrac{P - 2w}{2}$ **c.** The length is 103 m.

67. a. $C = 2\pi r$ **b.** $r = \dfrac{C}{2\pi}$ **c.** The radius is approximately 140 ft.

69. a. 415.48 m^2 **b.** 10,386.89 m^3

Section 2.7 Practice Exercises, pp. 161–165

1. a. $x = \dfrac{c + by}{a}$ **3.** $y = \dfrac{18 - 7x}{x}$ **5.** $\{4\}$

7. $200 - t$ **9.** $100 - x$ **11.** $3000 - y$
13. 53 tickets were sold at \$3 and 28 tickets were sold at \$2.
15. There were 17 songs purchased at \$1.29 and 8 songs purchased at \$1.49.
17. Amber bought 21 books at \$6.99 and 11 books at \$9.99.   **19.** $x + 7$
21. $d + 2000$ **23.** Mix 500 gal of 5% ethanol fuel mixture.
25. The pharmacist needs to use 21 mL of the 1% saline solution.
27. The contractor needs to mix 6.75 oz of 50% acid solution.
29. a. 300 mi   **b.** $5x$ **c.** $5(x + 12)$ or $5x + 60$ **31.** She walks 4 mph to the lake.   **33.** Bryan hiked 6 mi up the canyon.
35. The plane travels 600 mph in still air.   **37.** The slower car travels 48 mph and the faster car travels 52 mph.   **39.** The speeds of the vehicles are 40 mph and 50 mph.   **41.** Sarah walks 3.5 mph and Jeanette runs 7 mph.   **43. a.** 2 lb   **b.** $0.10x$
c. $0.10(x + 3) = 0.10x + 0.30$ **45.** Mix 10 lb of coffee sold at \$12 per pound and 40 lb of coffee sold at \$8 per pound.   **47.** The boats will meet in $\frac{3}{4}$ hr (45 min).   **49.** Sam purchased 16 packages of wax and 5 bottles of sunscreen.   **51.** 2.5 quarts of 85% chlorine solution
53. 20 L of water must be added.   **55.** The Japanese bullet train travels 300 km/hr and the Acela Express travels 240 km/hr.

Section 2.8 Practice Exercises, pp. 176–180

1. a. linear inequality   **b.** inequality   **c.** set-builder; interval

3. $\{-3\}$ **5.**   **7.**   **9.**

11.   **13.**   **15.**

Set-Builder Notation	Graph	Interval Notation
17. $\{x \mid x \ge 6\}$		$[6, \infty)$
19. $\{x \mid x \le 2.1\}$		$(-\infty, 2.1]$
21. $\{x \mid -2 < x \le 7\}$		$(-2, 7]$

Set-Builder Notation	Graph	Interval Notation
23. $\left\{x \mid x > \dfrac{3}{4}\right\}$		$\left(\dfrac{3}{4}, \infty\right)$
25. $\{x \mid -1 < x < 8\}$		$(-1, 8)$
27. $\{x \mid x \le -14\}$		$(-\infty, -14]$

Set-Builder Notation	Graph	Interval Notation
29. $\{x \mid x \ge 18\}$		$[18, \infty)$
31. $\{x \mid x < -0.6\}$		$(-\infty, -0.6)$
33. $\{x \mid -3.5 \le x < 7.1\}$		$[-3.5, 7.1)$

35. a. $\{3\}$
b. $\{x \mid x > 3\}$; $(3, \infty)$

37. a. $\{13\}$
b. $\{p \mid p \le 13\}$; $(-\infty, 13]$

39. a. $\{-3\}$
b. $\{c \mid c < -3\}$; $(-\infty, -3)$

41. a. $\left\{-\dfrac{3}{2}\right\}$
b. $\left\{z \mid z \ge -\dfrac{3}{2}\right\}$; $\left[-\dfrac{3}{2}, \infty\right)$

43. $(-1, 4]$

45. $(-3, 5)$

47. $[2, 6]$

49. a. $\{x \mid x \le 1\}$ **b.** $(-\infty, 1]$

51. a. $\{q \mid q > 10\}$
b. $(10, \infty)$

53. a. $\{x \mid x > 3\}$
b. $(3, \infty)$

55. a. $\{c \mid c > 2\}$
b. $(2, \infty)$

57. a. $\{c \mid c < -2\}$
b. $(-\infty, -2)$

59. a. $\{h \mid h \ge 14\}$
b. $[14, \infty)$

61. a. $\{x \mid x \ge -24\}$
b. $[-24, \infty)$

63. a. $\{p \mid -3 \le p < 3\}$
b. $[-3, 3)$

65. a. $\left\{h \mid 0 < h < \dfrac{5}{2}\right\}$
b. $\left(0, \dfrac{5}{2}\right)$

67. a. $\{x \mid 10 < x < 12\}$
b. $(10, 12)$

69. a. $\{x \mid -8 \le x < 24\}$
b. $[-8, 24)$

SA-6   Student Answer Appendix

71. a. $\{y|y > -9\}$

b. $(-9, \infty)$

73. a. $\left\{x\middle|x \ge -\dfrac{15}{2}\right\}$

b. $\left[-\dfrac{15}{2}, \infty\right)$

75. a. $\{x|x < -3\}$

b. $(-\infty, -3)$

77. a. $\left\{b\middle|b \ge -\dfrac{1}{3}\right\}$

b. $\left[-\dfrac{1}{3}, \infty\right)$

79. a. $\{n|n > -3\}$
b. $(-3, \infty)$

81. a. $\{x|x < 7\}$
b. $(-\infty, 7)$

83. a. $\{x|x \le -5\}$
b. $(-\infty, -5]$

85. a. $\{z|z \le -2\}$
b. $(-\infty, -2]$

87. a. $\left\{a\middle|a > -\dfrac{2}{3}\right\}$

b. $\left(-\dfrac{2}{3}, \infty\right)$

89. a. $\left\{p\middle|p \le \dfrac{15}{4}\right\}$

b. $\left(-\infty, \dfrac{15}{4}\right]$

91. a. $\{y|y < -9\}$
b. $(-\infty, -9)$

93. a. $\{a|a > -3\}$
b. $(-3, \infty)$

95. a. $\{x|x \le 0\}$ **b.** $(-\infty, 0]$

97. No   **99.** Yes   **101.** $L \ge 10$ **103.** $w > 75$
105. $t \le 72$ **107.** $L \ge 8$ **109.** $2 < h < 5$
111. More than 10.2 in. of rain is needed.   **113.** Trevor needs at least 86 to get a B in the course.   **115. a.** $1539
b. 200 birdhouses cost $1440. It is cheaper to purchase 200 birdhouses because the discount is greater.   **117.** Company A is better if more than 400 flyers are printed.   **119.** Madison needs to babysit a minimum of 39.5 hr.

Chapter 2 Review Exercises, pp. 187–190

1. a. Equation **b.** Expression **c.** Equation **d.** Equation
2. A linear equation can be written in the form $ax + b = c, a \ne 0$.
3. a. No **b.** Yes **c.** No **d.** Yes   **4. a.** No **b.** Yes
5. $\{-8\}$ **6.** $\{15\}$ **7.** $\left\{\dfrac{21}{4}\right\}$ **8.** $\{70\}$ **9.** $\left\{-\dfrac{21}{5}\right\}$

10. $\{-60\}$ **11.** $\left\{-\dfrac{10}{7}\right\}$ **12.** $\{27\}$ **13.** The number is 60.

14. The number is $\dfrac{7}{24}$.   **15.** The number is -8.

16. The number is -2.   **17.** $\{1\}$ **18.** $\left\{-\dfrac{3}{5}\right\}$ **19.** $\{2\}$

20. $\{-6\}$ **21.** $\{-3\}$ **22.** $\{18\}$ **23.** $\left\{\dfrac{3}{4}\right\}$ **24.** $\{-3\}$

25. $\{0\}$ **26.** $\left\{\dfrac{1}{8}\right\}$ **27.** $\{2\}$ **28.** $\{6\}$ **29.** A contradiction has no solution and an identity is true for all real numbers.
30. Identity   **31.** Conditional equation   **32.** Contradiction
33. Identity   **34.** Contradiction   **35.** Conditional equation
36. $\{6\}$ **37.** $\{22\}$ **38.** $\{13\}$ **39.** $\{-27\}$ **40.** $\{-10\}$
41. $\{-7\}$ **42.** $\left\{\dfrac{5}{3}\right\}$ **43.** $\left\{-\dfrac{9}{4}\right\}$ **44.** $\{2.5\}$ **45.** $\{-4\}$
46. $\{-4.2\}$ **47.** $\{2.5\}$ **48.** $\{-312\}$ **49.** $\{200\}$ **50.** $\{ \}$
51. $\{ \}$ **52.** The set of real numbers   **53.** The set of real numbers   **54.** The number is 30.   **55.** The number is 11.
56. The number is -7.   **57.** The number is -10.
58. The integers are 66, 68, and 70.   **59.** The integers are 27, 28, and 29.   **60.** The sides are 25 in., 26 in., and 27 in.

61. The sides are 36 cm, 37 cm, 38 cm, 39 cm, and 40 cm.
62. In 1975 the minimum salary was $16,000.
63. Indiana has 6.2 million people and Kentucky has 4.1 million.
64. 23.8   **65.** 28.8   **66.** 12.5%   **67.** 95%   **68.** 160
69. 1750   **70.** The dinner was $40 before tax and tip.
71. a. $840   **b.** $3840   **72.** He invested $12,000.
73. The novel originally cost $29.50.   **74.** $K = C + 273$

75. $C = K - 273$ **76.** $s = \dfrac{P}{4}$ **77.** $s = \dfrac{P}{3}$

78. $x = \dfrac{y - b}{m}$ **79.** $x = \dfrac{c - a}{b}$ **80.** $y = \dfrac{-2x - 2}{5}$

81. $b = \dfrac{Q - 4a}{4}$ or $b = \dfrac{Q}{4} - a$ **82.** The height is 7 m.

83. a. $h = \dfrac{3V}{\pi r^2}$ **b.** The height is 5.1 in.   **84.** The angles are $22°, 78°,$ and $80°$.   **85.** The angles are $50°$ and $40°$.

86. The length is 5 ft and the width is 4 ft.   **87.** $x = 20$. The angle measure is $65°$.   **88.** The measure of angle y is $53°$.
89. The truck travels 45 km/hr in bad weather and 60 km/hr in good weather.   **90.** Gus rides 15 mph and Winston rides 18 mph.
91. The cars will be 327.6 mi apart after 2.8 hr (2 hr and 48 min).
92. They meet in 2.25 hr (2 hr and 15 min).   **93.** 2 lb of 24% fat content beef is needed.   **94.** 20 lb of the 40% solder should be used.
95. $(-2, \infty)$

96. $\left(-\infty, \dfrac{1}{2}\right]$

97. $(-1, 4]$

98. a. $637   **b.** 300 plants cost $1410, and 295 plants cost $1416. 295 plants cost more.
99. $\{c|c < 17\}$; $(-\infty, 17)$

100. $\left\{w\middle|w > -\dfrac{1}{3}\right\}$; $\left(-\dfrac{1}{3}, \infty\right)$

101. $\{x|x \le -6\}$; $(-\infty, -6]$

102. $\left\{y\middle|y \le -\dfrac{14}{5}\right\}$; $\left(-\infty, -\dfrac{14}{5}\right]$

103. $\{a|a \ge 49\}$; $[49, \infty)$

104. $\{t|t < 34.5\}$; $(-\infty, 34.5)$

105. $\{k|k > 18\}$; $(18, \infty)$

106. $\left\{h\middle|h \le \dfrac{5}{2}\right\}$; $\left(-\infty, \dfrac{5}{2}\right]$

107. $\{x|x < -1\}$; $(-\infty, -1)$

108. $\{b|-3 < b \le 7\}$; $(-3, 7]$

109. $\{z|-6 \le z \le 5\}$; $[-6, 5]$

110. More than 2.5 in. is required.
111. Collette can have at most 18 wings.

Chapter 2 Test, pp. 190–191

1. b, d   **2. a.** $5x + 7$ **b.** $\{9\}$ **3.** $\left\{\dfrac{7}{3}\right\}$ **4.** $\{ \}$

5. $\{-16\}$ **6.** $\left\{\dfrac{13}{4}\right\}$ **7.** $\{12\}$ **8.** $\left\{\dfrac{20}{21}\right\}$ **9.** $\left\{-\dfrac{16}{9}\right\}$

10. $\{15\}$ **11.** The set of real numbers   **12.** $\{-3\}$
13. $\{-47\}$ **14.** $y = -3x - 4$ **15.** $r = \dfrac{C}{2\pi}$ **16.** 90

17. a. $(-\infty, 0)$ **b.** $[-2, 5)$

18. $\{x|x > -2\}$; $(-2, \infty)$ **19.** $\{x|x \le -4\}$; $(-\infty, -4]$

20. $\left\{y \mid y > -\frac{3}{2}\right\}; \left(-\frac{3}{2}, \infty\right)$

21. $\{p \mid -5 \le p \le 1\}; [-5, 1]$

22. The cost was $82.00.   **23.** Clarita originally borrowed $5000.
24. The numbers are 18 and 13.   **25.** One family travels 55 mph
and the other travels 50 mph.   **26.** More than 26.5 in. is required.
27. The sides are 61 in., 62 in., 63 in., 64 in., and 65 in.
28. Matthew needs 30 lb of macadamia nuts.
29. Each basketball ticket was $36.32, and each hockey ticket
was $40.64.   **30.** The measures of the angles are 32° and 58°.
31. The field is 110 m long and 75 m wide.   **32.** $y = 30$;
The measures of the angles are 30°, 39°, and 111°.

Chapters 1–2 Cumulative Review Exercises, pp. 191–192

1. $\frac{1}{2}$ **2.** -7 **3.** $-\frac{5}{12}$ **4.** 16   **5.** 4

6. $\sqrt{5^2 - 9}; 4$ **7.** $-14 + 12; -2$ **8.** $-7x^2y, 4xy, -6$

9. $9x + 13$ **10.** $\{4\}$ **11.** $\{-7.2\}$

12. The set of real numbers   **13.** $\{-8\}$ **14.** $\left\{-\frac{4}{7}\right\}$

15. $\{-80\}$ **16.** The numbers are 77 and 79.   **17.** The
cost before tax was $350.00.   **18.** The height is $\frac{41}{6}$ cm or $6\frac{5}{6}$ cm.
19. $\{x \mid x > -2\}; (-2, \infty)$ **20.** $\{x \mid -1 \le x \le 9\}; [-1, 9]$

Chapter 3

Section 3.1 Practice Exercises, pp. 198–203

1. a. x; y-axis   **b.** ordered   **c.** origin; $(0, 0)$ **d.** quadrants
e. negative   **f.** III   **3. a.** Month 10   **b.** 30   **c.** Between months 3
and 5 and between months 10 and 12   **d.** Months 8 and 9
e. Month 3   **f.** 80   **5. a.** On day 1 the price per share was $89.25.
b. $1.75   **c.** $-$2.75

7. 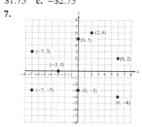   **9.**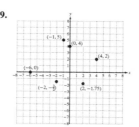

11. IV   **13.** II   **15.** III   **17.** I
19. $(0, -5)$ lies on the y-axis.   **21.** $\left(\frac{7}{8}, 0\right)$ is located on the x-axis.
23. $A(-4, 2), B(\frac{1}{2}, 4), C(3, -4), D(-3, -4), E(0, -3), F(5, 0)$
25. a. $A(400, 200), B(200, -150), C(-300, -200),$
$D(-300, 250), E(0, 450)$ **b.** 450 m   **27. a.** $(250, 225), (175, 193),$
$(315, 330), (220, 209), (450, 570), (400, 480), (190, 185)$; the ordered
pair $(250, 225)$ means that 250 people produce $225 in popcorn sales.
b.

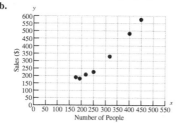

29. a. $(1, -10.2), (2, -9.0), (3, -2.5), (4, 5.7), (5, 13.0), (6, 18.3),$
$(7, 20.9), (8, 19.6), (9, 14.8), (10, 8.7), (11, 2.0), (12, -6.9)$
b.

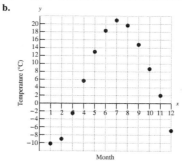

31. a.

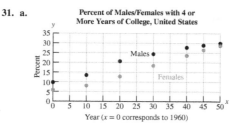

b. Increasing   **c.** Increasing

Section 3.2 Calculator Connections, pp. 211–212

1.
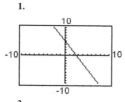

2.
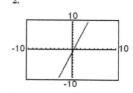

3.
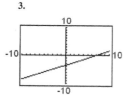

4.
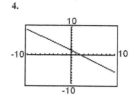

5.
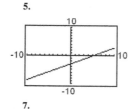

6.
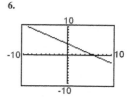

7.
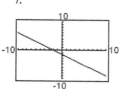

8.
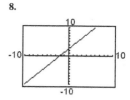

SA-8   Student Answer Appendix

9.

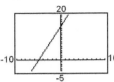

10.

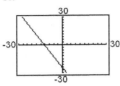

11.

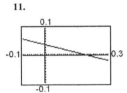

12.

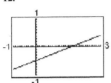

Section 3.2 Practice Exercises, pp. 212–218

1. a. $Ax + By = C$ **b.** x-intercept   **c.** y-intercept
d. vertical   **e.** horizontal   **3.** $(-2, -2)$; quadrant III
5. $(-5, 0)$; x-axis   **7.** $(-3, 2)$; quadrant II   **9.** Yes
11. Yes   **13.** No   **15.** No   **17.** Yes

19.

x	y
1	−3
−2	0
−3	1
−4	2

21.

x	y
−2	3
−1	0
−4	9

23.

x	y
0	4
2	0
3	−2

25.

x	y
0	−2
5	−5
10	−8

27.

x	y
0	−2
−3	−2
5	−2

29.

x	y
3/2	−1
3/2	2
3/2	−3

31.

x	y
0	4.6
1	3.4
2	2.2

33.

35.

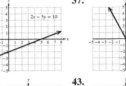

37.

39.

41.

43.

45. y-axis   **47.** x-intercept: $(-1, 0)$; y-intercept: $(0, -3)$
49. x-intercept: $(-4, 0)$; y-intercept: $(0, 1)$
51. x-intercept: $\left(-\dfrac{9}{4}, 0\right)$;   **53.** x-intercept: $\left(\dfrac{8}{3}, 0\right)$;
y-intercept: $(0, 3)$ y-intercept: $(0, 2)$

55. x-intercept: $(-4, 0)$;   **57.** x-intercept: $(0, 0)$;
y-intercept: $(0, 8)$ y-intercept: $(0, 0)$

59. x-intercept: $(10, 0)$;   **61.** x-intercept: $(0, 0)$;
y-intercept: $(0, 5)$ y-intercept: $(0, 0)$

63. True   **65.** True
67. a. Horizontal line   **69. a.** Vertical line
c. no x-intercept;   **c.** x-intercept: $(4, 0)$;
y-intercept: $(0, -1)$ no y-intercept

71. a. Horizontal line **c.** no x-intercept; y-intercept: $(0, 3)$

73. a. Vertical line **c.** All points on the y-axis are y-intercepts; x-intercept: $(0, 0)$

75. A horizontal line may not have an x-intercept. A vertical line may not have a y-intercept. **77.** a, b, d **79. a.** $y = 11,190$ **b.** $x = 3$ **c.** $(1, 11190)$ One year after purchase the value of the car is $11,190. $(3, 9140)$ Three years after purchase the value of the car is $9140.

Section 3.3 Practice Exercises, pp. 225–231

1. a. slope; $\dfrac{y_2 - y_1}{x_2 - x_1}$ **b.** parallel **c.** right **d.** -1
e. undefined; horizontal

3. x-intercept: $(6, 0)$; y-intercept: $(0, -2)$

5. x-intercept: none; y-intercept: $\left(0, \dfrac{3}{2}\right)$

7. $m = \dfrac{1}{3}$ **9.** $m = \dfrac{6}{11}$ **11.** undefined **13.** positive

15. Negative **17.** Zero **19.** Undefined **21.** Positive

23. Negative **25.** $m = \dfrac{1}{2}$ **27.** $m = -3$ **29.** $m = 0$

31. The slope is undefined. **33.** $\dfrac{1}{3}$ **35.** -3 **37.** $\dfrac{3}{5}$

39. Zero **41.** Undefined **43.** $\dfrac{28}{5}$ **45.** $-\dfrac{7}{8}$

47. -0.45 or $-\dfrac{9}{20}$ **49.** -0.15 or $-\dfrac{3}{20}$ **51. a.** -2 **b.** $\dfrac{1}{2}$

53. a. 0 **b.** undefined **55. a.** $\dfrac{4}{5}$ **b.** $-\dfrac{5}{4}$ **57.** Perpendicular

59. Parallel **61.** Neither **63.** l_1: $m = 2$, l_2: $m = 2$; parallel

65. l_1: $m = 5$, l_2: $m = -\dfrac{1}{5}$; perpendicular

67. l_1: $m = \dfrac{1}{4}$, l_2: $m = 4$; neither **69.** The average rate of change is $-\$160$ per year. **71. a.** $m = 47$ **b.** The number of male prisoners increased at a rate of 47 thousand per year during this time period. **73. a.** 1 mi **b.** 2 mi **c.** 3 mi **d.** $m = 0.2$; The distance between a lightning strike and an observer increases by 0.2 mi for every additional second between seeing lightning and hearing thunder.

75. $m = \dfrac{3}{4}$ **77.** $m = 0$

79. For example: $(4, -4)$ and $(-2, 0)$

81. For example: $(3, 5)$ and $(1, -1)$

83. For example: $(-3, 1)$ and $(-3, 4)$

85.

87.

89.

91. $\dfrac{3m - 3n}{2b}$ or $\dfrac{-3m + 3n}{-2b}$ **93.** $\left(\dfrac{c}{a}, 0\right)$

95. For example: $(7, 1)$

Section 3.4 Calculator Connections, p. 237

1. Perpendicular

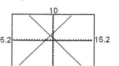

2. Parallel

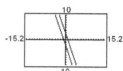

3. Neither

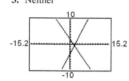

4. The lines may appear parallel; however, they are not parallel because the slopes are different. **5.** The lines may appear to coincide on a graph; however, they are not the same line because the y-intercepts are different. **6.** The line may appear to be horizontal, but it is not. The slope is 0.001 rather than 0.

Section 3.4 Practice Exercises, pp. 238–242

1. a. $y = mx + b$ **b.** standard **3.** x-intercept: $(10, 0)$; y-intercept: $(0, -2)$ **5.** x-intercept: none; y-intercept: $(0, -3)$
7. x-intercept: $(0, 0)$; y-intercept: $(0, 0)$ **9.** x-intercept: $(4, 0)$; y-intercept: none **11.** $m = -2$; y-intercept: $(0, 3)$ **13.** $m = 1$; y-intercept: $(0, -2)$ **15.** $m = -1$; y-intercept: $(0, 0)$

17. $m = \dfrac{3}{4}$; y-intercept: $(0, -1)$ **19.** $m = \dfrac{2}{5}$; y-intercept: $\left(0, -\dfrac{4}{5}\right)$ **21.** $m = 3$; y-intercept: $(0, -5)$

23. $m = -1$; y-intercept: $(0, 6)$ **25.** Undefined slope; no y-intercept **27.** $m = 0$; y-intercept: $\left(0, -\dfrac{1}{4}\right)$

29. $m = \dfrac{2}{3}$; y-intercept: $(0, 0)$

31.

33.

SA-10 Student Answer Appendix

35. b **37.** e **39.** c

41. $y = -2x + 9$

43. $y = \frac{1}{2}x - 3$

45. $y = -\frac{1}{2}x + \frac{3}{2}$

47. $y = -x$

49. $y = \frac{4}{5}x$

51. $y = -\frac{2}{3}$

53. Perpendicular **55.** Neither **57.** Parallel
59. Perpendicular **61.** Parallel **63.** Perpendicular
65. Neither **67.** Parallel **69.** $y = -\frac{1}{3}x + 2$
71. $y = 10x - 19$ **73.** $y = 6x - 8$ **75.** $y = \frac{1}{2}x - 3$
77. $y = -11$ **79.** $y = 5x$ **81.** $y = -2x + 3$
83. $y = -\frac{1}{3}x + 2$ **85.** $y = 4x - 1$ **87. a.** $m = 1203$;

The slope represents the rate of increase in the number of cases of Lyme disease per year. **b.** (0, 10006); In the year 1993 there were 10,006 cases reported. **c.** 30,457 cases **d.** $x = 27$; the year 2020
89. $y = -\frac{A}{B}x + \frac{C}{B}$; the slope is $-\frac{A}{B}$.
91. $m = -\frac{6}{7}$ **93.** $m = \frac{11}{8}$

Chapter 3 Problem Recognition Exercises, p. 242

1. a, c, d **2.** b, f, h **3.** a **4.** f **5.** b, f **6.** c
7. c, d **8.** f **9.** e **10.** g **11.** b **12.** h
13. g **14.** e **15.** c **16.** b, h **17.** e **18.** e
19. b, f, h **20.** c, d

Section 3.5 Practice Exercises, pp. 247–251

1. a. $Ax + By = C$ **b.** horizontal **c.** vertical **d.** slope; y-intercept **e.** $y - y_1 = m(x - x_1)$
3.

5.

7. 9 **9.** 0 **11.** $y = 3x + 7$ or $3x - y = -7$
13. $y = -4x - 14$ or $4x + y = -14$ **15.** $y = -\frac{1}{2}x - \frac{1}{2}$
or $x + 2y = -1$ **17.** $y = 2x - 2$ or $2x - y = 2$

19. $y = -x - 4$ or $x + y = -4$
21. $y = -0.2x - 2.86$ or $20x + 100y = -286$
23. $y = -2x + 1$ **25.** $y = 2x + 4$ **27.** $y = \frac{1}{2}x - 1$
29. $y = 4x + 13$ or $4x - y = -13$
31. $y = -\frac{3}{2}x + 6$ or $3x + 2y = 12$
33. $y = -2x - 8$ or $2x + y = -8$ **35.** $y = -\frac{1}{5}x - 6$ or
$x + 5y = -30$ **37.** iv **39.** vi **41.** iii **43.** $y = 1$
45. $x = 2$ **47.** $y = 2$ **49.** $y = \frac{1}{4}x + 8$ or $x - 4y = -32$
51. $y = 3x - 8$ or $3x - y = 8$ **53.** $y = 4.5x - 25.6$ or
$45x - 10y = 256$ **55.** $x = -6$ **57.** $y = -2$
59. $x = -4$ **61.** $y = 2x - 4$ **63.** $y = -\frac{1}{2}x + 1$

Section 3.6 Calculator Connections, p. 255

1. 13.3

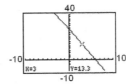

2. −42.3

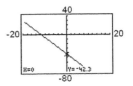

3. 345

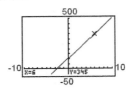

4. 95

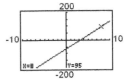

Section 3.6 Practice Exercises, pp. 255–259

1. $m = -\frac{5}{2}$ **3.** x-intercept: (6, 0); y-intercept: (0, 5)
5. x-intercept: (−2, 0); y-intercept: (0, −4) **7.** x-intercept: none; y-intercept: (0, −9) **9. a.** $3.00 **b.** $7.90 **c.** The y-intercept is (0, 1.6). This indicates that the minimum wage was $1.60 per hour in the year 1970. **d.** The slope is 0.14. This indicates that the minimum wage has risen approximately $0.14 per year during this period.
11. a. $m = \frac{2}{7}$ **b.** $m = \frac{4}{7}$ **c.** $m = \frac{2}{7}$ means that Grindel's weight increased at a rate of 2 oz in 7 days. $m = \frac{4}{7}$ means that Frisco's weight increased at a rate of 4 oz in 7 days. **d.** Frisco gained weight more rapidly. **13. a.** $106.95 **b.** $201.95 **c.** (0, 11.95). For 0 kilowatt-hours used, the cost consists of only the fixed monthly tax of $11.95. **d.** $m = 0.095$. The cost increases by $0.095 for each kilowatt-hour used. **15. a.** $m = -1.0$ **b.** $y = -1.0x + 1051$ **c.** The minimum pressure was approximately 921 mb.
17. a. $m = 21.5$ **b.** The slope means that the consumption of wind energy in the United States increased by 21.5 trillion Btu per year. **c.** $y = 21.5x + 57$ **d.** 272 trillion Btu **19. a.** $y = 0.10x + 5000$ **b.** $6130 **21. a.** $y = 90x + 105$ **b.** $1185.00
23. a. $y = 0.8x + 100$ **b.** $260.00

Chapter 3 Review Exercises, pp. 265–269

1.

2. $A(4, -3)$; $B(-3, -2)$; $C(\frac{5}{2}, 5)$; $D(-4, 1)$; $E(-\frac{1}{2}, 0)$; $F(0, -5)$

3. III   **4.** II   **5.** IV   **6.** I   **7.** IV   **8.** III   **9.** x-axis

10. y-axis   **11. a.** On day 1, the price was \$26.25.   **b.** Day 2

c. \$2.25   **12. a.** In 2003 (8 years after 1995), there was only one space shuttle launch. (This was the year that the Columbia and its crew were lost.)

b.

Number of Shuttles Launched

Year ($x = 0$ corresponds to 1995)

13. No   **14.** No   **15.** Yes   **16.** Yes

17.

x	y
2	1
3	4
1	-2

18.

x	y
0	2
-2	7/3
-6	3

19.

x	y
0	-1
3	1
-6	-5

20.

x	y
0	-3
-3	3
1	-5

21.

22.

23.

24.   **25.** Vertical   **26.** Vertical

27. Horizontal   **28.** Horizontal

29. x-intercept: $(-3, 0)$; y-intercept: $\left(0, \frac{3}{2}\right)$

30. x-intercept: $(3, 0)$; y-intercept: $(0, 6)$ **31.** x-intercept: $(0, 0)$; y-intercept: $(0, 0)$ **32.** x-intercept: $(0, 0)$; y-intercept: $(0, 0)$

33. x-intercept: none; y-intercept: $(0, -4)$ **34.** x-intercept: none; y-intercept: $(0, 2)$ **35.** x-intercept: $\left(-\frac{5}{2}, 0\right)$; y-intercept: none

36. x-intercept: $\left(\frac{1}{3}, 0\right)$; y-intercept: none   **37.** $m = \frac{12}{5}$

38. -2 **39.** $-\frac{2}{3}$ **40.** 8   **41.** Undefined   **42.** 0

43. a. -5 **b.** $\frac{1}{5}$ **44. a.** 0 **b.** Undefined

45. $m_1 = \frac{2}{3}$; $m_2 = \frac{2}{3}$; parallel   **46.** $m_1 = 8$; $m_2 = 8$; parallel

47. $m_1 = -\frac{5}{12}$; $m_2 = \frac{12}{5}$; perpendicular   **48.** m_1 is undefined; $m_2 = 0$; perpendicular   **49. a.** $m = 35$ **b.** The number of kilowatt-hours increased at a rate of 35 kilowatt-hours per day.

50. a. $m = -994$ **b.** The number of new cars sold in Maryland decreased at a rate of 994 cars per year.

51. $y = \frac{5}{2}x - 5$; $m = \frac{5}{2}$; y-intercept: $(0, -5)$

52. $y = -\frac{3}{4}x + 3$; $m = -\frac{3}{4}$; y-intercept: $(0, 3)$

53. $y = \frac{1}{3}x$; $m = \frac{1}{3}$; y-intercept: $(0, 0)$ **54.** $y = \frac{12}{5}$; $m = 0$; y-intercept: $\left(0, \frac{12}{5}\right)$ **55.** $y = -\frac{5}{2}$; $m = 0$; y-intercept: $\left(0, -\frac{5}{2}\right)$

56. $y = x$; $m = 1$; y-intercept: $(0, 0)$ **57.** Neither

58. Perpendicular   **59.** Parallel   **60.** Parallel

61. Perpendicular   **62.** Neither   **63.** $y = -\frac{4}{3}x - 1$ or $4x + 3y = -3$ **64.** $y = 5x$ or $5x - y = 0$ **65.** $y = -\frac{4}{3}x - 6$ or $4x + 3y = -18$ **66.** $y = 5x - 3$ or $5x - y = 3$

67. For example: $y = 3x + 2$ **68.** For example: $5x + 2y = -4$

69. $m = \frac{y_2 - y_1}{x_2 - x_1}$ **70.** $y - y_1 = m(x - x_1)$

71. For example: $x = 6$ **72.** For example: $y = -5$

73. $y = -6x + 2$ or $6x + y = 2$ **74.** $y = \frac{2}{3}x + \frac{5}{3}$ or $2x - 3y = -5$ **75.** $y = \frac{1}{4}x - 4$ or $x - 4y = 16$ **76.** $y = -5$

77. $y = \frac{6}{5}x + 6$ or $6x - 5y = -30$ **78.** $y = 4x + 31$ or $4x - y = -31$ **79. a.** 47.8 in.   **b.** The slope is 2.4 and indicates that the average height for girls increases at a rate of 2.4 in. per year.

80. a. $m = 137$ **b.** The number of prescriptions increased by 137 million per year during this time period.   **c.** $y = 137x + 2825$ **d.** 4880 million   **81. a.** $y = 20x + 55$ **b.** \$235

82. a. $y = 8x + 700$ **b.** \$1340

Chapter 3 Test, pp. 269–271

1. a. II **b.** IV **c.** III   **2.** 0   **3.** 0

4. a. $(4, 14)$ After 4 days the bamboo plant is 14 in. tall. $(8, 28)$, $(12, 42)$, $(16, 56)$, $(20, 70)$

b.

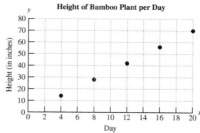

Height of Bamboo Plant per Day

Day

c. Approximately 35 in.

SA-12   Student Answer Appendix

5. a. No **b.** Yes **c.** Yes **d.** Yes

6.

x	y
0	-2
4	-1
6	$-\frac{1}{2}$

7.  **8.** 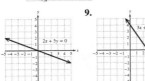 **9.**

10.   **11.** Horizontal **12.** Vertical

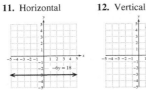

13. x-intercept: $\left(-\frac{3}{2}, 0\right)$; y-intercept: $(0, 2)$

14. x-intercept: $(0, 0)$; y-intercept: $(0, 0)$ **15.** x-intercept: $(4, 0)$; y-intercept: none   **16.** x-intercept: none; y-intercept: $(0, 3)$

17. $\frac{2}{5}$ **18. a.** $\frac{1}{3}$ **b.** $\frac{4}{3}$ **19. a.** $-\frac{1}{4}$ **b.** 4

20. a. Undefined **b.** 0   **21. a.** $m = 0.6$ **b.** The cost of renting a truck increases at a rate of $0.60 per mile.   **22.** Parallel

23. Perpendicular   **24.** $y = -\frac{1}{3}x + 1$ or $x + 3y = 3$

25. $y = -\frac{7}{2}x + 15$ or $7x + 2y = 30$ **26.** $y = \frac{1}{4}x + \frac{1}{2}$ or $x - 4y = -2$ **27.** $y = 3x + 8$ or $3x - y = -8$ **28.** $y = -6$

29. $y = -x - 3$ or $x + y = -3$ **30. a.** $y = 1.5x + 10$ **b.** $25

31. a. $m = 20$; The slope indicates that there is an increase of 20 thousand medical doctors per year. **b.** $y = 20x + 414$ **c.** 1114 thousand or, equivalently, 1,114,000

Chapters 1–3 Cumulative Review Exercises, pp. 271–272

1. a. Rational **b.** Rational **c.** Irrational **d.** Rational

2. a. $\frac{2}{3}; \frac{2}{3}$ **b.** $-5.3; 5.3$ **3.** 69   **4.** -13 **5.** 18

6. $\frac{3}{4} \div \left(-\frac{7}{8}\right); -\frac{6}{7}$ **7.** $(-2.1)(-6); 12.6$ **8.** The associative property of addition   **9.** $\{4\}$ **10.** $\{5\}$ **11.** $\left\{-\frac{9}{2}\right\}$

12. $\{-2\}$ **13.** 9241 mi^2 **14.** $a = \frac{c - b}{3}$

15.

16. x-intercept: $(-2, 0)$; y-intercept: $(0, 1)$

17. $y = -\frac{3}{2}x - 6$; slope: $-\frac{3}{2}$; y-intercept: $(0, -6)$

18. $2x + 3 = 5$ can be written as $x = 1$, which represents a vertical line. A vertical line of the form $x = k$ ($k \neq 0$) has an x-intercept of $(k, 0)$ and no y-intercept.   **19.** $y = -3x + 1$ or $3x + y = 1$

20. $y = \frac{2}{3}x + 6$ or $2x - 3y = -18$

Chapter 4

Section 4.1 Calculator Connections, pp. 278–279

1. $\{(2, 1)\}$ **2.** $\{(6, -1)\}$

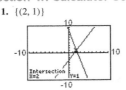 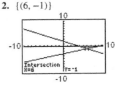

3. $\{(3, 1)\}$ **4.** $\{(-2, 0)\}$

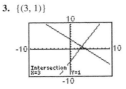 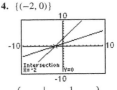

5. $\{\ \}$ **6.** $\left\{(x, y) \,\middle|\, y = -\frac{1}{4}x + 2\right\}$

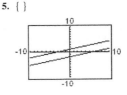 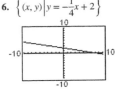

Section 4.1 Practice Exercises, pp. 279–284

1. a. system **b.** solution **c.** intersect **d.** consistent **e.** $\{\ \}$ **f.** dependent **g.** independent   **3.** Yes   **5.** No   **7.** Yes

9. No   **11.** b   **13.** d

15. a.   **b.**   **c.**

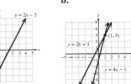

17. c   **19.** a   **21.** a   **23.** b   **25.** c

27. $\{(3, 1)\}$ **29.** $\{(1, -2)\}$ **31.** $\{(1, 4)\}$

33. No solution; $\{\ \}$; inconsistent system   **35.** Infinitely many solutions; $\{(x, y) \mid -2x + y = 3\}$; dependent equations

37. $\{(-3, 6)\}$ **39.** $\{(2, -2)\}$ **41.** No solution; $\{\ \}$; inconsistent system

43. {(4, 2)}   **45.** {(1, 2)}

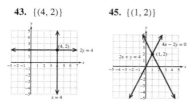

47. Infinitely many solutions;   **49.** {(−3, −1)}
{(x, y) | y = 0.5x + 2};
dependent equations

51. The same cost occurs when $2500 of merchandise is purchased.   **53.** The point of intersection is below the x-axis and cannot have a positive y-coordinate.   **55.** For example: $4x + y = 9; -2x - y = -5$ **57.** For example: $2x + 2y = 1$

Section 4.2 Practice Exercises, pp. 292–294

1. $y = 2x - 4; y = 2x - 4$; coinciding lines

3. $y = -\frac{2}{3}x + 2; y = x - 5$; intersecting lines

5. $y = 4x - 4; y = 4x - 13$; parallel lines   **7.** {(3, −6)}

9. {(0, 4)}   **11. a.** y in the second equation is easiest to isolate because its coefficient is 1.   **b.** {(1, 5)}   **13.** {(5, 2)}   **15.** {(10, 5)}

17. $\left\{\left(\frac{1}{2}, 3\right)\right\}$ **19.** {(5, 3)}   **21.** {(1, 0)}   **23.** {(1, 4)}

25. No solution; { }; inconsistent system   **27.** Infinitely many solutions; {(x, y) | 2x − 6y = −2}; dependent equations   **29.** {(5, −7)}

31. $\left\{\left(-5, \frac{3}{2}\right)\right\}$ **33.** {(2, −5)}   **35.** {(−4, 6)}   **37.** {(0, 2)}

39. Infinitely many solutions; {(x, y) | y = 0.25x + 1}; dependent equations   **41.** {(1, 1)}   **43.** No solution; { }; inconsistent system

45. {(−1, 5)}   **47.** {(−6, −4)}   **49.** The numbers are 48 and 58.   **51.** The numbers are 13 and 39.   **53.** The angles are 165° and 15°.   **55.** The angles are 70° and 20°.   **57.** The angles are 42° and 48°.   **59.** For example: (0, 3), (1, 5), (−1, 1)

Section 4.3 Practice Exercises, pp. 301–303

1. No   **3.** No   **5.** Yes   **7. a.** True   **b.** False, multiply the second equation by 5.   **9. a.** x would be easier.   **b.** {(0, −3)}

11. {(4, −1)}   **13.** {(4, 3)}   **15.** {(2, 3)}   **17.** {(1, −4)}

19. {(1, −1)}   **21.** {(−4, −6)}   **23.** $\left\{\left(\frac{7}{9}, \frac{5}{9}\right)\right\}$

25. The system will have no solution. The lines are parallel.

27. There are infinitely many solutions. The lines coincide.

29. The system will have one solution. The lines intersect at a point whose x-coordinate is 0.   **31.** No solution; { }; inconsistent system

33. Infinitely many solutions; {(x, y) | x + 2y = 2}; dependent equations   **35.** {(1, 4)}   **37.** {(−1, −2)}   **39.** {(2, 1)}

41. No solution; { }; inconsistent system   **43.** {(2, 3)}   **45.** {(3.5, 2.5)}

47. $\left\{\left(\frac{1}{3}, 2\right)\right\}$ **49.** {(−2, 5)}   **51.** $\left\{\left(-\frac{1}{2}, 1\right)\right\}$ **53.** {(0, 3)}

55. { }   **57.** {(1, 4)}   **59.** {(4, 0)}   **61.** Infinitely many solutions; {(a, b) | 9a − 2b = 8}   **63.** $\left\{\left(\frac{7}{16}, -\frac{7}{8}\right)\right\}$

65. The numbers are 17 and 19.   **67.** The numbers are −1 and 3.

69. The angles are 46° and 134°.   **71.** {(1, 3)}   **73.** One line within the system of equations would have to "bend" for the system to have exactly two points of intersection. This is not possible.

75. A = −5, B = 2

Chapter 4 Problem Recognition Exercises, p. 304

1. Infinitely many solutions. The equations represent the same line.   **2.** No solution. The equations represent parallel lines.

3. One solution. The equations represent intersecting lines.

4. One solution. The equations represent intersecting lines.

5. No solution. The equations represent parallel lines.

6. Infinitely many solutions. The equations represent the same line.

7. The y variable will easily be eliminated by adding the equations. The solution set is {(−3, 1)}.   **8.** The x variable will easily be eliminated by multiplying the second equation by 2 and then adding the equations. The solution set is {(3, 4)}.   **9.** Because the variable x is already isolated in the first equation, the expression −3y + 4 can be easily substituted for x in the second equation. The solution set is {(−2, 2)}.   **10.** Because the variable y is already isolated in the second equation, the expression x − 8 can be easily substituted for y in the first equation. The solution set is {(8, 0)}.   **11.** {(5, 0)}

12. {(1, −7)}   **13.** {(4, −5)}   **14.** {(2, 3)}   **15.** {(2, 0)}

16. {(8, 10)}   **17.** $\left\{\left(2, -\frac{5}{7}\right)\right\}$ **18.** $\left\{\left(-\frac{14}{3}, -4\right)\right\}$

19. No solution; { }; inconsistent system   **20.** No solution; { }; inconsistent system

21. {(−1, 0)}   **22.** {(5, 0)}   **23.** Infinitely many solutions; {(x, y) | y = 2x − 14}; dependent equations   **24.** Infinitely many solutions; {(x, y) | x = 5y − 9}; dependent equations

25. {(2200, 1000)}   **26.** {(3300, 1200)}   **27.** {(5, −7)}

28. {(2, −1)}   **29.** $\left\{\left(\frac{2}{3}, \frac{1}{2}\right)\right\}$ **30.** $\left\{\left(\frac{1}{4}, -\frac{3}{2}\right)\right\}$

Section 4.4 Practice Exercises, pp. 310–314

1. {(−1, 4)}   **3.** $\left\{\left(\frac{5}{2}, 1\right)\right\}$ **5.** The numbers are 4 and 16.

7. The angles are 80° and 10°.   **9.** A video game costs $21.50 and a DVD costs $15.00.   **11.** Technology stock costs $16 per share, and the mutual fund costs $11 per share.   **13.** Mylee bought thirty-five 47-cent stamps and fifteen 34-cent stamps.   **15.** Shanelle invested $3500 in the 10% account and $6500 in the 7% account.

17. $9000 was borrowed at 6%, and $3000 was borrowed at 9%.

19. Invest $12,000 in the bond fund and $18,000 in the stock fund.

21. 15 gal of the 50% mixture should be mixed with 10 gal of the 40% mixture.   **23.** 12 gal of the 45% disinfectant solution should be mixed with 8 gal of the 30% disinfectant solution.

25. She should mix 20 mL of the 13% solution with 30 mL of the 18% solution.   **27.** Chad needs 1 L of pure antifreeze and 5 L of the 40% solution.   **29.** The speed of the boat in still water is 6 mph, and the speed of the current is 2 mph.   **31.** The speed of the plane in still air is 300 mph, and the wind is 20 mph.   **33.** The speed of the plane in still air is 525 mph and the speed of the wind is 75 mph.   **35.** There are 17 dimes and 22 nickels.   **37.** 2 qt of water should be mixed.   **39. a.** 835 free throws and 1597 field goals   **b.** 4029 points   **c.** Approximately 50 points per game

41. The speed of the plane in still air is 160 mph, and the wind is 40 mph.   **43.** $15,000 was invested in the 5.5% account, and $45,000 was invested in the 6.5% account.   **45.** 12 lb of candy should be mixed with 8 lb of nuts.   **47.** Dallas scored 30 points, and Buffalo scored 13 points.   **49.** There were 300 women and 200 men in the survey.

Section 4.5 Practice Exercises, pp. 320–322

1. a. linear   **b.** ordered triples   **3.** { }   **5.** The speeds are 65 mph and 58 mph.   **7.** (4, 0, 2) is a solution.

9. (1, 1, 1) is a solution.   **11.** {(1, −2, 4)}

13. {(−1, 2, 0)}   **15.** {(−2, −1, −3)}   **17.** {(1, −4, −2)}

19. {(1, 2, 3)}   **21.** {(−6, 1, 7)}   **23.** $\left\{\left(\frac{1}{2}, \frac{2}{3}, -\frac{5}{6}\right)\right\}$

25. $\left\{\left(\frac{1}{2}, 2, -\frac{1}{2}\right)\right\}$ **27.** {(6, −3, −2)}   **29.** {(0, 4, −4)}

31. {(1, 0, −1)}   **33.** {(−20, 8, 0)}

35. Dependent equations   **37.** Inconsistent system

SA-14   Student Answer Appendix

39. $\{(1, 3, 1)\}$ **41.** $\left\{\left(-\dfrac{1}{2}, \dfrac{1}{3}, \dfrac{1}{6}\right)\right\}$
43. Dependent equations   **45.** $\{(1, 0, 1)\}$
47. $\{(0, 0, 0)\}$ **49.** Dependent equations

Section 4.6 Practice Exercises, pp. 325–327

1. $\{(-7, 0, 8)\}$ **3.** Inconsistent system   **5.** 67°, 82°, 31°
7. 25°, 56°, 99°   **9.** 10 cm, 18 cm, 27 cm   **11.** 11 in., 17 in.,
26 in.   **13.** The fiber supplement has 3 g; the oatmeal has 4 g; and
the cereal has 1.5 g.   **15.** Kyoki invested $2000 in bonds, $6000 in
mutual funds, and $2000 in the Treasury note.   **17.** $1500
at 5%, $2000 at 5.5%, $1000 at 4%   **19.** He made six free throws,
seven 2-point shots, and three 3-point shots.   **21.** 24 oz peanuts,
8 oz pecans, 16 oz cashews   **23.** 1500 seats in section A,
400 seats in section B, and 500 seats in section C were sold.

Chapter 4 Review Exercises, pp. 335–337

1. Yes   **2.** No   **3.** No   **4.** Yes   **5.** Intersecting lines
(The lines have different slopes.)   **6.** Intersecting lines (The lines have
different slopes.)   **7.** Parallel lines (The lines have the same slope but
different y-intercepts.)   **8.** Intersecting lines (The lines have different
slopes.)   **9.** Coinciding lines (The lines have the same slope and same
y-intercept.)   **10.** Intersecting lines (The lines have different slopes.)

11. $\{(0, -2)\}$ **12.** $\{(-2, 3)\}$

13. Infinitely many solutions;   **14.** Infinitely many solutions;
$\{(x, y) \mid 2x + y = 5\}$; $\{(x, y) \mid -x + 5y = -5\}$;
dependent equations   dependent equations

15. $\{(1, -1)\}$ **16.** $\{(-1, 2)\}$

17. No solution; $\{\ \}$;   **18.** No solution; $\{\ \}$;
inconsistent system   inconsistent system

19. Using 39 minutes per month, the cost per month for each
company is $9.75.   **20.** $\left\{\left(\dfrac{2}{3}, -2\right)\right\}$ **21.** $\{(-4, 1)\}$
22. $\{\ \}$ **23.** Infinitely many solutions; $\{(x, y) \mid y = -2x + 2\}$
24. a. x in the first equation is easiest to isolate because its
coefficient is 1.   **b.** $\left\{\left(6, \dfrac{5}{2}\right)\right\}$ **25. a.** y in the second equation is
easiest to isolate because its coefficient is 1.   **b.** $\left\{\left(\dfrac{9}{2}, 3\right)\right\}$

26. $\{(5, -4)\}$ **27.** $\{(0, 4)\}$ **28.** Infinitely many solutions;
$\{(x, y) \mid x - 3y = 9\}$ **29.** $\{\ \}$ **30.** The numbers are 50 and 8.
31. The angles are 41° and 49°.   **32.** The angles are $115\frac{1}{3}$° and $64\frac{2}{3}$°.
33. b. $\{(-1, 4)\}$ **34. b.** $\{(-3, -2)\}$ **35. b.** $\{(2, 2)\}$
36. $\{(2, -1)\}$ **37.** $\{(-6, 2)\}$ **38.** $\left\{\left(-\dfrac{1}{2}, \dfrac{1}{3}\right)\right\}$
39. $\left\{\left(\dfrac{1}{4}, -\dfrac{2}{5}\right)\right\}$ **40.** Infinitely many solutions;
$\{(x, y) \mid -4x - 6y = -2\}$ **41.** $\{\ \}$ **42.** $\{(-4, -2)\}$
43. $\{(1, 0)\}$ **44. a.** Use the substitution method because y is
already isolated in the second equation.   **b.** $\{(5, -3)\}$ **45. a.** Use the
addition method. The substitution method would be cumbersome because
isolating either variable from either equation would result in fractional
coefficients.   **b.** $\{(-2, -1)\}$
46. There were 8 adult tickets and 52 children's tickets sold.
47. He should invest $75,000 at 12% and $525,000 at 4%.
48. 20 gal of whole milk should be mixed with 40 gal of low fat milk.
49. The speed of the boat is 18 mph, and that of the current is 2 mph.
50. The plane's speed in still air is 320 mph. The wind speed is
30 mph.   **51.** A hot dog costs $4.50 and a drink costs $3.50.
52. The score was 72 on the first round and 82 on the second round.
53. $\{(2, -1, 5)\}$ **54.** Inconsistent system
55. Dependent equations   **56.** $\{(-1, -2, 2)\}$ **57.** $\{(1, -3, -2)\}$
58. $\{(-1, 4, 0)\}$ **59.** 5 ft, 12 ft, and 13 ft   **60.** The pumps can
drain 250, 300, and 400 gal/hr.   **61.** She invested $6000 in Fund A, $4000
in Fund B, and $2000 in Fund C.   **62.** The angles are 13°, 39°, and 128°.

Chapter 4 Test, pp. 338–339

1. $y = -\dfrac{5}{2}x - 3;\ y = -\dfrac{5}{2}x + 3$; Parallel lines

2. $\{(3, 2)\}$

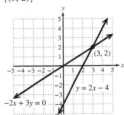

3. Infinitely many solutions; $\{(x, y) \mid 2x + 4y = 12\}$

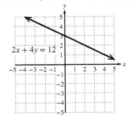

4. $\{(-2, 0)\}$ **5.** Swoopes scored 614 points and Jackson
scored 597.   **6.** $\left\{\left(2, -\dfrac{1}{3}\right)\right\}$ **7.** 12 mL of the 50%
acid solution should be mixed with 24 mL of the 20% solution.
8. a. No solution   **b.** Infinitely many solutions   **c.** One solution
9. $\{(-5, 4)\}$ **10.** $\{\ \}$ **11.** $\{(3, -5)\}$ **12.** $\{(-1, 2)\}$
13. Infinitely many solutions; $\{(x, y) \mid 10x + 2y = -8\}$
14. $\{(1, -2)\}$ **15.** CDs cost $8 each and DVDs cost $11 each.
16. a. $18 was required.   **b.** They used 24 quarters and 12 $1 bills.
17. $1200 was borrowed at 10%, and $3800 was borrowed at 8%.
18. They would be the same cost for a distance of approximately 24 mi.
19. The plane travels 500 mph in still air, and the wind speed is 45 mph.
20. The cake has 340 calories, and the ice cream has 120 calories.
21. 60 mL of 10% solution and 40 mL of 25% solution
22. $\{(16, -37, 9)\}$ **23.** $\{(2, -2, 5)\}$ **24.** $\{\ \}$

25. The sides are 5 ft, 15 ft, and 23 ft   **26.** $5500 was invested in Fund A. $4000 was invested in Fund B, and $2000 was invested in Fund C.   **27.** Joanne can process 142 orders, Kent can process 162 orders, and Geoff can process 200 orders.

Chapters 1–4 Cumulative Review Exercises, pp. 339–340

1. $\dfrac{11}{6}$ **2.** $\left\{-\dfrac{21}{2}\right\}$ **3.** $\{\ \}$ **4.** $y = \dfrac{3}{2}x - 3$ **5.** $x = 5z + m$

6. $\left[\dfrac{3}{11}, \infty\right)$

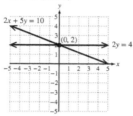

7. The angles are 37°, 33°, and 110°.   **8.** The rates of the hikers are 2 mph and 4 mph.   **9.** Jesse Ventura received approximately 762,200 votes.   **10.** 36% of the goal has been achieved.

11. The angles are 36.5° and 53.5°.   **12.** Slope: $-\dfrac{5}{3}$; y-intercept: $(0, -2)$

13. a. $-\dfrac{2}{3}$ **b.** $\dfrac{3}{2}$ **14.** $y = -3x + 3$

15. c. $\{(0, 2)\}$ **16.** $\{(0, 2)\}$

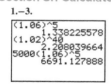

17. 20 gal of the 15% solution should be mixed with 40 gal of the 60% solution.   **18.** x is 27°; y is 63°   **19. a.** 1.4   **b.** Between 1920 and 1990, the winning speed in the Indianapolis 500 increased on average by 1.4 mph per year.   **20.** $\{(1, 0, 4)\}$

Chapter 5

Section 5.1 Calculator Connections, p. 348

1.–3.

```
(1.06)^5
        1.338225578
(1.02)^40
        2.208039664
5000(1.06)^5
        6691.127888
```

4.–6.

```
2000(1.02)^40
        4416.079327
3000(1+.06)^2
        3370.8
1000(1+.05)^3
        1157.625
```

Section 5.1 Practice Exercises, pp. 349–351

1. a. exponent   **b.** base; exponent   **c.** 1   **d.** $I = Prt$ **e.** compound interest   **3.** Base: x; exponent: 4   **5.** Base: 3; exponent: 5   **7.** Base: -1; exponent: 4   **9.** Base: 13; exponent: 1   **11.** Base: 10; exponent: 3   **13.** Base: t; exponent: 6

15. v **17.** 1   **19.** $(-6b)^2$ **21.** $-6b^2$ **23.** $(y + 2)^4$

25. $\dfrac{-2}{t^3}$ **27.** No; $-5^2 = -25$ and $(-5)^2 = 25$ **29.** Yes; -32

31. Yes; $\dfrac{1}{8}$ **33.** Yes; -16 **35.** 16   **37.** -1 **39.** $\dfrac{1}{9}$

41. $-\dfrac{4}{25}$ **43.** 48   **45.** 4   **47.** 9   **49.** 50   **51.** -100

53. 400   **55.** 1   **57.** 1   **59.** 1000   **61.** -800

63. a. $(x \cdot x \cdot x \cdot x)(x \cdot x \cdot x) = x^7$ **b.** $(5 \cdot 5 \cdot 5 \cdot 5)(5 \cdot 5 \cdot 5) = 5^7$

65. z^8 **67.** a^9 **69.** 4^{14} **71.** $\left(\dfrac{2}{3}\right)^4$ **73.** c^{14} **75.** x^{18}

77. a. $\dfrac{p \cdot p \cdot p \cdot p \cdot p \cdot p \cdot p \cdot p}{p \cdot p \cdot p} = p^5$

b. $\dfrac{8 \cdot 8 \cdot 8 \cdot 8 \cdot 8 \cdot 8 \cdot 8 \cdot 8}{8 \cdot 8 \cdot 8} = 8^5$ **79.** x^2 **81.** a^9 **83.** 7^7

85. 5^7 **87.** y **89.** h^4 **91.** 7^7 **93.** 10^9 **95.** $6x^7$

97. $40a^5b^5$ **99.** s^9t^{16} **101.** $-30v^8$ **103.** $16m^{20}n^{10}$

105. $2cd^4$ **107.** z^4 **109.** $\dfrac{25hjk^4}{12}$ **111.** $-8p^7q^9r^6$

113. $-3stu$ **115.** $5724.50   **117.** $4764.06   **119.** 201 in.^{2}

121. 268 in.^{3} **123.** x^{2n+1} **125.** p^{2m+3} **127.** z **129.** r^3

Section 5.2 Practice Exercises, pp. 355–356

1. 4^9 **3.** a^{20} **5.** d^9 **7.** 7^6 **9.** When multiplying expressions with the same base, add the exponents. When raising an expression with an exponent to a power, multiply the exponents.

11. 5^{12} **13.** 12^6 **15.** y^{14} **17.** w^{25} **19.** a^{36} **21.** y^{14}

23. They are both equal to 2^6.   **25.** $4^{3^2} = 4^9$; $(4^3)^2 = 4^6$; the expression 4^{3^2} is greater than $(4^3)^2$.   **27.** $25w^2$ **29.** $s^4r^4t^4$

31. $\dfrac{16}{r^4}$ **33.** $\dfrac{x^5}{y^5}$ **35.** $81a^4$ **37.** $-27a^3b^3c^3$ **39.** $-\dfrac{64}{x^3}$

41. $\dfrac{a^2}{b^2}$ **43.** $6^3u^6v^{12}$ or $216u^6v^{12}$ **45.** $5x^8y^4$ **47.** $-h^{28}$

49. m^{12} **51.** $\dfrac{4^5}{r^5s^{20}}$ or $\dfrac{1024}{r^5s^{20}}$ **53.** $\dfrac{3^5p^5}{q^{15}}$ or $\dfrac{243p^5}{q^{15}}$ **55.** y^{14}

57. x^{31} **59.** $200a^{14}b^9$ **61.** $16p^8q^{16}$ **63.** $-m^{35}n^{15}$

65. $25a^{18}b^6$ **67.** $\dfrac{4c^2d^6}{9}$ **69.** $\dfrac{c^{27}d^{31}}{2}$ **71.** $\dfrac{27a^9b^3}{c^6}$

73. $16b^{26}$ **75.** x^{2m} **77.** $125a^{6n}$ **79.** $\dfrac{m^{2b}}{n^{3b}}$ **81.** $\dfrac{3^na^{3n}}{5^nb^{4n}}$

Section 5.3 Practice Exercises, pp. 364–366

1. a. 1   **b.** $\left(\dfrac{1}{b}\right)^n$ or $\dfrac{1}{b^n}$ **3.** c^9 **5.** y **7.** 3^6 or 729

9. $7^4w^{28}z^8$ or $2401w^{28}z^8$ **11. a.** 1   **b.** 1   **13.** 1   **15.** 1

17. -1 **19.** 1   **21.** 1   **23.** -7 **25. a.** $\dfrac{1}{t^5}$ **b.** $\dfrac{1}{t^5}$

27. $\dfrac{343}{8}$ **29.** 25   **31.** $\dfrac{1}{a^3}$ **33.** $\dfrac{1}{12}$ **35.** $\dfrac{1}{16b^2}$ **37.** $\dfrac{6}{x^2}$

39. $\dfrac{1}{64}$ **41.** $-\dfrac{3}{y^4}$ **43.** $-\dfrac{1}{t^3}$ **45.** a^5

47. $\dfrac{x^4}{x^{-6}} = x^{4-(-6)} = x^{10}$ **49.** $2a^{-3} = 2 \cdot \dfrac{1}{a^3} = \dfrac{2}{a^3}$ **51.** $\dfrac{1}{x^4}$

53. 1   **55.** y^4 **57.** $\dfrac{n^{27}}{m^{18}}$ **59.** $\dfrac{81k^{24}}{j^{20}}$ **61.** $\dfrac{1}{p^6}$ **63.** $\dfrac{1}{r^3}$

65. a^8 **67.** $\dfrac{1}{y^8}$ **69.** $\dfrac{1}{7^7}$ **71.** 1   **73.** $\dfrac{1}{a^4b^6}$ **75.** $\dfrac{1}{w^{21}}$

77. $\dfrac{1}{27}$ **79.** 1   **81.** $\dfrac{1}{64x^6}$ **83.** $-\dfrac{16y^4}{z^2}$ **85.** $\dfrac{a^{12}}{6}$

87. $80c^{21}d^{24}$ **89.** $\dfrac{9y^2}{8x^5}$ **91.** $\dfrac{4d^{16}}{c^2}$ **93.** $\dfrac{9y^2}{2x}$ **95.** $\dfrac{9}{20}$

97. $\dfrac{9}{10}$ **99.** $\dfrac{5}{4}$ **101.** $\dfrac{10}{3}$ **103.** 2   **105.** -11

Chapter 5 Problem Recognition Exercises, p. 366

1. t^8 **2.** 2^8 or 256   **3.** y^5 **4.** p^6 **5.** r^4s^8 **6.** $a^3b^9c^6$

7. w^6 **8.** $\dfrac{1}{m^{16}}$ **9.** $\dfrac{x^4z^3}{y^7}$ **10.** $\dfrac{a^3c^8}{b^6}$ **11.** x^6 **12.** $\dfrac{1}{y^{10}}$

13. $\dfrac{1}{t^5}$ **14.** w^7 **15.** p^{15} **16.** p^{15} **17.** $\dfrac{1}{v^2}$ **18.** $c^{50}d^{40}$

19. 3   **20.** -4 **21.** $\dfrac{b^9}{2^{15}}$ **22.** $\dfrac{81}{y^6}$ **23.** $\dfrac{16y^4}{81x^4}$ **24.** $\dfrac{25d^6}{36c^2}$

25. $3a^7b^5$ **26.** $64x^7y^{11}$ **27.** $\dfrac{y^4}{x^8}$ **28.** $\dfrac{1}{a^{10}b^{10}}$ **29.** $\dfrac{1}{t^2}$ **30.** $\dfrac{1}{p^7}$

31. $\dfrac{8w^6x^9}{27}$ **32.** $\dfrac{25b^8}{16c^6}$ **33.** $\dfrac{q^3s}{r^4t^5}$ **34.** $\dfrac{m^2p^3q}{n^3}$ **35.** $\dfrac{1}{y^{13}}$

36. w^{10} **37.** $-\dfrac{1}{8a^{18}b^6}$ **38.** $\dfrac{4x^{18}}{9y^{10}}$ **39.** $\dfrac{k^8}{5h^6}$ **40.** $\dfrac{6n^{10}}{m^{12}}$

Section 5.4 Calculator Connections, p. 370

1.–2.

```
(5.2E6)*(4.6E-3)
        23920
(2.19E-8)*(7.84E
-4)
        1.71696E-11
```

3.–4.

```
(4.76E-5)/(2.38E
9)
        2E-14
(8.5E4)/(4.0E-1)
        212500
```

SA-16   Student Answer Appendix

5.

6.

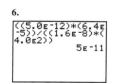

Section 5.4 Practice Exercises, pp. 371–373

1. scientific notation   **3.** b^{13} **5.** 10^{13} **7.** $\dfrac{1}{y^5}$ **9.** $\dfrac{x^{20}}{y^{12}}$

11. w^4 **13.** 10^4 **15.** Move the decimal point between the
2 and 3 and multiply by 10^{-10}; 2.3×10^{-10}.   **17.** 5×10^4
19. 2.08×10^5 **21.** 6.01×10^6 **23.** 8×10^{-6}
25. 1.25×10^{-4} **27.** 6.708×10^{-3} **29.** 1.7×10^{-24} g
31. $\$2.7 \times 10^{10}$ **33.** 6.8×10^7 gal; 1×10^2 miles
35. Move the decimal point nine places to the left; 0.000 000 0031.
37. 0.00005   **39.** 2800   **41.** 0.000603   **43.** 2,400,000
45. 0.019   **47.** 7032   **49.** 0.000 000 000 001 g
51. 1600 Cal and 2800 Cal   **53.** 5×10^4 **55.** 3.6×10^{11}
57. 2.2×10^4 **59.** 2.25×10^{-13} **61.** 3.2×10^{14}
63. 2.432×10^{-10} **65.** 3×10^{13} **67.** 6×10^5 **69.** 1.38×10^1
71. 5×10^{-14} **73.** 3.75 in.   **75.** $\$2.97 \times 10^{10}$
77. a. 6.5×10^7 **b.** 2.3725×10^{10} days   **c.** 5.694×10^{11} hr
d. 2.04984×10^{15} sec

Section 5.5 Practice Exercises, pp. 379–382

1. a. polynomial   **b.** coefficient; degree   **c.** 1   **d.** one
e. binomial   **f.** trinomial   **g.** leading; leading coefficient   **h.** greatest
i. zero   **3.** $\dfrac{45}{x^2}$ **5.** $\dfrac{2}{t^4}$ **7.** $\dfrac{1}{3^{12}}$ **9.** 4×10^{-2} is in scientific

notation in which 10 is raised to the -2 power. 4^{-2} is not in scientific
notation and 4 is being raised to the -2 power.

11. a. $-7x^5 + 7x^2 + 9x + 6$ **b.** -7 **c.** 5   **13.** Binomial; 75
15. Monomial; 54   **17.** Binomial; -12 **19.** Trinomial; 27
21. Monomial; -192 **23.** The exponents on the x-factors are
different.   **25.** $35x^2y$ **27.** $8b^5d^2 - 9d$ **29.** $4y^2 + y - 9$
31. $-x^3 + 5x^2 + 9x - 10$ **33.** $10.9y$ **35.** $4a - 8c$
37. $a - \dfrac{1}{2}b - 2$ **39.** $\dfrac{4}{3}z^2 - \dfrac{5}{3}$ **41.** $7.9t^3 - 3.4t^2 + 6t - 4.2$
43. $-4h + 5$ **45.** $2.3m^2 - 3.1m + 1.5$
47. $-3v^3 - 5v^2 - 10v - 22$ **49.** $-8a^3b^2$ **51.** $-53x^3$
53. $-5a - 3$ **55.** $16k + 9$ **57.** $2m^4 - 14m$
59. $3s^2 - 4st - 3t^2$ **61.** $-2r - 3s + 3t$ **63.** $\dfrac{3}{4}x + \dfrac{1}{3}y - \dfrac{3}{10}$
65. $-\dfrac{2}{3}h^2 + \dfrac{3}{5}h - \dfrac{5}{2}$ **67.** $2.4x^4 - 3.1x^2 - 4.4x - 7.9$
69. $4b^3 + 12b^2 - 5b - 12$ **71.** $-\dfrac{7}{2}x^2 + 5x - 11$
73. $4y^3 + 2y^2 + 2$ **75.** $3a^2 - 3a + 5$
77. $9ab^2 - 3ab + 16a^2b$ **79.** $4z^5 + z^4 + 9z^3 - 3z - 2$
81. $2x^4 + 11x^3 - 3x^2 + 8x - 4$ **83.** $-w^3 + 0.2w^2 + 3.7w - 0.7$
85. $-p^2q - 4pq^2 + 3pq$ **87.** 0   **89.** $-5ab + 6ab^2$
91. $11y^2 - 10y - 4$ **93.** For example: $x^3 + 6$
95. For example: $8x^5$ **97.** For example: $-6x^2 + 2x + 5$

Section 5.6 Practice Exercises, pp. 389–392

1. a. $5 - 2x$ **b.** squares; $a^2 - b^2$ **c.** perfect; $a^2 + 2ab + b^2$
3. $-2y^2$ **5.** $-8y^4$ **7.** $8uvw^2$ **9.** $7u^2v^2w^4$ **11.** $-12y$
13. $21p$ **15.** $12a^{14}b^8$ **17.** $-2c^{10}d^{12}$
19. $16p^2q^2 - 24p^2q + 40pq^2$ **21.** $-4k^3 + 52k^2 + 24k$
23. $-45p^3q - 15p^4q^3 + 30pq^2$ **25.** $y^2 + 19y + 90$
27. $m^2 - 14m + 24$ **29.** $12p^2 - 5p - 2$
31. $12w^2 - 32w + 16$ **33.** $p^2 - 14pw + 33w^2$
35. $12x^2 + 28x - 5$ **37.** $6a^2 - 21.5a + 18$

39. $9t^3 - 21t^2 + 3t - 7$ **41.** $9m^2 + 30mn + 24n^2$
43. $5s^3 + 8s^2 - 7s - 6$ **45.** $27w^3 - 8$
47. $p^4 + 5p^3 - 2p^2 - 21p + 5$ **49.** $6a^3 - 23a^2 + 38a - 45$
51. $8x^3 - 36x^2y + 54xy^2 - 27y^3$ **53.** $1.2x^2 + 7.6xy + 2.4y^2$
55. $y^2 - 36$ **57.** $9a^2 - 16b^2$ **59.** $81k^2 - 36$
61. $\dfrac{4}{9}t^2 - 9$ **63.** $u^6 - 25v^2$ **65.** $\dfrac{4}{9} - p^2$
67. $a^2 + 10a + 25$ **69.** $x^2 - 2xy + y^2$ **71.** $4c^2 + 20c + 25$
73. $9t^4 - 24st^2 + 16s^2$ **75.** $t^2 - 14t + 49$ **77.** $16q^2 + 24q + 9$
79. a. 36   **b.** 20   **c.** $(a + b)^2 \neq a^2 + b^2$ in general.
81. $4x^2 - 25$ **83.** $16p^2 + 40p + 25$
85. $27p^3 - 135p^2 + 225p - 125$ **87.** $15a^5 - 6a^2$
89. $49x^2 - y^2$ **91.** $25s^2 + 30st + 9t^2$ **93.** $21x^2 - 65xy + 24y^2$
95. $2t^2 + \dfrac{26}{3}t + 8$ **97.** $-30x^2 - 35x + 25$
99. $6a^3 + 11a^2 - 7a - 2$ **101.** $y^3 - 3y^2 - 6y - 20$
103. $\dfrac{1}{9}m^2 - \dfrac{2}{3}mn + n^2$ **105.** $42w^3 - 84w^2$ **107.** $16y^2 - 65.61$
109. $21c^4 + 4c^2 - 32$ **111.** $9.61x^2 + 27.9x + 20.25$
113. $k^3 - 12k^2 + 48k - 64$ **115.** $125x^3 + 225x^2 + 135x + 27$
117. $2y^4 + 3y^3 + 3y^2 + 5y + 3$ **119.** $6a^3 + 22a^2 - 40a$
121. $2x^3 - 13x^2 + 17x + 12$ **123.** $2x - 7$
125. $k = 10$ or -10 **127.** $k = 8$ or -8

Section 5.7 Practice Exercises, pp. 400–402

1. a. division; quotient; remainder   **b.** Synthetic
3. a. $-4a - 11b$ **b.** $5a^2 - 49ab - 10b^2$
5. a. $7x^2 + 2$ **b.** $6x^4 - 5x^3 + x^2 - 2x$
7. For example: $(5y + 1)^2 = 25y^2 + 10y + 1$
9. $-4t^3 + t - 5$ **11.** $12 + 8y + 2y^2$
13. $x^2 + 3xy - y^2$ **15.** $2y^2 + 3y - 8$
17. $-\dfrac{1}{2}p^3 + p^2 - \dfrac{1}{3}p + \dfrac{1}{6}$ **19.** $a^2 + 5a + 1 - \dfrac{5}{a}$
21. $-3s^2t + 4s - \dfrac{5}{t^2}$ **23.** $8p^2q^6 - 9p^3q^5 - 11p - \dfrac{4}{p^2q}$
25. a. Divisor: $(x - 2)$; quotient: $(2x^2 - 3x - 1)$;
remainder: (-3) **b.** Multiply the quotient and the divisor, then add
the remainder. The result should equal the dividend.
27. $x + 7 + \dfrac{-9}{x + 4}$ **29.** $3y^2 + 2y + 2 + \dfrac{9}{y - 3}$
31. $-4a + 11$ **33.** $6y - 5$ **35.** $6x^2 + 4x + 5 + \dfrac{22}{3x - 2}$
37. $4a^2 - 2a + 1$ **39.** $x^2 - 2x + 2$ **41.** $x^2 + 2x + 5$
43. $x^2 - 1 + \dfrac{8}{x^2 - 2}$ **45.** $n^3 + 2n^2 + 4n + 8$
47. $3y^2 - 3 + \dfrac{2y + 6}{y^2 + 1}$
49. The divisor must be of the form $x - r$.
51. No. The divisor is not of the form $x - r$.
53. a. $x - 5$ **b.** $x^2 + 3x + 11$ **c.** 58
55. $x + 6$ **57.** $t - 4$ **59.** $5y + 10 + \dfrac{11}{y - 1}$
61. $3y^2 - 2y + 2 + \dfrac{-3}{y + 3}$ **63.** $x^2 - x - 2$
65. $a^4 + 2a^3 + 4a^2 + 8a + 16$ **67.** $x^2 + 6x + 36$
69. $4w^3 + 2w^2 + 6$ **71.** $-x^2 - 4x + 13 + \dfrac{-54}{x + 4}$
73. $2x - 1 + \dfrac{3}{x}$ **75.** $4y - 3 + \dfrac{4y + 5}{3y^2 - 2y + 5}$
77. $2x^2 + 3x - 1$ **79.** $2k^3 - 4k^2 + 1 - \dfrac{5}{k^4}$
81. $x + \dfrac{9}{5} + \dfrac{2}{x}$

Chapter 5 Problem Recognition Exercises, p. 403

1. a. $8x^2$ **b.** $12x^4$ **2. a.** $9y^3$ **b.** $8y^6$ **3. a.** $16x^2 + 8xy + y^2$
b. $16x^2y^2$ **4. a.** $4a^2 + 4ab + b^2$ **b.** $4a^2b^2$ **5. a.** $6x + 1$
b. $8x^2 + 8x - 6$ **6. a.** $6m^2 + m + 1$ **b.** $5m^4 + 5m^3 + m^2 + m$
7. a. $9z^2 + 12z + 4$ **b.** $9z^2 - 4$ **8. a.** $36y^2 - 84y + 49$
b. $36y^2 - 49$ **9. a.** $2x^3 - 8x^2 + 14x - 12$ **b.** $x^2 - 1$
10. a. $-3y^4 - 20y^2 - 32$ **b.** $4y^2 + 12$ **11. a.** $2x$ **b.** x^2
12. a. $4c$ **b.** $4c^2$ **13.** $49m^2n^2$ **14.** $64p^2q^2$ **15.** $-x^2 - 3x + 4$
16. $5m^2 - 4m + 1$ **17.** $-7m^2 - 16m$

18. $-4n^5 + n^4 + 6n^2 - 7n + 2$ **19.** $8x^2 + 16x + 34 + \dfrac{74}{x-2}$

20. $-4x^2 - 10x - 30 + \dfrac{-95}{x-3}$ **21.** $6x^3 + 5x^2y - 6xy^2 + y^3$

22. $6a^3 - a^2b + 5ab^2 + 2b^3$ **23.** $x^3 + y^6$ **24.** $m^6 + 1$
25. $4b$ **26.** $-12z$ **27.** $a^6 - 4b^2$ **28.** $y^6 - 36z^2$

29. $4p + 4 + \dfrac{-2}{2p-1}$ **30.** $2v - 7 + \dfrac{29}{2v+3}$ **31.** $4x^2y^2$

32. $-9pq$ **33.** $\dfrac{9}{49}x^2 - \dfrac{1}{4}$ **34.** $\dfrac{4}{25}y^2 - \dfrac{16}{9}$

35. $-\dfrac{11}{9}x^3 + \dfrac{5}{9}x^2 - \dfrac{1}{2}x - 4$ **36.** $-\dfrac{13}{10}y^2 - \dfrac{9}{10}y + \dfrac{4}{15}$

37. $1.3x^2 - 0.3x - 0.5$ **38.** $5w^3 - 4.1w^2 + 2.8w - 1.2$
39. $-6x^3y^6$ **40.** $50a^4b^6$

Chapter 5 Review Exercises, pp. 408–411

1. Base: 5; exponent: 3 **2.** Base: x; exponent: 4
3. Base: -2; exponent: 0 **4.** Base: y; exponent: 1
5. a. 36 **b.** 36 **c.** -36 **6. a.** 64 **b.** -64 **c.** -64
7. 5^{13} **8.** a^{11} **9.** x^9 **10.** 6^9 **11.** 10^3 **12.** y^6
13. b^8 **14.** 7^7 **15.** k **16.** 1 **17.** 2^8 **18.** q^6
19. Exponents are added only when multiplying factors with the same base. In such a case, the base does not change.
20. Exponents are subtracted only when dividing factors with the same base. In such a case, the base does not change. **21.** $7146.10
22. $22,050 **23.** 7^{12} **24.** c^{12} **25.** p^{18} **26.** 9^{28}

27. $\dfrac{a^2}{b^2}$ **28.** $\dfrac{1}{3^4}$ **29.** $\dfrac{5^2}{c^4d^{10}}$ **30.** $\dfrac{m^{10}}{45n^{30}}$ **31.** $2^4a^4b^8$

32. $x^{14}y^2$ **33.** $-\dfrac{3^3x^9}{5^3y^6z^3}$ **34.** $\dfrac{r^{15}}{s^{10}t^{30}}$ **35.** a^{11} **36.** 8^2

37. $4h^{14}$ **38.** $2p^{14}q^{13}$ **39.** $\dfrac{x^6y^2}{4}$ **40.** a^9b^6 **41.** 1

42. 1 **43.** -1 **44.** 1 **45.** 2 **46.** 1 **47.** $\dfrac{1}{z^5}$

48. $\dfrac{1}{10^4}$ **49.** $\dfrac{1}{36a^2}$ **50.** $\dfrac{6}{a^2}$ **51.** $\dfrac{17}{16}$ **52.** $\dfrac{10}{9}$

53. $\dfrac{1}{t^8}$ **54.** $\dfrac{1}{r}$ **55.** $\dfrac{2y^7}{x^6}$ **56.** $\dfrac{4a^6bc}{5}$ **57.** $\dfrac{n^{16}}{16m^8}$

58. $\dfrac{u^{15}}{27v^6}$ **59.** $\dfrac{k^{21}}{5}$ **60.** $\dfrac{h^9}{9}$ **61.** $\dfrac{1}{2}$ **62.** $\dfrac{5}{4}$

63. a. 9.74×10^7 **b.** 4.2×10^{-3} in. **64. a.** 0.000 000 0001
b. $256,000 **65.** 9.43×10^5 **66.** 1.55×10^{10}
67. 2.5×10^8 **68.** 1.638×10^3 **69.** $\approx 9.5367 \times 10^{13}$.
This number has too many digits to fit on most calculator displays.
70. $\approx 1.1529 \times 10^{-12}$. This number has too many digits to fit on most calculator displays. **71. a.** $\approx 5.84 \times 10^8$ mi
b. $\approx 6.67 \times 10^4$ mph **72. a.** $\approx 2.26 \times 10^8$ mi
b. $\approx 1.07 \times 10^5$ mph **73. a.** Trinomial **b.** 4 **c.** 7
74. a. Binomial **b.** 7 **c.** -5 **75.** $7x - 3$
76. $-y^2 - 14y - 2$ **77.** $14a^2 - 2a - 6$
78. $\dfrac{15}{2}x^3 + \dfrac{1}{4}x^2 + \dfrac{1}{2}x + 2$ **79.** $10w^4 + 2w^3 - 7w + 4$
80. $0.01b^5 + b^4 - 0.1b^3 + 0.3b + 0.33$ **81.** $-2x^2 - 9x - 6$

82. $-5x^2 - 9x - 12$ **83.** For example, $-5x^2 + 2x - 4$
84. For example, $6x^5 + 8$ **85.** $6w + 6$ **86.** $-75x^6y^4$
87. $18a^8b^4$ **88.** $15c^4 - 35c^2 + 25c$ **89.** $-2x^3 - 10x^2 + 6x$
90. $5k^2 + k - 4$ **91.** $20t^2 + 3t - 2$ **92.** $6q^2 + 47q - 8$
93. $2a^2 + 4a - 30$ **94.** $49a^2 + 7a + \dfrac{1}{4}$ **95.** $b^2 - 8b + 16$
96. $8p^3 - 27$ **97.** $-2w^3 - 5w^2 - 5w + 4$
98. $4x^3 - 8x^2 + 11x - 4$ **99.** $12a^3 + 11a^2 - 13a - 10$
100. $b^2 - 16$ **101.** $\dfrac{1}{9}r^8 - s^4$ **102.** $49z^4 - 84z^2 + 36$
103. $2h^5 + h^4 - h^3 + h^2 - h + 3$ **104.** $2x^2 + 3x - 20$
105. $4y^2 - 2y$ **106.** $2a^2b - a - 3b$ **107.** $-3x^2 + 2x - 1$
108. $-\dfrac{z^5w^3}{2} + \dfrac{3zw}{4} + \dfrac{1}{z}$ **109.** $x + 2$ **110.** $2t + 5$

111. $p - 3 + \dfrac{5}{2p+7}$ **112.** $a + 6 + \dfrac{-4}{5a-3}$

113. $b^2 + 5b + 25$ **114.** $z + 4$ **115.** $y^2 - 4y + 2 + \dfrac{9y-4}{y^2+3}$

116. $t^2 - 3t + 1 + \dfrac{-2t-6}{3t^2+t+1}$ **117.** $w^2 + w - 1$

Chapter 5 Test, pp. 411–412

1. $\dfrac{(3 \cdot 3 \cdot 3 \cdot 3) \cdot (3 \cdot 3 \cdot 3)}{3 \cdot 3 \cdot 3 \cdot 3 \cdot 3 \cdot 3} = 3$ **2.** 9^6 **3.** q^8 **4.** 1

5. $\dfrac{1}{c^3}$ **6.** $\dfrac{5}{4}$ **7.** $\dfrac{3}{2}$ **8.** $27a^6b^3$ **9.** $\dfrac{16x^4}{y^{12}}$ **10.** 14

11. $49s^{18}t$ **12.** $\dfrac{4}{b^{12}}$ **13.** $\dfrac{16a^{12}}{9b^6}$ **14. a.** 4.3×10^{10}
b. 0.000 0056 **15.** 8.4×10^{-9} **16.** 7.5×10^6
17. a. 2.4192×10^8 m^3 **b.** 8.83008×10^{10} m^3
18. $5x^3 - 7x^2 + 4x + 11$ **a.** 3 **b.** 5
19. $5t^4 + 12t^3 + 7t - 19$ **20.** $24w^2 - 3w - 4$
21. $-10x^5 - 2x^4 + 30x^3$ **22.** $8a^2 - 10a + 3$
23. $4y^3 - 25y^2 + 37y - 15$ **24.** $4 - 9b^2$ **25.** $25z^2 - 60z + 36$
26. $15x^2 - x - 6$ **27.** $-4x^2 + 5x + 7$
28. $y^3 - 11y^2 + 32y - 12$ **29.** $15x^3 - 7x^2 - 2x + 1$
30. Perimeter: $12x - 2$; area: $5x^2 - 13x - 6$

31. $-3x^6 + \dfrac{x^4}{4} - 2x$ **32.** $-4a^2 + \dfrac{ab}{2} - 2$ **33.** $2y - 7$

34. $w^2 - 4w + 5 + \dfrac{-10}{2w+3}$ **35.** $3x^2 + x - 12 + \dfrac{15}{x^2+4}$

Chapters 1–5 Cumulative Review Exercises, pp. 412–413

1. $-\dfrac{35}{2}$ **2.** 4 **3.** $5^2 - \sqrt{4}$; 23 **4.** $\left\{ \dfrac{28}{3} \right\}$

5. { } **6.** Quadrant III **7.** y-axis

8. The measures are $31°$, $54°$, $95°$. **9. a.** 12 in. **b.** 19.5 in.
c. 5.5 hr **10.** $\{(-3, 4)\}$
11. $[-5, \infty)$ $\xrightarrow[\;-5\;]{}$

12. $5x^2 - 9x - 15$ **13.** $-2y^2 - 13yz - 15z^2$
14. $16t^2 - 24t + 9$ **15.** $\dfrac{4}{25}a^2 - \dfrac{1}{9}$
16. $-4a^3b^2 + 2ab - 1$ **17.** $4m^2 + 8m + 11 + \dfrac{24}{m-2}$
18. $\dfrac{c^2}{16d^4}$ **19.** $\dfrac{2b^3}{a^2}$ **20.** 4.1×10^3

SA-18   Student Answer Appendix

Chapter 6

Section 6.1 Practice Exercises, pp. 423–425

1. a. product   **b.** prime   **c.** greatest common factor
d. prime   **e.** greatest common factor (GCF)   **f.** grouping
3. 7   **5.** 6   **7.** y **9.** $4w^2z$ **11.** $2xy^4z^2$ **13.** $(x - y)$
15. a. $3x - 6y$ **b.** $3(x - 2y)$ **17.** $4(p + 3)$ **19.** $5(c^2 - 2c + 3)$
21. $x^3(x^2 + 1)$ **23.** $t(t^3 - 4 + 8t)$ **25.** $2ab(1 + 2a^2)$
27. $19x^2y(2 - y^3)$ **29.** $6xy^5(x^2 - 3y^4z)$ **31.** The expression is
prime because it is not factorable.   **33.** $7pq^2(6p^2 + 2 - p^3q^2)$
35. $t^2(t^3 + 2rt - 3t^2 + 4r^2)$ **37. a.** $-2x(x^2 + 2x - 4)$
b. $2x(-x^2 - 2x + 4)$ **39.** $-1(8t^2 + 9t + 2)$ **41.** $-15p^2(p + 2)$
43. $-3mn(m^3n - 2m + 3n)$ **45.** $-1(7x + 6y + 2z)$
47. $(a + 6)(13 - 4b)$ **49.** $(w^2 - 2)(8v + 1)$ **51.** $7x(x + 3)^2$
53. $(2a - b)(4a + 3c)$ **55.** $(q + p)(3 + r)$ **57.** $(2x + 1)(3x + 2)$
59. $(t + 3)(2t - 1)$ **61.** $(3y - 1)(2y - 3)$ **63.** $(b + 1)(b^3 - 4)$
65. $(j^2 + 5)(3k + 1)$ **67.** $(2x^6 + 1)(7w^6 - 1)$
69. $(y + x)(a + b)$ **71.** $(vw + 1)(w - 3)$ **73.** $5x(x^2 + y^2)(3x + 2y)$
75. $4b(a - b)(x - 1)$ **77.** $6t(t - 3)(s - t^2)$ **79.** $P = 2(l + w)$
81. $S = 2\pi r(r + h)$ **83.** $\frac{1}{7}(x^2 + 3x - 5)$ **85.** $\frac{1}{4}(5w^2 + 3w + 9)$
87. For example: $6x^2 + 9x$ **89.** For example: $16p^4q^2 + 8p^3q - 4p^2q$

Section 6.2 Practice Exercises, pp. 430–432

1. a. positive   **b.** different   **c.** Both are correct.
d. $3(x + 6)(x + 2)$ **3.** $3(t - 5)(t - 2)$ **5.** $(a + 2b)(x - 5)$
7. $(x + 8)(x + 2)$ **9.** $(z - 9)(z - 2)$ **11.** $(z - 6)(z + 3)$
13. $(p - 8)(p + 5)$ **15.** $(t + 10)(t - 4)$ **17.** Prime
19. $(n + 4)^2$ **21.** a   **23.** c   **25.** They are both correct
because multiplication of polynomials is a commutative operation.
27. The expressions are equal and both are correct.
29. It should be written in descending order.   **31.** $(x - 15)(x + 2)$
33. $(w - 13)(w - 5)$ **35.** $(t + 18)(t + 4)$ **37.** $3(x - 12)(x + 2)$
39. $8p(p - 1)(p - 4)$ **41.** $y^2z^2(y - 6)(y - 6)$ or $y^2z^2(y - 6)^2$
43. $-(x - 4)(x - 6)$ **45.** $-5(a - 3x)(a + 2x)$
47. $-2(c + 2)(c + 1)$ **49.** $xy^3(x - 4)(x - 15)$
51. $12(p - 7)(p - 1)$ **53.** $-2(m - 10)(m - 1)$
55. $(c + 5d)(c + d)$ **57.** $(a - 2b)(a - 7b)$ **59.** Prime
61. $(q - 7)(q + 9)$ **63.** $(x + 10)^2$ **65.** $(t + 20)(t - 2)$
67. The student forgot to factor out the GCF before factoring the
trinomial further. The polynomial is not factored completely, because
$(2x - 4)$ has a common factor of 2.   **69.** $x^2 + 9x - 52$
71. a. $3x^2 + 9x - 12$ **b.** $3(x + 4)(x - 1)$ **73.** $(x^2 + 1)(x^2 + 9)$
75. $(w^2 + 5)(w^2 - 3)$ **77.** 7, 5, −7, −5
79. For example: $c = -16$

Section 6.3 Practice Exercises, pp. 439–440

1. a. Both are correct.   **b.** $2(3x - 5)(x + 1)$ **3.** $(n - 1)(m - 2)$
5. $6(a - 7)(a + 2)$ **7.** a   **9.** b   **11.** $(3n + 1)(n + 4)$
13. $(2y + 1)(y - 2)$ **15.** $(5x + 1)(x - 3)$ **17.** $(4c + 1)(3c - 2)$
19. $(10w - 3)(w + 4)$ **21.** $(3q + 2)(2q - 3)$ **23.** Prime
25. $(5m + 2)(5m - 4)$ **27.** $(6y - 5x)(y + 4x)$
29. $2(m + 4)(m - 10)$ **31.** $y^3(2y + 1)(y + 6)$
33. $-(a + 17)(a - 2)$ **35.** $-10(4m + p)(2m - 3p)$
37. $(x^2 + 1)(x^2 + 9)$ **39.** $(w^2 + 5)(w^2 - 3)$ **41.** $(2x^2 + 3)(x^2 - 5)$
43. $-2(z - 9)(z - 1)$ **45.** $(q - 7)(q - 6)$ **47.** $(2t + 3)(3t - 1)$
49. $(2m - 5)^2$ **51.** Prime   **53.** $(2x - 5y)(3x - 2y)$
55. $(4m + 5n)(3m - n)$ **57.** $5(3r + 2)(2r - 1)$ **59.** Prime
61. $(2t - 5)(5t + 1)$ **63.** $(7w - 4)(2w + 3)$
65. $(a - 12)(a + 2)$ **67.** $(x + 5y)(x + 4y)$ **69.** $(a + 20b)(a + b)$
71. $(t - 7)(t - 3)$ **73.** $d(5d^2 + 3d - 10)$
75. $4b(b - 5)(b + 4)$ **77.** $y^2(x - 3)(x - 10)$
79. $-2u(2u + 5)(3u - 2)$ **81.** $(2x^2 + 3)(4x^2 + 1)$
83. a. 36 ft   **b.** $-4(4t + 5)(t - 2)$; Yes   **85. a.** $(x - 12)(x + 2)$
b. $(x - 6)(x - 4)$ **87. a.** $(x - 6)(x + 1)$ **b.** $(x - 2)(x - 3)$

Section 6.4 Practice Exercises, pp. 446–447

1. a. Both are correct.   **b.** $3(4x + 3)(x - 2)$ **3.** $(y + 5)(8 + 9y)$
5. 12, 1   **7.** −8, −1   **9.** 5, −4   **11.** 9, −2
13. $(x + 4)(3x + 1)$ **15.** $(w - 2)(4w - 1)$ **17.** $(x + 9)(x - 2)$
19. $(m + 3)(2m - 1)$ **21.** $(4k + 3)(2k - 3)$ **23.** $(2k - 5)^2$
25. Prime   **27.** $(3z - 5)(3z - 2)$ **29.** $(6y - 5z)(2y + 3z)$
31. $2(7y + 4)(y + 3)$ **33.** $-(3w - 5)(5w + 1)$
35. $-4(x - y)(3x - 2y)$ **37.** $6y(y + 1)(3y + 7)$
39. $(a^2 + 2)(a^2 + 3)$ **41.** $(3x^2 - 5)(2x^2 + 3)$
43. $(8p^2 - 3)(p^2 + 5)$ **45.** $(5p - 1)(4p - 3)$
47. $(3u - 2v)(2u - 5v)$ **49.** $(4a + 5b)(3a - b)$
51. $(h + 7k)(3h - 2k)$ **53.** Prime   **55.** $(2z - 1)(8z - 3)$
57. $(b - 4)^2$ **59.** $-5(x - 2)(x - 3)$ **61.** $(t - 3)(t + 2)$
63. Prime   **65.** $2(12x - 1)(3x + 1)$ **67.** $p(p + 3)(p - 9)$
69. $x(3x + 7)(x + 1)$ **71.** $2p(p - 15)(p - 4)$
73. $x^2(y + 3)(y + 11)$ **75.** $-(k + 2)(k + 5)$
77. $-3(n + 6)(n - 5)$ **79.** $(x^2 - 2)(x^2 - 5)$
81. No. $(2x + 4)$ contains a common factor of 2.
83. a. 128 customers   **b.** $-2(x - 18)(x - 2)$; 128; Yes
85. a. 42   **b.** $n(n + 1)$; 42; Yes

Section 6.5 Practice Exercises, pp. 453–454

1. a. difference; $(a + b)(a - b)$ **b.** sum   **c.** is not
d. square   **e.** $(a + b)^2$; $(a - b)^2$ **3.** $(3x - 1)(2x - 5)$
5. $5xy(3x - 2y)$ **7.** $(x + b)(a - 6)$ **9.** $(y + 10)(y - 4)$
11. $x^2 - 25$ **13.** $4p^2 - 9q^2$ **15.** $(x - 6)(x + 6)$
17. $3(w + 10)(w - 10)$ **19.** $(2a - 11b)(2a + 11b)$
21. $(7m - 4n)(7m + 4n)$ **23.** Prime   **25.** $(y + 2z)(y - 2z)$
27. $(a - b^2)(a + b^2)$ **29.** $(5pq - 1)(5pq + 1)$ **31.** $\left(c - \frac{1}{5}\right)\left(c + \frac{1}{5}\right)$
33. $2(5 - 4t)(5 + 4t)$ **35.** $(x + 4)(x - 4)(x^2 + 16)$
37. $(2 - z)(2 + z)(4 + z^2)$ **39.** $(x + 5)(x + 3)(x - 3)$
41. $(c - 1)(c + 5)(c - 5)$ **43.** $(x + 3)(x - 3)(2 + y)$
45. $(y + 3)(y - 3)(x + 2)(x - 2)$ **47.** $9x^2 + 30x + 25$
49. a. $x^2 + 4x + 4$ is a perfect square trinomial.
b. $x^2 + 4x + 4 = (x + 2)^2$; $x^2 + 5x + 4 = (x + 1)(x + 4)$
51. $(x + 9)^2$ **53.** $(5z - 2)^2$ **55.** $(7a + 3b)^2$ **57.** $(y - 1)^2$
59. $5(4z + 3w)^2$ **61.** $(3y + 25)(3y + 1)$ **63.** $2(a - 5)^2$
65. Prime   **67.** $(2x + y)^2$ **69.** $3x(x - 1)^2$ **71.** $y(y - 6)$
73. $(2p - 5)(2p + 7)$ **75.** $(-t + 2)(t + 6)$ or $-(t - 2)(t + 6)$
77. $(2a - 5 + 10b)(2a - 5 - 10b)$ **79. a.** $a^2 - b^2$
b. $(a - b)(a + b)$

Section 6.6 Practice Exercises, pp. 459–460

1. a. sum; cubes   **b.** difference; cubes   **c.** $(a - b)(a^2 + ab + b^2)$
d. $(a + b)(a^2 - ab + b^2)$ **3.** $5(2 - t)(2 + t)$ **5.** $(t + u)(2 + s)$
7. $(3v - 4)(v + 3)$ **9.** $-(c + 5)^2$ **11.** $x^3, 8, y^6, 27q^3, w^{12}, r^3s^6$
13. $t^3, -1, 27, a^3b^6, 125, y^6$ **15.** $(y - 2)(y^2 + 2y + 4)$
17. $(1 - p)(1 + p + p^2)$ **19.** $(w + 4)(w^2 - 4w + 16)$
21. $(x - 10y)(x^2 + 10xy + 100y^2)$ **23.** $(4t + 1)(16t^2 - 4t + 1)$
25. $(10a + 3)(100a^2 - 30a + 9)$ **27.** $\left(n - \frac{1}{2}\right)\left(n^2 + \frac{1}{2}n + \frac{1}{4}\right)$
29. $(5x + 2y)(25x^2 - 10xy + 4y^2)$ **31.** $(x^2 - 2)(x^2 + 2)$
33. Prime   **35.** $(t + 4)(t^2 - 4t + 16)$ **37.** Prime
39. $4(b + 3)(b^2 - 3b + 9)$ **41.** $5(p - 5)(p + 5)$
43. $\left(\frac{1}{4} - 2h\right)\left(\frac{1}{16} + \frac{1}{2}h + 4h^2\right)$ **45.** $(x - 2)(x + 2)(x^2 + 4)$
47. $\left(\frac{2}{3}x - w\right)\left(\frac{2}{3}x + w\right)$
49. $(q - 2)(q^2 + 2q + 4)(q + 2)(q^2 - 2q + 4)$
51. $(x^3 + 4y)(x^6 - 4x^3y + 16y^2)$ **53.** $(2x + 3)(x - 1)(x + 1)$
55. $(2x - y)(2x + y)(4x^2 + y^2)$ **57.** $(3y - 2)(3y + 2)(9y^2 + 4)$
59. $(a + b^2)(a^2 - ab^2 + b^4)$ **61.** $(x^2 + y^2)(x - y)(x + y)$
63. $(k + 4)(k - 3)(k + 3)$ **65.** $2(t - 5)(t - 1)(t + 1)$
67. $\left(\frac{4}{5}p - \frac{1}{2}q\right)\left(\frac{16}{25}p^2 + \frac{2}{5}pq + \frac{1}{4}q^2\right)$ **69.** $(a^4 + b^4)(a^8 - a^4b^4 + b^8)$
71. a. The quotient is $x^2 + 2x + 4$.   **b.** $(x - 2)(x^2 + 2x + 4)$
73. $x^2 + 4x + 16$ **75.** $2x + 1$

Chapter 6 Problem Recognition Exercises, pp. 461–462

1. A prime polynomial cannot be factored further.
2. Factor out the GCF.   **3.** Look for a difference of squares: $a^2 - b^2$, a difference of cubes: $a^3 - b^3$, or a sum of cubes: $a^3 + b^3$.   **4.** Grouping
5. a. Difference of squares   **b.** $2(a - 9)(a + 9)$
6. a. Nonperfect square trinomial   **b.** $(y + 3)(y + 1)$
7. a. None of these   **b.** $6w(w - 1)$
8. a. Difference of squares   **b.** $(2z + 3)(2z - 3)(4z^2 + 9)$
9. a. Nonperfect square trinomial   **b.** $(3t + 1)(t + 4)$
10. a. Sum of cubes   **b.** $5(r + 1)(r^2 - r + 1)$
11. a. Four terms-grouping   **b.** $(3c + d)(a - b)$
12. a. Difference of cubes   **b.** $(x - 5)(x^2 + 5x + 25)$
13. a. Sum of cubes   **b.** $(y + 2)(y^2 - 2y + 4)$
14. a. Nonperfect square trinomial   **b.** $(7p - 1)(p - 4)$
15. a. Nonperfect square trinomial   **b.** $3(q - 4)(q + 1)$
16. a. Perfect square trinomial   **b.** $-2(x - 2)^2$
17. a. None of these   **b.** $6a(3a + 2)$
18. a. Difference of cubes   **b.** $2(3 - y)(9 + 3y + y^2)$
19. a. Difference of squares   **b.** $4(t - 5)(t + 5)$
20. a. Nonperfect square trinomial   **b.** $(4t + 1)(t - 8)$
21. a. Nonperfect square trinomial   **b.** $10(c^2 + c + 1)$
22. a. Four terms-grouping   **b.** $(w - 5)(2x + 3y)$
23. a. Sum of cubes   **b.** $(x + 0.1)(x^2 - 0.1x + 0.01)$
24. a. Difference of squares   **b.** $(2q - 3)(2q + 3)$
25. a. Perfect square trinomial   **b.** $(8 + k)^2$
26. a. Four terms-grouping   **b.** $(t + 6)(s^2 + 5)$
27. a. Four terms-grouping   **b.** $(x + 1)(2x - y)$
28. a. Sum of cubes   **b.** $(w + y)(w^2 - wy + y^2)$
29. a. Difference of cubes   **b.** $(a - c)(a^2 + ac + c^2)$
30. a. Nonperfect square trinomial   **b.** Prime
31. a. Nonperfect square trinomial   **b.** Prime
32. a. Perfect square trinomial   **b.** $(a + 1)^2$
33. a. Perfect square trinomial   **b.** $(b + 5)^2$
34. a. Nonperfect square trinomial   **b.** $-(t + 8)(t - 4)$
35. a. Nonperfect square trinomial   **b.** $-p(p + 4)(p + 1)$
36. a. Difference of squares   **b.** $(xy - 7)(xy + 7)$
37. a. Nonperfect square trinomial   **b.** $3(2x + 3)(x - 5)$
38. a. Nonperfect square trinomial   **b.** $2(5y - 1)(2y - 1)$
39. a. None of these   **b.** $abc^2(5ac - 7)$
40. a. Difference of squares   **b.** $2(2a - 5)(2a + 5)$
41. a. Nonperfect square trinomial   **b.** $(t + 9)(t - 7)$
42. a. Nonperfect square trinomial   **b.** $(b + 10)(b - 8)$
43. a. Four terms-grouping   **b.** $(b + y)(a - b)$
44. a. None of these   **b.** $3x^2y^4(2x + y)$
45. a. Nonperfect square trinomial   **b.** $(7u - 2v)(2u - v)$
46. a. Nonperfect square trinomial   **b.** Prime
47. a. Nonperfect square trinomial   **b.** $2(2q^2 - 4q - 3)$
48. a. Nonperfect square trinomial   **b.** $3(3w^2 + w - 5)$
49. a. Sum of squares   **b.** Prime
50. a. Perfect square trinomial   **b.** $5(b - 3)^2$
51. a. Nonperfect square trinomial   **b.** $(3r + 1)(2r + 3)$
52. a. Nonperfect square trinomial   **b.** $(2s - 3)(2s + 5)$
53. a. Difference of squares   **b.** $(2a - 1)(2a + 1)(4a^2 + 1)$
54. a. Four terms-grouping   **b.** $(p + c)(p - 3)(p + 3)$
55. a. Perfect square trinomial   **b.** $(9u - 5v)^2$
56. a. Sum of squares   **b.** $4(x^2 + 4)$
57. a. Nonperfect square trinomial   **b.** $(x - 6)(x + 1)$
58. a. Nonperfect square trinomial   **b.** Prime
59. a. Four terms-grouping   **b.** $2(x - 3y)(a + 2b)$
60. a. Nonperfect square trinomial   **b.** $m(4m + 1)(2m - 3)$
61. a. Nonperfect square trinomial   **b.** $x^2y(3x + 5)(7x + 2)$
62. a. Difference of squares   **b.** $2(m^2 - 8)(m^2 + 8)$
63. a. Four terms-grouping   **b.** $(4v - 3)(2u + 3)$
64. a. Four terms-grouping   **b.** $(t - 5)(4t + s)$
65. a. Perfect square trinomial   **b.** $3(2x - 1)^2$
66. a. Perfect square trinomial   **b.** $(p + q)^2$
67. a. Nonperfect square trinomial   **b.** $n(2n - 1)(3n + 4)$
68. a. Nonperfect square trinomial   **b.** $k(2k - 1)(2k + 3)$

69. a. Difference of squares   **b.** $(8 - y)(8 + y)$
70. a. Difference of squares   **b.** $b(6 - b)(6 + b)$
71. a. Nonperfect square trinomial   **b.** Prime
72. a. Nonperfect square trinomial   **b.** $(y + 4)(y + 2)$
73. a. Nonperfect square trinomial   **b.** $(c^2 - 10)(c^2 - 2)$

Section 6.7 Practice Exercises, pp. 467–469

1. a. quadratic   **b.** $0; 0$ **3.** $4(b - 5)(b - 6)$
5. $(3x - 2)(x + 4)$ **7.** $4(x^2 + 4y^2)$ **9.** Neither   **11.** Quadratic
13. Linear   **15.** $\{-3, 1\}$ **17.** $\left\{\frac{7}{2}, -\frac{7}{2}\right\}$ **19.** $\{-5\}$
21. $\left\{0, \frac{1}{5}\right\}$ **23.** The polynomial must be factored completely.
25. $\{5, -3\}$ **27.** $\{-12, 2\}$ **29.** $\left\{4, -\frac{1}{2}\right\}$ **31.** $\left\{\frac{2}{3}, -\frac{2}{3}\right\}$
33. $\{6, 8\}$ **35.** $\left\{0, -\frac{3}{2}, 4\right\}$ **37.** $\left\{-\frac{1}{3}, 3, -6\right\}$ **39.** $\left\{0, 4, -\frac{3}{2}\right\}$
41. $\left\{0, -\frac{9}{2}, 11\right\}$ **43.** $\{0, 4, -4\}$ **45.** $\{-6, 0\}$
47. $\left\{\frac{3}{4}, -\frac{3}{4}\right\}$ **49.** $\{0, -5, -2\}$ **51.** $\left\{-\frac{14}{3}\right\}$ **53.** $\{5, 3\}$
55. $\{0, -2\}$ **57.** $\{-3\}$ **59.** $\{-3, 1\}$ **61.** $\left\{\frac{3}{2}\right\}$
63. $\left\{0, \frac{1}{3}\right\}$ **65.** $\{0, 2\}$ **67.** $\{3, -2, 2\}$ **69.** $\{-5, 4\}$
71. $\{-5, -1\}$

Chapter 6 Problem Recognition Exercises, p. 469

1. a. $(x + 7)(x - 1)$ **b.** $\{-7, 1\}$ **2. a.** $(c + 6)(c + 2)$
b. $\{-6, -2\}$ **3. a.** $(2y + 1)(y + 3)$ **b.** $\left\{-\frac{1}{2}, -3\right\}$
4. a. $(3x - 5)(x - 1)$ **b.** $\left\{\frac{5}{3}, 1\right\}$ **5. a.** $\left\{\frac{4}{5}, -1\right\}$
b. $(5q - 4)(q + 1)$ **6. a.** $\left\{-\frac{1}{3}, \frac{3}{2}\right\}$ **b.** $(3a + 1)(2a - 3)$
7. a. $\{-8, 8\}$ **b.** $(a + 8)(a - 8)$ **8. a.** $\{-10, 10\}$
b. $(v + 10)(v - 10)$ **9. a.** $(2b + 9)(2b - 9)$ **b.** $\left\{-\frac{9}{2}, \frac{9}{2}\right\}$
10. a. $(6t + 7)(6t - 7)$ **b.** $\left\{-\frac{7}{6}, \frac{7}{6}\right\}$
11. a. $\left\{-\frac{3}{2}, -\frac{1}{2}\right\}$ **b.** $2(2x + 3)(2x + 1)$
12. a. $\left\{-\frac{4}{3}, -2\right\}$ **b.** $4(3y + 4)(y + 2)$
13. a. $x(x - 10)(x + 2)$ **b.** $\{0, 10, -2\}$
14. a. $k(k + 7)(k - 2)$ **b.** $\{0, -7, 2\}$
15. a. $\{-1, 3, -3\}$ **b.** $(b + 1)(b - 3)(b + 3)$
16. a. $\{8, -2, 2\}$ **b.** $(x - 8)(x + 2)(x - 2)$
17. $(s - 3)(2s + r)$ **18.** $(2t + 1)(3t + 5u)$
19. $\left\{-\frac{1}{2}, 0, \frac{1}{2}\right\}$ **20.** $\{-5, 0, 5\}$ **21.** $\{0, 1\}$
22. $\{-3, 0\}$ **23.** $\left\{\frac{1}{3}\right\}$ **24.** $\left\{-\frac{7}{12}\right\}$
25. $(2w + 3)(4w^2 - 6w + 9)$ **26.** $(10q - 1)(100q^2 + 10q + 1)$
27. $\left\{-\frac{7}{5}, 1\right\}$ **28.** $\left\{-6, -\frac{1}{4}\right\}$ **29.** $\left\{-\frac{2}{3}, -5\right\}$ **30.** $\left\{-1, -\frac{1}{2}\right\}$
31. $\{3\}$ **32.** $\{0\}$ **33.** $\{-4, 4\}$ **34.** $\left\{-\frac{2}{3}, \frac{2}{3}\right\}$
35. $\{1, 6\}$ **36.** $\{-2, -12\}$

Section 6.8 Practice Exercises, pp. 474–477

1. a. $x + 1$ **b.** $x + 2$ **c.** $x + 2$ **d.** LW **e.** $\frac{1}{2}bh$
f. $a^2 + b^2 = c^2$ **3.** $\left\{0, -\frac{2}{3}\right\}$ **5.** $\{6, -1\}$ **7.** $\left\{-\frac{5}{6}, 2\right\}$
9. The numbers are 7 and −7.   **11.** The numbers are 10 and −4.
13. The numbers are −9 and −7, or 7 and 9.   **15.** The numbers are 5 and 6, or −6 and −5.   **17.** The height of the painting is 11 ft and the width is 9 ft.   **19. a.** The slab is 7 m by 4 m.   **b.** The perimeter is 22 m.   **21.** The base is 7 ft and the height is 4 ft.

SA-20   Student Answer Appendix

23. The base is 5 cm and the height is 8 cm.   **25.** The ball hits the ground in 3 sec.
27. The object is at ground level at 0 sec and 1.5 sec.
29.

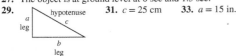

31. $c = 25$ cm   **33.** $a = 15$ in.

35. The brace is 20 in. long.   **37.** The kite is 19 yd high.
39. The bottom of the ladder is 8 ft from the house. The distance from the top of the ladder to the ground is 15 ft.
41. The hypotenuse is 10 m.

Chapter 6 Review Exercises, pp. 483–485

1. $3a^2b$ **2.** $x + 5$ **3.** $2c(3c - 5)$ **4.** $-2yz$ or $2yz$
5. $2x(3x + x^3 - 4)$ **6.** $11w^2y^3(w - 4y^2)$
7. $t(-t + 5)$ or $-t(t - 5)$ **8.** $u(-6u - 1)$ or $-u(6u + 1)$
9. $(b + 2)(3b - 7)$ **10.** $2(5x + 9)(1 + 4x)$
11. $(w + 2)(7w + b)$ **12.** $(b - 2)(b + y)$
13. $3(4y - 3)(5y - 1)$ **14.** $a(2 - a)(3 - b)$
15. $(x - 3)(x - 7)$ **16.** $(y - 8)(y - 11)$
17. $(z - 12)(z + 6)$ **18.** $(q - 13)(q + 3)$
19. $3w(p + 10)(p + 2)$ **20.** $2m^2(m + 8)(m + 5)$
21. $-(t - 8)(t - 2)$ **22.** $-(w - 4)(w + 5)$
23. $(a + b)(a + 11b)$ **24.** $(c - 6d)(c + 3d)$
25. Different   **26.** Both negative   **27.** Both positive
28. Different   **29.** $(2y + 3)(y - 4)$ **30.** $(4w + 3)(w - 2)$
31. $(2z + 5)(5z + 2)$ **32.** $(4z - 3)(2z + 3)$ **33.** Prime
34. Prime   **35.** $10(w - 9)(w + 3)$ **36.** $-3(y - 8)(y + 2)$
37. $(3c - 5d)^2$ **38.** $(x + 6)^2$ **39.** $(3g + 2h)(2g + h)$
40. $(6m - n)(2m - 5n)$ **41.** $(v^2 + 1)(v^2 - 3)$
42. $(x^2 + 5)(x^2 + 2)$ **43.** $5, -1$ **44.** $-3, -5$
45. $(c - 2)(3c + 1)$ **46.** $(y - 3)(4y + 1)$ **47.** $(t + 12w)(t + w)$
48. $(4x^2 - 3)(x^2 + 5)$ **49.** $(w^2 + 5)(w^2 + 2)$
50. $(p - 3q)(p - 5q)$ **51.** $-2(4v + 3)(5v - 1)$
52. $10(4s - 5)(s + 2)$ **53.** $ab(a - 6b)(a - 4b)$
54. $2z^4(z + 7)(z - 3)$ **55.** Prime   **56.** Prime   **57.** $(7x + 10)^2$
58. $(3w - z)^2$ **59.** $(a - b)(a + b)$ **60.** Prime
61. $(a - 7)(a + 7)$ **62.** $(d - 8)(d + 8)$ **63.** $(10 - 9t)(10 + 9t)$
64. $(2 - 5k)(2 + 5k)$ **65.** Prime   **66.** Prime   **67.** $(y + 6)^2$
68. $(t + 8)^2$ **69.** $(3a - 2)^2$ **70.** $(5x - 4)^2$ **71.** $-3(v + 2)^2$
72. $-2(x - 5)^2$ **73.** $2(c^2 - 3)(c^2 + 3)$ **74.** $2(6x - y)(6x + y)$
75. $(p + 3)(p - 4)(p + 4)$ **76.** $(k - 2)(2 - k)(2 + k)$ or $-(k - 2)^2(2 + k)$ **77.** $(a + b)(a^2 - ab + b^2)$
78. $(a - b)(a^2 + ab + b^2)$ **79.** $(4 + a)(16 - 4a + a^2)$
80. $(5 - b)(25 + 5b + b^2)$ **81.** $(p^2 + 2)(p^4 - 2p^2 + 4)$
82. $\left(q^2 - \frac{1}{3}\right)\left(q^4 + \frac{1}{3}q^2 + \frac{1}{9}\right)$ **83.** $6(x - 2)(x^2 + 2x + 4)$
84. $7(y + 1)(y^2 - y + 1)$ **85.** $x(x - 6)(x + 6)$
86. $q(q - 4)(q^2 + 4q + 16)$ **87.** $4(2h^2 + 5)$ **88.** $m(m - 8)$
89. $(x + 4)(x + 1)(x - 1)$ **90.** $5q(p^2 - 2q)(p^2 + 2q)$
91. $n(2 + n)(4 - 2n + n^2)$ **92.** $14(m - 1)(m^2 + m + 1)$
93. $(x - 3)(2x + 1) = 0$ can be solved directly by the zero product rule because it is a product of factors set equal to zero.
94. $\left\{\frac{1}{4}, -\frac{2}{3}\right\}$ **95.** $\left\{9, \frac{1}{2}\right\}$ **96.** $\left\{0, -3, -\frac{2}{5}\right\}$
97. $\left\{0, 7, \frac{9}{4}\right\}$ **98.** $\left\{-\frac{5}{7}, 2\right\}$ **99.** $\left\{-\frac{1}{4}, 6\right\}$
100. $\{12, -12\}$ **101.** $\{5, -5\}$ **102.** $\left\{0, \frac{1}{5}\right\}$ **103.** $\{4, 2\}$
104. $\left\{-\frac{5}{6}\right\}$ **105.** $\left\{-\frac{2}{3}\right\}$ **106.** $\left\{\frac{2}{3}, 6\right\}$ **107.** $\left\{\frac{11}{2}, -12\right\}$
108. $\{0, 7, 2\}$ **109.** $\{0, 2, -2\}$ **110.** The height is 6 ft, and the base is 13 ft.   **111.** The ball is at ground level at 0 and 1 sec.
112. The ramp is 13 ft long.   **113.** The legs are 6 ft and 8 ft; the hypotenuse is 10 ft.   **114.** The numbers are -8 and 8.
115. The numbers are 29 and 30, or -2 and -1.
116. The height is 4 m, and the base is 9 m.

Chapter 6 Test, p. 485

1. $3x(5x^3 - 1 + 2x^2)$ **2.** $(a - 5)(7 - a)$
3. $(6w - 1)(w - 7)$ **4.** $(13 - p)(13 + p)$
5. $(q - 8)^2$ **6.** $(2 + t)(4 - 2t + t^2)$ **7.** $(a + 4)(a + 8)$
8. $(x + 7)(x - 6)$ **9.** $(2y - 1)(y - 8)$ **10.** $(2z + 1)(3z + 8)$
11. $(3t - 10)(3t + 10)$ **12.** $(v + 9)(v - 9)$ **13.** $3(a + 6b)(a + 3b)$
14. $(c - 1)(c + 1)(c^2 + 1)$ **15.** $(y - 7)(x + 3)$ **16.** Prime
17. $-10(u - 2)(u - 1)$ **18.** $3(2t - 5)(2t + 5)$ **19.** $5(y - 5)^2$
20. $7q(3q + 2)$ **21.** $(2x + 1)(x - 2)(x + 2)$
22. $(y - 5)(y^2 + 5y + 25)$ **23.** $(mn - 9)(mn + 9)$
24. $16(a - 2b)(a + 2b)$ **25.** $(4x - 3y^2)(16x^2 + 12xy^2 + 9y^4)$
26. $3y(x - 4)(x + 2)$ **27.** $\left\{\frac{3}{2}, -5\right\}$ **28.** $\{0, 7\}$ **29.** $\{8, -2\}$
30. $\left\{\frac{1}{5}, -1\right\}$ **31.** $\{3, -3, -10\}$
32. The tennis court is 12 yd by 26 yd.   **33.** The two integers are 5 and 7, or -5 and -7.   **34.** The base is 12 in., and the height is 7 in.
35. The shorter leg is 5 ft.   **36.** The stone hits the ground in 2 sec.

Chapters 1–6 Cumulative Review Exercises, p. 486

1. $\frac{7}{5}$ **2.** $\{-3\}$ **3.** $y = \frac{3}{2}x - 4$
4. There are 10 quarters and 7 dimes.
5. $[-4, \infty)$ **6. a.** Yes   **b.** 1
c. $(0, 4)$ **d.** $(-4, 0)$ **e.**

7. a. Vertical line   **b.** Undefined   **c.** $(5, 0)$ **d.** Does not exist
8. $y = 3x + 14$ **9.** $\{(5, 2)\}$ **10.** $-\frac{7}{2}y^2 - 5y - 14$
11. $8p^3 - 22p^2 + 13p + 3$ **12.** $4w^2 - 28w + 49$
13. $r^3 + 5r^2 + 15r + 40 + \frac{121}{r - 3}$ **14.** c^4 **15.** $\frac{a^4}{9b^2}$
16. 1.6×10^3 **17.** $(w - 2)(w + 2)(w^2 + 4)$
18. $(a + 5b)(2x - 3y)$ **19.** $(2x - 5)(2x + 1)$
20. $\left\{0, \frac{1}{2}, -5\right\}$

Chapter 7

Section 7.1 Practice Exercises, pp. 495–498

1. a. rational   **b.** denominator; zero   **c.** $\frac{p}{q}$ **d.** $1; -1$ **3.** 0
5. $-\frac{1}{8}$ **7.** $-\frac{1}{2}$ **9.** Undefined   **11. a.** $3\frac{1}{5}$ hr or 3.2 hr
b. $1\frac{3}{4}$ hr or 1.75 hr   **13.** $k = -2$ **15.** $x = \frac{5}{2}, x = -8$
17. $m = -2, m = -3$ **19.** There are no restricted values.
21. There are no restricted values.   **23.** $t = 0$
25. For example: $\frac{1}{x - 2}$ **27.** For example: $\frac{1}{(x + 3)(x - 7)}$
29. a. $\frac{2}{5}$ **b.** $\frac{2}{5}$ **31. a.** Undefined   **b.** Undefined
33. a. $y = -2$ **b.** $\frac{1}{2}$ **35. a.** $t = -1$ **b.** $t - 1$
37. a. $w = 0, w = \frac{5}{3}$ **b.** $\frac{1}{3w - 5}$ **39. a.** $x = -\frac{2}{3}$ **b.** $\frac{3x - 2}{2}$
41. a. $a = -3, a = 2$ **b.** $\frac{a + 5}{a + 3}$ **43.** $\frac{b}{3}$ **45.** $-\frac{3xy}{z^2}$
47. $\frac{p - 3}{p + 4}$ **49.** $\frac{1}{4(m - 11)}$ **51.** $\frac{2x + 1}{4x^2}$ **53.** $\frac{1}{4a - 5}$
55. $\frac{x - 2}{3(y + 2)}$ **57.** $\frac{2}{x - 5}$ **59.** $a + 7$ **61.** Cannot simplify

63. $\dfrac{y+3}{2y-5}$ **65.** $\dfrac{5}{(q+1)(q-1)}$ **67.** $\dfrac{c-d}{2c+d}$ **69.** $5x+4$

71. $\dfrac{x+y}{x-4y}$ **73.** They are opposites.   **75.** -1 **77.** -1

79. $-\dfrac{1}{2}$ **81.** Cannot simplify   **83.** $\dfrac{5x-6}{5x+6}$ **85.** $\dfrac{x+3}{4+x}$

87. $\dfrac{3x-2}{x+4}$ **89.** $-\dfrac{1}{2}$ **91.** $-\dfrac{w+2}{4}$ **93.** $\dfrac{3t^2}{2}$ **95.** $\dfrac{2r-s}{s+2r}$

97. $-\dfrac{3}{2(x-y)}$ **99.** $\dfrac{1}{t(t-5)}$ **101.** $w-2$ **103.** $\dfrac{z+4}{z^2+4z+16}$

Section 7.2 Practice Exercises, pp. 503–505

1. $\dfrac{3}{10}$ **3.** 2   **5.** $\dfrac{5}{2}$ **7.** $\dfrac{15}{4}$ **9.** $\dfrac{3}{2x}$ **11.** $3xy^4$

13. $\dfrac{x-6}{8}$ **15.** $\dfrac{2}{y}$ **17.** $-\dfrac{5}{8}$ **19.** $-\dfrac{b+a}{a-b}$ **21.** $\dfrac{y+1}{5}$

23. $\dfrac{2(x+6)}{2x+1}$ **25.** 6   **27.** $\dfrac{m^6}{n^2}$ **29.** $\dfrac{10}{9}$ **31.** $\dfrac{6}{7}$

33. $-m(m+n)$ **35.** $\dfrac{3p+4q}{4(p+2q)}$ **37.** $\dfrac{p}{p-1}$ **39.** $\dfrac{w}{2w-1}$

41. $\dfrac{4r}{2r+3}$ **43.** $\dfrac{5}{6}$ **45.** $\dfrac{1}{4}$ **47.** $\dfrac{y+9}{y-6}$ **49.** 1

51. $\dfrac{3t+8}{t+2}$ **53.** $\dfrac{x+4}{x+1}$ **55.** $-\dfrac{w-3}{2}$ **57.** $\dfrac{k+6}{k+3}$ **59.** $\dfrac{2}{a}$

61. $2y(y+1)$ **63.** $x+y$ **65.** 2   **67.** $\dfrac{1}{a-2}$ **69.** $\dfrac{p+q}{2}$

Section 7.3 Practice Exercises, pp. 509–511

1. multiple; denominators   **3.** $x=1, x=-1; \dfrac{3}{5(x-1)}$

5. $\dfrac{a+5}{a+7}$ **7.** $\dfrac{2}{3y}$ **9.** a, b, c, d   **11.** x^5 is the greatest power of x that appears in any denominator.   **13.** 45   **15.** 48
17. 63   **19.** $9x^2y^3$ **21.** w^2y **23.** $(p+3)(p-1)(p+2)$
25. $9t(t+1)^2$ **27.** $(y-2)(y+2)(y+3)$ **29.** $3-x$ or $x-3$
31. Because $(b-1)$ and $(1-b)$ are opposites, they differ by a factor of -1.   **33.** $\dfrac{6}{5x^2}; \dfrac{5x}{5x^2}$ **35.** $\dfrac{24x}{30x^3}; \dfrac{5y}{30x^3}$

37. $\dfrac{10}{12a^2b}; \dfrac{a^3}{12a^2b}$ **39.** $\dfrac{6m-6}{(m+4)(m-1)}; \dfrac{3m+12}{(m+4)(m-1)}$

41. $\dfrac{6x+18}{(2x-5)(x+3)}; \dfrac{2x-5}{(2x-5)(x+3)}$

43. $\dfrac{6w+6}{(w+3)(w-8)(w+1)}; \dfrac{w^2+3w}{(w+3)(w-8)(w+1)}$

45. $\dfrac{6p^2+12p}{(p-2)(p+2)^2}; \dfrac{3p-6}{(p-2)(p+2)^2}$

47. $\dfrac{1}{a-4}; \dfrac{-a}{a-4}$ or $\dfrac{-1}{4-a}; \dfrac{a}{4-a}$

49. $\dfrac{8}{2(x-7)}; \dfrac{-y}{2(x-7)}$ or $\dfrac{-8}{2(7-x)}; \dfrac{y}{2(7-x)}$

51. $\dfrac{1}{a+b}; \dfrac{-6}{a+b}$ or $\dfrac{-1}{-a-b}; \dfrac{6}{-a-b}$

53. $\dfrac{-9}{24(3y+1)}; \dfrac{20}{24(3y+1)}$ **55.** $\dfrac{3z+12}{5z(z+4)}; \dfrac{5z}{5z(z+4)}$

57. $\dfrac{z^2+3z}{(z+2)(z+7)(z+3)}; \dfrac{-3z^2-6z}{(z+2)(z+7)(z+3)};$
$\dfrac{5z+35}{(z+2)(z+7)(z+3)}$

59. $\dfrac{3p+6}{(p-2)(p^2+2p+4)(p+2)}; \dfrac{p^3+2p^2+4p}{(p-2)(p^2+2p+4)(p+2)};$
$\dfrac{5p^3-20p}{(p-2)(p^2+2p+4)(p+2)}$

Section 7.4 Practice Exercises, pp. 518–520

1. a. $-\dfrac{1}{2}, -2, 0,$ undefined, undefined

b. $(x-5)(x-2); x=5, x=2$ **c.** $\dfrac{x+1}{x-2}$ **3.** $\dfrac{2(2x-3)}{(x-3)(x-1)}$

5. $\dfrac{5}{4}$ **7.** $\dfrac{3}{8}$ **9.** 2   **11.** 5   **13.** $\dfrac{-2(t-2)}{t-8}$ **15.** $3x+7$

17. $m+5$ **19.** 2   **21.** $x-5$ **23.** $\dfrac{1}{r+1}$ **25.** $\dfrac{1}{y+7}$

27. $\dfrac{15x}{y}$ **29.** $\dfrac{5a+6}{4a}$ **31.** $\dfrac{2(6+x^2y)}{15xy^3}$ **33.** $\dfrac{2s-3t^2}{s^4t^3}$

35. $-\dfrac{2}{3}$ **37.** $\dfrac{19}{3(a+1)}$ **39.** $\dfrac{-3(k+4)}{(k-3)(k+3)}$ **41.** $\dfrac{a-4}{2a}$

43. $\dfrac{(x+6)(x-2)}{(x-4)(x+1)}$ **45.** $\dfrac{x(4x+9)}{(x+3)^2(x+2)}$

47. $\dfrac{5p-1}{3}$ or $\dfrac{-5p+1}{-3}$ **49.** $\dfrac{9}{x-3}$ or $\dfrac{-9}{3-x}$

51. $\dfrac{6n-1}{n-8}$ or $\dfrac{-6n+1}{8-n}$ **53.** $\dfrac{2(4x+5)}{x(x+2)}$ **55.** $\dfrac{3y}{2(2y+1)}$

57. $\dfrac{2(w-3)}{(w+3)(w-1)}$ **59.** $\dfrac{4a-13}{(a-3)(a-4)}$ **61.** $\dfrac{3x(x+7)}{(x+5)^2(x-1)}$

63. $\dfrac{-y(y+8)}{(2y+1)(y-1)(y-4)}$ **65.** $\dfrac{1}{2p+1}$ **67.** $\dfrac{-2mn+1}{(m+n)(m-n)}$

69. 0   **71.** $\dfrac{2(3x+7)}{(x+3)(x+2)}$ **73.** $\dfrac{1}{n}$ **75.** $\dfrac{5}{n+2}$

77. $n+\left(7 \cdot \dfrac{1}{n}\right); \dfrac{n^2+7}{n}$ **79.** $\dfrac{1}{n}-\dfrac{2}{n}; -\dfrac{1}{n}$

81. $\dfrac{-w^2}{(w+3)(w-3)(w^2-3w+9)}$ **83.** $\dfrac{p^2-2p+7}{(p+2)(p+3)(p-1)}$

85. $\dfrac{-m-21}{2(m+5)(m-2)}$ or $\dfrac{m+21}{2(m+5)(2-m)}$ **87.** $\dfrac{3k+5}{4k+7}$ **89.** $\dfrac{1}{a}$

Chapter 7 Problem Recognition Exercises, p. 521

1. $\dfrac{-2x+9}{3x+1}$ **2.** $\dfrac{1}{w-4}$ **3.** $\dfrac{y-5}{2y-3}$ **4.** $\dfrac{7}{(x+3)(2x-1)}$

5. $-\dfrac{1}{x}$ **6.** $\dfrac{1}{3}$ **7.** $\dfrac{c+3}{c}$ **8.** $\dfrac{x+3}{5}$ **9.** $\dfrac{a}{12b^4c}$

10. $\dfrac{2a-b}{a-b}$ **11.** $\dfrac{p-q}{5}$ **12.** 4   **13.** $\dfrac{10}{2x+1}$ **14.** $\dfrac{w+2z}{w+z}$

15. $\dfrac{3}{2x+5}$ **16.** $\dfrac{y+7}{x+a}$ **17.** $\dfrac{1}{2(a+3)}$

18. $\dfrac{2(3y+10)}{(y-6)(y+6)(y+2)}$ **19.** $(t+8)^2$ **20.** $6b+5$

Section 7.5 Practice Exercises, pp. 527–529

1. complex   **3.** $\dfrac{1}{2a-3}$ **5.** $\dfrac{3(2k-5)}{5(k-2)}$ **7.** $\dfrac{7}{4y}$ **9.** $\dfrac{1}{2y}$

11. $\dfrac{24b}{a^3}$ **13.** $\dfrac{2r^5t^4}{s^6}$ **15.** $\dfrac{35}{2}$ **17.** $k+h$ **19.** $\dfrac{n+1}{2(n-3)}$

21. $\dfrac{2x+1}{4x+1}$ **23.** $m-7$ **25.** $\dfrac{2y(y-5)}{7y^2+10}$ **27.** $\dfrac{-a+8}{a-2}$ or $\dfrac{a+8}{2-a}$

29. $\dfrac{t-2}{t-4}$ **31.** $\dfrac{t+3}{t-5}$ **33.** $\dfrac{1}{2}$ **35.** $\dfrac{\frac{1}{2}+\frac{2}{3}}{5}; \dfrac{7}{30}$

37. $\dfrac{3}{\frac{2}{3}+\frac{3}{4}}; \dfrac{36}{17}$ **39. a.** $\dfrac{6}{5}\,\Omega$ **b.** $6\,\Omega$ **41.** $\dfrac{xy}{y+x}$ **43.** $\dfrac{y+4x}{2y}$

45. $\dfrac{1}{n^2+m^2}$ **47.** $\dfrac{2z-5}{3(z+3)}$ **49.** $\dfrac{x+1}{x-1}$ or $\dfrac{x+1}{1-x}$ **51.** $\dfrac{3}{2}$

Section 7.6 Practice Exercises, pp. 537–539

1. a. linear; quadratic   **b.** rational   **c.** denominator   **3.** $\dfrac{2}{4x-1}$

5. $5(h+1)$ **7.** $\dfrac{(x+4)(x-3)}{x^2}$ **9.** $\{3\}$ **11.** $\left\{\dfrac{5}{11}\right\}$

SA-22   Student Answer Appendix

13. $\left\{\dfrac{1}{3}\right\}$ **15. a.** $z = 0$ **b.** $5z$ **c.** $\{5\}$ **17.** $\left\{-\dfrac{200}{19}\right\}$

19. $\{-7\}$ **21.** $\left\{\dfrac{47}{6}\right\}$ **23.** $\{3, -1\}$ **25.** $\{4\}$

27. $\{5\}$ (The value 0 does not check.)   **29.** $\{-5\}$

31. $\{\ \}$ (The value 4 does not check.)   **33.** $\{4\}$ **35.** $\{4, -3\}$

37. $\{-4\}$; (The value 1 does not check.)   **39.** $\{\ \}$ (The value -4 does not check.)   **41.** $\{4\}$ (The value -6 does not check.)

43. $\{-25\}$ **45.** $\{-2, 7\}$ **47.** The number is 8.

49. The number is -26.   **51.** $m = \dfrac{FK}{a}$ **53.** $E = \dfrac{IR}{K}$

55. $R = \dfrac{E - Ir}{I}$ or $R = \dfrac{E}{I} - r$

57. $B = \dfrac{2A - hb}{h}$ or $B = \dfrac{2A}{h} - b$ **59.** $h = \dfrac{V}{r^2\pi}$

61. $t = \dfrac{b}{x - a}$ or $t = \dfrac{-b}{a - x}$ **63.** $x = \dfrac{y}{1 - yz}$ or $x = \dfrac{-y}{yz - 1}$

65. $h = \dfrac{2A}{a + b}$ **67.** $R = \dfrac{R_1 R_2}{R_2 + R_1}$

Chapter 7 Problem Recognition Exercises, p. 540

1. $\dfrac{y - 2}{2y}$ **2.** $\{6\}$ **3.** $\{2\}$ **4.** $\dfrac{3a - 17}{a - 5}$ **5.** $\dfrac{4p + 27}{18p^2}$

6. $\dfrac{b(b - 5)}{(b - 1)(b + 1)}$ **7.** $\{5\}$ **8.** $\dfrac{2w + 5}{(w + 1)^2}$ **9.** $\{7\}$ **10.** $\{5\}$

11. $\dfrac{3x + 14}{4(x + 1)}$ **12.** $\left\{\dfrac{11}{3}\right\}$ **13.** $\left\{\dfrac{41}{10}\right\}$ **14.** $\dfrac{7 - 3t}{t(t - 5)}$

15. $\dfrac{8a + 1}{2a - 1}$ **16.** $\{5\}$ (The value 2 does not check.)

17. $\{-1\}$ (The value 3 does not check.)   **18.** $\dfrac{11}{12k}$

19. $\dfrac{h + 9}{(h - 3)(h + 3)}$ **20.** $\{7\}$

Section 7.7 Practice Exercises, pp. 548–552

1. a. proportion   **b.** proportional

3. Expression; $\dfrac{m^2 + m + 2}{(m - 1)(m + 3)}$ **5.** Expression; $\dfrac{3}{10}$

7. Equation; $\{2\}$ **9.** $\{95\}$ **11.** $\{1\}$ **13.** $\left\{\dfrac{40}{3}\right\}$ **15.** $\{40\}$

17. $\{3\}$ **19.** $\{-1\}$ **21.** $\{1\}$ **23. a.** $V_f = \dfrac{V_i T_f}{T_i}$ **b.** $T_f = \dfrac{T_i V_f}{V_i}$

25. Toni can drive 297 mi on 9 gal of gas.   **27.** Mix 14.82 mL of plant food.   **29.** 5 oz contains 12 g of carbohydrate.

31. The minimum length is 20 ft.   **33.** $x = 4$ cm; $y = 5$ cm

35. $x = 3.75$ cm; $y = 4.5$ cm   **37.** The height of the pole is 7 m.

39. The light post is 24 ft high.   **41.** The speed of the boat is 20 mph.   **43.** The plane flies 210 mph in still air.   **45.** He runs 8 mph and bikes 16 mph.   **47.** Floyd walks 4 mph and Rachel walks 2 mph.   **49.** Sergio rode 12 mph and walked 3 mph.

51. $5\frac{5}{11}$ $(5.\overline{45})$ min   **53.** $22\frac{2}{9}$ $(22.\overline{2})$ min   **55.** 48 hr

57. $3\frac{1}{3}$ $(3.\overline{3})$ days   **59.** There are 40 smokers and 140 nonsmokers.

61. There are 240 men and 200 women.

Chapter 7 Review Exercises pp. 558–560

1. a. $-\dfrac{2}{9}, -\dfrac{1}{10}, 0, -\dfrac{5}{6}$, undefined   **b.** $t = -9$

2. a. $-\dfrac{1}{5}, -\dfrac{1}{2}$, undefined, $0, \dfrac{1}{7}$ **b.** $k = 5$ **3.** a, c, d

4. $x = \dfrac{5}{2}, x = 3$; $\dfrac{1}{2x - 5}$ **5.** $h = -\dfrac{1}{3}, h = -7$; $\dfrac{1}{3h + 1}$

6. $a = 2, a = -2$; $\dfrac{4a - 1}{a - 2}$ **7.** $w = 4, w = -4$; $\dfrac{2w + 3}{w - 4}$

8. $z = 4$; $-\dfrac{z}{2}$ **9.** $k = 0, k = 5$; $-\dfrac{3}{2k}$ **10.** $b = -3$; $\dfrac{b - 1}{2}$

11. $m = -1$; $\dfrac{m - 5}{3}$ **12.** $n = -3$; $\dfrac{1}{n + 3}$ **13.** $p = -7$; $\dfrac{1}{p + 7}$

14. y^2 **15.** $\dfrac{u^2}{2}$ **16.** $v + 2$ **17.** $\dfrac{3}{2(x - 5)}$ **18.** $\dfrac{c(c + 1)}{2(c + 5)}$

19. $\dfrac{q - 2}{4}$ **20.** $-2t(t - 5)$ **21.** $4s(s - 4)$ **22.** $\dfrac{1}{7}$

23. $\dfrac{1}{n - 2}$ **24.** $-\dfrac{1}{6}$ **25.** $\dfrac{1}{m + 3}$ **26.** $\dfrac{-1}{(x + 3)(x + 2)}$

27. $\dfrac{2y - 1}{y + 1}$ **28.** LCD $= (n + 3)(n - 3)(n + 2)$

29. LCD $= (m + 4)(m - 4)(m + 3)$ **30.** $c - 2$ or $2 - c$

31. $3 - x$ or $x - 3$ **32.** $\dfrac{4b}{10ab}$; $\dfrac{3a}{10ab}$ **33.** $\dfrac{21y}{12xy}$; $\dfrac{22x}{12xy}$

34. $\dfrac{y}{x^2y^5}$; $\dfrac{3x}{x^2y^5}$ **35.** $\dfrac{5c^2}{ab^3c^2}$; $\dfrac{3b^3}{ab^3c^2}$

36. $\dfrac{5p - 20}{(p + 2)(p - 4)}$; $\dfrac{p^2 + 2p}{(p + 2)(p - 4)}$ **37.** $\dfrac{6q + 48}{q(q + 8)}$; $\dfrac{q}{q(q + 8)}$

38. 2   **39.** 2   **40.** $a + 5$ **41.** $x - 7$

42. $\dfrac{-y - 18}{(y - 9)(y + 9)}$ or $\dfrac{y + 18}{(9 - y)(y + 9)}$ **43.** $\dfrac{t^2 + 2t + 3}{(2 - t)(2 + t)}$

44. $\dfrac{m + 8}{3m(m + 2)}$ **45.** $\dfrac{3(r - 4)}{2r(r + 6)}$ **46.** $\dfrac{p}{(p + 4)(p + 5)}$

47. $\dfrac{q}{(q + 5)(q + 4)}$ **48.** $\dfrac{1}{2}$ **49.** $\dfrac{1}{3}$ **50.** $\dfrac{a - 4}{a - 2}$

51. $\dfrac{3(z + 5)}{z(z - 5)}$ **52.** $\dfrac{w}{2}$ **53.** $\dfrac{8}{y}$ **54.** $y - x$ **55.** $-(b + a)$

56. $\dfrac{2p + 7}{2p}$ **57.** $-\dfrac{k + 10}{k + 4}$ **58.** $\{-8\}$ **59.** $\{-2\}$

60. $\{0\}$ **61.** $\{2\}$ **62.** $\{-2\}$ **63.** $\{-1\}$ (The value 3 does not check.)   **64.** $\{\ \}$ (The value 2 does not check.)   **65.** $\{-11, 1\}$

66. The number is 4.   **67.** $h = \dfrac{3V}{\pi r^2}$ **68.** $b = \dfrac{2A}{h}$

69. $\left\{\dfrac{6}{5}\right\}$ **70.** $\left\{\dfrac{96}{5}\right\}$ **71.** It contains 10 g of fat.

72. Ed travels 60 mph, and Bud travels 70 mph.

73. Together the pumps would fill the pool in 16.8 min.

74. $x = 11$; $b = 26$

Chapter 7 Test, pp. 560–561

1. a. $x = 2$ **b.** $-\dfrac{x + 1}{6}$ **2. a.** $a = 6, a = -2, a = 0$

b. $\dfrac{7}{a + 2}$ **3.** b, c, d   **4. a.** $15(x + 3)$ **b.** $3x^2y^2$

5. $\dfrac{y + 7}{3(y + 3)(y + 1)}$ **6.** $-\dfrac{b + 3}{5}$ **7.** $\dfrac{1}{w + 1}$ **8.** $\dfrac{t + 4}{t + 2}$

9. $\dfrac{x(x + 5)}{(x + 4)(x - 2)}$ **10.** $\dfrac{2y + 7}{y - 6}$ or $\dfrac{-2y - 7}{6 - y}$ **11.** $\dfrac{1}{m + 4}$

12. $\left\{\dfrac{8}{5}\right\}$ **13.** $\{2\}$ **14.** $\{1\}$ **15.** $\{\ \}$ (The value 4 does not check.)   **16.** $\{-5\}$ (The value 2 does not check.)

17. $r = \dfrac{2A}{C}$ **18.** $\{-8\}$ **19.** $1\frac{1}{4}$ (1.25) cups of carrots

20. The speed of the current is 5 mph.   **21.** It would take the second printer 3 hr to do the job working alone.

22. $a = 5.6$; $b = 12$

Chapters 1–7 Cumulative Review Exercises, pp. 561–562

1. 32   **2.** 7   **3.** $\left\{\dfrac{10}{9}\right\}$

4.

Set-Builder Notation	Graph	Interval Notation
$\{x \mid x \geq -1\}$	(graph) -1	$[-1, \infty)$
$\{x \mid x < 5\}$	(graph) 5	$(-\infty, 5)$

5. The width is 17 m and the length is 35 m.
6. The base is 10 in. and the height is 8 in. **7.** $\dfrac{x^2yz^{17}}{2}$
8. a. $6x + 4$ **b.** $2x^2 + x - 3$ **9.** $(5x - 3)^2$
10. $(2c + 1)(5d - 3)$ **11.** $x = 5, x = -\dfrac{1}{2}$ **12.** $\{(1, -4)\}$
13. $\dfrac{1}{5(x + 4)}$ **14.** -3 **15.** $\{1\}$ **16.** $\left\{-\dfrac{7}{2}\right\}$
17. a. x-intercept: $(-4, 0)$; y-intercept: $(0, 2)$
b. x-intercept: $(0, 0)$; y-intercept: $(0, 0)$
18. a. $m = -\dfrac{7}{5}$ **b.** $m = -\dfrac{2}{3}$ **c.** $m = 4$ **d.** $m = -\dfrac{1}{4}$
19. $y = 5x - 3$ **20.** One large popcorn costs \$4.50, and one drink costs \$3.00.

Chapter 8

Section 8.1 Practice Exercises, pp. 569–572
1. a. relation **b.** domain **c.** range
3. a. {(Northeast, 54.1), (Midwest, 65.6), (South, 110.7), (West, 70.7)} **b.** Domain: {Northeast, Midwest, South, West}; Range: {54.1, 65.6, 110.7, 70.7} **5. a.** {(USSR, 1961), (USA, 1962), (Poland, 1978), (Vietnam, 1980), (Cuba, 1980)} **b.** Domain: {USSR, USA, Poland, Vietnam, Cuba}; range: {1961, 1962, 1978, 1980}
7. a. {(A, 1), (A, 2), (B, 2), (C, 3), (D, 5), (E, 4)}
b. Domain: {A, B, C, D, E}; range: {1, 2, 3, 4, 5}
9. a. {(6, A), (6, B), (6, C)} **b.** Domain: {6}; range: {A, B, C}
11. a. {(−4, 1), (0, 3), (1, −1), (3, 0)}
b. Domain: {−4, 0, 1, 3}; range: {−1, 0, 1, 3}
13. a. {(−4, 4), (1, 1), (2, 1), (3, 1), (4, −2)}
b. Domain: {−4, 1, 2, 3, 4}; range: {−2, 1, 4}
15. Domain: [0, 4]; range: [−2, 2] **17.** Domain: [−5, 3]; range: [−2.1, 2.8] **19.** Domain: (−∞, 2]; range: (−∞, ∞)
21. Domain: (−∞, ∞); range: (−∞, ∞) **23.** Domain: {−3}; range: (−∞, ∞) **25.** Domain: (−∞, 2); range: [−1.3, ∞)
27. Domain: {−3, −1, 1, 3}; range: {0, 1, 2, 3}
29. Domain: [−4, 5); range: {−2, 1, 3} **31. a.** 2.85
b. 9.33 **c.** Dec. **d.** Nov. **e.** 7.63 **f.** {Jan., Feb., Mar., Apr., May, June, July, Aug., Sept., Oct., Nov., Dec.}
33. a. 33.484 million or 33,484,000 **b.** The year 2015
35. a. For example: {(Julie, New York), (Peggy, Florida), (Stephen, Kansas), (Pat, New York)} **b.** Domain: {Julie, Peggy, Stephen, Pat}; range: {New York, Florida, Kansas}
37. $y = 2x - 1$ **39.** $y = x^2$

Section 8.2 Practice Exercises, pp. 580–584
1. a. function **b.** vertical **c.** $2x + 1$ **d.** x values **e.** y values **f.** denominator **g.** negative
3. a. {(−2, −4), (−1, −1), (0, 0), (1, −1), (2, −4)}
b. {−2, −1, 0, 1, 2} **c.** {−4, −1, 0} **5.** Function
7. Not a function **9.** Function **11.** Not a function
13. Function **15.** Not a function **17.** When x is 2, the function value y is 5. **19.** (0, 2) **21.** −11 **23.** 1
25. 2 **27.** $6t - 2$ **29.** 7 **31.** 4 **33.** 4
35. $6x + 4$ **37.** $-4x^2 - 8x + 1$ **39.** $-\pi^2 + 4\pi + 1$
41. 7 **43.** $-6a - 2$ **45.** $|-c - 2|$ **47.** 1 **49.** 7
51. −18.8 **53.** −7 **55.** 2π **57.** −5 **59.** 4
61. a. 3 **b.** 1 **c.** 1 **d.** $x = -3$ **e.** $x = 0, x = 2$
f. (−∞, 3] **g.** (−∞, 5] **63. a.** 3 **b.** $H(4)$ is not defined because 4 is not in the domain of H. **c.** 4 **d.** $x = -3$ and $x = 2$ **e.** All x on the interval [−2, 1] **f.** [−4, 4) **g.** [2, 5)
65. a. −4 **b.** 0 **c.** −3 **d.** $x = -1$ **e.** There are no such values of x. **f.** (−∞, ∞) **g.** (−∞, −3] ∪ (−2, ∞)
67. $\{-3, -7, -\frac{3}{2}, 1.2\}$ **69.** {6, 0}

71. $x = -3$ and $x = 1.2$ **73.** $x = 6$ and $x = 1$ **75.** −3
77. The domain is the set of all real numbers for which the denominator is not zero. Set the denominator equal to zero, and solve the resulting equation. The solution(s) to the equation must be excluded from the domain. In this case, setting $x - 2 = 0$ indicates that $x = 2$ must be excluded from the domain. The domain is (−∞, 2) ∪ (2, ∞). **79.** (−∞, −6) ∪ (−6, ∞)
81. (−∞, 0) ∪ (0, ∞) **83.** (−∞, ∞) **85.** [−7, ∞)
87. [3, ∞) **89.** (−∞, $\frac{1}{2}$] **91.** (−∞, ∞) **93.** (−∞, ∞)
95. a. $h(1) = 64$ and $h(1.5) = 44$ **b.** $h(1) = 64$ means that after 1 sec, the height of the ball is 64 ft. $h(1.5) = 44$ means that after 1.5 sec, the height of the ball is 44 ft. **97. a.** $d(1) = 11.5$ and $d(1.5) = 17.25$ **b.** $d(1) = 11.5$ means that after 1 hr, the distance traveled is 11.5 mi. $d(1.5) = 17.25$ means that after 1.5 hr, the distance traveled is 17.25 mi. **99.** $f(x) = 2x + 3$
101. $f(x) = |x| - 10$ **103.** (−2, ∞)

Section 8.2 Graphing Calculator Exercises, p. 584
105.

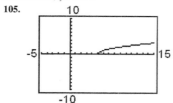

106.

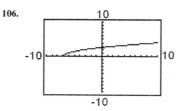

Section 8.3 Practice Exercises, pp. 592–596
1. a. linear **b.** constant **c.** quadratic **d.** parabola **e.** 0 **f.** y **3. a.** Yes **b.** {7, 2, −5} **c.** {3}
5. $f(3) = 9$ means that 9 lb of force is required to stretch the spring 3 in. $f(10) = 30$ means that 30 lb of force is required to stretch the spring 10 in. **7.** horizontal
9. Domain (−∞, ∞); range {2}

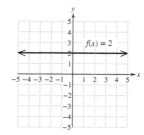

11.

x	$f(x)$	x	$f(x)$
−2	$-\frac{1}{2}$	$\frac{1}{4}$	4
−1	−1	$\frac{1}{2}$	2
$-\frac{1}{2}$	−2	1	1
$-\frac{1}{4}$	−4	2	$\frac{1}{2}$

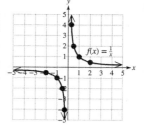

SA-24   Student Answer Appendix

13.

x	$h(x)$
-2	-8
-1	-1
0	0
1	1
2	8

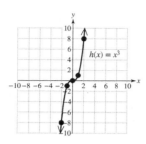

15.

x	$q(x)$
-2	4
-1	1
0	0
1	1
2	4

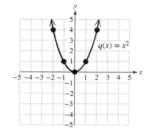

17. Quadratic   **19.** Linear   **21.** Constant
23. None of these   **25.** Linear   **27.** None of these
29. x-intercept: $(2, 0)$; y-intercept: $(0, -10)$

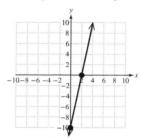

31. x-intercept: $\left(\dfrac{5}{6}, 0\right)$; y-intercept: $(0, 5)$

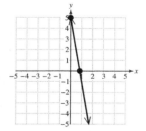

33. x-intercept: none; y-intercept: $(0, 18)$

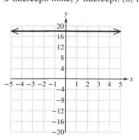

35. x-intercept: $(-3, 0)$; y-intercept: $(0, 2)$

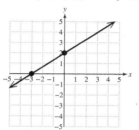

37. a. $x = -1$ **b.** $f(0) = 1$ **39. a.** $x = -2$ and $x = 2$
b. $f(0) = -2$ **41. a.** None   **b.** $f(0) = 2$
43. a. $(-\infty, \infty)$ **b.** $(0, 0)$ **c.** vi   **45. a.** $(-\infty, \infty)$
b. $(0, 1)$ **c.** viii   **47. a.** $[-1, \infty)$ **b.** $(0, 1)$ **c.** vii
49. a. $(-\infty, 3) \cup (3, \infty)$ **b.** $\left(0, -\dfrac{1}{3}\right)$ **c.** ii
51. a. $(-\infty, \infty)$ **b.** $(0, 2)$ **c.** iv   **53. a.** Linear
b. $G(90) = 82.5$. This means that if the student gets a 90% score
on her final exam, then her overall course average is 82.5%.
c. $G(50) = 72.5$. This means that if the student gets a 50% score on her
final exam, then her overall course average is 72.5%.
55. $f(x) = x^2 + 2$ **57.** $f(x) = 3$ **59.** $f(x) = \frac{1}{2}x - 2$

**Section 8.3 Graphing Calculator
Exercises, pp. 596–597**

61.

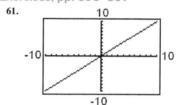

62.

63.

64.

65.

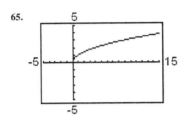

66.

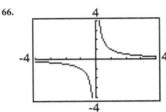

67. x-intercept: $(8, 0)$; y-intercept: $(0, 1)$ **68.** x-intercept: $(-6, 0)$; y-intercept: $(0, -3)$ **69.** x-intercept: $(-5, 0)$; y-intercept: $(0, 4)$ **70.** x-intercept: $(2, 0)$; y-intercept: $(0, -7)$

Chapter 8 Problem Recognition Exercises, p. 597

1. a, c, d, f, g   **2.** a, b, d, f, h   **3.** 4   **4.** 2
5. $\{0, 1, \frac{1}{2}, -3, 2\}$ **6.** $\{4, 3, 6, 1, 10\}$ **7.** $[-2, 4]$

8. $[0, \infty)$ **9.** 0   **10.** $\left(\frac{9}{5}, 0\right)$ **11.** $(0, -1), (0, 1)$

12. 1   **13.** c   **14.** d   **15.** 3

Section 8.4 Practice Exercises, pp. 602–604

1. a. $f(x)$; $g(x)$ **b.** $g(x)$; $g(x)$ **c.** $f(g(x))$
3. $(f + g)(x) = 2x^2 + 5x + 4$
5. $(g - f)(x) = 2x^2 + 3x - 4$
7. $(f \cdot h)(x) = x^3 + 4x^2 + x + 4$
9. $(g \cdot f)(x) = 2x^3 + 12x^2 + 16x$

11. $\left(\dfrac{h}{f}\right)(x) = \dfrac{x^2 + 1}{x + 4}, x \neq -4$

13. $\left(\dfrac{f}{g}\right)(x) = \dfrac{x + 4}{2x^2 + 4x}, x \neq 0, x \neq -2$

15. $(f \circ g)(x) = 2x^2 + 4x + 4$
17. $(g \circ f)(x) = 2x^2 + 20x + 48$ **19.** $(k \circ h)(x) = \dfrac{1}{x^2 + 1}$

21. $(k \circ g)(x) = \dfrac{1}{2x^2 + 4x}, x \neq 0, x \neq -2$ **23.** No

25. $(f \circ g)(x) = 25x^2 - 15x + 1$; $(g \circ f)(x) = 5x^2 - 15x + 5$
27. $(f \circ g)(x) = |x^3 - 1|$; $(g \circ f)(x) = |x|^3 - 1$
29. $(h \circ h)(x) = 25x - 24$ **31.** 0   **33.** -64 **35.** 2

37. 1   **39.** $\dfrac{1}{64}$ **41.** 0   **43.** Not a real number

45. $\dfrac{4}{9}$ **47.** -2 **49.** 2   **51.** 0   **53.** 1   **55.** 0

57. Undefined   **59.** -1 **61.** 2   **63.** 2   **65.** -1
67. -2 **69.** 3   **71.** -6 **73.** -1 **75.** 4
77. 0   **79.** 2   **81. a.** $P(x) = 3.78x - 1$ **b.** \$188
83. a. $F(t) = 0.2t + 6.4$; $F(t)$ represents the amount of child support (in billion dollars) not paid for year t.   **b.** $F(4) = 7.2$ means that in year 4, \$7.2 billion of child support was not paid.
85. a. $(D \circ r)(t) = 560t$; This function represents the total distance Joe travels as a function of time that he rides.   **b.** 5600 ft

Section 8.5 Practice Exercises, pp. 610–613

1. a. kx **b.** $\dfrac{k}{x}$ **c.** kxw **3.** $x^2 - 4x + 4$ **5.** $x^2 - 2$

7. -1 **9.** Inversely   **11.** $T = kq$ **13.** $b = \dfrac{k}{c}$

15. $Q = \dfrac{kx}{y}$ **17.** $c = kst$ **19.** $L = kw\sqrt{v}$ **21.** $x = \dfrac{ky^2}{z}$

23. $k = \dfrac{9}{2}$ **25.** $k = 512$ **27.** $k = 1.75$ **29.** $x = 70$

31. $b = 6$ **33.** $Z = 56$ **35.** $Q = 9$ **37.** $L = 9$

39. $B = \dfrac{15}{2}$ **41. a.** The heart weighs 0.92 lb.
b. Answers will vary.   **43. a.** 3.6 g   **b.** 4.5 g   **c.** 2.4 g
45. a. \$0.40   **b.** \$0.30   **c.** \$1.00   **47.** 355,000 tons
49. 42.6 ft   **51.** 300 W   **53.** 18.5 A   **55.** 20 lb
57. \$3500

Chapter 8 Review Exercises, pp. 618–621

1. Domain; $\left\{\dfrac{1}{3}, 6, \dfrac{1}{4}, 7\right\}$; range; $\left\{10, -\dfrac{1}{2}, 4, \dfrac{2}{5}\right\}$

2. Domain; $\{-3, -1, 0, 2, 3\}$; range; $\left\{-2, 0, 1, \dfrac{5}{2}\right\}$

3. Domain; $[-3, 9]$; range; $[0, 60]$ **4.** Domain; $[-4, 4]$; range; $[1, 3]$

5.   **6.**

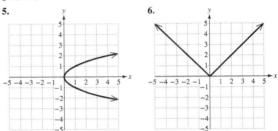

7. a. Not a function   **b.** $[1, 3]$ **c.** $[-4, 4]$
8. a. Function   **b.** $(-\infty, \infty)$ **c.** $(-\infty, 0.35]$
9. a. Function   **b.** $\{1, 2, 3, 4\}$ **c.** $\{3\}$
10. a. Not a function   **b.** $\{0, 4\}$ **c.** $\{2, 3, 4, 5\}$
11. a. Not a function   **b.** $\{4, 9\}$ **c.** $\{2, -2, 3, -3\}$
12. a. Function   **b.** $\{6, 7, 8, 9\}$ **c.** $\{9, 10, 11, 12\}$
13. -4 **14.** 2   **15.** 2   **16.** $6t^2 - 4$ **17.** $6b^2 - 4$
18. $6\pi^2 - 4$ **19.** $6a^2 - 4$ **20.** 20   **21.** $(-\infty, \infty)$
22. $(-\infty, 11) \cup (11, \infty)$ **23.** $[8, \infty)$ **24.** $[-2, \infty)$
25. a. \$150   **b.** \$175   **c.** \$200
26.   **27.**

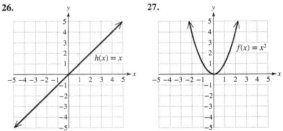

28.   **29.**

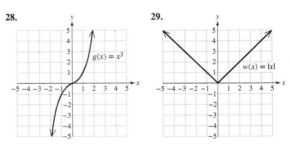

SA-26   Student Answer Appendix

30.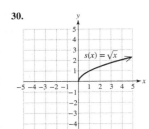

31.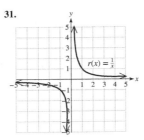

32.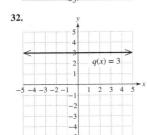

33.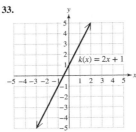

4.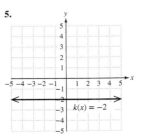

5.

6.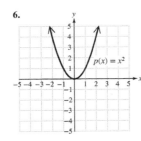

7.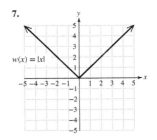

34. a. $s(4) = 4, s(-3) = 25, s(2) = 0, s(1) = 1, s(0) = 4$
b. $(-\infty, \infty)$ **35. a.** $r(2)$ is not a real number,
$r(4) = 0, r(5) = 2, r(8) = 4$ **b.** $[4, \infty)$

36. a. $h(-3) = -\dfrac{1}{2}, h(0) = -1, h(2) = -3, h(5) = \dfrac{3}{2}$
b. $(-\infty, 3) \cup (3, \infty)$

37. a. $k(-5) = -2, k(-4) = -1, k(-3) = 0,$
$k(2) = -5$ **b.** $(-\infty, \infty)$ **38.** x-intercept: $\left(\dfrac{7}{4}, 0\right)$;
y-intercept: $(0, -7)$

39. x-intercept: $\left(\dfrac{9}{2}, 0\right)$; y-intercept: $(0, 9)$

40. a. $b(0) = 28.3$. In 2010 consumption was 28.3 gal of bottled water per capita. $b(5) = 36.5$. In 2015 consumption was 36.5 gal of bottled water per capita.   **b.** $m = 1.64$. Consumption increased at a rate of 1.64 gal/year.
41. -1 **42.** 0 **43.** $x = 0$ and $x = 4$
44. There are no values of x for which $g(x) = 4$.
45. $(-4, \infty)$ **46.** $(-\infty, 1]$ **47.** $(f - g)(x) = 2x^3 + 9x - 7$
48. $(f + g)(x) = -2x^3 - 7x - 7$ **49.** $(f \cdot n)(x) = \dfrac{x - 7}{x - 2}, x \neq 2$

50. $(f \cdot m)(x) = x^3 - 7x^2$ **51.** $\left(\dfrac{f}{g}\right)(x) = \dfrac{x - 7}{-2x^3 - 8x}; x \neq 0$

52. $\left(\dfrac{g}{f}\right)(x) = \dfrac{-2x^3 - 8x}{x - 7}, x \neq 7$
53. $(m \circ f)(x) = (x - 7)^2$ or $x^2 - 14x + 49$

54. $(n \circ f)(x) = \dfrac{1}{x - 9}, x \neq 9$ **55.** 100 **56.** $\dfrac{1}{8}$

57. -167 **58.** -10 **59. a.** $(2x + 1)^2$ or $4x^2 + 4x + 1$

b. $2x^2 + 1$ **c.** No, $f \circ g \neq g \circ f$ **60.** $\dfrac{1}{4}$ **61.** -3

62. 0 **63.** -1 **64.** 4 **65.** 1 **66. a.** $F = kd$

b. $k = 3$ **c.** 12.6 lb   **67.** $y = \dfrac{8}{3}$ **68.** $y = 12$ **69.** 48 km

Chapter 8 Test, pp. 621–622
1. a. Not a function   **b.** $\{-3, -1, 1, 3\}$
c. $\{-2, -1, 1, 3\}$ **2. a.** Function   **b.** $(-\infty, \infty)$
c. $(-\infty, 0]$ **3.** To find the x-intercept(s), solve for the real solutions of the equation $f(x) = 0$. To find the y-intercept, find $f(0)$.

8. $(-\infty, -7) \cup (-7, \infty)$ **9.** $[-7, \infty)$ **10.** $(-\infty, \infty)$
11. a. $r(-2) = 9, r(0) = 1, r(3) = 4$ **b.** $(-\infty, \infty)$
12. $s(0) = 0.96$. At the beginning of the study (year 0) the per capita consumption was 0.96 c per day. $s(20) = 0.8$. In year 20, the per capita consumption was 0.8 c per day.
13. 1 **14.** 2 **15.** $(-1, 7]$ **16.** $[-1, 4)$
17. False   **18.** $(6, 0)$ **19.** $x = 6$ **20.** All x in the interval $[1, 3]$ and $x = 5$ **21.** Quadratic   **22.** Linear
23. Constant   **24.** None of these
25. x-intercept: $(-12, 0)$; y-intercept: $(0, 9)$

26. $\left(\dfrac{f}{g}\right)(x) = \dfrac{x - 4}{x^2 + 2}$ **27.** $(h \cdot g)(x) = \dfrac{x^2 + 2}{x}, x \neq 0$

28. $(g \circ f)(x) = x^2 - 8x + 18$ **29.** $(h \circ f)(x) = \dfrac{1}{x - 4}, x \neq 4$

30. -48 **31.** $-\dfrac{3}{2}$ **32.** $\dfrac{1}{18}$ **33.** 18

34. $\left(\dfrac{g}{f}\right)(x) = \dfrac{x^2 + 2}{x - 4}, x \neq 4$ **35.** 8.25 mL

36. 200 drinks are sold.

Chapters 1–8 Cumulative Review Exercises, p. 623
1. -1 **2.** $21x - 62y + 12$ **3.** $\{-15\}$ **4.** $\{\ \}$

5. $[-3, \infty)$ **6.** x-intercept: $\left(\dfrac{10}{3}, 0\right)$ y-intercept: $(0, -2)$

7. $m = -\dfrac{1}{5}$ **8.** $m = \dfrac{5}{2}$ **9.** $\{(2, -1)\}$ **10.** $\{(-4, 0, 5)\}$

11. $\dfrac{9x^2}{y^6}$ **12.** $5x^2 - 8x + 7$ **13.** $-10x^3 + 47x^2 - 42x$

14. $(2x + 1)(x + 3)$ **15.** $5(x - 4)(x + 4)$ **16.** $\dfrac{x^2 + 5}{(x - 5)(x + 1)}$

17. $\dfrac{x + 2}{x^2}$ **18.** Domain: $\{2, -1, 9, -6\}$ Range: $\{4, 2, 8\}$

19. $(-\infty, 0) \cup (0, \infty)$ **20.** $(f \circ g)(x) = x^2 + 2x - 5$

Chapter 9

Section 9.1 Practice Exercises, pp. 634–638

1. a. union; $A \cup B$ **b.** intersection; $A \cap B$ **c.** intersection
d. $a < x < b$ **e.** union   **3.** $(-\infty, 2]$ **5.** $(-\infty, 15)$
7. a. $\{-3, -1\}$ **b.** $\{-4, -3, -2, -1, 0, 1, 3, 5\}$
9. $[-7, -4)$ **11.** $(-\infty, -4) \cup (2, \infty)$ **13.** $\{\ \}$ **15.** $[-7, \infty)$
17. $[0, 5)$ **19.** $[-7, \infty)$ **21. a.** $[-1, 5)$ **b.** $(-2, \infty)$
23. a. $(-1, 3)$ **b.** $\left(-\dfrac{5}{2}, \dfrac{9}{2}\right)$ **25. a.** $(0, 2]$ **b.** $(-4, 5]$

27. $[-2, 3]$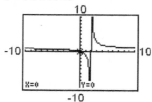
        $-2 \quad 3$

29. $(3, 6)$
        $3 \quad\quad 6$

31. $(-\infty, 2]$
                2

33. $[8, \infty)$
        8

35. $\{\ \}$ **37.** $-4 \le t$ and $t < \dfrac{3}{4}$ **39.** The statement $6 < x < 2$
is equivalent to $6 < x$ and $x < 2$. However, no real number is
greater than 6 and also less than 2.
   41. The statement $-5 > y > -2$ is equivalent to $-5 > y$ and
$y > -2$. However, no real number is less than -5 and also greater
than -2.

43. $\left[\dfrac{5}{2}, 7\right)$
                $\dfrac{5}{2} \quad 7$

45. $(-6, 6]$
        $-6 \quad\quad 6$

47. $(2, 8)$
        $2 \quad\quad 8$

49. $\left[-\dfrac{10}{3}, -\dfrac{7}{3}\right]$
        $-\dfrac{10}{3} \quad\quad -\dfrac{7}{3}$

51. $\left[-\dfrac{1}{2}, \dfrac{3}{2}\right)$
        $-\dfrac{1}{2} \quad\quad \dfrac{3}{2}$

53. $(-0.4, 0.2)$
        $-0.4 \quad\quad 0.2$

55. $(-\infty, -2) \cup [2, \infty)$
                $-2 \quad 2$

57. $(-\infty, 2]$
                2

59. $[-6, \infty)$
        -6

61. $(-\infty, \infty)$

63. $(-\infty, -4] \cup (4.5, \infty)$
                $-4 \quad\quad 4.5$

65. a. $(-10, 8)$ **b.** $(-\infty, \infty)$
67. a. $(-\infty, -8] \cup [1.3, \infty)$ **b.** $\{\ \}$
69. $\left(-\dfrac{11}{2}, \dfrac{7}{2}\right]$ **71.** $\left(-\dfrac{13}{2}, \infty\right)$ **73.** $(-\infty, 1) \cup (5, \infty)$
75. a. $4800 \le x \le 10{,}800$ **b.** $x < 4800$ or $x > 10{,}800$
77. a. $44\% < x < 48\%$ **b.** $x \le 44\%$ or $x \ge 48\%$
79. All real numbers between $-\dfrac{3}{2}$ and 6
81. All real numbers greater than 2 or less than -1
83. a. Amy would need 82% or better on her final exam.
b. If Amy scores at least 32% and less than 82% on her final exam
she will receive a "B" in the class.
   85. $32° \le F \le 42.08°$

Section 9.2 Practice Exercises, pp. 645–648

   1. a. quadratic   **b.** solutions; undefined   **c.** test point   **d.** true
e. rational   **f.** zero
   3. $(-\infty, -4) \cup \left(\dfrac{1}{3}, \infty\right)$ **5.** $\left[3, \dfrac{16}{5}\right]$ **7.** $[-1, 3]$
   9. a. $(-\infty, -2) \cup (3, \infty)$ **b.** $(-2, 3)$ **c.** $[-2, 3]$
d. $(-\infty, -2] \cup [3, \infty)$ **11. a.** $(-2, 0) \cup (3, \infty)$
b. $(-\infty, -2) \cup (0, 3)$ **c.** $(-\infty, -2] \cup [0, 3]$
d. $[-2, 0] \cup [3, \infty)$ **13. a.** $\{4, -\frac{1}{2}\}$ **b.** $(-\infty, -\frac{1}{2}) \cup (4, \infty)$
c. $(-\frac{1}{2}, 4)$ **15. a.** $\{-10, 3\}$ **b.** $[-10, 3)$ **c.** $(-\infty, -10) \cup (3, \infty)$
   17. a. $\left\{-\dfrac{1}{2}, 3\right\}$ **b.** $\left[-\dfrac{1}{2}, 3\right]$ **c.** $\left(-\infty, -\dfrac{1}{2}\right] \cup [3, \infty)$
   19. $(1, 7)$ **21.** $(-\infty, -2) \cup (5, \infty)$ **23.** $[-5, 0]$ **25.** $[4, 8]$
   27. $\left(-\infty, -\dfrac{1}{5}\right) \cup (1, \infty)$ **29.** $(-11, 11)$
   31. $\left(-\infty, -\dfrac{1}{3}\right] \cup [3, \infty)$ **33.** $(-\infty, -3] \cup [0, 4]$
   35. $(-2, -1) \cup (2, \infty)$ **37. a.** $(-1, 1]$
b. $(-\infty, -1) \cup [1, \infty)$ **c.** $(-\infty, -1) \cup (1, \infty)$ **d.** $(-1, 1)$
   39. a. $(-\infty, -1) \cup (2, \infty)$ **b.** $(-1, 2)$ **c.** $[-1, 2)$
d. $(-\infty, -1] \cup (2, \infty)$ **41. a.** $\{7\}$ **b.** $(-\infty, 5) \cup (7, \infty)$ **c.** $(5, 7)$
   43. a. $\{4\}$ **b.** $[4, 6)$ **c.** $(-\infty, 4] \cup (6, \infty)$ **45.** $(1, \infty)$
   47. $(-\infty, -4) \cup (4, \infty)$ **49.** $\left(2, \dfrac{7}{2}\right)$ **51.** $(5, 7]$
   53. $(-\infty, 0) \cup \left[\dfrac{1}{2}, \infty\right)$ **55.** $(0, \infty)$ **57.** Quadratic; $[-4, 4]$
   59. Quadratic; $(-\infty, -\frac{4}{5}) \cup (0, \infty)$ **61.** Linear; $(-\frac{5}{2}, \infty)$
   63. Rational; $(-\infty, -1)$ **65.** Polynomial (degree > 2);
$(0, 5) \cup (5, \infty)$ **67.** Polynomial (degree > 2); $(2, \infty)$
   69. Polynomial (degree > 2); $(-\infty, 5]$ **71.** Quadratic; $(-2, 2)$
   73. Rational; $(-\infty, -2] \cup (5, \infty)$ **75.** Linear; $(-\infty, 5]$
   77. $(-\infty, \infty)$ **79.** $\{\ \}$ **81.** $\{0\}$ **83.** $\{\ \}$ **85.** $\{\ \}$
   87. $(-\infty, \infty)$ **89.** $(-\infty, -11) \cup (-11, \infty)$ **91.** $\{\frac{3}{2}\}$

Section 9.2 Graphing Calculator Exercises, p. 648

   93. $(-\infty, 0) \cup (2, \infty)$

   94. $(0, 2)$

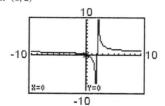

   95. $(-1, 1)$

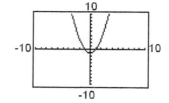

SA-28   Student Answer Appendix

96. $(-\infty, -1) \cup (1, \infty)$

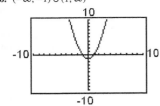

97. $\{-5\}$

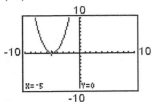

98. $\{5\}$

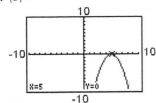

99. $\{\ \}$

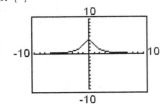

100. $\{\ \}$

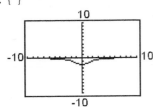

Section 9.3 Practice Exercises, pp. 654–655

1. a. absolute; $\{a, -a\}$ **b.** Subtract 5 from both sides.
c. $y; -y$ **d.** $\{\ \}; \{-4\}$

3. $(-\infty, -1] \cup [1, \infty)$ **5.** $(-\infty, -1) \cup \left[\dfrac{1}{2}, \infty\right)$

7. $\{7, -7\}$ **9.** $\{6, -6\}$ **11.** $\{\ \}$ **13.** $\{-2, 2\}$

15. $\{0\}$ **17.** $\left\{4, -\dfrac{4}{3}\right\}$ **19.** $\left\{\dfrac{9}{2}, -\dfrac{1}{2}\right\}$ **21.** $\left\{\dfrac{10}{7}, -\dfrac{8}{7}\right\}$

23. $\{\ \}$ **25.** $\{-12, 28\}$ **27.** $\left\{\dfrac{5}{2}, -\dfrac{7}{2}\right\}$ **29.** $\left\{\dfrac{7}{3}\right\}$

31. $\{\ \}$ **33.** $\left\{\dfrac{3}{2}\right\}$ **35.** $\left\{-4, \dfrac{16}{5}\right\}$ **37.** $\left\{-\dfrac{1}{2}, \dfrac{7}{6}\right\}$

39. $\left\{\dfrac{5}{2}, -\dfrac{3}{2}\right\}$ **41.** $\left\{-4, \dfrac{1}{3}\right\}$ **43.** $\left\{\dfrac{1}{2}\right\}$ **45.** $\left\{-\dfrac{1}{16}\right\}$

47. $\left\{\dfrac{1}{4}\right\}$ **49.** $\{-1.44, -0.4\}$ **51.** $\{\ \}$

53. $\{w \mid w$ is a real number$\}$ **55.** $\{\ \}$ **57.** $|x| = 6$

59. $|x| = \dfrac{4}{3}$

Section 9.3 Graphing Calculator Exercises, p. 655

61. $\left\{2, -\dfrac{1}{2}\right\}$

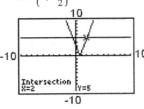 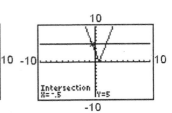

62. $\{7, 1\}$

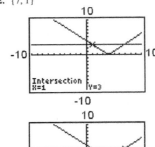

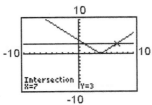

63. $\{\ \}$

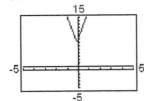

64. $\{\ \}$

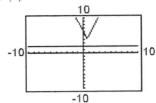

65. $\left\{\dfrac{1}{2}\right\}$

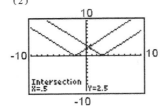

66. $\{-1\}$

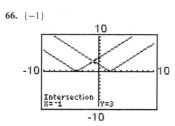

Section 9.4 Practice Exercises, pp. 663–665

1. a. $-a; a$ **b.** $-a; >$ **c.** $\{\ \}; (-\infty, \infty)$ **d.** includes; excludes

3. $\left\{\dfrac{4}{7}, \dfrac{6}{7}\right\}$ **5.** $(-3, -1]$ ———

7. $(-\infty, \infty)$ ——— **9. a.** $\{-5, 5\}$

b. $(-\infty, -5) \cup (5, \infty)$ ———

c. $(-5, 5)$ ——— **11. a.** $\{10, -4\}$

b. $(-\infty, -4) \cup (10, \infty)$ ———

c. $(-4, 10)$ ———

13. a. $\{\ \}$ **b.** $(-\infty, \infty)$ ———

c. $\{\ \}$ **15. a.** $\{\ \}$
b. $(-\infty, \infty)$ ——— **c.** $\{\ \}$

17. a. $\{0\}$ **b.** $(-\infty, 0) \cup (0, \infty)$ ———

c. $\{\ \}$ **19. a.** $\{7\}$
b. $(-\infty, 7) \cup (7, \infty)$ ——— **c.** $\{\ \}$

21. $(-\infty, -6) \cup (6, \infty)$ ———

23. $[-3, 3]$ ———

25. $(-\infty, \infty)$ ———
27. $(-\infty, -2] \cup [3, \infty)$ ———

29. $\{\ \}$ **31.** $[-10, 14]$ ———

33. $\left(-\infty, -\dfrac{5}{4}\right] \cup \left[\dfrac{23}{4}, \infty\right)$ ———

35. $\left(-\dfrac{21}{2}, \dfrac{19}{2}\right)$ ———

37. $(-\infty, \infty)$ ———
39. $\{\ \}$ **41.** $\{-5\}$ ———

43. $(-\infty, 6) \cup (6, \infty)$ ———

45. $(-\infty, 2] \cup [4, \infty)$ ———

47. $(4, 8)$ ———

49. $(-10.5, 4.5)$ ———

51. $|x| > 7$ **53.** $|x - 2| \le 13$ **55.** $|x - 32| \le 0.05$

57. $\left| x - 6\dfrac{3}{4} \right| \le \dfrac{1}{8}$

59. The solution set is $\{w \mid 1.99 \le w \le 2.01\}$ or, equivalently in interval notation, $[1.99, 2.01]$. This means that the actual width of the bolt could be between 1.99 cm and 2.01 cm, inclusive. **61.** b **63.** a

Section 9.4 Graphing Calculator Exercises, p. 666

65. $(-\infty, -6) \cup (2, \infty)$

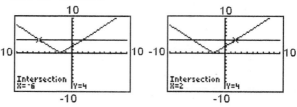

66. $(-\infty, -3) \cup (9, \infty)$

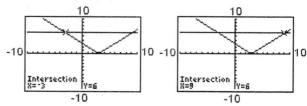

67. $(-7, 5)$

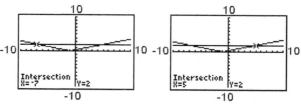

68. $(-3, 5)$

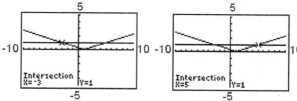

69. $\{\ \}$

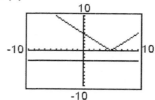

70. $\{\ \}$

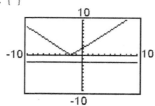

SA-30   Student Answer Appendix

71. $(-\infty, \infty)$

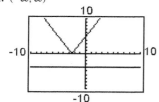

72. $(-\infty, \infty)$

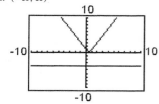

73. $\left\{-\dfrac{1}{6}\right\}$

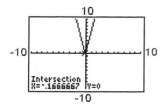

74. $\left\{\dfrac{4}{3}\right\}$

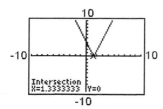

Chapter 9 Problem Recognition Exercises, p. 666

1. Quadratic; $(-\infty, -9) \cup (-1, \infty)$ **2.** Linear; $\{-26\}$
3. Rational; $[-8, -2)$ **4.** Quadratic; $\left\{-\dfrac{1}{4}, 2\right\}$
5. Absolute value; $\left(-\dfrac{1}{3}, 1\right)$ **6.** Quadratic; $\{\ \}$
7. Linear; $(-\infty, -10)$ **8.** Quadratic; $[-4, 1]$
9. Quadratic; $(-\infty, -1] \cup \left[\dfrac{2}{3}, \infty\right)$ **10.** Rational; $\left\{-\dfrac{11}{3}\right\}$
11. Linear; $\left[\dfrac{16}{7}, \infty\right)$ **12.** Absolute value; $\{\ \}$
13. Polynomial; $\left[-5, -\dfrac{1}{2}\right] \cup [3, \infty)$ **14.** Quadratic; $(-\infty, \infty)$
15. Rational; $(-\infty, -1) \cup (2, \infty)$ **16.** Quadratic; $\{-1, 5\}$
17. Absolute value; $(-\infty, -8) \cup (-8, \infty)$
18. Quadratic; $(-6, 6)$ **19.** Polynomial; $\left\{2, -2, -\dfrac{5}{3}\right\}$
20. Absolute value; $\{12, -4\}$ **21.** Linear; $\{0\}$
22. Rational; $(-\infty, 0] \cup (5, \infty)$ **23.** Absolute value; $\left\{-\dfrac{1}{2}\right\}$
24. Polynomial; $\left(-\dfrac{3}{2}, 0\right)$

Section 9.5 Practice Exercises, pp. 674–679

1. **a.** linear **b.** is not; is **c.** dashed; is not **d.** solid; is
3. $[1, 3)$ **5.** $(-\infty, -4] \cup (-2, \infty)$ **7. a.** No **b.** No
c. Yes **d.** Yes   **9. a.** No **b.** Yes **c.** Yes **d.** No
11. $>$ **13.** $\geq$ **15.** $\geq, \leq$

17.
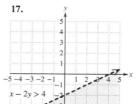
$x - 2y > 4$

19.
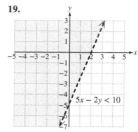
$5x - 2y < 10$

21.
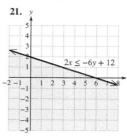
$2x \leq -6y + 12$

23.
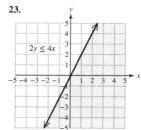
$2y \leq 4x$

25.
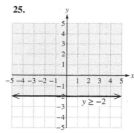
$y \geq -2$

27.
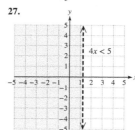
$4x < 5$

29.
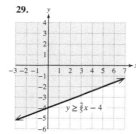
$y \geq \dfrac{2}{5}x - 4$

31.
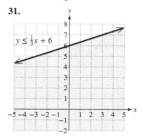
$y \leq \dfrac{1}{3}x + 6$

33.
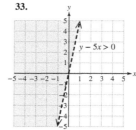
$y - 5x > 0$

35.
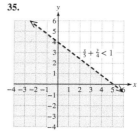
$\dfrac{x}{5} + \dfrac{y}{4} < 1$

37.
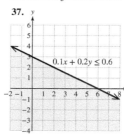
$0.1x + 0.2y \leq 0.6$

39.
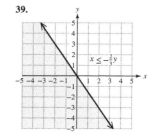
$x \leq -\dfrac{2}{3}y$

41.

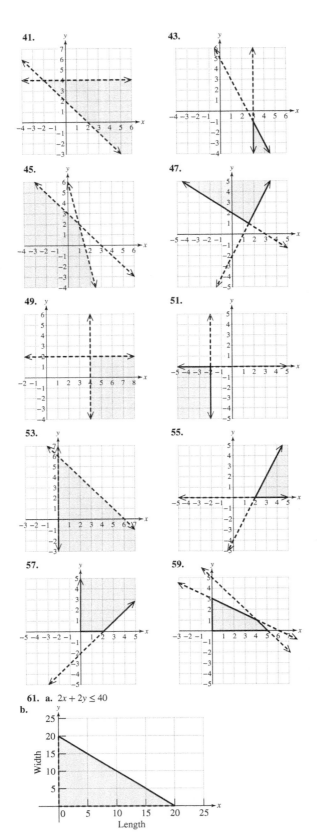

43.

45.

47.

49.

51.

53.

55.

57.

59.

61. a. $2x + 2y \le 40$
b.

63. a. $x \ge 0, y \ge 0$ **b.** $x \le 40, y \le 40$ **c.** $x + y \ge 65$
d.

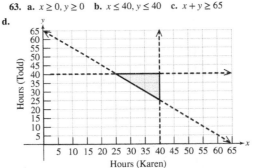

e. Yes; The point (35, 40) means that Karen works 35 hr and Todd works 40 hr.   **f.** No; The point (20, 40) means that Karen works 20 hr and Todd works 40 hr. This does not satisfy the constraint that there must be at least 65 hr total.

Chapter 9 Review Exercises, pp. 686–689

1. $C \cap D$ is the set of elements common to both sets C and D.

$C \cup D$ is the set of elements in either set C, set D, or both sets.

2. $[-10, 1)$ **3.** $(-\infty, \infty)$ **4.** $(-\infty, \infty)$ **5.** $(-1, 1)$

6. $(-\infty, -3] \cup (-1, \infty)$ **7.** $\{ \}$ **8.** $\left(-\frac{11}{4}, 4\right]$

9. $[-5, 2)$ **10.** $(-\infty, 6] \cup (12, \infty)$

11. $(-\infty, -2) \cup [2, \infty)$ **12.** $\left[0, \frac{4}{3}\right]$ **13.** $[-7, -2)$

14. a. $140 \le x \le 225$ **b.** $x < 140$ or $x > 225$
15. a. $125 \le x \le 200$ **b.** $x < 125$ or $x > 200$
16. a. $(-2, 0)$ and $(2, 0)$ are the x-intercepts.   **b.** On the interval $(-2, 2)$ the graph is below the x-axis.   **c.** On the intervals $(-\infty, -2)$ and $(2, \infty)$ the graph is above the x-axis.
17. a. $x = 0$; $(0, 0)$ is the x-intercept.   **b.** $x = 2$ is the vertical asymptote.   **c.** On the intervals $(-\infty, 0]$ and $(2, \infty)$ the graph is on or above the x-axis.   **d.** On the interval $[0, 2)$ the graph is on or below the x-axis.   **18.** $(-2, 6)$ **19.** $(-\infty, \infty)$ **20.** $(-\infty, -2) \cup [0, \infty)$
21. $(-\infty, -1] \cup (1, \infty)$ **22.** $(-2, 0) \cup (5, \infty)$

23. $(-2, 0) \cup \left(\frac{5}{2}, \infty\right)$ **24.** $[-3, -1]$

25. $(-\infty, -5) \cup (1, \infty)$ **26.** $(3, \infty)$ **27.** $(-3, \infty)$
28. $\{-5\}$ **29.** $(-\infty, -2) \cup (-2, \infty)$ **30.** $\{10, -10\}$
31. $\{17, -17\}$ **32.** $\{1.3, 7.4\}$ **33.** $\{-0.44, 2.54\}$
34. $\{5, -9\}$ **35.** $\{3, 1\}$ **36.** $\{ \}$

37. $\{ \}$ **38.** $\left\{\frac{3}{7}\right\}$ **39.** $\left\{-\frac{5}{4}\right\}$ **40.** $\left\{6, \frac{4}{5}\right\}$

41. $\left\{-\frac{1}{2}\right\}$ **42.** Both expressions give the distance between 3 and -2.   **43.** $|x| > 5$ **44.** $|x| < 4$

45. $|x| < 6$ **46.** $|x| > \frac{2}{3}$

47. $(-\infty, -14] \cup [2, \infty)$

48. $[-11, -5]$

49. $\left(-\infty, \frac{1}{7}\right) \cup \left(\frac{1}{7}, \infty\right)$

50. $\left(-\infty, -\frac{1}{5}\right) \cup \left(-\frac{1}{5}, \infty\right)$

SA-32 Student Answer Appendix

51. $\left[-2, -\frac{2}{3}\right]$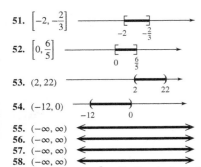

52. $\left[0, \frac{6}{5}\right]$

53. $(2, 22)$

54. $(-12, 0)$

55. $(-\infty, \infty)$
56. $(-\infty, \infty)$
57. $(-\infty, \infty)$
58. $(-\infty, \infty)$
59. $\{\ \}$ **60.** $\{\ \}$ **61.** If an absolute value is less than a negative number, there will be no solution.   **62.** If an absolute value is greater than a negative number, then all real numbers are solutions.   **63.** $0.17 \le p \le 0.23$ or, equivalently in interval notation, $[0.17, 0.23]$. This means that the actual percentage of viewers is estimated to be between 17% and 23%, inclusive.

64. $3\frac{1}{8} \le L \le 3\frac{5}{8}$ or, equivalently in interval notation, $[3\frac{1}{8}, 3\frac{5}{8}]$. This means that the actual length of the screw may be between $3\frac{1}{8}$ in. and $3\frac{5}{8}$ in., inclusive.

65. 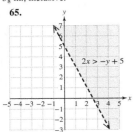   **66.**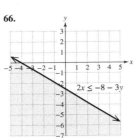

67. 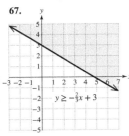   **68.**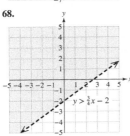

69. 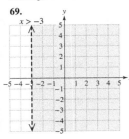   **70.**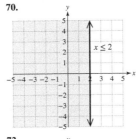

71. 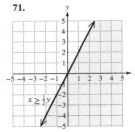   **72.**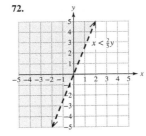

73. 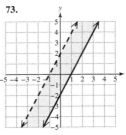   **74.**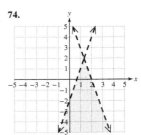

75. 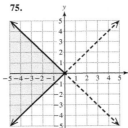   **76.**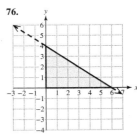

77. a. $x \ge 0, y \ge 0$ **b.** $x + y \le 100$ **c.** $x \ge 4y$

d.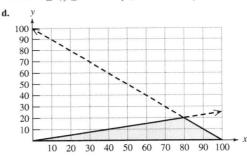

Chapter 9 Test, pp. 689–690

1. $\left[-\frac{1}{3}, 2\right]$ **2.** $(-\infty, -24] \cup [-15, \infty)$ **3.** $[-3, 0)$

4. $(-\infty, \infty)$ **5.** $\{\ \}$ **6. a.** $9 \le x \le 33$

b. $x < 9$ or $x > 33$ **7.** $(-5, 5)$ **8.** $(-\infty, -3) \cup (-2, 2)$

9. $\{\ \}$ **10.** $\{-11\}$ **11.** $\left[\frac{1}{2}, 6\right)$ **12.** $\left(-3, -\frac{3}{2}\right)$

13. $\{10, -22\}$ **14.** $\{-8, 2\}$ **15.** $\{\ \}$

16. $\left(-\infty, -\frac{1}{3}\right) \cup \left(\frac{17}{3}, \infty\right)$ **17.** $(-18.75, 17.25)$

18. $(-\infty, \infty)$ **19.** $|x - 15.41| \le 0.01$
20. 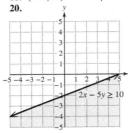   **21.**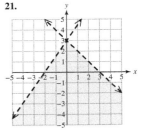

22.

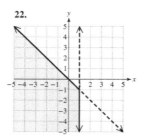

23. a. $x \geq 0, y \geq 0$ **b.** $300x + 400y \geq 1200$

c.

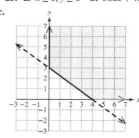

Chapters 1–9 Cumulative Review Exercises, pp. 690–692

1. $x^2 - x - 13$ **2.** $\left\{-\dfrac{3}{2}, 1\right\}$

3. a. $\{0, 6\}$ **b.** $(0, 6)$ **c.** $(-\infty, 0) \cup (6, \infty)$

4. a. $\{14, -10\}$ **b.** $(-10, 14)$ **c.** $(-\infty, -10) \cup (14, \infty)$

5.

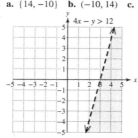

6. a. $t(1) = 9$. After one trial the rat requires 9 min to complete the maze. $t(50) = 3.24$. After 50 trials the rat requires 3.24 min to complete the maze. $t(500) = 3.02$. After 500 trials the rat requires 3.02 min to complete the maze.   **b.** The limiting time is 3 min.   **c.** More than 5 trials

7. a. $\left(-\infty, -\dfrac{5}{2}\right] \cup [2, \infty)$ **b.** On these intervals the graph is on or above the x-axis.

8.

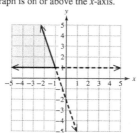

9. $-7x + 13$

10. a. Quotient: $2x^2 - 5x + 12$; remainder: $-24x + 5$

11. a. $b_1 = \dfrac{2A - hb_2}{h}$ or $b_1 = \dfrac{2A}{h} - b_2$ **b.** 10 cm

12. 75 mph   **13.** $57°, 123°$ **14.** $8000 in the 6.5% account; $5000 in the 5% account   **15.** Neither

16. a. x-intercept $(1, 0)$; no y-intercept; undefined slope   **b.** x-intercept $(8, 0)$; y-intercept $(0, 4)$; slope $-\frac{1}{2}$

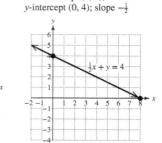

17. $y = -\dfrac{2}{3}x - \dfrac{13}{3}$ **18.** $\{(-1, 3, -2)\}$ **19.** $\dfrac{6}{x^4 y^5}$

20. Plane: 500 mph; wind: 20 mph   **21. a.** Quadratic
b. $P(0) = -2600$. The company will lose $2600 if no desks are produced.   **c.** $P(x) = 0$ for $x = 20$ and $x = 650$. The company will break even ($0 profit) when 20 desks or 650 desks are produced.
22. $3(x - 2)^2(x + 2)$

23. $-\dfrac{xy}{x + y}$ **24.** $-\dfrac{a + 1}{a}$ **25.** $\dfrac{2x + 5}{(x - 5)(x - 2)(x + 10)}$

Chapter 10

Section 10.1 Practice Exercises, pp. 702–705

1. a. $b; a$ **b.** principal   **c.** $b^n; a$ **d.** index; radicand
e. cube   **f.** is not; is   **g.** even; odd   **h.** Pythagorean; c^2
i. $[0, \infty); (-\infty, \infty)$ **j.** -5 and -4

3. a. $8, -8$ **b.** 8   **c.** There are two square roots for every positive number. $\sqrt{64}$ identifies the positive square root.

5. a. 9   **b.** -9 **7.** There is no real number b such that $b^2 = -36$.   **9.** 7   **11.** -7 **13.** Not a real number

15. $\dfrac{8}{3}$ **17.** 0.9   **19.** -0.4 **21. a.** 8   **b.** 4

c. -8 **d.** -4 **e.** Not a real number   **f.** -4

23. -3 **25.** $\dfrac{1}{2}$ **27.** 2   **29.** $-\dfrac{5}{4}$ **31.** Not a real number   **33.** 10   **35.** -0.2 **37.** 0.5   **39.** $|a|$

41. a **43.** $|a|$ **45.** $|x + 1|$ **47.** $|x| y^2$ **49.** $-\dfrac{x}{y}$

51. $\dfrac{2}{|x|}$ **53.** -92 **55.** 2   **57.** -923 **59.** y^4

61. $\dfrac{a^3}{b}$ **63.** $-\dfrac{5}{q}$ **65.** $3xy^2z$ **67.** $\dfrac{hk^2}{4}$ **69.** $-\dfrac{t}{3}$

71. $2y^2$ **73.** $2p^2q^3$ **75.** 9 cm   **77.** 13 ft

79. They were 5 mi apart.   **81.** They are 25 mi apart.

83. a. Not a real number   **b.** Not a real number
c. 0   **d.** 1   **e.** 2; Domain: $[2, \infty)$ **85. a.** -2 **b.** -1

c. 0   **d.** 1; Domain: $(-\infty, \infty)$ **87.** $\left(-\infty, \dfrac{5}{2}\right]$

89. $(-\infty, \infty)$ **91.** $[5, \infty)$ **93.** $(-\infty, \infty)$

95. a. $(-\infty, 1]$ **97. a.** $[-3, \infty)$

b.

b.

SA-34   Student Answer Appendix

99. a. $[0, \infty)$
b.

101. a. $(-\infty, \infty)$
b.

103. $q + p^2$ **105.** $\dfrac{6}{\sqrt[3]{x}}$ **107.** 8 in.

Section 10.1 Graphing Calculator Exercises, p. 705

109. 8.3066   **110.** 76.1446   **111.** 3.7100
112. -0.5566 **113.** 15.6525   **114.** -6.2403
115. -0.1235 **116.** 1.0622
117.

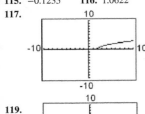

118.

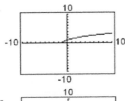

119.

120.

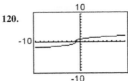

Section 10.2 Practice Exercises, pp. 710–713

1. a. $\sqrt[n]{a}$ **b.** $(\sqrt[n]{a})^m$ or $\sqrt[n]{a^m}$ **c.** $\dfrac{1}{\sqrt{x}}$ **d.** $2; \dfrac{1}{2}$

3. 5   **5.** 3   **7.** 12   **9.** -12 **11.** Not a real number

13. -4 **15.** $\dfrac{1}{5}$ **17.** $-\dfrac{1}{7}$

19. $a^{m/n} = \sqrt[n]{a^m}$; The numerator of the exponent represents the power of the base. The denominator of the exponent represents the index of the radical.   **21. a.** 8   **b.** -8 **c.** Not a real number
d. $\dfrac{1}{8}$ **e.** $-\dfrac{1}{8}$ **f.** Not a real number

23. a. 125   **b.** -125 **c.** Not a real number   **d.** $\dfrac{1}{125}$
e. $-\dfrac{1}{125}$ **f.** Not a real number   **25.** $\dfrac{1}{512}$ **27.** 27

29. $-\dfrac{1}{81}$ **31.** $\dfrac{27}{1000}$ **33.** Not a real number   **35.** -2

37. -2 **39.** 6   **41.** 10   **43.** $\dfrac{3}{4}$ **45.** 1   **47.** $\dfrac{9}{2}$

49. $\sqrt[3]{q^2}$ **51.** $6\sqrt[4]{y^3}$ **53.** $\sqrt[3]{x^2 y}$ **55.** $\dfrac{6}{\sqrt[5]{r^2}}$

57. $x^{1/3}$ **59.** $10b^{1/2}$ **61.** $y^{2/3}$ **63.** $(a^2 b^3)^{1/4}$

65. $\dfrac{1}{x}$ **67.** p **69.** y^2 **71.** $6^{2/5}$ **73.** $\dfrac{4}{t^{5/3}}$

75. a^7 **77.** $\dfrac{25a^4 d}{c}$ **79.** $\dfrac{y^9}{x^8}$ **81.** $\dfrac{2z^3}{w}$ **83.** $5xy^2 z^3$

85. $x^{13} z^{4/3}$ **87.** $\dfrac{x^3 y^2}{z^5}$ **89. a.** 10.9%   **b.** 8.8%
c. The account in part (a).   **91.** 2.7 in.   **93.** $\sqrt{y}$
95. $\sqrt[4]{z}$ **97.** $\sqrt[3]{x^2}$ **99.** $y\sqrt{x}$ **101.** $4x^4 y^3$
103. $2x\sqrt[3]{y^2 z}$ **105.** $\sqrt[6]{x}$ **107.** $\sqrt[15]{w}$ **109.** 3
111. 0.3761   **113.** 2.9240   **115.** 31.6228

Section 10.3 Practice Exercises, pp. 718–720

1. a. $\sqrt[n]{a}$; $\sqrt[n]{b}$ **b.** The exponent within the radicand is greater than the index.   **c.** is not   **d.** 3   **e.** t^{12} **f.** No. $\sqrt{2}$ is an irrational number and the decimal form is a nonterminating, nonrepeating decimal.

3. $\dfrac{p}{q^5}$ **5.** $\sqrt[7]{x^4}$ **7.** $y^{9/2}$ **9.** $x^2\sqrt{x}$ **11.** $q^2\sqrt[3]{q}$

13. $a^2 b^2 \sqrt{a}$ **15.** $-x^2 y^3 \sqrt[4]{y}$ **17.** $2\sqrt{7}$ **19.** $2\sqrt{5}$
21. $15\sqrt{2}$ **23.** $3\sqrt[3]{2}$ **25.** $5b\sqrt{ab}$ **27.** $2x^2\sqrt[3]{5x}$
29. $-2x^2 z\sqrt[3]{2y}$ **31.** $2wz\sqrt[4]{5z^3}$ **33.** x **35.** p^2

37. 5   **39.** $\dfrac{1}{2}$ **41.** $\dfrac{5\sqrt{2}}{3}$ **43.** $\dfrac{5\sqrt[3]{9}}{6}$ **45.** $4\sqrt{5}$

47. $-30\sqrt{3}$ **49.** $5x^2 y\sqrt{y}$ **51.** $3yz\sqrt[3]{x^2 z}$ **53.** $2w^2$

55. $\dfrac{1}{10y^6}$ **57.** $\dfrac{2}{b}$ **59.** $2a^7 b^4 c^{15} d^{11}\sqrt{2c}$

61. $3a^2 b\sqrt[3]{2b}$ **63.** $-10a^2 b^2 \sqrt[3]{3ac}$ **65.** $x\sqrt[4]{7xy}$

67. $3a^2 b\sqrt{6}$ **69.** $2\sqrt{3}$ **71.** $\dfrac{3\sqrt{5}}{4}$

73. $\dfrac{1}{\sqrt[3]{w^6}}$ simplifies to $\dfrac{1}{w^2}$ **75.** $\sqrt{k^3}$ simplifies to $k\sqrt{k}$

77. $2\sqrt{41}$ ft   **79.** $6\sqrt{5}$ m   **81.** The distance is $90\sqrt{2}$ ft or approximately 127.3 ft.   **83.** The path from A to B and B to C is faster.

Section 10.4 Practice Exercises, pp. 723–725

1. a. index; radicand   **b.** $2\sqrt{3x}$ **c.** cannot; can   **d.** $4\sqrt{2}$

3. $-xy\sqrt[4]{x^3}$ **5.** $\dfrac{b^2}{2}$ **7.** $(x^3 y)^{1/4}$ **9.** $y^{11/12}$

11. a. Not *like* radicals   **b.** *Like* radicals
c. Not *like* radicals   **13. a.** Both expressions can be simplified by using the distributive property.   **b.** Neither expression can be simplified because the terms do not contain *like* radicals or *like* terms.   **15.** $9\sqrt{5}$ **17.** $2\sqrt[3]{tw}$
19. $5\sqrt{10}$ **21.** $8\sqrt[4]{3} - \sqrt[4]{14}$ **23.** $2\sqrt{x} + 2\sqrt{y}$
25. Cannot be simplified further
27. Cannot be simplified further   **29.** $\dfrac{29}{18}z\sqrt[3]{6}$

31. $0.7x\sqrt{y}$ **33.** Simplify each radical: $3\sqrt{2} + 35\sqrt{2}$. Then add *like* radicals: $38\sqrt{2}$ **35.** 15   **37.** $8\sqrt{3}$
39. $3\sqrt{7}$ **41.** $-5\sqrt{2} + 3\sqrt{3}$ **43.** $\sqrt[3]{3}$ **45.** $-5\sqrt{2a}$
47. $8s^2 t^2\sqrt[3]{s^2}$ **49.** $6x\sqrt[3]{x}$ **51.** $14p^2\sqrt{5}$
53. $-\sqrt[3]{a^2 b}$ **55.** $(5x + 6)\sqrt{x}$ **57.** $(5x - 6)\sqrt{2}$
59. $33d\sqrt[3]{2c}$ **61.** $2a^2 b\sqrt{6a}$ **63.** $5x\sqrt[3]{2} - 6\sqrt[3]{x}$
65. False; $\sqrt{9} + \sqrt{16} \neq \sqrt{9 + 16}$; $7 \neq 5$ **67.** True
69. False; $\sqrt{y} + \sqrt{y} = 2\sqrt{y} \neq \sqrt{2y}$
71. False; $2w\sqrt{5} + 4w\sqrt{5} = 6w\sqrt{5} \neq 6w^2\sqrt{5}$
73. $\sqrt{48} + \sqrt{12}$ simplifies to $6\sqrt{3}$
75. $5\sqrt[3]{x^6} - x^2$ simplifies to $4x^2$ **77.** The difference of the principal square root of 18 and the square of 5
79. The sum of the principal fourth root of x and the cube of y
81. $9\sqrt{6}$ cm ≈ 22.0 cm   **83.** $x = 2\sqrt{2}$ ft
85. a. $10\sqrt{5}$ yd   **b.** 22.36 yd   **c.** \$105.95

Section 10.5 Practice Exercises, pp. 731–733

1. a. $\sqrt[n]{ab}$ **b.** x **c.** a **d.** conjugates   **e.** $m - n$
f. $c + 8\sqrt{c} + 16$ **3.** $-2ab\sqrt{5bc}$ **5.** $x^{1/6} y^{7/12}$ **7.** $2\sqrt[3]{7}$
9. $\sqrt[3]{21}$ **11.** $2\sqrt{5}$ **13.** $4\sqrt[4]{4}$ **15.** $8\sqrt[3]{20}$
17. $-24ab\sqrt{a}$ **19.** $6\sqrt{10}$ **21.** $6x\sqrt{2}$ **23.** $10a^3 b^2\sqrt{b}$
25. $-24x^2 y^2\sqrt{2y}$ **27.** $6ab\sqrt[3]{2a^2 b^2}$ **29.** $12 - 6\sqrt{3}$
31. $2\sqrt{3} - \sqrt{6}$ **33.** $-2x - \dfrac{7}{3}\sqrt{x}$ **35.** $-8 + 7\sqrt{30}$

37. $x - 5\sqrt{x} - 36$ **39.** $\sqrt[3]{y^2} - \sqrt[3]{y} - 6$
41. $9a - 28\sqrt{ab} + 3b$ **43.** $8\sqrt{p} + 3p + 5\sqrt{pq} + 16\sqrt{q} - 2q$
45. 15 **47.** $3y$ **49.** 6 **51.** 709 **53. a.** $x^2 - y^2$
b. $x^2 - 25$ **55.** $29 + 8\sqrt{13}$ **57.** $p - 2\sqrt{7p} + 7$
59. $2a - 6\sqrt{2ab} + 9b$ **61.** $3 - x^2$ **63.** 4
65. $\frac{4}{9}x - \frac{1}{4}y$ **67. a.** $3 - x$ **b.** $3 + 2\sqrt{3x} + x$
c. $3 - 2\sqrt{3x} + x$ **69.** True **71.** False;
$(x - \sqrt{5})^2 = x^2 - 2x\sqrt{5} + 5$ **73.** False; 5 is multiplied by 3 only.
75. True **77.** $6x$ **79.** $3x + 1$
81. $x + 19 - 8\sqrt{x + 3}$ **83.** $2t + 10\sqrt{2t - 3} + 22$
85. $12\sqrt{5}$ ft^2 **87.** $18\sqrt{15}$ in.^{2} **89.** $\sqrt[4]{x^3}$
91. $\sqrt[15]{(2z)^8}$ **93.** $p^2\sqrt[6]{p}$ **95.** $u\sqrt[6]{u}$
97. $\sqrt[6]{x^2y}$ **99.** $\sqrt[4]{2^3 \cdot 3^2}$ or $\sqrt[4]{72}$ **101.** $\sqrt[12]{2^4 5^3 x^7 y^7}$
103. $2m\sqrt[6]{3^3 2mn^5}$ **105.** $a + b$

Chapter 10 Problem Recognition Exercises, p. 734
1. a. $2\sqrt{6}$ **b.** $2\sqrt[3]{3}$ **2. a.** $3\sqrt{6}$ **b.** $3\sqrt[3]{2}$
3. a. $10y^3\sqrt{2}$ **b.** $2y^2\sqrt[3]{25}$ **4. a.** $4z^7\sqrt{2z}$ **b.** $2z^5\sqrt[3]{4}$
5. a. $4\sqrt{5}$ **b.** $2\sqrt[3]{10}$ **c.** $2\sqrt{5}$ **6. a.** $4\sqrt{3}$ **b.** $2\sqrt[3]{6}$ **c.** $2\sqrt[4]{3}$
7. a. $x^2y^3\sqrt{x}$ **b.** $xy^2\sqrt[3]{x^2}$ **c.** $xy\sqrt[4]{xy^2}$
8. a. $a^5b^4\sqrt{b}$ **b.** $a^3b^3\sqrt[3]{a}$ **c.** $a^2b^2\sqrt[4]{a^2b}$ **9. a.** $2st^2\sqrt[3]{4s^2}$
b. $2st\sqrt[4]{2st^2}$ **c.** $2st\sqrt[5]{t}$ **10. a.** $2v^2w^6\sqrt[3]{12vw^2}$
b. $2vw^5\sqrt[4]{6v^3}$ **c.** $2vw^4\sqrt[5]{3v^2}$ **11. a.** $2\sqrt{5}$ **b.** 5
12. a. $2\sqrt{10}$ **b.** 10 **13. a.** $-3\sqrt{6}$ **b.** 60
14. a. $-7\sqrt{7}$ **b.** 210 **15. a.** $3\sqrt{2}$ **b.** 4
16. a. $3\sqrt{3}$ **b.** 6 **17. a.** $7\sqrt{2}$ **b.** 240
18. a. $-\sqrt{2}$ **b.** 60 **19. a.** $14\sqrt[3]{3}$ **b.** $48\sqrt[3]{9}$
20. a. $\sqrt[3]{2}$ **b.** $30\sqrt[3]{4}$

Section 10.6 Practice Exercises, pp. 741–744
1. a. radical **b.** $\frac{\sqrt[n]{a}}{\sqrt[n]{b}}$ **c.** $\frac{4}{x^2}$ **d.** rationalizing **e.** is; is not
f. denominator **3.** $12y\sqrt{5}$ **5.** $-18y + 3\sqrt{y} + 3$
7. $64 - 16\sqrt{t} + t$ **9.** -5 **11.** $\frac{7x^2}{y^3}$ **13.** $\frac{2a\sqrt{2}}{x^3}$
15. $\frac{-2j\sqrt[3]{2}}{k}$ **17.** $3b^2$ **19.** $\frac{1}{2b^2}$ **21.** $\frac{z\sqrt{3y}}{w^2}$ **23.** $\frac{\sqrt{5}}{\sqrt{5}}$
25. $\frac{\sqrt[3]{x^2}}{\sqrt[3]{x^2}}$ **27.** $\frac{\sqrt{3z}}{\sqrt{3z}}$ **29.** $\frac{\sqrt[4]{2a^2}}{\sqrt[4]{2a^2}}$ **31.** $\frac{\sqrt{3}}{3}$
33. $\frac{\sqrt{x}}{x}$ **35.** $\frac{3\sqrt{2y}}{y}$ **37.** $\frac{a\sqrt{2a}}{2}$ **39.** $\frac{3\sqrt{2}}{2}$
41. $\frac{3\sqrt[3]{4}}{2}$ **43.** $\frac{-6\sqrt[4]{x^3}}{x}$ **45.** $\frac{7\sqrt[3]{2}}{2}$ **47.** $\frac{\sqrt[3]{4w}}{w}$
49. $\frac{2\sqrt[4]{27}}{3}$ **51.** $\frac{\sqrt[3]{2x}}{x}$ **53.** $\frac{2\sqrt{6}}{21}$ **55.** $\frac{\sqrt{x}}{x^4}$
57. $\frac{\sqrt{2x}}{2x^3}$ **59.** $\sqrt{2} + \sqrt{6}$ **61.** $\sqrt{x} - 23$
63. $\frac{4\sqrt{2} - 12}{-7}$ or $\frac{-4\sqrt{2} + 12}{7}$ **65.** $4\sqrt{6} + 8$
67. $-\sqrt{21} + 2\sqrt{7}$ **69.** $\frac{-\sqrt{p} + \sqrt{q}}{p - q}$ **71.** $\sqrt{x} - \sqrt{5}$
73. $\frac{w + 11\sqrt{w} + 18}{81 - w}$ **75.** $\frac{4\sqrt{xy} - 3x - y}{y - x}$
77. $5 - \sqrt{10}$ **79.** $\frac{5 + \sqrt{21}}{4}$ **81.** $-6\sqrt{5} - 13$
83. $\frac{16}{\sqrt[3]{4}}$ simplifies to $8\sqrt[3]{2}$
85. $\frac{4}{x - \sqrt{2}}$ simplifies to $\frac{4x + 4\sqrt{2}}{x^2 - 2}$

87. $\frac{\pi\sqrt{2}}{4}$ sec ≈ 1.11 sec **89. a.** $\frac{\sqrt{2}}{2}$ **b.** $\frac{\sqrt[3]{4}}{2}$
91. a. $\frac{\sqrt{5a}}{5a}$ **b.** $\frac{\sqrt{5} - a}{5 - a^2}$ **93.** $\frac{2\sqrt{6}}{3}$ **95.** $\frac{17\sqrt{15}}{15}$
97. $\frac{8\sqrt[3]{25}}{5}$ **99.** $\frac{-33}{2\sqrt{3} - 12}$ **101.** $\frac{a - b}{a + 2\sqrt{ab} + b}$
103. $\frac{3}{\sqrt{5 + 3h} + \sqrt{5}}$ **105.** $\frac{5}{\sqrt{4 + 5h} + 2}$

Section 10.7 Practice Exercises, pp. 751–754
1. a. radical **b.** isolate; 7 **c.** extraneous **d.** third
3. $\frac{3w\sqrt{w}}{4}$ **5.** $3c\sqrt[3]{2c}$ **7.** $4x - 6$ **9.** $9p + 7$
11. $\{100\}$ **13.** $\{4\}$ **15.** $\{3\}$ **17.** $\{42\}$ **19.** $\{2\}$
21. $\{29\}$ **23.** $\{140\}$ **25.** $\{ \}$ (The value 25 does not check.)
27. $\{7\}$ (The value -1 does not check.)
29. $\{ \}$ (The value 3 does not check.)
31. $V = \frac{4\pi r^3}{3}$ **33.** $h^2 = \frac{r^2 - \pi^2 r^2}{\pi^2}$ or $h^2 = \frac{r^2}{\pi^2} - r^2$
35. $a^2 + 10a + 25$ **37.** $5a - 6\sqrt{5a} + 9$
39. $r + 22 + 10\sqrt{r - 3}$ **41.** $\{-3\}$
43. $\{ \}$ (The value $\frac{1}{2}$ does not check.)
45. $\{2\}$ (The value 18 does not check.) **47.** $\{9\}$
49. $\{-4\}$ **51.** $\left\{\frac{9}{5}\right\}$ **53.** $\{2\}$
55. $\{ \}$ (The value 9 does not check.)
57. $\left\{-\frac{11}{4}\right\}$ **59.** $\{ \}$ (The value $\frac{8}{3}$ does not check.)
61. $\{-1\}$ (The value 3 does not check.) **63.** $\left\{\frac{1}{3}, -1\right\}$
65. $\{ \}$ (The values 3 and 23 do not check.)
67. $\{6\}$ **69.** $\{2\}$ (The value 18 does not check.)
71. a. 30.25 ft **b.** 34.5 m **73. a.** \$2 million
b. \$1.2 million **c.** 50,000 passengers **75. a.** 12 lb
b. $t(18) = 5.1$. An 18-lb turkey will take about 5.1 hr to cook.
77. $b = \sqrt{25 - h^2}$ **79.** $a = \sqrt{k^2 - 196}$

Section 10.7 Graphing Calculator Exercises, p. 754
80. The x-coordinate of the point of intersection is the solution to the equation.
81. The x-coordinate of the point of intersection is the solution to the equation.

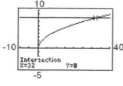

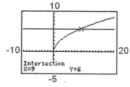

82.

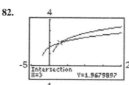

83.

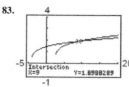

Section 10.8 Practice Exercises, pp. 762–764
1. a. imaginary **b.** $\sqrt{-1}$; -1 **c.** $i\sqrt{b}$ **d.** $a + bi$; $\sqrt{-1}$
e. real; b **f.** $a + bi$ **g.** True **h.** True
3. $9 - x$ **5.** $\{-8\}$ **7.** $\left\{\frac{1}{25}\right\}$ **9.** $\sqrt{-1} = i$ and
$-\sqrt{-1} = -1$ **11.** $12i$ **13.** $i\sqrt{3}$ **15.** $-2i\sqrt{5}$

SA-36   Student Answer Appendix

17. -60 **19.** $13i\sqrt{7}$ **21.** -7 **23.** -12
25. $-3\sqrt{10}$ **27.** $i\sqrt{2}$ **29.** 3 **31.** $-i$ **33.** 1
35. i **37.** 1 **39.** $-i$ **41.** -1 **43.** $a - bi$
45. Real: -5; imaginary: 12 **47.** Real: 0; imaginary: -6
49. Real: 35; imaginary: 0 **51.** Real: $\frac{3}{5}$; imaginary: 1
53. $7 + 6i$ **55.** $\frac{3}{10} + \frac{3}{2}i$ **57.** $5i\sqrt{2}$
59. $-1 + 10i$ **61.** $-24 + 0i$ **63.** $18 + 6i$
65. $26 - 26i$ **67.** $-29 + 0i$ **69.** $-9 + 40i$
71. $35 + 20i$ **73.** $-20 + 48i$ **75.** $\frac{13}{16} + 0i$
77. $\frac{1}{5} - \frac{3}{5}i$ **79.** $\frac{3}{25} - \frac{4}{25}i$ **81.** $\frac{21}{29} + \frac{20}{29}i$
83. $-\frac{17}{10} - \frac{1}{10}i$ **85.** $-\frac{1}{2} - \frac{5}{2}i$ **87.** $\frac{1}{2} - \frac{1}{3}i$
89. $1 + 10i$ **91.** $\frac{1}{4} + \frac{1}{2}i$ **93.** $-1 + i\sqrt{2}$
95. $-2 - i\sqrt{3}$ **97.** $-\frac{1}{2} + \frac{\sqrt{2}}{2}i$ **99.** Yes   **101.** Yes

Chapter 10 Review Exercises, pp. 772–774

1. a. False; $\sqrt{0} = 0$ is not positive.   **b.** False; $\sqrt[3]{-8} = -2$
2. $\sqrt{(-3)^2} = \sqrt{9} = 3$ **3. a.** False   **b.** True
4. $\frac{5}{4}$ **5.** 5 **6.** 6 **7. a.** 3 **b.** 0 **c.** $\sqrt{7}$
d. $[1, \infty)$ **8. a.** 0 **b.** 1 **c.** 3 **d.** $[-5, \infty)$
9. $\frac{\sqrt[3]{2x}}{\sqrt[4]{2x}} + 4$ **10. a.** $|x|$ **b.** x **c.** $|x|$ **d.** $x + 1$
11. a. $2|y|$ **b.** $3y$ **c.** $|y|$ **d.** y **12.** 8 cm
13. Yes, provided the expressions are defined. For example: $x^5 \cdot x^3 = x^8$ and $x^{1/5} \cdot x^{2/5} = x^{3/5}$ **14.** n represents the root.
15. Take the reciprocal of the base and change the exponent to positive.   **16.** -5 **17.** $\frac{1}{2}$ **18.** 4
19. b^{10} **20.** $\frac{16y^{12}}{xz^9}$ **21.** $\frac{a^3c}{b^2}$ **22.** $x^{3/4}$
23. $(2y^2)^{1/3}$ **24.** 2.1544 **25.** 6.8173 **26.** 54.1819
27. a. The radicand has no factor raised to a power greater than or equal to the index.   **b.** The radicand does not contain a fraction.
c. There are no radicals in the denominator of a fraction.
28. $6\sqrt{3}$ **29.** $xz\sqrt[4]{xy}$
30. $-10ab^3\sqrt[3]{2b}$ **31.** $-\frac{2a}{b}$
32. a. The principal square root of the quotient of 2 and x
b. The cube of the sum of x and 1   **33.** 31 ft
34. They are *like* radicals.   **35.** Cannot be combined; the indices are different.   **36.** Cannot be combined; one term has a radical, but the other does not.   **37.** Can be combined: $3\sqrt[4]{3xy}$ **38.** Can be added after simplifying: $19\sqrt{2}$
39. $5\sqrt{7}$ **40.** $9\sqrt[3]{2} - 8$ **41.** $10\sqrt{2}$ **42.** $13x\sqrt[3]{2x^2}$
43. False; 5 and $3\sqrt{x}$ are not *like* radicals.
44. False; $\sqrt{y} + \sqrt{y} = 2\sqrt{y}$ (add the coefficients).
45. 6 **46.** $2\sqrt[4]{2}$ **47.** $-2\sqrt{21} + 6\sqrt{33}$
48. $-6\sqrt{15} + 15$ **49.** $4x - 9$ **50.** $y - 16$
51. $7y - 2\sqrt{21xy} + 3x$ **52.** $12w + 20\sqrt{3w} + 25$
53. $-2z - 9\sqrt{6z} - 42$ **54.** $3a + 5\sqrt{5a} - 10$
55. $u^2\sqrt[6]{u^5}$ **56.** $\sqrt[4]{4w^3}$ **57.** $\frac{y^2\sqrt{3y}}{5x^3}$
58. $\frac{-2x^2y^2\sqrt[3]{2x}}{z^3}$ **59.** $9w^2$ **60.** $\frac{t^4}{4}$ **61.** $\frac{\sqrt{14y}}{2y}$

62. $\frac{\sqrt{15w}}{3w}$ **63.** $\frac{4\sqrt[3]{3p}}{3p}$ **64.** $-\frac{\sqrt[3]{4x^2}}{x}$
65. $\sqrt{10} - \sqrt{15}$ **66.** $3\sqrt{5} - 3\sqrt{7}$ **67.** $\sqrt{t} + \sqrt{3}$
68. $\sqrt{w} + \sqrt{7}$ **69.** The quotient of the principal square root of 2 and the square of x
70. $\left\{\frac{49}{2}\right\}$ **71.** $\{31\}$ **72.** $\{-12\}$ **73.** $\{7\}$
74. $\{9\}$ **75.** $\{\ \}$ (The value -2 does not check.)
76. $\left\{\frac{1}{2}, 4\right\}$ **77.** $\{-2\}$ (The value 2 does not check.)
78. $6\sqrt{5}$ m ≈ 13.4 m   **79. a.** $v(20) \approx 25.3$ ft/sec. When the water depth is 20 ft, a wave travels about 25.3 ft/sec.
b. 8 ft   **80.** $a + bi$, where a and b are real numbers and $i = \sqrt{-1}$
81. $a + bi$, where $b \neq 0$
82. Multiply the numerator and denominator by $4 - 6i$, which is the complex conjugate of the denominator.
83. $4i$ **84.** $-i\sqrt{5}$ **85.** -15 **86.** $-2i$ **87.** -1
88. i **89.** $-i$ **90.** 0 **91.** $-5 + 5i$ **92.** $9 + 17i$
93. $25 + 0i$ **94.** $24 - 10i$
95. $-\frac{17}{4} + i$; real part: $-\frac{17}{4}$; imaginary part: 1
96. $-2 - i$; real part: -2; imaginary part: -1
97. $\frac{4}{13} - \frac{7}{13}i$ **98.** $3 + 4i$ **99.** $-\frac{3}{2} + \frac{5}{2}i$
100. $-\frac{4}{17} + \frac{16}{17}i$ **101.** $-\frac{2}{3} + \frac{\sqrt{10}}{6}i$ **102.** $2 - 4i$

Chapter 10 Test, pp. 775–776

1. a. 6 **b.** -6 **2. a.** Real   **b.** Not real   **c.** Real
d. Real   **3. a.** y **b.** $|y|$ **4.** 3 **5.** $\frac{4}{3}$ **6.** $2\sqrt[3]{4}$
7. $a^2bc^2\sqrt{bc}$ **8.** $3x^2yz^2\sqrt{2xy}$ **9.** $4w^2\sqrt{w}$ **10.** $\frac{x^2}{5y}$
11. $\frac{3\sqrt{2}}{2}$ **12. a.** $f(-8) = 2\sqrt{3}$; $f(-6) = 2\sqrt{2}$; $f(-4) = 2$; $f(-2) = 0$ **b.** $(-\infty, -2]$ **13.** -0.3080
14. -3 **15.** $\frac{20x^2y^3}{z}$ **16.** $\sqrt[6]{7y^3}$ **17.** $\sqrt[12]{10}$
18. $3\sqrt{5}$ **19.** $3\sqrt{2x} - 3\sqrt{5x}$ **20.** $40 - 10\sqrt{5x} - 3x$
21. $\frac{-2\sqrt[3]{x^2}}{x}$ **22.** $\frac{x + 6 + 5\sqrt{x}}{9 - x}$ **23. a.** $2i\sqrt{2}$ **b.** $8i$
c. $\frac{1}{2} + \frac{\sqrt{2}}{2}i$ **24.** $1 - 11i$ **25.** $30 + 16i$ **26.** -28
27. $-33 - 56i$ **28.** 104 **29.** $\frac{17}{25} + \frac{6}{25}i$
30. $-\frac{15}{17} + \frac{9}{17}i$ **31.** $r(10) \approx 1.34$; the radius of a sphere of volume 10 cubic units is approximately 1.34 units.
32. 21 ft   **33.** $\{-16\}$ **34.** $\left\{\frac{17}{5}\right\}$
35. $\{2\}$ (The value 42 does not check.)

Chapters 1–10 Cumulative Review Exercises, pp. 776–777

1. 54 **2.** $15x - 5y - 5$ **3.** $\{-3\}$ **4.** $(-\infty, -5)$
5. $[-9, -3)$ **6.** $\{\ \}$ **7.** $y = -2x + 5$ **8.** $x = -5$
9. $\left\{\left(\frac{1}{2}, \frac{1}{3}\right)\right\}$ **10.** $\left(2, -2, \frac{1}{2}\right)$ is not a solution.
11. Together it will take them $1\frac{7}{8}$ hr.

12. a. $f(-2) = -10; f(0) = -2; f(4) = 14; f\left(\dfrac{1}{2}\right) = 0$

b. $(-2, -10), (0, -2), (4, 14), \left(\dfrac{1}{2}, 0\right)$

c.

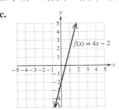

13. $a^6 b^{12} c^4$ **14. a.** 1.4×10^{-4} **b.** 3.14×10^9

15. $2x^2 - x - 15$; 2nd degree   **16.** $\sqrt{15} + 3\sqrt{2} + 3$

17. $x - 4$ **18.** $-\dfrac{1}{6}$ **19.** $\dfrac{3c\sqrt[3]{2}}{d}$ **20.** $32b\sqrt{5b}$

21. $2 + 3i$ **22.** $\{10\}$ **23.** $\dfrac{x - 15}{x(x + 5)(x - 5)}$

24. $\dfrac{-1}{(2a + 1)(a + 2)}$ **25.** $-14x^2 + 26x - 17$

26. $2\sqrt{3} + 2\sqrt{5}$ **27.** $\dfrac{6}{17} + \dfrac{10}{17}i$ **28.** $\left\{\dfrac{7}{6}, -\dfrac{3}{2}\right\}$

29. $(x + 3 - y)(x + 3 + y)$ **30.** $(x^2 + 2)(x^4 - 2x^2 + 4)$

Chapter 11

Section 11.1 Practice Exercises, pp. 786–789

1. a. $0; 0$ **b.** 0 **c.** $\sqrt{k}; -\sqrt{k}$ **d.** $2; \{3, -3\}$ **e.** completing
f. 100 **g.** $4; 1$ **h.** 8

3. $\{\pm 2\}$ **5.** $\{\pm\sqrt{7}\}$ **7.** $\left\{\dfrac{11}{6}, -\dfrac{11}{6}\right\}$ **9.** $\{\pm 5i\}$

11. $\{-1, -5\}$ **13.** $\left\{\dfrac{-3 \pm \sqrt{7}}{2}\right\}$ **15.** $\{-5 \pm 3i\sqrt{2}\}$

17. $\left\{\pm\dfrac{\sqrt{33}}{3}\right\}$ **19.** $\left\{-\dfrac{4}{5} \pm \dfrac{\sqrt{3}}{5}i\right\}$ **21.** $\{4i, -4i\}$

23. 1. Factoring and applying the zero product rule. 2. Applying the square root property. $\{\pm 6\}$ **25. a.** $\{16\}$ **b.** $\{2, -2\}$

27. $n = 9; (x - 3)^2$ **29.** $n = 16; (t + 4)^2$

31. $n = \dfrac{1}{4}; \left(c - \dfrac{1}{2}\right)^2$ **33.** $n = \dfrac{25}{4}; \left(y + \dfrac{5}{2}\right)^2$

35. $n = \dfrac{1}{25}; \left(b + \dfrac{1}{5}\right)^2$ **37.** $n = \dfrac{1}{9}; \left(p - \dfrac{1}{3}\right)^2$

39. 1. Divide both sides by a to make the leading coefficient 1.
2. Isolate the variable terms on one side of the equation. 3. Complete the square. 4. Apply the square root property and solve for x.

41. $\{-3, -5\}$ **43.** $\{-3 \pm i\sqrt{7}\}$ **45.** $\{-2 \pm i\sqrt{2}\}$

47. $\{5, -2\}$ **49.** $\left\{-1 \pm \dfrac{\sqrt{6}}{2}i\right\}$ **51.** $\left\{2 \pm \dfrac{2}{3}i\right\}$

53. $\left\{\dfrac{1}{5} \pm \dfrac{\sqrt{3}}{5}\right\}$ **55.** $\left\{-\dfrac{3}{4} \pm \dfrac{\sqrt{65}}{4}\right\}$ **57.** $\{2 \pm \sqrt{11}\}$

59. $\{1, -7\}$ **61. a.** $t = \dfrac{\sqrt{d}}{4}$ **b.** 8 sec

63. $r = \sqrt{\dfrac{A}{\pi}}$ or $r = \dfrac{\sqrt{A\pi}}{\pi}$ **65.** $a = \sqrt{d^2 - b^2 - c^2}$

67. $r = \sqrt{\dfrac{3V}{\pi h}}$ or $r = \dfrac{\sqrt{3V\pi h}}{\pi h}$ **69.** The shelf extends 4.2 ft.

71. The sides are 7.1 in.   **73. a.** 4.5 thousand textbooks or 35.5 thousand textbooks   **b.** Profit increases to a point as more books are produced. Beyond that point, the market is "flooded," and profit decreases. There are two points at which the profit is $20,000. Producing 4.5 thousand books makes the same profit using fewer resources as producing 35.5 thousand books.

Section 11.2 Practice Exercises, pp. 800–803

1. a. quadratic; $\dfrac{-b \pm \sqrt{b^2 - 4ac}}{2a}$ **b.** $ax^2 + bx + c = 0$
c. $8; -42; -27$ **d.** $7; 97$ **e.** $b^2 - 4ac$; discriminant **f.** imaginary
g. real **h.** less than

3. $4 - 2\sqrt{5}$ **5.** $2 - i\sqrt{3}$ **7.** linear   **9.** $\{-12, 1\}$

11. $\left\{\dfrac{1}{9} \pm \dfrac{2\sqrt{11}}{9}i\right\}$ **13.** $\left\{\dfrac{1}{6} \pm \dfrac{\sqrt{14}}{6}i\right\}$ **15.** $\{7, -5\}$

17. $\left\{\dfrac{-3 \pm \sqrt{41}}{2}\right\}$ **19.** $\left\{\dfrac{2}{5}\right\}$ **21.** $\{3 \pm i\sqrt{5}\}$

23. $\left\{\dfrac{1 \pm \sqrt{29}}{2}\right\}$ **25.** $\left\{\dfrac{-1 \pm \sqrt{13}}{4}\right\}$

27. $\left\{-\dfrac{2}{3} \pm \dfrac{2\sqrt{2}}{3}i\right\}$ **29.** $\left\{\dfrac{-5 \pm \sqrt{13}}{2}\right\}$

31. $\{-2, -4\}$ **33.** $\left\{\dfrac{-7 \pm \sqrt{109}}{6}\right\}$

35. a. $(x - 3)(x^2 + 3x + 9)$ **b.** $\left\{3, -\dfrac{3}{2} \pm \dfrac{3\sqrt{3}}{2}i\right\}$

37. a. $3x(x^2 - 2x + 2)$ **b.** $\{0, 1 \pm i\}$ **39.** The length of each side is 3 ft.   **41.** The legs are approximately 1.6 in. and 3.6 in.
43. The legs are approximately 8.2 m and 6.1 m.
45. a. Approximately 4.5 fatalities per 100 million miles driven
b. Approximately 1 fatality per 100 million miles driven
c. Approximately 4.2 fatalities per 100 million miles driven
d. For drivers 26 yr old and 71 yr old

47. The times are $\dfrac{3 + \sqrt{5}}{2}$ sec ≈ 2.62 sec or
$\dfrac{3 - \sqrt{5}}{2}$ sec ≈ 0.38 sec.   **49. a.** $x^2 + 2x + 1 = 0$
b. 0 **c.** 1 rational solution   **51. a.** $19m^2 - 8m + 0 = 0$ **b.** 64
c. 2 rational solutions   **53. a.** $5p^2 + 0p - 21 = 0$ **b.** 420
c. 2 irrational solutions   **55. a.** $n^2 + 3n + 4 = 0$ **b.** -7
c. 2 imaginary solutions   **57.** Discriminant: 16; two x-intercepts
59. Discriminant: 0; one x-intercept
61. Discriminant: -39; no x-intercepts

63. x-intercepts: $\left(\dfrac{5 + \sqrt{13}}{2}, 0\right), \left(\dfrac{5 - \sqrt{13}}{2}, 0\right)$;
y-intercept: $(0, 3)$ **65.** x-intercepts: none; y-intercept: $(0, -1)$

67. x-intercepts: $\left(\dfrac{-5 - \sqrt{41}}{4}, 0\right), \left(\dfrac{-5 + \sqrt{41}}{4}, 0\right)$;
y-intercept: $(0, -2)$ **69.** $\{-1 \pm 3i\}$

71. $\left\{-\dfrac{1}{3}, 6\right\}$ **73.** $\left\{\dfrac{5}{2} \pm \dfrac{3\sqrt{2}}{2}i\right\}$ **75.** $\left\{-\dfrac{1}{2} \pm 2i\right\}$

77. $\left\{\dfrac{3 \pm \sqrt{7}}{2}\right\}$ **79.** $\{1 \pm 3i\sqrt{2}\}$ **81.** $\{2 \pm \sqrt{2}\}$

83. $\left\{-\dfrac{1}{8}, \dfrac{3}{4}\right\}$ **85.** $\left\{\pm\dfrac{\sqrt{21}}{2}\right\}$

87. a. $\{-3 \pm \sqrt{14}\}$ **b.** $\{-3 \pm \sqrt{14}\}$ **c.** Answers will vary

Section 11.2 Graphing Calculator Exercises, p. 803

89. **90.**

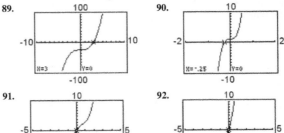

91. **92.**

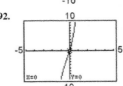

SA-38   Student Answer Appendix

Section 11.3 Practice Exercises, pp. 807–809

1. a. quadratic **b.** $3x - 1$ **c.** $p^{1/3}$

3. $\left\{\dfrac{3}{2} \pm \dfrac{\sqrt{7}}{2}\right\}$ **5.** $\{-4\}$ **7.** $\{2 \pm \sqrt{26}\}$

9. a. $\{-4, -6\}$ **b.** $\{-4, -1, -2, -3\}$

11. $\{1 \pm i\sqrt{2}, 1 \pm \sqrt{2}\}$ **13.** $\{5, -1, 2\}$ **15.** $\{27, -8\}$

17. $\left\{-\dfrac{1}{32}, -243\right\}$ **19.** $\{4\}$ (The value 64 does not check.)

21. $\left\{\dfrac{1}{4}\right\}$ (The value 4 does not check.)

23. $\{-7\}$ **25.** $\{16\}$; yes   **27.** $\{\pm 3i, \pm\sqrt{5}\}$

29. $\left\{\pm\dfrac{\sqrt{3}}{2}, \pm i\sqrt{5}\right\}$ **31.** $\left\{\dfrac{-5 \pm \sqrt{13}}{2}\right\}$

33. $\left\{\dfrac{9 \pm \sqrt{73}}{4}\right\}$ **35.** $\{2 \pm \sqrt{3}\}$ **37.** $\{\pm 2, \pm 2i\}$

39. $\left\{-\dfrac{7}{4}, -\dfrac{3}{2}\right\}$ **41.** $\left\{\dfrac{1}{2}, -\dfrac{1}{2}, \sqrt{2}, -\sqrt{2}\right\}$

43. $\left\{2, 1, -1 \pm i\sqrt{3}, -\dfrac{1}{2} \pm \dfrac{\sqrt{3}}{2}i\right\}$ **45.** $\{5, 4\}$ **47.** $\{0, 2\}$

49. $\left\{1, \dfrac{17}{2}\right\}$ **51.** $\{64, -125\}$ **53.** $\{\pm\sqrt{2}, \pm 2i\}$

55. $\{\pm 4i, 1\}$ **57.** $\{4, \pm i\sqrt{5}\}$ **59.** $\left\{\dfrac{8}{3}, 2\right\}$

Section 11.3 Graphing Calculator Exercises, p. 809

61. a. $\{\pm i\sqrt{2}\}$ **b.** Two imaginary solutions; no real solutions
c. No x-intercepts
d.
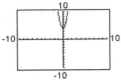

62. a. $\{1, -1\}$ **b.** Two real solutions; no imaginary solutions
c. Two x-intercepts
d.
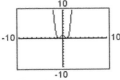

63. a. $\{0, 3, -2\}$ **b.** Three real solutions; no imaginary solutions
c. Three x-intercepts
d.
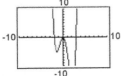

64. a. $\{\pm 1, \pm 3\}$ **b.** Four real solutions; no imaginary solutions
c. Four x-intercepts
d.
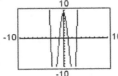

Chapter 11 Problem Recognition Exercises, pp. 809–810

1. $\{-5 \pm \sqrt{22}\}$ **2.** $\{8 \pm \sqrt{59}\}$ **3.** $\left\{-\dfrac{1}{6} \pm \dfrac{\sqrt{47}}{6}i\right\}$

4. $\left\{-\dfrac{3}{8} \pm \dfrac{\sqrt{71}}{8}i\right\}$ **5. a.** Quadratic **b.** $\{2, -7\}$

6. a. Quadratic **b.** $\{4, 5\}$ **7. a.** Quadratic form
b. $\{-3, -1, 1, 3\}$ **8. a.** Quadratic form **b.** $\{2, -2, i, -i\}$
9. a. Quadratic form (or radical) **b.** $\{16\}$ (The value 1

does not check.)   **10. a.** Quadratic **b.** $\left\{\dfrac{9 \pm \sqrt{89}}{2}\right\}$

11. a. Linear **b.** $\{4\}$ **12. a.** Linear **b.** $\{-1\}$
13. a. Quadratic **b.** $\{\pm i\sqrt{2}\}$ **14. a.** Quadratic
b. $\{\pm i\sqrt{6}\}$ **15. a.** Rational **b.** $\{2, -1\}$
16. a. Rational **b.** $\{-2, 4\}$
17. a. Quadratic **b.** $\{10 \pm \sqrt{101}\}$
18. a. Quadratic **b.** $\{-9 \pm \sqrt{77}\}$

19. a. Quadratic **b.** $\left\{\dfrac{1 \pm \sqrt{17}}{2}\right\}$

20. a. Quadratic **b.** $\left\{\dfrac{1 \pm \sqrt{13}}{2}\right\}$

21. a. Radical **b.** $\{3\}$ (The value -1 does not check.)
22. a. Radical **b.** $\{6\}$ (The value -1 does not check.)
23. a. Quadratic form (or radical) **b.** $\{-125, 27\}$
24. a. Quadratic form (or radical) **b.** $\{-64, -1\}$

Section 11.4 Practice Exercises, pp. 819–823

1. a. parabola **b.** $>$; $<$ **c.** lowest; highest **d.** (h, k);
upward; downward **e.** vertex; $x = h$

3. $\{3 \pm 2i\}$

5. $\left\{\dfrac{5 \pm \sqrt{10}}{5}\right\}$

7. $\{-27, -8\}$

9. The value of k shifts the graph of $f(x) = x^2$ vertically.

11.

13.

15.

17.

19.

21.

23.

25.

27. The value of a vertically stretches or shrinks the graph of $f(x) = x^2$.

29.

31.

33.

35.

37. d   **39.** g   **41.** a   **43.** e

45.

47.

Domain: $(-\infty, \infty)$; range: $[2, \infty)$ Domain: $(-\infty, \infty)$; range: $[-3, \infty)$

49.

51.

Domain: $(-\infty, \infty)$; range: $(-\infty, -2]$ Domain: $(-\infty, \infty)$; range: $(-\infty, 3]$

53.

55.

Domain: $(-\infty, \infty)$; range: $[1, \infty)$ Domain: $(-\infty, \infty)$; range: $[0, \infty)$

57.

59.

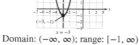

Domain: $(-\infty, \infty)$; range: $(-\infty, 3]$ Domain: $(-\infty, \infty)$; range: $[-1, \infty)$

61.

63.

Domain: $(-\infty, \infty)$; range: $(-\infty, 2]$ Domain: $(-\infty, \infty)$; range: $[1, \infty)$

65. a. $y = x^2 + 3$ is $y = x^2$ shifted up 3 units.
b. $y = (x + 3)^2$ is $y = x^2$ shifted left 3 units.
c. $y = 3x^2$ is $y = x^2$ with a vertical stretch.
67. Vertex $(6, -9)$; minimum point; minimum value: -9
69. Vertex $(2, 5)$; maximum point; maximum value: 5
71. Vertex $(-8, 0)$; minimum point; minimum value: 0
73. Vertex $\left(0, \dfrac{21}{4}\right)$; maximum point; maximum value: $\dfrac{21}{4}$
75. Vertex $\left(7, -\dfrac{3}{2}\right)$; minimum point; minimum value: $-\dfrac{3}{2}$
77. Vertex $(0, 0)$; minimum point; minimum value: 0
79. True   **81.** False   **83. a.** $(60, 30)$ **b.** 30 ft **c.** 70 ft
85. a. The fireworks will explode at a height of 150 ft.
b. Yes, because the ordered pair $(3, 150)$ is the vertex.

Section 11.5 Practice Exercises, pp. 830–834

1. a. $\dfrac{-b}{2a}; \dfrac{-b}{2a}$ **b.** True **c.** True **d.** True **e.** False
3. The graph of p is the graph of $y = x^2$ shrunk vertically by a factor of $\frac{1}{4}$.

5. The graph of r is the graph of $y = x^2$ shifted up 7 units.
7. The graph of t is the graph of $y = x^2$ shifted to the left 10 units.
9. $16; (x - 4)^2$ **11.** $\dfrac{49}{4}; \left(y + \dfrac{7}{2}\right)^2$
13. $\dfrac{1}{81}; \left(b + \dfrac{1}{9}\right)^2$ **15.** $\dfrac{1}{36}; \left(t - \dfrac{1}{6}\right)^2$
17. $g(x) = (x - 4)^2 - 11; (4, -11)$
19. $n(x) = 2(x + 3)^2 - 5; (-3, -5)$
21. $p(x) = -3(x - 1)^2 - 2; (1, -2)$
23. $k(x) = \left(x + \dfrac{7}{2}\right)^2 - \dfrac{89}{4}; \left(-\dfrac{7}{2}, -\dfrac{89}{4}\right)$
25. $F(x) = 5(x + 1)^2 - 4; (-1, -4)$
27. $P(x) = -2\left(x - \dfrac{1}{4}\right)^2 + \dfrac{1}{8}; \left(\dfrac{1}{4}, \dfrac{1}{8}\right)$ **29.** $(2, 3)$
31. $(-1, -2)$ **33.** $(-4, -15)$ **35.** $(-1, 2)$ **37.** $(1, 3)$
39. $\left(\dfrac{3}{2}, \dfrac{3}{4}\right)$ **41.** $(-4, -15)$ **43.** $(-1, 4)$
45. a. $(-1, -4)$ **b.** $(0, -3)$ **47. a.** $\left(\dfrac{1}{2}, \dfrac{7}{2}\right)$ **b.** $(0, 4)$
c. $(1, 0), (-3, 0)$ **c.** No x-intercepts
d.   **d.**

49. a. $\left(\dfrac{3}{2}, 0\right)$ **b.** $\left(0, -\dfrac{9}{4}\right)$ **51. a.** $(-1, 4)$ **b.** $(0, 3)$
c. $\left(\dfrac{3}{2}, 0\right)$ **c.** $(1, 0), (-3, 0)$
d.   **d.**

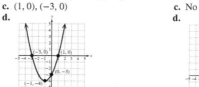

53. a. 164.25 ft **b.** 3.125 sec   **55. a.** 45 mph **b.** 32 mpg
57. a. 48 hr **b.** 2 g   **59.** $a = -9, b = 5, c = 4; y = -9x^2 + 5x + 4$
61. $a = 2, b = -1, c = -5; y = 2x^2 - x - 5$
63. $a = -3, b = 4, c = 0; y = -3x^2 + 4x$
65. a. The sum of the sides must equal the total amount of fencing.
b. $A = x(200 - 2x)$ **c.** 50 ft by 100 ft

Section 11.5 Graphing Calculator Exercises, p. 834

67.

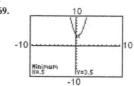

68.

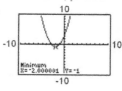

69.

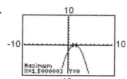

70.

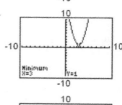

71.

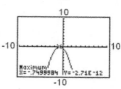

72.

SA-40   Student Answer Appendix

Chapter 11 Review Exercises, pp. 840–843

1. $\{\pm\sqrt{5}\}$ **2.** $\{\pm 2i\}$ **3.** $\{\pm 9\}$ **4.** $\left\{\pm\dfrac{\sqrt{57}}{3}i\right\}$

5. $\{2 \pm 6\sqrt{2}\}$ **6.** $\left\{\dfrac{5}{2}\pm\dfrac{3}{2}i\right\}$ **7.** $\left\{\dfrac{1\pm\sqrt{3}}{3}\right\}$

8. $\{4\pm\sqrt{5}\}$ **9.** $5\sqrt{3}$ in. ≈ 8.7 in.   **10.** 9 in.
11. $5\sqrt{6}$ in. ≈ 12.2 in.   **12.** $n = 64$; $(x + 8)^2$

13. $n = \dfrac{81}{4}$; $\left(x - \dfrac{9}{2}\right)^2$ **14.** $n = \dfrac{1}{16}$; $\left(y + \dfrac{1}{4}\right)^2$

15. $n = \dfrac{1}{25}$; $\left(z - \dfrac{1}{5}\right)^2$ **16.** $\{-2\pm 3i\}$ **17.** $\{1\pm\sqrt{6}\}$

18. $\{3 \pm 2\sqrt{3}\}$ **19.** $\{4\pm 3i\}$ **20.** $\left\{\dfrac{1}{3}, -1\right\}$

21. $\left\{\dfrac{1}{2}, -4\right\}$ **22.** $r = \sqrt{\dfrac{V}{\pi h}}$ or $r = \dfrac{\sqrt{V\pi h}}{\pi h}$

23. $s = \sqrt{\dfrac{A}{6}}$ or $s = \dfrac{\sqrt{6A}}{6}$

24. There will be two imaginary solutions.
25. Two rational solutions   **26.** Two rational solutions
27. Two irrational solutions   **28.** Two imaginary solutions
29. One rational solution   **30.** Two imaginary solutions

31. $\{2\pm\sqrt{3}\}$ **32.** $\left\{\dfrac{5}{2}\pm\dfrac{5\sqrt{3}}{2}i\right\}$ **33.** $\left\{2, -\dfrac{5}{6}\right\}$

34. $\left\{2, \dfrac{4}{3}\right\}$ **35.** $\left\{\dfrac{4}{5}, -\dfrac{1}{5}\right\}$ **36.** $\left\{\dfrac{1}{10}, -\dfrac{1}{2}\right\}$

37. $\{2\pm 2i\sqrt{7}\}$ **38.** $\{4\pm\sqrt{6}\}$ **39.** $\left\{\dfrac{2\pm\sqrt{22}}{3}\right\}$

40. $\{8, -2\}$ **41.** $\{-7\pm\sqrt{3}\}$ **42.** $\{-1\pm\sqrt{11}\}$
43. a. 1822 ft   **b.** 115 ft/sec   **44. a.** $\approx 53{,}939$ thousand
b. 2021   **45.** The dimensions are approximately 3.1 ft by 7.2 ft.
46. The distance between Lincoln and Omaha is approximately
50 mi.   **47.** $\{49\}$ (The value 9 does not check.)

48. $\{4, 16\}$ **49.** $\{\pm 3, \pm\sqrt{2}\}$ **50.** $\left\{\pm\dfrac{\sqrt{6}}{2}, \pm i\right\}$

51. $\{-243, 32\}$ **52.** $\{32, 1\}$ **53.** $\{3\pm\sqrt{10}\}$

54. $\left\{\dfrac{1\pm\sqrt{181}}{6}\right\}$ **55.** $\{\pm 3i, \pm i\sqrt{3}\}$ **56.** $\{\pm\sqrt{7}, \pm 2\}$

57.   **58.**

Domain: $(-\infty, \infty)$; range: $[-5, \infty)$ Domain: $(-\infty, \infty)$; range: $[3, \infty)$

59.   **60.**

Domain: $(-\infty, \infty)$; range: $[0, \infty)$ Domain: $(-\infty, \infty)$; range: $[0, \infty)$

61.   **62.**

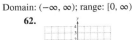

Domain: $(-\infty, \infty)$; range: $(-\infty, 0]$ Domain: $(-\infty, \infty)$; range: $(-\infty, 0]$

63.   **64.**

Domain: $(-\infty, \infty)$; range: $(-\infty, -5]$ Domain: $(-\infty, \infty)$; range: $(-\infty, 3]$

65. $\left(4, \dfrac{5}{3}\right)$ is the minimum point. The minimum value is $\dfrac{5}{3}$.

66. $\left(1, -\dfrac{1}{7}\right)$ is the maximum point. The maximum value is $-\dfrac{1}{7}$.

67. $x = -\dfrac{2}{11}$ **68.** $x = \dfrac{3}{16}$

69. $z(x) = (x - 3)^2 - 2$; $(3, -2)$
70. $b(x) = (x - 2)^2 - 48$; $(2, -48)$
71. $p(x) = -5(x + 1)^2 - 8$; $(-1, -8)$
72. $q(x) = -3(x + 4)^2 - 6$; $(-4, -6)$ **73.** $(1, -15)$

74. $(-1, 7)$ **75.** $\left(\dfrac{1}{2}, \dfrac{41}{4}\right)$ **76.** $\left(-\dfrac{1}{3}, -\dfrac{22}{3}\right)$

77. a. $(2, -3)$ **b.** $(0, 0), (4, 0)$
c.

78. a. $(-2, 4)$ **b.** $(0, 0), (-4, 0)$
c.

79. a. 3 sec   **b.** 144 ft   **80. a.** 150 meals   **b.** $1200
81. $a = 1, b = 4, c = -1$; $y = x^2 + 4x - 1$
82. $a = 1, b = -1, c = 6$; $y = x^2 - x + 6$

Chapter 11 Test, pp. 843–844

1. $\{2, -8\}$ **2.** $\{2\pm 2\sqrt{3}\}$ **3.** $\{-1\pm i\}$

4. $n = \dfrac{121}{4}$; $\left(d + \dfrac{11}{2}\right)^2$ **5.** $\{-3\pm 3\sqrt{3}\}$

6. $\left\{\dfrac{3}{4}\pm\dfrac{\sqrt{47}}{4}i\right\}$ **7. a.** $x^2 - 3x + 12 = 0$

b. $a = 1, b = -3, c = 12$ **c.** -39 **d.** Two imaginary solutions
8. a. $y^2 - 2y + 1 = 0$ **b.** $a = 1, b = -2, c = 1$ **c.** 0   **d.** One
rational solution

9. $\left\{1, \dfrac{1}{3}\right\}$ **10.** $\left\{\dfrac{-7\pm\sqrt{5}}{2}\right\}$ **11.** The height is
approximately 4.6 ft and the base is 6.2 ft.   **12.** The radius
is approximately 12.0 ft.   **13.** $\{9\}$ (The value 4 does not

check.)   **14.** $\{8, -64\}$ **15.** $\left\{\dfrac{11}{3}, 6\right\}$

16. $\{\pm\sqrt{6}, \pm 3\}$ **17.** $\left\{\dfrac{5\pm\sqrt{57}}{2}\right\}$ **18.** $\left\{5, -\dfrac{1}{2}\right\}$

19. $\{4\pm\sqrt{15}\}$ **20.** $\{-7\pm 2i\sqrt{6}\}$ **21.** $\{6\pm\sqrt{23}\}$
22. The vertex is $(3, -17)$.

23.   **24.**

Domain: $(-\infty, \infty)$; range: $[-4, \infty)$ Domain: $(-\infty, \infty)$; range: $(-\infty, 0]$

25.

Domain: $(-\infty, \infty)$; range: $[-3, \infty)$

26. The rocket will hit the ground 256 ft away.
27. a. 1320 million   **b.** 1999   **28.** The graph of $y = x^2 - 2$ is the graph of $y = x^2$ shifted down 2 units.   **29.** The graph of $y = (x + 3)^2$ is the graph of $y = x^2$ shifted 3 units to the left.
30. The graph of $y = -4x^2$ is the graph of $y = 4x^2$ opening downward instead of upward.   **31. a.** (4, 2)
b. Downward   **c.** Maximum point   **d.** The maximum value is 2.
e. $x = 4$ **32. a.** $g(x) = 2(x - 5)^2 + 1$; (5, 1)
b. (5, 1)   **33. a.** $f(x) = (x + 2)^2 - 16$.   **b.** Vertex: $(-2, -16)$
c. x-intercepts: $(-6, 0)$ and $(2, 0)$; y-intercept: $(0, -12)$
d. The minimum value is -16.   **e.** $x = -2$
34. a. 200 ft   **b.** 20,000 ft^2

Chapters 1–11 Cumulative Review Exercises, pp. 844–846

1. a. $\{2, 4, 6, 8, 10, 12, 16\}$ **b.** $\{2, 8\}$ **2.** $-3x^2 - 13x + 1$
3. -16 **4.** 1.8×10^{10} **5. a.** $(x + 2)(x + 3)(x - 3)$
b. Quotient: $x^2 + 5x + 6$; remainder: 0   **6.** $x - 2$
7. $\dfrac{2\sqrt{2x}}{x}$ **8.** $8000 in 12\% account; $2000 in 3\% account
9. $\{(8, 7)\}$ **10. a.** 720 ft   **b.** 720 ft   **c.** 12 sec
11. $\{3 \pm 4i\}$ **12.** $\left\{\dfrac{-5 \pm \sqrt{33}}{4}\right\}$ **13.** $n = 25$; $(x + 5)^2$
14. $2(x + 5)(x^2 - 5x + 25)$
15.

16. a. $\left(\dfrac{5}{2}, 0\right)$, (2, 0)   **b.** (0, 10)   **17.** The domain element 3 has more than one corresponding range element.
18.

19. $y = 39$ **20. a.** Linear   **b.** (0, 300,000). If there are no passengers, the airport runs 300,000 flights per year. (These flights are cargo flights only.)   **c.** $m = 0.008$ or $m = \frac{8}{1000}$. There are eight additional flights per 1000 passengers.
21. a. $[-4, \infty)$ **b.** $(-\infty, \infty)$
22. a. $(-\infty, 2]$ **b.** $(-\infty, 4]$ **c.** 4   **d.** 3   **e.** $x = -1$
23. $\left\{\dfrac{1}{18}, \dfrac{1}{2}\right\}$ **24.** $f = \dfrac{pq}{p + q}$ **25.** $\{7\}$
26. $\dfrac{y + 1}{y - 3}$ **27. a.** (3, 1)   **b.** Upward   **c.** (0, 19)
d. No x-intercept
e.

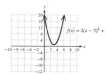

28. Vertex: (8, −62)

Chapter 12

Section 12.1 Practice Exercises, pp. 854–857

1. a. $\{(2, 1), (3, 2), (4, 3)\}$ **b.** one-to-one; y **c.** is not   **d.** is
e. $y = x$ **f.** x; x **g.** f^{-1} **h.** (b, a) **3.** Yes   **5.** No
7. Yes   **9.** $g^{-1} = \{(5, 3), (1, 8), (9, -3), (2, 0)\}$
11. $r^{-1} = \{(3, a), (6, b), (9, c)\}$ **13.** The function is not one-to-one.
15. Yes   **17.** No   **19.** Yes
21. a. $(f \circ g)(x) = 6\left(\dfrac{x - 1}{6}\right) + 1 = x$
b. $(g \circ f)(x) = \dfrac{(6x + 1) - 1}{6} = x$
23. a. $(f \circ g)(x) = \dfrac{\sqrt[3]{8x^3}}{2} = x$ **b.** $(g \circ f)(x) = 8\left(\dfrac{\sqrt[3]{x}}{2}\right)^3 = x$
25. a. $(f \circ g)(x) = (\sqrt{x - 1})^2 + 1 = x$
b. $(g \circ f)(x) = \sqrt{(x^2 + 1) - 1} = x$ **27.** $h^{-1}(x) = x - 4$
29. $m^{-1}(x) = 3(x + 2)$ **31.** $p^{-1}(x) = -x + 10$
33. $n^{-1}(x) = \dfrac{5x - 2}{3}$ **35.** $h^{-1}(x) = \dfrac{3x + 1}{4}$
37. $f^{-1}(x) = \sqrt[3]{x - 1}$ **39.** $g^{-1}(x) = \dfrac{x^3 + 1}{2}$
41. $g^{-1}(x) = \sqrt{x - 9}$
43. a. 1.2192 m, 15.24 m   **b.** $f^{-1}(x) = \dfrac{x}{0.3048}$ **c.** 4921.3 ft
45. False   **47.** True   **49.** False   **51.** True   **53.** $(b, 0)$
55. a. Domain: $[1, \infty)$, range: $[0, \infty)$ **b.** Domain: $[0, \infty)$, range: $[1, \infty)$ **57. a.** $[-4, 0]$ **b.** $[0, 2]$ **c.** $[0, 2]$ **d.** $[-4, 0]$

59. a. $[0, 2]$ **b.** $[0, 4]$ **c.** $[0, 4]$ **d.** $[0, 2]$

61. $q^{-1}(x) = x^2 - 4, x \geq 0$ **63.** $z^{-1}(x) = x^2 - 4, x \leq 0$
65. $f^{-1}(x) = \dfrac{x + 1}{1 - x}$ **67.** $t^{-1}(x) = \dfrac{x + 2}{x}$
69. $n^{-1}(x) = -\sqrt{x - 9}$

Section 12.1 Graphing Calculator Exercises, p. 857
71. $f^{-1}(x) = x^3 - 5$ **72.** $k^{-1}(x) = \sqrt[3]{x + 4}$

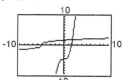

73. $g^{-1}(x) = \sqrt[3]{2x + 4}$ **74.** $m^{-1}(x) = \dfrac{x + 4}{3}$

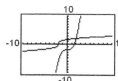
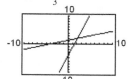

SA-42　　Student Answer Appendix

Section 12.2 Practice Exercises, pp. 863–866

1. a. b^x　**b.** is not; is　**c.** increasing　**d.** decreasing
e. $(-\infty, \infty); (0, \infty)$　**f.** $(0, 1)$　**g.** $y = 0$　**h.** is not

3. $-2x^2 + 2x - 3$　**5.** $\dfrac{3x - 1}{2x^2 + x + 2}$　**7.** $6x^2 + 3x + 5$

9. 25　**11.** $\dfrac{1}{1000}$　**13.** 6　**15.** 8　**17.** 5.8731

19. 1385.4557　**21.** 0.0063　**23.** 0.8950

25. a. $x = 2$　**b.** $x = 3$　**c.** Between 2 and 3
27. a. $x = 4$　**b.** $x = 5$　**c.** Between 4 and 5

29. $f(0) = 1, f(1) = \dfrac{1}{5}, f(2) = \dfrac{1}{25}, f(-1) = 5, f(-2) = 25$

31. $h(0) = 1, h(1) = 3, h(-1) = \dfrac{1}{3}, h(\sqrt{2}) \approx 4.73, h(\pi) \approx 31.54$

33. If $b > 1$, the graph is increasing. If $0 < b < 1$, the graph is decreasing.

35.

37.

39.

41.

43. a. 0.25 g　**b.** $\approx 0.16\ g$　**45. a.** 758,000　**b.** 379,000
c. 144,000　**47. a.** $P(t) = 153,000,000(1.0125)^t$
b. $P(41) \approx 255,000,000$　**49. a.** $1640.67　**b.** $2691.80
c. $A(0) = 1000$. The initial amount of the investment is $1000.
$A(7) = 2000$. The amount of the investment doubles in 7 yr.

Section 12.2 Graphing Calculator Exercises, p. 866

51.
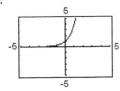

52.
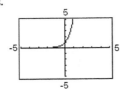

53.
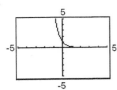

54.
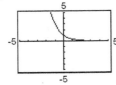

55.
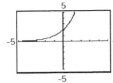

56.
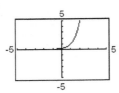

57.
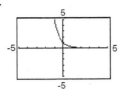

58.
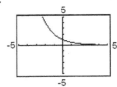

Section 12.3 Practice Exercises, pp. 875–879

1. a. logarithmic; b　**b.** logarithm; base; argument
c. $(0, \infty); (-\infty, \infty)$　**d.** exponential　**e.** common
f. increasing; decreasing　**g.** 2, 3, and 4　**h.** $y = x$　**3.** i

5. a. $s(-2) = \dfrac{25}{4}, s(-1) = \dfrac{5}{2}, s(0) = 1, s(1) = \dfrac{2}{5}, s(2) = \dfrac{4}{25}$
b.

7. $g(-2) = \dfrac{1}{9}, g(-1) = \dfrac{1}{3}, g(0) = 1, g(1) = 3, g(2) = 9$

9. $b^y = x$　**11.** $5^4 = 625$　**13.** $10^{-4} = 0.0001$　**15.** $6^2 = 36$

17. $b^x = 15$　**19.** $3^x = 5$　**21.** $\left(\dfrac{1}{4}\right)^{10} = x$　**23.** $\log_3 81 = x$

25. $\log_5 25 = 2$　**27.** $\log_7\left(\dfrac{1}{7}\right) = -1$　**29.** $\log_b y = x$

31. $\log_e y = x$　**33.** $\log_{1/3} 9 = -2$　**35.** 2　**37.** -1　**39.** $\dfrac{1}{2}$

41. 0　**43.** 5　**45.** 1　**47.** 3　**49.** $\dfrac{1}{2}$　**51.** 1　**53.** 3

55. 6　**57.** -2　**59.** 0.7782　**61.** 0.4971　**63.** -1.5051
65. -2.2676　**67.** 5.5315　**69.** -7.4202
71. a. Slightly less than 2　**b.** Slightly more than 1
c. $\log 93 \approx 1.9685, \log 12 \approx 1.0792$

73. a. $f\left(\dfrac{1}{64}\right) = -3, f\left(\dfrac{1}{16}\right) = -2, f\left(\dfrac{1}{4}\right) = -1, f(1) = 0,$
$f(4) = 1, f(16) = 2, f(64) = 3$

b.

75. $3^y = x$

x	y
$\frac{1}{9}$	-2
$\frac{1}{3}$	-1
1	0
3	1
9	2

77. $\left(\dfrac{1}{2}\right)^y = x$

x	y
4	-2
2	-1
1	0
$\frac{1}{2}$	1
$\frac{1}{4}$	2

79. $(5, \infty)$ **81.** $(-\infty, 2)$ **83.** $\left(\frac{1}{3}, \infty\right)$ **85.** $(-1.2, \infty)$

87. $(-\infty, 2)$ **89.** $(-\infty, 0) \cup (0, \infty)$ **91.** ≈ 7.35

93. a.

t (months)	0	1	2	6	12	24
$S_1(t)$	91	82.0	76.7	65.6	57.6	49.1
$S_2(t)$	88	83.5	80.8	75.3	71.3	67.0

b. Group 1: 91; Group 2: 88 **c.** Method II

Section 12.3 Graphing Calculator Exercises, p. 879

95. Domain: $(-6, \infty)$;
asymptote: $x = -6$

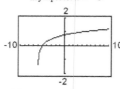

96. Domain: $(-2, \infty)$;
asymptote: $x = -2$

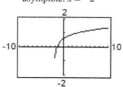

97. Domain: $(2, \infty)$;
asymptote: $x = 2$

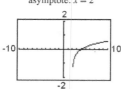

98. Domain: $(-8, \infty)$;
asymptote: $x = -8$

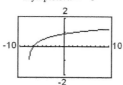

99. Domain: $(-\infty, 2)$;
asymptote: $x = 2$

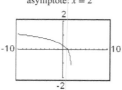

100. Domain: $(-\infty, 3)$;
asymptote: $x = 3$

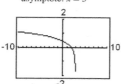

Chapter 12 Problem Recognition Exercises, p. 880

1. e **2.** l **3.** j **4.** g **5.** c **6.** a
7. k **8.** b **9.** i **10.** h **11.** f **12.** d

Section 12.4 Practice Exercises, pp. 886–889

1. a. $1; 0; x; x$ **b.** $\log_b x + \log_b y$; $\log_b x - \log_b y$ **c.** $p \log_b x$
d. False **e.** False **f.** False

3. 4 **5.** $\frac{1}{6}$ **7.** 0.9031 **9.** 5.0475 **11.** a **13.** c

15. a, b, c **17.** 1 **19.** 4 **21.** 11 **23.** 3 **25.** 0

27. 9 **29.** 0 **31.** 3 **33.** 1 **35.** $2x$ **37.** 4 **39.** 0

41. Expressions a and c are equivalent.

43. Expressions a and c are equivalent.

45. $\log_3 x - \log_3 5$ **47.** $\log 2 + \log x$ **49.** $4 \log_5 x$

51. $\log_4 a + \log_4 b - \log_4 c$

53. $\frac{1}{2} \log_b x + \log_b y - 3 \log_b z - \log_b w$

55. $\log_2(x + 1) - 2 \log_2 y - \frac{1}{2} \log_2 z$

57. $\frac{1}{3} \log a + \frac{2}{3} \log b - \frac{1}{3} \log c$ **59.** $-5 \log w$

61. $\frac{1}{2} \log_b a - 3 - \log_b c$ **63.** 3 **65.** 2 **67.** $\log_3\left(\frac{x^2 z}{y^3}\right)$

69. $\log_3\left(\frac{a^2 c}{\sqrt[4]{b}}\right)$ **71.** $\log_b x^2$ **73.** $\log_8 (8a^5)$ or $\log_8 a^5 + 1$

75. $\log\left[\frac{(x + 6)^2 \sqrt[3]{y}}{z^5}\right]$ **77.** $\log_b\left(\frac{1}{x - 1}\right)$ **79.** 1.792

81. 2.485 **83.** 4.396 **85.** 0.916 **87.** 13.812 **89.** 16.09

91. a. $B = 10 \log I - 10 \log I_0$ **b.** $10 \log I + 160$

Section 12.4 Graphing Calculator Exercises, p. 889

93. a. Domain: $(-\infty, 0) \cup (0, \infty)$ **b.** Domain: $(0, \infty)$

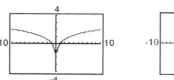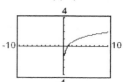

c. They are equivalent for all x in the intersection of their
domains, $(0, \infty)$.

94. a. Domain: $(-\infty, 1) \cup (1, \infty)$ **b.** Domain: $(1, \infty)$

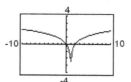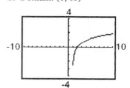

c. They are equivalent for all x in the intersection of their
domains, $(1, \infty)$.

Section 12.5 Practice Exercises, pp. 897–901

1. a. e **b.** e **c.** natural; $\ln x$ **d.** $0; 1; p, x$ **e.** $\ln x + \ln y$;
$\ln x - \ln y$ **f.** $p \ln x$ **g.** $\log_a b$

3. $\log_3\left(\frac{a\sqrt{d}}{c^5}\right)$ **5.** $\frac{1}{4} \log_6 x + \frac{1}{2} \log_6 y - \frac{3}{4} \log_6 z$

7.

x	y
-4	0.05
-3	0.14
-2	0.37
-1	1
0	2.72
1	7.39

Domain: $(-\infty, \infty)$

9.

x	y
-2	2.14
-1	2.37
0	3
1	4.72
2	9.39
3	22.09

Domain: $(-\infty, \infty)$

11. a. \$12,209.97 **b.** \$13,488.50 **c.** \$14,898.46 **d.** \$16,050.09
An investment grows more rapidly at higher interest rates.
13. a. \$12,423.76 **b.** \$12,515.01 **c.** \$12,535.94 **d.** \$12,546.15
e. \$12,546.50 More money is earned at a greater number of
compounding periods per year. **15. a.** \$6920.15 **b.** \$9577.70
c. \$13,255.84 **d.** \$18,346.48 **e.** \$35,143.44 More money is earned
over a longer period of time.

17.

x	y
2.25	−1.39
2.50	−0.69
2.75	−0.29
3	0
4	0.69
5	1.10
6	1.39

Domain: $(2, \infty)$

19.

x	y
0.25	−2.39
0.5	−1.69
0.75	−1.29
1	−1.00
2	−0.31
3	0.10
4	0.39

Domain: $(0, \infty)$

21. a.

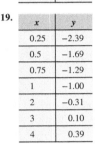

b. Domain: $(-\infty, \infty)$; range: $(0, \infty)$
c. Domain: $(0, \infty)$; range: $(-\infty, \infty)$

23. 1　**25.** 0　**27.** −6　**29.** $2x + 3$　**31.** $\ln(p^6 \sqrt[3]{q})$

33. $\ln \sqrt{\dfrac{x}{y^3}}$　**35.** $\ln\left(\dfrac{a^2}{b\sqrt[3]{c}}\right)$　**37.** $\ln\left(\dfrac{x^4}{y^3 z}\right)$

39. $2\ln a - 2\ln b$　**41.** $2\ln b + 1$　**43.** $4\ln a + \dfrac{1}{2}\ln b - \ln c$

45. $\dfrac{1}{5}\ln a + \dfrac{1}{5}\ln b - \dfrac{2}{5}\ln c$　**47. a.** 2.9570　**b.** 2.9570

c. They are the same.　**49.** 2.8074　**51.** 1.5283

53. −2.1269　**55.** 0　**57.** −3.3219　**59.** −3.8124

61. a. 15.4 yr　**b.** 6.9 yr　**c.** 13.8 yr　**63. a.** 19.8 yr

b. 13.9 yr　**c.** 27.8 yr

Section 12.5 Graphing Calculator Exercises,
pp. 901–902

65. a–b

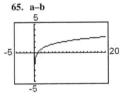

c. They appear to be the same.

66. a–b

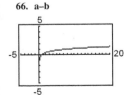

c. They appear to be the same.

67.

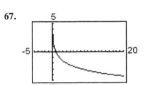

68.

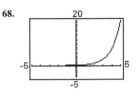

69.

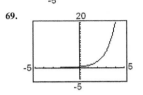

Chapter 12 Problem Recognition
Exercises, p. 902

	Exponential Form	Logarithmic Form
1.	$2^5 = 32$	$\log_2 32 = 5$
2.	$3^4 = 81$	$\log_3 81 = 4$
3.	$z^y = x$	$\log_z x = y$
4.	$b^c = a$	$\log_b a = c$
5.	$10^3 = 1000$	$\log 1000 = 3$
6.	$10^1 = 10$	$\log 10 = 1$
7.	$e^a = b$	$\ln b = a$
8.	$e^q = p$	$\ln p = q$
9.	$\left(\frac{1}{2}\right)^2 = \frac{1}{4}$	$\log_{1/2}\left(\frac{1}{4}\right) = 2$
10.	$\left(\frac{1}{3}\right)^{-2} = 9$	$\log_{1/3} 9 = -2$
11.	$10^{-2} = 0.01$	$\log 0.01 = -2$
12.	$10^x = 4$	$\log 4 = x$
13.	$e^0 = 1$	$\ln 1 = 0$
14.	$e^1 = e$	$\ln e = 1$
15.	$25^{1/2} = 5$	$\log_{25} 5 = \frac{1}{2}$
16.	$16^{1/4} = 2$	$\log_{16} 2 = \frac{1}{4}$
17.	$e^t = s$	$\ln s = t$
18.	$e^r = w$	$\ln w = r$
19.	$15^{-2} = \frac{1}{225}$	$\log_{15}\left(\frac{1}{225}\right) = -2$
20.	$3^{-1} = p$	$\log_3 p = -1$

Section 12.6 Practice Exercises, pp. 911–915

1. a. $x = y$　**b.** $x = y$　**3.** $\log_b [x(2x + 3)]$

5. $\log_b\left(\dfrac{x + 2}{3x - 5}\right)$　**7.** {9}　**9.** $\{10^{42}\}$　**11.** $\{e^{0.08}\}$

13. $\{10^{-9.2} - 40\}$　**15.** {5}　**17.** {10}　**19.** {25}　**21.** {59}

23. {1}　**25.** {0}　**27.** $\left\{-\dfrac{37}{9}\right\}$

29. {3} (The value −3 does not check.)　**31.** {4}　**33.** {3}

35. {2}　**37.** { } (The value −3 does not check.)　**39.** {4}

41. {−6}　**43.** $\left\{\dfrac{1}{2}\right\}$　**45.** {2}　**47.** $\left\{\dfrac{11}{12}\right\}$　**49.** {1}

51. $\left\{\dfrac{4}{19}\right\}$　**53.** {−2, 1}　**55.** $\left\{\dfrac{\ln 21}{\ln 8}\right\}$　**57.** {ln 8.1254}

59. {log 0.0138}　**61.** $\left\{\dfrac{\ln 15}{0.07}\right\}$　**63.** $\left\{\dfrac{\ln 3}{1.2}\right\}$

65. $\left\{\dfrac{\ln 3}{\ln 5 - \ln 3}\right\}$　**67.** $\left\{\dfrac{2\ln 2}{\ln 6 - \ln 2}\right\}$　**69.** $\left\{\dfrac{\ln 4}{0.04}\right\}$

71. $\left\{ 3\ln\left(\dfrac{125}{6}\right)\right\}$ **73.** $\left\{\dfrac{\ln 20}{\ln 5}+2\right\}$

75. a. ≈ 1285 million (or 1,285,000,000) people   **b.** ≈ 1466.5 million (or 1,466,500,000) people   **c.** The year 2049 ($t \approx 50.8$)

77. a. 500 bacteria   **b.** ≈ 660 bacteria   **c.** ≈ 25 min

79. It will take 9.9 yr for the investment to double.   **81.** 5 yr

83. a. 7.8 g   **b.** 18.5 days   **85.** The intensity of sound of heavy traffic is $10^{-3.07}$ W/m^2.   **87.** It will take 38.4 yr.   **89. a.** 1.42 kg

b. No   **91.** $\{10^5, 10^{-3}\}$ **93.** $\left\{\dfrac{1}{27}, \dfrac{1}{9}\right\}$

Section 12.6 Graphing Calculator Exercises, p. 915

95.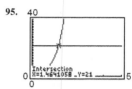

96.

Chapter 12 Review Exercises, pp. 921–924

1. No   **2.** Yes   **3.** $\{(5, 3), (9, 2), (-1, 0), (1, 4)\}$

4. $q^{-1}(x) = \dfrac{4}{3}(x + 2)$ **5.** $g^{-1}(x) = (x - 3)^5$

6. $f^{-1}(x) = \sqrt[3]{x} + 1$ **7.** $n^{-1}(x) = \dfrac{2x + 4}{x}$

8. $(f \circ g)(x) = 5\left(\dfrac{1}{5}x + \dfrac{2}{5}\right) - 2 = x + 2 - 2 = x$

$(g \circ f)(x) = \dfrac{1}{5}(5x - 2) + \dfrac{2}{5} = x - \dfrac{2}{5} + \dfrac{2}{5} = x$

9. The graphs are symmetric about the line $y = x$.

10. a. Domain: $[-1, \infty)$; range: $[0, \infty)$ **b.** Domain: $[0, \infty)$; range: $[-1, \infty)$ **11.** $p^{-1}(x) = (x - 2)^2, x \geq 2$

12. 1024   **13.** $\dfrac{1}{36} \approx 0.028$ **14.** 2   **15.** 10

16. 8.825   **17.** 16.242   **18.** 1.627   **19.** 0.681

20.

21.

22.

23.

24. a. Horizontal   **b.** $y = 0$ **25. a.** 15,000 mrem **b.** 3750 mrem   **c.** Yes   **26.** -3 **27.** 0   **28.** 1

29. 8   **30.** 4   **31.** 4   **32.** 5   **33.** -1

34.

35.

36. a. Vertical asymptote   **b.** $x = 0$ **37. a.** 2.5   **b.** 9.5

38. 1   **39.** 6   **40.** 0   **41.** 7

42. a. $\log_b x + \log_b y$ **b.** $\log_b\left(\dfrac{x}{y}\right)$ **c.** $p \log_b x$

43. $\log_b\left(\dfrac{\sqrt[4]{x^3 y}}{z}\right)$ **44.** $\log_3\left(\dfrac{\sqrt{ab}}{c^2 d^4}\right)$ **45.** $\log 5$

46. 0   **47.** b   **48.** a   **49.** 148.4132   **50.** 14.0940

51. 32.2570   **52.** 57.2795   **53.** 1.7918   **54.** -2.1972

55. 1.3424   **56.** 1.3029   **57.** 3.3219   **58.** 1.9943

59. -0.8370 **60.** -3.6668 **61. a.** \$33,361.92

b. \$33,693.90   **c.** \$33,770.48   **d.** \$33,809.18

62. a. $S(0) = 95$; the student's score is 95 at the end of the course. **b.** $S(6) \approx 23.7$; the student's score is 23.7 after 6 months. **c.** $S(12) \approx 20.2$; the student's score is 20.2 after 1 yr.

63. $(-\infty, \infty)$ **64.** $(-\infty, \infty)$ **65.** $(-\infty, \infty)$

66. $(0, \infty)$ **67.** $(-5, \infty)$ **68.** $(7, \infty)$ **69.** $\left(\dfrac{4}{3}, \infty\right)$

70. $(-\infty, 5)$ **71.** $\{125\}$ **72.** $\left\{\dfrac{1}{49}\right\}$ **73.** $\{216\}$

74. $\{3^{1/12}\}$ **75.** $\left\{\dfrac{1001}{2}\right\}$ **76.** $\{9\}$

77. $\{5\}$ (The value -2 does not check.)   **78.** $\left\{\dfrac{190}{321}\right\}$

79. $\{-1\}$ **80.** $\left\{\dfrac{4}{7}\right\}$ **81.** $\left\{\dfrac{\ln 21}{\ln 4}\right\}$ **82.** $\left\{\dfrac{\ln 18}{\ln 5}\right\}$

83. $\{-\ln 0.1\}$ **84.** $\left\{-\dfrac{\ln 0.06}{2}\right\}$ **85.** $\left\{\dfrac{\log 1512}{2}\right\}$

86. $\left\{\dfrac{\log 821}{3}\right\}$ **87.** $\left\{\dfrac{3\ln 2}{\ln 7 - \ln 2}\right\}$

88. $\left\{\dfrac{5\ln 14}{\ln 14 - \ln 6}\right\}$ **89. a.** 1.09 μg   **b.** 0.15 μg

c. 16.08 days   **90. a.** 150 bacteria   **b.** ≈ 185 bacteria **c.** ≈ 99 min   **91. a.** $V(0) = 15,000$; the initial value of the car is \$15,000.   **b.** $V(10) = 3347$; the value of the car after 10 years is \$3347.   **c.** 7.3 yr

Chapter 12 Test, pp. 924–926

1. A function is one-to-one if it passes the horizontal line test.

2. b   **3.** $f^{-1}(x) = 4x - 12$ **4.** $g^{-1}(x) = \sqrt{x} + 1$

5.

6. a. 4.6416   **b.** 32.2693   **c.** 687.2913

7.

8. a. $\log_{16} 8 = \dfrac{3}{4}$ **b.** $x^5 = 31$

SA-46   Student Answer Appendix

9.

10. $\dfrac{\log_a n}{\log_a b}$ **11. a.** 1.3222   **b.** 1.8502   **c.** −2.5850

12. a. $1 + \log_3 x$ **b.** −5   **13. a.** $\log_b(\sqrt{x}y^3)$

b. $\log\left(\dfrac{1}{a^3}\right)$ or $-\log a^3$ **14. a.** 1.6487   **b.** 0.0498

c. −1.0986   **d.** 1   **15. a.** $y = \ln x$ **b.** $y = e^x$

16. a. $p(4) \approx 59.8$; 59.8% of the material is retained after
4 months.   **b.** $p(12) \approx 40.7$; 40.7% of the material is retained
after 1 yr.   **c.** $p(0) = 92$; 92% of the material is retained at the end
of the course.   **17. a.** 9762 thousand (or 9,762,000) people
b. The year 2020 ($t \approx 20.4$)

18. a. $P(0) = 300$; there are 300 bacteria initially.
b. 35,588 bacteria   **c.** 1,120,537 bacteria   **d.** 1,495,831 bacteria
19. {25} (The value −4 does not check.)

20. {32}   **21.** $\{e^{2.4} - 7\}$ **22.** {−7}   **23.** $\left\{\dfrac{\ln 50}{\ln 4}\right\}$

24. $\left\{\dfrac{\ln 250}{2.4}\right\}$ **25.** $\left\{\dfrac{\ln 58}{\ln 2} + 3\right\}$ **26.** $\left\{\dfrac{7 \ln 4}{\ln 5 - \ln 4}\right\}$

27. a. $P(2500) = 560.2$; at 2500 m the atmospheric pressure is
560.2 mm Hg.   **b.** 760 mm Hg   **c.** 1498.8 m
28. a. $2909.98   **b.** 9.24 yr to double

**Chapters 1–12 Cumulative Review Exercises,
pp. 926–928**

1. $-\dfrac{5}{4}$ **2.** $-1 + \dfrac{p}{2} + \dfrac{3p^3}{4}$

3. Quotient: $t^3 + 2t^2 - 9t - 18$; remainder: 0   **4.** $|x - 3|$

5. $\dfrac{2\sqrt[3]{25}}{5}$ **6.** $2\sqrt{7}$ in.   **7.** $\dfrac{4d^{1/10}}{c}$

8. $(\sqrt{15} - \sqrt{6} + \sqrt{30} - 2\sqrt{3})\,\text{m}^2$ **9.** $-\dfrac{7}{29} - \dfrac{26}{29}i$

10. $\left\{6, \dfrac{3}{2}\right\}$ **11.** 4.8 L   **12.** 24 min   **13.** {(7, −1)}

14. $\left\{-\dfrac{23}{11}\right\}$ **15.** $x = \dfrac{c + d}{a - b}$ **16.** $t = \dfrac{\sqrt{2sg}}{g}$

17. $\left\{\dfrac{4 \pm \sqrt{34}}{3}\right\}$ **18.** (7, 0), (3, 0)

19. a. $-30t$ **b.** $-10t^2$ **c.** $2t^2 + 5t$ **20.** {0}

21. a. $x = 2$ **b.** $y = 6$ **c.** $y = \dfrac{1}{2}x + 5$

22. 40°, 80°, 60°   **23.** Infinitely many solutions;
$\{(x, y)\,|\,-2x + y = -4\}$; dependent equations

24. $\left[\dfrac{1}{2}, \infty\right)$ **25.** $f^{-1}(x) = \dfrac{1}{5}x + \dfrac{2}{15}$ **26.** 40 m³

27. $\dfrac{-x^2 + 5x - 25}{(2x + 1)(x - 2)}$ **28.** $1 + x$ **29. a.** Yes; $x \neq 4, x \neq -2$
b. {8}   **c.** $(-\infty, -2) \cup (4, 8]$

30. The numbers are $-\dfrac{3}{4}$, 4.   **31.** {−4} (The value −9

does not check.)   **32.** $(-\infty, \infty)$
33. a. $P(6) = 2,000,000$, $P(12) = 1,000,000$, $P(18) = 500,000$,
$P(24) = 250,000$, $P(30) = 125,000$ **b.** 48 hr
34. a. 2   **b.** −3   **c.** 6   **d.** 3   **35. a.** 217.0723
b. 23.1407   **c.** 0.1768   **d.** 3.7293   **e.** −0.4005   **f.** 2.6047

36. $\left\{\dfrac{2}{3}\right\}$ **37.** {ln 100}   **38.** {3} (The value −9

does not check.)   **39.** $\log\left(\dfrac{\sqrt{z}}{x^2 y^3}\right)$ **40.** $\dfrac{2}{3}\ln x - \dfrac{1}{3}\ln y$

Chapter 13

Section 13.1 Practice Exercises, pp. 936–940

1. a. $\sqrt{(x_2 - x_1)^2 + (y_2 - y_1)^2}$ **b.** circle; center   **c.** radius

d. $(x - h)^2 + (y - k)^2 = r^2$ **e.** $\left(\dfrac{x_1 + x_2}{2}, \dfrac{y_1 + y_2}{2}\right)$

3. $3\sqrt{5}$ **5.** $\sqrt{34}$ **7.** $\dfrac{\sqrt{73}}{8}$ **9.** 4   **11.** 8

13. $4\sqrt{2}$ **15.** $\sqrt{42}$ **17.** Subtract 5 and −7. This becomes
$5 - (-7) = 12.$ **19.** $y = 13, y = 1$
21. $x = 0, x = 8$ **23.** Yes   **25.** No

27. Center (4, −2); $r = 3$ **29.** Center (−1, −1); $r = 1$

31. Center (0, 2); $r = 2$ **33.** Center (3, 0); $r = 2\sqrt{2}$

35. Center (0, 0); $r = \sqrt{6}$ **37.** Center $\left(-\dfrac{4}{5}, 0\right)$; $r = \dfrac{8}{5}$

39. Center (1, 3); $r = 6$ **41.** Center: (0, 3); $r = 2$

43. Center (0, −3); $r = \dfrac{4}{3}$ **45.** Center: (−1, −2); $r = 3$

47. Center (0, 0); $r = 1$

49. $x^2 + y^2 = 4$ **51.** $x^2 + (y-2)^2 = 4$
53. $(x+2)^2 + (y-2)^2 = 9$ **55.** $x^2 + y^2 = 49$
57. $(x+3)^2 + (y+4)^2 = 36$ **59.** $(x-5)^2 + (y-3)^2 = 2.25$
61. $(1, 2)$ **63.** $(-1, 0)$ **65.** $(-1, 6)$
67. $(0, 3)$ **69.** $\left(-\frac{1}{2}, \frac{3}{2}\right)$ **71.** $(-0.4, -1)$
73. $(40, 7\frac{1}{2})$; they should meet 40 mi east, $7\frac{1}{2}$ mi north of the warehouse.   **75. a.** $(1, 3)$ **b.** $(x-1)^2 + (y-3)^2 = 5$
77. a. $(0, 3)$ **b.** $x^2 + (y-3)^2 = 4$
79. $(x-4)^2 + (y-4)^2 = 16$

81. $(x-1)^2 + (y-1)^2 = 29$

Section 13.1 Graphing Calculator Exercises, p. 940

83.
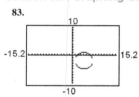

84.
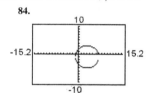

85.
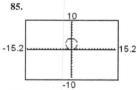

86.
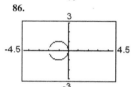

87.
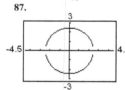

88.
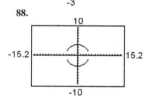

Section 13.2 Practice Exercises, pp. 947–950

1. a. conic; plane   **b.** parabola; directrix; focus   **c.** vertex; symmetry   **d.** $y = k$
3. 5
5. Center: $(0, -1)$; radius: 4

7. $\left(\frac{11}{2}, 1\right)$

9.

11.
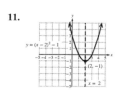

13.
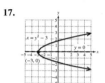

15.

17.
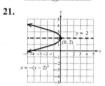

19.

21.

23.

25. $(2, -1)$ **27.** $(5, -1)$ **29.** $\left(2, \frac{7}{4}\right)$ **31.** $\left(\frac{3}{2}, -\frac{1}{4}\right)$
33. $(10, -1)$ **35.** The maximum height of the water is 22 ft.
37. A parabola whose equation is in the form $y = a(x-h)^2 + k$ has a vertical axis of symmetry. A parabola whose equation is in the form $x = a(y-k)^2 + h$ has a horizontal axis of symmetry.
39. Vertical axis of symmetry; opens upward
41. Vertical axis of symmetry; opens downward
43. Horizontal axis of symmetry; opens right
45. Horizontal axis of symmetry; opens left
47. Vertical axis of symmetry; opens downward
49. Horizontal axis of symmetry; opens right

Section 13.3 Practice Exercises, pp. 955–959

1. a. ellipse; foci   **b.** ellipse   **c.** hyperbola; foci   **d.** transverse
e. $\frac{x^2}{a^2} - \frac{y^2}{b^2} = 1$ **f.** $\frac{y^2}{b^2} - \frac{x^2}{a^2} = 1$
3. Center: $(8, -6)$; radius: 10
5. Vertex: $(-3, -1)$; $x = -3$
7. $\left(x - \frac{1}{2}\right)^2 + \left(y - \frac{5}{2}\right)^2 = \frac{1}{4}$

9.
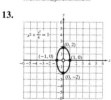

11.
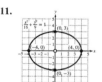

13.
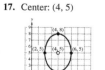

15.
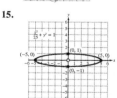

17. Center: $(4, 5)$ **19.** Center: $(-1, 2)$

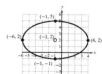

SA-48   Student Answer Appendix

21. Center: (2, −3)

23. Center: (0, 1)

17. {(−3, 0), (2, 5)}

19. {(0, 1), (−1, 0)}

25. Vertical   **27.** Horizontal   **29.** Horizontal
31. Vertical

33.

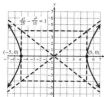

35.

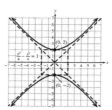

21. {(√2, 2), (−√2, 2)}

23. {(1, 1)}   **25.** {(0, 0)}   **27.** $\left\{\left(\dfrac{3}{2}, \dfrac{9}{4}\right)\right\}$
29. {(0, 0), (−2, −8)}   **31.** {(1, 4)}
33. {(1, 0), (−1, 0)}   **35.** {(2, 0), (−2, 0)}
37. {(3, 2), (−3, 2), (3, −2), (−3, −2)}
39. {(8, 6), (−8, −6)}   **41.** {(0, −2), (0, 2)}
43. {(2, 0), (0, 1)}   **45.** {(4, 5), (−4, −5)}

47. $\left\{\left(-\sqrt{2}, \dfrac{\sqrt{2}}{2}\right), \left(\sqrt{2}, -\dfrac{\sqrt{2}}{2}\right)\right\}$

49. The numbers are 3 and 4.
51. The numbers are 5 and √7, −5 and √7,
5 and −√7, or −5 and −√7.

37.

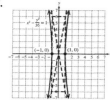

39.

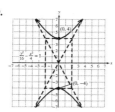

41. Hyperbola   **43.** Ellipse
45. Ellipse   **47.** Hyperbola
49. Ellipse   **51.** Hyperbola
53. The height 10 ft from the center is approximately 49 ft.
55.

57.

Section 13.3 Problem Recognition Exercises, pp. 959–960

1. Standard equation of a circle   **2.** Ellipse centered at the origin   **3.** Distance between two points
4. Midpoint between two points   **5.** Parabola with vertical axis of symmetry   **6.** Hyperbola with horizontal transverse axis
7. Hyperbola with vertical transverse axis
8. Parabola with horizontal axis of symmetry
9. Parabola   **10.** Hyperbola   **11.** Circle   **12.** Circle
13. Hyperbola   **14.** Ellipse   **15.** None of these
16. Circle   **17.** Parabola   **18.** Hyperbola   **19.** Parabola
20. Circle   **21.** None of these   **22.** Parabola
23. Ellipse   **24.** Circle   **25.** Parabola   **26.** Ellipse
27. Hyperbola   **28.** Circle   **29.** Ellipse   **30.** Parabola

Section 13.4 Practice Exercises, pp. 964–967

1. a. nonlinear   **b.** intersection

3. 7√2   **5.** $(x + 5)^2 + (y - 3)^2 = 64$ **7.** $\left(-\dfrac{1}{2}, -\dfrac{7}{2}\right)$

9. Zero, one, or two   **11.** Zero, one, or two
13. Zero, one, two, three, or four   **15.** Zero, one, two, three, or four

Section 13.4 Graphing Calculator Exercises, p. 967

53.

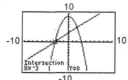

54.

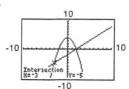
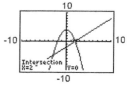

55.

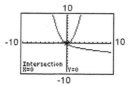

56.

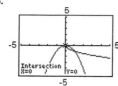
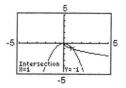

57. { }

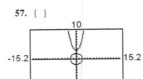

58. { }

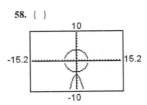

43.

45.

Section 13.5 Practice Exercises, pp. 971–975

1. k   **3.** e   **5.** i   **7.** j   **9.** a   **11.** d
13. True   **15.** False
17. a.

b. The set of points on and "outside" the circle $x^2 + y^2 = 9$
c. The set of points on the circle $x^2 + y^2 = 9$

19. a.

b. The parabola $y = x^2 + 1$ would be drawn as a dashed curve.

47. { }
49.

51.

53.

55.

21. $(x-3)^2 + (y+4)^2 \le 625$

23.

25.

27.

29.

31.

33.

35.

37.

39.

41.

Chapter 13 Review Exercises, pp. 982–985

1. $2\sqrt{10}$ **2.** $\sqrt{89}$ **3.** $x = 5$ or $x = -1$
4. $x = -3$ **5.** Center $(12, 3)$; $r = 4$
6. Center $(-7, 5)$; $r = 9$ **7.** Center $(-3, -8)$; $r = 2\sqrt{5}$
8. Center $(1, -6)$; $r = 4\sqrt{2}$ **9. a.** $x^2 + y^2 = 64$
b. $(x-8)^2 + (y-8)^2 = 64$ **10.** $(x+6)^2 + (y-5)^2 = 10$
11. $(x+2)^2 + (y+8)^2 = 8$

12. $\left(x - \dfrac{1}{2}\right)^2 + (y-2)^2 = 4$

13. $(x-3)^2 + \left(y - \dfrac{1}{3}\right)^2 = 9$ **14.** $x^2 + y^2 = \dfrac{49}{4}$

15. $x^2 + (y-2)^2 = 9$ **16.** $(-4, -2)$ **17.** $(-1, 8)$
18. Vertical axis of symmetry; parabola opens downward
19. Horizontal axis of symmetry; parabola opens right
20. Horizontal axis of symmetry; parabola opens left
21. Vertical axis of symmetry; parabola opens upward

22.

23.

24.

25.

26. $y = (x-3)^2 - 4$; vertex: $(3, -4)$;
axis of symmetry: $x = 3$
27. $x = (y+2)^2 - 2$; vertex: $(-2, -2)$;
axis of symmetry: $y = -2$

28. $x = -4\left(y - \dfrac{1}{2}\right)^2 + 1$; vertex: $\left(1, \dfrac{1}{2}\right)$;

axis of symmetry: $y = \dfrac{1}{2}$

29. $y = -2\left(x + \dfrac{1}{2}\right)^2 + \dfrac{1}{2}$; vertex: $\left(-\dfrac{1}{2}, \dfrac{1}{2}\right)$;

axis of symmetry: $x = -\dfrac{1}{2}$

SA-50 Student Answer Appendix

30.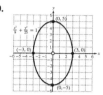

31.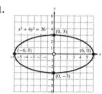

32. Center: (5, −3)

33. Center: (0, 2)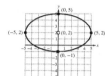

34. Horizontal **35.** Vertical
36. Vertical **37.** Horizontal

38.

39.

40. Hyperbola **41.** Ellipse
42. Ellipse **43.** Hyperbola

44. a. Line and parabola
b.

45. a. Line and parabola
b.

c. $\left\{\left(\dfrac{5}{2}, \dfrac{5}{4}\right), (-4, 11)\right\}$

c. $\{(-5, 15), (3, -1)\}$

46. a. Circle and line
b.

47. a. Circle and line
b.

c. $\left\{(0, 3), \left(\dfrac{12}{5}, -\dfrac{9}{5}\right)\right\}$

c. $\left\{(0, -4), \left(\dfrac{16}{5}, -\dfrac{12}{5}\right)\right\}$

48. $\left\{(0, -2), \left(\dfrac{16}{9}, \dfrac{14}{9}\right)\right\}$ **49.** $\left\{\left(-\dfrac{7}{5}, \dfrac{13}{5}\right), (-5, -1)\right\}$

50. $\{(8, 4), (2, -2)\}$ **51.** $\{(2, 4), (-2, 4), (\sqrt{2}, 2), (-\sqrt{2}, 2)\}$
52. $\{(3, 1), (3, -1), (-3, 1), (-3, -1)\}$
53. $\{(6, 5), (-6, 5), (6, -5), (-6, -5)\}$

54.

55.

56.

57.

58.

59.

60.

61.

Chapter 13 Test, pp. 985–986

1. $4\sqrt{2}$ **2.** Center: $\left(\dfrac{5}{6}, -\dfrac{1}{3}\right)$; $r = \dfrac{5}{7}$
3. Center: (0, 2); $r = 3$ **4. a.** $\sqrt{5}$ **b.** $x^2 + (y - 4)^2 = 5$
5. The center is the midpoint (3.8, 1.95).

6.

7.

8.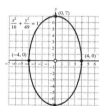

9.

10.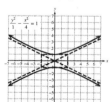

11. $\{(-3, 0), (0, 4)\}$; graph b **12.** $\{\ \}$; graph a
13. The addition method can be used if the equations have corresponding *like* terms. **14.** $\{(2, 0), (-2, 0)\}$

15.

16.

17.

18.

Chapters 1–13 Cumulative Review Exercises, pp. 987–988

1. $\{x \mid x \text{ is a real number}\}$

2. $\left(\dfrac{10}{3}, \infty\right)$

3. The integers are 10 and 15.   **4. a.** $(-5, 0), (0, 3)$ **b.** $m = \dfrac{3}{5}$

c.

5. slope: $\dfrac{3}{4}$; y-intercept: $\left(0, -\dfrac{3}{2}\right)$

6. There are 12 dimes and 5 quarters.

7. $\{(2, -3, 1)\}$ **8.** $\left\{\left(\dfrac{5}{2}, \dfrac{3}{2}\right)\right\}$ **9.** $\{(6, 3)\}$

10. $f(0) = -12; f(-1) = -16; f(2) = -10; f(4) = -16$

11. $(-4, -2)$ **12.** $z = 32$ **13.** $(g \circ f)(x) = x + 7;$
$x \ge -1$ **14. a.** -5 **b.** $(x + 1)(x^2 + 1); -5$

c. They are the same.   **15.** $(x + y)(x - y - 6)$

16. $x^3 - 2x^2 - 7x - 4$ **17.** $\left\{6, \dfrac{3}{2}\right\}$ **18.** $\dfrac{a-1}{a+2}$

19. $\dfrac{-x^2 - x - 4}{(x+3)(x-2)}$ **20.** $\{0, -1\}$ **21. a.** $\{\ \}$

b. $\{-11\}$ **22.** $-30 + 24i$ **23.** $\dfrac{12}{41} + \dfrac{15}{41}i$

24. $2\sqrt{7}$ m   **25. a.** 17.6 ft; 39.6 ft; 70.4 ft   **b.** 8 sec

26. $\left\{-\dfrac{1}{5}, \dfrac{1}{10} \pm \dfrac{\sqrt{3}}{10}i\right\}$ **27.** $\{2 \pm \sqrt{11}\}$

28. $(-5, -36)$

29. a. $(-3, 0), (1, 0)$ **b.** $(0, 3)$ **c** $(-1, 4)$

30. $(-1, 19)$ **31.** $\left(-\infty, \dfrac{1}{2}\right] \cup \left[\dfrac{9}{2}, \infty\right)$ **32.** $\log_8 32 = \dfrac{5}{3}$

33. $\left\{\dfrac{2}{3}\right\}$ **34.** $h^{-1}(x) = \sqrt[3]{x + 1}$

35. $x^2 + (y - 5)^2 = 16$

36.

37. $\left(-\dfrac{1}{2}, 0\right)$ **38.** $\{(0, -4)\}$

39.

40.

Chapter 14

Section 14.1 Practice Exercises, pp. 995–996

1. a. $a^2 + 2ab + b^2$; $a^3 + 3a^2b + 3ab^2 + b^3$; binomial
b. $n(n - 1)(n - 2) \cdots (2)(1)$; factorial   **c.** 6; 2; 1; 1
d. binomial   **e.** Pascal's   **3.** $a^3 + 3a^2b + 3ab^2 + b^3$
5. $1 + 4g + 6g^2 + 4g^3 + g^4$
7. $p^7 + 7p^6q^2 + 21p^5q^4 + 35p^4q^6 + 35p^3q^8 + 21p^2q^{10} + 7pq^{12} + q^{14}$
9. $s^5 - 5s^4t + 10s^3t^2 - 10s^2t^3 + 5st^4 - t^5$
11. $625 - 500u^3 + 150u^6 - 20u^9 + u^{12}$
13. $x^6 - 12x^4 + 48x^2 - 64$ **15.** 120   **17.** 1   **19.** False
21. True   **23.** $6! = 6 \cdot (5 \cdot 4 \cdot 3 \cdot 2 \cdot 1) = 6 \cdot 5!$ **25.** 1680
27. 6   **29.** 56   **31.** 1   **33.** $m^{11} + 11m^{10}n + 55m^9n^2$
35. $u^{24} - 12u^{22}v + 66u^{20}v^2$ **37.** 9 terms
39. $s^6 + 6s^5t + 15s^4t^2 + 20s^3t^3 + 15s^2t^4 + 6st^5 + t^6$
41. $b^3 - 9b^2 + 27b - 27$ **43.** $16x^4 + 32x^3y + 24x^2y^2 + 8xy^3 + y^4$
45. $c^{14} - 7c^{12}d + 21c^{10}d^2 - 35c^8d^3 + 35c^6d^4 - 21c^4d^5 + 7c^2d^6 - d^7$

47. $\dfrac{1}{32}a^5 - \dfrac{5}{16}a^4b + \dfrac{5}{4}a^3b^2 - \dfrac{5}{2}a^2b^3 + \dfrac{5}{2}ab^4 - b^5$

49. $x^4 + 16x^3y + 96x^2y^2 + 256xy^3 + 256y^4$
51. $-462m^6n^5$ **53.** $495u^{16}v^4$ **55.** g^9

Section 14.2 Practice Exercises, pp. 1002–1004

1. a. infinite; finite   **b.** terms; nth   **c.** alternating   **d.** series
e. summation   **f.** index; $(3)^2 + (4)^2 + (5)^2$
3. 28   **5.** $16x^4 + 32x^3z + 24x^2z^2 + 8xz^3 + z^4$

7. 4, 7, 10, 13, 16   **9.** $\sqrt{3}, 2, \sqrt{5}, \sqrt{6}$ **11.** $-\dfrac{2}{3}, \dfrac{3}{4}, -\dfrac{4}{5}, \dfrac{5}{6}$

13. $0, -3, 8$ **15.** 0, 2, 6, 12, 20, 30   **17.** $-3, 9, -27, 81$
19. When n is odd, the term is negative. When n is even, the term is
positive.   **21.** $a_n = 2n$ **23.** $a_n = 2n - 1$

25. $a_n = \dfrac{1}{n^2}$ **27.** $a_n = (-1)^{n+1}$ **29.** $a_n = (-1)^n 2^n$

31. $a_n = \dfrac{3}{5^n}$ **33.** \$60, \$58.80, \$57.62, \$56.47

35. 25,000; 50,000; 100,000; 200,000; 400,000; 800,000; 1,600,000
37. A sequence is an ordered list of terms. A series is the sum of
the terms of a sequence.

39. 90   **41.** $\dfrac{31}{16}$ **43.** 30   **45.** 10   **47.** $\dfrac{73}{12}$ **49.** 38

51. -1 **53.** 55   **55.** $\displaystyle\sum_{n=1}^{6} n$ **57.** $\displaystyle\sum_{i=1}^{5} 4$ **59.** $\displaystyle\sum_{j=1}^{5} 4j$

61. $\displaystyle\sum_{k=1}^{4} (-1)^{k+1} \dfrac{1}{3^k}$ **63.** $\displaystyle\sum_{i=1}^{6} \dfrac{i+4}{11i}$ **65.** $\displaystyle\sum_{n=1}^{5} x^n$

67. $-3, 2, 7, 12, 17$ **69.** 5, 21, 85, 341, 1365
71. 1, 1, 2, 3, 5, 8, 13, 21, 34, 55

Section 14.3 Practice Exercises, pp. 1009–1010

1. a. arithmetic   **b.** difference   **c.** $a_1 + (n - 1)d; d$
d. series   **e.** $\dfrac{n}{2}(a_1 + a_n)$

3. $-1, 1, -1, 1$ **5.** -55 **7.** 3, 11, 19, 27, 35

9. 80, 60, 40, 20, 0   **11.** $3, \dfrac{15}{4}, \dfrac{9}{2}, \dfrac{21}{4}, 6$ **13.** 2   **15.** -3

17. -2 **19.** 3, 8, 13, 18, 23   **21.** $2, \dfrac{5}{2}, 3, \dfrac{7}{2}, 4$

23. $2, -2, -6, -10, -14$ **25.** $a_n = -5 + 5n$

27. $a_n = -2n$ **29.** $a_n = \dfrac{3}{2} + \dfrac{1}{2}n$ **31.** $a_n = 25 - 4n$

33. $a_n = -14 + 6n$ **35.** $a_6 = 17$ **37.** $a_9 = 47$
39. $a_7 = -30$ **41.** $a_{11} = -48$ **43.** 19   **45.** 22
47. 23   **49.** 11   **51.** $a_1 = -2, a_2 = -5$ **53.** 670
55. 290   **57.** -15 **59.** 95   **61.** 924   **63.** 300
65. -210 **67.** 5050   **69.** 980 seats; \$14,700

SA-52   Student Answer Appendix

Section 14.4 Practice Exercises, pp. 1016–1019

1. a. geometric **b.** ratio **c.** $a_1 r^{n-1}$ **d.** $\dfrac{a_1(1-r^n)}{1-r}$

e. $\dfrac{a_1}{1-r}$; 1   **3.** $a_n = 4n - 8$ **5.** 25   **7.** 1, 10, 100, 1000

9. 64, 32, 16, 8   **11.** $8, -2, \dfrac{1}{2}, -\dfrac{1}{8}$ **13.** 2   **15.** $-\dfrac{1}{4}$

17. -2 **19.** $-3, 6, -12, 24, -48$ **21.** $6, 3, \dfrac{3}{2}, \dfrac{3}{4}, \dfrac{3}{8}$

23. $-1, -6, -36, -216, -1296$ **25.** $a_n = 3(4)^{n-1}$

27. $a_n = -5(-3)^{n-1}$ **29.** $a_n = \dfrac{1}{2}(4)^{n-1}$ **31.** $\dfrac{1}{64}$

33. $-\dfrac{243}{8}$ **35.** -48 **37.** -9 **39.** $\dfrac{1}{8}$ **41.** 4

43. A geometric sequence is an ordered list of numbers in which the ratio between each term and its predecessor is constant. A geometric series is the sum of the terms of such a sequence.
45. a. $3 + 12 + 48 + 192$ **b.** 255

47. $\dfrac{1562}{125}$ **49.** $-\dfrac{11}{8}$ **51.** $\dfrac{3124}{27}$ **53.** $\dfrac{665}{243}$

55. -172 **57. a.** \$1050.00, \$1102.50, \$1157.63, \$1215.51
b. $a_{10} = \$1628.89$; $a_{20} = \$2653.30$; $a_{40} = \$7039.99$

59. $r = \dfrac{1}{6}$; sum is $\dfrac{6}{5}$ **61.** $r = -\dfrac{1}{4}$; sum is $\dfrac{4}{5}$

63. $r = -\dfrac{3}{2}$; sum does not exist   **65.** The sum is \$800 million.

67. The total vertical distance traveled is 28 ft.

69. a. $\dfrac{7}{10}$ **b.** $\dfrac{1}{10}$ **c.** $\dfrac{7}{9}$ **71. a.** \$1,429,348

b. \$1,505,828 **c.** \$76,480

Section 14.4 Problem Recognition Exercises, p. 1019

1. Geometric, $r = -\dfrac{1}{2}$ **2.** Arithmetic, $d = \dfrac{1}{2}$

3. Geometric, $r = 2$ **4.** Neither   **5.** Arithmetic, $d = \dfrac{2}{3}$

6. Geometric, $r = -\dfrac{3}{2}$ **7.** Neither   **8.** Geometric, $r = -1$

9. Arithmetic, $d = -2$ **10.** Neither   **11.** Neither

12. Arithmetic, $d = 4$ **13.** Arithmetic, $d = \dfrac{1}{4}\pi$

14. Geometric, $r = -1$ **15.** Neither

16. Arithmetic, $d = \dfrac{1}{3}e$ **17.** Neither   **18.** Geometric, $r = 3$

Chapter 14 Review Exercises, pp. 1024–1025

1. 40,320   **2.** 120   **3.** 66   **4.** 84
5. $x^{10} + 20x^8 + 160x^6 + 640x^4 + 1280x^2 + 1024$
6. $c^4 - 12c^3d + 54c^2d^2 - 108cd^3 + 81d^4$
7. $a^{11} - 22a^{10}b + 220a^9b^2$ **8.** $1512x^{10}y^3$
9. $-15,000x^3y^{21}$ **10.** $160a^3b^3$ **11.** $1, -2, -5, -8, -11$

12. $-2, -16, -54$ **13.** $\dfrac{1}{3}, -\dfrac{1}{2}, \dfrac{3}{5}, -\dfrac{2}{3}$ **14.** $-\dfrac{2}{3}, \dfrac{4}{9}, -\dfrac{8}{27}, \dfrac{16}{81}$

15. $a_n = \dfrac{n}{n+1}$ **16.** $a_n = (-1)^n \cdot \dfrac{3}{2^n}$ **17.** k **18.** 5

19. 5   **20.** -22 **21.** $\displaystyle\sum_{i=1}^{7} \dfrac{i+3}{i}$ **22.** $a_n = n^2 + \left(\dfrac{n}{2}\right)h$

23. $-12, -10.5, -9, -7.5, -6$ **24.** $\dfrac{2}{3}, 1, \dfrac{4}{3}, \dfrac{5}{3}, 2$

25. $a_n = 10n - 9$ **26.** $a_n = -14n + 20$ **27.** $a_{17} = \dfrac{9}{2}$

28. $a_{25} = -155$ **29.** 24 terms   **30.** 19 terms
31. $d = 10$ **32.** $a_n = -5n + 19$ **33.** -620
34. 92.5   **35.** 294   **36.** 5989   **37.** $r = 3$

38. $r = 1.2$ **39.** $-1, \dfrac{1}{4}, -\dfrac{1}{16}, \dfrac{1}{64}$ **40.** 10, 20, 40, 80

41. $a_n = -4(2)^{n-1}$ **42.** $a_n = 6\left(-\dfrac{1}{3}\right)^{n-1}$ **43.** $a_6 = \dfrac{128}{243}$

44. $a_4 = 270$ **45.** $a_1 = 4$ **46.** $a_1 = 1$ **47.** 1275

48. $-\dfrac{182}{3}$ **49.** 18   **50.** $\dfrac{25}{2}$

51. a. \$10,700, \$11,449, \$12,250.43   **b.** The account is worth \$12,250.43 after 3 yr.   **c.** \$19,671.51

Chapter 14 Test, pp. 1025–1026

1. 1   **2.** 210   **3.** $a^4 + 4a^3b + 6a^2b^2 + 4ab^3 + b^4$
4. $81y^4 - 216y^3x^2 + 216y^2x^4 - 96yx^6 + 16x^8$

5. $-56a^3c^{15}$ **6.** $-1, -\dfrac{3}{4}, -\dfrac{3}{5}, -\dfrac{1}{2}$ **7.** 65

8. a. 8, 9.5, 11, 12.5, 14 **b.** $a_n = 1.5n + 6.5$ **9.** $\displaystyle\sum_{n=1}^{4} x^{3n}$

10. $d = \dfrac{1}{4}$ **11.** $r = \dfrac{1}{3}$ **12. a.** $-15, -18, -21, -24$

b. $a_n = -3n - 12$ **c.** $a_{40} = -132$ **13. a.** $4, -8, 16, -32$

b. $a_n = 4(-2)^{n-1}$ **c.** -2048 **14.** $a_n = \dfrac{3}{5} \cdot \left(\dfrac{1}{2}\right)^{n-1}$

15. $a_n = -2n + 22$ **16.** 31 terms   **17.** 7 terms

18. 10,900   **19.** $\dfrac{1023}{64}$ **20.** 8   **21.** $a_1 = \dfrac{1}{27}$

22. $a_{18} = -202$ **23. a.** \$2007.50 **b.** \$2087.80
c. \$6260.69 **d.** \$112,590.51

Chapters 1–14 Cumulative Review Exercises, pp. 1027–1028

1. $x^2 - x - 13$ **2.** $\dfrac{20a^6}{b^{10}}$ **3.** $\dfrac{1}{16}$ **4.** $\dfrac{\sqrt{10}}{2}$

5. $\dfrac{2c+5}{2(c+4)}$ **6.** $-\dfrac{xy}{x+y}$ **7.** 4   **8.** $3xy^4\sqrt[3]{2x^2z^2}$

9. $-\dfrac{a+1}{a}$ **10.** $\dfrac{2x+5}{(x-5)(x-2)(x+10)}$ **11.** $7x^2\sqrt{2x}$

12. $x - 9y$ **13.** $2x^3 + 3x^2 + 6x + 17 + \dfrac{27}{x-2}$

14. $(2a - 7)(3a + 2)$ **15.** $3c(5c - 2)(5c + 2)$
16. $(3x + 4y^2)(9x^2 - 12xy^2 + 16y^4)$
17. $(w + 9)(w - 2)(w + 2)$ **18.** $\{4\}$ **19.** $\{0\}$

20. $\left\{\dfrac{5}{4}\right\}$ **21.** $\left\{\dfrac{2}{5} \pm \dfrac{\sqrt{3}}{5}i\right\}$ **22.** $\{4, -4, 1, -1\}$

23. $\left\{\dfrac{7}{2}, -\dfrac{3}{4}\right\}$ **24.** $\{1\}$ **25.** $\{2\}$ (The value -5

does not check.)   **26.** $\ln\left(\dfrac{x\sqrt{z}}{y^5}\right)$ **27.** 3.4929

28. $[-2, 5)$ **29.** $[-5, 0] \cup [1, \infty)$ **30.** $\{5\}$
31. $(-\infty, -4) \cup [-1, \infty)$ **32.** $(-\infty, 1) \cup (3, \infty)$
33.   **34.**

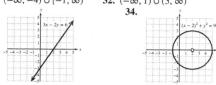

35.   **36.**

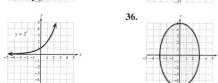

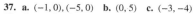

37. a. $(-1, 0), (-5, 0)$ **b.** $(0, 5)$ **c.** $(-3, -4)$
38. slope -4; y-intercept $(0, 6)$ **39.** $y = -5x + 18$
40. a. 2 **b.** undefined **c.** $x = 2$ **d.** $(-\infty, 4)$ **e.** $(-\infty, 3]$

41. $(-\infty, 5]$ **42.** $\{(3, -1)\}$ **43.** $\{(1, 2, 3)\}$
44. a. $2\sqrt{13}$ **b.** $(6, -2)$ **45.** $b_1 = \dfrac{2A - hb_2}{h}$

46. $t(9) = 4.2$; This means that it will take the rat 4.2 min if the rat has practiced 9 times. **47.** The car is moving 75 mph. **48.** The angles are 57° and 123°. **49.** She invested $8000 at 6.5% and $5000 at 5%. **50.** The plane travels 500 mph in still air. The wind speed is 50 mph.

Additional Topics Appendix

Section A.1 Practice Exercises, pp. A-4–A-6

1. Let $u = 3x - 2$. **3.** Factor the first three terms as $(x - 2)^2$.
5. $2(4t + 3)(2t - 1)$ **7.** $(2w - 3)(w - 5)$
9. $(5x + 20 - y)(5x + 20 + y)$ **11.** $(15a - 7)(15a - 11)$
13. $-1(t + 3)(3t - 1)$ **15.** $(a + b + c)(a^2 + 2ab + b^2 - ac - bc + c^2)$
17. $(3c - d - 2)(9c^2 + 3cd + 6c + d^2 + 4d + 4)$
19. $(2x + 14y + 7)^2$ **21.** $(x - 5 - y)(x - 5 + y)$
23. $(a - x - 9y)(a + x + 9y)$ **25.** $(5a + 2b - 10c)(5a + 2b + 10c)$
27. $(8w - 3t + 4p)(8w + 3t - 4p)$ **29.** $(x + 2y)(x - 2y - 1)$
31. $(w + 2)(w^2 - 2w + 4)(w^2 + 1)(w - 1)(w + 1)$
33. $(y - 4)(x + 2z - 2)$ **35.** $(x - y)(x + 2y + 1)$
37. $(n - 4)(n^2 + 4n + 16)(n + 1)(n^2 - n + 1)$
39. $(a + b - 3c + 3d)^2$ **41.** $2x(2x - 5)(x + 3)(x - 3)$
43. $(a + b)(a + b - 1)$ **45.** $(x - y)(x + y)^2$
47. $(a + 3)^3(a + 9)$ **49.** $18(3x + 5)^2(4x + 5)$
51. $\left(\dfrac{1}{10}x + \dfrac{1}{7}\right)^2$ **53.** $5x^2(5x^2 - 6)$
55. $(4p^2 + q^2)(2p - q)(2p + q)$ **57.** $\left(y + \dfrac{1}{4}\right)\left(y^2 - \dfrac{1}{4}y + \dfrac{1}{16}\right)$
59. $(a + b)(a - b)(6a + b)$ **61.** $\left(\dfrac{1}{3}t + \dfrac{1}{4}\right)^2$
63. $(3a + b)(2x - y)$ **65.** $(x^4 + 1)(x^2 + 1)(x + 1)(x - 1)$
67. $(5c - 3d)(5c + 3d + 1)$

Section A.2 Practice Exercises, pp. A-11–A-15

1. 88 **3.** 5 **5.** 6 **7.** −15.8 **9.** 5.8 hr
11. a. 397 Cal **b.** 386 Cal **c.** There is only an 11-Cal difference in the means. **13. a.** 86.5% **b.** 81% **c.** The low score of 59% decreased Zach's average by 5.5%. **15.** 17 **17.** 110.5
19. −52.5 **21.** 3.93 deaths per 1000 **23.** 0
25. 51.7 million passengers **27.** 4 **29.** −21 and −24
31. No mode **33.** 3.66 in. **35.** 5.2% and 5.8%
37. Mean: 85.5%; median: 94.5%; The median gives Jonathan a better overall score. **39.** Mean: $250; median: $256; mode: There is no mode. **41.** Mean: $942,500; median: $848,500; mode: $850,000 **43.** 2.38 **45.** 2.77 **47.** 3.3; Elmer's GPA improved from 2.5 to 3.3.

49.

Number of Residents in Each House	Number of Houses	Product
1	3	3
2	9	18
3	10	30
4	9	36
5	6	30
Total:	37	117

The mean number of residents is approximately 3.2.

Section A.3 Practice Exercises, pp. A-25–A-31

1. Perimeter **3.** 32 m **5.** 17.2 mi **7.** $11\frac{1}{2}$ in.
9. 31.4 ft **11.** a, f, g **13.** 33 cm² **15.** 16.81 m²
17. 84 in.² **19.** 10.12 km² **21.** 13.8474 ft² **23.** 66 in.²

25. 31.5 ft² **27.** c, d, h **29.** 307.72 cm³ **31.** 39 in.³
33. 113.04 cm³ **35.** 1695.6 cm³ **37.** 3052.08 in.³
39. 113.04 cm³ **41. a.** $0.25/ft² **b.** $104 **43.** Perimeter
45. 54 ft **47. a.** 57,600 ft² **b.** 19,200 pieces
49. a. 50.24 in.² **b.** 113.04 in.² **c.** One 12-in. pizza
51. 289.3824 cm³ **53.** True **55.** True **57.** True
59. Not possible **61.** For example: 100°, 80°
63. 45° **65. a.** $\angle 1$ and $\angle 3$, $\angle 2$ and $\angle 4$
b. $\angle 1$ and $\angle 2$, $\angle 2$ and $\angle 3$, $\angle 3$ and $\angle 4$, $\angle 1$ and $\angle 4$
c. $m(\angle 1) = 100°$, $m(\angle 2) = 80°$, $m(\angle 3) = 100°$
67. 57° **69.** 78° **71.** 147° **73.** 58°
75. 7 **77.** 1 **79.** 1 **81.** 5
83. $m(\angle a) = 45°$, $m(\angle b) = 135°$, $m(\angle c) = 45°$, $m(\angle d) = 135°$, $m(\angle e) = 45°$, $m(\angle f) = 135°$, $m(\angle g) = 45°$
85. Scalene **87.** Isosceles **89.** True
91. No, a 90° angle plus an angle greater than 90° would make the sum of the angles greater than 180°. **93.** 40°
95. 37° **97.** $m(\angle a) = 80°$, $m(\angle b) = 80°$, $m(\angle c) = 100°$, $m(\angle d) = 100°$, $m(\angle e) = 65°$, $m(\angle f) = 115°$, $m(\angle g) = 115°$, $m(\angle h) = 35°$, $m(\angle i) = 145°$, $m(\angle j) = 145°$
99. $m(\angle a) = 70°$, $m(\angle b) = 65°$, $m(\angle c) = 65°$, $m(\angle d) = 110°$, $m(\angle e) = 70°$, $m(\angle f) = 110°$, $m(\angle g) = 115°$, $m(\angle h) = 115°$, $m(\angle i) = 65°$, $m(\angle j) = 70°$, $m(\angle k) = 65°$
101. 82 ft **103.** 36 in.² **105.** 15.2464 cm²

Section A.4 Practice Exercises, pp. A-38–A-40

1. a. matrix; rows; columns **b.** column; one; square
c. coefficient; augmented **d.** row echelon
3. $\left\{\left(12, \dfrac{1}{2}\right)\right\}$ **5.** $\{(1, 3, -3)\}$ **7. a.** 3×1 **b.** column matrix
9. a. 2×2 **b.** square matrix **11. a.** 1×4 **b.** row matrix
13. a. 2×3 **b.** none of these
15. $\begin{bmatrix} 1 & -2 & | & -1 \\ 2 & 1 & | & -7 \end{bmatrix}$ **17.** $\begin{bmatrix} 1 & -2 & 1 & | & 5 \\ 2 & 6 & 3 & | & -2 \\ 3 & -1 & -2 & | & 1 \end{bmatrix}$
19. $4x + 3y = 6$; $12x + 5y = -6$ **21.** $x = 4, y = -1, z = 7$
23. a. 7 **b.** −2 **25.** $\begin{bmatrix} 1 & \frac{1}{2} & | & \frac{11}{2} \\ 2 & -1 & | & 1 \end{bmatrix}$
27. $\begin{bmatrix} 1 & -4 & | & 3 \\ 5 & 2 & | & 1 \end{bmatrix}$ **29.** $\begin{bmatrix} 1 & 5 & | & 2 \\ 0 & 11 & | & 5 \end{bmatrix}$
31. a. $\begin{bmatrix} 1 & 3 & 0 & | & -1 \\ 0 & -11 & -5 & | & 10 \\ -2 & 0 & -3 & | & 10 \end{bmatrix}$ **b.** $\begin{bmatrix} 1 & 3 & 0 & | & -1 \\ 0 & -11 & -5 & | & 10 \\ 0 & 6 & -3 & | & 8 \end{bmatrix}$
33. True **35.** True **37.** Interchange rows 1 and 2.
39. Multiply row 1 by −3 and add to row 2. Replace row 2 with the result. **41.** $\{(-3, -1)\}$ **43.** $\{(-21, 9)\}$ **45.** Infinitely many solutions; $\{(x, y) \mid x + 3y = 3\}$; dependent equations
47. $\{(3, -1)\}$ **49.** $\{(-10, 3)\}$ **51.** No solution; { }; inconsistent system **53.** $\{(1, 2, 3)\}$ **55.** $\{(1, -2, 0)\}$

Section A.4 Graphing Calculator Exercises, p. A-40

57. **58.** **59.**

60. **61.** **62.**

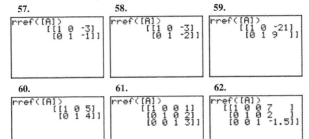

SA-54   Student Answer Appendix

Section A.5 Practice Exercises, pp. A-49–A-52

1. a. determinant; $ad - bc$ **b.** minor   **c.** a_2; $\begin{vmatrix} b_1 & c_1 \\ b_2 & c_2 \end{vmatrix}$

3. 16   **5.** 1   **7.** 4   **9.** 6   **11.** 26   **13.** 6

15. 46   **17. a.** 30   **b.** 30   **19.** Choosing the row or column with the most zero elements simplifies the arithmetic when evaluating a determinant.

21. 12   **23.** −15   **25.** 0   **27.** $8a - 2b$

29. $4x - 3y + 6z$ **31.** 0

33. $D = 16$; $D_x = -63$; $D_y = 66$ **35.** $\{(2, -1)\}$ **37.** $\{(4, -1)\}$

39. $\left\{ \left(\dfrac{23}{13}, \dfrac{9}{13} \right) \right\}$ **41.** $x = 1$ **43.** $z = \dfrac{1}{2}$ **45.** $y = \dfrac{16}{41}$

47. Cramer's rule does not apply when the determinant $\mathbf{D} = 0$.

49. No solution; $\{\ \}$; inconsistent system   **51.** $\{(0, 0)\}$

53. Infinitely many solutions; $\{(x, y) \mid x + 5y = 3\}$; dependent equations   **55.** $\{(3, 2, 1)\}$

57. No solution; $\{\ \}$; inconsistent system   **59.** $x = -19$

61. $w = 1$ **63.** 36   **65. a.** 2   **b.** −2   **c.** $x = -1$

67. The measures are 37.5° and 52.5°.

69. 900 tickets in section A, 1500 tickets in section B, and 600 tickets in section C were sold.

71. There were 560 women and 440 men in the survey.

Chapter 15

Section 15.1 Practice Exercises, pp. 8–14

1. The graph of g is the graph of $y = x^2$ shifted to the left 2 units and shifted downward 8 units.

3. c   **5.** e   **7.** b

9. Domain: $(-\infty, \infty)$; range: $[-4, \infty)$

11. Domain: $[3, \infty)$; range: $[0, \infty)$

13. Domain: $(-\infty, \infty)$; range: $(-\infty, \infty)$

15. Domain: $(-\infty, \infty)$; range: $(-\infty, \infty)$

17. Domain: $(-\infty, \infty)$; range: $[0, \infty)$

19. Domain: $[-1, \infty)$; range: $[-4, \infty)$

21. Domain: $(-\infty, \infty)$; range: $[2, \infty)$

23. Domain: $[0, \infty)$; range: $(-\infty, 0]$

25. Domain: $(-\infty, \infty)$; range: $(-\infty, -3]$

27. Domain: $(-\infty, \infty)$; range: $(-\infty, -2]$

29. Domain: $(-\infty, \infty)$; range: $[1, \infty)$

31. a   **33. a.** 7   **b.** –3   **c.** –2   **d.** 4

35. a. 2   **b.** 7   **c.** 4   **d.** 5   **e.** 2

37. a.

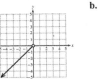

b.

c.

39. Domain: $(-\infty, \infty)$; range: $(-1, \infty)$

41. Domain: $(-\infty, \infty)$; range: $(-\infty, 3)$

43. Domain: $(-\infty, \infty)$; range: $[-4, \infty)$

45. Domain: $(-\infty, \infty)$; range: $[0, \infty)$;

47. a. $s(30) = 16$; This means that 30 min into the ride, the bicyclist was riding 16 mph.

b. $s(40) = 10$; This means that 40 min into the ride, the bicyclist was riding 10 mph.

c. $s(65) = 20$; This means that 65 min into the ride, the bicyclist was riding 20 mph.

d. The ride ended after 67 min. Therefore, since $s(67) = 24$, the cyclist was riding 24 mph at the end of the ride.

e.

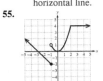

49. $f(x) = \begin{cases} -2 & \text{for } x < -1 \\ 3 & \text{for } x \geq -1 \end{cases}$

51. $f(x) = \begin{cases} x^2 & \text{for } x \leq 1 \\ 2 & \text{for } x > 1 \end{cases}$

53. b. Constant speed is a constant function whose graph is a horizontal line.

55.

SA-2   Student Answer Appendix

Section 15.2 Practice Exercises, pp. 20–23

1. 120   **3.** 40,320   **5.** 1   **7.** $4 \cdot 3 \cdot 8 \cdot 6 = 576$

9. $6! = 720$ **11.** $16 \cdot 15 \cdot 14 \cdot 13 = 43,680$

13. 720; There are 720 ways in which 3 items can be selected from 10 in a specific order.   **15.** 95,040   **17.** 7   **19.** 40,320

21. 5040   **23.** $_8P_2 = 56$ **25.** $_6P_6 = 720$

27. 120; There are 120 ways in which 3 items can be selected from 10 items in *no* specific order.   **29.** 220   **31.** 7   **33.** 1

35. 7   **37.** $_{15}C_{12} = 455$ **39.** $_5C_2 = 10$

41. a. WX, XW, WY, YW, WZ, ZW, XY, YX, XZ, ZX, YZ, ZY
b. WX, WY, WZ, XY, XZ, YZ   **43.** $_{10}P_3 = 720$ **45.** $_{11}C_6 = 462$

47. $_{10}C_5 = 252$ **49.** $_8P_2 = 56$ **51.** $2 \cdot 25 \cdot 24 \cdot 23 = 27,600$

53. $_{10}C_4 = 210$ **55.** $3 \cdot 3 \cdot 2 \cdot 2 \cdot 1 \cdot 1 = 36$ **57.** $_9P_9 = 362,880$

59. $_{40}C_{12} = 5,586,853,480$ **61.** $_{10}C_3 \cdot _8C_1 = 960$ **63.** $2^3 = 8$

65. $2^{10} = 1024$ **67. a.** $9! = 362,880$ **b.** $6 \cdot 5 \cdot 7! = 151,200$
c. $6! \cdot 3! = 4320$ **69. a.** $7^3 = 343$ **b.** $7 \cdot 6 \cdot 5 = 210$
c. $7 \cdot 7 \cdot 4 = 196$ **71.** $_{26}C_5 = 65,780$ **73.** $_{13}C_3 \cdot _{13}C_2 = 22,308$

Section 15.3 Practice Exercises, pp. 29–32

1. $_{10}C_4 = 210$ **3.** $5! = 120$ **5.** a, c, d   **7.** c, e, f   **9.** $\frac{1}{2}$

11. $\frac{2}{3}$ **13.** $\frac{3}{16}$ **15. a.** $\frac{_3C_2}{_8C_2} = \frac{3}{28}$ **b.** $\frac{_5C_2}{_8C_2} = \frac{5}{14}$

17. a. $\frac{1}{575,757}$ **b.** $\frac{575,756}{575,757}$ **c.** The events of winning the grand prize and losing are not equally likely events.

19. a. $\frac{8}{59}$ **b.** $\frac{15}{59}$ **21. a.** $\frac{1}{8}$ **b.** $\frac{3}{4}$ **c.** $\frac{5}{8}$ **d.** $\frac{11}{40}$

23. a. 0.08 or 8%   **b.** 0.83 or 83%   **25.** $\frac{27}{130}$ **27.** $\frac{103}{130}$

29. $\frac{56}{65}$ **31.** $\frac{2}{3}$ **33.** $\frac{3}{5}$ **35.** $\frac{11}{15}$ **37.** $\frac{1}{4}$ **39.** $\frac{1}{2}$

41. $\frac{4}{13}$ **43.** $\frac{1}{4}$ **45.** $\frac{1}{2}$ **47.** $\frac{4}{13}$

49. a. $\frac{120}{600} = \frac{1}{5}$ **b.** $\frac{160}{600} = \frac{4}{15}$ **c.** $\frac{580}{600} = \frac{29}{30}$

d. $\frac{140}{480} = \frac{7}{24}$ **e.** $\frac{20}{120} = \frac{1}{6}$ **f.** $\frac{7}{24} \approx 0.292; \frac{1}{6} \approx 0.167$; male firefighters are more likely to be promoted.

Chapter 15 Review Exercises, pp. 35–36

1.   **2.**

3.   **4.**

5. a. 2   **b.** 4   **c.** 1   **d.** 2
6. a. $-\frac{1}{2}$ **b.** -1 **c.** 0   **d.** 8
7. a. -5 **b.** -1 **c.** $\sqrt{3}$ **d.** 3
8. a. 25   **b.** 9   **c.** -3 **d.** -7

9.   **10.**

11.   **12.**

13. 20   **14.** 6   **15.** 10   **16.** 6   **17.** 6   **18.** 1

19. $_{30}C_5 = 142,506$ **20.** $_4P_4 = 24$

21. $_{10}P_4$ or $10 \cdot 9 \cdot 8 \cdot 7 = 5040$ **22.** $3 \cdot 4 \cdot 3 = 36$

23. a, b, c, d, f   **24.** a, c, d, e   **25.** $\frac{_6C_6}{_{46}C_6} = \frac{1}{9,366,819}$

26. $\frac{_{26}C_3}{_{52}C_3} = \frac{2600}{22,100} = \frac{2}{17}$ **27.** $\frac{2}{25}$ **28.** $\frac{2}{3}$

29. a. $\frac{12}{245}$ **b.** $\frac{37}{245}$ **c.** $\frac{16}{35}$ **30.** $\frac{1}{52}$

31. $\frac{1}{13}$ **32.** $\frac{3}{13}$ **33.** $\frac{4}{13}$

Chapter 15 Test, pp. 36–38

1. a. Domain: $(-\infty, \infty)$; range: $[0, \infty)$ **b.** Domain: $(-\infty, \infty)$; range: $[0, \infty)$

2. a. Domain: $(-\infty, \infty)$; range: $[0, \infty)$ **b.** Domain: $(-\infty, \infty)$; range: $(-\infty, 2]$

3. a. Domain: $[0, \infty)$; range: $[0, \infty)$ **b.** Domain: $[-2, \infty)$; range: $[-3, \infty)$

4. a. Domain: $(-\infty, \infty)$; range: $(-\infty, \infty)$ **b.** Domain: $(-\infty, \infty)$; range: $(-\infty, \infty)$

5. a. 2   **b.** 4   **c.** -1 **d.** -9 **6. a.** 3   **b.** 0   **c.** 0   **d.** $-\frac{1}{3}$

7. Domain: $(-\infty, \infty)$;
range: $[3, \infty)$

8. Domain: $(-\infty, \infty)$;
range: $[0, \infty)$

9. Domain: $(-\infty, \infty)$;
range: $(-\infty, 2]$

10. Domain: $(-\infty, \infty)$;
range: $[-2, \infty)$

11. 12   **12.** 6   **13.** 2520   **14.** 40,320   **15.** 1

16. $7! = 5040$ **17.** $_{18}P_3$ or $18 \cdot 17 \cdot 16 = 4896$

18. $_6P_4 = 360$ **19.** $_{20}C_9 = 167,960$ **20.** $_{12}C_5 = 792$

21. $_4P_3 = 24$ **22.** $\dfrac{2}{6} = \dfrac{1}{3}$ **23.** $\dfrac{3}{5}$ **24. a.** $\dfrac{12}{42} = \dfrac{2}{7}$ **b.** $\dfrac{34}{42} = \dfrac{17}{21}$

25. a. $\dfrac{102}{200} = \dfrac{51}{100}$ **b.** $\dfrac{61}{200}$ **c.** $\dfrac{139}{200}$ **d.** $\dfrac{145}{200} = \dfrac{29}{40}$

Section B.1 Practice Exercises, pp. B-7–B-9

1. $\left\{-6, -\frac{7}{8}, -0.\overline{3}, 0, \frac{4}{9}, 7, 10.4\right\}$ **2.** $\{-\sqrt{5}, \pi\}$ **3.** $\{-6, 0, 7\}$

4. $\{0, 7\}$ **5.** $\{1, 8\}$ **6.** $\{-2, 0, 1, 8\}$ **7.** $\{-\pi, \sqrt{3}\}$

8. $\left\{-2, -\frac{1}{2}, 0, 1, \frac{5}{4}, 8\right\}$ **9.** 9   **10.** 13   **11.** $-\frac{2}{3}$ **12.** $-\frac{1}{4}$

13. 4   **14.** 12.6   **15.** 8.5   **16.** 3   **17.** -22 **18.** -8
19. -13 **20.** -7 **21.** 5 is greater than -2
22. 8 is less than or equal to 9   **23.** -3 is greater than or equal to -4
24. $\frac{1}{2}$ is greater than $-\frac{1}{2}$ **25.** 10 is between 6 and 12
26. 0 is between -1 and 1   **27.** 2 is not equal to -5
28. $\frac{2}{3}$ is not equal to $-\frac{2}{3}$ **29.** $6 \cdot 3$ **30.** $7 - 4$ **31.** $20 \div 5$
32. $2 + 12$ **33.** $|-5|$ **34.** $|-13|$ **35.** $2 + |-8|$
36. $10 - |-1|$ **37.** $4 \cdot \frac{1}{3}$ **38.** $8 \div \sqrt{16}$ **39.** -2 **40.** 14
41. 19   **42.** -3 **43.** 16   **44.** 26   **45.** -33 **46.** -35
47. -4.3 **48.** -4.5 **49.** -16 **50.** 21   **51.** -19
52. -41 **53.** 5.6   **54.** 1.23   **55.** $-\frac{9}{8}$ **56.** $-\frac{8}{3}$
57. $-\frac{20}{9}$ **58.** $\frac{1}{10}$ **59.** -27 **60.** -16 **61.** 35   **62.** 33
63. 0   **64.** 0   **65.** -8.61 **66.** -36.38 **67.** $\frac{5}{6}$ **68.** $\frac{2}{7}$
69. 7   **70.** 17   **71.** -6 **72.** -7 **73.** 0   **74.** 0
75. Undefined   **76.** Undefined   **77.** $\frac{1}{2}$ **78.** $-\frac{2}{7}$ **79.** 9
80. 5   **81.** 8   **82.** 3   **83.** 2   **84.** 12   **85.** -16
86. -19 **87.** 5   **88.** -3 **89.** 15   **90.** 26   **91.** $-\frac{8}{3}$
92. $-\frac{1}{2}$ **93.** -16 **94.** 8   **95.** -11 **96.** 0
97. 460 in.^{2} **98.** 72.5 m^2 **99.**   Associative property of
multiplication   **100.** Associative property of addition
101. Distributive property of multiplication over addition
102. Commutative property of multiplication
103. Commutative property of addition
104. Distributive property of multiplication over addition
105. 1; for example $1(3) = 3$ **106.** 0; for example $0 + 8 = 8$
107. a. reciprocal   **b.** $\frac{1}{4}$ **108. a.** opposite   **b.** -6
109. $5a + 45$ **110.** $3x + 36$ **111.** $-7y + 7z$ **112.** $-2a + 2b$
113. $2b + 3c - 5$ **114.** $2h - 4k - 1$ **115.** $-2x + 3y - 8$
116. $3p + q - 9$ **117.** $7a + 14$ **118.** $3b - 12$ **119.** $5y - 25$
120. $6k + 20$ **121.** $-w + 12u$ **122.** $-3m + n$
123. $14g - 48h$ **124.** $-29p + 8q + 32$

Section B.2 Practice Exercises, pp. B-13–B-15

1. $\{-21\}$ **2.** $\{-24\}$ **3.** $\{60\}$ **4.** $\{39\}$ **5.** $\{-20\}$
6. $\{-18\}$ **7.** $\{3\}$ **8.** $\{-1\}$ **9.** $\left\{-\frac{3}{2}\right\}$ **10.** $\left\{-\frac{12}{5}\right\}$
11. $\{23\}$ **12.** $\{-13\}$ **13.** $\left\{-\frac{7}{2}\right\}$ **14.** $\{-3\}$ **15.** $\left\{-\frac{10}{7}\right\}$
16. $\left\{\frac{3}{2}\right\}$ **17.** $\left\{-\frac{19}{3}\right\}$ **18.** $\left\{\frac{6}{11}\right\}$ **19.** $\{5.5\}$ **20.** $\{2\}$
21. $\{2.3\}$ **22.** $\{-42.5\}$ **23.** $\{0\}$ **24.** $\{19\}$ **25.** $\{2\}$
26. $\{-2\}$ **27.** $\{9\}$ **28.** $\{1\}$ **29.** $\{-33\}$ **30.** $\{6\}$
31. $\frac{1}{2}$ **32.** -2 **33.** $-20, -19, -18$ **34.** $35, 37, 39$
35. 4.5%   **36.** 5%   **37.** $2100 in the 4.2% account, $1400 in the
3.8% account   **38.** $700   **39.** Car: 64 mph; truck: 60 mph
40. 5 mph   **41.** $(-\infty, -2)$

42. $(-1, \infty)$

43. $[-6, \infty)$

44. $\left(-\infty, \frac{40}{3}\right)$

45. $(-2, \infty)$

46. $(-4, \infty)$

47. $\left(\frac{3}{4}, \infty\right)$

48. $[4, \infty)$

49. $\left(-\frac{7}{4}, 1\right]$

50. $[-3, 2]$

51. $(-1, 7)$

52. $\left[0, \frac{10}{3}\right]$

53. $\left(-\infty, \frac{35}{3}\right)$

54. $\left[-\frac{3}{7}, \infty\right)$

55. $(-\infty, -0.2]$

56. $(20, \infty)$

Section B.3 Practice Exercises, pp. B-21–B-24

1–8.

9. IV   **10.** III   **11.** III   **12.** I   **13.** I   **14.** IV
15. II   **16.** II
17.

x	y
3	1
5	-1
0	4

18.

x	y
2	0
7/3	1
1	-3

19.

x	y
0	0
$\frac{2}{5}$	2
-1	-5

20.

x	y
1	1
$\frac{1}{2}$	2
-1	5

21.

x	y
3	3
-3	-1
0	1

22.

x	y
3	-2
0	2
-1	10/3

SA-2 Student Answer Appendix

23. x-intercept $(6, 0)$; y-intercept $(0, -9)$ **24.** x-intercept $(16, 0)$; y-intercept $(0, -4)$ **25.** x-intercept $(-3, 0)$; y-intercept $(0, -15)$
26. x-intercept $(-1, 0)$; y-intercept $(0, -6)$ **27.** x-intercept $(4, 0)$; y-intercept $(0, 2)$ **28.** x-intercept $(-4, 0)$; y-intercept $(0, 12)$
29. x-intercept $(0, 0)$; y-intercept $(0, 0)$ **30.** x-intercept $(0, 0)$; y-intercept $(0, 0)$ **31.** x-intercept $\left(-\frac{9}{2}, 0\right)$; y-intercept $(0, -3)$
32. x-intercept $\left(-\frac{5}{3}, 0\right)$; y-intercept $(0, 1)$ **33.** x-intercept $\left(\frac{5}{6}, 0\right)$; y-intercept $(0, -5)$ **34.** x-intercept $\left(-\frac{3}{2}, 0\right)$; y-intercept $(0, -3)$
35. $x = 3$; vertical   **36.** $y = 2$; horizontal   **37.** $y = -\frac{1}{3}$; horizontal
38. $x = \frac{4}{7}$; vertical   **39.** $x = 0$; vertical   **40.** $y = 0$; horizontal
41. 2   **42.** 1   **43.** $\frac{8}{3}$ **44.** $\frac{1}{2}$ **45.** $-\frac{13}{3}$ **46.** $-\frac{4}{9}$
47. $y = \frac{4}{5}x - \frac{6}{5}$; slope is $\frac{4}{5}$; y-intercept $\left(0, -\frac{6}{5}\right)$
48. $y = \frac{2}{5}x - \frac{11}{5}$; slope is $\frac{2}{5}$; y-intercept $\left(0, -\frac{11}{5}\right)$
49. $y = 3x + \frac{3}{2}$; slope is 3; y-intercept $\left(0, \frac{3}{2}\right)$
50. $y = \frac{1}{3}x + \frac{4}{3}$; slope is $\frac{1}{3}$; y-intercept $\left(0, \frac{4}{3}\right)$ **51.** $x = 1$; undefined slope; no y-intercept   **52.** $y = \frac{3}{2}$; slope is 0; y-intercept $\left(0, \frac{3}{2}\right)$
53. $y = -\frac{1}{4}x$; slope is $-\frac{1}{4}$; y-intercept $(0, 0)$ **54.** $y = -4x$; slope is -4; y-intercept $(0, 0)$ **55.** $y = 4$; slope is 0; y-intercept is $(0, 4)$
56. $x = 8$; undefined slope; no y-intercept
57.   **58.**
59.   **60.**
61.   **62.**
63.   **64.**
65.   **66.**
67.   **68.**

69.   **70.**
71.   **72.**
73.   **74.**

75. Parallel   **76.** Neither   **77.** Neither   **78.** Neither
79. Perpendicular   **80.** Parallel   **81.** Parallel
82. Perpendicular   **83.** $y = -3x - 17$; $3x + y = -17$
84. $y = \frac{1}{2}x - \frac{5}{2}$; $x - 2y = 5$ **85.** $y = 4x + 8$; $4x - y = -8$
86. $y = -2x + 5$; $2x + y = 5$ **87.** $y = 2x - 6$; $2x - y = 6$
88. $y = 4x + 26$; $4x - y = -26$ **89.** $y = -2x$; $2x + y = 0$
90. $y = 3x - 9$; $3x - y = 9$ **91.** $x = 4$ **92.** $x = -7$

Section B.4 Practice Exercises, pp. B-29–B-30

1. $\{(1, -2)\}$ **2.** $\{(0, 3)\}$

3. $\{(4, 2)\}$ **4.** $\{(-1, -2)\}$

5. $\{(1, -1)\}$ **6.** $\{(25, 6)\}$ **7.** $\{(1, 0)\}$ **8.** $\{(2, 3)\}$
9. $\{(1, -7)\}$ **10.** $\{(4, 5)\}$ **11.** $\{(2, -1)\}$ **12.** $\{(3, -1)\}$
13. No solution; $\{\ \}$; inconsistent system   **14.** No solution; $\{\ \}$; inconsistent system   **15.** $\{(5, -7)\}$ **16.** $\{(2, -1)\}$
17. Infinitely many solutions; $\{(x, y) \mid y = 2x - 14\}$; dependent equations
18. Infinitely many solutions; $\{(x, y) \mid y = 0.4x - 0.3\}$; dependent equations
19. $\{(2200, 1000)\}$ **20.** $\{(3300, 1200)\}$ **21.** $\{(2, 0)\}$
22. $\left\{\left(-5, \frac{3}{4}\right)\right\}$ **23.** $\left\{\left(\frac{1}{2}, -\frac{5}{4}\right)\right\}$ **24.** $\{(-1, -1)\}$
25. He invested $8000 at 6% interest and $2000 at 4.5% interest.
26. Greg invested $5000 at 5.5% interest and $3500 at 4% interest.
27. The angles are 52° and 38°.   **28.** The angles are 165° and 15°.
29. Denisha is 26 and her sister is 22.   **30.** The angles are 70° and 20°.

Section B.5 Practice Exercises, pp. B-36–B-37

1. 6^7; multiplication of like bases   **2.** x^{12}; power rule
3. y^3, division of like bases   **4.** $10^5 p^5$; power of a product
5. $\frac{w^4}{256}$; power of a quotient   **6.** x^{14}; multiplication of like bases
7. q^{30}; power rule   **8.** 1; division of like bases   **9.** 1
10. $\frac{1}{5}$ **11.** 2   **12.** 1   **13.** $\frac{1}{25}$ **14.** $\frac{9}{4}$ **15.** $\frac{7}{6}$ **16.** $\frac{3}{8}$
17. $\frac{1}{r^2}$ **18.** $\frac{1}{t^3}$ **19.** b^2 **20.** c **21.** $27x^6$ **22.** $49y^8$

23. $3w^2z^2$ **24.** $\dfrac{-2m^4}{n^5}$ **25.** $\dfrac{b^2c^6}{a^4d^8}$ **26.** $\dfrac{p^9r^6}{q^3s^3}$ **27.** $\dfrac{1}{wz^3}$

28. $\dfrac{4q^5}{p^5}$ **29.** 3.05×10^6 **30.** 8.25×10^7 **31.** 2.51×10^{-5}

32. 3.8×10^{-3} **33.** 8.96×10^7 **34.** 1.58×10^4

35. 3.9×10^{-4} **36.** 6.9×10^{-16} **37.** 3.6×10^4

38. 9.6×10^4 **39.** 2.1×10^{16} **40.** 2.4×10^{-15}

41. 2.19×10^{-2} **42.** 1.05×10^{12} **43.** 8×10^{-12}

44. 1.6×10^{12} **45.** $13p^3 - 4p^2 + 2p + 11$ **46.** $5m^2 - 5m + 17$

47. $-n^2 - n + 8$ **48.** $-3a^3 + \dfrac{3}{2}a^2 - 5a - 3$

49. $-10u^2v + 16u^2 + 2uv^2$ **50.** $14a^2b + ab + 16ab^2$

51. $4p^4 - 20p^3 + 8p^2 + 32p$ **52.** $-15m^3n + 30m^2n^2 + 5mn^3$

53. $-6x^2 - 17xy - 5y^2$ **54.** $12u^2 - 25uv + 7v^2$

55. $16b^2 - 16b - 12$ **56.** $-25a^2 + 25a - 6$

57. $x^3 - 6x^2y + 14xy^2 - 15y^3$ **58.** $3p^2 - 6p^2q - 2pq + 10pq^2 - 5q^2$

59. $9h^2 - 64$ **60.** $k^2 - 25$ **61.** $16x^2 - 40x + 25$

62. $9y^2 + 48y + 64$ **63.** $\dfrac{1}{9}t^4 - 81$ **64.** $a^2b^2 - \dfrac{9}{16}$

65. $0.04x^4 - 1.2x^2 + 9$ **66.** $1.44y^4 + 9.6y^2 + 16$

67. $2a^2b - 6ab + b - 3$ **68.** $2x^2y^2 + x - 3y^2 + 1$

69. $x^2 - 5x + 11$ **70.** $2y^2 - 3y - 5$ **71.** $2p^2 - 7p + 4 + \dfrac{10}{p-5}$

72. $t^2 - 4t + 2 + \dfrac{-2}{t+3}$ **73.** $-5m^4 + 8m^3 - 4m^2 - 4m + 1$

74. $5b^3 - 2b^2 + b + 7$ **75.** $4a^2 + 6a + 9 + \dfrac{18}{2a-3}$

76. $16k^2 + 8k + 4 + \dfrac{9}{2k-1}$

Section B.6 Practice Exercises, pp. B-41–B-42

1. $a^2 - b^2 = (a+b)(a-b)$ **2.** $a^3 - b^3 = (a-b)(a^2 + ab + b^2)$

3. $a^3 + b^3 = (a+b)(a^2 - ab + b^2)$ **4.** No

5. a. Difference of squares **b.** $(t-10)(t+10)$

6. a. Difference of squares **b.** $(2m-7n)(2m+7n)$

7. a. Sum of cubes **b.** $(y+3)(y^2 - 3y + 9)$

8. a. Sum of cubes **b.** $(x+1)(x^2 - x + 1)$

9. a. Trinomial (non-perfect square trinomial) **b.** $(d-4)(d+7)$

10. a. Trinomial (nonperfect square trinomial) **b.** $(c+8)(c-3)$

11. a. Trinomial (perfect square trinomial) **b.** $(x-6)^2$

12. a. Trinomial (perfect square trinomial) **b.** $(p+8)^2$

13. a. Four terms—grouping **b.** $(ax+b)(2x-5)$

14. a. Four terms—grouping **b.** $(4x+a)(2x-b)$

15. a. Trinomial (non-perfect square trinomial) **b.** $(2y-1)(5y+4)$

16. a. Trinomial (non-perfect square trinomial) **b.** $(3z+2)(4z+1)$

17. a. Difference of squares **b.** $10(p-8)(p+8)$

18. a. Difference of squares **b.** $2(5a-6)(5a+6)$

19. a. Difference of cubes **b.** $z(z-4)(z^2 + 4z + 16)$

20. a. Difference of cubes **b.** $t(t-2)(t^2 + 2t + 4)$

21. a. Trinomial (non-perfect square trinomial) **b.** $b(b+5)(b-9)$

22. a. Trinomial (nonperfect square trinomial) **b.** $y(y-4)(y-10)$

23. a. Trinomial (perfect square trinomial) **b.** $(3w+4x)^2$

24. a. Trinomial (perfect square trinomial) **b.** $(2k-5p)^2$

25. a. Four terms—grouping **b.** $10(2x+a)(3x-1)$

26. a. Four terms—grouping **b.** $10(5x+c)(x-4)$

27. a. Four terms—grouping **b.** $(x-3)(x+3)(x+4)$

28. a. Four terms—grouping **b.** $(m+5)(m-2)(m+2)$

29. a. Difference of squares **b.** $(w^2+4)(w-2)(w+2)$

30. a. Difference of squares **b.** $(k^2+9)(k-3)(k+3)$

31. a. Difference of cubes **b.** $(t^2-2)(t^4 + 2t^2 + 4)$

32. a. Sum of cubes **b.** $(p^2+3)(p^4 - 3p^2 + 9)$

33. a. Trinomial (non-perfect square trinomial) **b.** $(4p-1)(2p-5)$

34. a. Trinomial (non-perfect square trinomial) **b.** $(3m+4)(3m-5)$

35. a. Trinomial (perfect square trinomial) **b.** $(6y-1)^2$

36. a. Trinomial (perfect square trinomial) **b.** $(3a+7)^2$

37. a. Four terms—grouping **b.** $(x+4)(x-y)$

38. a. Four terms—grouping **b.** $(m-6)(m+n)$

39. a. Sum of squares **b.** $2(x^2+25)$

40. a. Sum of squares **b.** $4(y^2+16)$

41. a. Trinomial (nonperfect square trinomial) **b.** $s^2(3r-2)(4r+5)$

42. a. Trinomial (nonperfect square trinomial) **b.** $w^2(7z+4)(z-2)$

43. a. Trinomial (nonperfect square trinomial) **b.** $(x-3y)(x+11y)$

44. a. Trinomial (nonperfect square trinomial) **b.** $(s+3t)(s-12t)$

45. a. Sum of cubes **b.** $(m^2+n)(m^4 - m^2n + n^2)$

46. a. Difference of cubes **b.** $(a-b^2)(a^2 + ab + b^4)$

47. a. Trinomial (nonperfect square trinomial) **b.** $(a+b)(x-4)(x+3)$

48. a. Trinomial (nonperfect square trinomial) **b.** $(y+2)(y+1)(y+9)$

49. a. None of these **b.** $x(x-4)$

50. a. None of these **b.** $y(y-9)$

51. $\left\{-\dfrac{5}{2}, 3\right\}$ **52.** $\left\{\dfrac{1}{4}, -6\right\}$ **53.** $\{0, 5\}$ **54.** $\{0, -7\}$

55. $\{-3\}$ **56.** $\{10\}$ **57.** $\{4, -2\}$ **58.** $\{16, -1\}$

59. $\left\{\dfrac{5}{3}, -\dfrac{1}{2}\right\}$ **60.** $\left\{-\dfrac{7}{4}, 2\right\}$ **61.** $\left\{\dfrac{3}{2}, 4\right\}$ **62.** $\{5, 7\}$

63. $\{1, -1\}$ **64.** $\{4, -4\}$

Section B.7 Practice Exercises, pp. B-48–B-50

1. $x \neq -4$ **2.** $x \neq 1$ **3.** $x \neq \dfrac{3}{5}$ and $x \neq -\dfrac{3}{5}$

4. $y \neq \dfrac{7}{2}$ and $y \neq -\dfrac{7}{2}$ **5.** There are no restricted values.

6. There are no restricted values. **7.** $\dfrac{x^3}{4y}$ **8.** $\dfrac{3b}{a^2}$ **9.** $\dfrac{t+2}{2}$

10. $\dfrac{m+3}{3}$ **11.** $\dfrac{y+4}{y+2}$ **12.** $\dfrac{x+4}{2(x-6)}$ **13.** $\dfrac{y^3}{10x}$

14. $\dfrac{t^3}{6s^2}$ **15.** $\dfrac{1}{2}$ **16.** $\dfrac{x+6}{x-6}$ **17.** $3ab^2c$ **18.** $\dfrac{3}{2m^4n^4}$

19. $\dfrac{p(p-6)}{4}$ **20.** $\dfrac{y(y-1)}{5(y+3)}$ **21.** $-\dfrac{t^2}{t-7}$ **22.** $-(x-5)$

23. $8x^3y^{10}$ **24.** $48a^2b^4$ **25.** $(x-4)(x+3)(x-3)$

26. $(x+1)(x+9)(x-9)$ **27.** $-\dfrac{1}{3x}$ **28.** $-\dfrac{1}{3t}$ **29.** $\dfrac{5x^2+2y}{4x^3y^2}$

30. $\dfrac{7b^3+3}{9a^2b^4}$ **31.** $x-7$ **32.** $z-10$ **33.** $\dfrac{17x}{2(2x-1)}$

34. $\dfrac{-9}{2(5x+4)}$ **35.** $\dfrac{x^2-3x+6}{(x+4)(x-3)(x-1)}$ **36.** $\dfrac{4y^2-17y-6}{(y-2)^2(y-5)}$

37. $\dfrac{-3}{y+3}$ **38.** $\dfrac{x+4}{x+2}$ **39.** -1 **40.** -1

41. $\dfrac{3b+4a}{7b-a}$ **42.** $\dfrac{2(q-2p)}{2q+p}$ **43.** $2(4x+1)$ **44.** $\dfrac{t}{2(t+1)}$

45. $u-v$ **46.** $\dfrac{a+b}{2}$ **47.** $\dfrac{y+5}{2y-9}$ **48.** $\dfrac{3(x-1)}{x+3}$

49. $\{10\}$ **50.** $\{6\}$ **51.** $\{\ \}$ **52.** $\{\ \}$ **53.** $\{-2, -4\}$

54. $\{3, 5\}$ **55.** $\{7\}$ **56.** $\{5, -2\}$

Online Supplements

MATH
Hosted by **ALEKS Corp.**

Connect Math Hosted by ALEKS Online Access 52 Weeks for Beginning and Intermediate Algebra, Fifth Edition

Connect Math Hosted by ALEKS® is an online homework system that offers everything you and your students need in one, intuitive platform:

- Content developed to precisely match the author's content
- Integrated ALEKS Assessment to diagnose student gaps in prerequisite knowledge
- Integrated SmartBook provides a personalized, interactive reading experience
- Seamless print and digital integration with 99.97% uptime

The following steps are for new users registering with Connect Math for the first time. (If you already have a Connect Math account, simply go to www.connectmath.com. Enter your login name and password and click on "LOGIN.") To register you will need the access code printed on the inside back cover of your book.

IMPORTANT: You will also need to obtain a 10-character course code from your instructor.

1. Go to www.connectmath.com.
2. Click on the link marked "**NEW USER? Sign up now!**"
3. Enter the **10-character course code** and click on "Continue."
4. Verify the course information and click on "Continue."
5. Enter the access code located on either the back cover of your Create printed textbook or located on the user's Create eBookshelf and click on "Continue."
6. Answer the questions to complete your registration.
7. During the registration process, you will be given a login name. WRITE IT DOWN; you will need it to access your account in the future.

Once you have completed your registration, click on "Continue" to automatically log into your Connect Math account.

Visit: http://support.connectmath.com or Call: (949) 390-2095

Monday – Thursday | 7:00 A.M. – 1:00 A.M.
Friday: 7:00 AM – 9:00 P.M.
Sunday: 4:00 PM – 1:00 A.M.
(All times Eastern)